ROUTE SURVEYS
AND CONSTRUCTION

ENGINEERING SURVEYS SERIES

A completely coordinated set

ENGINEERING SURVEYS: ELEMENTARY
  by Rubey, Lommel, and Todd

ENGINEERING SURVEYS: ELEMENTARY AND
  APPLIED
  by Rubey, Lommel, and Todd

ROUTE SURVEYS AND CONSTRUCTION
  by Rubey

PRACTICAL PHOTOGRAMMETRY
  by Sharp

ROUTE SURVEYS AND CONSTRUCTION

A Pocket and Reference Book with Tables
for the Survey, Design, and Construction
of Highways, Railways, Airways, Tramways,
Beltways, Canals, Flumes, Levees, Pipe Lines,
Transmission Lines, and Other Route
Constructions

for

Students, Professional Engineers,
Construction Engineers, and Contractors

BY

HARRY RUBEY, B.S., C.E., P.E.

LIFE MEMBER, AMERICAN SOCIETY OF CIVIL ENGINEERS
MEMBER, NATIONAL SOCIETY OF PROFESSIONAL ENGINEERS
MEMBER, AMERICAN SOCIETY FOR ENGINEERING EDUCATION
CHAIRMAN, DEPARTMENT OF CIVIL ENGINEERING,
UNIVERSITY OF MISSOURI

THIRD EDITION OF *Route Surveys*

THE MACMILLAN COMPANY, NEW YORK

PREFACE

This third edition is based on 50 years of the practice and teaching of routes. It has been revised through three editions and numerous printings to serve as a text and permanent reference book emphasizing professional civil engineering and its trend towards the profitable fields of engineered construction, contracting, professional management, and the expanding practical uses of photogrammetry. Fundamentals and disciplines are retained but the traditional field surveying flavor is diminished.

It has been kept in mind that the course in route surveys must provide the engineering approach and the broad basic treatment underlying highways, railways, airways, canals, pipe lines, transmission lines, cableways, beltways and all transportation and communication constructions. Obviously it cannot provide complete coverage of such a wide variety of fields in any of which the graduate may practice. Furthermore, corporations or governmental branches engaged in these fields have varying standards of practice, accompanied by pride of opinion. Since the work of the graduate varies so widely, it would be misleading and narrowing to concentrate on any one field or any single standard practice, as was once done for railways and as is now being done for highways. While highway, railway, and hydraulic constructions are emphasized in this text, other applications are indicated. It is the author's conviction that the engineer should be educated broadly and professionally, not trained narrowly in the techniques of a special field.

Few engineering curricula allow adequate courses and time for engineered construction with its relation to professional management and for modern photogrammetric applications; hence their inclusion in this edition. It is suggested that the economic studies, estimates, and bids of chapters XV and XVII may be made as part of a project investigation in the routes, construction, or professional management courses. Perhaps in this indirect manner a little additional time may become available for consideration of routes.

Regardless of whether the study of routes be limited to an unduly brief geometric treatment in the sophomore year, a more elaborate study in the junior year, or preferably a professional design and economic project study in the senior year; all civil engineering students, constructors, practitioners, and managers need complete reference material and tables for routes close at hand throughout their careers. The book has been prepared for this overall permanent use as well as for class use in all types of routes courses. Selected chapters may be assigned and covered to any extent desired but the treatment is comprehensive. Any shorter text or any specialized treatment such as is given in railway, highway, and similiar manuals necessarily must be on a sub-professional or technician basis unsuited to professional collegiate curricula or for broad professional reference.

Better, broader, and more comprehensive coverage is provided in this book than in other texts for such matters as:

1. More tables, with latest revisions and corrections.

2. Tables and text suitable for arc, chord, and other definitions of degree of curve, including latest methods and tables for staking curves with a tape on secondary roads, logging roads, canals, and the like.

3. Tables and text suitable for the American Railway Engineering Association (railway), the Barnett (highway), and other spirals, treated fundamentally.

4. The latest developments for both string lining (from A.R.E.A. Manual and newest mechanical equipment) and transit lining, on existing railway curves.

5. Several methods of staking railway turnouts.

6. Highway and photogrammetric applications.

7. New chapters and emphasis on the growing and remunerative fields of engineered construction, professional management, and contracting, including estimating and bidding.

8. The long-established Macmillan five-place natural trigonometric and log tables that are most efficient for general use. For

rare usage, eight-place natural sines and cosines have been added. No such precise tables are available to most engineers.

9. Facilitating reference by continuing to number all figures, tables, and formulas to correspond to the section in which they occur and giving the chapter and section numbers at the top of each page.

10. Perfecting and expanding the index to increase the reference value of the book and tables.

11. Including extensive problems with answers to the (a) problem in each case so that the student can check them while studying. Similiar (b), (c), and (d) problems with varying numerical data are added for examining or quizzing the student.

12. Retaining the type which is more easily read than is that of most pocket books.

13. Avoiding verbose description or formulation which makes a text difficult to follow and removes the student's incentive to reason from a figure and to exercise his own initiative and judgment. On the contrary, figures are ample but simple and the student must give his own thoughtful study to the figures, formulas, and text. Reasoning on the part of the student thus becomes necessary in solving the problems, in explaining simple missing steps in the development of formulas, and in his economic design of location on maps and profiles or on the ground. Open or closed book examinations may then use both problems and objective questions.

14. Perfecting the text and tables through a score of printings and editions.

15. Outlining a project method for teaching a route surveys course, as given in Section 12a.

16. Furnishing teaching aids, on request from teachers, especially designed for this book and for the larger classes.

17. Encouraging a professional, rather than a sub-professional, approach.

The more notable changes in this edition place emphasis on professional engineering, engineered-construction, professional management, contracting, and practical photogrammetry; these being the more promising and profitable outlets for the majority of civil engineers.   Here their future is unlimited, whichever way their interests and opportunities develop.

The cooperation of associates in teaching and practice, of students, of manufacturers, of transportation agencies, and of governmental agencies is gratefully acknowledged.   The author will be most appreciative of further suggestions for improvement that may be brought to his attention.

HARRY RUBEY

Columbia, Mo.

CONTENTS

NOTE: See also Index and list at beginning of Tables.

CHAPTER I

SECTION INTRODUCTION PAGE

1. Importance of Route Surveys and Construction.......... 1
2. Selection of Routes.................................... 2
3. General Types of Route Surveys........................ 4

CHAPTER II

THE RECONNAISSANCE

4. General Considerations................................ 5
5. Topography.. 6
6. Controlling Points................................... 8
7. Gradients... 8
8. Compensated Grades.................................. 9
9. Curvature... 10
10. Reconnaissance Instruments.......................... 11
11. Obtaining Elevations with the Aneroid Barometer........ 11
12. Aerial Surveys...................................... 20
12a.A Project Method for Teaching Route Surveys.......... 23
13. Reconnaissance Procedure............................ 23
14. The Reconnaissance Report........................... 24

CHAPTER III

THE PRELIMINARY

15. Purpose of Preliminary............................... 26
16. The Standard Type of Preliminary..................... 26
17. Long Tape Preliminaries.............................. 34
18. Stadia Preliminary................................... 38
19. Rapid Stadia Preliminary............................. 38
19a.Aerial Preliminaries................................. 38
20. Precision of Preliminaries............................ 38
21. Checking and Coordinating the Preliminary............. 39
22. Miscellany.. 40

CHAPTER IV

LOCATION

23. General... 47
24. Procedure... 47
25. Grade Contour....................................... 49

26. Balanced Cuts and Fills........................   50
27. Exploration of Excavation......................   51
28. Obtaining Permission to Construct..............   51
29. Monumenting the Location.......................   52
30. Location Maps and Profiles.....................   52
30a.Construction...................................   57

CHAPTER V

SIMPLE CIRCULAR CURVES

31. Introduction...................................   58
32. Degree of Curve................................   58
33. Functions of Simple Curves.....................   60
34. Curve Notes....................................   63
35. Field Work.....................................   66
36. Staking Curves with a Tape.....................   70
37. Triangulating a Curve..........................   75
38. Locating a Curve from the Center...............   75
39. Special Problems...............................   75
40. Some Solutions by Trial........................   79
41. In Conclusion..................................   80

CHAPTER VI

COMPOUND AND REVERSE CURVES

42. Compound Curves................................   81
43. Reverse Curves.................................   86

CHAPTER VII

SOLUTION BY TRAVERSE

44. Solution by Traverse...........................   89
45. Traversing around Obstacles....................   90
46. Conclusion.....................................   91

CHAPTER VIII

VERTICAL AND OTHER PARABOLIC CURVES

47. Parabolic Curves...............................   93
48. Vertical Parabola..............................   93
49. Low Point on Vertical Curve....................   97
50. Adjacent Vertical Curves.......................   98
51. Length of Vertical Curves......................   99
52. Laying out Parabolas with a Tape...............   101

CHAPTER IX

SPIRALS

53. Introduction.. 103
54. Basic Equation of the Spiral............................ 104
55. American Railway Engineering Association Ten-Chord
    Spiral.. 106
56. Properties of the A. R. E. A. Spiral.................... 108
57. Precise Definition of A. R. E. A. Spiral................ 115
58. Spiral Field Notes.................................... 117
59. Spiral Field Notes when Stationing Is Preferred......... 120
60. The Osculating Circle................................. 120
61. Intermediate Setups and Compound Curves.............. 121
62. Field Work... 124
63. Field Work by Offsets................................. 125
64. Spiral Tables... 126
65. Spiraling Existing Curves............................. 126
66. Superelevation....................................... 128
67. Length of Spirals..................................... 135
67a. Barnett Transition Curves for Highways................ 138

CHAPTER X

RAILWAY TURNOUTS AND TRACK LAYOUTS

68. General.. 139
69. Definitions... 139
70. Staking a Turnout from Straight Track.................. 141
71. Turnouts on Curves................................... 143
72. Tracks Curved after Leaving Turnout................... 144
73. Turnouts from Straight Track.......................... 145
74. Connecting Tracks.................................... 146
75. "Y" Track Layouts.................................... 146
76. Crossovers... 146
77. Crossings.. 146
78. Other Track Layouts.................................. 147

CHAPTER XI

STRING LINING OF CURVES

79. General.. 148
80. String Lining of Railway Curves by Chord Method....... 148
81. Tools Required....................................... 150
82. Procedure.. 150
82a. Improved Mechanized String Lining................... 156
83. String Lining as Applied to Park Roads................ 160

CHAPTER XII

84. Purpose of the Study.................................... 161
85. General Procedure..................................... 161
86. Cross-Section Forms................................... 166
87. Setting Slope Stakes................................... 167
88. Precision in Measurements............................. 169
89. Computing End Areas.................................. 169
90. Coordinate Method of Computing End Areas........... 171
91. The Grade Triangle Method............................ 173
92. End Areas by Planimeter............................... 174
93. Sections in Earth and Rock............................ 174
94. Canal Cross-Sections.................................. 177
95. Averaging End Areas.................................. 177
96. Prismoidal Formula.................................... 178
97. Prismoidal Correction................................. 179
98. Excavation Tables and Diagrams....................... 181
99. Embankment Openings................................. 183
100. Curvature Correction.................................. 184
101. Borrow Pits... 187
102. Computation of Grading Over an Area—or Borrow-Pit
     Method.. 188
103. Shrinkage and Swell................................... 192
104. Settlement.. 193
105. Classification of Excavation........................... 193
106. Grading Equipment and Methods....................... 194

CHAPTER XIII

HAUL AND THE MASS DIAGRAM

107. Haul.. 195
108. Free Haul... 195
109. Overhaul.. 195
110. Station to Station Method............................. 197
111. Economic Limit of Haul............................... 199
112. Mass Diagram... 200
113. Properties of the Mass Diagram....................... 202
114. Purpose of the Mass Diagram.......................... 203
115. Procedure in Using the Mass Diagram................. 203

CHAPTER XIV

RIGHTS OF WAY

116. Influence of Rights of Way on the Selection of Routes.. 207
117. The Right of Eminent Domain.......................... 207

SECTION   PAGE

118. Right of Way Agents.................................... 208
119. Deeds and Easements................................... 208
120. Right of Way Description............................... 208
121. Surveys of Right of Way............................... 209
122. Legal Rights of Surveyors.............................. 210

CHAPTER XV

CONSTRUCTION

CONSTRUCTION PROCEDURE

123. General... 212
124. Re-establishing a Final Location and Ordering Materials.. 212
125. Cross-Sectioning...................................... 212
126. Staking Appurtenant Structures........................ 212
127. "Change Orders"...................................... 218
128. Inspection.. 218
129. Contracts... 218
130. Monthly Estimates.................................... 219
131. "Progress Reports"................................... 219
132. Final Estimate....................................... 219
133. Summary... 220
134. Operation after Construction.......................... 220
135. Management and Administration........................ 221

CONSTRUCTION DATA

136. Allowable Bearing Power of Soils...................... 221
137. Bearing Power of Piles................................ 222
138. Strength of Building Materials......................... 225
139. Concrete Data.. 227
140. Waterway Size for Culverts or Bridges................. 229
141. Flow of Water in Pipes and Open Channels............. 232
142. Flow of Water over Weirs............................. 232
143. Conversion Factors.................................... 239
144. Weights of Materials.................................. 240
145. Cost of Various Constructions......................... 240
146. Estimating by Cost per Complete Unit.................. 240
147. Estimates Made from Quantity Surveys................. 243

CHAPTER XVI

THE CONSTRUCTION ENGINEER AND PROFESSIONAL MANAGEMENT

148. Introduction.. 248
149. The Construction Engineer............................. 248

SECTION   PAGE

150. Organization of the Construction Management Department 250
151. Professional Management............................ 251
152. The Rise and Fall of Engineers as Managers........... 252

CHAPTER XVII
THE ENGINEER-CONTRACTOR

153. Introduction.................................... 255
154. The Contractor's Equipment....................... 255
155. The Contractor's Organization...................... 256
156. The Contractor's Bid............................. 256
157. Contracting as a Career........................... 261
158. The Contractor's Work............................ 264

CHAPTER XVIII
COMPARISON OF VARIOUS DEFINITIONS OF DEGREE
OF CURVE

159. General....................................... 265
160. Even-Radius Curves.............................. 265
161. Radius of 5730 Feet.............................. 266
162. Metric Curves.................................. 267
163. Discrepancies.................................. 267
164. Comparison of Values under Various Definitions......... 268

CHAPTER XIX
HIGHWAY PRACTICE

165. Purpose of this Chapter........................... 271
166. Geometric Practice.............................. 271
167. Location and Design.............................. 280
168. An Overall Transportation Policy.................... 285
168a.Present Highway Standards........................ 285

CHAPTER XX
AERIAL PHOTOGRAPHY IN ROUTE SURVEYING

169. General Considerations........................... 295
170. Example Number I............................... 298
171. Example Number II.............................. 300
172. Addendum.................................... 303

CHAPTER XXI
PROBLEMS

Chapts. I–XVIII.................................. 304
Tables. ....following page 315

ROUTE SURVEYS
AND CONSTRUCTION

CHAPTER I

INTRODUCTION

1. Importance of Route Surveys and Construction. Construction, with its accompanying replacement and maintenance, has become our largest industry, accounting for one-seventh of our expenditures. It is a most profitable field for civil engineers and offers preferred entree into management. Much of this rapidly growing activity is based on the fundamental data contained herein.

This book presents the principles underlying the design of location, survey, and construction of highways; railways; airways; gas, oil, and water pipe lines; canals and water conveying conduits and flumes; electrical transmission lines; telephone and telegraph lines; tunnels and underground conduits; cableways; beltways; and other means of conveying or transmitting goods, materials, power, or power impulses over long distances on the surface of the earth.

The foregoing routes comprise America's multimillion-mile system of transportation and communication where perhaps one-fifth of our national wealth is invested. The cost per mile for constructing routes varies from a few thousands to many millions of dollars, and operating equipment is equally costly.

Present civilization, its future development, and the high standard of living of this country are dependent to a considerable extent upon its elaborate transportation and communication system. Kipling has said "Transportation is civilization."

In the past, most route construction projects were designed to meet only existing needs, with the result that a large part of this construction is now obsolete. Railways have become partially obsolete in a generation; many highways are inadequate for present speeds and volume of traffic though constructed within the past fifteen years; and irrigation and drainage projects, while satisfying individual or local needs, do not conform to a comprehensive plan of development. The engineer who plans a route of communication or transportation, therefore, should be a man of vision who endeavors to anticipate future trends and to locate his construction in accordance with them, so that it may be readily adaptable to future demands. After construction, the engineer is engaged in a continuous process of revision and of operation calling for a high degree of skill.

Location, construction, maintenance, operation, and management of transportation facilities provide employment for many engineers. In this connection, it is interesting to note that a large proportion of the executives of our largest railroads, highway organizations, oil companies, and so on, are civil engineers whose early work was concerned with the practices dealt with in this book.

Transportation projects are sometimes initiated and financed by private corporations with the expectation of profit; sometimes they are undertaken by governmental agencies as a part of a social and economic program; but by one, or by the other, or by both, they are being developed continually. In one generation the major emphasis may be placed on railways; in another it may be on highways, waterways, irrigation, or electric power; but some form of development of transportation is always absorbing a large part of the money and the activity of the community. There is no serious prospect of a decrease in importance of this general field of endeavor; rather, there is evidence of ever increasing activity.

2. Selection of Routes. In originally providing transportation, it is necessary first to select the most practicable means and then to choose the best route for that means of transportation which has been adopted. For

example, an industry or a community may be served by
waterway, canal, flume, pipe line, highway, railway, cableway, transmission line, and so on. It is necessary to investigate these several means and to choose the best one.
For each of these means of transportation, frequently several
routes are possible, each possessing some advantages as to
markets, or production, or physical location, or economy of
operation, or low first-cost, or similar factor. As a specific
illustration, a transmission line between an electrical generating station and an important market in a distant large
city may have other valuable markets along one possible
location, or it may have desirable hydro-electric or mine-
mouth steam-electric generating sites along another location.

In some instances, as in locating a highway, æsthetic
factors may influence the selection of a route.

The highest type of engineering and business judgment
is essential in making selection from the many alternative
means and routes that may be feasible, and such selection
should be entrusted only to a broadly experienced engineer.
It is desirable that he should not be a specialist to such an
extent as to be committed to one particular means of transportation and thus to overlook other more desirable means.
In some instances it may be necessary for the engineer to
refer to books, technical periodicals, or the catalogs of manufacturers of equipment regarding matters with which he is
not entirely familiar. For example, it may be necessary to
obtain data about a cableway. Most engineers would know
little about cableways as a means of transportation, yet
under some conditions they are quite satisfactory.

Frequently, a thorough study may show that none of the
alternative means or routes is possible at a reasonable cost
and that, consequently, the industry or the community
can not be served.

All these types of projects—railways, highways, waterways, cableways, transmission lines, pipe lines, canals,
ditches, flumes, levees, and so on—are located and constructed according to the same general principles, although

modifications of details of application of the principles are
necessary, depending on the needs of a special type of work.
For example, railway surveys are generally among the more
accurate ones, while those for pipe lines and transmission
lines are among the less accurate. Even in a particular
type of work, as for example highway construction, the
highway departments of the various states and counties
have slightly different standards of precision, of details,
and of procedure. The engineer must, therefore, understand the basic principles underlying all of these projects
and modify them according to the type of work he is doing
and according to the standards and procedure of his organization.

3. General Types of Route Surveys. In his effort to
provide the most satisfactory transportation service with
the "cheapest in the long run" cost (considering both the
first cost and the operating cost) the engineer follows these
successive steps:

(1) The reconnaissance survey determines the general
route and type of transportation. Most such surveys are
only partial, in that the type has been decided beforehand.

(2) The preliminary survey provides a map and other
data from which a "paper location" may be made that
further defines the desirable location.

(3) The final location survey stakes the precise location
on the ground and provides the best cost estimates available
before construction actually starts. Complete maps, profiles, plans, and specifications are drawn up at this time.

(4) The construction survey provides stakes, inspection,
and supervision for the contractor or construction forces.

The foregoing steps are followed by operation and management where the engineer continues to provide engineering surveys and supervision, including management. It is
here that the engineer often leaves engineering and enters
management, frequently reaching the top positions therein.

CHAPTER II

THE RECONNAISSANCE

4. General Considerations. The reconnaissance is a rapid and approximate examination of the entire area surrounding the proposed project, made with a view to eliminating from consideration the impracticable means and routes so that the more promising ones may be studied in greater detail through further surveys and investigations.

It is neither desirable nor permissible for the reconnaissance engineer to assume that some one means or route of communication or transportation is superior to others and to examine that one only. He must examine *all* possible means and routes. This often involves the examination of an entire area rather than a mere strip of country. Natural aptitude and experience in sensing topography and its effect on the selection of a means and a route of transportation are needed. The less the reconnaissance engineer possesses these qualities, the more maps and other data he will need to aid him. Such aids can seldom or never replace native endowment and experience entirely, however.

Consultation with geologists regarding formations and with soils experts regarding soils properties and stabilization is frequently helpful. Aerial reconnaissance is increasingly used with excellent results, as described later.

Throughout the reconnaissance, the engineer must confer with other officials of the organization and secure and utilize their judgments. Usually this can be accomplished in the headquarters office by referring to the reconnaissance map, but the more interested officials should occasionally visit the field.

It is particularly necessary for the reconnaissance engineer to sense the trend of the times and to plan his project for the future, rather than to work entirely on the basis of precedent. He must possess what may be termed "practical imagination." Thousands of miles of highways in this country have become obsolete within fifteen years of their construction, due to increased speeds, greater loads, and other changed conditions. While the cost of providing for all possible future needs is frequently prohibitive, yet present construction often may be planned so as to minimize the cost of future changes. Unusually good judgment is required in deciding just how much money may be expended at present to provide for a probable, but not certain, future requirement.

5. Topography. A route must generally conform to one or more types of topography as follows:

(1) *Along valleys* where flat grades are possible but where floods and washouts may introduce difficulties in construction and operation, and where many curves and side-drainage bridges are necessitated in following a winding stream.

(2) *Along ridges* (or drainage divides) where somewhat steeper grades are necessary but where drainage and alignment problems are minimized.

(3) *Across drainage*, that is, crossing the streams approximately at right angles. Here grades are necessarily fairly steep and expensive structures are needed at stream crossings.

(4) *Along hillsides* where the gradient may often be made as flat or as steep as desired but where following the curve of the side hill frequently necessitates rather sharp (short radius) curves in the horizontal alignment.

(5) *Through comparatively level country* where little difficulty in gradient or drainage is encountered and where the route may frequently be straight for long distances, sometimes following section lines and thus causing the least damage to property.

(6) *With relative disregard of topography* where heavy and important construction is involved.

Usually more than one of these types of location is encountered on a long survey. It will thus be seen that the valleys and ridges (broadly spoken of as the drainage of the country) will frequently have a controlling influence on the

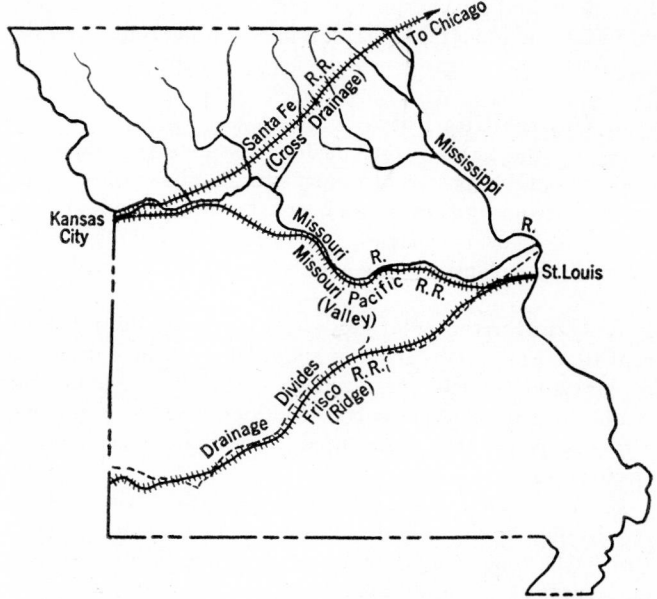

FIG. 5. Drainage as Affecting Routes.

route location, and must consequently be studied carefully. Fortunately, most available maps show the drainage with more or less completeness. On Fig. 5 will be found:

(1) The *Missouri Pacific* Railway following a major valley.

(2) The *Frisco* Railway following the drainage divides, or ridges.

(3) The *Santa Fe* Railway crossing the streams at approximately right angles.

Topography is especially important in selecting the routes for railways, first-class highways, canals, aqueducts, and flumes. For the less difficult types of location, such as for electrical transmission lines, pipe lines, cableways, temporary or low-type roads, and so on, where the steepness of the grades and the sharpness of the curves are relatively immaterial, the topography has less effect on the route, and the line is run more nearly straight between controlling points

6. Controlling Points.   The controlling points of a route are the termini; intermediate markets or production centers; saddles, passes, or tunnel sites in hills or mountains; major stream crossings; and, for highways and streets, underpasses or overpasses. Sites involving danger from snow slides or land slips should, of course, be avoided.

7. Gradients.   Flat grades are generally desirable except that a minimum grade of about 0.1 percent is desirable in cuts and tunnels, for drainage. Maximum permissible grades for various types of construction are about as follows, although they may be varied somewhat under special circumstances:

Canals, flumes, levees, and most *hydraulic constructions* require flat grades, usually of the order of 0.0002 to 0.005 (from 0.02 foot to 0.5 foot vertically for each hundred feet horizontally). The decimal form of expressing gradient is used in hydraulic work.

First-class railways will ordinarily have maximum grades of from 0.3 percent to 0.6 percent (from 0.3 foot to 0.6 foot vertically for each 100 feet horizontally), except in mountainous country. *Industrial tracks* and *mountain railways* may have grades up to 2 percent or 3 percent, or even more in special instances.

First-class highways for very heavy hauling will have grades under 3 percent. First-class highways for combined trucking and passenger traffic should not exceed 5 percent in gradient. *Secondary roads* for light traffic, such as farm to market roads, may use as high as 7 percent grades. All of these highway grades may be necessarily exceeded in rough country. Gradients for *temporary* or *construction* roads should not exceed 15 percent.

Transmission lines, pipe lines, telephone lines, and *cableways* have no special limit on gradient.

8. Compensated Grades. As a train or vehicle moves around a curve, energy is required to overcome the "curve resistance." At the same time energy may be required to climb a grade. It is frequently desirable to reduce the portions of steep grades that occur on curves so that the total energy required to overcome the combined grade resistance and curve resistance shall not exceed that required to mount the established maximum grade which occurs on the straight portion of the roadway.

On railroads, the grade compensation for curvature varies from 0.03 to 0.05 percent per degree of curve. Recommendations regarding the proper rate to be used for varying conditions may be found in the latest Manual of the American Railway Engineering Association. As an example, let us assume that a proper rate of compensation is 0.04 percent per degree of curve, and let us further assume that the maximum permissible grade on straight track is 1.00 percent. If the degree of curve is five degrees, then the compensation will be 0.04 times 5 or 0.20 percent, and the actual grade around the curve should not exceed 0.80 percent.

On highways, grades have not usually been compensated around curves, but many engineers consider such compensation advisable, especially on heavy grades and sharp curves. The California Division of Highways compensates maximum ruling grades of 6 percent and over on curves up to 1000-foot radius according to the formula

$$\text{Compensation in percent} = \frac{125}{\text{radius of curve in feet}}.$$

9. Curvature. Flat curves are usually desirable. However, a degree of curve * of less than one degree generally serves no special purpose and makes the curve longer and consequently more difficult to maintain. Maximum permissible curvatures, to be modified in special cases, are about as follows:

The curvature of a *first class railway* should not ordinarily exceed two or three degrees. The modern, high-speed, streamlined trains, traveling at speeds in excess of 100 miles per hour will need curves as flat as one degree, and even higher speeds than this should be anticipated. (Competent railway officials predict speeds of 125 miles per hour within the next five years.) On *industrial tracks* where ordinary road engines are used, an attempt is made to keep the degree of curve under twelve degrees. If only switch engines are used, as in *railway yards*, somewhat higher degrees of curve may be used, but they are apt to result in derailments and in excessive maintenance costs.

Modern, *first-class*, *high-speed highways* should not have curvatures exceeding two or three degrees. Flatter curves are necessary on superhighways such as those in Germany which are designed for speeds of 112 miles per hour, although it is doubtful if such speeds will be tolerated in this country. Ten-degree curves are not seriously objectionable on *moderate-speed farm to market roads*. On *temporary* and *low-type roads* and on *city streets* where speeds are low, we will continue to encounter and use very sharp curves, even the rounded off right angle turns which are in evidence at street corners.

For most *canals*, *flumes*, and *pipe line*, very sharp curves are permitted, say 20 degrees to 30 degrees or even sharper on unimportant construction.

For *telegraph*, *telephone*, and *transmission lines*, the turns are made at a single pole or tower, so that no curves are used unless the construction follows a curved railway or highway.

* See definition of degree of curve in § 32.

10. Reconnaissance Instruments. Few instruments or no instruments whatever are required on the reconnaissance survey. The map is taken into the field, a compass may be used for direction, and distances may be roughly estimated.

Field notes are usually kept in narrative or log form, or they may be entered directly on the map. Errors and omissions found on the map are corrected as they are discovered.

Distances are most frequently scaled from the map. An automobile odometer (or, less precisely, distance reading on the speedometer) is often used. When the reconnaissance is made on foot, the pedometer (measuring distances) or the passometer (measuring number of paces) is convenient.

Directions are obtained by means of a compass, frequently used in connection with a map. The Brunton pocket compass is an excellent reconnaissance instrument. A compass may be attached to an automobile, but it must be compensated against local attraction of the car. The compass used by the Forest Service, mounted on a Jacob staff, is an instrument of more precision and is desirable for the better types of reconnaissance.

Elevations are sometimes available on the map. The hand level, or preferably the clinometer, is used to measure the slope angle of the ground surface. The Brunton pocket compass will measure vertical angles approximately and will serve roughly as a hand level. The aneroid barometer, described in the next section, is useful for obtaining approximate elevations, especially in rough and wooded country.

11. Obtaining Elevations with the Aneroid Barometer. Because of improved theory, methods, and barometric equipment, it appears desirable to include an adequate treatment of modern procedure.

Approximate elevations, correct to within 10 to 20 feet, may be obtained quickly and cheaply with an aneroid barometer, which measures atmospheric pressure. This pressure is greater at low elevations than at high ones.

For the theory of the barometer, one is referred to texts on physics or on higher surveying, or to other reference sources. Only the latest customary practices of using the aneroid barometer will be described here.

Two types of aneroids are commonly used, the old standard form and the newer and more precise altimeters which are operated somewhat differently, as described in the instructions accompanying the instrument. With either type, it is desirable to hold the aneroid at the known elevation, usually a bench mark, and to adjust it so that the pointer reads the known elevation. Then as the instrument is moved to other places the pointer will read the approximate elevation of those places (such readings to be corrected for temperature and for changes in barometric pressure, as described later). Each reading is entered in the notes as in Fig. 11. The following points should be observed in reading:

(1) The air temperature is taken with a thermometer separate from the aneroid. All, or nearly all, aneroids are "compensated" and are so marked on their face or elsewhere. This simply means that temperatures inside of the instrument will not affect readings. However, when the instrument is taken suddenly through a considerable range of temperature, time must be allowed for the temperature inside of the instrument to become uniform.

(2) Upon reaching a new station or point, the barometer should be allowed a few minutes to adjust itself—more time is required with the older type than with the newer. When the older type is used, it may be well to tap the instrument with a pencil to assist it in adjusting itself to the new conditions. It is best to leave the instrument in its case, and it is necessary to hold it horizontally. The instrument should be exposed to direct sunlight as little as possible.

(3) It is desirable, when convenient, as for example at lunch time, to take one reading upon reaching a point, and a second reading when leaving the point. This is

done in order to note the change in reading at a constant elevation with varying temperatures and varying atmospheric pressures.

PAULIN ALTIMETER RECORD

INSTRUMENT NO. 585 DATE January 11 19

LOCATION

Along Foothills Back of Alhambra

and on Line of Conduit.

REMARKS

Foggy in Morning.

Wind Started Shortly after Noon.

Cloudy in the Afternoon.

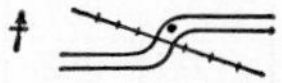

"a"

622
620
621

"b"

965
963
964

"c"

1753
1753
✓

"d"

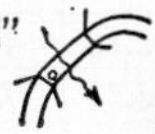

882
881
(870)
881

"e"

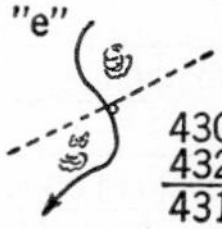

430
432
431

COMPUTER

OBSERVER

Courtesy of the Paulin Company.

FIG. 11. (*Continued on following pages.*)

Temperature Correction. The observer should then correct the field readings for *air temperatures* as in columns 9, 10, 11, and 12, of Fig. 11, noting that column 11 is a cumu-

ALTIMETER OBSERVATIONS   ....Jan. 11. 19......

1	2	3	4	5	6
NO.	DESCRIPTION	DIST.	HOUR	READING	TEMP. °F.
1	U.S.G.S. B.M. at Alhambra		7:02	398	38
2	Same as No. 1		7:08	402	38
3	R.R. X'ing 2 mi. East		7:32	565	40
4	Alder Creek at Highway		7:50	300	44
5	Creek Bed ½ mi. South		8:30	270	50
6	Road intersection North of R.R.		9:10	491	56
7	Transmission Tower No. 2876		9:47	864	62
8	East End of Sycamore Syphon	0+00	10:15	1631	67
9	Top Steep Slope	2+40	10:22	1546	68
10	Toe Steep Slope	3+70	10:28	1370	68
11	Creek Bed	6+50	10:32	1238	69
12	Toe Steep Slope	8+60	10:43	1344	69
13	Top Steep Slope	10+20	10:56	1490	70
14	West End of Syphon	16+75	11:02	1650	70
15	Same as No. 8		11:30	1654	72
16	Upper Bridge - Sycamore Creek		12:16	837	72
17	Same as No. 16		1:00	852	72
18	Same as No. 6		1:25	573	72
19	Same as No. 3		1:51	627	72
20	Alder Creek at Syphon X'ing		2:25	460	70
21	East End Alder Syphon		3:05	785	68
22	Same as No. 20		3:18	470	67
23	West End Alder Syphon		3:44	789	65
24	Saddle ½ mi. North		4:12	1122	64
25	Sycamore Canyon Road Junction		4:18	971	64
26.	Sycamore Road ½ mi. East of Bridge		4:32	908	64
27	Same as No. 16		4:40	873	63
28	Same as No. 7		4:55	960	63
29	U.S.G.S. B.M. at Alhambra		5:21	467	62

Fig. 11.   (Continued.)

lative algebraic total temperature correction and that column 12 is obtained by applying the correction of column 11 to the observed readings of column 5.   Column 9 is found from the formula

CALCULATION OF ELEVATIONS ..... Jan. 11, 19 ....

7	8	9	10	11	12	13	14	15	16
DIFF. OF READ'S	SUM OF TEMPS.	TEMP. ADJUSTMENT			ADJUSTED READING	BAROMETRIC CORRECTION	ELEVATION		NO.
		PER CENT	FEET	TOTAL			COMP.	ACTUAL	
+4	76	-2.4	-0.1	0	398	+64*	—	462	1
+163	78	-2.2	-3.6	0	402	+60*	—	462	2
-265	84	-1.6	+4.3	-4	561	+61	622	a	3
-30	94	-0.6	+0.2	+1	301	+63	364		4
+221	106	+0.6	+1.3	+1	271	+74	345		5
+373	118	+1.8	+6.7	+2	493	+86*	—	579	6
+767	129	+3.0	+23.0	+9	873	+92	965	b	7
-85	135	+3.6	-3.1	+32	1663	+90	1753	c	8
-176	136	+3.7	-6.5	+29	1575	+89	1664		9
-132	137	+3.8	-5.0	+22	1392	+88	1480		10
+106	138	+3.9	+4.1	+17	1255	+87	1342		11
+146	139	+4.0	+5.9	+21	1365	+85	1450		12
+160	140	+4.1	+6.6	+27	1517	+80	1597		13
+4	142	+4.3	+0.2	+34	1684	+79*	—	1763	14
-817	144	+4.5	-36.8	+34	1688	+65	1753	c	15
+15	144	+4.5	+0.7	-2	835	+47	882	d	16
-279	144	+4.5	-12.6	-1	851	+30	881	d	17
+54	144	+4.5	+2.4	-14	559	+20*	—	579	18
-167	142	+4.3	-7.2	-12	615	+5	620	a	19
+325	138	+3.9	+12.7	-19	441	-11	430	e	20
-315	135	+3.6	-11.3	-6	779	-20	759		21
+319	132	+3.3	+10.5	-18	452	-20	432	e	22
+333	129	+3.0	+10.0	-7	782	-16*	—	766	23
-151	128	+2.9	-4.4	+3	1125	-9	1116		24
-63	128	+2.9	-1.8	-1	970	-6	964		25
-35	127	+2.8	-1.0	-3	905	-1	904		26
+87	126	+2.7	+2.3	-4	869	+1	870	d	27
-493	125	+2.5+	-12.5	-2	958	+5	963	b	28
				-15	452	+10*	—	462	29

Fig. 11. (Concluded.)

(11) temperature correction, in percent of the difference in aneroid readings,

$$= \frac{t_1 + t - 100}{1000},$$

* On known bench marks.

where t_1 and t are the Fahrenheit temperatures of the air at two adjacent points. Column 7 times column 9 gives column 10.

If desired, column 10 may be found directly from Table XXXIII.

It will be noted by examination of formula 11 or Table XXXIII that the temperature correction is small when the sum of the temperatures is not far from 100° F, and/or when the difference in elevation between adjacent points is small.

Barometric Correction. A barometer kept at a fixed location may vary during a day, sometimes within an hour or two, by an amount equivalent to from 50 feet to several hundred feet. This is due to the following causes:

(1) *The diurnal or daily variation*, which is a somewhat irregular cycle with the low observed elevation occurring about 3 hours after sunrise and the high observed elevation about 9 hours after sunrise. A secondary low elevation also occurs during the night and a secondary high elevation occurs about sunrise. In latitude 30° this range is about 100 feet, the amount in the tropics being greater and in high latitudes smaller. In other words, in latitude 30° one would expect an elevation reading taken some 3 hours after sunrise to be about 100 feet lower than the same reading taken about 9 hours after sunrise. Naturally the best results in barometric leveling will be obtained when the barometer is varying the least, usually from 2 to 4 hours after sunrise and between 8 and 10 hours after sunrise. During the middle of the day, the rate of barometric diurnal variation is maximum—frequently as great as 30 feet per hour.

(2) *The effect of major storms and of local disturbances on the barometric pressure.* During the 1927 tornado in St. Louis, the barometer readings changed an amount equivalent to some 1300 feet of elevation in two or three hours. It is evidently difficult or impossible to do satisfactory elevation work with a barometer except in reasonably stable atmospheric conditions. A sharp rise in pressure (lowering

of observed elevations) frequently follows a thunderstorm.

In order most satisfactorily to obtain elevations with the aneroid, we must, then, do the field work when the barometric pressure is varying the least, and we must correct the observed elevations (which have previously been corrected for air temperature) for barometric pressure changes, as in Fig. 11. The barometric correction, taken from the chart of Fig. 11a, is entered in column 13 of Fig. 11 and is applied to the entry of column 12 to give columns 14 and 15.

The barometric correction chart of Fig. 11a is constructed from the observations taken in the field notes of Fig. 11. For points 1 and 2, the known bench mark elevation, 462, minus the 398 and 402 of column 12 gives the barometric correction of $+64$ and $+60$ in column 13. These are plotted as open circles on the barometric correction chart at 7:02 and 7:08 A.M. Points 6, 14, 18, 23, and 29 (all points of known elevation) are similarly entered in column 13 and are also plotted as open circles on the barometric correction chart. The dashed line drawn through these open circles gives a curve which is approximately correct. For improving this curve somewhat, especially where few or no known elevations are available except the initial one, readings are taken a second or third time on the same point, as for example on Fig. 11 in the cases of numbers 8 and 15; 16, 17, and 27; 6 and 18; 3 and 19; 20 and 22; and 7 and 28. As an example of the use of the duplicate readings, points 8 and 15 show a barometric variation of $1688 - 1663$ or 25 feet, whereas the dashed trial curve on the barometric correction chart shows a difference of 16 feet, indicating that one or the other, or both, points must be raised or lowered so that they will show a difference of 25 feet on the chart. A pair of dividers set to 25 feet for point c and moved up and down, aids in determining where the c points should be finally located. The solid circles at c on the chart show such an adjustment. Similarly points a, b, d, and e are adjusted and plotted as solid circles and the solid curve drawn through them as well as through the open circles.

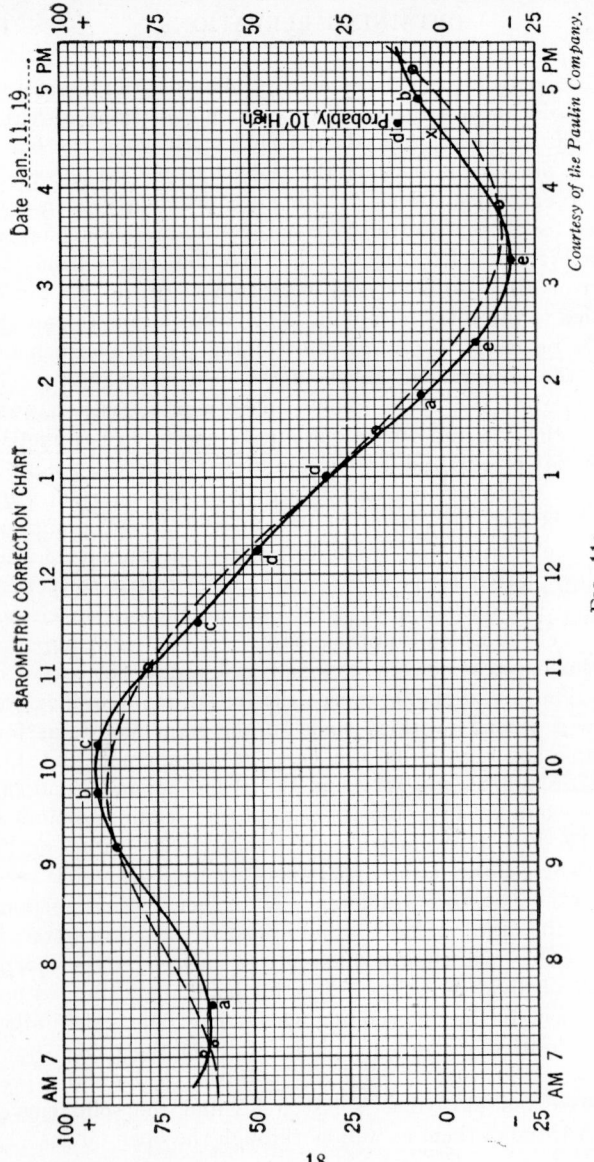

BAROMETRIC CORRECTION CHART   Date Jan. 11, 19......

Probably 10′ High

Courtesy of the Paulin Company.

FIG. 11a.

18

If a second barometer and a second observer are available, then the second barometer is kept at a constant elevation near the points whose elevations are being obtained with the moving barometer, and the barometric correction chart is plotted directly from the readings of the stationary barometer. It is desirable, although not essential, that both barometers be adjusted simultaneously to the same true elevation reading on the bench mark. Readings of the stationary barometer should usually be taken every half hour, and at 10 minute intervals if precise results are needed and/or if the barometric pressures are varying rapidly. If the moving barometer can be seen by the fixed barometer observer then the readings of both barometers may be taken at the same time. Of course the stationary barometer method can be used only to control points within a territory over which barometric pressures are varying in the same manner.

A careful compliance with the foregoing systematic procedure should give readings which will generally be within 10 feet or so of the correct elevations. We add some suggestions for insuring the accuracy of the work:

(1) The Paulin barometer seems to be superior to the older types, which are subject to sudden derangement and which require more time to accommodate themselves to changes in temperature, elevation, or other factors that affect barometric pressure.

(2) Barometric leveling should not be undertaken when the barometric pressure is changing rapidly.

(3) As in leveling with the engineer's level, the circuits should always be "closed" on the initial point (preferably a bench mark) or on some other point of known elevation, preferably a bench mark.

(4) During the lunch hour and whenever it can conveniently be done, readings should be taken upon reaching (after allowing the barometer time to adjust itself), and upon leaving, the station. A variation in readings will aid in drawing the barometric correction chart.

(5) If it is necessary to change inches of mercury to feet of elevation, the following formula, or a similar one, is generally used

$$(11a) \quad \text{Feet of elevation} = 62,943 \log \frac{30}{\text{inches of mercury}},$$

where 0 elevation at sea level is assumed to be equal to 30 inches of mercury. Tables are provided in some surveying books on this basis, and elevation scales are so divided on many barometers.

(6) When the atmospheric pressure at the moment of observation, reduced to mean sea level, varies from the normal zero of the graduated scale on the barometer (mentioned as 30 inches in (5) above), then a correction of 4 percent, plus or minus, per 1000 feet (about 1 inch of mercury) of variation should be applied to the difference in elevation between any points as read on the barometer. It will be noted that this correction is ordinarily negligible.

(7) The recent improved aneroids may be used for much approximate reconnaissance and preliminary leveling for dam sites, topography, contours, reservoir sites, pipe lines, ditches, grade contours, and so on.

(8) For an explanation of Precision Altimetry with newer and improved types of aneroid barometers, see Professor Philip Kissam's article in *Photogrammetric Engineering*, January–March, 1944.

If a third barometer and a third observer are available, the most precise results may be obtained by a "two-base" method as explained in the reference in (8), or as described more simply on pages 540–541 of Rubey, Lommel, and Todd, *Engineering Surveys—Elementary and Applied*.

12. Aerial Surveys. From the 1949 "Highway Practice in the United States of America" published by the Public Roads Administration of the Federal Works Agency, a brief summary is here quoted which indicates the present use of aerial surveys in the field of highway engineering. Similar practices are used in other fields of route surveying.

Reconnaissance of the Region

"The first stage of highway location is the determination, not of a single route or highway location, but of all feasible routes in the region through which the proposed new or relocated highway will pass. This survey stage is largely based on existing maps where available, supplemented by aerial photographs and mosaics obtainable from various sources.

Reconnaissance of Alternate Routes

"The second stage has as its purpose the selection and comparison of a series of possible alternate routes. As now carried out by aerial survey methods, this reconnaissance usually covers a series of strips or zones of land from 1 to 5 miles, or more, in width. Best adapted for such aerial coverage are strip photographs at scales of from 400 to 600 feet per inch. In highly developed suburban or urban areas photogrammetric maps made from such photographs to scales as large as 200 feet per inch, with a contour interval of 5 feet, have been used. In very heavy, mountainous topography such large scale maps are often useful, both in this stage and in the preliminary location stage following. Under usual conditions, in open, undeveloped country, photogrammetric contour maps at a scale of 400 to 500 feet per inch, with a 10-foot contour interval, are satisfactory.

Aerial Surveys

"Main features of aerial surveys for alternate route reconnaissance may be summarized as follows:

(1) Flight lines are laid out covering a series of strips or zones of land from 1 to 5 miles wide containing possible alternate routes. The small-scale topographic maps or mosaics, mentioned under stage 1, are used for this purpose.

(2) The strips shown on the small-scale mosaics or maps are flown over and photographs are taken at desired scales, preferably 400 to 600 feet per inch. These photographs will

normally have about 55 percent overlap along the strip, with 25 to 35 percent of side lap.

(3) The photographs are examined under the stereoscope, and ground traverses and base lines are run to locate control points, such as road intersections, building corners, and the like. These control points, to be usable, should be easily recognized both on photographs and on the ground.

(4) After ground control surveys are run and bench marks established by level parties, these known control points are located on base map sheets.

(5) Photogrammetric maps can then be made, within the scale limits mentioned, by commercial mapping organizations. Costs of such mapping at 500 feet per inch and 10-foot contour interval in 1945 were in the neighborhood of 50 cents per acre, a map of 200-foot-per-inch scale and 5-foot contour interval costing about $1.00 per acre.

"Points of importance are: (1) that such maps must be correct up to the minute; (2) that they must be accurate in horizontal measurement to the limits of accurate measurement at the scales provided; and (3) that contours can be provided with elevation accuracy on 90 percent of areas covered to within half the contour interval.

"The usual final operation in this stage of reconnaissance will be the selection of the most direct and economical route for the preliminary surveys to follow.

GROUND RECONNAISSANCE

"The above description of aerial survey procedures should not be understood to imply that ground reconnaissance is not of great value. By ground processes, however, only the individual locator can retain full knowledge of the strips over which alternate routes will pass. In rough topography, or in developed suburban or urban areas, the vision of the reconnaissance party on the ground is limited and many details must be supplied by memory and from field notes. Reconnaissance by aerial methods, in contrast, removes the possibility of individual errors in judgment. Alternate routes shown on paired photographs under the stereoscope and on good photogrammetric maps are recorded in every detail. With such paired photographs and the contour maps made from them, there should be no possibility of doubt that the best and most economical route has been selected for preliminary location survey."

Chapters XIX and XX of this volume contain further information regarding aerial surveys.

12a. A Project Method for Teaching Route Surveys. An entire course in route surveys can be developed from the reconnaissance tabulation of Fig. 146 (page 244), and as described in §§ 146, 147, and 156. Beginning with a comprehensive statement of the project to be investigated, following with a reconnaissance survey and report, continuing with a preliminary map and paper location, and concluding with an engineer's estimate (Fig. 147) or a contractor's bid (Fig. 156 and 156a); the complete course of text assignments, lectures, problems, designs, and quizzes are introduced at appropriate intervals when need, interest, and motivation are keenest.

In such a project, the student develops a professional, rather than a sub-professional, attitude and closely associates route surveys with the profitable construction, contracting, and professional management of Chapters XV, XVI, and XVII. Furthermore, he will cultivate the important engineering and business judgments described on pages 5, 6, 24, and 25.

The assignment of a local, not an imaginary, project gives a practical flavor, provides opportunity for a field reconnaissance following the map reconnaissance, and facilitates the selection of field practice on a judgment-building project background rather than as isolated exercises which develop a sub-professional, rather than a professional, viewpoint.

13. Reconnaissance Procedure. The first step is a study of the possible profits, from a broad promotional viewpoint, with special emphasis on the future trends for which one is attempting to provide.

The second step is to secure the best available maps. The United States Geological Survey quadrangle sheets, the township plats of the United States Bureau of Public Lands, and other maps obtainable from Federal, state, county, city, and private sources, should be purchased or otherwise secured. An appreciable portion of the United States is now covered by aerial maps made by Federal, state, or county authorities. In many cases, special aerial surveys are justified. Usually it is desirable to complete and assemble all information which is available on one large map, or on a set of maps, either by mounting adjacent maps on cloth, or by preparing a comprehensive tracing. Frequently, the available maps are incomplete or insufficient, and rough supplemental surveys must be made on the ground before the map can be completed.

With the reconnaissance map in hand, trips by plane, automobile, on horseback, or on foot are made over the territory. With due respect to topography and other features, the approximate routes can be sketched on the map. If controlling points can be flagged on the ground, this will facilitate the later surveys.

In new or unsettled country where maps are inadequate, aerial surveys and field astronomical observations for latitude, longitude, and meridian will be found useful, and frequently indispensable.

It is sometimes desirable to traverse the route roughly, using a small compass and measuring distances by pacing or by an automobile speedometer. A complex but rapid method developed for the Army is described in Civil Engineering, December 1944.

14. The Reconnaissance Report. Such a report should include the following items:

(1) *A summary of the business prospects for the project.* This should be given in some detail if the matter is not covered in other available reports, or reference to such available business reports should be included in the engi-

neering reconnaissance report.   There should be available somewhere estimates corresponding to the balance sheet and the profit and loss statements of an operating business, including first cost of construction, income and operating costs, probable net earnings, and so on.

(2) *One or more recommended means of transportation* or communication and recommended routes.   It is usually desirable to discuss somewhat fully other means and routes which were considered and why they were discarded.

(3) *A recommendation against the entire undertaking,* if that should seem advisable.

The more carefully and accurately the reconnaissance is conducted and the report rendered, the easier, cheaper, and more quickly the preliminary surveys will be accomplished, as described in the following sections.   It pays very definitely to make a careful and painstaking reconnaissance, both because of savings in the preliminary surveys and because the very life of the project depends on the reconnaissance, as stated in (3) in the following paragraph.

The following points must be emphasized regarding the reconnaissance:

(1) *It is best undertaken with a broad, promotive, administrative, and engineering viewpoint* by a mature and competent engineer who possesses excellent judgment.

(2) *It is largely a one-man job in its execution,* although the best ideas of competent, experienced, and informed executives and financiers must be enlisted and incorporated in the final recommendations and conclusions.

(3) *It is apt seriously to harm or ruin the project if erroneous recommendations are made,* since it is usually impossible later to alter a general plan which has been adopted in the reconnaissance, and the project will remain permanently handicapped by an unwise selection of a means or route of transportation or communication.   This condition will encourage competitors to build a more efficient or more effective project.

CHAPTER III

THE PRELIMINARY

15. Purpose of Preliminary. After the reconnaissance has eliminated the obviously unsuitable routes, one or more promising routes usually remain about which more exact and detailed information is needed. The preliminary survey fulfills this need and usually provides a map on which the "map location" of § 24 may be made.

16. The Standard Type of Preliminary. The older, simpler, slower, surer, and more expensive preliminary involves the survey of a traverse of distances measured with a 100-foot tape and of deflection angles measured with a transit. Stakes are left in the ground 100 feet apart and numbered successively 0, 1, 2, 3, and so on. Elevations are taken with an engineer's level.

Three parties are necessary in this type of preliminary, each one having definite duties to perform:

> The Transit Party
> The Level Party
> The Topographic Party.

The *transit party* (field notes shown in Fig. 16) comprises a transitman, occasionally a notekeeper, a head tapeman, a rear tapeman, a flagman, and sufficient axmen to clear the line and to set stakes. A small truck for transportation should be provided. It is generally necessary to have a chief of party or a locating engineer who acts in an executive capacity and who scouts out the territory ahead of the transit party and sets successive objectives ahead on the ground for them. The speed of the transit party is largely dependent on the head tapeman; he should be an alert man, physically and mentally active. The work of the party must be planned so that it proceeds according to a routine in which a minimum number of delays for the entire party occur while some one member of the party performs his duties; in other words, so that all keep reasonably busy at the same time.

The *level party* (field notes shown in Fig. 16a) follows immediately behind the transit party, so that elevations are available to the locating engineer. Level data are especially needed by the transit party in the evening, in order that it may plan its work for the following day. This party comprises a levelman and a rodman with a small automobile for transportation. Sometimes part-time use of the transit party's truck will suffice for this.

The level party runs a profile over the preliminary transit line with an engineer's level, establishing bench marks along the route about 1,000 feet apart and determining the elevation of the ground at each station and at important breaks in the ground (at pluses between stations). The United States Coast and Geodetic Survey or the United States Geological Survey datum should be used if possible. The maximum permissible error of closure of levels in feet of elevation is usually $0.05\sqrt{M}$, occasionally $0.10\sqrt{M}$, where M is the length of circuit in miles. The level party should determine the high water elevations of streams and the elevation of exposed rock ledges.

The *topographic party* (field notes shown in Fig. 16b) follows the level party and includes a topographer, a rodman, and perhaps an instrument man. They must have some means of transportation, usually the automobile or truck of the level or transit party. It is desirable that the topographer be innately skilled and highly experienced.

This party locates all buildings, improvements, streams, contours, property lines, and so on, far enough on either or on both sides of the preliminary transit line so as to cover any reasonable possible final location of the engineering work to be undertaken. In a narrow valley, the topography will be needed for a width of several hundred feet or less, since here it is merely necessary to go high enough up the

sides of the valley to include any possible location; it is not
necessary to cover a particular width of territory.   In level

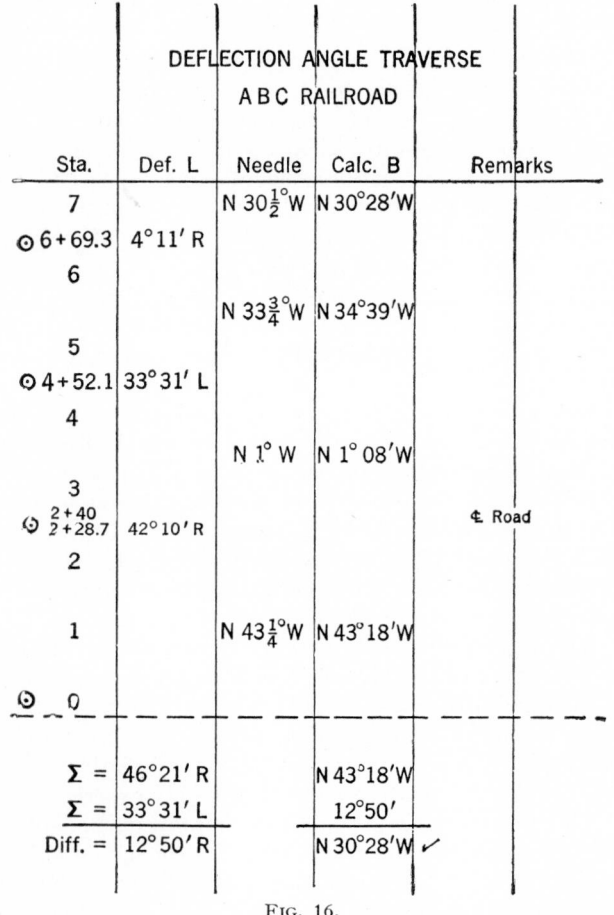

Sta.	Def. L	Needle	Calc. B	Remarks
7		N 30½°W	N 30°28′W	
⊙ 6+69.3	4°11′ R			
6				
		N 33¾°W	N 34°39′W	
5				
⊙ 4+52.1	33°31′ L			
4				
		N 1° W	N 1°08′W	
3				
⊙ 2+40 2+28.7	42°10′ R			℄ Road
2				
1		N 43¼°W	N 43°18′W	
⊙ 0				
Σ =	46°21′ R		N 43°18′W	
Σ =	33°31′ L		12°50′	
Diff. =	12°50′ R		N 30°28′W ✓	

DEFLECTION ANGLE TRAVERSE

A B C RAILROAD

Fig. 16.

or rolling country, where the final location may be a half-
mile or more from the preliminary, the map must cover that

much territory. The map, Fig. 16c, is customarily drawn to a scale of $1'' = 400'$ with a 5-foot contour interval, a—

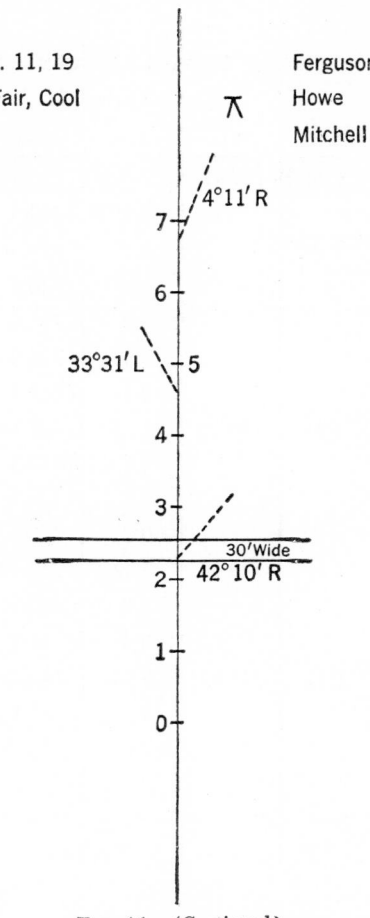

Jan. 11, 19
Fair, Cool

Ferguson
Howe
Mitchell

4°11' R

7

6

33°31' L — 5

4

3

30'Wide

2 — 42°10' R

1

0

FIG. 16. *(Continued.)*

though other scales are used in more difficult country, such as $1'' = 200'$ or $1'' = 100'$. One-foot or two-foot contours

ăre used occasionally, as for example in locating small canals.
For some surveys, such as for small pipe lines and trans-

Sta.	B. S.	H. I.	F. S.	Elev.
PROFILE OF A B C RAILROAD				
B.M. 1	9.30	729.41		720.11
0			8.3	721.1
1			3.7	725.7
+50			3.0	726.4
2			3.8	725.6
+40			4.6	724.8
3			2.3	727.1
T.P. 1	10.91	739.06	1.26	728.15
4			5.8	733.3
+42			2.7	736.4
5			0.3	738.8
B.M. 2	11.42	749.86	0.62	738.44
6			4.0	745.9
+5			3.4	746.5
T.P. 2	1.16	741.51	9.51	740.35
7			8.4	733.1
B.M. 3			9.02	732.49

FIG. 16a.

mission lines, little or no topography is required.   On highway work, topography is needed only on the more difficult
portions of the route.   On railways, large canals, large pipe

lines, and on important construction, topography must be taken over most of the route.

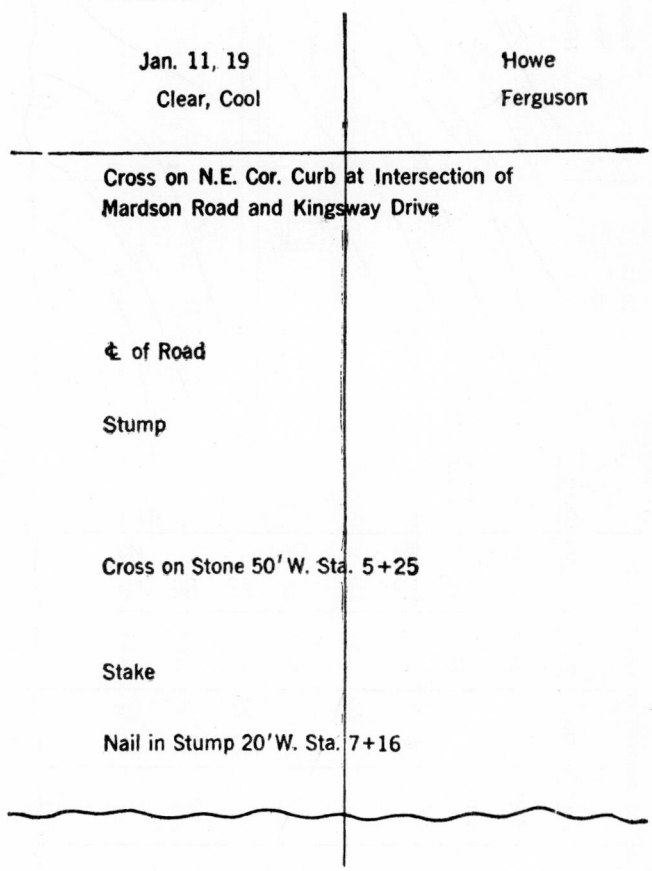

Jan. 11, 19
Clear, Cool

Howe
Ferguson

Cross on N.E. Cor. Curb at Intersection of Mardson Road and Kingsway Drive

₵ of Road

Stump

Cross on Stone 50′ W. Sta. 5+25

Stake

Nail in Stump 20′ W. Sta. 7+16

FIG. 16a. (*Continued.*)

The topographic party ties the land lines and property corners to the preliminary survey, usually approximately, but occasionally with precision.

TOPOGRAPHY OF A B C RAILROAD

Sta.	Left Contours			℄ Elev.	Right Contours			
7	+4°20′/170			733.1	730/80	725/197		
6 ⊙	−1°50′/250			740.9	740/60	735/102	730/125	725/198
5		730/345	735/51	738.8	742/126	728/295		
4			730/65	733.1	735/82			
3				727.1	730/64	735/181		
2		720/327	725/112	725.6	730/130			
1	−2°0′/250	720/111	725/6	725.7	730/205			
0		715/67	720/18	721.1	725/55	730/261		

Jan. 10, 19
Cloudy, Cool

⊼ Ferguson
Howe
Mitchell

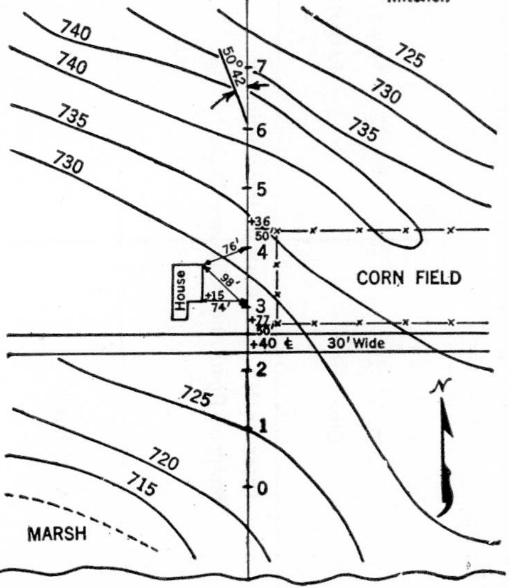
740
740
735
730
725
730
735
50°
42
7
6
5
4
3
2
1
0
+36
50
76′
98′
+15
74′
+77
50
+40 ℄
30′ Wide
House
CORN FIELD
725
720
715
MARSH
N

FIG. 16b.

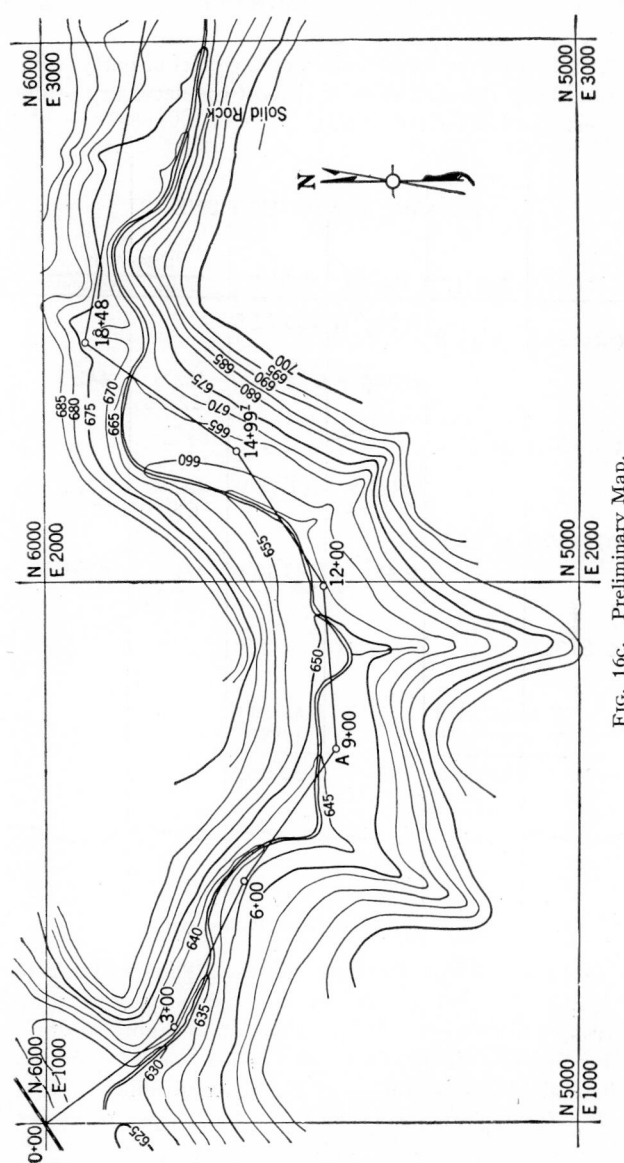

FIG. 16c. Preliminary Map.

33

At this time the topographer, or the chief of party, should note at least the approximate sizes of the necessary bridges, culverts, and other structures.

110 KVA TRANSMISSION LINE

Sta.	Def. L	Needle	Calc. B	Distances Slope	Distances Horizontal
⊙ 21+95.8	4°11′ R	N 30½° W	N 30°28′W		
		N 34½° W	N 34°39′W	453.0 +12°20′	442.5
⊙ 17+52.8	33°31 L				
		N 1° W	N 1°08′W	422.8 0°0′	422.8
⊙ 13+30.0	42°10′ R				
		N 43¼° W	N 43°18′W	471.3 −21°20′	439.0
⊙ 8+91.0					
Σ =	46°21′ R		N 43°18′W		
Σ =	33°31′ L		12°50′		
	12°50′ R		N 30°28′W		

Fig. 17. Long Tape Preliminary.

17. Long Tape Preliminaries. The speed or rate of progress of a preliminary survey traverse may be greatly increased and equal or better precision in taping secured by using 300-foot or 500-foot tapes instead of 100-foot tapes. The United States Bureau of Public Lands and the United States Geological Survey both use long tapes extensively, and they are also being used increasingly in private surveys, especially in rough open country. Figure 17 shows notes for such a survey. It is usually convenient to set stakes

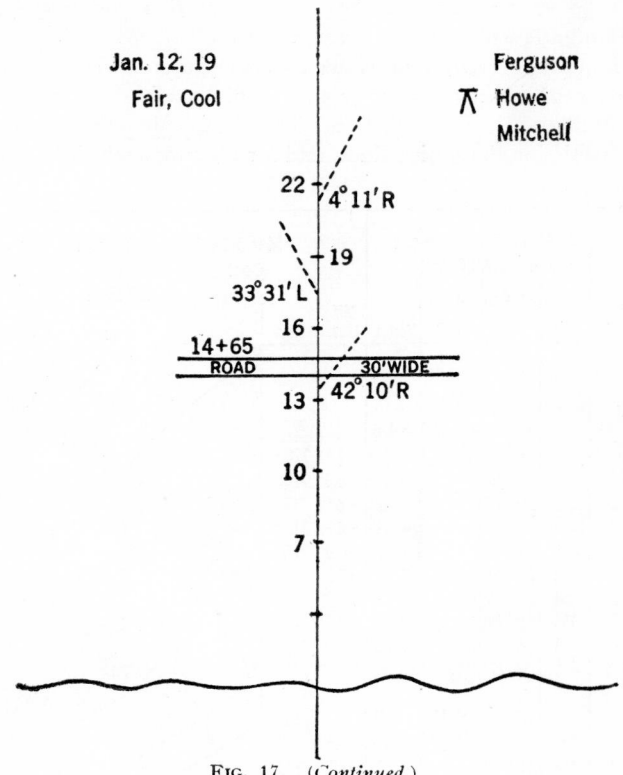

Jan. 12, 19
Fair, Cool

Ferguson
Ⲙ Howe
Mitchell

22 ┼ 4°11′R

┼ 19

33°31′L

16 ┼

14+65
ROAD   30′WIDE

13 ┼ 42°10′R

10 ┼

7 ┼

Fig. 17. (*Continued.*)

at pluses rather than at full stations. Table XXX facilitates the reduction of slope distances to the horizontal.* Rough elevations may be carried forward from the measured vertical angles, although this is seldom done.

* For further details regarding the use of long tapes, refer to pages 20–22 of Rubey, Lommel, and Todd, *Engineering Surveys*, The Macmillan Company, 1950.

Since the topographic cross-sections are several hundred feet apart, the topography must be carefully plotted and sketched in the field, and even then this topography will not be so accurate as the 100-foot station topography, although it will be taken more rapidly.

Long-tape preliminaries are especially useful where little topography is necessary, or where only moderate accuracy in topography is needed, as for example in surveys for transmission lines, pipe lines, and for highways which follow old rights of way.

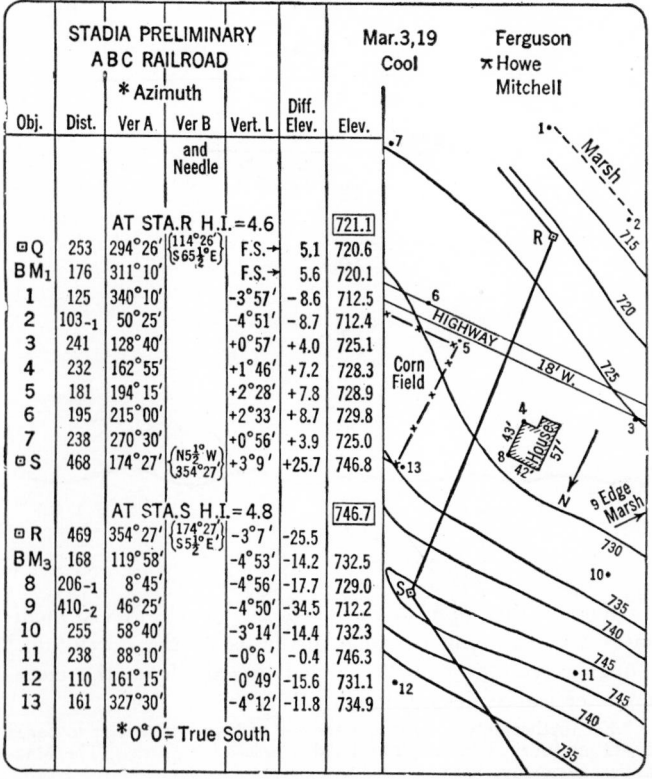

Fig. 18.

Object	Dist.	Needle	Vert. L	Diff. Elev.	Elev.
			RAPID STADIA PRELIMINARY		
			ABC RAILROAD		
⊙ Q	253	At Sta. R.	H.I. =	4.6	721.1
B.M. 1	176	S 65½° E		F.S. 5.1	720.6
1	232	S 48¾° E		F.S. 5.6	720.1
⊙ S	468	N 17° W	+ 1°46′	+ 7.2	728.3
		N 5½° W	+ 3°09′	+ 25.7	746.8
⊙ S	389	At Sta. T.	H.I. =	4.9	720.5
2	484	S 60½° E	+ 3°53′	+ 26.3	746.8
⊙ U	246	S 33¼° E	+ 0°58′	+ 8.2	728.7
		N 7½° W	− 2°14′	− 9.6	710.9

FIG. 19.

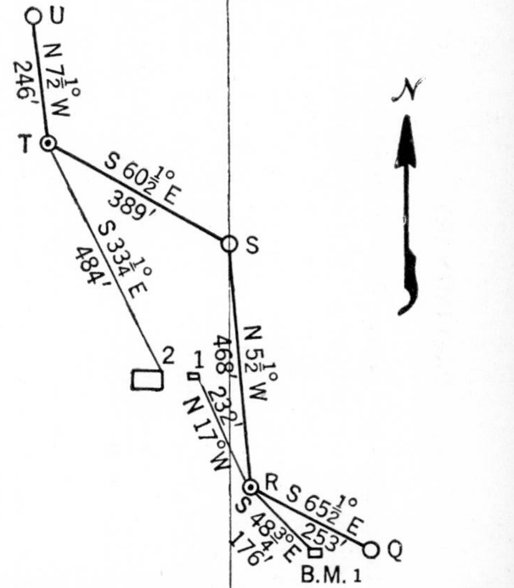

37

18. Stadia Preliminary. A more rapid and economical preliminary, and one that is being used increasingly, is that executed by the transit and stadia method. It is somewhat less precise than the preceding methods although frequently sufficiently precise, and it requires a more experienced personnel. Alignment, elevation, and topography are carried along by a single party. The procedure in this type of survey is shown in the field notes of Fig. 18. This method is best adapted to open country where a considerable range of topography, either in width or elevation, is to be taken. Timber, brush, or high crops seriously interfere with the many sights needed in using this method and excessive clearing is required. Rarely, the plane table is used instead of the transit.

19. Rapid Stadia Preliminary. The speed of the preliminary may be increased, at the expense of accuracy, by occupying only every other stadia station and by taking a reduced number of side shots as shown in the notes of Fig. 19. Topography is sketched in the notebook or on separate sheets of ruled paper. This is really a low grade of preliminary or a very high grade of reconnaissance. Direction is secured by *the magnetic needle only.*

19a. Aerial Preliminaries. These are increasingly used as indicated in § 12, Chapters XIX and XX.

20. Precision of Preliminaries. Opinions differ as to the precision needed in a preliminary survey. Some engineers believe that the preliminary should be run as precisely as the "final location," described later. It is desirable or necessary to secure such precision:

(1) when only one preliminary is to be surveyed;

(2) when parts of the preliminary may be used as the final location;

(3) when the preliminary is used to check the final location by means of computing coordinates or by other computation, as mentioned in § 21;

(4) when the final location is to be located accurately on the preliminary map and then transferred exactly to the same location on the ground. This is desirable, for example, when the country is heavily timbered or brushy, so that it is difficult to see the lay of the land when locating and it is advisable therefore to locate accurately on, and from, the map; and

(5) in the relatively rare cases where construction is to be started, or contracts for construction are to be entered into, as soon as the paper location is made and before the final location is completely staked on the ground.

Most engineers consider less precision than that just mentioned sufficient, however. and they are thus enabled to run more of the cheaper preliminaries with the time and money available. It will be recalled that the reconnaissance was stated to be the most important part of the survey as viewed from the business or financial standpoint. Where more preliminaries of a cheaper and less precise nature are run, they really serve the purpose of improving the reconnaissance; that is, they insure that no more satisfactory route has been overlooked. The less precise the preliminary, the more it may be considered a part of a high-grade reconnaissance.

21. Checking and Coordinating the Preliminary.

Any extensive route or line survey, say over a mile or two in length, should be coordinated. Coordinates should be computed for each angle point on the preliminary and from these data each angle point should be plotted on ten-inch squares which have previously been carefully drawn on the map. The plotting of the preliminary is then checked, almost error proof, by scaling the distances between angle points on the map and comparing these distances with the survey lengths.

It is desirable that the coordinates be referred or tied to existing official survey monuments whose coordinates are known from previous surveys, and thus to give permanence to the survey and to secure an inexpensive and excellent check on the work. Monuments of the United States Coast and Geodetic Survey, the United States Geological Survey, city surveys, or corporation surveys are all useful for this purpose. If the North American Datum can be used, so much the better. Highway data are occasionally available.

The coordinates are later computed from the same origin for the final location (mentioned later) and this final location survey is "tied" to the preliminary survey or to the monuments above mentioned in such a manner as to furnish a check or "closure" on all the survey work.

Such checking by coordinates generally more than pays for itself by insuring against blunders, sometimes serious ones, and by facilitating precision in mapping and in various computations. If coordinates are not used, it becomes increasingly important to secure the most careful field and office work; as, for example, to take frequent and careful astronomic observations to check bearings. It is surprising to find how many errors can creep into an unchecked survey and map.

Route surveys require traverse bearings precise to within a few minutes. This involves tying the route traverse by angle to previous precise surveys or to true meridians established by astronomical observations. Such ties should be made every several miles, or perhaps every 50 angle points, and the calculated bearings of the traverse should be checked between them. Due allowance must be made for the convergence of meridians, as given in Table XXVIII.

22. Miscellany. It may be well to repeat that a careful choice of survey and mapping methods is most important on the preliminary and location surveys to the end that rapid and correct results of sufficient precision may be obtained, and that the engineer in charge (often one of the younger men) may gain prestige among his superior officers.

It is frequently helpful to draw the preliminary map in pencil (and to ink it as opportunity offers) on the best grade of tracing paper so that blueprints may be made promptly for field use before the map is entirely complete. The map may be traced later on cloth for finished results and for permanent record. Where very careful scaling is required from the map, it is necessary to use the best grade of paper that will shrink and expand as little as possible, although such distortion may be allowed for if the map contains 10-inch squares for coordinates.

The computation, office work, and mapping of surveys should be done in the afternoon or evening of the day on which the survey was made so that errors and omissions in the field work may be discovered and brought to the attention of the field parties and so that corrections or additions may be secured by the field parties on the following day. This usually means that a draftsman and computer should be maintained at field headquarters.

Stakes. In both preliminary and location surveys, it is necessary to stake the surveys in a workmanlike manner according to uniform and conventional standards which may vary slightly with different organizations. Relative permanence is the aim. Even with careful procedure in this respect, it is usually difficult to find stakes after a few weeks or months and almost impossible to do so after a year or more.

Hubs. $2'' \times 2'' \times 8''$ stakes, occasionally larger and longer, are driven flush with the ground at each point occupied by the transit, and the exact point is marked with a tack.

Guard Stakes are driven in a sloping position about $8''$ from the hub at right angles from the line. They extend several inches or more above ground and are marked with lumber crayon or keel to designate the relation of the hub to the survey, as for example, T.C. (tangent-curve) 134 + 94.6, or P.O.T. (point on tangent) 139 + 48.7, or P.O.C. (point on the curve) 147 + 17.9. Frequently other letters may be needed; as, for example, *PB* (Preliminary *B*) or *LA* (Location *A*) and so on.

Reference Stakes or Marks are established to facilitate the relocation of lost hubs.

Station Stakes marking the station, usually without tacks, extending several inches or more vertically above the ground, are marked with the station number and perhaps the *PB* or *LA*, as mentioned above.

Equations are written in the notes and on the map, and are lettered on the stakes wherever two or more surveys cross or join; as, for example, $LA \; 13 + 17.6 = PA \; 19 + 38.4$. Equations must be clearly indicated and must be self-explanatory.

Instructions for the Guidance of Field Parties. The following instructions of the American Railway Engineering Association will be useful in calling attention to points to be considered in organizing and supervising field parties.

Purpose and Scope. The amount and kind of information to be obtained and the degree of precision required depend upon the purpose and scope of the survey; hence careful and constant consideration of these features is essential to the proper planning and execution of field work.

The error, if any, should be in the direction of too much information or excess precision; but large errors in either direction are inexcusable, as they constitute an economic waste.

Before Going into the Field. The "Chief of Party," being responsible to his superiors for results and to his men for their welfare, should familiarize himself as thoroughly as possible with the conditions to be encountered before starting field work.

With the advice and under the instructions of his superiors the Chief of Party should consider the following items and make his preparations accordingly:

The size of the party should be adapted to the work to be done, i.e., a sufficient number of engineering assistants with ample training for their respective positions, and of intelligent helpers, should be provided to handle the work expeditiously and economically.

The Chief of Party should have the right to select the members of the party whenever feasible; especially on extensive surveys, when he should satisfy himself that the men will be able to stand the work under the climatic and other conditions encountered.

Local people should be employed as helpers whenever possible so that advantage may be taken of their knowledge of local conditions. Sometimes the sympathetic interest of the community may be enlisted by this practice.

The relative rank of the various members of the party or sub-parties under any and all circumstances should be specified clearly, but with the understanding that changes may be made by the Chief of Party as the exigencies of the work require.

The Chief of Party should instruct the men as to the amount and kind of clothing and personal supplies with which to provide themselves, setting limits of weight or bulk whenever necessary, with due consideration to the following:

Transportation facilities,

Climate, including extremes of temperature, rainfall, etc.,

Country to be traversed,

Duration of trip or expedition, and

Possibility of securing clothes and supplies on the work.

Mode or modes of travel are as follows:

Steam railway,

Electric railway,

Automobile,

Motor car,

Horse and wagon,

Pack train,

Boats or canoes, and

Dog sleds, etc.

Check availability of forage for animals, and gasoline, oils, and repair parts for motor vehicles.

Provide for overcoming difficulties with the mode or modes of travel selected.

If housing and boarding of men are in hotels, the spacing and capacity,

If in farm houses, the spacing and capacity,

If in camp cars, the number and kind required, and

If in tents, the number necessary and the proper design to withstand storms, animals and insects. Also whether stoves, wooden floors, flies, etc., are needed.

Check food supplies—articles and amount of each required to take care of party until it can be replenished. Use of local foods should be encouraged.

Provide first aid outfits and instructions for their use.

Provide additional medical supplies and instructions for their use, the quantity and assortment to depend upon possibility of securing such supplies in the country to be traversed.

Provide methods of preserving foods and substitutes for those that can not be preserved.

Instrumental equipment, including drafting, should be ample, with duplicates of those articles difficult or impossible to secure in the country traversed or within a reasonable time.

The cooking outfit should be reasonably complete, considering the difficulties of transportation.

In addition to tents, mosquito head nets, mosquito proof tents, snow shoes, snow glasses, portable boats, ropes, hammocks, cots, blankets, etc., may be necessary in some localities.

Camp sites should be carefully selected with due regard to:

Supply of potable water,

Sanitary facilities required and method of providing them,

Protection from storms, and

Healthfulness.

Provide facilities and methods of securing mail, and other sources of communication that can be arranged.

After the party arrives in the field, the Chief of Party should not be overburdened with details, but should have ample time to plan the work and anticipate requirements. He should first, therefore, give instructions covering the following items:

The duties of the various members of the party under differing circumstances and for different periods of the day should be outlined, insofar as is practicable, such as:

When starting the day,
When completing the day,
When setting up camp,
When breaking camp, and
When in camp.

The assembling of each party, or sub-party, at the close of the day's work should be insisted upon, so that no one may be lost or left alone in case of accident.

Care should be used in the handling and use of all supplies and equipment so that injuries and waste may be avoided.

Special instructions should be given in regard to leaving instruments and other equipment in the field over night.

Personal property of each man should bear individual marks or be of distinctive color sufficient to keep it from being mixed with the property of others.

Specify the amount of care to be exercised when passing through cultivated fields.

Specify the general rules as to when timber should be cut and when to triangulate or offset around it.

Specify the cutting of stakes from timber, or material at hand, to avoid using property upon which others may set a value.

Specify the kind of stakes to be used through fields to avoid injuries to farm machinery; or specify the removal of stakes after the party has passed.

The conduct of party should be such as to create and maintain a good feeling among the residents; local customs should be observed and care should be taken not to stir up local prejudices.

Conduct at farm houses should indicate an appreciation of the fact that the people have inconvenienced themselves in order to accommodate you.   Meddling with their belongings should be prohibited.

The forms for field notes should be specified and kept uniform throughout the survey, with due regard to ease of plotting and their use by others not connected with the survey.

All notes should be titled, dated and indexed, and should show the name of the engineer in charge and of the person making the notes.

The title should indicate the name, letter or number of the line, and notes for all abandoned lines should be crossed out and marked "Abandoned."

Transit and topography notes should run up the page and the latter should give the scale at the beginning and end of each line.

An index of all field books and their contents should also be kept.

Maps should be kept up to date and should conform in all respects to the required standards.

When a line is finally established, bench marks should be placed at permanent locations and a large number of alignment points should be referenced in a permanent manner. Reference points should be so placed as to make the recovery of the alignment point as convenient as possible and in such positions that they will not be disturbed by the processes of construction.

The preliminary survey is completed by the preparation of the preliminary map which is used as described in § 24.

CHAPTER IV

LOCATION

23. General. The location survey follows the preliminary and is the final fitting of the line to the ground. Curves are used, where necessary, to connect the straight lines or "tangents," and the alignment is completely staked on the ground; following this, the final map and the final profile are completed in the office.

Obviously the final location must conform to good engineering practice for the construction to be undertaken, and the locator must have specific engineering knowledge and experience to guide him. Here the judgment is somewhat more detailed and more technical, and involves less of a broad business viewpoint than is required in the reconnaissance. Judgment is required particularly regarding alignment, curves, spirals, gradients, construction methods, and construction and operation cost, all of which come primarily from experience but may be obtained to some extent by observation or by study from technical literature.

24. Procedure. The simpler location surveys may be made with little or no reconnaissance, preliminary, or map work, but usually the "map location" method is used. In applying this method, the chief of party or the locating engineer draws a proposed location on the map which was prepared from the preliminary survey. As he studies this "paper location," he sees where it can be improved and makes the change. After two or three such trial and error procedures, he steps around the penciled location with his dividers, marking each 100-foot station along the proposed location and perhaps emphasizing each fifth station. He then prepares a profile from the map and designs a tentative grade line on the profile. It will now be apparent that because of excessive cutting and filling or for other reasons the location must be modified further. This process is continued and ultimately results in an acceptable paper location.   One or more trips into the field may be necessary to clear up questions which have arisen in the office.

In establishing the final location on the map, and in establishing the grade line on the profile, it is desirable to use a fine silk thread passing around needles at the angle points.   The final location or the profile grade line, as indicated by the silk thread, can then be shifted as the study proceeds without excessive erasing on the map or profile.

Blueprints of this paper location are taken into the field and it is staked on the ground, again in order to improve alignment and grades so as to reduce construction and operation costs, or otherwise to improve the location.   In transferring the location from the map to a staked position on the ground, the engineer should ordinarily stake the tangents or straight lines first, locating them with reference to such of the preliminary stakes or other marks shown on the map as may be found and identified on the ground, and continually watching for map errors which may modify the location, although these modifications are usually slight.

The position of points on the map location which are to be transferred to the ground are usually scaled from the map with a protractor and scale, using right-angle offsets, intersection of lines, or angle and distance.   Occasionally, the distances and angles on the proposed final location are precisely computed from coordinates.   Rarely, the location field notes are prepared in the office from the paper location, and then run in the field.

Profile levels are run over the final location and the grade line is established on the profile.   The final location, as staked in the field, is then plotted on the map.

A topographic, or "land line," party now locates the property lines and various improvements, and ties these to the location survey so that definite descriptions for the necessary right of way may be prepared as described in

Chapter XIV. At this time, if not previously accomplished, data are secured for estimating and designing the culverts, bridges, transmission-tower footings, and other needed structures.

The organization of the survey work is quite similar to that used for the preliminary survey. Various standard types of field notes and drawings are required by different organizations. Usually the larger organizations have a pamphlet of instructions which is issued to the interested engineers and which shows standard field notes and drawings; or samples of their previous work may be consulted.

Contracts for construction may be let immediately after the paper location is made, especially if the preliminary survey and mapping have been carried out accurately. However, it is customary to let the contracts only after the final location has been staked on the ground and the final profile is available, even though this may involve months of delay.

If speed is essential, work may be started by company forces or under a "cost plus percentage" contract (see § 129) as soon as a short portion of the final location has been staked on the ground.

25. Grade Contour.

A grade contour is frequently useful where it is desired to lay out some construction, such as railway, highway, canal, or flume on a continuous and uniform grade, as is the case where a railway ascends toward a pass in the mountains or where a canal is being located along the foothills bordering a valley. Suppose, for example, that we desire so to locate a line on the map as to maintain the flattest possible uniform grade between two points which are 110 stations, or 11,000 feet, apart (measured along a probable location) and at a difference in elevation of 220 feet. This requires a continuous 2 percent grade. Assuming a 5-foot contour interval, a horizontal distance of 250 feet on the ground will be required to rise an amount equal to the 5-foot contour interval. Further, assuming the map to be drawn to a scale of $1'' = 400'$, we set a pair of dividers with a spread of 250/400 inch, representing 250 feet on the ground. Beginning on grade at the more definitely fixed end on the map, as we step from contour to contour with the dividers, we establish a sinuous line every part of which is on a 2 percent grade, and we will finally reach the point on grade at the other end which we chose originally. A perfect theoretical grade contour is not used, but it must approximate the final location and consequently must occasionally step across contours, reaching a proper contour again after a corresponding number of intervals. It will be impossible for our location to follow even this modified grade contour exactly, since it will curve too sharply and too frequently, but the nearer we can follow it, the less cutting and filling will be necessary and the more nearly will our construction fit the natural ground. This method is thus useful in making the paper location.

In the field, a similar grade contour is frequently used in locating hydraulic construction or on flat grades used for other purposes. The predetermined rate of grade is staked off on the ground by taping or pacing distances and by determining elevations with an engineers' level. Lath with cloth flags are thus set along the grade contour on the ground. The transit party follows these flags as nearly as may be possible, straightening out the alignment so that it may be a practicable one.

A similar process is used for setting lath or stakes on a grade contour where a construction or temporary road must climb a hill rapidly. A clinometer, set on the required grade, is used to run from lath to lath. With the laths set on the grade contour, the road building foreman can usually construct a passable road without further engineering aid.

26. Balanced Cuts and Fills. In railway, highway, and similar construction, the grade line on the profile is adjusted to balance the cuts and fills by longitudinal hauling along the center line, as explained in Chapter XIII.   Suitable construction equipment includes trucks, narrow gauge or standard gauge railway cars, carryalls, and the like.

In most hydraulic work, such as canals and levees, the profile grade line is adjusted so that the cut will just make the fill by moving the excavated material transversely— at right angles—to the center line, as in Table XXIV.   This requires a "balanced cut" as nearly as possible at every point along the center line.   Thus, material is not hauled for any considerable distance longitudinally, and power shovels (for side casting), drag line excavators, trenching machines, elevating graders, bulldozers, fresnos with tractors, and similar equipment are ordinarily used.

27. Exploration of Excavation.   During the location, if it has not been accomplished beforehand, it is frequently desirable to explore the material to be excavated, as mentioned in § 93.   By means of such exploration, the suitability of the excavation as a foundation is determined and a basis is established upon which to classify material and to estimate the costs of excavation.

The soil survey investigates the nature, methods of handling, and suitability of soils.   It determines the soil profile, the selection of samples, and the mapping of the profile. Test pits, auger borings, wash borings, soundings, geophysical exploration, and aerial photography are used.

"Exploration of Soil Conditions and Sampling Operations" by H. A. Mohr, Harvard Graduate School of Engineering, Bulletin No. 208, and pages 175 and 221 of this text give additional information.

28. Obtaining Permission to Construct.   During or near the completion of the location, it is customary to open negotiations with persons, corporations, or governmental bodies whose permission is needed before construction may be initiated.   This includes right of way, as mentioned in Chapter XIV; crossings of railways, pipe lines, canals, transmission lines, highways, streets; and other invasion of vested interests.

29. Monumenting the Location. The *hubs*, or transit point stakes (see § 22), are of substantial size and are driven flush with the ground. Their positions are marked by guard stakes on which the point is described and its station number given. However, these hubs are often destroyed or lost, so that as a precaution their position is referred to nearby permanent objects, such as trees, buildings, and so on. These references are entered in the field note books for use later by the construction engineer.

30. Location Maps and Profiles. Some of the more typical maps and profiles are shown in this section. Few organizations use precisely the same standards in executing their drawings, but most organizations have their own standards which must be followed.

On railways, Fig. 30, it is desirable to show the transverse slope of the ground (as at the top of the profile), the quantities of construction to be accomplished, the regular profile, and the alignment of tangents and curves (as at the bottom of the profile).

On highways, Fig. 30a, the map and profile are customarily shown on the same sheet.

On transmission lines, Fig. 30b, the map is a rather simple one, usually without topography. The profile (not shown) is also rather simple and is used primarily for locating the towers so as to give the best tower spacing and at the same time to keep the conductors the required minimum distance above the ground. This last requirement is usually covered by a statute of the state in which the construction is located.

On canals, Fig. 30c, the profile customarily shows the cross-section of the various portions of the canal and also gives the hydraulic properties of the various sections. The standards of the United States Reclamation Service are among the best for canal work.

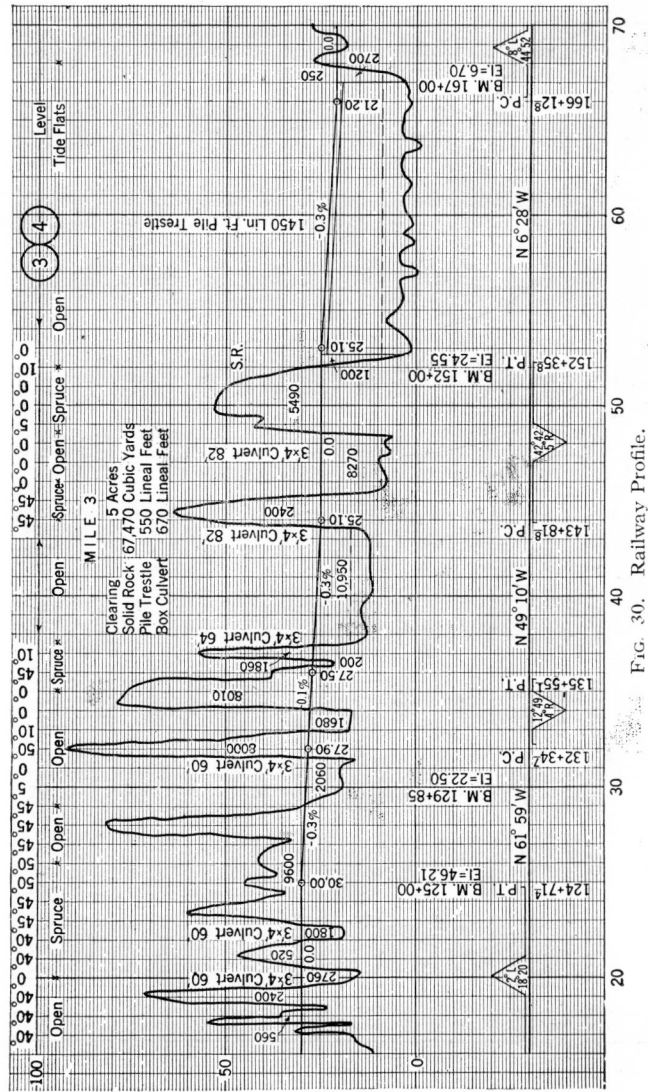

Fig. 30. Railway Profile.

53

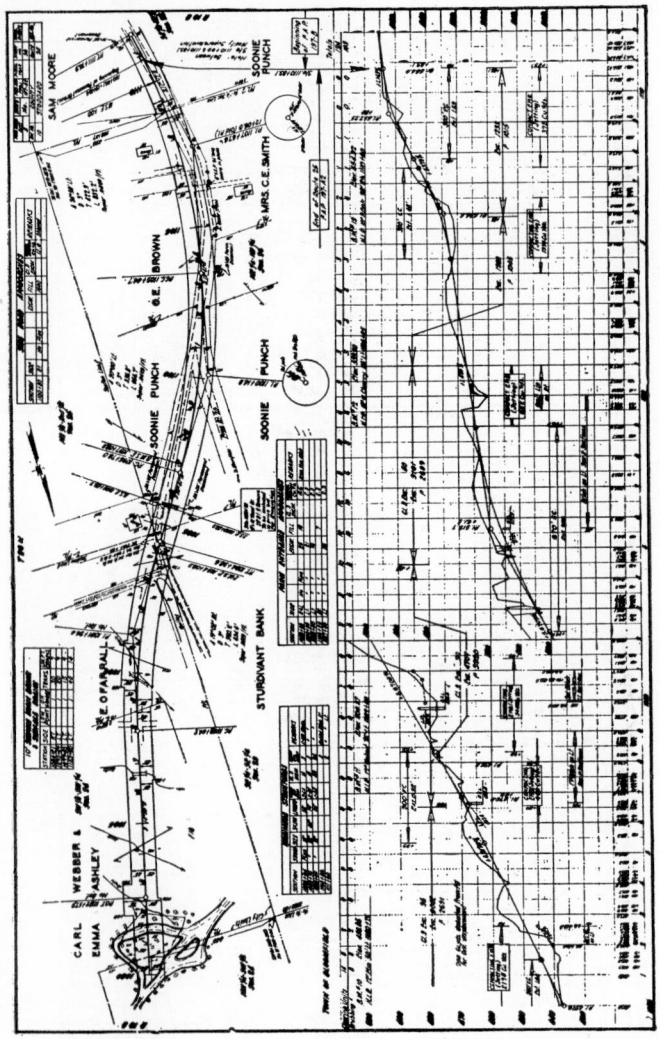

Fig. 30a. Highway Location. (Missouri Highway Department.)

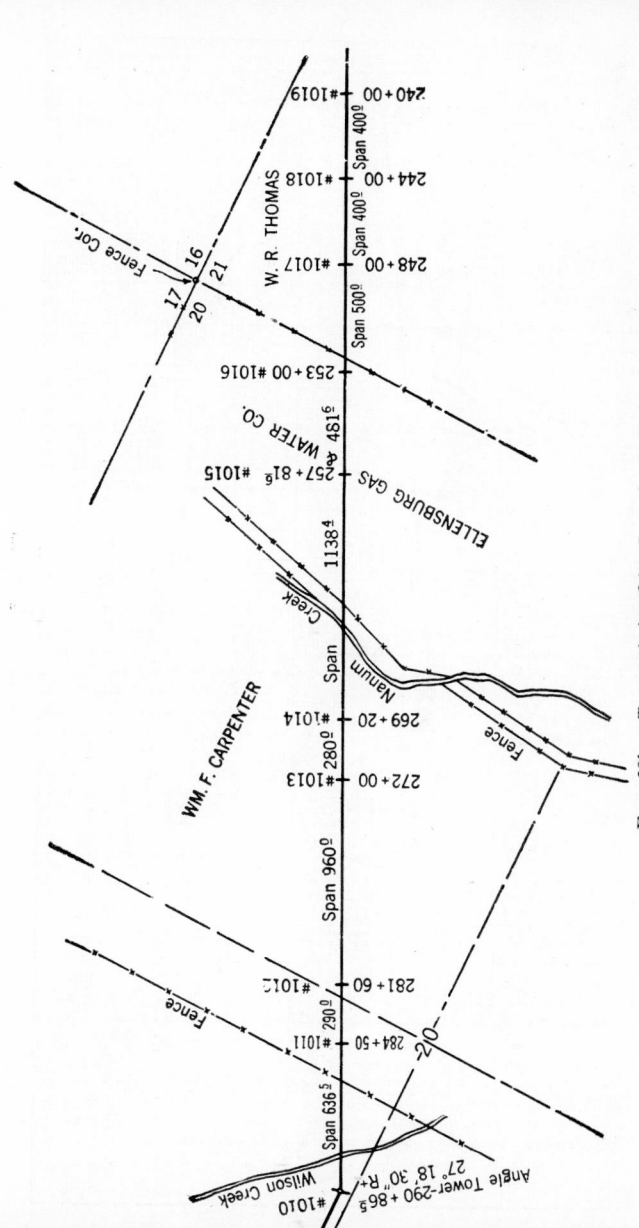

Fig. 30b. Transmission Line Location.

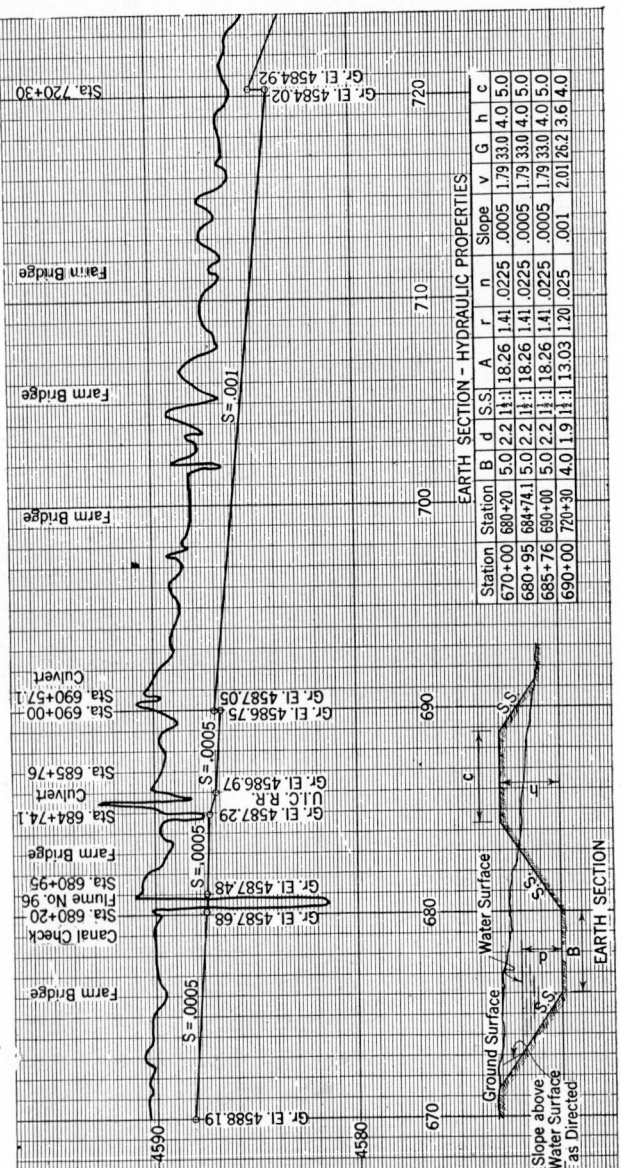

FIG. 30c.   Canal Profile.

EARTH SECTION – HYDRAULIC PROPERTIES

Station	Station	B	d	S.S	A	r	n	Slope	v	G	h	c
670+00	680+20	5.0	2.2	1½:1	18.26	1.41	.0225	.0005	1.79	33.0	4.0	5.0
680+95	684+74.1	5.0	2.2	1½:1	18.26	1.41	.0225	.0005	1.79	33.0	4.0	5.0
685+76	690+00	5.0	2.2	1½:1	18.26	1.41	.0225	.0005	1.79	33.0	4.0	5.0
690+00	720+30	4.0	1.9	1:1	13.03	1.20	.025	.001	2.01	26.2	3.6	4.0

On pipe lines, Fig. 30d, the profile is of the simplest type, since the lines are not necessarily laid very accurately to grade.

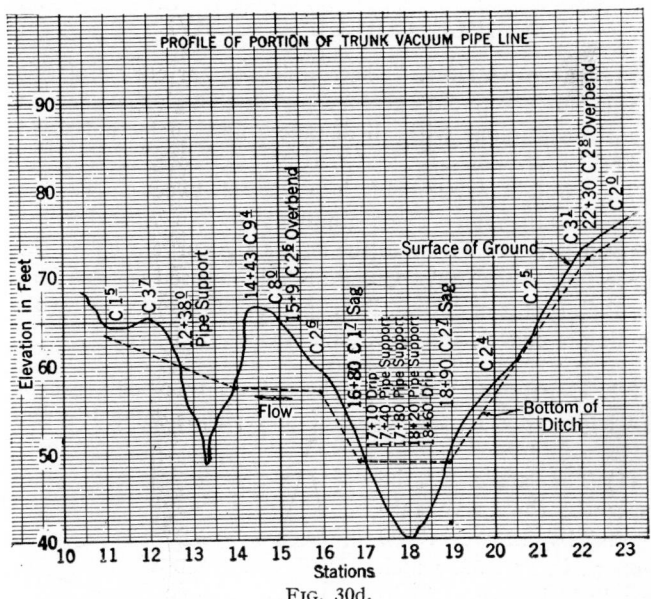

Fig. 30d.

As to *underground utilities*, the reader is referred to the American Society of Civil Engineers' pamphlet *Location of Underground Utilities*, 1937, and the work of the Cleveland, Ohio, Regional Surveys.

30a. Construction. Chapters XV, XVI, and XVII explain the ensuing construction procedure, usually done by contract. Promotion for engineers is often from surveys to construction supervision, and thence with increasing remuneration to contracting or to upper levels of corporate or governmental management.

CHAPTER V

SIMPLE CIRCULAR CURVES

31. Introduction. The simple circular curves of this chapter are computed and surveyed as though they were in a horizontal plane with all distances and angles measured in horizontal planes.

The straight portions of the survey between curves are known as tangents. The beginning of the curve is called the tangent-curve or T.C. and the end of the curve is called the curve-tangent or C.T. Older and seldom used designations are P.C. (point of curve), P.T. (point of tangent), B.C. (beginning of curve), and E.C. (end of curve).

32. Degree of Curve. Throughout this book, except in Chapter XVIII, the degree of curve, D, is defined in two ways:

(1) The angle at the center of the curve subtended by an arc of 100 feet, as in Fig. 32, which is called the arc or highway definition. This definition is used on much highway and other work.

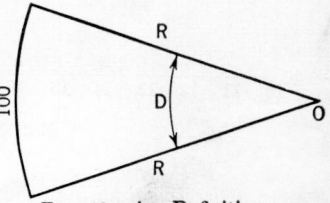

FIG. 32. Arc Definition.

(2) The angle at the center of the curve subtended by a chord of 100 feet, as in Fig. 32a, which is called the chord or railway definition. This definition is used on nearly all railways and on much highway and other work.

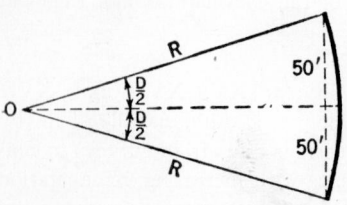

FIG. 32a. Chord Definition.

Chapter XVIII explains other rarely used definitions.

In all tables regular type is used for chord definition data, *while lighter italic type is used for arc definition data. In* *sections 32 and 33 the same distinction is made in connection* *with the formulas, insofar as possible.*

In practice, the engineer must inform himself as to which *definition of degree of curve is being used on his project and* *govern himself accordingly. Otherwise his work will not check.*

FOR THE ARC DEFINITION, *Fig. 32,* $D_a : 360° :: 100 : 2\pi R_a$ *from which*

$$(32) \qquad any\ radius = R_a = \frac{5729.58}{D_a}, \qquad exactly,$$

and from which it will be noted that for D = 1°, R = 5729.58 *feet. It will be noted further that this corresponds to the* *57.2958 degrees in one radian.*

FOR THE CHORD DEFINITION, the relation between the degree of curve and the radius, R, is found from Fig. 32a:

$$(32a) \qquad \sin\frac{D}{2} = \frac{50}{R} \quad and \quad R = \frac{50}{\sin(D/2)}, \qquad exactly.$$

Substituting in formula (32a) for a curve with D = 1° (that is, a curve such that a 100-foot chord subtends an angle of 1° at the center of the curve), we find R to be 5729.65 feet.

For small values of D_a, since small angles vary closely with their sines, the radius for any degree of curve, R_a, is

$$(32b) \qquad R_a = \frac{5729.65}{D_a}, \qquad approximately.$$

Thus the radius of a 1° curve is 5729.6 for both arc and chord definitions. This value should be memorized, at least to the precision of 5730 feet. As illustrating the increasing discrepancy between the two definitions as the curves become sharper, we may substitute D = 10° in formulas 32 and 32a whence we find the respective values of R to be

572.96 and 573.69, an appreciable difference. The difference is smaller for flatter curves and larger for sharper curves. Table I gives values for both definitions.

33. Functions of Simple Curves. From Fig. 33, the following fundamental formulas are apparent:

TANGENT OR T. The intersection of two adjacent tangents is called the P.I. (point of intersection). The distance from the T.C. to the P.I. or the distance from the C.T. to the P.I. is computed from Fig. 33 as follows:

$$(33) \qquad T = R \tan \frac{I}{2}, \text{ exactly for both definitions.}$$

Table II gives the tangents for a 1° curve (R = 5729.6, which is correct for both definitions of degree of curve), for various values of I. For any other degree of curve, T may be found from the formula

$$(33a) \qquad T_a = \frac{T_1}{D_a}, \qquad \begin{array}{l} \textit{exactly for arc def.} \\ \text{approximately for chord def.} \end{array}$$

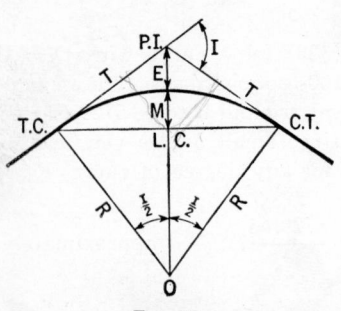

FIG. 33.

For example, if D = 3° 42′, and I = 39° 18′ we find T_1 from Table II to be 2045.9 feet, then

$$T_{3° 42′} = \frac{2045.9}{3.7} = 552.9 \text{ feet,}$$

exactly for arc def.; approximately for chord def.

To secure an exact value of $T_{3° 42′}$ for the chord definition, it is necessary to add a correction taken from Table III. For example,

$$T_{3° 42′} = 552.9 + 0.1 = 553.0 \text{ feet, exactly.}$$

LONG CHORD OR L.C. This distance from the T.C. to the C.T. is not used frequently. It may be computed from Fig. 33 as follows:

(33b) $L.C. = 2R \sin \dfrac{I}{2}$, exactly for both defs.

EXTERNAL OR E.   The distance from the P.I. to the center of the arc is computed from Fig. 33 as follows:

(33c) $E_a = \dfrac{R}{\cos I/2} - R = R \operatorname{exsec} \dfrac{I}{2}$,

exactly for both defs.

Table II gives externals of a 1° curve for varying values of I.   For any other degree of curve, E_a may be found from the equation

(33d) $E_a = \dfrac{E_1}{D_a}$,

exactly for arc def.
approximately for chord def.

For example, for D = 3° 42′ and I = 39° 18′, we find E_1 from Table II to be 354.28 feet; then

$$E_{3° \, 42′} = \frac{354.28}{3° \, 42′} = \frac{354.28}{3.7} = 95.75 \text{ feet},$$

exactly for arc def.
approximately for chord def.

To secure an exact value of $E_{3° \, 42′}$ for the chord definition it is necessary to add a correction taken from Table III, and

$$E_{3° \, 42′} = 95.75 + 0.02 = 95.77 \text{ feet}.$$

LENGTH OF CURVE OR L.   This is the total length around the curve as measured around the 1. *Actual 100-foot arc* *stations * and short end arcs (for the arc definition),* or 2. The 100-foot chords and the shorter chords at the ends of the curve as in Fig. 33a (for the chord definition).* Its value is

$$(33e) \qquad L = \left(\frac{I}{D} \right)(100), \qquad \begin{array}{l} \textit{exactly for arc def.} \\ \text{approximately for chord def.} \end{array}$$

Due to the short chords at the end of the curve, the formula is slightly in error for the chord definition, but it is sufficiently precise for nearly all purposes, and is generally used. Arc lengths may be found from Tables IV or XVIII.

Table II provides a convenient means of computing L, for either definition.

DEFLECTION ANGLE. This is the angle from the tangent (with the transit at the T.C.) to any particular point on the curve, as in Fig. 33a. It is exactly equal to half of the angle at the center of the curve between the radius at the T.C. and the radius at the particular point in question.

The deflection angle corresponding to a 100-foot chord (or arc) is exactly equal to $D/2$.

The sub-deflection angle corresponding to some other length of chord, the sub-chord (or arc), is approximately proportional to the length of chord (or arc), or

$$(33f) \qquad \text{sub-deflection angle} = \left(\frac{D}{2} \right)\left(\frac{c}{100} \right),$$
$$\begin{array}{l} \textit{exactly for arc def.} \\ \text{approximately for chord def.} \end{array}$$

A convenient formula which should be memorized, since it is generally used, derived from formula (33f), expresses the sub-deflection angle in minutes as follows:

$$(33g) \quad \begin{array}{l} \text{sub-deflec-} \\ \text{tion angle} \end{array} = 0.3cD, \qquad \begin{array}{l} \textit{exactly for arc def} \\ \text{approximately for chord def.} \end{array}$$

* If shorter chords than for the 100-foot chord (or arc) are used in staking, see Table IV.

Should a precise value of the sub-deflection angle (chord definition) be needed, use the formula

(33h) $\sin \text{(sub-deflection angle)} = \dfrac{c}{2R}$,   exactly.

FINAL DEFLECTION ANGLE. This is the total deflection angle to the C.T. and is equal to $I/2$, as in Fig. 33a.

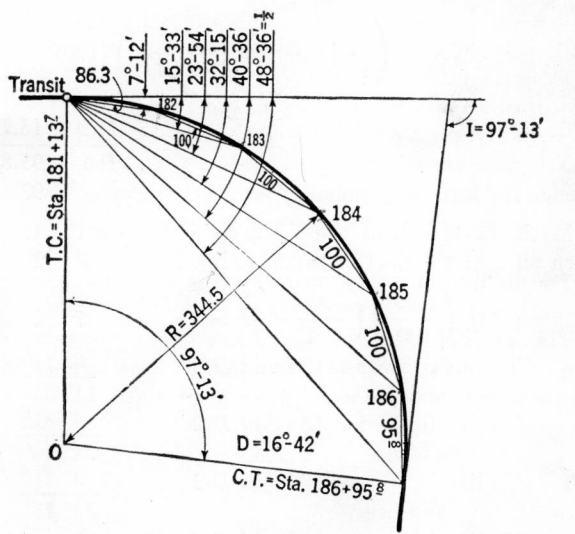

FIG. 33a.   Field Data for Staking a Curve.

34. Curve Notes.

An example of curve notes for both definitions, with the transit at the T.C., is given in Fig. 34.

The stationing of the survey is carried forward around the curve, either by 100-foot *arcs* or chords. As a consequence, the T.C. and the C.T. nearly always fall at plus stations, which necessitates *sub-arcs* or sub-chords of less than 100 feet and sub-deflection angles at both ends of the curve, as in Fig. 33a.

Regardless of the position on the curve which is to be occupied by the transit in staking the curve, the curve notes are always best computed and recorded as though the transit were at the T.C., as in Fig. 34.

With the transit at the T.C., the deflection angles from the tangent, Fig. 33a, are calculated as follows:

First full station to be set	182 + 00.0
T.C.	181 + 13.7
First *arc* (or chord) length =	86.3 feet

$$\text{Length of curve} = \left(\frac{I}{D}\right)(100) = \left(\frac{97° \, 13'}{16° \, 42'}\right)(100)$$

	= 582.1 feet
T.C.	181 + 13.7
C.T.	186 + 95.8
Hence the last *arc* (or chord) =	95.8 feet

With the transit at the T.C., sighted along the tangent, turn off a first deflection angle to line in station 182

using $\left(\dfrac{86.3}{100}\right)\left(\dfrac{16° \, 42'}{2}\right)^{*} =$	7° 12'
To line in station 183 add $D/2$	8° 21'
and use	15° 33'
To line in station 184 add $D/2$	8° 21'
and use	23° 54'
To line in station 185 add $D/2$	8° 21'
and use	32° 15'
To line in station 186 add $D/2$	8° 21'
and use	40° 36'
To line in the C.T. = 186 + 95.8	
use $I/2$	48° 36'
This leaves an angle corresponding	
to the last chord of	8° 00'
As a check on all deflection angles	
$\left(\dfrac{95.8}{100}\right)\left(\dfrac{16° \, 42'}{2}\right)^{*} =$	8° 00'

* Formulas (33g) or (33h), or Table I, may be used here.

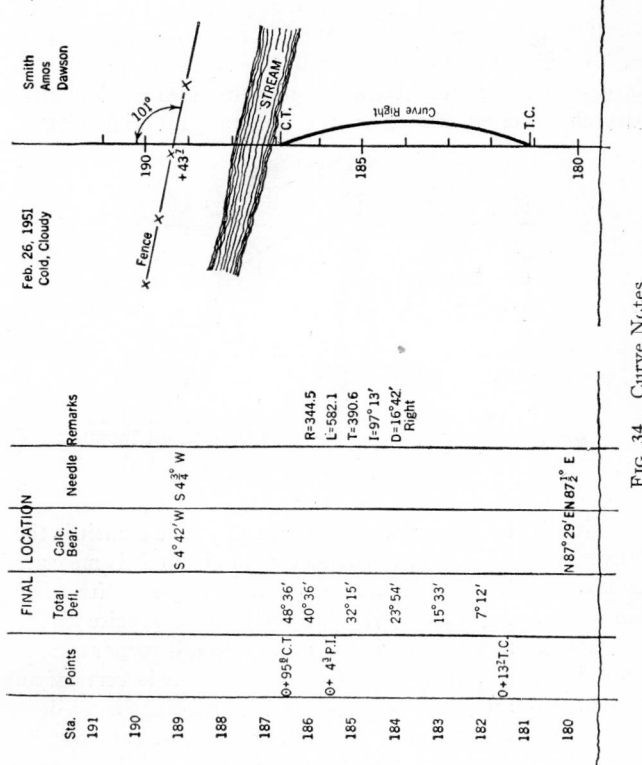

FIG. 34. Curve Notes.

Sta.	Points	FINAL		LOCATION		Remarks
		Total Defl.	Calc. Bear.	Needle		
191						
190						
189			S 4° 42' W	S 4¾° W		
188						
187						R=344.5
186	0+95⁸C.T.	48° 36'				L=582.1
185	0+ 4³ P.I.	40° 36'				T=390.6
184		32° 15'				I=97° 13'
183		23° 54'				D=16° 42'
182		15° 33'				Right
181		7° 12'				
180	0+13¹T.C.		N 87° 29'E N 87½° E			

Feb. 26, 1951
Cold, Cloudy

Smith
Amos
Dawson

35. Field Work.   The tangents, or straight portions
of the survey, are usually laid out first to meet required
conditions, since most of the construction is straight.   In
Fig. 35 the regular stationing is carried forward along the
back tangent towards the yet undetermined P.I.   The forward tangent from Z toward the P.I. is then usually "backed
in" with a hub line (a transit line without taping) and
intersected with the back tangent by means of a string
stretched across stakes on the one tangent and with the

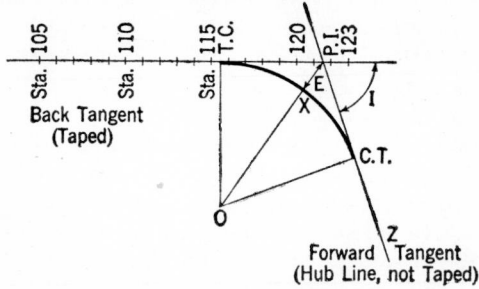

Fig. 35.   Field Work.

transit aligned along the other tangent.   The transit is then
moved to the P.I. and the deflection angle, or I, is measured
and doubled.   The double deflection angle is free from
blunders and slippage; it is slightly more precise than a
single measurement; and it contains no adjustment errors,
provided the vertical axis of the instrument is vertical and
provided the mean of A and B vernier readings is used.

The degree of curve is now selected to suit the construction, the topography, the funds available, and the other
requirements, as mentioned in § 9.   Sometimes the available
length of tangent controls the degree of curve that may be
used.   It is frequently helpful to pace or tape along the
bisector of the angle at the P.I. towards the center of the
curve at O until one reaches what seems on the ground to
be a topographically suitable point (point X on Fig. 35) for

the curve to pass through.   With the value of either T or E known, D and R may be computed from formulas, using the measured value of I.   Better still, the value of T_1 or E_1 for a 1° curve may be taken from Table II and D computed from formulas 33a or 33d as follows:

$$D = \frac{T_1}{T} \quad \text{or} \quad D = \frac{E_1}{E}, \qquad \begin{array}{l} \textit{exactly for arc def.} \\ \text{approximately for chord def.} \end{array}$$

The value of D is generally selected as the nearest degree or half degree to that computed, although this approximation is of course simply a convenience and not always advisable.

The computed value of T is measured forward from the P.I. towards the C.T. which is then set in proper position. It is not necessary to tape the distance from the P.I. to the T.C., since the station of the P.I. (already taped) minus the computed T will give the station and plus of the T.C., and the T.C. is then set in proper position by taping the plus from the nearest station which has already been set.

If the curve is long and/or a high degree of precision is needed, it is desirable to bisect the angle at the P.I. with a transit and to measure E as precisely computed towards O, setting a stake at the center of the arc at X, and checking later on this point as the curve is run in.

For short curves and/or for approximate work, it is sometimes sufficient to set the T.C., the C.T., and X only. Generally, however, the transit is moved to the C.T. and/or the T.C. and/or one or more intermediate points on the curve, and full 100-foot stations are set around the curve, as in Fig. 33a.   If the entire curve can be run in from the C.T., it is usually preferable to do so, since the transit is then in position to line in stations ahead on the forward tangent and since accumulated errors are minimized.   With the transit at the C.T., the longer transit sights are taken before the instrument has, perhaps, shifted slightly and before errors in taping have accumulated.

If the curve is a long one and is difficult to check, it is desirable to run forward from the T.C. and backward from the C.T., so that the unavoidable error will accumulate less and may be adjusted on the curve rather than at the ends as described in § 62.

WITH THE TRANSIT AT THE T.C. and the plates on 0° 00′, the transit is sighted along the tangent towards the P.I. Then as each station is set, the transit plates are rotated to read the angle opposite that station in the field notes, and finally the C.T. is set with the transit plates reading the angular value opposite C.T. in the notes, namely $I/2$.

The stakes which have been set along the back tangent, Fig. 35, are pulled up and set over on the curve.

Each station is set at the end of the chord from the previous point, usually 100 feet apart. Shorter distances are used at the end sub-chords and occasionally between stations, as mentioned later, to aid in more precise construction.

WITH THE TRANSIT AT THE C.T., it is sighted on the long chord towards the T.C. with the plates clamped on the angular value opposite the T.C. in the notes (0° 00′). Then as the curve is taped forward towards the C.T., the angular value opposite each station in the notes is used and finally the plates will read $I/2$ on the P.I.

WHEN IT IS NECESSARY TO SET UP AT AN INTERMEDIATE POINT ON THE CURVE (in which case the first setup will usually have been at the T.C.) the transit is backsighted on the T.C. (inverted position, bubble up) with the plates reading 0° (which is the angular value opposite the T.C. in the notes). After plunging the transit vertically (the transit must be in adjustment), the angle opposite each succeeding station in the notes is used to set each succeeding station. In precise work, deflection angles are doubled between transit points not over 400 feet apart. Setups are preferably at full stations.

IF YET AN ADDITIONAL SETUP IS NECESSARY, then the transit is backsighted on the last transit point with the telescope inverted and the plates reading the angular value of that point as recorded in the notes. The transit telescope is then plunged vertically and the angle opposite each succeeding station in the notes is then used to set that station.

As a rule of thumb, it may therefore be stated that whenever the transit is pointed at a station, the plates must read the angle opposite that station in the notes.

With the transit procedure as outlined above, whenever the transit is set up and properly oriented at a station, and the transit plates read the angular value opposite that station in the notes, then the line of sight is tangent to the curve at that station.   It is necessary not infrequently to establish such an auxiliary tangent.

In order to secure better intersections and consequently more precise location of points on the curve, it is necessary to limit the angle between the original line of sight and the tape as held, or the maximum total deflection angle, to less than about 30°.

As previously mentioned, for long curves and for precise work, it is desirable to check the midpoint of the arc by measuring E and locating the midpoint while the transit is still on the P.I.

When D is large, say over 7°, and/or precise location of the curve is essential, it is customary to locate points on the arc approximately 50 feet or 25 feet or some other short distance apart.   In locating a point midway between two stations which are 100 feet apart, it is evident that the chords must somewhat exceed 50 feet in length, this excess increasing with D.   Table IV gives the correction here necessary, although for many purposes, and/or on flat curves, it may be neglected.

In the computation of the curve notes it was seen that a check exists when the deflection angle corresponding to the last chord is checked, as on page 63.

In the field, a check on all computation and field work (except field alignment errors on stations around the arc) occurs when the last stake or point on the arc (generally the T.C. or the C.T.) which has previously been set on the ground, is finally located from the last setup of the transit. This is an inclusive, overall check.   See page 125 for a method of distributing the actual unavoidable error of closure.

It is interesting to note that the field work comprises a closed transit-tape traverse composed of the two tangents and of the various chords around the arc. The final field error mentioned above is the linear error of closure of the traverse.

The tapemen measure the sub-chord from the T.C. to the first station on the curve, and are lined in by the transitman, who has set off the proper angle from his computed curve notes. This is continued completely around the curve. Careful taping is essential and is checked when the final sub-chord, as measured in the field, corresponds with the computed station of the C.T. The head tapeman, after setting a station, moves 100 feet forward on the back 100-foot chord produced, and then inward toward the center of the curve by a distance (measured in feet) equal to $(1\frac{3}{4})\mathbf{D}$ (the chord offset C.O. of § 36), which brings him very closely onto the arc and checks and minimizes the aligning of the head tapeman by the transitman.

36. Staking Curves with a Tape.

Curves may be staked by means of a tape, using the chord offset (C.O.), the tangent offset (T.O.), and/or the middle ordinate (M); either without, or in connection with, a transit.

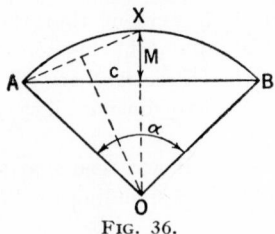

FIG. 36.

MIDDLE ORDINATE OR M. The distance from the center of the arc to the center of any chord is computed from Fig. 36 as follows:

$$(36) \qquad M = R - R\cos\frac{\alpha}{2} = R \text{ vers } \frac{\alpha}{2}, \text{ exactly for both defs.}$$

An approximate M is derived as follows:

$$M : XA = \frac{XA}{2} : R$$

when XA is small as compared to R, then $XA = \dfrac{c}{2}$ and

(36a) $M = \dfrac{c^2}{8R}$,   approximately for both definitions.

TANGENT OFFSET OR T.O.   The perpendicular offset from the tangent to the arc, at any given distance measured along the tangent, from Fig. 36a is

(36b)   T.O. = (length along tangent) $\left(\tan \dfrac{\alpha}{2} \right)$, exactly; or

(36c)   T.O. = (length along chord) $\left(\sin \dfrac{\alpha}{2} \right)$,

exactly for both defs.

Also   T.O. = R versine α,   exactly for both defs.

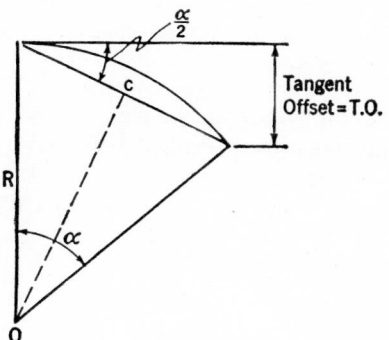

FIG. 36a.

Another formula is derived as follows:

$$\text{T.O.} : c = \dfrac{c}{2} : R$$

(36d)   T.O. = $\dfrac{c^2}{2R}$ exactly for both defs.

Table I provides a convenient means of obtaining the T.O.

CHORD OFFSET OR C.O.   The chord offset C.O. of Fig. 36b is

(36e)   C.O. $= 2c \sin \dfrac{\alpha}{2}$, exactly for both defs.

Also   C.O. $= 2$ T.O.,   exactly for both defs.

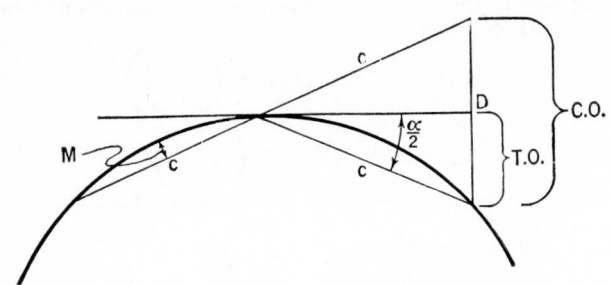

FIG. 36b.   Chord Offset.

RELATIONS BETWEEN C.O., T.O., AND M.   It is frequently helpful to use the following simple relationships. From the foregoing formulas, it is evident that

(36f)   C.O. $= \dfrac{c^2}{R} = 2$ T.O.,   exactly for both defs.

(36g)   T.O. $= \dfrac{c^2}{2R} =$ T.O.,   exactly for both defs.

(36h) $M = \dfrac{c^2}{8R} = \frac{1}{4}$ T.O., approximately for both defs.

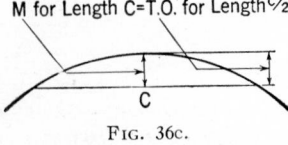

FIG. 36c.

This ratio of 2 to 1 to $\frac{1}{4}$ should be memorized.   Drawing simple figures similar to Figs. 36b and 36c will enable one to distinguish which is which.

In Table I, we find the T.O. of a 100′ chord for any degree of curve.   The exact value of the C.O. and the approximate

value of M may be computed easily by multiplying by 2
and by dividing by 4, respectively.   It is desirable to mem-
orize the **C.O. for a 1° curve as 1.746, or very closely $1\frac{3}{4}$ feet, for
a 100-foot chord.**

Another useful fact that may be memorized to advantage
is that **M in inches = D, for a 62-foot chord, approximately.**

From these memorized facts, it is possible to lay out,
relocate, or check a curve without a transit and without
tables of any kind.

See Tables I, IIIA, and XXVI for values of offsets and
ordinates to be used in the following procedures for staking
curves with a tape.

CHORD OFFSETS.   In Fig. 36d, the tangent offset for station
182 is computed and the station located on the ground.   An
auxiliary tangent is estab-
lished at station 182, and
station 183 is located by
using the tangent offset.
Stations 184, 185, and 186
are set by chord offsets.
The C.T., station 186 + 95.8,
is set by tangent offset from
the auxiliary tangent at station 186.

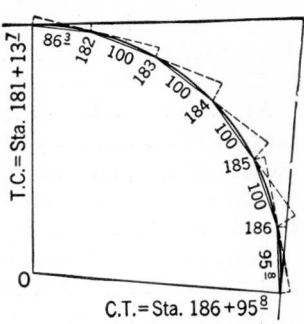

FIG. 36d.   Staking a Curve by
Chord Offsets.

TANGENT OFFSETS.   For
staking a curve, tangent offsets are calculated as follows:

STATION	DISTANCE ALONG TANGENT	RIGHT ANGLE OFFSET FROM TANGENT
182	R sin d	R vers d
183	R sin(d + D)	R vers(d + D)
184	R sin(d + 2D)	R vers(d + 2D)
185	R sin(d + 3D)	R vers(d + 3D)
185 + 95.8	R sin(d + 3D + d')	R vers(d + 3D + d')
	R sin I	R vers I

It is often better to calculate and stake the curve from both ends, checking on some intermediate station. Measuring the distances between the 100-foot stations provides a desirable check.

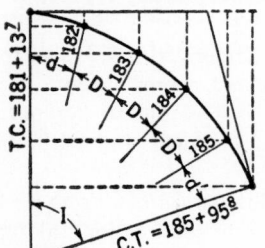

FIG. 36e. Staking a Curve by Tangent Offsets.

MIDDLE ORDINATES. This method is preferred generally for staking the sharp curves often found on secondary highways, logging roads, and canals where it is customary to set stakes 50 feet, or $\frac{1}{2}$ station, apart. A minimum of clearing and surveying is involved.

Set station $181 + 50$ by a tangent offset taken from Table IIIA. Set station 182 by the same tangent offset method or by the procedure of Table XXVI.

At station 182, lay off radially the tangent offset from Table IIIA for 50 feet of the given D (this is the middle ordinate for a 100-foot chord or arc) and set the temporary point T.

Set station $182 + 50$ in line with T and station $181 + 50$ at 50 feet (see Table IV for the usually negligible correction) from station 182.

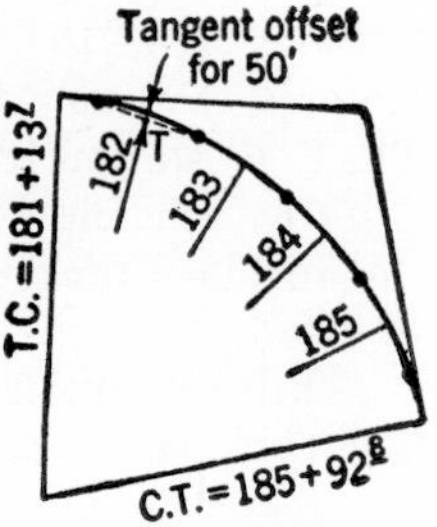

Proceed similarly to locate all subsequent stations and half stations on

FIG. 36f.

the curve. Finally set, or check, the C.T. by the method of Table XXVI.

Values from Table I of tangent offsets and middle ordinates for 100-foot chords are exact for the chord definition of degree of curve and *less than 0.1 foot in error for the arc definition* when D is less than 21°.

As previously mentioned, Tables I, IIIA, and XXVI have been prepared especially to facilitate staking curves with a tape. Logging engineers, highway engineers, pipe line engi-

neers, and hydraulic engineers all have expressed their need for
such tables and methods. They have developed the procedures which are described in the foregoing sections.

Under many circumstances adequate precision will result
from staking curves with a tape and usually considerable time
will be saved.

37. Triangulating a Curve. Occasionally, it is difficult or impossible to tape the 100-foot distances (as for
example in water or swamp), in which case two transits, one
at the T.C. and one at the C.T. or at other points, can
locate the successive stations by intersection of lines of
sight; in reality this is a sort of triangulation where well
shaped triangles are essential in securing the most accurate
results.

38. Locating a Curve from the Center. Where
the radius of the curve is less than 100 feet, rarely with
longer radii, and where the ground lies so that a tape or
wire may be used as a swinging radius, it is sometimes
advisable to establish the center of the curve and to set
points around the arc by swinging a radius from the center.
Such a procedure is common practice in setting curb stakes
at street intersections where the radii may be from 15 feet
to 100 feet, and for other constructions of relatively minor
importance.

39. Special Problems. In staking curves while locating the line, in modifying them after construction, and
in office computations, many problems arise to tax the ingenuity of the engineer. If the foregoing fundamentals are
thoroughly in mind, the required special computations may
be made. Occasionally the problem may be solved by a
cut and try method on a drawing made carefully to scale,
although such a solution is rarely precise enough and the
drafting equipment is seldom available in the field. On
other occasions, and perhaps as a last resort, a cut and try

method may be used in the field, but this is ordinarily costly, since the field work proceeds slowly and the time of an entire

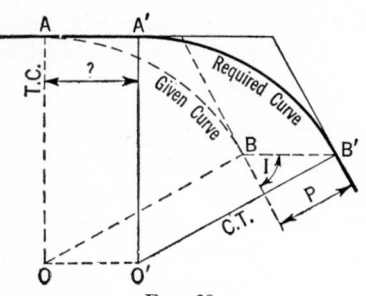

party is wasted in trials.

Chapter VII is frequently useful in such computations.

A few of the more commonly encountered problems and their solutions follow. This geometric and trigonometric type of solution is essential in the office and is usually most effective in the field.

FIG. 39.

GIVEN A SIMPLE CIRCULAR CURVE JOINING TWO TANGENTS, as in Fig. 39. It is required to shift one tangent parallel to itself through a distance p. How far must the T.C. be shifted?

$$(39) \qquad AA' = OO' = BB' = \frac{p}{\sin I}.$$

The same formula will apply if the required curve lies inside and to the left of the given curve (A' being then left of A).

GIVEN A SIMPLE CIRCULAR CURVE JOINING TWO TANGENTS, as in Fig. 39a. It is required to shift one tangent parallel to itself through a distance p, using the same T.C. Find R.

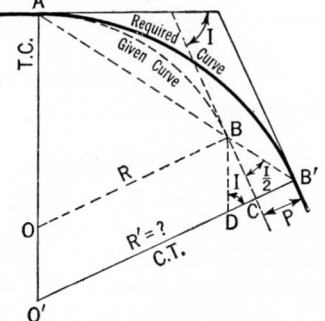

FIG. 39a.

$$BD \text{ vers } I = p$$

$$(39a) \qquad R' - R = OO' = BD = B'D = \frac{p}{\text{vers } I}.$$

The point B' may be set by producing AB a distance of

(39b) $$BB' = \frac{p}{\sin \dfrac{I}{2}}.$$

The same formula will apply if the required curve lies inside of the original curve, but in that case, of course, $R' < R$.

WHAT RADIUS MUST BE USED TO RUN A SIMPLE CIRCULAR CURVE THROUGH A GIVEN POINT SO THAT IT WILL CONNECT TWO GIVEN TANGENTS? In other words, in Fig. 39b, given I, α, and VZ, find R.

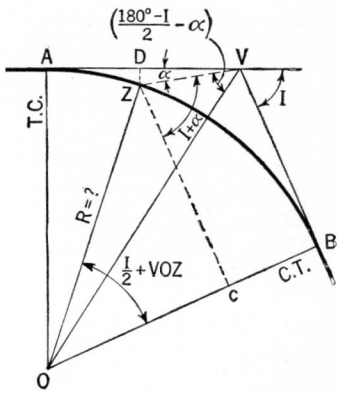

Fig. 39b.

In triangle VOZ:

$$VO : OZ = \sin VZO : \sin OVZ,$$

$$\frac{R}{\cos \dfrac{I}{2}} : R = \sin VZO : \sin \left(\frac{180 - I}{2} - \alpha \right).$$

But $\sin \left(\dfrac{180 - I}{2} - \alpha \right) = \sin \left[90 - \left(\dfrac{I}{2} + \alpha \right) \right]$

$$= \cos \left(\frac{I}{2} + \alpha \right).$$

Substituting above and solving, we find

(39c) $$\sin VZO = \frac{\cos \left(\dfrac{I}{2} + \alpha \right)}{\cos \dfrac{I}{2}}.$$

Triangle VOZ may now be solved for R.

If the angle VOZ is very small (occasioning a considerable error in R), the following solution (after finding angle VOZ) is better:

$$R \text{ vers } BOZ = VZ \sin VZC$$

(39d)
$$R = \frac{VZ \sin (I + \alpha)}{\text{vers} \left(\dfrac{I}{2} + VOZ \right)}.$$

This problem may also be solved by trial. For example, if $DZ = 25'$, $DV = 200'$ (measured or computed), and $I = 43° 20'$; assume a 5° curve and from Table II obtain a tangent length of $2276.5/5 = 455.3$ feet. Hence $DA = 455.3 - 200 = 255.3$ feet. The chord distance AZ will be slightly more, say 257 feet. From Table I, the tangent offset will be $4.362 \left(\dfrac{257}{100} \right)^2 = 28.8$ feet, instead of the required 25 feet. A slightly sharper curve is needed. Trying 5° 20′ and following the same procedure, we calculate a value of $4.653 \left(\dfrac{228}{100} \right)^2 = 24.2$ feet instead of the required 25 feet. Another trial calculation may be made, or a slightly flatter curve, say 5° 18′, may be run in the field, and it will pass within a few tenths of a foot of the required point Z.

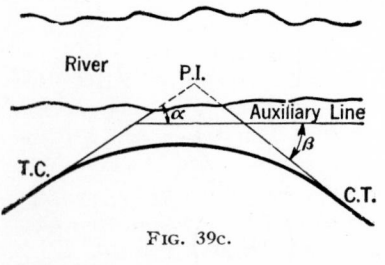

Fig. 39c.

IF IT IS DIFFICULT OR IMPOSSIBLE TO OCCUPY THE P.I. as in Fig. 39c, the taped length of the auxiliary line and the angles α and β will furnish I and will permit T to be calculated so that the T.C. and the C.T. may be located.

Rarely, even more difficult problems are encountered which involve considerable ingenuity in so adapting the foregoing general methods of attack as to reach a solution.

40. Some Solutions by Trial.

TO CHANGE THE DIRECTION OF THE FORWARD TANGENT, run
the curve beyond, or short of, the C.T. by a distance around
the curve equivalent to the required change of angular
direction. In Fig. 40, the original curve stopped at A, and
it is required to establish a new tangent passing through B.
The angle α is measured and the length from A to A' is

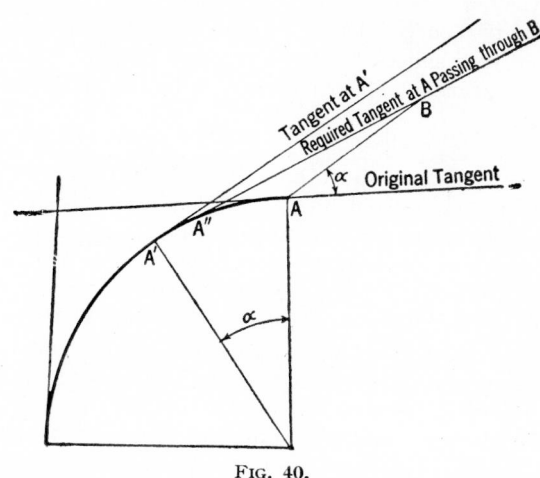

FIG. 40.

computed as $(100)(\alpha/D)$. The stationing of A' is computed
by subtracting AA' from the stationing of A. The stationing of A'', slightly to the right of A', is assumed and the
transit is set up at A'' and turned tangent to the curve at
that point. This tangent will pass close to B, perhaps
sufficiently close. The process may be repeated to secure
greater precision in passing the new tangent through B.

A similar process may be used in connecting two already
established curves by a common tangent.

TO FIND THE POINT WHERE A STRAIGHT LINE INTERSECTS
THE CURVE, set several plus stakes on the curve (with a

transit-tape or by offsets from the chord) in the vicinity of
the intersection and establish the point of intersection by
trial.

WHERE IT IS NECESSARY TO CHANGE BOTH THE DIRECTION
OF THE TANGENT AND ALSO TO SHIFT ITS POSITION, it is usually best to align the new tangent on the ground, to establish
a new P.I., and to compute and run in the new curve regardless of the old curve.

Often a trial curve is surveyed around an existing embankment and then shifted to fit the tangents instead of surveying the tangents. This is explained in the reference on
page 128.

41. In Conclusion. Only by deriving formulas and
by working many problems can the engineer become sufficiently skilled in curve computation to meet the many and
varied demands of practice in the field and in the office.
A mere knowledge of geometry and trigonometry is insufficient unless augmented by a considerable and specific
application of this knowledge to curve theory and curve
problems such as are given in this and the succeeding chapters of this book.

In all geometric and trigonometric solutions, it is most
helpful to draw the figure at least approximately to scale
so that equal angles, similar triangles, and approximate
values of angles and distances become apparent. Portions
of the figure may be greatly enlarged for a specific computation. However, these are still best kept roughly to scale.

Working curve problems provides excellent training in
the practical applications of geometry and trigonometry,
those branches of mathematics which the engineer uses most
throughout his lifetime.

CHAPTER VI

COMPOUND AND REVERSE CURVES

42. Compound Curves. A compound curve is a multi-centered curve in which two or more simple curves bend in the same direction and lie on the same side of their common tangent, as in Fig. 42.

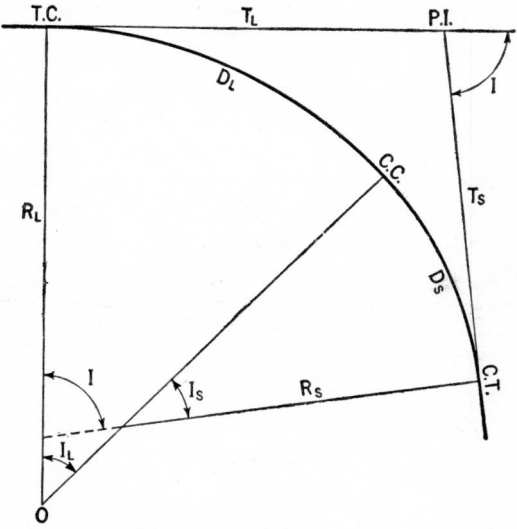

Fig. 42.

When four of the seven variables, R_S, R_L, T_S, T_L, I_S, I_L, and I (Fig. 42), are known (of which one must be, and not more than two may be, angles), the other three may be computed and the curve is definitely fixed. If D_S is known, then it may be assumed that R_S is known, since they are related to one another in the simple manner of Fig. 32; similarly for D_L and R_L. The subscript $_S$ refers to the simple curve with the shorter radius while the subscript $_L$ refers to the simple curve with the longer radius.

The most useful solution of compound-curve problems is accomplished by solving the triangle ABC in Fig. 42a. In this solution the tangent length for each of the component simple curves is used, that is, T for I_L and D_L is the

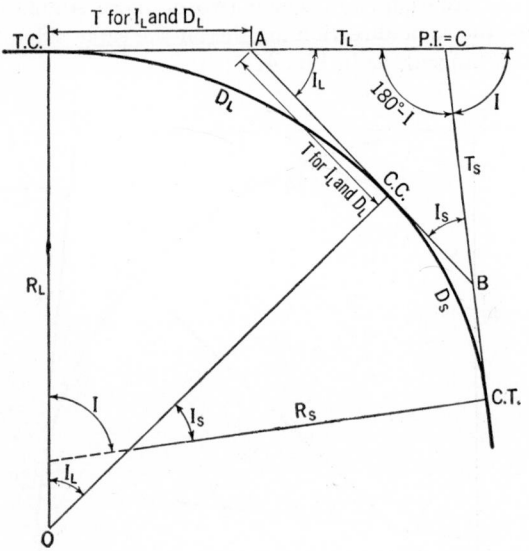

FIG. 42a.

line between A and C.C.; and similarly for the line C.C. to B. The angle at A is I_L, the angle at B is I_S and the angle at the P.I. is $180° - I$.

As an illustrative example of the several cases which may arise requiring a solution through the use of the triangle ABC, suppose that R_S, R_L, and two of the three angles I, I_S, and I_L are known. Since $I = I_S + I_L$, all angles are known. The value of T for I_L and R_L may be computed; likewise the value of T for I_S and R_S. The sum of the two values of T gives AB and the triangle ABC may be solved for AC and BC. Then

(42a) $T_L = AC + T$ (for I_L and D_L),

(42b) $T_S = BC + T$ (for I_S and D_S).

Other less simple solutions of compound curves may be made by drawing arcs nearer the centers of the curve. As

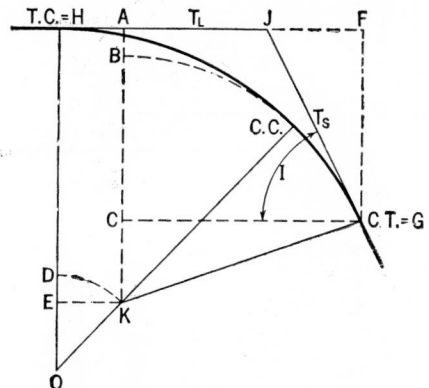

FIG. 42b.

an example of this type of solution, we are given in Fig. 42b, T_S, R_S, R_L, and I; then

$$AB = \quad DE \quad = AC \quad - BC,$$
$$(R_L - R_S) \text{ vers } I_L = T_S \sin I - R_S \text{ vers } I,$$

$$\text{vers } I_L = \frac{T_S \sin I - R_S \text{ vers } I}{R_L - R_S},$$

$$I_S = I - I_L,$$
$$HJ = EK \qquad\qquad + CG \qquad - FJ,$$
(42c) $$T_L = (R_L - R_S) \sin I_L + R_S \sin I - T_S \cos J$$

In another type of compound-curve solution, triangles near the C.T. and at the center of the longer radius curve may be so chosen as to simplify the computation of the required data. As an example, in Fig. 42c the original compound curve is shown in light line and its known parts are R_L, R_S, and I_S. It is required to shift the tangent

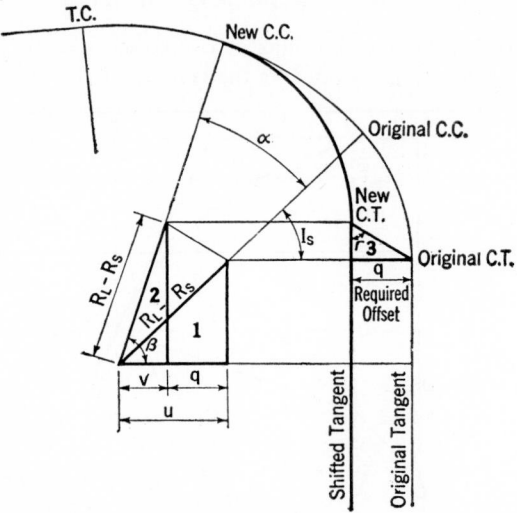

Fig. 42c. Compound Curve to Be Shifted.

inward a distance q, with the radii remaining the same lengths. The C.C. moves from the original to a new position as indicated.

In triangle 1, the angle at the left is I_S and the hypotenuse is $R_L - R_S$, from which the base u may be computed. From this, $v = u - q$.

In triangle 2, the hypotenuse and base are known and the angle β may be computed. From this, $\alpha = \beta - I_S$. With α and R_L known, we may compute the distance around the curve from the original C.C. to the new C.C., thus securing the stationing of the new C.C.

In triangle 3, the angle $\gamma = \frac{1}{2}\alpha + I_S$ and q is known, from which the triangle may be solved. Thus the new

C.T. may be located from the original C.T. by right-angle offsets.

Other compound-curve problems may frequently be solved in a similar manner.

A trial solution is frequently used where the compound curve is confined between a rock bluff and a river, so that various radii are necessary. Compound curves should not be used where a simple curve is reasonably possible. However, where needed, they are permissible on most types of work except on highways, where any considerable change in curvature is deceptive and dangerous to drivers.

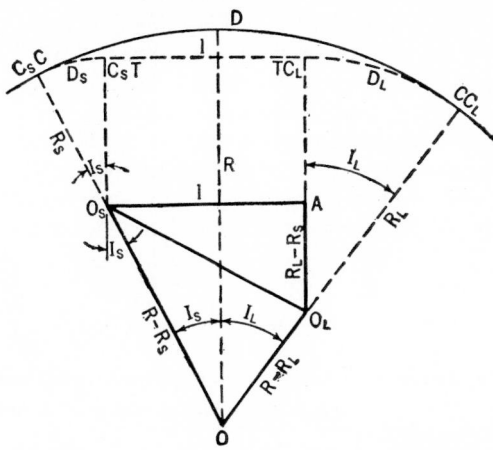

Fig. 42d.   Elimination of a Broken-Back Curve.

A "broken-back" curve (Fig. 42d), where a rather short tangent separates two curves in the same direction, is not good practice. On most work, it is better to replace the "broken-back" curve by a single simple curve, or to use a third flatter curve in place of the short tangent, as in Fig. 42d. In the solution of this figure, the heavy lined triangles are solved for all angles. Angles I_S and I_L are then found by addition and subtraction, I_S being equal to

$90° − AO_SO$.   The positions of C_SC and CC_L and all curve
data may then be computed, a small station equation developing at one of these points.

The curve notes for a compound curve should usually be
computed as two separate simple curves, and the curves
should be run in the field as separate simple curves from
the T.C. and from the C.T., checking on the C.C., where
permissible discrepancies may best be cared for.   Other procedures are rarely advisable.

43. Reverse Curves.   A reverse curve consists of two
simple curves bending in opposite directions with a common
tangent at their junction, as in Figs. 43a and 43b.

Reverse curves are used on pipe lines, flumes, levees,
canals, and sometimes on roads and railroads, but only on
those designed for low velocities.   Such curves are used
sometimes for railroad yards and industrial tracks.

Reverse curves *must not* be used on highways or railroads
where speeds are high, largely because the curves cannot be
superelevated properly at their junction.   Also, the sudden

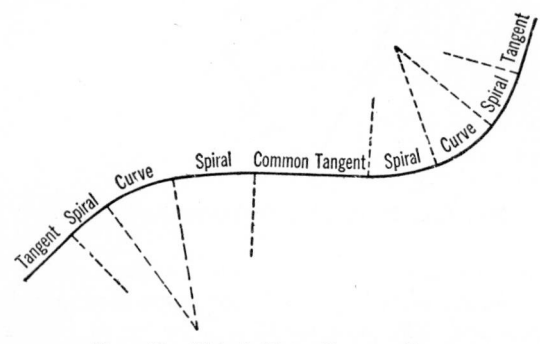

FIG. 43.   This Is Not a Reverse Curve.

change in direction is objectionable and, in the case of
highways, steering is extremely dangerous.   Neither can
reverse curves be used on all canals, because steering of

vessels may be difficult and dangerous, and the sudden change in direction may cause scouring of the canal. In such cases several hundred feet of tangent should be left between the two simple curves, and frequently spirals (Chapter IX) should be provided to connect the curves with the tangent, as in Fig. 43. This, of course, requires the curves to be inset from the common tangent as described in § 62, and as shown in Fig. 55. For slow speeds of vehicles or slow velocities of water where spirals are unnecessary, a "reversing tangent" of 50 to 100 feet may prove sufficient, and data can be computed by a slight modification of the solution immediately following.

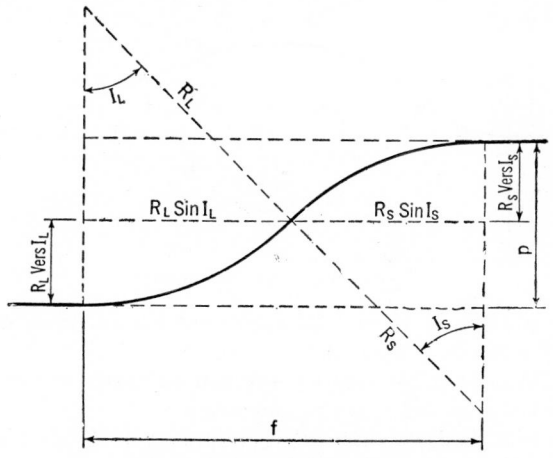

FIG. 43a.   Reverse Curve.

Two of the more common cases of reverse curves are solved in Figs. 43a and 43b. Another solution is given in § 44. In Fig. 43a, $I_L = I_S = I$.

(43) $(R_L + R_S) \sin I = f,$

(43a) $(R_L + R_S) \text{ vers } I = p.$

When $R_L = R_S$

(43b)
$$R = \frac{f}{2 \sin I},$$

(43c)
$$R = \frac{p}{2 \operatorname{vers} I}.$$

In Fig. 43b, angle I can be found in the field, and some of the values of R_L, R_S, T_L, and T_S are known or assumed, from which the other required values may be computed from the following relations:

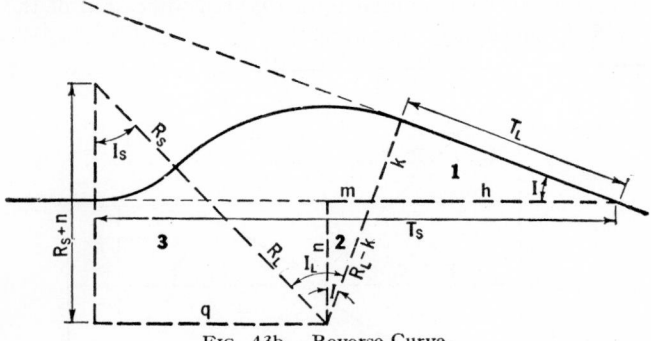

FIG. 43b.   Reverse Curve.

In triangle **1**, T_L and all angles are known, from which h and k can be computed.

In triangle **2**, the side $R_L - k$ and all angles are known, from which m and n can be computed.

In triangle **3**, two sides $R_S + n$ and $R_S + R_L$ are known, so that I_S and q can be calculated from the formulas

$$I_L = I_S + I,$$

and

$$T_S = h + m + q.$$

The curve notes for a reverse curve should be computed as two separate simple curves, and the curves should be run in the field as two separate simple curves from the T.C. and from the C.T., checking on the C.C. where the permissible discrepancies may best be cared for.

CHAPTER VII

SOLUTION BY TRAVERSE

44. Solution by Traverse. Many of the problems in this volume and other similar ones, as well as a great variety of computations which arise in field and office work,

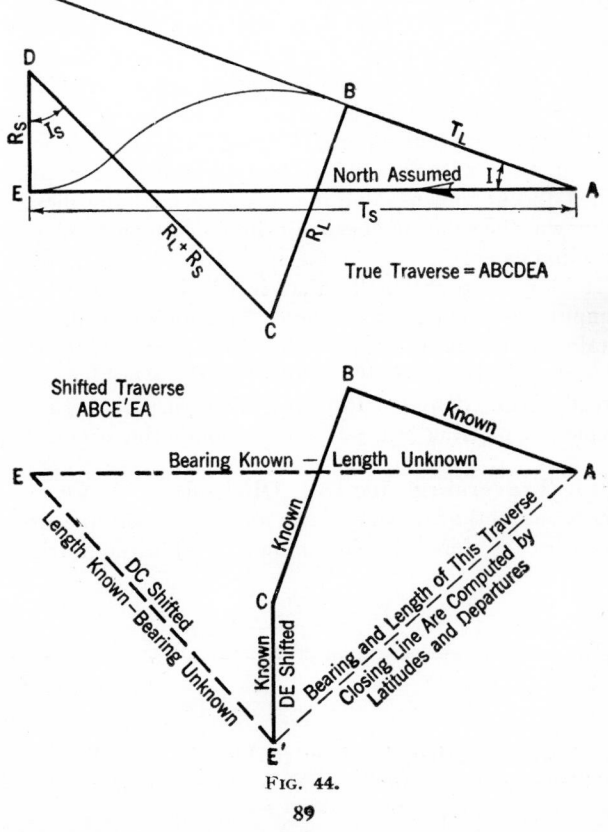

FIG. 44.

are solved most satisfactorily and systematically by computing latitudes and departures and finding the missing data in a closed traverse. The principles involved in such a determination of missing traverse data are given in most books on surveying.

As an example, in Fig. 44 the same problem is solved as that of Fig. 43b in § 43. Assuming AE as north, the lengths and bearings of AB, BC, and DE are known. The line DE is shifted to the position CE' in the lower figure. Then the length and bearing of the closing traverse line AE' can be computed. Sufficient data are then available in the triangle AEE' to compute the length of AE and the bearing of EE', which has the same bearing as DC. This gives I_S and T_S. Also, $I_L = I_S + I$.

It is most convenient to pick some suitable direction and to assume it as north, which simplifies the computation. When the unknown value is a distance, and the direction is known, the solution is usually simplified by assuming this direction as north.

It happens occasionally that it will be worth while to compute coordinates of the several points involved, and to attain the result by computations from these coordinates. This method is especially useful when the coordinates have already been computed for some other purpose, as, for example, for plotting (see § 21), or for computing areas.

45. Traversing around Obstacles. A somewhat analogous method of surveying a straight transit line around obstacles (as, for example, around trees) without trigono-

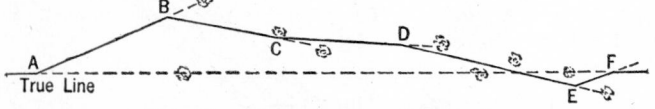

FIG. 45. Traversing around Obstacles.

metric computation, is given in Fig. 45. No line of the auxiliary traverse should make an angle greater than one degree with the true line. The method assumes that the sines of angles are proportional to the angles themselves. For each auxiliary course, the angle between that course and the true line, in minutes, is multiplied by the length of the course (usually measured to an even ten feet or an even 100 feet to facilitate taping and multiplication), and the results are tabulated as follows:

Station	Deflection in Minutes	Distance in Feet	Factors	Products	
				Right	Left
A	19 L		−19×210		3990
		210			
B	28 R		+ 9×160	1440	
		160			
C	7 L		+ 2×190	380	
		190			
D	10 R		+12×260	3120	
		260			
E	27 L		−15×?	....	
		?			
F	?				
	0			4940	3990

The length of the line EF is $\dfrac{4940 - 3990}{15} = 63.3$ feet.

At point F, an angle of 15 minutes *right* must be turned to give the direction of the original, or true, tangent.

The stationing around the auxiliary courses will give nearly the same stationing at F as though the straight line AF had been taped, although a slight allowance may be deducted if precision demands.

46. Conclusion. The method of solution by traverse has not been extensively used for curve problems although it is a valuable tool for this purpose. It is not deemed advisable to cover a great variety of solutions in this volume, but those interested will be able, through the exercise of ingenuity, to apply this method to unusual cases, especially to those not now covered by such of the older standard geometric and trigonometric solutions as are given in this and similar texts.

Most compound curves can be solved by the traverse method. Often it is the best method. Such a solution by traverse for a compound curve, with spirals at both ends and between the curves, is suggested at the end of § 61, page 124. It should be studied in connection with spiraling compound curves.

Figure 46 shows this case. We are given R_L, R_S, I_L, I_S, and the three spiral offsets O_L, O, and O_S. It is required to find the tangent lengths T_L and T_S, and I.

Latitudes and departures are computed around the traverse $ABCD$, the length and bearing of the missing closed traverse line AD are computed, and the triangle ADE is then solved for T_L–Z_L and T_S–Z_S. Z_L and Z_S are known.

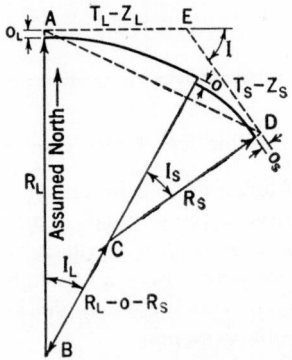

Fig. 46. Tangent Lengths for Compound Curve with Spirals.

CHAPTER VIII

VERTICAL AND OTHER PARABOLIC CURVES

47. Parabolic Curves. The parabola, instead of the circular curve, is used in virtually all cases for vertical curves. An exception may occur in riveted steel pipe lines where a simple circular curve permits the use of the same standard steel plates throughout the curve. The parabola is used occasionally for horizontal curves, and in some other instances—especially when a more pleasing appearance is desired, as in landscaping, or where two tangents of unequal length can not be connected by means of a simple circular curve. A small arc of the flatter parabolas gives substantially the same curve as does a circular curve. It is only the longer arcs of rather sharp parabolas which give the pleasing appearance. Short parabolas are also used in forming the crowns of roads and pavements.

48. Vertical Parabola. A very simple and substantially symmetric form of parabola is ordinarily used for vertical curves. Simplicity and symmetry are attained by placing the vertex of the parabola at a full station, and by terminating the parabola at full stations equidistant horizontally from the vertex, as in Fig. 48.* The curve used is a parabola with skewed axes whose equation is of the form $y = kx^2$, where k is a constant. Vertical distances are y coordinates and distances along AVC from A or along BV from B are x coordinates.

Referring to Fig. 48, it is seen that $VE = CB/2$ (from similar triangles). From the equation $y = kx^2$, it follows

---

* If it is desired or necessary to set stakes 50 feet or 25 feet apart, then the vertical curve may be terminated the same number of these intervals on either side of the vertex.

(48) $$VD = (\tfrac{1}{2})^2 CB = \tfrac{1}{4}CB,$$

and consequently that $VD = VE/2$. From $y = kx^2$

(48a) $$aa' = dd' = (\tfrac{1}{3})^2 VD = \tfrac{1}{9}VD,$$

(48b) $$bb' = cc' = (\tfrac{2}{3})^2 VD = \tfrac{4}{9}VD,$$

since the offsets from either tangent to the parabola vary as the square of the distance along the tangents AVC and BV, beginning at A or B, respectively, either being an origin. Horizontal distances are actually used but this does not alter the proportions.

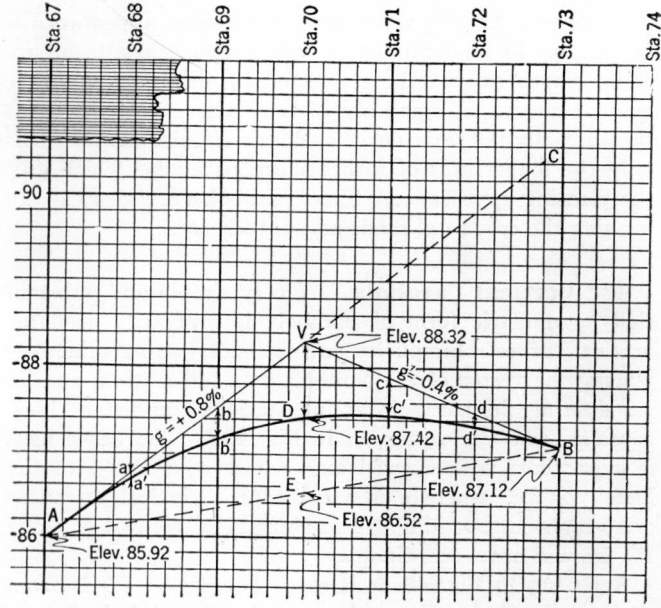

Fig. 48. Vertical Curve.

A numerical example, referred to Fig. 48, may be worked in either of the following manners, both being exact.

First Method

Find the elevation of A and B. Their mean value gives the elevation of E. The mean of the elevations of V and E gives the elevation of D, on the vertical curve. Subtracting the elevation of D from that of V, we find the value of the ordinate VD. Check this by formula 48d. The following example will illustrate this method.

$$A = 85.92$$
$$B = \underline{87.12}$$

$$x = \left(\frac{T_1}{T_2}\right)^2 E$$

$$E = \frac{173.04}{2} = 86.52$$

$$V = 88.32 \qquad\qquad = 88.32$$

$$D = \frac{174.84}{2} \qquad\qquad = 87.42$$

$$DV \qquad\qquad\qquad = 0.90$$

From formula 48c on page 97, we have

$$DV = \tfrac{1}{8}L(g - g') = \tfrac{1}{8}[6][0.8 + 0.4] = 0.90 \text{ check.}$$

Station	Tangent elevations along AV and VB	Vertical offsets from AV and VB	Elevations on vertical curve	Differences in elevation	
				First	Second
67	85.92	0.00	85.92		
				0.70	
68	86.72	$1/9(0.90) = 0.10$	86.62		0.20
				0.50	
69	87.52	$4/9(0.90) = 0.40$	87.12		0.20
				0.30	
70	88.32	0.90	87.42		0.20
				0.10	
71	87.92	$4/9(0.90) = 0.40$	87.52		0.20
				-0.10	
72	87.52	$1/9(0.90) = 0.10$	87.42		0.20
				-0.30	
73	87.12	0.00	87.12		

In the foregoing tabulation the differences in elevation, first and second, are computed only to check the intermediate points on the vertical curve. The second differences for equal horizontal distances must be constant, as in the tabulation, and equal to the value r below. A slide rule is sometimes used to compute the vertical offsets.

SECOND METHOD

Pay *careful attention* to *algebraic signs* in this method. The gradients of the tangents, in percent, are g and g'; the rate of change of gradient per 100 feet is called r; and L is the length of the vertical curve, in stations.

$$r = \frac{g - g'}{L} = \frac{0.8 - (-0.4)}{6} = \frac{1.2}{6} = +0.2$$

STATION	ELEVATION	
		$+0.80 = g$
67	85.92	$0.10 = \frac{1}{2}r$
	$0.70 \leftarrow$	$+0.70 = g - \frac{1}{2}r$
68	$\overline{86.62}$	$0.20 = r$
	$0.50 \leftarrow$	$+0.50 = g - 1\frac{1}{2}r$
69	$\overline{87.12}$	$0.20 = r$
	$0.30 \leftarrow$	$+0.30 = g - 2\frac{1}{2}r$
70	$\overline{87.42}$	$0.20 = r$
	$0.10 \leftarrow$	$+0.10 = g - 3\frac{1}{2}r$
71	$\overline{87.52}$	$0.20 = r$
	$-0.10 \leftarrow$	$-0.10 = g - 4\frac{1}{2}r$
72	$\overline{87.42}$	$0.20 = r$
	$-0.30 \leftarrow$	$-0.30 = g - 5\frac{1}{2}r$
73	$\overline{87.12}$	

This checks the predetermined elevation at the end of the vertical curve, and all intermediate elevations on the vertical curve.

In the somewhat rare case where elevations of points on the vertical curve between stations are needed, it is simpler to compute them by the first method on pages 95 and 96.

Where short vertical curves are used, it is frequently sufficient to stake only the points A, B, and D.

A value for DV may be computed directly from formula 48c which is derived from Fig. 48 as follows:

Difference in gradient between VC and $VB = g - g'$.

Difference in elevation between C and $B = \dfrac{L}{2}(g - g') = CB$.

The values g and g' must be given their proper algebraic signs, then from formula 48,

$$DV = \tfrac{1}{4}CB, \text{ hence}$$

(48c) $$DV = \tfrac{1}{8}L(g - g'), \quad \text{exactly.}$$

Where unequal tangents may be necessary, the same general properties hold, although in the first method of this section, the intermediate offsets corresponding to aa' and bb' are different from those offsets corresponding to cc' and dd'. Moreover, in this case,

(48d) $$DV = \frac{ll'}{2(l + l')}(g - g'),$$

where l and l' are the respective tangent lengths, in 100-foot stations, and DV is in feet.

For equal tangents, $l = l' = L/2$, and

$$DV = \tfrac{1}{8}L(g - g').$$

49. Low Point on Vertical Curve.

Sometimes this point, needed for installing drainage, may be located sufficiently closely from the vertical curve elevations in the notes, when staking is being done.

It is possible to compute the position of the low point as follows, referring to Fig. 49.

Since the parabola has equal tangents and is level at the low point, we have $g - rx = 0$. Also $r = \dfrac{g - g'}{L}$. Substituting, we find

(49) $$x = \frac{Lg}{g - g'}.$$

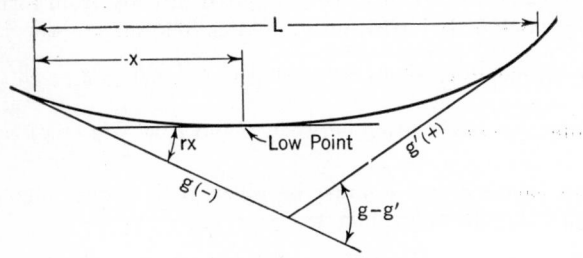

Fig. 49.   Low Point on Vertical Curve.

The elevation of the low point may be computed in the same manner as for any other point on the vertical curve.

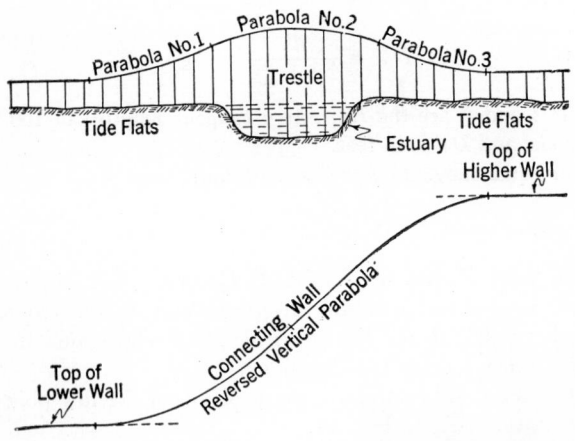

Fig. 50.   Adjacent Vertical Curves.

50. Adjacent Vertical Curves. It sometimes happens, though rarely, that circumstances call for two or more adjacent vertical curves, either compounded or reversed at a point of common tangency, as might be needed for a high trestle crossing tide flats and an estuary, or for connecting two walls at different elevations, as in Fig. 50. Such curves are laid out as separate parabolas, sometimes with an intervening tangent.

51. Length of Vertical Curves. It is desirable to use long vertical curves for appearance, for easy riding, for long sight distances on summits, and for safer operation. Frequently, the amount of earthwork tends to be less with the longer vertical curves, if the tangents and vertical curves are carefully adjusted mutually with this in view.

Ordinarily where two grades differ by only a few tenths of one percent (0.1 percent for first-class railways or slightly more for highways), it is not necessary to use a vertical curve, since ordinary construction methods will round off the intersection sufficiently. Hence vertical curves are rarely used on canals, flumes, levees, or similar constructions using flat grades. No use is made of vertical curves on transmission lines.

For railways, the American Railway Engineering Association Manual recommends: "For high-speed main tracks, the rate of change (in gradient) should not be more than 0.054 foot per station (of 100 feet) in sags and not more than 0.10 foot per station on summits. For secondary main tracks, the rates of change may be twice those for high-speed main tracks. For tracks of lesser importance, rates of change may be relatively large but should not be greater than practical considerations will permit."

For highways, the minimum length of vertical curves is controlled by the sight distance, S. Ideas regarding sight distances are somewhat involved and have changed from time to time. Present practice is given in the 1949 publication of the Public Roads Administration, "Highway Practice in the United States of America," and in Chapter XIX. The desirable sight distance is a matter of judgment based on curvature, grades, amount of traffic to be handled, number of traffic lanes, etc.—subjects beyond the scope of this book.

It must not be overlooked that horizontal, as well as vertical, sight distances must be adequate. These are often scaled on the maps.

One phase of sight distance which can be treated geo-metrically is how far two vehicles are visible to one another over a vertical curve. Here it is assumed that the eye and the top of the other vehicle are both four and one-half feet above the roadway.

Then if both vehicles are on the vertical curve, with S and L in stations, and g and g' in percent,

$$(51) \qquad S < L \text{ and } S^2 = \frac{36L}{g - g'}.$$

If both vehicles are on the tangents approaching the vertical curve, then

$$(51a) \qquad S > L \text{ and } S = \frac{L}{2} + \frac{18}{g - g'}.$$

These formulas are diagrammed in Fig. 51.

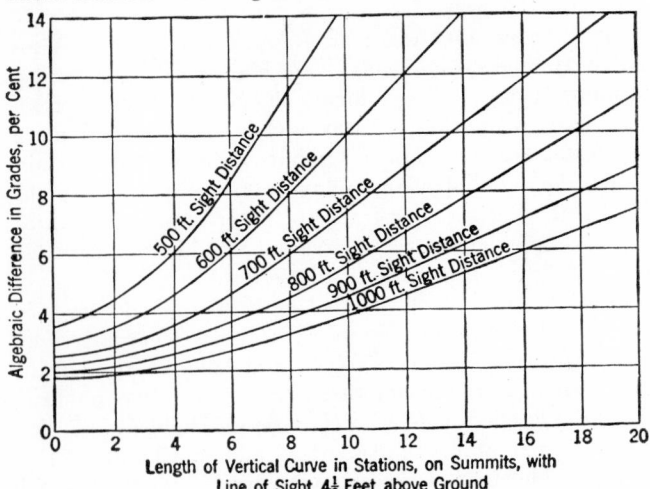

Fig. 51. Sight Distances.

Much shorter vertical curves may be used in sags, although not so short that headlight rays intersect the road too near the car to provide sufficient illuminated roadway.

For pipe lines, the special type of construction employed will govern the minimum length of vertical curve.   Bell and spigot joint pipe of cast iron, concrete, or wood can usually be specially ordered in short lengths to permit laying around rather sharp curves.   Manufacturers, or their catalogs and hand books, should be consulted.

52. Laying out Parabolas with a Tape.   Heretofore the vertical parabola has been described as laid out with a level.   Parabolas can not be laid out conveniently with transit angles, except the cubic parabola mentioned in Chapter IX.

Figure 52 shows two customary methods of laying out parabolas, usually in a horizontal plane, with a tape.   While this figure is drawn for unequal tangents, the same procedure is used for equal tangents.

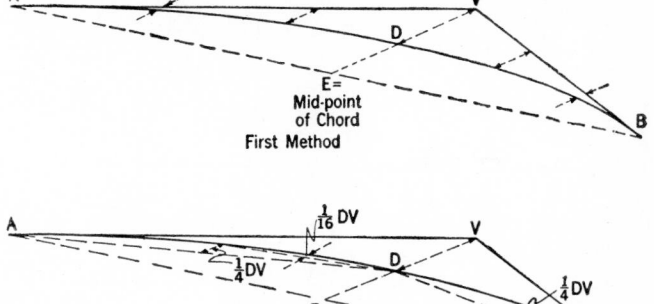

Fig. 52.   Laying out Parabolas with a Tape.

In the first method, either *A* or *B* may be used as the origin of coordinates.   The offsets from the tangent to the parabola will then vary as the square of the distance along the tangent from either A or B. The positions of A, V, and B are given on the ground, the midpoint of the chord is established as E, VE is measured, and the computed offsets from the tangents are laid off parallel to VE. This parallelism is accomplished by eye, or by establishing points proportioned along the chord, if more precision is required. The point D, of course, bisects VE, and the value DV is the basis for computing the offsets.

In the second method, ordinates to the parabola from the midpoint of successively smaller chords are laid off in a direction parallel to VE. Each successive offset is one-fourth of the preceding one.

CHAPTER IX

SPIRALS

53. Introduction. For many constructions, such as high-speed railways and highways, and for very sharp low-speed curves such as occur on street railways, it is essential to provide a spiral connecting the tangent with the circular curve so as to increase gradually the sharpness of the curve until the main body of the simple circular curve is reached. This is shown in Fig. 53. Spirals are also used sometimes to connect the two arcs of a compound curve.

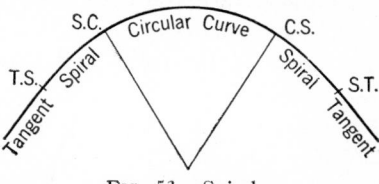

Fig. 53. Spirals.

The several purposes served by spirals are listed below in order of importance:

(1) To provide a satisfactory means of increasing the elevation of the outer rail of a railway or tipping crosswise a highway, from no "superelevation" on the tangent to the required amount of superelevation on the main body of the curve, as described in § 66.

(2) Gradually to change the direction of motion from a straight line to a curve, or vice versa, thus reducing lurching and strains.

(3) On highways; to aid in steering, to minimize skidding, and to keep traffic from cutting across the opposite traffic lane. The steering mechanism of automobiles naturally follows a spiral when entering or leaving a curve.

(4) To provide the most effective means of widening highways on curves. Since the rear wheels of automobiles do not track, and since it is perhaps psychologically

desirable, highways are generally widened on curves.

(5) To minimize scouring or to aid navigation in canals.

54. Basic Equation of the Spiral.   The spiral or transition curve which will best serve the foregoing purposes is one having a varying degree of curvature, zero at the beginning and increasing uniformly as one proceeds around the spiral until it finally equals that of the circular curve where the spiral joins it; thus the degree varies directly as the length along the spiral from its initial point on the tangent, the T.S.   Expressed in another manner, the radius of the spiral is infinite at the beginning of the spiral on the tangent, and it continues to decrease as one proceeds around the spiral until the simple circular curve is reached, at which point the radius of the spiral and that of the simple circular

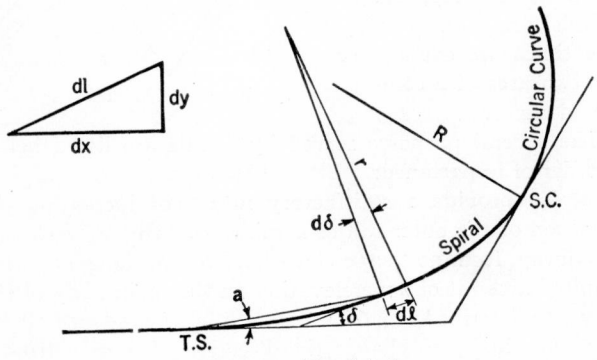

Fig. 54.   The Spiral.

curve are the same.   The basic equation of such a spiral is derived from Fig. 54 as follows: By calculus, with radians and feet as units, and with the nomenclature of § 55, except that d indicates the differential, we have

$$r\,d\delta = dl, \qquad \text{or} \qquad d\delta = \frac{dl}{r}.$$

Because r varies inversely* with l, $\dfrac{r}{R} = \dfrac{L}{l}$, and we have

(54) $$d\delta = \frac{ldl}{RL},$$

and, by integration,

(54a) $$\delta = \frac{l^2}{2RL}, \qquad \text{approximately.}$$

At the S.C., where the spiral joins the simple circular curve, $l = L$ and $\delta = \Delta$, so that we have

(54b) $$\Delta = \frac{L^2}{2RL} = \frac{L}{2R}, \qquad \text{approximately,}$$

with the units still radians and feet. If we substitute the closely approximate relation $R = \dfrac{5729.6}{D}$ and express the angle Δ in degrees instead of in radians, we have

(54c) $$\Delta = \frac{LD}{200}, \quad \text{exactly.}$$

Moreover, since $\sin \delta = \delta$, approximately,

$$dy = \delta dl = \frac{l^2 dl}{2RL},$$

and, by integration,

(54d) $$y = \frac{l^3}{6RL}, \qquad \text{approximately,}$$

which is called a "cubic spiral" or an "easement curve."

Several spirals, such as the cubic parabola,† the Talbot, the Searles, the Crandall, and the Barnett spirals, have been based on these formulas or a slight modification of them. All of them are satisfactory and give substantially the same easement curve as actually staked out. The ten-chord spiral

---

* This is not a precise statement since r and d vary approximately, but not precisely, in inverse ratio.

† $y = \dfrac{x^3}{6RL}$.

of the American Railway Engineering Association, commonly
called the A.R.E.A. spiral, was developed after considering
all of the older spirals; it is widely used; it promises to continue in use; and it will be developed and used in this book.
Once it has been mastered, the other types may be learned
easily if need arises.

The Barnett highway transition curve is explained at the
ends of this chapter and Chapter XVIII.

**55. American Railway Engineering Association
Ten-Chord Spiral.**   The study of spiral curves introduces so many new relationships and symbols that it seems
advisable to define them here, with reference to Fig. 55, in
order to simplify the discussion that follows.   A.R.E.A.
nomenclature is used.

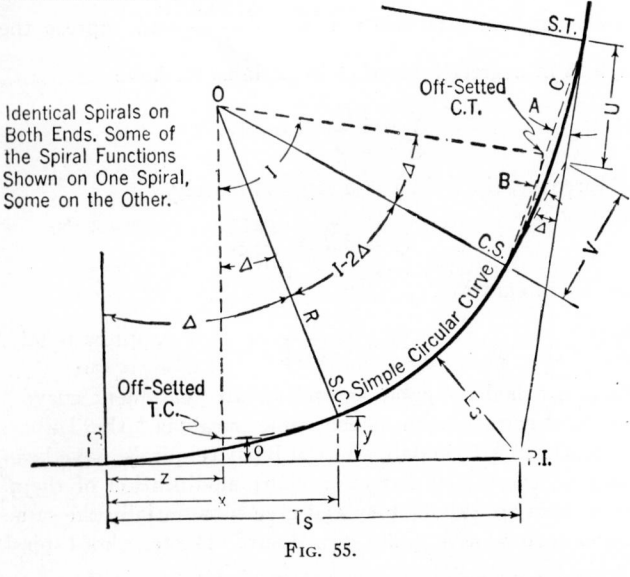

F𝚒ɢ. 55.

N𝚘𝚝𝚊𝚝𝚒𝚘𝚗

"For curve points, the first initial represents the alignment on
the side toward station zero, the second that away from station zero.

T.C.   The point of change in alignment from tangent to circular curve.

C.T.   The point of change from circular curve to tangent.

C.C.   The point of change in degree of circular curve; the point of compound curve.

T.S.   The point of change from tangent to spiral.

S.C.   The point of change from spiral to circular curve.

C.S.   The point of change from circular curve to spiral.

S.T.   The point of change from spiral to tangent.

S.S.   The point of change from one spiral to another.
      The symbols T.C. and C.T., T.S. and S.T., and S.C. and C.S. become transposed when the direction of stationing is changed.

a The angle between the tangent at the T.S. and the chord from the T.S. to any point on the spiral.

A The angle between the tangent at the T.S. and the chord from the T.S. to the S.C.

b The angle at any point on the spiral, between the tangent at that point and the chord from the T.S.

B The angle at the S.C. between the chord from the T.S. and the tangent at the S.C.

c The chord from the T.S. to any point on the spiral.

C The chord from the T.S. to the S.C.

d The degree of curve at any point on the spiral.

D The degree of central circular curve.

f The angle between any chord of the spiral (produced if necessary) and the tangent through the T.S.

I The angle between the initial and final tangents; the total central angle of circular curve and spirals.

k The increase in degree of curve per station on the spiral.

l The length of the spiral in feet from the T.S. to any given point.

L The length of the spiral in feet from the T.S. to the S.C.

o The ordinate of the offsetted T.C.; the distance between the tangent and a parallel tangent to the offsetted curve.

s The length of the spiral in station from the T.S. to any given point.

S The length of the spiral in station from the T.S. to the S.C.

r The radius of the osculating circle at any given point of the spiral.

R The radius of the central circular curve.

u The distance on the tangent from the T.S. to the intersection with the tangent through any given point on the spiral.

U The distance on the tangent from the T.S. to the inter-section with a tangent through the S.C.; the longer spiral tangent.

v The distance on the tangent through any given point from that point to the intersection with the tangent through the T.S.

V The distance on the tangent through the S.C. from the S.C. to the intersection with the tangent through the T.S.; the shorter spiral tangent.

x The abscissa or tangent distance of any given point, referred to the T.S.

X The abscissa or tangent distance of the S.C., referred to the T.S.

y The ordinate or tangent offset of any point on the spiral.

Y The ordinate or tangent offset of the S.C.

Z The abscissa or tangent distance of the offsetted T.C. referred to the T.S.: $Z = \dfrac{X}{2}$, approximately.

δ The central angle of the spiral from the T.S. to any given point.

Δ The central angle of the whole spiral.

T_S The tangent distance of the spiraled curve; distance from T.S. to P.I. (point of intersection of tangents).

E_S The external distance of the offsetted curve."

The A.R.E.A. spiral is based on equation (54c) in which the lengths around the spiral are measured in ten equal chords rather than around the actual arc. The A.R.E.A. spiral closely approximates a cubic parabola of the form $y = x^3/6RL$, and likewise a "cubic spiral" of the form $y = l^3/6RL$.

56. Properties of the A.R.E.A. Spiral. The A.R.E.A. spiral (Fig. 55) has the properties given in this section, stated with sufficient accuracy for field work. If more exact values are needed, as for example in preparing tables, the reader is referred to § 57 immediately following, and to the Proceedings or the Manual of the American Railway Engineering Association. All examples given here are for a spiral with D (of circular curve) = 5°, $L = 300$ feet; and point 4 on the spiral (0.4 of the spiral length from the T.S.) is used as a typical intermediate point:

(1) The degree of curve of the spiral varies directly as the length of the spiral from the T.S., or

$$(56) \qquad \frac{d}{D} = \frac{l}{L}, \qquad \text{exactly.}$$

For the above example the degree of the spiral at point 4 is

$$d_4 = \frac{120}{300}(5°) = 2°.$$

(2) Similarly, the radius of the spiral varies approximately inversely as the distance from the T.S., or

$$(56a) \qquad \frac{r}{R} = \frac{L}{l}, \qquad \text{approximately,}$$

and for the example given above where $R = 1146.3$ feet, r at point 4 is

$$r_4 = \frac{300}{120}(1146.3) = \frac{10}{4}(1146.3) = 2865.7 \text{ feet.}$$

(3) The final value of the spiral angle is

$$(56b) \qquad \Delta = \frac{LD}{200}, \qquad \text{exactly,}$$

or, for the foregoing example,

$$\Delta = \frac{(300)(5°)}{200} = 7.5 \text{ degrees.}$$

(4) The spiral angle for any point on the spiral varies directly as the square of the distance from the T.S., or

$$(56c) \qquad \frac{\delta}{\Delta} = \frac{l^2}{L^2}, \qquad \text{exactly.}$$

or, for the foregoing example,

$$\delta_4 = \left(\frac{120}{300}\right)^2 (7.5°) = 0.16(7.5°) = 1.2 \text{ degrees.}$$

(5) The deflection angle to any point on the spiral from the original tangent, that is, with the transit at the T.S., is

$$(56d) \qquad\qquad a = \frac{\delta}{3}, \qquad\qquad \text{approximately,}$$

and for the final point, S.C., the deflection angle is

$$(56e) \qquad\qquad A = \frac{\Delta}{3}, \qquad\qquad \text{approximately;}$$

for the foregoing example,

$$a_4 = \frac{\delta_4}{3} = \frac{1.2}{3} = 0.4 \text{ degrees} = 24 \text{ minutes,}$$

$$A = \frac{\Delta}{3} = \frac{7.5}{3} = 2.5 \text{ degrees.}$$

If the value of Δ lies between 15° and 45° and if very exact values of the deflection angles to intermediate or final points on the spiral are desired, the American Railway Engineering Association recommends use of the formula

$$(56f) \qquad\qquad a = \frac{\delta}{3} - 0.00297\delta^3, \qquad\qquad \text{exactly,}$$

where a and δ are in degrees and the correction $0.00297\delta^3$ is in seconds. Values for this correction are given in Table XI.

The values in Tables VII to IX include this correction. In field work, the foregoing correction may be eliminated, if desired, by setting up the transit at intermediate points on the spiral so as to keep a less than about 7°.

(6) The deflection angle to any point on the spiral from the T.S. may also be determined from the following relationship:

$$(56g) \qquad\qquad \frac{a}{A} = \frac{l^2}{L^2}, \qquad\qquad \text{approximately,}$$

or, for the foregoing example,

$$a_4 = \left(\frac{120}{300}\right)^2 (2.5°) = 0.4 \text{ degrees} = 24 \text{ minutes.}$$

It is sometimes desirable to compute the deflection angle by means of the formula

$$a = \frac{kl^2}{1000} \text{ minutes,} \qquad \text{approximately.}$$

For example,

$$a_4 = \frac{(1\frac{2}{3})(120)^2}{1000} = 24 \text{ minutes.}$$

Another way of computing the ten deflection angles is to multiply the first deflection angle, a_1, by the squares of the numbers of the chord points. That is, the first deflection angle would be multiplied by 1^2, 2^2, 3^2, 4^2, 5^2, 6^2. 7^2, 8^2, 9^2, and 10^2 to secure the ten successive deflection angles. Actually, then, the first deflection angle would be multiplied by 1, 4, 9, 16, 25, 36, 49, 64, 81, and 100. For large values of Δ, say between 15° and 45°, the small correction given by formula 56f, or from Table XI, must be applied if precise results are needed.

(7) The tangent offsets vary closely as the cube of the spiral length from the T.S., measured as chords, or

(56h)
$$\frac{y}{Y} = \frac{l^3}{L^3}, \qquad \text{approximately,}$$

or, for the foregoing example (Y being taken from Table VIII),

$$y_4 = (13.07)\left(\frac{120}{300}\right)^3 = 0.84 \text{ feet.}$$

The procedure may be simplified by computing the middle, quarter, and three-quarter points of the spiral as $(1/4)^3$, $(2/4)^3$, and $(3/4)^3$ of Y.

(8) The values measured along the tangent vary closely as the spiral length from the T.S., measured as chords, or

(56i) $$\frac{x}{X} = \frac{l}{L},$$ approximately,

or, for the foregoing example, at point 4,

$$x_4 = \left(\frac{120}{300}\right)(299.49) = 119.80.$$

The *exact* values of X and Y are best taken from Table VII or Table VIII, since the *exact* computation is laborious, as explained in the following paragraphs.

The American Railway Engineering Association has computed the values of X and Y precisely by a method in which the length of each spiral chord is multiplied by the cosine and sine, respectively, of the angle f which that chord makes with the original tangent; the total of these components giving X and Y, or

$$l_1 \cos f_1 + l_2 \cos f_2 + l_3 \cos f_3 \cdots + l_{10} \cos f_{10} = X,$$
$$l_1 \sin f_1 + l_2 \sin f_2 + l_3 \sin f_3 \cdots + l_{10} \sin f_{10} = Y.$$

The values f_1, f_2, f_3, $\cdots f_{10}$ of the angles made by the successive spiral chords with the original tangent are $1/300\Delta$, $7/300\Delta$, $19/300\Delta$, $\cdots 271/300\Delta$. The American Railway Engineering Association explains the derivation of these values as follows, with reference to Fig. 56.

"Dividing the spiral into ten equal parts, the angle between the tangent at the T.S. and the chord from a spiral point $(n - 1)$ to the next point (n), is equal to the central angle of the spiral from the T.S. to the point $(n - 1)$, plus the degree of curve at the point $(n - 1)$ times half the distance in stations from $(n - 1)$ to (n), plus the deflection from the tangent at the T.S. to the chord subtending the first tenth of the spiral. This is shown on Fig. 56 and is partly explained in § 61. It is referred to again in § 57.

"Substituting the successive numerals 1 to 10 for n, the successive values of f are 1, 7, 19. 37, 61, 91, 127, 169, 217, and 271, each multiplied by $\Delta/300$." See §§ 60 and 61 before attempting to follow Fig. 56.

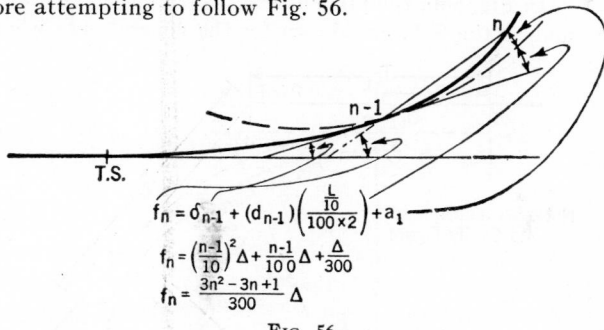

$$f_n = \delta_{n-1} + (d_{n-1})\left(\frac{\frac{L}{10}}{100 \times 2}\right) + a_1$$

$$f_n = \left(\frac{n-1}{10}\right)^2 \Delta + \frac{n-1}{100}\Delta + \frac{\Delta}{300}$$

$$f_n = \frac{3n^2 - 3n + 1}{300} \Delta$$

Fig. 56.

(9) The line O–5 in Fig. 56a bisects the spiral, very closely, 5 being point 5 on the spiral. The point 5 is midway, very closely, between the offsetted T.C. and the tangent.

(56j) $o = KJ = CN - CQ = Y - R \text{ vers } \Delta$,   exactly.

(56k) $Z = HJ = HN - JN = X - R \sin \Delta$,   exactly.

Also, $o = \dfrac{L^2}{24R} = 0.0727 DS^2$ and $Z = \dfrac{L}{2}$, approximately

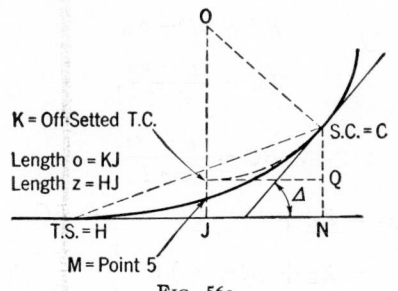

Fig. 56a.

In the foregoing example,
$$o = 13.07 - (1146.3)(0.00856) = 3.26 \text{ feet},$$
$$Z = 299.49 - (1146.3)(0.13053) = 149.86 \text{ feet}.$$

The values of o and of Z are usually taken from Table VII or Table VIII, or they may be computed from the preceding formulas.

(10) In Fig. 56b, the tangent lengths from the P.I. to the T.S. and to the S.T. are shown for the general case where

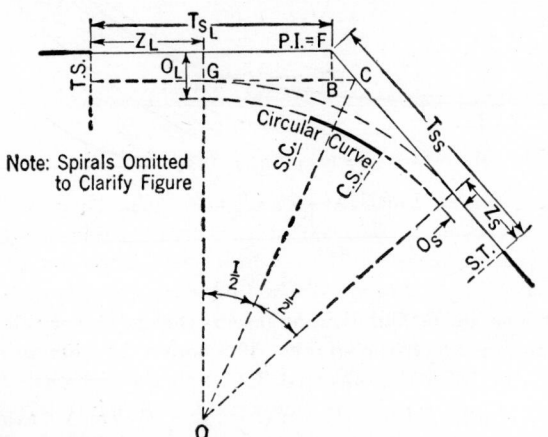

FIG. 56b. Spiral Tangents.

the spirals are of unequal length, and derived as follows:

$$FB = o_L - o_S,$$

$$FC = \frac{o_L - o_S}{\sin I},$$

$$BC = \frac{o_L - o_S}{\tan I},$$

$$T_{S_L} = Z_L + \qquad GC \qquad - BC,$$

(56l) $$T_{S_L} = Z_L + (R + o_S) \tan \frac{I}{2} - \frac{o_L - o_S}{\tan I},$$

and similarly

(56m) $$T_{S_S} = Z_S + (R + o_S) \tan \frac{I}{2} + \frac{o_L - o_S}{\sin I}.$$

The direction of traffic, speed, grade, and frost action often justify spirals of different lengths. However, if identical spirals are used, the two tangents are equal and $o_L - o_S = o$. Then

(56n) $$T_{SL} = T_{SS} = Z + (R + o) \tan \frac{I}{2},$$

(56o) $$= Z + T_C + \left(o \tan \frac{I}{2} \right),$$

where T_C is the tangent length for a simple circular curve with D and I as given, and may be taken from Table II.

57. Precise Definition of A.R.E.A. Spiral.

Because the usual field procedures frequently follow slightly approximate formulas, it may be well to introduce at this point a precise definition of the A.R.E.A. Ten-Chord Spiral as formulated for this volume by Colonel J. B. Jenkins, the outstanding authority of the Association on this subject. He states:

"The exact nature of the Ten-Chord Spiral has been widely misunderstood, some thinking it a compound curve and others an irregular curve passing through certain chord points.

"The Ten-Chord Spiral is based upon the requirement that the degree of curve as defined by the A.R.E.A.—the angle subtended at the center of a simple (circular) curve by a 100-foot chord—shall be proportional to the distance, measured in ten equal chords, from the origin of the spiral. The true definition is as follows:

"The Ten-Chord Spiral is the locus of a point at the extremity of the tenth chord of ten equal consecutive chords, the sum of which is variable, the angles of the several chords with the tangent through the point of origin being respectively 1, 7, 19, 37, 61, 91, 127, 169, 217 and 271 three-hundredths of Δ, which is proportional to the square of the chord-length. The A.R.E.A. formulas which follow conform to this definition and the tables at the end of this volume are calculated in accordance therewith.

"Of the basic formulas (57) to (57e), inclusive, two are empirical—that for the long chord, in which the maximum error up to $\Delta = 45$ degrees is less than one part in a million, and that for the deflection angle, in which the maximum error is less than one second. Formulas (57f) to (57n), inclusive, are trigonometrical derivatives.

"*Formulas for the Exact Determination of the Functions of the Ten-Chord Spiral when the Central Angle Does Not Exceed 45 Degrees*

(57) $$d = ks = \frac{kl}{100},$$

(57a) $$D = kS = \frac{kL}{100},$$

(57b) $$\begin{cases} \delta = \dfrac{ks^2}{2} = \dfrac{ds}{2} = \dfrac{kl^2}{20000} = \dfrac{dl}{200}, \\ \Delta = \dfrac{kS^2}{2} = \dfrac{DS}{2} = \dfrac{kL^2}{20000} = \dfrac{DL}{200}, \end{cases}$$

(57c) $$A = \tfrac{1}{3}\Delta - 0.00297\Delta^3 \text{ seconds},$$

(57d) $$B = \Delta - A,$$

(57e) $$C = L(\cos 0.3\Delta + 0.004 \text{ exsec } \tfrac{3}{4}\Delta).$$

(57f) $$X = C \cos A,$$

(57g) $$Y = C \sin A,$$

(57h) $$U = C\frac{\sin B}{\sin \Delta},$$

(57i) $$V = C\frac{\sin A}{\sin \Delta},$$

(57j) $$R = \frac{50}{\sin \tfrac{1}{2}D},$$

(57k) $Z = X - R \sin \Delta,$

(57l) $o = Y - R \operatorname{vers} \Delta,$

(57m) $Ts = (R + o) \tan (\tfrac{1}{2}I) + Z,$

(57n) $Es = (R + o) \operatorname{exsec} (\tfrac{1}{2}I) + o.$

"*Formulas for Field Use.* The formulas presented above are best adapted for the preparation of tables. For use in the field, the following empirical formulas are sufficiently accurate and have the advantage that they do not require the computation of the long chord. The formulas can all be applied for the functions of any parts of the spiral without serious error, though they are derived for the completed spiral.

(57o) $\begin{cases} a = \tfrac{1}{3}\delta, \\ A = \tfrac{1}{3}\Delta, \end{cases}$

(57p) $a = 10ks^2 \text{ minutes,}$

(57q) $A = 10kS^2 \text{ minutes.}$

"Formulas 57o, 57p, and 57q are sufficiently accurate for turning deflection when δ (or Δ) does not exceed 15 degrees.

"A similar approximation may be used when the transit is set at an intermediate point on the spiral if the included central angle from the transit point to the point of sight, less the included angle from the T.S. to the transit point, does not exceed 15 degrees."

58. Spiral Field Notes.

The following is an example of the computations for a curve with spirals of different lengths on the ends, which is the general case. Where the same spiral is used on both ends, the solution is somewhat simplified.

Required to connect given tangents by a 4° curve with an approaching spiral of 180 feet and a leaving spiral of 100 feet. $I = 22° \ 14'$ and the P.I. is at station $46 + 72.5$.

From table I,

$R_4 = 1432.69$ feet, $\tan I = 0.40877$,

From Tables VII and/or VIII, or from formulas,

$o_S = 0.29$ feet, $Z_S = 49.99$ feet, $\sin I = 0.37838$,

$o_L = 0.94$ feet, $Z_L = 89.97$ feet, $\tan \dfrac{I}{2} = 0.19649$.

$$T_{SL} = 89.97 + (1432.69 + 0.29)0.19649 - \frac{0.94 - 0.29}{0.40877}$$

$$= 369.95 \text{ feet,}$$

$$T_{SS} = 49.99 + (1432.69 + 0.29)0.19649 + \frac{0.94 - 0.29}{0.37838}$$

$$= 333.27 \text{ feet.}$$

From 54c, $\Delta_L = \dfrac{180 \times 4}{200} = 3.6°$,

$$\Delta_S = \frac{100 \times 4}{200} = 2.0°,$$

$$\overline{5.6°} = \Delta_L + \Delta_S,$$

P.I. =	46 + 72.5
	3 + 69.9 $= T_{SL}$
T.S. =	43 + 02.6
	1 + 80.0 $= L_L$
S.C. =	44 + 82.6
	4 + 15.8 $= L_C$
C.S. =	48 + 98.4
	1 + 00.0 $= L_S$
S.T. =	49 + 98.4

$I = 22.2333°$

$4°)\overline{16.6333°} = I - (\Delta_L + \Delta_S)$

$\overline{4.1583} \times 100 = L_C$

Deflection angles for long spiral with transit at T.S.

	SPIRAL DEFLECTION	STATION
	Instrument at T.S. =	$43 + 02.6$
	$a_1 = 0° 01'$	$43 + 20.6$
	$03'$	$43 + 38.6$
	$06'$	$43 + 56.6$
From table IX: Val-	$11'$	$43 + 74.6$
ues of a for $\Delta = 3.6°$	$18'$	$43 + 92.6$
	$26'$	$44 + 10.6$
	$35'$	$44 + 28.6$
	$46'$	$44 + 46.6$
	$58'$	$44 + 64.6$
	$A = a_{10} = 1° 12'$	$44 + 82.6 =$ S.C.

$$\frac{\Delta}{3} = a_{10} = \frac{3.6}{3} = 1° 12' \quad Check.$$

Deflection angles for circular curve with transit at the S.C.

$$\Delta = 3° 36'$$
$$a_{10} = 1° 12'$$
$$\text{Back deflection to T.S.} = 2° 24'$$

	DEFLECTION ANGLE	STATION
	Instrument at S.C. =	$44 + 82.6$
for chord = 17.4 feet, $d/2$	$= 0° 21'$	$45 + 00.0$
	$= 2° 21'$	$46 + 00.0$
	$= 4° 21'$	$47 + 00.0$
	$= 6° 21'$	$48 + 00.0$
for chord = 98.4 feet, $d/2$	$= 8° 19'$	$48 + 98.4 =$ C.S.

$$Check: \frac{I - (\Delta_L + \Delta_S)}{2} = \frac{22.2333° - 5.6°}{2} = 8.3166° = 8° 19'$$

Deflection angles for short spiral with transit at S.T. (spiral run backwards).

	SPIRAL DEFLECTION		STATION
	$A = a_{10} = 40'$	to	$48 + 98.4 =$ C.S.
	$32'$		$49 + 08.4$
	$26'$		$49 + 18.4$
	$20'$		$49 + 28.4$
From table IX: Val-	$14'$		$49 + 38.4$
ues of a for $\Delta = 2°$	$10'$		$49 + 48.4$
	$6'$		$49 + 58.4$
	$4'$		$49 + 68.4$
	$2'$		$49 + 78.4$
	$0.5'$		$49 + 88.4$
	$a_0 = 00'$		$49 + 98.4 =$ S.T.

59. Spiral Field Notes when Stationing is Preferred. Many engineers prefer to carry the regular stationing around the spiral, as mentioned in § 62. Here

$$k = \frac{4°}{1.8} = 2.222+.$$

Deflection angles are computed from formula 57p and stakes would be set at

STATION	DEFLECTION ANGLE
43 + 02.6	0° 0′
43 + 50	5′
44	21′
44 + 50	48′
44 + 82.6	72′ = 1° 12′

Any necessary intermediate point, such as the center of a bridge pier, may be set similarly.

If this method is to be used, computation is simplified by choosing values of S and of k so as to use Table VIII. For example, in the above case, S might be chosen as 2.00 with $k = 2$, and all spiral data except deflection angles might be taken directly from the Table. The deflection angles could be interpolated from the Table for lengths of 0.474, 0.974, 1.474, and 2.00 (values of S), usually by inspection.

Should a shorter spiral be preferred, $S = 1.60$ and $k = 2\frac{1}{2}$ (Table VIII) could be used similarly.

60. The Osculating Circle. At any point of the spiral, as at point 4 in Fig. 61, a circle may be drawn having a common tangent with the spiral and having a degree of curve equal to that of the spiral at that point. This is known as an *osculating circle*.

An important property of the spiral is that *the spiral departs from the osculating circle, in both angle and offset, in the same manner as the spiral departs from the tangent at the T.S.* This property is referred to in the following section

61. Intermediate Setups and Compound Curves.

Intermediate Setups on Spiral. It rarely happens that an intermediate setup is necessary, but in such cases the deflection angles are computed as shown below, where an intermediate setup is required at point 4. On Fig. 61, the dashed circular curve (the osculating circle) through the

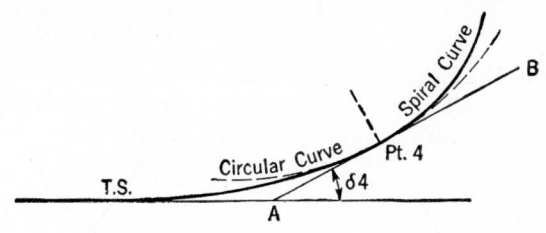

Fig. 61.

point 4 has the same degree as the spiral at that point, namely (4/10) D. The spiral between the points 4 and 5 departs from the dashed circular curve the same amount in angle or in offset as the spiral between the points 0 and 1 departs from the original tangent through the T.S. In other words, with the transit on the point 4 and sighting along the tangent to the spiral at that point, we turn toward the point 5 through the deflection angle for a circular curve of (4/10) D degrees, and then onward to the point 5 through an angle of a_1 (the deflection angle which we would use to set point 1 on the spiral with the transit at the T.S.). An example of this computation follows:

Required deflection angles from tangent at point 4 on 180-foot spiral of preceding problem of § 58.

The tangent AB is found by turning an angle from chord from 4 to T.S. equal to twice the forward deflection to point 4 (a_4), or $2 \times 11\frac{1}{2} = 23'$.

$$d \text{ at point } 4 = 0.4 \times 4° = 1° 36'.$$

Deflection for 18 feet on a 1° 36′ curve = 8.64′.

Forward deflection to point	5	08.6'+ 0.7'	= 9'	43+92.6
	6	17.3'+03'	=20'	44+10.6
	7	25.9'+06'	=32'	44+28.6
	8	34.6'+11'	=46'	44+46.6
	9	43.2'+18'	=61'	44+64.6
	10	51.9'+26'	=78'	44+82.6=S.C.
Back deflection to point	3	08.6'−01'	=08'	43+56.6
	2	17.3'−03'	=14'	43+38.6
	1	25.9'−06'	=20'	43+20.6
	0	34.6'−11'	=24'	43+02.6=T.S.

Table X of the American Railway Engineering Association gives coefficients for determining directly the deflection angles to be used at an intermediate setup.

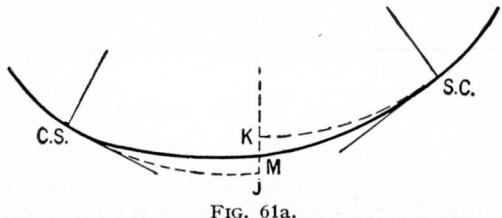

FIG. 61a.

Spiraling Compound Curves. It is often desirable to insert a spiral between two arcs of a compound curve as in Fig. 61a. This is done as follows:

From Tables VIII and IX find the spiral deflections for a spiral that would be used to connect with a curve of degree $D_S - D_L$, and of the selected length. Find the deflection angles of one of the circular curves for chords equal to the successive spiral chords. The total deflection angles, with the transit at the C.S., are

$$\text{point } 1 = \left(\frac{L}{10 \times 100} \right) \frac{D_S}{2} + a_1,$$

$$\text{point } 2 = \left(\frac{2L}{10 \times 100} \right) \frac{D_S}{2} + a_2,$$

$$\cdots \text{point } 10 = \left(\frac{10L}{10 \times 100} \right) \frac{D_S}{2} + a_{10}.$$

If the transit is at the S.C., and the spiral is being run backwards, the total deflection angles are

$$\text{point 1} = \left(\frac{L}{10 \times 100} \right) \frac{D_L}{2} - a_1,$$

$$\text{point 2} = \left(\frac{2L}{10 \times 100} \right) \frac{D_L}{2} - a_2,$$

$$\cdots \text{point 10} = \left(\frac{10L}{10 \times 100} \right) \frac{D_L}{2} - a_{10}.$$

These computations are somewhat similar to those of the intermediate setup on spiral, in the first part of this section.

EXAMPLE: Required to connect two curves of 2° and 5°, respectively, with a spiral 200 feet long.

The deflection angle for 20 feet (one chord length) of a 2° curve is 0° 12′, and the successive spiral deflections for a curve of $D = 5° - 2° = 3°$ and $L = 200$ feet, are obtained from Tables VIII and IX.

The following table gives the total deflection angles at the successive points of the spiral, with the transit at the C.S.

	2° curve deflection	+	spiral deflection	=	total deflection
For point 1	0° 12′	+	0° 01′	=	0° 13′
2	0° 24′	+	0° 02′	=	0° 26′
3	0° 36′	+	0° 05′	=	0° 41′
4	0° 48′	+	0° 10′	=	0° 58′
5	1° 00′	+	0° 15′	=	1° 15′
6	1° 12′	+	0° 22′	=	1° 34′
7	1° 24′	+	0° 29′	=	1° 53′
8	1° 36′	+	0° 38′	=	2° 14′
9	1° 48′	+	0° 49′	=	2° 37′
10	2° 00′	+	1° 00′	=	3° 00′

If the transit is at the S.C.. an equivalent table may be made, total deflections being equal to the deflections for the 5° curve *minus* the successive spiral deflections.

In the field, J and K are usually fixed by topographical requirements. Measure $L/2$ of the selected spiral along each of the circular curves from J and K to establish the C.S. and the S.C., respectively. With the transit at the C.S. or the S.C., turn off the proper spiral angles.

The tangent lengths T_{SL} and T_{SS} are best computed as the closing lines of a traverse. See Fig. 46, page 92.

The spiral can be located also from the previously located circular curves by measuring offsets inward from the flatter curve and outward from the sharper curve, the offset along the common radius being half of o. Other offsets are proportional to the cube of the distances from the nearest end of the spiral.

62. Field Work. On location surveys prior to construction, it is usually sufficient to stake the offsetted circular curve and to run in the spiral later in connection with construction. This, of course, involves the selection of the spiral and especially of the value of o. In running the offsetted circular curve an offsetted P.I. must be used.

Frequently, it may be sufficient to set only part of the spiral points such as 0,5,10; or 0,3,7,10; or 0,2,4,6,8,10.

As an alternative procedure, stakes are often set at full stations and at fractions thereof, as for example 50 feet apart up to $d = 3$ degrees and 25 feet apart for sharper spirals.

Not infrequently, it is necessary to set stakes at odd points, such as the center of a bridge pier.

In the usual case, I and D are known. Select L to fit the requirements; or perhaps o has already been established as in the preceding paragraph and L must be chosen to correspond with o. Compute the *field notes* as in § 58.

Run in the first spiral with the transit at the T.S. Move the transit to the S.C., turn tangent to the curve and spiral by backsighting on the T.S. with the transit plates clamped on $(\Delta - A)$ degrees (twice A is sufficiently precise when Δ is less than $15°$), and the plates will be on zero degrees when the transit is on the common auxiliary tangent mentioned above. Run in the circular curve to the C.S. Move the transit to the S.T. and run in the second spiral backwards, checking on the C.S. which was previously set. If the check is not satisfactory, it may be necessary to repeat the work. Occasionally, it may be sufficient to run in part of the circular curve backward from the last set C.S., and to throw the error of closure on the main circular curve rather than at the C.S. The limits of precision for the construction in hand will determine which of these alternatives should be used.

Sometimes it may be desirable to run in the circular curve entirely from the C.S. in order to avoid accumulating errors, as mentioned in § 35.

Linear closing errors are usually relatively unimportant but alignment closing errors often should be adjusted by shifting a few stakes sidewise on one or both sides of the closing point so as gradually to "run out" the error, unless the error is great enough to necessitate re-running the entire curve and spirals.

In many instances it may be desirable to maintain the 100-foot stations around the spiral, in which case the transit index angle for the exact station to be set is computed from the formula (56g) or (57p).

63. Field Work by Offsets. Occasionally, it is desirable to locate the spiral by offsets figured as mentioned in item 7, § 56. This may be useful especially where the off-setted circular curve has been run without spirals, as described in § 62. In this case, offsets from the tangents to the first half of the spiral may be computed and used. These same offsets for the last half of the spiral may then be used from, and normal to, the circular curve, since the offsets from an original tangent are the same as the offsets from the osculating circle (in this case the main circular curve).

If very precise results are needed, use x and y coordinates from the tables, since they are exact. For example, Table

VIII not only gives exact spiral data at the end of the spiral, the S.C., but the x and y values may be read directly from Table VIII, for successive points along the spiral.

64. Spiral Tables. Tables VII to XI will facilitate computation of the A.R.E.A. spiral. Their form and content was chosen, after consultation with the leading authorities on spirals, as being the most useful and practical type of tables, including spirals for high-speed operation. Tables covering other spirals will be found in use in various organizations. All of them give substantially the same spiral on the ground, although the use of the tables and the field work vary slightly. A little study of these other spirals will acquaint one with their use, after the A.R.E.A. ten-chord spiral given here has been mastered.

The use of the tables in this book, in connection with the Barnett highway transition spiral, is explained in §67a.

65. Spiraling Existing Curves. Different procedures are followed in spiraling existing railroad curves, depending upon whether the curve has been previously spiraled, on the perfection of alignment necessary, and on the money available for the work, as follows:

(1) To smooth out old curves which are already spiraled but are out of line, the stringlining method of Chapter XI is cheapest and minimizes shifting of existing track.

(2) To secure the most perfect alignment, it is frequently necessary to realign the track entirely in the same manner as though the work were being laid out new, without much reference to the existing track.

(3) To introduce spirals on an existing unspiraled circular curve or to introduce longer and flatter spirals, one of the following procedures is ordinarily used:

(a) The circular curve is moved inward parallel to its original position so that the spiral may be inserted as in Fig. 65. Because this method frequently involves too much shifting of the track, it is seldom used.

(b) The curve, if relatively short, is thrown outward at the center of the arc and sharpened and thrown inward at

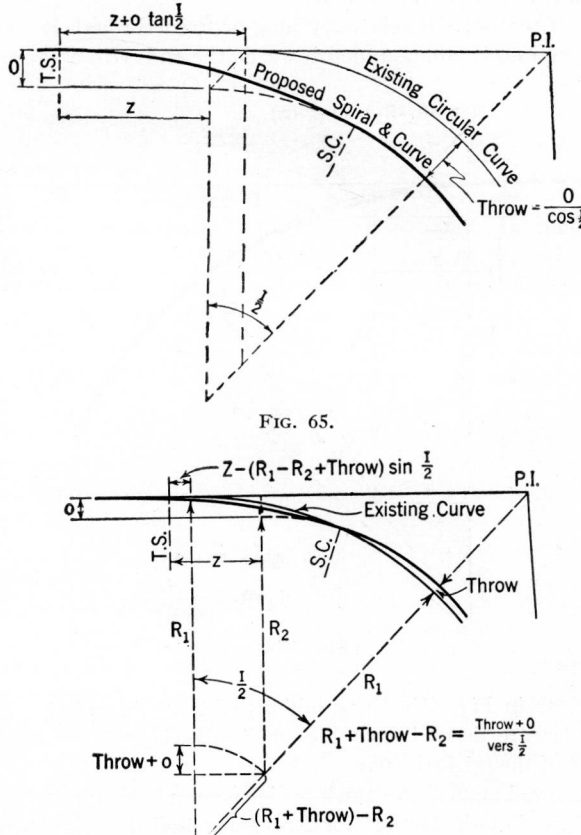

Fig. 65.

Fig. 65a.

the end as in Fig. 65a, to allow for the insertion of a spiral. The formulas are derived by considering the small triangle and arc at the center of the original curve. The value of

L having been chosen, R_2 is assumed and successive trial values of o and of the throw finally result in satisfactory ones. The value of Z is then fixed.

(*c*) The curve, if relatively long or fixed through its central portion, is compounded towards the end with a sharper

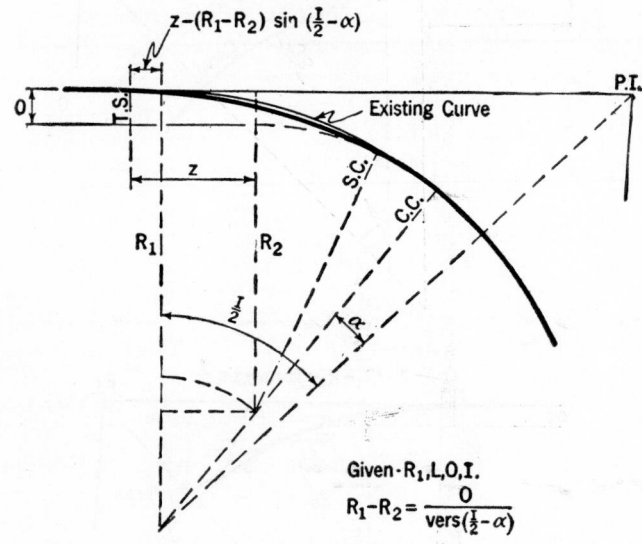

$$z - (R_1 - R_2) \sin (\tfrac{I}{2} - \alpha)$$

Given · $R_1, L, O, I.$

$$R_1 - R_2 = \frac{O}{\text{vers}(\tfrac{I}{2} - \alpha)}$$

Fig. 65b.

curve, as in Fig. 65b, to permit insertion of the spiral. The formulas are derived from the small triangle and arc at the center of the original curve.

Improved methods for track realignment are given in Rubey's "A New Transit Method for Realigning Railway Curves and Spirals," Bulletin 34, University of Missouri Engineering Experiment Station; and A.S.C.E. Trans., Vol. 120, 1955, pages 521 through 538.

66. Superelevation. On curves a highway or a railway is tilted or "superelevated" sufficiently to balance as nearly as possible the centrifugal force generated by a vehicle moving around a curve, this being designed to care for the various speeds of traffic encountered. Ordinarily, it is not possible to provide sufficient superelevation entirely to overcome the centrifugal force of vehicles moving at high speeds, since superelevation on railways or highways exceeding one-tenth of a foot per foot introduces difficulties in operation and maintenance, including the possibility of overturning, side slipping, and rail wear.

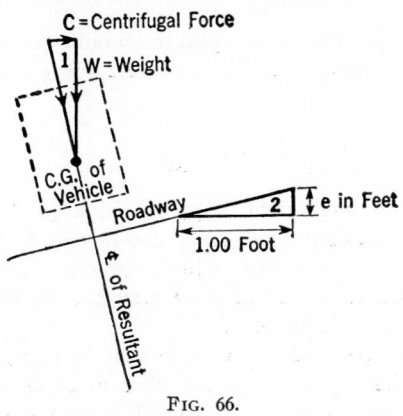

Fig. 66.

In Fig. 66 are shown the forces involved in computing the amount of superelevation needed to balance exactly the centrifugal force generated by a vehicle moving around a curve, namely, the weight W acting vertically, the centrifugal force C acting nearly horizontally, and the resultant of these two forces acting at right angles to the roadway—all of these forces passing through the center of gravity of the vehicle. Since triangles 1 and 2 are similar, we have

$$\frac{W}{C} = \frac{1.00}{e}.$$

The centrifugal force is $C = \dfrac{WV^2}{gR}$, approximately, where V is the velocity in feet per second and g is the acceleration of gravity in feet per second per second. Substituting, we find

$$\frac{W}{\dfrac{WV^2}{gR}} = \frac{1.00}{e}, \qquad \text{or} \qquad e = \frac{V^2}{gR}.$$

To change V from feet per second to miles per hour, we must multiply the right side of the equation by $\left(\dfrac{88}{60}\right)^2$, since 88 feet per second is equal to 60 miles per hour. Substituting the numerical value of 32.2 for g and reducing, we have

$$(66) \qquad\qquad e = \frac{v^2}{15R}, \qquad\qquad \text{approximately}$$

where e is the theoretical superelevation (in feet per foot of width of roadway) necessary completely to balance the centrifugal force, v is the velocity of the vehicle in miles per hour, and R is the radius of curvature in feet. Values of e are given in Table XII.

When the speed of the vehicle exactly equals the speed for which the superelevation is chosen, as in Fig. 66 and Table XII, the resultant of the weight and the centrifugal force passes through the center of the base and at right angles to it, and, consequently, the height of the center of gravity of the vehicle does not enter into the formula, so that there is no overturning effect. For higher or for lower speeds, the height of the center of gravity does affect the overturning tendency of the vehicle. In recent years, the center of gravity of automotive vehicles and of high-speed trains has been lowered, thus increasing their stability against overturning. This lowering of the center of gravity *does not* reduce any unbalanced centrifugal force, but it does, of course, reduce the overturning moment of the force.

Usually the theoretical amount of superelevation is obtained by means of formula (66), and then it is arbitrarily reduced to practical limits, as suggested in the following paragraphs.

Railway practice raises the outer rail as summarized in Table 66, from the A.R.E.A. Manual. It will be noticed that the tabulation gives two speeds, one for equilibrium elevation and the other for a 3-inch unbalanced elevation.

Formula 66 also can be expressed in the following form, where E is the balanced superelevation of a railway track about 4.9 feet wide between bearing points on the rails.

(66a) $$E = 0.00069Dv^2$$

The A.R.E.A. Manual states: "If it were possible to operate all classes of traffic at the same speed around a curve, the ideal condition of smooth riding and minimum rail wear could be obtained by elevating for equilibrium. However, a section of track must usually handle several classes of traffic operating at different speeds. A slow train passing over a curve that is elevated for a much higher speed tends to throw the track out of surface and to cause excessive wear on the inside rail.

"Safety and comfort limit the speed at which a passenger train may negotiate a curve. Any speed that gives comfortable riding on a curve is well within the limits of safety. Experience has shown that the usual passenger coach, pullman car or light-weight equipment will ride comfortably around a curve at a speed which would require an elevation about three inches higher for equilibrium. As far as speed traffic is concerned, it may therefore be said that passenger comfort governs train speed on curves and that trains may be operated over curves at speeds somewhat greater than equilibrium speed. Advantage is taken of this condition in operating high-speed trains on track that must also carry slower traffic.

"Since the elevation required is a function of the train speed, this speed is the first element to be determined.

"Ordinarily an elevation of 6 inches should not be exceeded for a track carrying both fast and slow traffic; and

TABLE 66—SPEED

MAXIMUM SPEED IN MILES PER HOUR RECOM-
SAFETY) WHERE CENTER OF GRAVITY IS
E = Speed at Equilibrium Elevation

DEGREE OF CURVE	ELEVATION OF OUTER RAIL →	¼"	½"	¾"	1"	1¼"	1½"	1¾"	2"	2¼"	2½"	2¾"	3"	3¼"	3½"
0° 30′	E	30	40	50	55	60	65	70	75	80	85	90	95	100	
	M	100		105	110										
1° 00′	E	20	25	35		40	45	50	55		60	65		70	
	M	70		75		80		85		90		95			
1° 30′	E			25	30	35		40	45		50		55		
	M		55	60		65		70			75				80
2° 00′	E		20		25	30		35		40		45		50	
	M	50			55			60		65					70
2° 30′	E					30			35		40				45
	M	45				50			55			60			
3° 00′	E			20		25		30			35			40	
	M	40			45			50			55				
3° 30′	E					25		30			35				
	M			40			45			50					
4° 00′	E				20		25			30			35		
	M	35				40				45					
4° 30′	E										30				
	M			35			40						45		
5° 00′	E				20			25			30				
	M			35				40							
5° 30′	E					20				25			30		
	M				35						40				
6° 00′	E						20			25					30
	M	30						35				40			40
7° 00′	E						20				25				
	M					30				35					
8° 00′	E								20				25		
	M	25					30								35
9° 00′	E							20							
	M			25				30							
10° 00′	E								20						
	M					25					30				
11° 00′	E								20						
	M						25								30
12° 00′	E								20						
	M	20						25							

The limits as shown will also serve for use on any lower height center of gravity.

TABLE FOR CURVES

MENDED AS GOOD PRACTICE (NOT LIMITS OF
84 INCHES ABOVE THE TOP OF RAIL
M = Maximum Speed = Speed at 3″ Unbalanced Elevation

3¾″	4″	4¼″	4½″	4¾″	5″	5¼″	5½″	5¾″	6″	6¼″	6½″	6¾″	7″	← Elevation of Outer Rail	Degree of Curve
105	110													E	0° 30'
														M	
75		80	85			90		95			100			E	1° 00'
100	105			110										M	
60		65		70			75			80				E	1° 30'
			85					95					100	M	
	55		60			65			70					E	2° 00'
				75			80			85				M	
		50			55			60						E	2° 30'
	65					70								M	
	45			50				55						E	3° 00'
		60				65					70			M	
40			45			50								E	3° 30'
	55							60						M	
				45			55							E	4° 00'
50										60				M	
35								45						E	4° 30'
		50							55					M	
		35					40	45						E	5° 00'
45							50						55	M	
				35		40								E	5° 30'
			45						50					M	
						35			40					E	6° 00'
												50		M	
		30					35							E	7° 00'
			40							45				M	
			30							35				E	8° 00'
							40							M	
25							30							E	9° 00'
		35									40			M	
		25						30						E	10° 00'
					35									M	
			25							30				E	11° 00'
								35						M	
				25										E	12° 00'
		30										35		M	

CURVE SPEED TABLE

MAXIMUM PERMISSIBLE SPEED IN MILES PER HOUR

Super-elevation of outer rail in inches   Minimum length of spiral

Degree of Curve	SPEED IN MILES PER HOUR																								Degree of Curve
	80		75		70		65		60		55		50		45		40		35		30		25		
	E	L	E	L	E	L	E	L	E	L	E	L	E	L	E	L	E	L	E	L	E	L	E	L	
0°-30'	3/4	70	1/2	44	1/4	20	—	—	—	—	—	—	—	—	—	—	—	—	—	—	—	—	—	—	0°-30'
0°-45'	1 3/4	164	1 1/4	110	1	82	1/2	38	1/4	18	—	—	—	—	—	—	—	—	—	—	—	—	—	—	0°-45'
1°-00'	2 3/4	258	2 1/4	198	1 3/4	144	1 1/4	96	1	70	1/2	32	1/4	16	—	—	—	—	—	—	—	—	—	—	1°-00'
1°-15'	3 3/4	352	3 1/4	286	2 1/2	206	2	152	1 1/2	106	1	64	1/2	30	1/4	14	—	—	—	—	—	—	—	—	1°-15'
1°-30'	5	468	4 1/4	374	3 1/2	288	2 3/4	208	2	140	1 1/2	96	1	58	1/2	26	—	—	—	—	—	—	—	—	1°-30'
1°-45'	6"	562	5	438	4 1/4	348	3 1/2	266	2 3/4	194	2	128	1 1/2	88	1	52	1/2	24	—	—	—	—	—	—	1°-45'
2°-00'	—	—	6	526	5	410	4 1/4	324	3 1/4	228	2 1/2	162	2	118	1 1/4	66	3/4	36	1/4	10	—	—	—	—	2°-00'
2°-15'	—	—	—	—	6	492	4 3/4	362	4	280	3	194	2 1/4	132	1 1/2	80	1	48	1/4	10	—	—	—	—	2°-15'
2°-30'	—	—	—	—	—	—	5 1/2	418	4 1/2	316	3 1/2	226	2 3/4	162	2	106	1 1/4	60	1/2	22	—	—	—	—	2°-30'
2°-45'	—	—	—	—	—	—	—	—	5	350	4	258	3	176	2 1/4	120	1 1/2	70	3/4	30	1/4	10	—	—	2°-40'
3°-00'	—	—	—	—	—	—	—	—	5 3/4	404	4 1/2	290	3 1/2	206	2 1/2	132	1 3/4	82	1	42	1/4	10	—	—	3°-00'
3°-15'	—	—	—	—	—	—	—	—	—	—	5"	322	4	234	3	158	2	94	1 1/4	52	1/2	18	—	—	3°-15'
3°-30'	—	—	—	—	—	—	—	—	—	—	5 1/2	354	4 1/2	264	3 1/4	172	2 1/4	106	1 1/2	62	1/2	18	—	—	3°-30'
3°-45'	—	—	—	—	—	—	—	—	—	—	6	388	4 3/4	278	3 1/2	184	2 1/2	118	1 1/2	62	3/4	26	—	—	3°-45'
4°-00'	—	—	—	—	—	—	—	—	—	—	—	—	5 1/4	308	4	212	2 3/4	130	1 3/4	72	1	36	1/4	8	4°-00'
4°-30'	—	—	—	—	—	—	—	—	—	—	—	—	6	352	4 1/2	238	3 1/4	152	2 1/4	92	1 1/4	44	1/2	14	4°-30'
5°-00'	—	—	—	—	—	—	—	—	—	—	—	—	—	—	5 1/4	278	3 3/4	176	2 1/2	102	1 1/2	52	1/2	14	5°-00'
5°-30'	—	—	—	—	—	—	—	—	—	—	—	—	—	—	6	316	4 1/4	200	3	124	1 3/4	62	3/4	22	5°-30'
6°-00'	—	—	—	—	—	—	—	—	—	—	—	—	—	—	—	—	5	234	3 1/2	144	2	70	1	30	6°-00'
7°-00'	—	—	—	—	—	—	—	—	—	—	—	—	—	—	—	—	6	282	4 1/4	174	2 3/4	96	1 1/2	44	7°-00'
8°-00'	—	—	—	—	—	—	—	—	—	—	—	—	—	—	—	—	—	—	5	206	3 1/4	114	1 3/4	52	8°-00'
9°-00'	—	—	—	—	—	—	—	—	—	—	—	—	—	—	—	—	—	—	6	246	4	140	2 1/4	66	9°-00'

$E = \frac{v^2 D}{1500} - 1.5$ $L = 1.1733\,Ev$ $v = \sqrt{\frac{1500\,(E+1.5)}{D}}$

E = Elevation of outer rail in inches
L = Length of spiral in feet
v = Speed in miles per hour
D = Degree of curve

★ Maximum super-elevation = 6 inches

FIG. 66a.

an elevation of 7 inches where one class of traffic is carried exclusively."

A table of standard practice on one railroad is given as Fig. 66a on page 134. Note that 1.5 inches of unbalanced superelevation is used.

On highways, superelevation is not well standardized. Here unbalanced centrifugal force must be taken up by the friction between the tires and the pavement, a highly variable factor.

The Public Roads Administration, in its Highway Practice, 1949, states: "Maximum superelevation of 0.12 foot per foot is recommended by the American Association of State Highway Officials. Where snow and ice conditions prevail, 0.08 foot per foot is the maximum that should be used. In recent practice, superelevations of 0.16 foot per foot have been found to be very satisfactory on ramps at interchanges, especially on the down ramps where design must generally provide for higher speeds than on up ramps. In obtaining superelevation, it is desirable that the slope of the outer edge of pavement with respect to the profile of the center line should not be greater than 1 in 200."

That portion of the roadway over which superelevation is attained is called the *runoff*, and it corresponds to the spiral length. If spirals are not used, then the runoff is on the tangent immediately adjacent to the circular curve.

67. Length of Spirals. Since there is usually no rigid requirement as to length, it is often desirable to use some multiple of ten for the total spiral length so that each of the ten chords may be an exact foot, rather than contain decimals of a foot.

If the spiral stakes are to be set on stations, half-stations, and so on rather than at ten chord points, then some value of k should be chosen which will permit the use of Table VIII.

On railways, the A.R.E.A. states: "Spirals need not be used when the elevation required for the highest permissible speed is less than 2 inches. [Present practice often spirals for 1 inch.] In this case the use of easement curves should be a matter of judgment considering the amount of offset, speed, and other features.

"Length of easement curves should be based on the maximum allowable speed and should not be less than that which will cause a rise of not more than 2.2 inches per second for the maximum speed. If the physical conditions permit, the length of the easement curve should be based on a rise of not more than 1¼ inches per second.

"Curve elevations should run out uniformly over the easement curve.

"Any form of easement curve is satisfactory which is of the general form of a cubic parabola."

The spiral tables in this volume are extended to cover the longer and flatter spirals which may be required for speeds up to 125 miles per hour.

Using the recommended rise per second given above as 1¼ inches per second, the length of the spiral becomes

$$L = \frac{E}{1\frac{1}{4}} V$$

where E is the total superelevation between rails in inches and V is in feet per second. Changing V from feet per second to v in miles per hour we have

(67) $$L = \frac{E}{1\frac{1}{4}} \left(\frac{88}{60} \right) v = 1.17Ev$$

It is to be noted that E is the actual superelevation and v is the maximum speed. Usually these are not the values for a "balanced" superelevation.

On highways, widening of the pavement on curves, attaining of superelevation, securing good riding qualities, and keeping traffic in its own lane are the essential factors in selecting the proper length of spirals. The minimum length, according to the United States Public Roads Administration in its Highway Practice, 1949, is determined as follows:

"Transitions should be applied to all curves of such radii

that the offset from the circular arc is greater than 1 foot
for a transition of the required length L_S, as determined by
the formula

(67a)
$$L_S = \frac{1.6v^3}{R}$$

"In this formula, v is the assumed design speed in miles
per hour and R, the radius in feet.

"Where possible, superelevation should be attained within
the limits of the transition, which should be of such length
that the slope of the outer edge of pavement with respect to
the profile of the center line is no greater than 1 in 200."

The Missouri Highway Department uses spirals where the
degree of the curve exceeds two.

*Example of the rational selection of superelevation and
length of spiral.* Assume a high-speed passenger train with
53-inch center of gravity rounding a 1° 30′ curve, with an
actual superelevation of 6 inches. From formula (66) or
from Table XII (using 6 inches of actual superelevation and
3 inches of unbalanced superelevation, a total of 9 inches),
we find a maximum permissible speed of 95 miles per hour,
or 140 feet per second.

To attain 6 inches of superelevation (at the optimum rate
of 1¼ inches per second) will require 4.8 seconds or a
run-off length of 672 feet. The spiral will normally be made
about this length, unless too much expense is involved.

From Table VIII, we might select a 750-foot spiral with
$k = 0.2$, or a 500-foot spiral with $k = 0.3$, or a 600-foot
spiral with $k = 0.25$ (interpolated); depending on the policy
and the standard of the particular railway.

If the 600-foot spiral is chosen, it will be necessary to reduce the speed to 85 miles per hour, or to extend the run-off
72 feet backward along the tangent; in both of which cases a
rate of rise of 1¼ inches per second is maintained. Or, as
another alternative, the 600-foot length and 95-mile per
hour speed may be retained by increasing the rate of rise
slightly.

67a. Transition Curves for Highways. A book of
this title by Mr. Joseph Barnett of the United States Bureau
of Public Roads is now widely used by highway engineers
since its extensive tables were developed for convenience
in handling that type of work where the arc definition of
degree of curve is often used. First published in 1938, it
had minor revision in 1940 and no major revision has been
made nor is contemplated. These tables have been widely
adopted by highway departments and may be obtained for a
nominal charge from the Superintendent of Documents,
Washington, D.C. Those interested in these tables should
secure the latest edition of them rather than use some re-
production of a part of them in a textbook. But little basic
theory is included.

Mr. Barnett uses the same spiral as the A.R.E.A. spiral
used in this text except that it is based on the 100-foot arc
definition of degree of curve rather than the 100-foot chord
definition. All tables and formulas in this text give values
which are identical with those of Mr. Barnett's book except
for values of o and Z in Tables VII and VIII. Even for o and
Z the differences are negligible on all but the sharpest and
longest spirals, as indicated in the explanation accompanying Table VII on page 57 and Table VIII on page 79.

Some highway engineers use the A.R.E.A. spiral and tables
and some use Mr. Barnett's tables. Either is satisfactory. So
far as is known, no railways use the Barnett tables.

CHAPTER X

RAILWAY TURNOUTS AND TRACK LAYOUTS

68. General. Only cases that are more frequently encountered can be studied in a single chapter, and the railway engineer is referred for further details to more elaborate treatments here mentioned and to the standards of the railway with which he is connected. Table XXV and the latest Trackwork Plans of the American Railway Engineering Association are, of course, the best available references for standard railway turnouts and track layouts. They should be studied by the railway engineer.

Few engineers, and these largely employed by frog and switch manufacturing companies, will delve deeply into the laborious computations which are involved in preparing the detailed plans for the manufacture of special track constructions. For most railway engineers, it is only necessary that they stake the track layout on the ground and furnish a plan of this general layout to the frog and switch manufacturing companies from whom the special work is to be ordered and by whom it is detailed in accordance with standards and specifications furnished by the railway company.

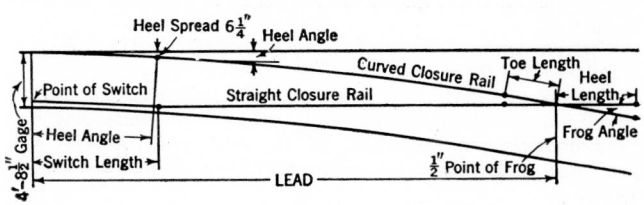

Fig. 69. Split Switch Turnout.

69. Definitions. Figure 69 shows the track features which occur in a "split switch" turnout. The turnout track

139

is straight through the frog. The switch rail is usually straight but may be curved. The switch rail and frog are connected by a circular curve. The "stub switch" turnout is obsolete in good railway practice and is therefore omitted from this chapter. The following definitions in italics have been adopted by the American Railway Engineering Association.

TURNOUT. *An arrangement of a switch and a frog with "closure rail," by means of which rolling stock may be diverted from one track to another.*

SWITCH. *A device consisting of two movable rails, necessary connections and operating parts, designed to turn an engine or train from a track on which it is running to another track.*

FROG. *A device used where two running rails intersect and providing flangeways to permit wheels and wheel flanges on either rail to cross the other.*

CLOSURE RAILS. *The rails connecting the heels of the switch rails with the toe end of the frog.*

SWITCH RAIL OR POINT RAIL. *The tapered rail of a split switch.*

HEEL OF SWITCH. *The end of a switch rail farther from the point of switch.*

POINT OF SWITCH (*Actual*). *The point where the spread between the gage lines of the main track and the turnout is sufficient to allow for a practical switch point.* (*The standard width of switch point is ¼ inch.* It becomes sharper with wear.) The switch stand is installed at the point of switch.

STOCK RAIL. *A running rail against which the switch rail operates.*

STOCK RAIL BEND. *The bend or set which must be given the stock rail at the vertex of a switch to allow it to follow the gage line of the turnout.*

SWITCH ANGLE. *The angle included between the gage lines of the switch rail and the stock rail.*

THROW OF SWITCH. *The distance through which the point of switch rails is moved sidewise, measured along the center line of the rod nearest the point connecting the two switch rails, to bring either point against the stock rail. This distance is standardized at 4¾ inches.*

SPRING RAIL FROG. *A frog having a movable wing rail held against the point rail by springs, normally presenting an unbroken running surface to wheels using one track while the flanges of wheels on the other track force the wing rail away from the point rail to provide opening.*

FROG ANGLE. *The angle formed by the intersecting gage lines of a frog.*

FROG NUMBER. *One-half the cotangent of one-half the frog angle, or the number of units of center line length in which the spread is one unit.* The Am. Ry. Eng. Assoc. suggests that, so far as practicable, the frog numbers used be Nos. 8, 10, 12, 16, and 20, so as to minimize stock sizes and reduce costs through such standardization.

HEEL END OF FROG. *The end of a frog farthest from the switch and where the running surfaces, diverging from the point, terminate.*

TOE END OF FROG. *The end of a frog in front of the point and towards the switch.*

POINT OF FROG (*Theoretical*). *The point of intersection of gage lines of the frog.*

POINT OF FROG (*Half-Inch Point*). *A point located at a distance from the theoretical point towards the heel and equal in inches to one-half the frog number and at which the spread between the gage lines is one-half inch. It is the origin from which shop measurements are made.*

POINT OF FROG (*Actual*). *A point at which the spread between the gage lines is sufficient to allow for a practical width of manufactured point.*

LEAD (*Theoretical*). *The distance from the theoretical point of a uniform turnout curve to the theoretical point of the frog, measured on the line of the parent track.* This is not used in practice.

LEAD (*Actual*). *The length between the actual point of the switch and the half-inch point of the frog measured on the line of parent track.* It is slightly modified (by using a short tangent adjacent to the switch rail or frog) so that the "closure rails" on Fig. 69 will cut with minimum waste and labor from standard rails. No harm results from this slight modification of what would be the truly circular "lead curve." Such practical leads are given in Table XXV from the Am. Ry. Eng. Assoc. Many railways have their own tables of practical leads.

TURNOUT NUMBER. *The number corresponding to the frog number of the frog used in the turnout.*

70. Staking a Turnout from Straight Track.

It is only necessary for the engineer to set a stake at half the gage distance (2′ 4¼″ for standard gage) from the gage line of the main line rail, directly opposite the actual ½″ point of frog, as shown in Fig. 70. The stake is marked (for example) P.F. #10 to indicate the actual point of frog for a #10 turnout. The track foreman places the frog here and constructs the turnout from his standard turnout plans. The engineer may mark this P.F. #10 on the rail flange.

It is desirable to face the turnout away from the direction of predominant traffic so that the greater volume of traffic, especially of speedy traffic, will "trail" through the turnout rather than "face" the turnout; thus opportunities for derailments due to a wheel flange catching in the point of the switch or frog will be minimized. In selecting the position of the P.S. and P.F., it is best to place the point of switch, the P.S., some 12 to 14 feet toward the frog from the main line rail joints which are located from the P.S. away from the frog. Such dimensions are shown on standard track plans of the A.R.E.A. and of various railways. This distance may be shorter in yards and on secondary track where clearance is limited. All of these requirements make it necessary to examine the position of the joints of the main track in the vicinity of the proposed turnout (and sometimes to shift them), if the turnout is from existing track. When a new turnout is staked before construction of the main track, the engineer must see that the main line rail joints in the vicinity of the turnout are properly placed. The novice should consult his track foreman regarding main line rail joints.

In order to line the track as it leaves the frog beyond the turnout, some engineers set up the transit over the stake marked P.F. #10 (or other frog number) with plates clamped

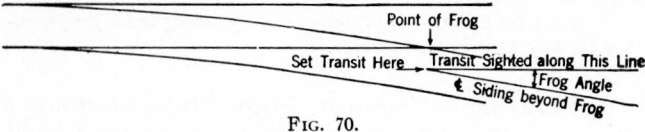

Fig. 70.

on the frog angle (5° 43′ for a #10 turnout) and the transit sighted parallel to the main track (Fig. 70). When the plates are turned to zero, the transit will be sighting along the straight track as it leaves the far end of the frog.

Another method is shown in Fig. 70a where the transit is set up at A, the intersection of center lines.

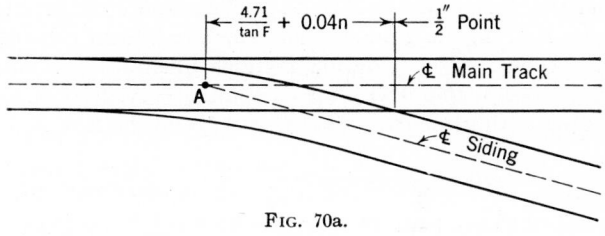

Fig. 70a.

71. Turnouts on Curves. Turnouts should not be located on curves, especially on the outside of a curve; nor should they face high-speed traffic. When it is necessary to locate a turnout on a curve, it is staked in the same manner as for straight track, using the same "lead" as given in Table XXV for straight track. When the transit is set up over the P.F. stake and the plates are clamped on the frog angle, the transit is sighted tangent to the curve (by the method of Fig. 71) instead of parallel to the main track (as

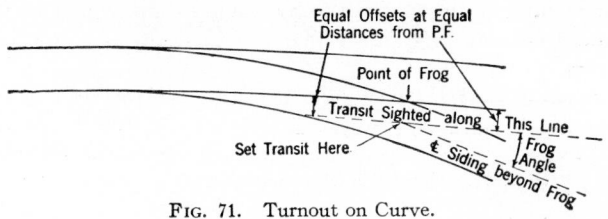

Fig. 71. Turnout on Curve.

in Fig. 70). The degree of curve of the lead curve as given in Table XXV is increased or decreased by the amount of the main track curvature, as for example a #10 turnout leaving a 4° main line would have a degree of curve equal to 7° 27′ (from Table XXV) minus 4°, or 3° 27′, if on the outside of the main track curve; and 7° 27′ plus 4°, or 11° 27′, if on the inside of the main line. This conception is slightly approximate but sufficiently precise for most practical work.

72. Tracks Curved After Leaving Turnout.   Problems of this nature are best solved by computing the values from the dimensions in Fig. 72.   This permits the location of the P.F. on the ground, from which trackmen construct the turnout.   The following sections illustrate the more simple uses of this device for computing curved track connections with turnouts.   The curve beyond the frog is pro-

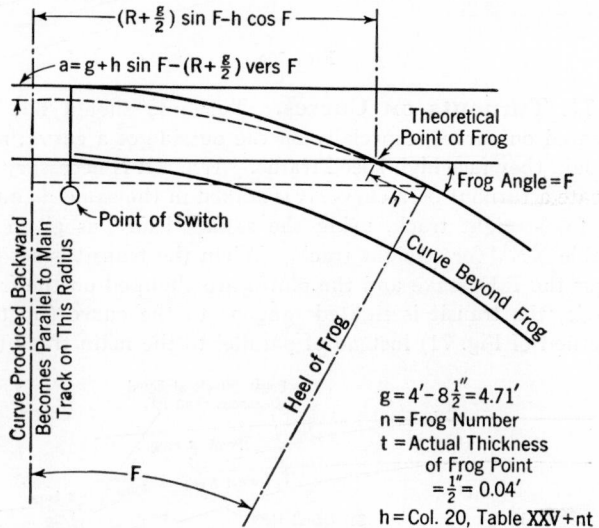

Fig. 72.   Curved Track Connection with Turnout.

duced backward (dashed line) until it is parallel to the main track.

If the curve starts at the heel of the frog, h equals the entry in column 20 of Table XXV plus nt.   If possible, 20 feet or more should be added as straight track beyond the frog.

Track and Turnout Engineering by C. M. Kurtz, Simmons-Boardman Company, 1944 contains an elaboration of this section, with special tables, and is very useful for railway engineers who encounter this problem repeatedly.

73. Turnouts from Straight Track. Figure 73 shows the simplified figure from which the computations are made when a given tangent is to be connected with an

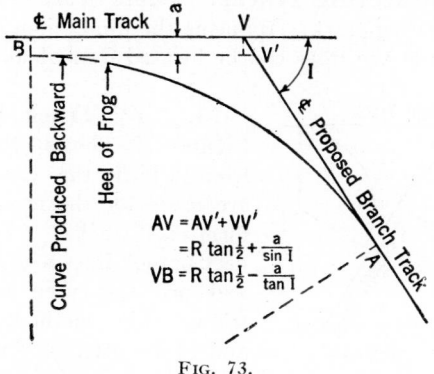

$$AV = AV' + VV'$$
$$= R \tan\tfrac{1}{2} + \frac{a}{\sin I}$$
$$VB = R \tan\tfrac{1}{2} - \frac{a}{\tan I}$$

Fig. 73.

existing straight track by a curve which begins at the heel of the frog. The values of I and R are known, and a is

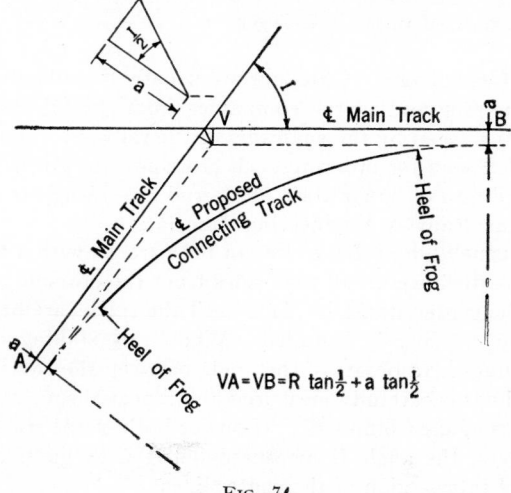

$$VA = VB = R \tan\tfrac{1}{2} + a \tan\tfrac{1}{2}$$

Fig. 74.

computed from Fig. 72. The distance from the point B to the point of frog is computed from the dimensions in Fig. 72.

74. Connecting Tracks. Figure 74 shows the layout of a connecting track. By using the dimensions of Fig. 72, the points of the frogs can be located from A and from B.

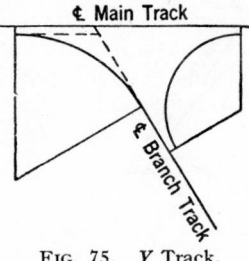

FIG. 75.   *Y* Track.

75. "Y" Track Layouts. Figure 75 shows the layout from which the computations are made for the most common form of *Y* track.   *Y* tracks connect branch lines with main lines and are also used in turning trains. The methods of §§ 72 and 73 are used for this solution.

76. Crossovers. Details for crossovers may be found in the Trackwork Plans mentioned in § 68.   Usually, though not necessarily, the track is straight between the two frogs which are used in the crossover.

77. Crossings. Crossings are usually manufactured to order by frog and switch companies from careful measurements furnished by the engineers of the railway.   Data and Record Sheets for ordering such crossings are given in the latest edition of Trackwork Plans and Specifications of the American Railway Engineering Association.

It is usually desirable to line in both tracks with a transit for some distance on all four sides from the crossing and to leave the center stakes in place until the tracks are lined up and the crossing is installed.   While this staking of the center lines is in progress, the angle between the two staked center lines is carefully measured and repeated several times to insure against blunders.   If one or both of the tracks are on curves, the angle is measured between tangents at the point of intersection of the center lines.

78. Other Track Layouts. A wide range of additional problems are somewhat rarely encountered, and the railway engineer must refer to books on railway track or on railway terminals for information regarding them. Among these problems are three-throw switches, slip switches, ladder tracks, and many layouts involving curved tracks.

It has been found that the coverage in this chapter is adequate for the railway practice encountered by most engineers. Even those engineers employed in large city terminals or by frog and switch companies find this fundamental treatment basically sufficient although, as specialists, they use many other volumes, plans, specifications, etc.— far more than can be even mentioned to advantage in college.

CHAPTER XI

STRING LINING OF CURVES

79. General. In the last twenty years string lining has been extensively used to supplement transit lining of certain types of curves, especially for perfecting the alignment of existing railway track and for laying out roads in landscaping. In the following sections the recommended procedure of the A.R.E.A. Manual* is quoted.

Minor modifications of this procedure are in effect on various railways. For example, in the usual case of realigning existing track, the tangent near the T.S. is found to have been thrown outward in a slight reverse curve, causing negative measured ordinates. Here some engineers prefer to establish the original or true position of the tangent by setting up and "balancing in" a transit on the gage line of the outer rail, produced. Rarely, it is necessary slightly to change the position of the existing tangent so as to avoid excessive throw on the curve. Offsets from the transit tangent are measured and tabulated. The new T.S. will normally occur near where the tangent offset is zero. After this preliminary procedure, the standard A.R.E.A. method is used, as in § 80. The exact procedure in using tangent offsets from the transit line varies on different railways.

Some railways use 39-foot stations (with a station opposite the end of every splice bar on the high rail, a considerable advantage where all rails are of this length) and measure the mid-ordinates in hundredths of feet, rather than the 31-foot stations and the tenths of inches as used in § 80.

Originally perfected by Mr. Charles H. Bartlett,† many engineers have developed modifications in use on particular railways which may be followed easily if the following A.R.E.A. method is understood. See also Railway Engineering and Maintenance, Aug. 1948 to Feb. 1949; Mar. 1952.

80. String Lining of Railway Curves by Chord Method. "String lining of curves may be used advan-

---

* From Manual of the American Railway Engineering Association.
† Simmons-Boardman Company, 1925.

tageously to supplement the engineer's transit. Briefly, the method consists in dividing the curve to be lined into 31-foot stations, recording the mid-ordinates of chords spanning each two stations and laying out a reasonable amount of throw, if necessary, to each station. No rule can be laid down to insure a satisfactory realignment at the first trial. At best, this is a cut and try method with sufficient definite rules and instructions to enable the user to lay out throws at each station throughout the curve that will give an alignment, if the work is carefully done, approaching transit survey accuracy.

"Any number of combinations of throws with balanced results may be obtained—some bad and others good—so that the work should be placed in the hands of a person with dependable judgment. Such person should also have at least a working knowledge of high school algebra and considerable experience in track work.

"The purpose is to secure an alignment in which the ordinates at each station of the circular parts of the curve are as nearly uniform as possible. A considerable difference in the ordinates of the circular parts of the curve must be carefully avoided in the interest of smooth riding and safe track.

"String lining is based on the following principles: The mid-ordinates of a circular curve are indicative of its degree of curvature. Hence, the ordinates of a circular curve are equal for a chord of uniform length. The ordinates of a spiral curve will vary in accordance with a specified progress.

"The length of spiral for any given degree will vary, not only with the natural conditions, but also with the maximum allowable speed and superelevation; the higher the speed, the greater the length of the spiral should be.

"The angle between tangents is the sum of the angles subtended by the chords of the curve. For all practical purposes, on curves of more than 193-feet radius (less than 30 degrees curvature) the mid-ordinate of a given length of chord varies directly with the degree of curvature, or, in other words, varies directly with the subtended angle. Hence, the sum of the mid-ordinates is a measure of the angle between tangents.

"On most curves where it is desired to string line, the angle between the tangents will not have to be changed and where this is the case the sum of the mid-ordinates before lining must equal the sum of the mid-ordinates of the re-aligned curve.

"The throw at any station on a curve will change the ordinate at that point by an amount equal to the throw and will increase or decrease the ordinates at adjacent stations by an amount equal to half the throw, always increasing when the throw decreases and decreasing when the throw increases the ordinates."

81. Tools Required. A strong fish line or chord of 62-foot length and a 50-foot steel tape; marking crayon; a suitable rule graduated to inches and tenths thereof with the graduations beginning at the extreme end of the rule or scale; and a pad of forms (described later).

82. Procedure. "All work is done on the outside rail of the curve. First stand on tangent several rail lengths back from the curve and locate the beginning of the curve as closely as possible by eye. This point is Station 0 and should be so marked.

"The station 31 feet back along the tangent is Station −1.

"Beginning at Station −1, lay off with steel tape and mark each 31-foot point and number consecutively as Stations −1, 0, 1, 2, 3, etc., and continue the stationing at least two stations beyond the point of tangent, which is also located by eye. These station numbers are entered in Column 1 of the sample form.

"Beginning at Station 0, measure mid-ordinates in tenths of inches from the outside rail to the line joining Stations −1 and 1. This is entered in Column 2 of the same form. Proceed around the curve to the PT, measuring the mid-ordinate at each station and entering on the form

"Take track centers at frequent intervals where there is more than one track and record any obstacle which might affect lining, noting same in Column 10 of the sample form.

"Column 1 is for station numbers.

"Column 2 is for measured mid-ordinates in inches and tenths thereof.

"Column 3 is for revised mid-ordinates.

"Column 4 is for the difference between ordinates in Columns 2 and 3.

"Columns 5 and 6 are explained by the headings.

"Column 7 is for the full throw which is double the figures shown in Column 6. Negative throw indicates that the track at

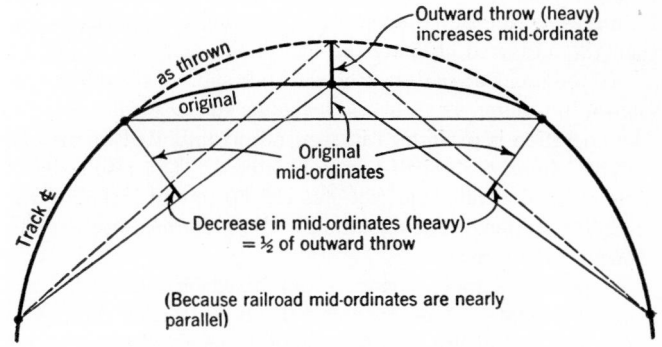

Fig. 80. Effect of a Track Throw on Mid-Ordinates.

NOTE: Original stations are shown as dots. When the track is thrown outward, the mid-ordinate at that station is increased by the amount of the outward throw, while each adjacent mid-ordinate is decreased by one-half of the outward throw, because of nearly similar triangles.

Inward throws have similar, but opposite, effects. See the last paragraph of § 80.

that station is to be thrown in, while positive throw indicates that the track is to be thrown out.

"Column 8 is obtained by subtracting algebraically the full throw from one-half the gage, 28.25 in.

"Column 9 is for revised superelevation to be used on the curve, and, of course, is contingent upon the maximum speed of trains running over this curve.

"By inspection of measured ordinates in Column 2, the beginning and ending of the spiral curves can be located as nearly correct as possible.

"In the example in Table 82 the end of the east spiral is taken at Station 7, while the end of the west spiral is taken at Station 24.

"In Column 4 are entered the differences between the measured ordinate, Column 2, and the revised ordinate, Column 3, in tenths of an inch. If the ordinate in Column 3 at any station is larger than that in Column 2, the sign of the difference in Column 4 is minus. Conversely, if the revised ordinate is less than the measured ordinate the sign of the difference is plus.

"In Column 5 are entered the algebraic sums of the differences (shown in Column 4) up to and including stations being entered. The operation is performed in sequence as indicated by arrows.

"In Column 6 the half-throw is entered. The result shown here is the algebraic sum of Column 5 up to and including the preceding station. The operation is also performed in the order shown by the arrows.

"In the example, computations based on selected revised spiral ordinates in sub-column A Table 82, carried through to Column 6, indicate a half-throw of 31 or a full-throw of 6.2 in at Station 7, which is too great. The minus sign of the half-throw indicates that ordinates slightly smaller should be selected. Slightly smaller spiral ordinates are therefore entered in subcolumn B and the curve ordinate of 45 is carried out through Station 11. This gives too great a throw in the positive direction.

"Therefore, interpolate a spiral between those used in sub-columns A and B, and enter these new spiral ordinates in subcolumn C. The curve ordinate of 46 is carried out a few stations below the S.C. (spiral curve) at Station 7. Computing a third time through to Column 6, the half-throw at Station 7 is −26 and at Station 11 is −10 which gives a practical throw. For trial the circular curve ordinate of 46 in Column 3 is carried through to Station 23 (one station back on the circular curve from the C.S., or curve spiral) and extension made to Column 6, where the half-throw is +31.

"Sum up in Column 2 the measured ordinates from Stations 24 to 32, inclusive, in the original spiral, which total 190. The sum of the measured ordinates from Stations 0 to 23, inclusive, is 922, bringing the total sum of measured ordinates to 1112. The sum of the revised ordinates from Stations 0 to 23, inclusive is 921. To assure that Column 5 will end in 0, the sum of the revised spiral ordinates from Stations 24 to 32, inclusive, must equal 191. Such revised spiral ordinates are entered in subcolumn 'C.'

"Carrying the calculations through to Column 6, the sum of differences check out 0, but the final half-throw is +17, indicating that the trial spiral ends in a parallel tangent. To end in the original tangent, both Columns 5 and 6 must balance; therefore, an adjustment of the revised ordinates is necessary and is made according to the following rule.

"When the final half-throw is positive, subtract from the revised ordinates having high station numbers and add an equal amount to the ordinates having low station numbers, choosing stations in pairs such that the sum of the differences of station numbers, taken in pairs, equals the numerical amount of the final half-throw. When the final half-throw is negative, reverse the procedure, subtracting from the ordinates having low station numbers and adding to those having high station numbers.

"Since in Table 82 the final half-throw is +17, an ordinate (or ordinates) of a low station number will have to be increased and that of a high station number decreased. As it is desirable to keep the spiral uniform, let us change Station 24 from 47 to 46 and Station 22 from 46 to 47. This change will decrease the final half-throw by 2 or 1 × (Sta. 24 − Sta. 22). Let us

TABLE 82

STATIONING FROM EAST TO WEST

Station Numbers	Measured	Revised A	B	C	D	Diff A	B	C	D	Sum A	B	C	D	Half A	B	C	D	Full Throw	Gage to Tack	Remarks
1	2	3				4				5				6				7	8	9
-1	0	0	0	0		0	0	0		0	0	0		0	0	0		0	28.25	
T.S. 0	1	1	1	1		0	0	0		0	0	0		0	0	0		0	28.25	
1	5	7	6	7		-2	-1	-2		-2	-1	-2		0	0	0		0	28.25	
2	14	13	13	13		+1	+1	+1		-1	0	-1		-2	-1	-2		-.4	28.65	
3	16	20	19	20		-4	-3	-4		-5	-3	-5		-3	-1	-3		-.6	28.85	
4	26	27	26	26		-1	0	0		-6	-3	-5		-8	-4	-8		-1.6	29.85	
5	30	34	32	33		-4	-2	-3		-10	-5	-8		-14	-7	-13		-2.6	30.85	
6	43	40	39	40		+3	+4	+3		-7	-1	-5		-24	-12	-21		-4.2	32.45	
S.C. 7	56	46	44	45		+10	+12	+11		+3	+11	+6		-31	-13	-26		-5.2	33.45	
8	49	47	45	46		+2	+4	+3		+5	+15	+9			-2	-20		-4.0	32.25	
9	35	47	45	46		-12	-10	-11		-7	+5	-2			+13	-11		-2.2	30.45	
10	51	47	45	46		+4	+6	+5		-3	+11	+3			+18	-13		-2.6	30.85	
11	49	47	45	46		+2	+4	+3		-1	+15	+6			+29	-10		-2.0	30.25	
12	43			46				+3				+3			+44	-4		-.8	29.05	
13	45			46				-1				+2				-1		-.2	28.45	
14	50			46	47			+4	+3			+6	+5			+1	+1	+.2	28.05	
15	49			46				+3				+9	+8			+7	+6	+1.2	27.05	
16	43			46				-3				+6	+5			+16	+14	+2.8	25.45	
17	38			46				-8				-2	-3			+22	+19	+3.8	24.45	
18	50			46				+4				+2	+1			+20	+16	+3.2	25.05	
19	55			46				+9				-11	+10			+22	+17	+3.4	24.85	
20	33			46				-13				-2	-3			+33	+27	+5.4	22.85	
21	44			46				-2				-4	-5			+31	+24	+4.8	23.45	
22	50			46	47			+4	+3			0	-2			+27	+19	+3.8	24.45	
23	47			46				+1				+1	-1			+27	+17	+3.4	24.85	
C.S. 24	48			47	46			+1	+2			+2	+1			+28	+16	+3.2	25.05	
25	38			41				-3				-1	-2			+30	+17	+3.4	24.85	
26	37			34				+3				+2	+1			+29	+15	+3.0	25.25	
27	21			27				-6				-4	-5			+31	+16	+3.2	25.05	
28	18			20				-2				-6	-7			+27	+11	+2.2	26.05	
29	17			14	13			+3	+4			-3	-3			+21	+4	+.8	27.45	
30	9			7				+2				-1	-1			+18	+1	+.2	28.05	
S.T. 31	2			1				+1				0	0			+17	0	0	28.25	
32	0			0				0				0	0			+17	0	0	28.25	
Sum	1112				1112															

now change Station 29 from ordinate 14 to ordinate 13.
Then following the rule, subtract (17 − 2 = 15) from Station

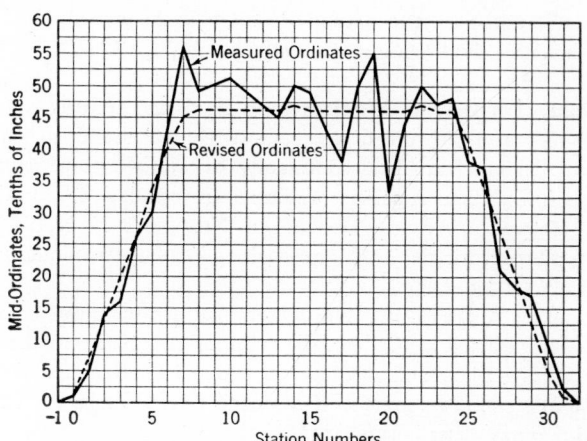

FIG. 82.   Determining Optimum Mid-Ordinates
Graphically.

29, leaving 14 and increase the ordinate at Station 14 from
46 to 47.   Enter these revised ordinates in subcolumn 'D,'
carrying out these computations again to Column 6, the final
half-throw becomes 0 and the ordinates are balanced.

   "Computations are simplified by treating the entries in
Columns 2, 3, 4, 5 and 6 as whole numbers, and placing
decimal points in Column 7, as shown in Table 1.

   "In working out string lining problems considerable assistance
can be gained by plotting the measured mid-ordinates against
the station numbers.   Fig. 82 shows the results for the curve
given in Table 82.   By plotting the mid-ordinates in this manner,
the ends of the spiral, as well as points of compounding, can be
determined readily and an estimate of the average ordinate to
use on the circular curve section can be closely determined.

   "When tabulations are completed and the curve staked, a
copy of the form should be given the track foreman to enable him

to apply the proper superelevation at the various stations as the track is lined."

The foregoing quotation is from the latest A.R.E.A. Manual.

A new and elaborate method of realigning the tangents is given in the A.S.C.E. Proceedings mentioned on page 128.

82a. Improved Mechanized String Lining.　It is the duty and pleasure of professional engineers and of professional engineer-managers continually to improve processes and procedures.　The American Railroad Curvelining Corporation, 137 Hollywood Avenue, Douglaston, New York 63, N. Y., has thus pioneered in devising improved equipment, techniques, and procedures for string lining.

Looking to the future, they contemplate string lining for roads (now being tried in France), the transposition of this method to the vertical plane and so adapting it to track surfacing and spot tamping, the development of a machine for shifting the track, and perhaps other improvements.

The objectives here as always are to cut cost and improve quality.　ARC states that forty railroads report money-saving advantages and increased track stability.　One chief engineer reports that, ". . . We estimate the savings made by the use of the Curveliners during the 26-month period up to and including September 30, amount to $59,949, which is divided as follows:

"Track labor account reduced throws	$30,535
Labor driving stakes	12,945
Engineering force	8,360
Center stakes	5,364
Labor handling and distributing stakes	2,682
Other supplies, stake tacks, etc.	63
	$59,949 "

Since their precision of measuring chord offsets mechanically is greater (1/32 inch), they use stations of $15\frac{1}{2}$ or $19\frac{1}{2}$ feet instead of the older 31 and 39 feet.　Since twice as many points are available, the lining can be finished in one pass instead of the wasteful back and forth motion of the track gang, and the track is left with more stability and a minimum of future curve alignment. This permits greater use of cyclical maintenance. The three-step procedure recommended by the manufacturer (who will furnish complete information on request) follows:

Step 1, Collecting the Data. Using overlapping 31- or 39-foot chords, stations are marked at half these distances and ordinates measured as shown in Fig. 80. The accuracy of this job determines the quality of the final alignment.

The Roll-ordinator performs these three operations in one pass. One man measures four ordinates a minute. Accuracy to 1/32 inch. See Fig. 82a.

FIG. 82a.   Roll-Ordinator.

Pushing the Roll-ordinator from station to station, one man marks the stations on the track and records ordinates, track condition and field limitations in his field book.

Step 2, Calculating New Line. The Curveliner (Fig. 82a-a,

which looks and works like a calculating machine) gives a visual
solution.   The data collected in Step 1 is set on the machine.

The operator sees on the machine a mechanical graph of
ordinates, like Fig. 82, as he selects the best throws for the most
economical solution.

Fig. 82a-a.   Curveliner.

The Panel of the Curveliner has movable indexes which obey
the basic principle of stringlining, see Fig. 80, three moving at
once such that the middle one moving in one direction shows
changes in middle ordinate while the two adjacent, moving in
the reverse direction, record applied half throws.   Full throws
are indicated on dials at the left of the panel.

The operator selects the best line by keeping throws to a
minimum, obtaining a maximum number of zero throws, locking
"Fixed points" (which have no throw and which anchor the
track), and considering field limitations.   Full throws are

directly recorded in the same units as ordinates. A graphic
record of old and new alignment is produced as solution progresses. Throws are recorded in the field book opposite the
corresponding ordinates.

Step 3, Lining Track. Lining track is where the largest savings
are made in the ARC 3-step method. Through progressive
lining, gang movement, and precise controlled throws, up to
one-third of the usual track labor can be saved.

The close stationing permits the gang to advance from station
to station producing a finished line in one pass. All the usual
back and forth motion of the gang has been eliminated, thus
reducing labor costs. Throwmeters (Fig. 82 a-b) at each station

Fig. 82a-b.　See Throwmeter at Lower Left of Track Gang. Other
Throwmeters Are on Both Sides of Gang at Each Station.

indicate the progress of the throw (accuracy to 1/32 inch). No
stakes need to be set. No undetected disturbance of adjacent
stations can occur as the gang is always bracketed by Throwmeters.

Eight throwmeters are rotated from station to station as the
work progresses (minimum four meters). One man places them
in position, setting them to indicate the desired throw. In this
manner, up to two miles of track can be lined in one day.

83. String Lining as Applied to Park Roads.*

Here the curve is frequently to be laid out new, although realignment of existing curves may rarely be encountered. To lay out a new curve, it must first be staked approximately by eye, then the Ms measured, then a suitable curve adopted similarly to the procedure of A.R.E.A. The authors recommend the following procedures:

(1) Use Ms in ¼-inch units (instead of 1/10-inch as in railway practice).

(2) Simple curves, compound curves, reversed curves, spirals, or parabolas may be staked as occasion demands.

(3) In staking a reversed curve it is desirable to establish the common tangent and two points on it on each side of the C.C., so that each curve may be string lined separately. It is possible, but somewhat confusing, to string line across a C.C., but such a procedure is not recommended for beginners.

(4) At least two points should be taken on the tangent at each end of the curve, as in railway practice.

(5) The authors suggest about 25-foot stations, but it may be better to use the 31-foot stations suggested for railway work. It should be noted that with a 62-foot chord, M in inches equals the degree of curve, and consequently D at any point along the string lined curve is evident by inspecting the value of M in the tabulation.

If much of this work is to be done, the reader should consult the reference in the footnote.

It is to be noted in all string lining that a great variety of solutions is possible and that consequently a final form for the curve must be chosen with *excellent judgment*.

* By R. B. H. Begg and H. P. C. Vandenberg. Bulletin XXVIII, No. 6, April, 1935, Virginia Polytechnic Institute.

CHAPTER XII

EXCAVATION AND EMBANKMENT

84. Purpose of the Study. The subject matter of this chapter is employed for the following purposes:

(1) For making preliminary estimates of the cubic yardage of earth, loose rock, solid rock, and possibly other classes of excavated material, and for estimating the cost of such yardage as a part of the costs of engineering projects.

(2) For making the more precise estimates of quantities and costs required during construction,

(*a*) so that payments may be made to the contractor, as the work progresses, on the basis of the cubic yardage he has moved up to a particular date (usually monthly or semi-monthly) and so that complete payment may be made to him after the "final estimate"; and

(*b*) so that the company or the contractor doing the work may keep cost accounts of the operation with a view to reducing costs while the work is in progress, to reducing costs on subsequent work, and for estimating the cost of future work.

(3) For setting construction stakes.

85. General Procedure. Preliminary or rough estimates of quantities of excavation and embankment may be made by scaling or computing the depth of cut or fill on the profile at each station and at a few intermediate points along the center line of the construction. Somewhat greater precision may be obtained by considering the transverse slope (at right angles to the center line of the construction), from Table XX. More precise estimates are made after the work has been cross-sectioned on the ground.

Figure 85 shows some typical earthwork cross-sections and Fig. 85a indicates the plan or top view of the same

161

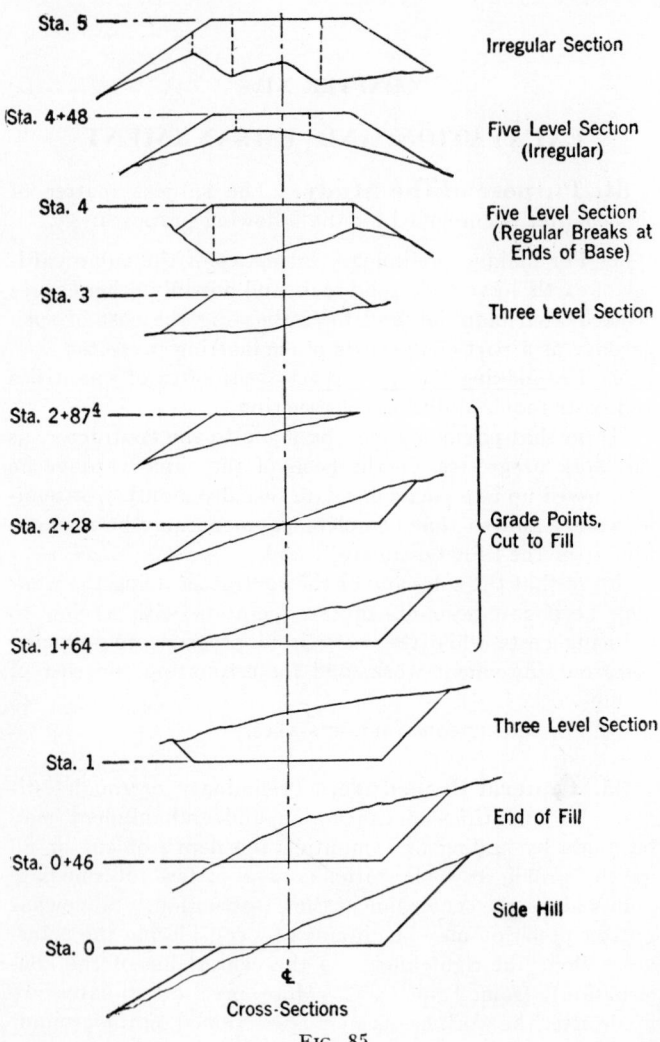

Sta. 5 — Irregular Section

Sta. 4+48 — Five Level Section (Irregular)

Sta. 4 — Five Level Section (Regular Breaks at Ends of Base)

Sta. 3 — Three Level Section

Sta. 2+87⁴ —

Sta. 2+28 — Grade Points, Cut to Fill

Sta. 1+64 —

Three Level Section

Sta. 1 —

End of Fill

Sta. 0+46 —

Side Hill

Sta. 0 —

℄

Cross-Sections

FIG. 85.

162

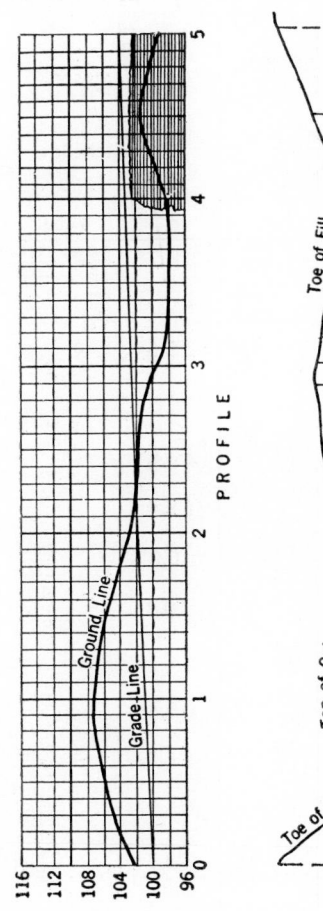

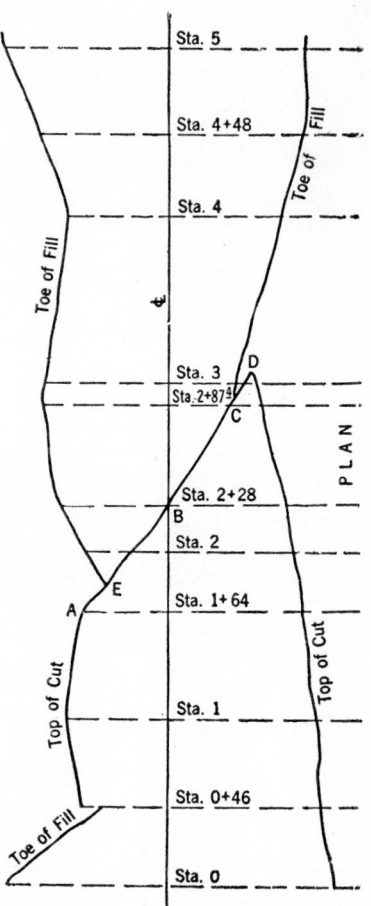

FIG. 85a.

sections and the corresponding profile.   The field notes are
shown in Fig. 85b.   Slope-stakes are set where the side

		Base 24; 1 to 18; $1\frac{1}{2}$ to	CROSS SECTIONS 1. Cut 1. Fill			Ferguson ㅠ Howe Mitchell		
Sta.	**Surface Elev., ft.**	**Grade Elev., ft.**	**Left**			**Cross Sections** **₵**	**Right**	
5	99.2	105.00	F $\frac{9.9}{23.9}$	F $\frac{4.6}{11.6}$	F $\frac{7.4}{6.4}$	F 5.8	F $\frac{8.6}{5.2}$	F $\frac{6.6}{18.9}$
4+48	101.8	104.48	F $\frac{6.4}{18.6}$	F $\frac{2.3}{6.0}$		F 2.7	F $\frac{2.9}{3.9}$	F $\frac{6.9}{19.4}$
4	98.4	104.00	F $\frac{3.4}{14.1}$	F $\frac{6.9}{9.0}$		F 5.6	F $\frac{3.0}{9.0}$	F $\frac{4.9}{16.4}$
3+04^Z							$\frac{0.0}{12.0}$	
3	99.4	103.00	F $\frac{5.8}{17.7}$			F 3.6	F $\frac{0.7}{10.1}$	
2+87 $\frac{1}{4}$	100.5	102.87	F $\frac{6.2}{18.3}$			F 2.4	$\frac{0.0}{9.0}$	
2+28	102.3	102.28	F $\frac{4.9}{16.4}$			0.0	C $\frac{5.1}{17.1}$	
2	102.8	102.00	F $\frac{2.2}{12.3}$	$\frac{0.0}{3.5}$		C 0.8	C $\frac{6.8}{18.8}$	
1+71^4			$\frac{0.0}{9.0}$					
1+64	105.0	101.64	$\frac{0.0}{12.0}$			C 3.4	C $\frac{7.4}{19.4}$	
1	107.3	101.00	C $\frac{2.7}{14.7}$			C 6.3	C $\frac{9.3}{21.3}$	
0+46	105.7	100.46	$\frac{0.0}{9.0}$			C 5.2	C $\frac{9.4}{21.4}$	
0	102.3	100.00	F $\frac{9.6}{23.4}$	$\frac{0.0}{3.1}$		C 2.3	C $\frac{11.6}{23.6}$	

Fig. 85b.

slope of the construction intersects the natural ground line
and, if the transverse slope of the ground is not uniform

between the center stake and the slope stakes, additional elevations are taken where the slope of the ground changes. The elevation at the center stake is always taken. The amount of cut (C) or fill (F) is marked on the slope stakes.

| Excavation | | Embank-ment | Jan. 11, 1938 |
Class A Earth	Class C Rock		General Notes

NOTE: While all engineers use C and F on the stakes, most of them use + for cut and − for fill in the notes. Less confusion results, however, if the letters C and F are also used in the notes, as in this example.

NOTE: Classification of Earth and of Rock may be entered as an estimated percentage during cross-sectioning, and/or entered as cubic yards as computed later.

FIG. 85b.   (Continued.)

and on the center stake. Cross-sections of this nature are taken at every 100-foot station along the line survey, and at such intermediate (or plus) points as may be necessitated by the fact that the ground does not slope uniformly along the line from one station to the next.

Where the work passes from cut to fill and where the roadbeds are of different widths as in Fig. 85, it is necessary to take additional cross-sections at stations $1 + 64.0$ and $2 + 87.4$. The station and plus should also be taken of the points D and E, although they are frequently omitted. Sufficient data are then available to compute two pyramidal volumes, one in cut and one in fill, lying between stations $1 + 64.0$ and $2 + 87.4$. Stakes marked "Grade" or 0.0 are set at points A, B, and C.

When the line ABD is nearly at right angles to the center line, only one cross-section (at right angles at B) is needed.

In general it may be said that cross-section notes must be taken wherever necessary to aid in computing cubic yardage, and that stakes must be set wherever they will facilitate construction.

86. Cross-Section Forms.

The base is frequently wider in cuts than on fills to allow for the side ditches in the cuts, as in Fig. 85. Usually the volumes of earth excavated to form side ditches are computed separately; but if the cross-sections are plotted and planimetered, then the actual shape of the bottom of the cut including the side ditches may be drawn with a template on the cross-section and the entire cross-sectional area measured at one operation.

The side slopes, s, of the finished grading are made sufficiently flat to stand up with little or no maintenance. Here s = horizontal to vertical; for example, $s = 3$ to 1 means 3 feet horizontally for a rise of 1 foot. In military usage and in the U. S. Engineer Corps, exactly the opposite is meant by their 3 on 1 slope, which they interpret as 3 vertical to 1 horizontal. In this volume we shall use the first definition of slope, which is customary in engineering.

USUAL SIDE SLOPES

	Cut	Fill
Solid rock	vertical to $\frac{1}{4}$: 1	
Loose rock	$\frac{1}{4}$: 1 to 1 : 1	1 : 1
Firm earth	$\frac{1}{2}$: 1 to 1$\frac{1}{2}$: 1	1$\frac{1}{2}$: 1
Average earth or sand	1$\frac{1}{2}$: 1 to 2 : 1	1$\frac{1}{2}$: 1 to 2 : 1
Average earth or sand, saturated with water	2 : 1 to 3 : 1	3 : 1
Large levees or dams in porous soil, up to		7 : 1

87. Setting Slope Stakes. Slope stakes are usually set with a 50-foot metallic tape and an engineer's level. Occasionally a hand level or a long straight edge with a bubble, called a *slope board*, replaces the tape and the engineer's level. The "Rhodes Arc" (California Highway Department) is an instrument recently developed for securing vertical and horizontal distances graphically and rapidly.

Slope stakes are placed by a method of trial and error. A levelman, a rodman, and an axman, constitute the cross-section party. The zero end of the tape is held on the center stake by the levelman, or is attached in some way to the stake. The rodman (handling the level) reads the rod as held by the axman on the ground at the center stake and computes the cut or fill, which is then *marked on the stake*. From this computed center cut or fill, it is possible to estimate the cut or fill for a slope stake (Fig. 87), and from this estimate to compute a corresponding horizontal distance. The rod is then held at the computed distance from the center stake, and from the rod reading it is possible to compute the cut or fill more exactly. Should this more exact value correspond with the estimated cut or fill, then the slope stake is driven at that point and *the cut or fill marked thereon*, as for example C 2.7. If the computed value of the cut or fill does not correspond within one or two-tenths of the assumed value, then the rod is moved toward or away from the center stake, a new rod reading is taken, and the new cut or fill compared with the actual distance from the center stake. Usually the second or third trial will locate the slope stake with sufficient precision. All cuts or fills are figured from the horizontal plane of the base of the roadbed and the distances from the center stake are computed as shown in Fig. 87. The result of this field

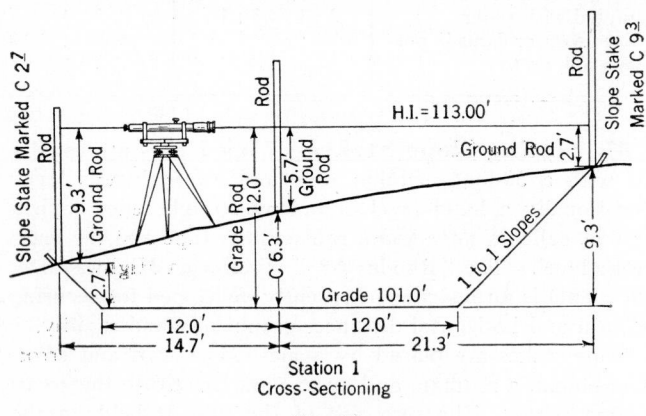

Station 1
Cross-Sectioning

FIG. 87.

procedure is entered in the notes of Fig. 85b. Where the ground does not slope uniformly from the center stake to the slope stakes, and where cut and fill occur on the same cross-section, it is necessary to take one or more extra readings, as indicated at stations 0, 2, 4, 4 + 48, and 5 of Fig. 85.

The levelman directs the work and keeps the notes, checking the computations which are made by the rodman.

The height of instrument for cross-sectioning is carried forward by differential leveling, the notes for which are kept on a separate page.* The *grade rod* is the difference between the *height of instrument* and the *grade elevation*. The

---

* Many engineers prefer to keep the differential level notes, including grade elevations, on the left page of the field note book, and the cross-section notes on the right page.

ground rod is the actual rod reading. Grade rod minus
ground rod equals *cut* or *fill*. This method of computation
simplifies field work and minimizes errors. This is shown
on Fig. 87.

Rarely, for heavy cuts or fills, it may be useful to set a
transit over the center stake and to measure a vertical angle
and a taped slope distance to the position of a proposed
slope stake on the ground. The horizontal and vertical
components of these slope distances are then used as a basis
for setting the slope stakes.

88. Precision in Measurements. Any particular
level rod reading taken on the ground may vary as much as
0.1 foot from the value which would be obtained by another
levelman. Several such errors occur on each cross-section
and tend to compensate. An error of 0.1 foot in *half* of the
cuts or fills on a particular section will cause an error of
about 1.7 square feet (for base = 20 feet, slopes of 1½ to 1,
and cut or fill of 5 feet) in the area of the cross-section, or
6 cubic yards per 100 feet of length. Such errors, over a
large number of cross-sections, will tend to compensate.

We may therefore conclude, in general, that computation
of end areas to the nearest square foot and of cubic yardage
to the nearest cubic yard per 100 feet of line is amply
precise.

89. Computing End Areas. The shape of the end
areas varies with the configuration of the original and finished ground surfaces. Dimensions are taken from the
cross-section notes such as those of Fig. 85b. In computing,
it is frequently possible to select triangles in pairs, and thus
to simplify the work.

The following notation will be used hereafter:

c = height at center line,
c_G = height of grade triangle,
h_L = height of ground at left slope stake,
h_R = height of ground at right slope stake,

$H = h_L + h_R,$

d_L = horizontal distance from center line to left slope stake,

d_R = horizontal distance from center line to right slope stake,

$D = d_L + d_R,$

s = side slope, as for example $1\frac{1}{2}$ horizontal to 1 vertical, expressed as $1\frac{1}{2}$ to 1,

A = net area of cross-section.

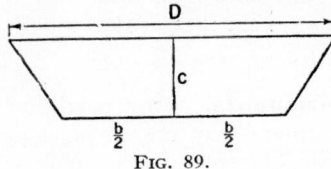

FIG. 89.

Level Cross-Section. In Fig. 89, considering the area as a trapezoid, we have

$$A = c\left(\frac{b + D}{2}\right).$$

It is sometimes desirable to express A in terms of s rather than D, in the form

$$A = c(b + cs).$$

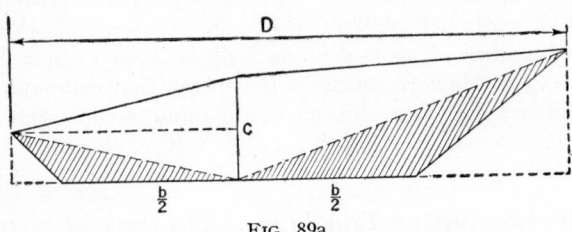

FIG. 89a.

Three Level Cross-Section. In Fig. 89a, the area for the two cross-hatched triangles equals $\frac{(b/2)H}{2}$ and the area of the two triangles with the common base c is $\frac{cD}{2}$. The total area of the four triangles is

$$A = \frac{cD + (b/2)H}{2}.$$

Five Level Cross-Section, Regular.   In Fig. 89b, the intermediate elevations are taken over the ends of the base.

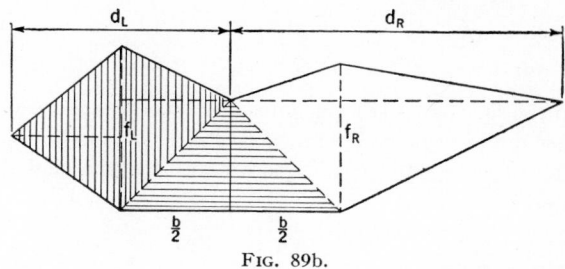

Fig. 89b.

The area for two horizontally cross-hatched triangles is $\dfrac{bc}{2}$. The area of two vertically cross-hatched triangles with base of f_L, and the combined altitude of d_L is $\dfrac{f_L d_L}{2}$.   Similarly, the area of the two unhatched triangles is $\dfrac{f_R d_R}{2}$, and

$$A = \frac{bc + f_L d_L + f_R d_R}{2}.$$

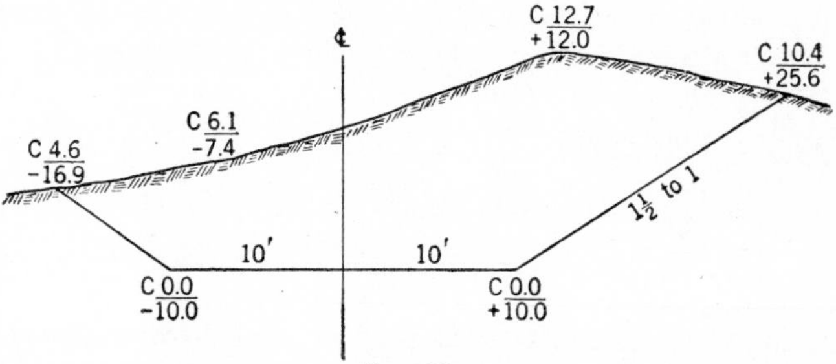

Fig. 90.

90. Coordinate Method of Computing End Areas.   This method is used for the more irregular cross-sections, one of which is shown in Fig. 90 for which the cross-section field notes are:

	Left		Right	
C 4.6	C 6.1	C 8.3	C 12.7	C 10.4
16.9	7.4	0.0	12.0	25.6

To the field cross-section notes are added readings which represent the respective ends of the base, so that the notes become a complete set of coordinates for the figure, as follows:

0.0	4.6	6.1	8.3	12.7	10.4	0.0
−10.0	−16.9	−7.4	0.0	+12.0	+25.6	+10.0

The origin for the foregoing coordinates is at the center of the base. To each figure in the denominators of the frac-tions is now added an algebraic sign opposite to that which precedes it and the notes become:

0.0	4.6	6.1	8.3	12.7	10.4	0.0
−10.0+	−16.9+	−7.4+	0.0	+12.0−	+25.6−	+10.0−

Each numerator is multiplied by the algebraic sum of the adjacent denominators, using the algebraic signs for the denominators which face the numerator being used. Half of the algebraic sum of these products is the area of the cross-section. For example:

$$\text{Area} = \tfrac{1}{2}[4.6(10.0 - 7.4) + 6.1(16.9) + 8.3(7.4 + 12.0)$$
$$+ 12.7(25.6) + 10.4(- 12.0 + 10.0)]$$
$$= \frac{580}{2} = 290 \text{ square feet.}$$

After making several such calculations it becomes unnec-essary to go through all of this detail. Should the section be in fill, the ordinates are really measured downward from the roadbed, but they are still considered as algebraically positive, since this assumption will not alter the resulting area.

The computations above are facilitated by using a computing machine or by using the Triangular Prism Table (XXI), with the results in cubic yards for a 50-foot length.

91. The Grade Triangle Method.   This alternative method is widely used in canal work and is especially useful for the three-level cross-sections which comprise so much of the work in computing excavation and embankment.   It is particularly easy and rapid when used in connection with the Triangular Prism Diagram of Table XXI.

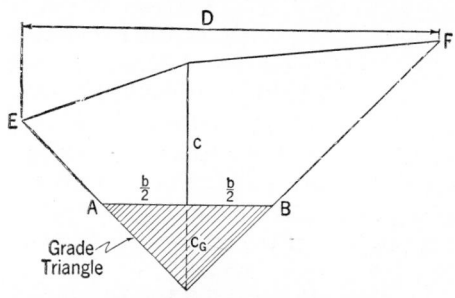

FIG. 91.   Grade Triangle Method.

In Fig. 91 the side slopes EA and FB are extended downward to the vertex V.   The gross area of the figure, including the cross-hatched grade triangle, is

$$\text{Gross } A = D \left(\frac{C + C_G}{2} \right).$$

The area of the cross-hatched grade triangle is $\frac{b C_G}{2}$.   The area of the net section is

(91) $$\text{Net } A = D \left(\frac{C + C_G}{2} \right) - \frac{b C_G}{2}.$$

This simplifies a long series of computations of cross-sections, especially where the same grade triangle and the same value of C_G occur over a considerable number of cross-sections. Some engineers subtract the grade triangle at each cross-section, while others prefer to subtract the grade triangle from the gross yardage for lengths of say one thousand feet or one mile.

92. End Areas by Planimeter. Still another method of securing the end area is to plot the cross-section on cross-section paper and to run a planimeter around the area twice, noting that the second reading is closely twice the first. The usual scale is 1 inch equals 10 feet both ways, although sometimes the vertical scale is reduced to 1 inch equals 20 feet. This method is generally used in highway work and it may well be the best method in other fields of engineering where the cross-sections are more complicated than the usual three level cross-section, and where the office force is not particularly well trained. While the precision is less than a geometric computation, yet it is not inconsistent with the precision of the field work. See Table XXIII.

93. Sections in Earth and Rock. In making cuts along a route, it happens frequently that rock is encountered beneath an overburden of earth. In making such excavations, it is customary for the contractor first to remove the earth, then to drill, blast and remove the rock. Construction contracts usually provide for payment of the rock and the earth portions of the excavation under different items of the contract, as described in §§ 105 and 129, the price per cubic yard moved differing for the two classes of material. The cost per cubic yard of rock is frequently from five to ten times that for earth. Occasionally, particularly if the earth overburden is shallow, the contractor may elect to "shoot" the entire mass of earth and rock at once and to remove, or "muck," it in one operation with a power shovel. In either case, however, if rates of payment for the earth and rock are different, it is necessary to measure the two separately. This is a comparatively simple matter if the contractor first uncovers the rock before beginning his blasting. The engineer then takes level shots to the rock surface on the regular sections on which earth sections have been taken or slope stakes set. Because the unit price paid for rock is often high, because the total amount of payment for rock is sometimes a large fraction of the entire contract, and because uncertainty as to the actual volume of rock removed is sometimes a fruitful source of dispute, cross-sections are often taken at closer intervals than 100 feet, particularly if the upper surface of the rock is irregular.

If the entire upper surface of the ledge (solid rock is frequently referred to by the term "ledge") is not uncovered before blasting is done, it is necessary to employ some other means of measuring it than simple levelling. These methods are all alike in making "soundings" through the earth overburden. The three commonest methods are, respectively, to drive a steel bar through the earth by hammering with a sledge until, from the ring of the blow on the bar, it appears that rock has been encountered. This method, called that of "punch borings," is unsatisfactory if the overburden includes boulders, or large fragments of loose rock, or large gravel. A second method is to make "wash borings." These are essentially small tubular wells sunk by the jetting method. The most reliable, but most expensive, method is to locate the rock by digging small holes, or test pits, and measuring the rock in the usual manner through them. Such methods as these are essential not only in case the contractor elects to remove earth and rock at one operation, but also if volumes of earth and rock must be estimated separately (as when the total estimated value of the proposed contract is needed) in advance of construction. Pages 51 and 241 give soil survey references.

Figure 93 shows a typical cross-section in earth and rock for a railway excavation. It will be noted that the rock slopes are $\frac{1}{6}$ to 1, whereas the earth slopes are $1\frac{1}{2}$ to 1, and that a small berm, or offset, is made at the bottom of the earth slopes.

Figure 93a shows a form of cross-section that is encountered in types of construction where a structure, such as a
masonry aqueduct or a sewer, is to be constructed in the cut.
Because the lines of the structure are fixed and the distance

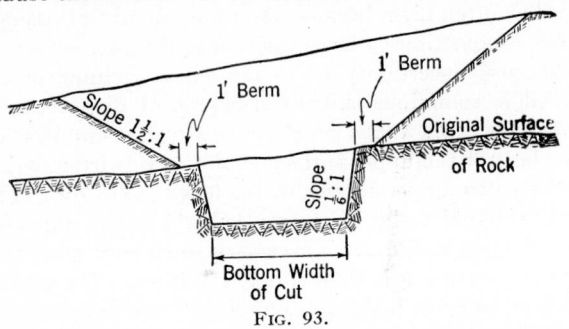

FIG. 93.

from inside of structure to face of rock must be within pre-
scribed limits (as when the "owner" pays separately for
the cement used on the job) two lines relating to the excavation are often indicated on the drawings, that may be
called the "A" and "B" lines.   One is the extreme line to

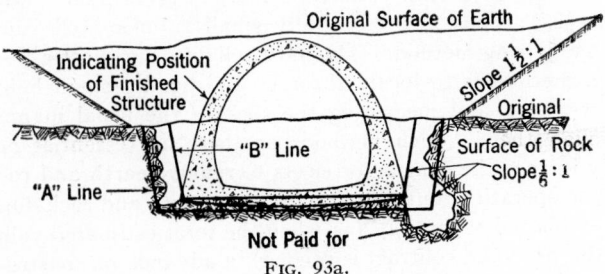

FIG. 93a.

which the contractor may be paid for his rock excavation;
the other is the line beyond which no rock shall project.
   Methods of computing volumes of earth and of rock in
"mixed" sections are the same as those employed where
earth is the only material encountered.   It should be re-

marked, however, that whenever a relatively exact method may be used instead of a relatively approximate one, the more precise of the two is preferable in the case of rock because of the greater money value involved.

When contractors' are bidding, it is necessary that the quantities of earth and of rock be definitely known, so as to avoid "unbalanced bids."

94. Canal Cross-Sections. Canals may have the usual cross-sections found in cuts on other types of construction, but they are frequently composed of two banks, or of somewhat irregular cross-sections, as shown in Fig. 94.

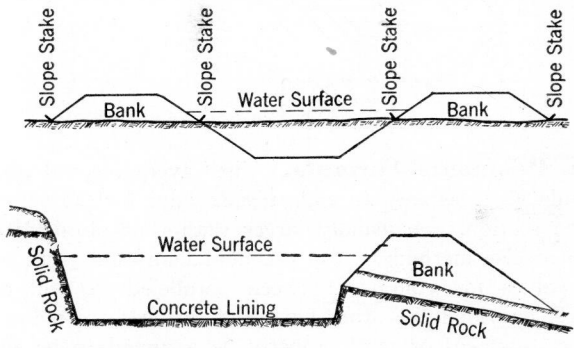

FIG. 94.   Canal Cross-Sections.

Computations are made in the ways described above. It is usually unnecessary to compute the quantities in the banks precisely, since payment is ordinarily made for cut, rather than fill, yardage.   Many canals are lined with concrete to prevent water growths, to exclude burrowing animals, to increase velocity and capacity, and to insure against breaks in the banks.

95. Averaging End Areas. Quantities of excavation or embankment (cubic yardage) are usually computed by the "averaging end area" method.   In Fig. 95, we have

(95)   Volume (in cubic yards) = V_{ea}

$$= \left(\frac{A_0 + A_1}{2} \right) \times \frac{l}{27}, \quad \text{approximately.}$$

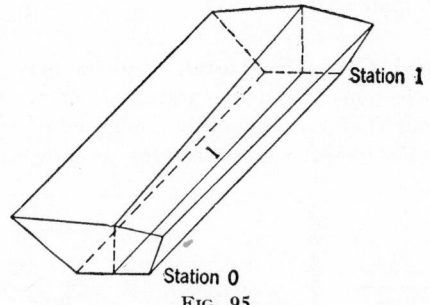

FIG. 95.

96. Prismoidal Formula.   The "averaging end area"

formula 95 gives only an *approximate* value for the volume
of the section, one usually larger than that obtained by
more precise methods.   The prismoidal formula gives *precise* values for volumes between paralleled vertical end
planes, provided the other bounding surfaces are plane or
warped surfaces or may properly be assumed to be such
surfaces.   *The prismoidal formula (96) should be memorized.*

(96) $$V_p = \left(\frac{A_0 + 4A_m + A_1}{6} \right) \times \frac{l}{27},$$

where A_m is the area of a cross-section mid-way between the
end cross-sections. A_m is *not* the mean of the areas A_0 and
A_1, but its dimensions are the mean of the corresponding
end dimensions.

Aside from its use for excavation and embankment computations, the prismoidal formula has a wide variety of
uses elsewhere in engineering.   It applies to any "pris-

moid," which may be defined as a solid between two parallel planes, each base having the same number of sides (although not necessarily similar in shape), all faces of the prismoid

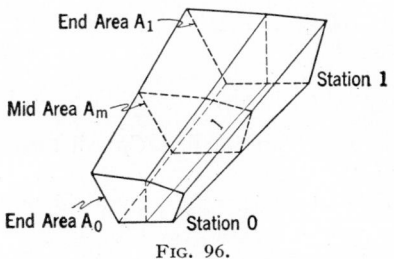

End Area A_1

Station **1**

Mid Area A_m

End Area A_0 Station 0

FIG. 96.

being planes. It will be noted in the preceding discussion of excavation and embankment solids, that they are not precisely prismoids, since natural earth surfaces are usually warped surfaces rather than planes; nevertheless the prismoidal formula gives the exact results in these cases also.

The prismoidal formula also applies to the frustra of pyramids and of all conic sections of revolution such as cones, spheres, ellipsoids of revolution, paraboloids of revolution, hyperboloids of revolution, and so on. In fact, this formula is precisely accurate whenever the area of the cross-section varies as any quadratic function of the distance to that cross-section, measured along a line perpendicular to the cross-sections, from any point in that line. This is true for the solids just mentioned and for many others.

97. Prismoidal Correction. In excavation and embankment computations, formula (96) is not convenient for use. It is easier to apply a correction C_p to the volume as figured by averaging end areas (V_{ea}), as in formula (97):

(97) $$V_p = V_{ea} - C_p,$$

where C_p may be positive or negative, usually positive. Usually, therefore, C_p is subtracted from V_{ea}.

Exactly for a three-level section, and sufficiently precisely for most other sections, we may write

(97a) C_p (in cubic feet) $= (l/12)(c_1 - c_0)(D_1 - D_0)$.

Where $l = 100$ feet, then for a three-level section, this formula becomes

(97b) C_{p100} (in cubic yards) $= (1/3.24)(c_1 - c_0)(D_1 - D_0)$.

For lengths other than 100 feet, C_p is directly proportional to the length.

The prismoidal correction for a pyramid or cone is

(97c) $$C_p = \frac{V_{ea}}{3}.$$

The prismoidal correction for grading usually amounts to only a few percent of V_{ea}, and is ordinarily neglected. It will be noted from the form of equation (97a) that C_p increases as either or both $(c_1 - c_0)$ and $(D_1 - D_0)$ increase, which means that C_p becomes larger and more important as the overall dimensions of any cross-section differ considerably from those of an adjacent cross-section. Consequently, it is important to apply C_p to those types of excavation and embankment where this condition exists, and where more precise quantities are needed.

Several facts doubtless account for the fact that C_p is rarely used: it is generally small; it involves added computation; it usually reduces the yardage for which the contractor is paid, and the owner who pays the contractor is usually unaware of the extra yardage involved by omitting the prismoidal correction. Figure 97 illustrates another reason for omitting C_p.

Since the method of average end areas is generally used, and will in all probability continue to be used, it may be desirable occasionally to specify in excavation and embankment contracts a maximum limit of $(c_1 - c_0)$,* say three or

* $(D_1 - D_0)$ might be used but it is not so evident from the field notes.

four feet, and to specify further that sufficient intermediate sections (between regular 100-foot sections) shall be taken so that this limit for $(c_1 - c_0)$ is not exceeded, or that the prismoidal correction will be applied when it is exceeded.

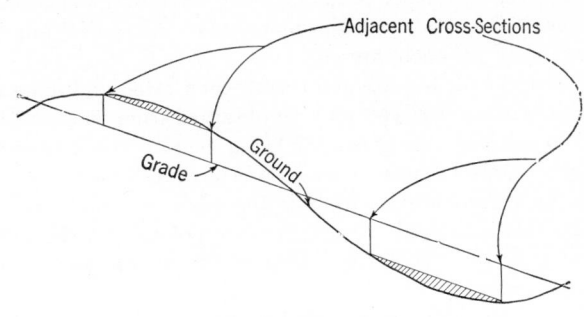

FIG. 97.

Such a specification would keep the errors of computation within reasonable limits. While perhaps it is generally recognized that omission of prismoidal corrections favors the contractor, few contractors or engineers realize that this favor varies from less than one percent of the yardage on some jobs to several percent on others, and consequently introduces a corresponding uncertainty to both contractor and engineer.

Unless mention is made in the grading specifications of the manner in which field cross-sections and office computations shall be accomplished, the courts will hold that common custom in that locality (usually averaging end areas 100 feet apart with extra sections at breaks in the ground between stations) must be followed.

98. Excavation Tables and Diagrams. The computation of excavation and embankment quantities may be accomplished by geometric solutions; by using the planimeter to find the areas of the plotted cross-sections; by means of earthwork tables; or by means of earthwork diagrams.

It is not possible to include in a single volume such as this all of the great variety of tables and diagrams which are needed in the wide range of excavation computations; only the more commonly useful and suggestive ones are given here.   On large projects it may be found advisable to prepare tables and/or diagrams to cover the special requirements that are encountered.

Examples for use are given with each table and diagram.

Preliminary estimates may be obtained from Tables XIX, XX, and XXII, center heights being usually taken from the profile to the nearest foot.   Intermediate tenths of feet may be interpolated with fair precision, but not exactly, where this is desired.   Since the interpolation in the tables is not exact, it is better to interpolate from the nearest foot, plus or minus.

Final estimates, more precise, may be obtained from Tables XXI and XXIII.

Prismoidal correction tables and diagrams have been omitted, since they are seldom used and since they can be obtained from the table of *Triangular Prisms* (Table XXI), as explained in the examples on that diagram. The relation is as follows:

Prismoidal Correction (yardage per 100 feet)

$$= \frac{1}{3.24} (c_0 - c_1)(D_0 - D_1),$$

Triangular Prisms (yardage per 50 feet)

$$= \frac{50}{54} \text{(height)(width)}.$$

The relation between the two formulas is

$$\frac{1}{3.24} \div \frac{50}{54} = \frac{1}{3}.$$

In other words, the prismoidal correction per 100 feet is ⅓ of the triangular prisms yardage per 50 feet, using the

$(c_0 - c_1)$ and $(D_0 - D_1)$ as the dimensions of the height and width of the triangular prism.

Table XXI, *Triangular Prisms* (three sheets), is sufficiently precise for excavation computation, and is more quickly and more easily used than are tables or other diagrams. Furthermore, this one diagram covers any reasonable range of base widths and of side slopes. For these reasons it has been enlarged and extended beyond the limits of other published tables and diagrams, so that it may be available for the following and other uses:

(1) To obtain the volumes of triangular prisms for the irregular earthwork solidities adjacent to grade points; and for securing solidities where the cross-sections contain more than the usual three-level readings.

(2) To obtain solidities for the usual three-level cross-sections.

(3) Rather rarely, for obtaining the Prismoidal Correction.

99. Embankment Openings. When an opening is left in an embankment for a bridge or other structure, there remains outside the regular cross-section the mass $EFLKM$ (Fig. 99). Its volume may be computed approximately by

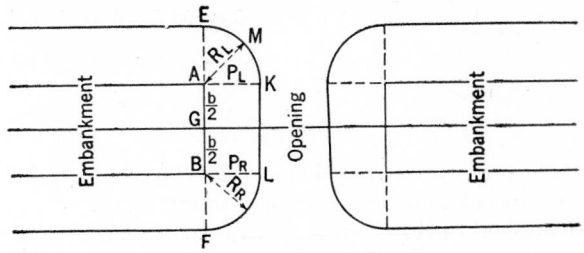

FIG. 99.   Embankment Opening.

dividing it into three parts: AEK, $ABLK$, and BFL. Let us assume that

$$R_L = AM = \frac{AE + AK}{2}, \quad \text{and} \quad R_R = \frac{BL + BF}{2}.$$

The vertical height at A is called f_L and the vertical height at B is called f_R. The total solidity in cubic yards is composed of two $\frac{1}{4}$ cones (see footnote on page 185) and a wedge.

$$EFLKM = \quad AEK \quad + \quad BFL \quad + \quad ABLK$$

$$(99) \quad = 0.0097 f_L R_L{}^2 + 0.0097 f_R R_R{}^2 + \frac{(f_L P_L + f_R P_R)b}{4 \times 27}$$

100. Curvature Correction. In calculating the volumes of earthwork, we have assumed the end-areas to be parallel, as is the case in the straight portions of the construction. In the case of a curve, this is equivalent to taking the cross-sections perpendicular to the chord (3–4 or 4–5 in Fig. 100) of the curve between the two stations.

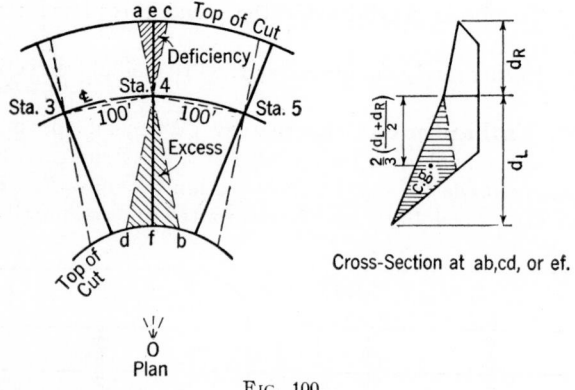

Cross-Section at ab,cd, or ef.

Fig. 100.

Actually the cross-sections in a curved volume of earthwork are staked radially, that is, normal to the curve.

Figure 100 shows the top view of earthwork on a curve, and the cross-section at station 4. If the volume has been computed in the usual manner, the cross-sections have been assumed as shown by the dashed lines ab and cd at right angles to the dotted chords 3–4 and 4–5. The volume thus computed will exceed the true quantities by the volume marked "excess," and will be less than the true quantities by the volume marked "deficiency." If the center of gravity of the cross-section is vertically over the center line of the survey, then excess and deficiency are equal and no curvature correction is necessary.

When it is necessary (as seldom happens) to compute the correction for curvature, it may be done as in Fig. 100. The correction desired per 100 feet of length is the cross-hatched area of the cross-section (Fig. 100) times the arc distance through which that area's center of gravity moves around a vertical axis through station 4 in generating the "excess minus deficiency" volumes,* or

$$C_c = \frac{[\text{area, in sq. ft.}][\text{arc, in feet}]}{27} \quad \text{(cu. yds.)}.$$

Since the arc, in feet, is equal to the radius, $\dfrac{2}{3}\left(\dfrac{d_L + d_R}{2}\right)$, times the angle between lines ab and cd, in radians; and since this angle, in degrees, is D (because 100 foot chords are used),

$$C_c = \left[\left(\frac{b}{2} + sc\right)\left(\frac{h_L - h_R}{2}\right)\right]$$
$$\times \left[\frac{2}{3}\left(\frac{d_L + d_R}{2}\right)\left(\frac{D}{57.3}\right)\right] \div 27$$

$$(100) \quad C_c = \left(\frac{b}{2} + sc\right)(h_L - h_R)(d_L + d_R)$$
$$\times (0.00011D) \text{ cu. yds.}$$

When the two adjacent chords are each less than 100 feet in length, then the formula becomes

$$(100a) \quad C_c = \left(\frac{b}{2} + sc\right)(h_L - h_R)(d_L + d_R)$$
$$\times \left(\frac{L_0 + L_1}{200}\right)(0.00011D) \text{ cu. yds.}$$

* A plane area revolving about a straight line in that plane but outside of the area, generates a solid of revolution whose volume is the product of that area times the length through which its center of gravity moves.

Since curves, concave towards the hills, generally occur in passing around sloping side hills, since the contractor is usually paid for excavation, and since excavation in such situations will generally be greater on the inside of the curve than on the outside, then uncorrected quantities (upon which the contractor is paid) will usually be larger than true excavated quantities, such as would be obtained after applying a correction for curvature. The correction as given in formula (100) is usually small and is not ordinarily used. Some idea of its amount may be obtained for a typical side-hill cross-section similar to Fig. 100 where, for example, the base is 20 ft., side slopes $1\frac{1}{2}$ to 1, $c = 5$ feet, $h_L - h_R = 10'$, $d_L + d_R = 44$ feet, $D = 10°$; and the correction would be $8\frac{1}{2}$ cubic yards, or some 2 percent of the yardage per 100 feet as computed without the correction. Since the correction varies directly with D, it is smaller for flat curves; and since it occurs only on curves, it is generally a small percentage of the *total* yardage which includes large lengths of straight route.

The correction C_c becomes appreciable on sharp curves, on steep transverse slopes, and in heavy work. It is relatively large in side hill work, such as Fig. 100 where the cut portion of the cross-section lies largely on one side of the center line.

Since the prismoidal and the curvature corrections are of the same order of magnitude, it would be generally, though not always, inconsistent to apply one and not the other. Both corrections, if applied, tend to reduce the calculated yardage.

The foregoing derivation and formulas for C_c apply almost exactly to three-level sections. They are closely approximate for most other sections where intermediate ground readings between the center line and the slope stakes have been taken. If the cross-section is very irregular, then an approximately equivalent three-level section may be used, or the cross-section may be plotted and the center of gravity determined graphically.

Where cross-sections have been plotted to scale, as in highway work, it may be easier to planimeter the cross-hatched area and to establish the c.g. graphically. Such a procedure is also useful for difficult figures such as occur on side-hill cross-sections which are partly in cut and partly in fill.

For a rough approximation for the total curvature correction to apply to a considerable length of line, an average percentage increase may be figured for a few typical cross-sections.

If it is intended to apply the curvature correction, it must be so specified in the grading contract, since otherwise the courts would probably hold that the general custom (of omitting curvature correction) must be followed.

101. Borrow Pits. It is customary to pay the contractor for material as measured in cuts,* and, when this material is insufficient to construct the fills, to pay him additionally for the borrowed materials as measured in the borrow pits.

When the borrow pit is adjacent to the main construction, it should be cross-sectioned at every 100-foot station and at necessary intermediate plus stations. After excavation, the borrow pit is again cross-sectioned at the original stations,

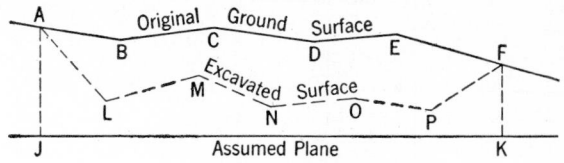

Fig. 101.   Borrow-Pit.

and excavated yardages are computed. Cross-sections are usually similar to that in Fig. 101. The cross-sectional area may be planimetered, or obtained as in § 90, or computed to an assumed plane JK. In the latter case, the net area

---

* Occasionally, as for example in Federal levee work, the contractor is paid for the yardage within the theoretical lines of the finished fill.

is equal to the difference of the areas $ABCDEFKJA$ and $ALMNOPFKJA$.

A "berm" of original ground of from 5 feet to 40 feet, according to necessity in the particular construction, must be left between the toe of the fill and the borrow pit. A contractor is generally required to leave the borrow pit in a sightly condition and so drained that water will not stand in it.

102. Computation of Grading Over an Area—or Borrow-Pit Method.

When the work covers a broad area rather than a narrow strip, as is the case in grading for a large building or industrial yard, or when a borrow pit is not adjacent to the route survey, it is frequently desirable to lay out a system of rectangles (usually squares) say fifty feet or one hundred feet on a side, depending on the roughness and topography of the ground and the precision with which the quantities are required.

Sometimes the rectangular dimensions may be chosen so as to facilitate computation, as for example rectangles 50×54 feet giving 100 cubic yards for each foot of depth. Usually it is more important that they be chosen to fit the ground, to give the required precision, and to minimize field work.

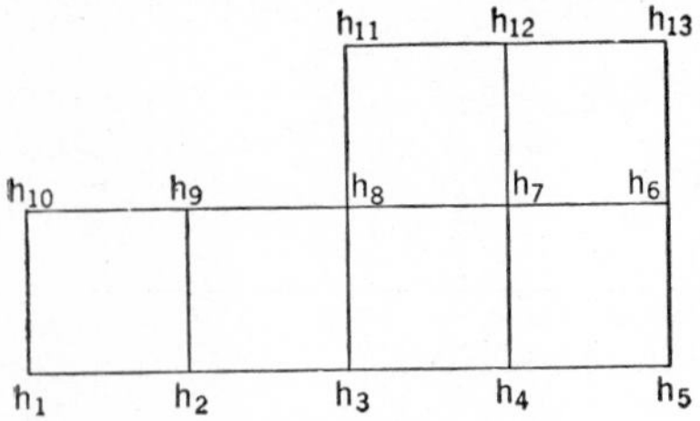

Fig. 102.

Elevations are then taken on the corners of the rectangles, and on such additional points as may be needed to define the ground surface with the necessary precision, as in Fig. 102. After excavation, the rectangles are reestablished and elevations are taken a second time and are marked on the plat with red ink. The difference of the first and second elevations at each point gives the h for that point, cut or fill.

Truncated Triangular Prism.   In Fig. 102a, the area of BCD is represented by A.

V (cu. ft.) = the right rectangular prism $BCDEFG$
$$+ \text{ the pyramid } EFGHI$$

$$= Ah_1 + (FGHI)\left(\frac{a}{3}\right)$$

$$= Ah_1 + \frac{(h_2 - h_1) + (h_3 - h_1)}{2} \ (FG)\left(\frac{a}{3}\right)$$

$$= A\left(\frac{3h_1}{3}\right) + \frac{(h_2 - h_1) + (h_3 - h_1)}{3}(FG)\left(\frac{a}{2}\right)$$

$$(102) \qquad = A\left(\frac{h_1 + h_2 + h_3}{3}\right).$$

This formula also applies when the triangular prism is truncated both top and bottom, since the same derivation could be applied if the triangular prism of Fig. 102a were extended downward to a truncated bottom.

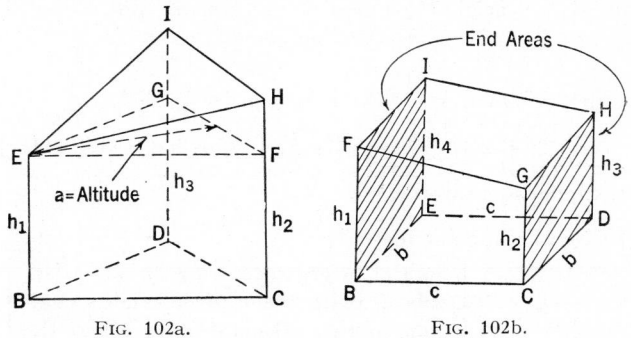

Fig. 102a.   Fig. 102b.

Truncated Rectangular Prism.   In Fig. 102b, the area of $BCDE$ is represented by A. Using the "averaging end area" method, we find

$$V \text{ (in cubic feet)} = c \left[\frac{\left(\dfrac{h_1 + h_4}{2}\right) b + \left(\dfrac{h_2 + h_3}{2}\right) b}{2} \right]$$

$$= bc \left(\frac{h_1 + h_2 + h_3 + h_4}{4} \right)$$

$$(102a) \qquad = A \left(\frac{h_1 + h_2 + h_3 + h_4}{4} \right).$$

Since the spread on these end areas (corresponding to D in the Prismoidal Correction Formula (97a)) is zero, the prismoidal correction is zero and formula (102a) is exact. Furthermore, $FIGH$ may be a warped surface (see § 96) and formula (102a) is still exact. As in the preceding paragraph, formula (102a) will also apply if the rectangular prism is truncated at top and bottom.

Assembly of Prisms. Some simplification of computation results when many rectangular prisms adjoin one another as in Fig. 102. Here h_7 is a height common to four prisms, h_8 is a height common to three prisms, h_2, h_3, h_4, h_6, h_9, and h_{12} are heights common to two prisms, and h_1, h_5, h_{10}, h_{11}, and h_{13} are heights affecting one prism only.

$$V \text{ (in cubic feet)} = \frac{A}{4} \left[(h_1 + h_5 + h_{10} + h_{11} + h_{13}) \right.$$
$$\left. + 2(h_2 + h_3 + h_4 + h_6 + h_9 + h_{12}) + 3h_8 + 4h_7 \right],$$

or, expressed in words,

(102b) V (in cubic feet)

$$= \frac{A}{4} \left[\begin{array}{l} \text{Sum of heights occurring on one prism} \\ \text{only} + \text{twice the sum of heights com-} \\ \text{mon to two prisms} + \text{three times the} \\ \text{sum of heights common to three prisms} \\ + \text{four times the sum of heights com-} \\ \text{mon to four prisms} \end{array} \right]$$

Special Prism Solutions. In Fig. 102c, we have

(102c)　V (in cubic feet) $= A \left(\dfrac{h_1 + h_2 + h_3 + h_4}{4} \right)$

$$+ \frac{A}{3} \left(h_5 - \frac{h_1 + h_2 + h_3 + h_4}{4} \right).$$

In Fig. 102d,

(102d)　V (in cubic feet) $= A \left(\dfrac{h_1 + h_2 + h_3 + h_4}{4} \right)$

$$+ \frac{A}{3} \left(h_5 - \frac{h_4 + h_3}{2} \right).$$

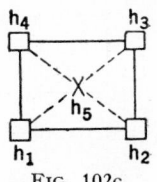

FIG. 102c.

In more irregular cases, the prisms must be divided somewhat as shown in Fig. 102e. Stakes and elevations are available at the points marked with squares. Elevations only are available from ground readings at the points marked X. Elevations may be taken on the ground at the points marked with an X in a circle, or such elevations may be interpolated from the ground elevations at the adjacent stakes.

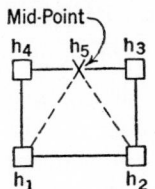

FIG. 102d.

Inexpensive Rectangular Layout. A layout such as Fig. 102f is cheaper, quicker, and nearly as precise as those described in the foregoing paragraphs. Elevations are taken at the center of the sides and at the center of the rectangle, although the stakes are not driven at these points. Only about one-third of

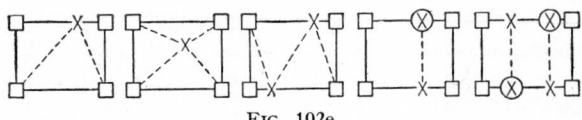

FIG. 102e.

the stake driving is here necessary, as compared with the methods previously described.

This is an economic method also where rectangles are to be staked out and contours are to be drawn as well. Contours are plotted by interpolation. It is best, however, to compute grading from the actual ground elevations rather than from contour elevations.

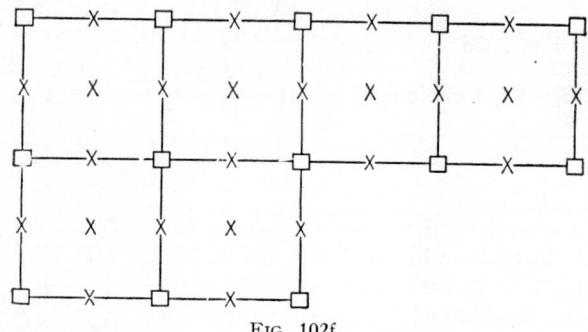

Fig. 102f.

Any isolated mass of material such as a boulder, or any hole such as may be caused by removing a large stump, is not ordinarily covered by the regular elevations and should be computed separately.

103. Shrinkage and Swell. Practically all material excavated from its natural site swells in volume. On the way to the fill where it is deposited, some of the material is lost. As and after it is deposited in the fill, it consolidates and shrinks; some of it is washed away by rain, some of it may thaw out, and the foundation under the fill may settle. All of these effects grouped together are referred to as "shrinkage" or "swell." In a general way, with considerable variation in special cases, it may be said that to make 1 cubic yard of fill or embankment, it is required to excavate from 1.10 to 1.15 cubic yards of earth; about 0.95 cubic yards of shale; about 0.85 cubic yards of shatter or loose rock; and about 0.70 cubic yards of solid rock. The amount of shrinkage or swell varies with the material, with the construction equipment and methods, with the water present in the material, and so on.

104. Settlement. In making a new fill or embankment, the foregoing shrinkage results in a vertical settlement for a considerable period after placing—of perhaps from one percent of the vertical height for a rock fill or for a hydraulic fill, to perhaps 25 percent or more for a high fill constructed without compacting the material as it is

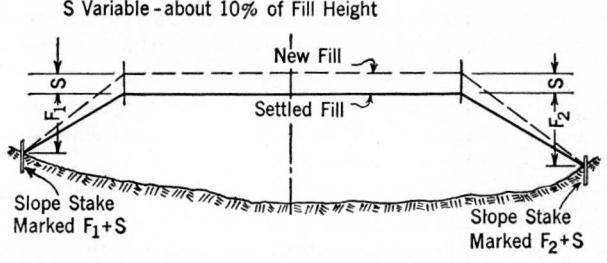

S Variable–about 10% of Fill Height

New Fill

Settled Fill

Slope Stake Marked F_1+S

Slope Stake Marked F_2+S

Fig. 104.

placed, and/or using frozen earth, and/or where there may be some subsidence of the foundation soil, as in levees. Such an estimated percentage of the vertical height of the finished fill is ordinarily added above the desired final grade, as shown in Fig. 104.

105. Classification of Excavation. Excavation is usually bid upon by the contractor, and paid for to him, according to specifications similar to the following, which are quoted from the Standard Specifications of the Missouri State Highway Commission, 1950:

"*Class A Excavation.* This item shall consist of all excavation under this item which cannot be classified under either of the other headings of classification.

"*Class C Excavation.* This item shall consist of the removal of stone in ledges six (6) inches or more in thickness, and any detached rock or boulder when the volume of same is more than two and one-half (2½) cubic yards.

"A ledge shall be considered to be a continuous body of rock which may or may not include thin, interbedded seams of shale or other soft material. The vertical limits of each ledge shall be determined by beds of soft material more than twelve (12) inches thick and such beds of soft material shall be included in the measurement of Class A Excavation only.

"Shale, fire clay, chert (known as joint flint rock) which is broken by intermittant clayey partings or clay seams, stratified chert cemented with clay seams (known as hardpan), and plain or bituminous-bound bases or surface courses of macadam, gravel, broken stone or other similar materials will not be considered as or paid as Class C Excavation."

The specifications go on to classify *Sandstone Excavation* and *Igneous Rock Excavation* in some detail.

Sometimes excavation is "unclassified," in which case all classes of material encountered are paid for at a single unit price. Still other classifications are used for the several types of excavation encountered in building structures.

106. Grading Equipment and Methods. The equipment and methods used in grading are being improved constantly. Consequently, they should be observed in practice or studied from articles and advertisements in engineering periodicals or from catalogs of equipment manufacturers. Special equipment is available in stock, or may be made to order for special jobs.

Dredges with pipe lines, and hydraulic giants with flumes, provide the cheapest methods of moving the looser material when conditions are favorable to their use.

Blasting of rock and other hard materials must necessarily be handled by an experienced foreman. More difficult work of this nature should be done under the direction of specialists, who are available in private consulting practice, or who are connected with companies manufacturing explosives.

CHAPTER XIII

HAUL AND THE MASS DIAGRAM

107. Haul. The word "haul" may have one of two meanings: first, the distance through which excavated material is moved; and second, the product of the volume moved (in cubic yards) and the distance (in stations) between its center of gravity in excavation and its center of gravity when it is placed in the fill, as shown by Fig. 107. In this latter usage of the word, the unit of measurement is the station-yard, meaning one cubic yard moved 100 feet.

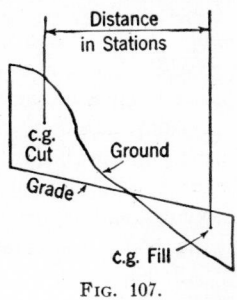

FIG. 107.

108. Free Haul. In cases where the contractor is paid for excavating material and further paid for hauling, as explained in § 109 immediately following this section, limits of free haul often are established as shown on Fig. 108, and no payment for hauling is made to the contractor for material excavated and placed within the free-haul limits nor for hauling between the free-haul limits of that material which is excavated and placed outside of the free-haul limits.

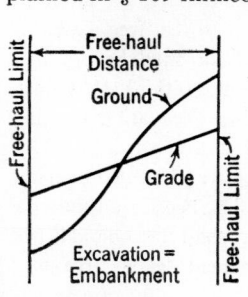

FIG. 108.

109. Overhaul. Part, sometimes all, of the cost of hauling is included in the price paid the contractor for excavation. That portion of the haul, if any, for which the contractor is paid in addition to the payment for excavation is called "overhaul." The computation of overhaul aids the contractor in bidding and provides the basis of payment to him for haul. Overhaul is best computed by the "station to station" method or by the "mass diagram," as explained in §§ 110 to 115 inclusive.

The 1955 Standard Specifications of the Missouri State Highway Commission describe overhaul as follows:

"The limits of free haul will be determined by fixing on the profile two points two thousand (2,000) feet apart, one on each side of the neutral grade point, selected in such a way that the included quantities of excavation will balance the included quantities of embankment plus the proper allowance for shrinkage or swell. All material within the balance points (see § 115) beyond this limit of two thousand (2,000) feet will be estimated, and payment will be made on the basis of the following method of computation,

"All material, whether roadway or borrow excavation, within the limits of two thousand (2,000) feet will be eliminated from further consideration in overhaul computations.

"The overhaul distance will be the distance between the center of gravity of the remaining mass of excavation and the center of gravity of the resulting embankments, measured to the nearest station, less two thousand (2,000) feet free haul.

"The amount of overhaul to be paid for shall be obtained by multiplying the overhaul distance in stations (100 feet) by the quantity of the remaining mass of excavation in cubic yards and shall be expressed in units of station yards.

"If material is obtained from borrow pits and hauled over the shortest practicable route, the overhaul distance for all material hauled over two thousand (2,000) feet shall be one-half the round-trip distance made by the equipment less a free haul distance of two thousand (2,000) feet. The amount of overhaul to be paid for shall be obtained as set forth above, and shall be expressed in units of station yards."

Longer free hauls and units may be used, such as one-half mile free haul and one-quarter mile yards units.

The American Railway Engineering Association has a
condensed overhaul specification which reads as follows:
"Payment in such units (station cubic yards of overhaul)
shall only be made for haul in excess of .... feet.
Haul shall be the distance along the center line of the roadway, or along the most direct practicable route, between the
center of mass before excavation and the center of mass as
finally placed."

Other specifications are occasionally used but the foregoing or similar ones are those adopted most widely.

The limit of free haul in the past was commonly fixed at
500 feet, a good figure for most small and medium sized
excavation jobs.   For larger jobs and with more modern
equipment, a free haul of 1,000 feet is more frequently
specified.   If the excavating equipment is such that, after
the material is loaded, it can be hauled a considerable distance cheaply (as by industrial or standard gage railway,
by carryalls or trucks, or by hydraulic methods), then the
free haul may be made much longer.   If, however, teams or
tractors haul the material in scrapers or fresnos, or if "bulldozers" are used, the free haul should be shorter.   The
length of free haul is specified by the engineer in his call for
bids.

110. Station to Station Method.   Figure 110 shows
the profile and Table 110 shows the computations for overhaul as made by this method.   The station to station
method has the great advantages of speed and simplicity.
It assumes that the center of gravity of the earthwork
between adjacent cross-sections, usually 100 feet apart, may
be considered midway between the two cross-sections, which
generally is a satisfactory approximation.   In this simple
example, from the Manual of the Associated General Contractors (which organization recommends this method), no
allowance is included for shrinkage or swell.   Such allowance is, however, always made in practice and usually applied to embankment quantities.

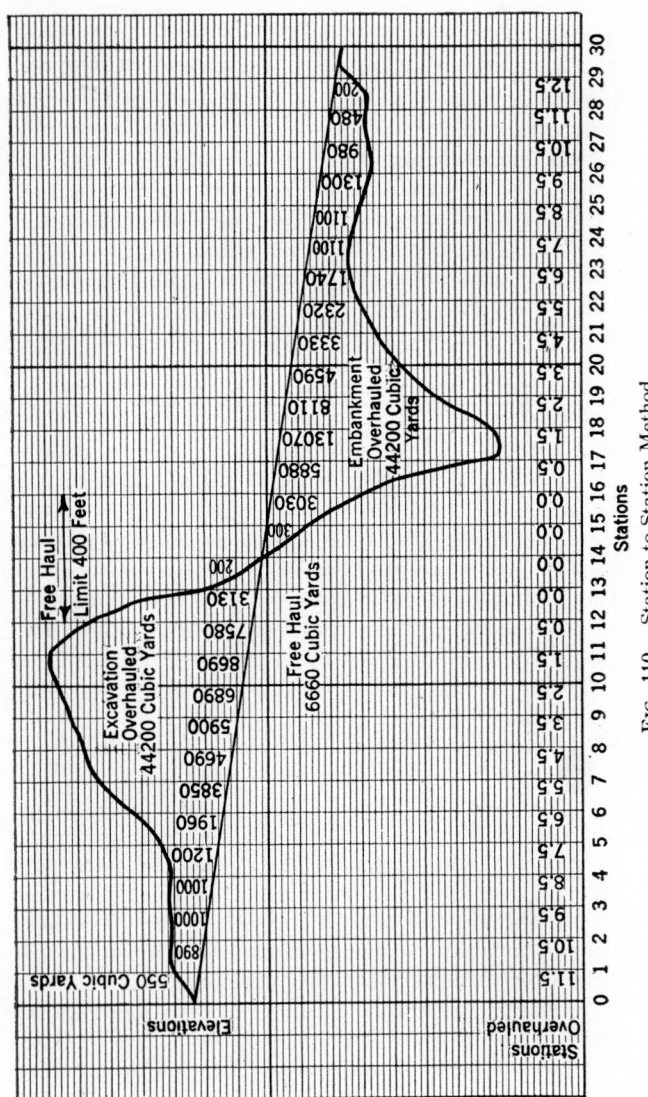

FIG. 110.   Station to Station Method.

198

TABLE 110

STATION	YARDAGE	STATIONS OVERHAULED	OVERHAULED STATION YARDS
0 to 1	550	11.5	6325
1 2	890	10.5	9345
2 3	1000	9.5	9500
3 4	1000	8.5	8500
4 5	1200	7.5	9000
5 6	1960	6.5	12740
6 7	3850	5.5	21175
7 8	4690	4.5	21105
8 9	5900	3.5	20650
9 10	6890	2.5	17225
10 11	8690	1.5	13035
11 12	7580	.5	3790
12 13	3130 (free)	0	0
13 14	200 (free)	0	0
14 15	300 (free)	0	0
15 16	3030 (free)	0	0
16 17	5880	.5	2940
17 18	13070	1.5	19605
18 19	8110	2.5	20275
19 20	4590	3.5	16065
20 21	3330	4.5	14985
21 22	2320	5.5	12760
22 23	1740	6.5	11310
23 24	1100	7.5	8250
24 25	1100	8.5	9350
25 26	1300	9.5	12350
26 27	980	10.5	10290
27 28	480	11.5	5520
28 29	200	12.5	2500
	95060		298590

111. Economic Limit of Haul. The material is hauled from cuts to fills until the cost of overhaul exceeds the cost of borrowing from pits or cuts immediately adjacent to the fills. For instance, assume that embankment is not paid for, that overhaul costs 4¢ per cubic yard per station (500 feet free haul), and that borrow costs 40¢ per cubic yard. It is economical to waste and borrow material when the haul is longer than 40/4 + 5 stations, or 15 stations.   If added right of way is needed for the borrow-pit and the cost of borrow is thus increased to say 44¢, then the limit of economic haul would be 44/4 + 5, or 16 stations.

112. Mass Diagram.   In constructing the mass diagram, the first step is to tabulate the accumulated algebraic sum of the yardage, cut or fill, at each station, as shown in Table 112.   On side-hill work, where both cut and fill occur on certain cross-sections, the net difference between cut and fill is entered in the tabulation.   These accumulated yardages are plotted above the horizontal axis if in cut and below

TABLE 112

MASS DIAGRAM TABULATION

Station	Center Height	Cubic Yards		Shrinkage Per Cent	Accumulated Yardage
		Cut	Fill		
0	F 5		343	+10 (earth)	F 378
1	F 10		778	+10	F 1233
2	F 12		293	+10	F 1555
+30	F 14		835	−30 (rock)	F 2140
3	F 17		1543	−30	F 3220
4	F 20		1926	−30	F 4569
5	F 23		2343	−30	F 6214
6	F 19		1794	+10 (earth)	F 8189
7	F 8		237	+10	F 8449
+40 Grade	C 2	37			F 8412
+60	C 4	154			F 8258
8	C 7	713			F 7545
9	C 9	950			F 6595
10	C 13	1469			F 5126
11	C 17	2046			F 3080
12	C 19	2357			F 723
13	C 21	2683			C 1960
14	C 20	2519			C 4479
15	C 16	1896			C 6375
16					

it if in fill. The points thus found are then joined by curved (not straight) lines. The mass diagram is best drawn immediately below the profile and to the same horizontal scale, so that corresponding stations will be on the same vertical line.

EXAMPLE: Construction of mass diagram from profile of Fig. 115. Base of cross-sections is taken as 16 feet in fills and 24 feet in cuts, ½ : 1 side slopes. Table 112 shows the tabulation.

Column 2 is needed for computing approximate or preliminary estimates. The center height of a cross-section is taken from the field notes or is scaled off the profile to the nearest foot. Cubic yardages (columns 3 and 4) are then taken from Table XXII, for given slope and base in cut and fill. When more precise yardages are available, as when, for example, cross-section notes have been taken, they should be used.

Column 5 shows the percentage allowance for shrinkage and swell of materials used in fills, as mentioned in § 103.

Column 6 gives the algebraic sums of yardage from origin. These accumulated yardages are plotted on Fig. 115.

Conditions or classification of excavation will determine which of the following two methods can be applied most conveniently, that is, whether excavation yardage is kept at unity or whether embankment yardage is made unity.

Method A. Excavation yardage is held the unit in ordinates for the mass diagram and swell or shrinkage factor is applied to the embankment quantities. This form is to be used when a shrinkage or swell factor is uniform throughout or for a major portion of the project, when the factors change so infrequently that the disposition of the cuts at the exceptions could be ascertained readily by trial without resorting to Method B, or when one cubic yard of excavation will make one cubic yard of embankment over a long stretch and there are no shrinkage or swell factors to consider. This method is applied in Table 112, and is the one generally used.

Method B. Embankment yardage is kept at unity and swell or shrinkage is applied to the excavation ordinates only. This method is to be used where frequent changes in classification cause varying factors of swell and shrinkage, and is necessary in order to determine graphically the distribution from a continuous mass curve. It will permit more rapid derivation of the most economical balance line and most advantageous hauls. In computing overhaul under Method B where the excavation pay quantity has had a factor applied in platting the ordinates of that yardage, the scaled yardage for overhaul must be divided by that factor.

113. Properties of the Mass Diagram. The mass diagram has the following properties:

(1) the ordinate at any point represents the cumulative yardage to that point, cut if above the axis and fill if below the axis;

(2) the difference in the lengths of any two ordinates is equal to the yardage between the two stations at which the ordinates are erected;

(3) ascending lines represent cut, descending lines represent fill;

(4) maximum and minimum points occur where grade points exist on the profile;

(5) the loops convex upward indicate that the haul from cut to fill is to be in one direction (in this case from left to right); loops concave upward indicate that the haul is in the opposite direction;

(6) between any two points where a horizontal line intersects the mass diagram, cut and fill are equal, or balanced, such points being called "balance points";

(7) haul along the profile is represented by areas in the mass diagram, and the amount of haul and/or overhaul may be secured by measuring the proper areas. For example, in Fig. 113 the cubic yard of excavation at C, shown solid, is hauled and deposited in the fill at B. The actual haul along

the profile is evidently one cubic yard multiplied by the length of haul, measured in station-yards. On the mass diagram the trapezoidal area represents this same amount of haul in station-yards. Since all of the haul along the profile between A and D could be represented by similar trapezoids on the mass diagram, the total area on the mass diagram, $ABECD$, in station-yards, represents the total amount of haul, in station-yards, along the profile between D and A.

When the mass diagram is being drawn, it should be roughly checked against the profile to see that the relations exist as mentioned in the foregoing paragraph.

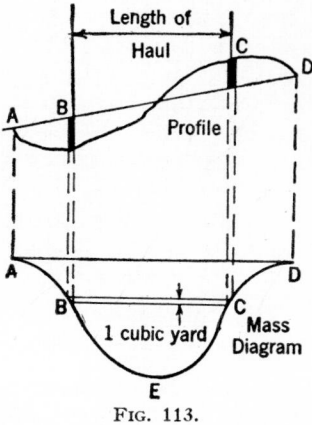

Fig. 113.

114. Purpose of the Mass Diagram. The mass diagram is used to study questions of excavation and embankment, borrow and waste, economic haul, overhaul, and direction of haul, so that the *total cost* of grading may be a minimum. Such a study is made when the corporation does its own work, not employing a contractor. When a contractor is employed, the same questions are studied, especially overhaul, with a view to keeping the *total payments to the contractor* to a minimum, regardless of the cost to the contractor.

115. Procedure in Using the Mass Diagram. If we assume a free haul of 500 feet and a limit of economic haul of 1100 feet, the procedure necessary to obtain a minimum cost of grading on Fig. 115 is as follows:

(1) *Establish the balance points.* In each of the larger loops, draw a horizontal line 1100 feet long, touching the

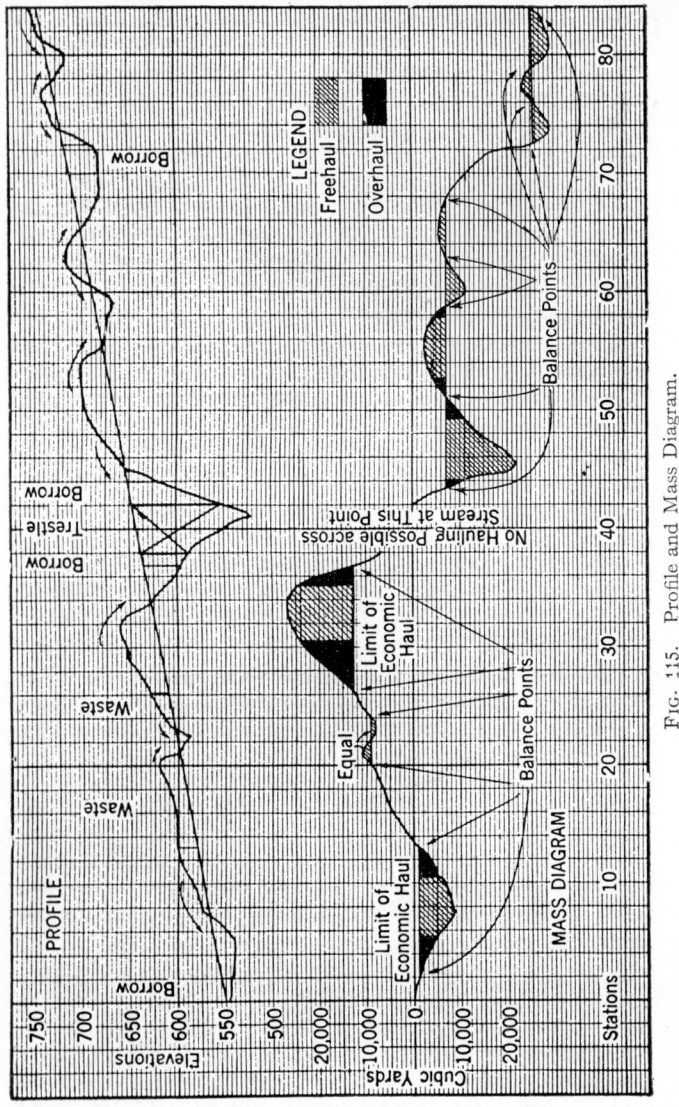

FIG. 115. Profile and Mass Diagram.

204

diagram at each end, as between stations 2 and 13 and between stations 26 and 37. In an analogous manner, draw a horizontal line from station 43 to station 68, each of the segments of this line being less than 1100 feet, and minimum overhaul occurring when tops equal bottoms of overhaul strips. Balance points are established at stations 20, 22, and 24 by drawing a horizontal line, the two segments of which are equal, and the total length being less than 1100 feet. All balance points are indicated in the figure. All material outside of the balances will be wasted (stations 13 to 20 and 24 to 26), or borrowed immediately adjacent to the fill (stations 0 to 2, 37 to trestle, trestle to 43, and 68 to 72 + 50), as shown on the figure. Other cases not shown in Fig. 115 must be studied to give the least cost, or to meet other requirements.

(2) *Establish free haul limits.* Whenever a pair of balance points are more than 500 feet apart, a horizontal line 500 feet long is drawn, as shown between stations 5 + 50 and 10 + 50, 30 + 50 and 35 + 50, 44 and 49, 52 + 50 and 57 + 50, and so on. The single cross-hatched areas represent free haul. For example, between stations 30 + 50 and 35 + 50, the area above the 500-foot line represents and measures the free haul originating and being deposited within the free haul limit. The rectangular area below the 500-foot line represents the free haul on material originating and being deposited outside of the free haul limit.

(3) *Overhaul.* The solid black areas as marked on the diagram represent and measure overhaul, as for example between stations 2 to 5 + 50, 10 + 50 to 13, 26 to 30 + 50, and so on.

More complex situations are occasionally encountered. Study of the mass diagram provides the solution. Economic use of equipment, the requirement that certain work must be completed by a scheduled date, or other practical considerations, may sometimes modify the conclusions drawn in the foregoing example, where the object was to keep the cost a minimum. In most cases, the mass diagram provides the best method of studying the disposition of excavation along a line of construction.

Before construction, the number of station-yards of overhaul *may be estimated* in one of the following ways:

(1) By planimetering the area of an enlarged section of the diagram, or by geometrical computation of the area on the original diagram, bearing in mind that the area must be modified by a shrinkage or swell factor.

(2) The approximate distance between the centers of gravity of the overhauled material in excavation and in embankment may be found by drawing a horizontal line midway between the free haul line and the balance line. This length, minus the free haul, multiplied by the net yardage (from the tabulation), gives the station-yards of overhaul.

(3) By the station to station method of § 110.

After construction, the contractor *is paid* for the *actual amount* of overhaul, using the balance points which actually occurred during construction.

The yardage of cut and borrow for which payment is made will be taken from the cross-section notes after noting on the mass diagram where such cut and borrow occur.

The mass diagram is of greatest usefulness where the contractor must be paid for overhaul.

Grading contracts are sometimes let on a lump sum basis of payment. In other cases, payment is made only for cut and borrow, no payment being made for overhaul. In still other cases, the work is not let by contract, but is done by company forces. While in none of these methods is payment made for overhaul, yet it is desirable to draw a mass diagram and to show thereon the balance points and the waste and borrow, so that the contractor or the company superintendent may see graphically what disposition of material is necessary.

The use of the mass diagram is sometimes complicated by specifications such as for mixing and consolidating soils. These cases require special study.

CHAPTER XIV

RIGHTS OF WAY

116. Influence of Rights of Way on the Selection of Routes. All line constructions, such as railways, highways, pipe lines, flumes, canals, levees, transmission lines, and the like, require the acquisition of property, or at least the right to use property. This requirement frequently influences the reconnaissance, preliminary, and location surveys. For example, when high property values exist along the line of the best location, it may be advisable to choose a less desirable location over cheaper land. At other times, it is anticipated that a serious delay will result from the objection of certain property owners. At still other times, it may take months to secure right of way from the Federal Government, or to secure the permission of some large corporation to cross their property, for example to cross railway tracks. It is obvious that it would be desirable frequently to alter the route to avoid such difficulties.

117. The Right of Eminent Domain. Most government units, and those corporations known as public utilities, possess the legal right to condemn private property for public use. By court action they may acquire property for right of way against the wish of the owner, though he must be suitably recompensed. The usual experience with courts in condemnation proceedings leads one to expect that the cost of land acquired by condemnation, including legal expenses, severance damages, and the like is considerably above its value. Furthermore, condemnation proceedings make enemies and require considerable time, though it is possible to proceed with the construction, providing a suitable bond has been posted to insure the property owner against damage. *Every effort should be made to avoid such proceedings.* Condemnation is used only rarely.

118. Right of Way Agents. It is usually advisable to assign the acquisition of right of way to one who is especially qualified by experience and training best to handle the necessary contacts and negotiations. Usually, such men have experience in real estate and the law, and are good contact men. In other words, the direct negotiation for right of way is not ordinarily made by an engineer. However, it is the function of the engineer to furnish the description of the right of way, and to aid indirectly in securing it. In connection with this last duty, the engineer should cultivate the good will and friendship of the leading citizens of the community, and he should acquaint them with his organization so that they will, in a way, sponsor the project. It is especially necessary that friendly relations be maintained with the persons whose land is affected by the construction, and on whose land surveys are being made.

119. Deeds and Easements. Right of way may be granted by a deed conveying complete right to the land used, in other words, by a title in "fee simple."

A cheaper type of grant permits only a limited use of the land occupied for a specified purpose, and is called an "easement." An easement may, for example, grant "the right of ingress and egress for constructing and maintaining (including necessary clearing of timber) an electrical transmission line across ———————, with towers at the points as now staked and to be constructed, and as shown on the map attached hereto." Such an easement allows the owner to use the land for all other purposes, as for example for farming or mining.

A lease, permit, license. or agreement is occasionally used.

120. Right of Way Description. Right of way descriptions take many forms according to the standard practice of the constructing organization, and according to the statutory law of the state in which the property lies. Only two examples will be given here, although many variations of them exist.   Usually a map similar to Fig. 120 accompanies the description.   Referring to the figure, one type of description would be as follows:

A right of way for a transmission line across Section Fifteen (15), Township Nineteen (19) North, Range Six (6) East, Willamette Meridian, Kittitas County, State of Washington, the center line of which is described as follows: Entering said Section at a point twenty hundred fifty-five and three-tenths (2055.3) feet easterly from the northwest corner of said Section, thence on a course South thirty (30) degrees and thirty-one (31) minutes West across the West half of

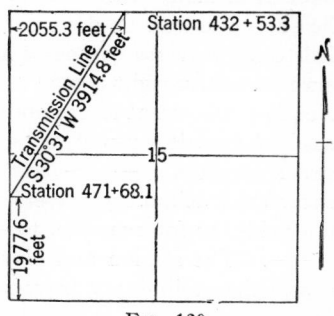

Fig. 120.

said Section for a distance of thirty-nine hundred fourteen and eight-tenths (3914.8) feet, and leaving said Section at a point nineteen hundred seventy-seven and six-tenths (1977.6) feet northerly from the southwest corner of said Section, as shown on the accompanying plat.

In many cases it is not desirable so precisely to describe the center line, more dependence being placed on the position which the line actually occupies on the ground.   Here the description would begin *"A right of way for a transmission line as now staked and to be constructed across ————, and so on."*   In such a case it is not infrequently advisable to insert the words *"more or less"* after such dimensions as are not definite and precise.

121. Surveys of Right of Way.   While surveys for rights of way may be made at any time, it is usually desirable that they be made early, so that the right of way agents may have ample time to become acquainted with the land owners and to establish friendly relations with them.

At this time, right of way difficulties may become apparent which will require a change of location. As mentioned in §12, aerial surveys made early in the project will help greatly.

As soon as the preliminary survey traverse is staked, and even while the traverse is being run if possible, it is desirable to locate as many of the needed property corners adjacent to the survey as can be done conveniently. They should be tied to the traverse by course and distance. This not only serves tentative right of way purposes, but permits property lines to be shown at least approximately on the preliminary map. A transit is usually set up, for example, at the ———— corner of section ———— and the property line is taped across the preliminary traverse to a property corner on the other side, as for example, to the ———— corner of section ————. The station and plus at which the property line crosses the preliminary traverse, and the angle of intersection at the point are recorded, as well as the taped distance to the property corners. Sometimes stadia location of the property corners is used. Rarely, where the survey is coordinated, coordinate positions of property corners are computed, especially if state plane coordinates are to be used in the description.

Frequently, such property surveys are made after the final location is staked on the ground and tied to the final location.

In searching for property corners, the engineer must avoid reviving old neighborhood quarrels as to their location. It is frequently desirable to enlist the aid of the county surveyor, city engineer, or other local persons best acquainted with the corners, and to have him identify them, after which the regular survey party can tie them to the preliminary or to the final location traverse. The location of these corners often gives considerable trouble, especially to one unfamiliar with the territory.

122. Legal Rights of Surveyors. The surveyor, whether a private engineer or a government official, has no right to trespass on private property without permission from the owner. Generally there is no objection, but occasionally violent protest is raised by the owner, and the surveyor must retire from the land. It is possible nearly always to traverse or triangulate around or across the prohibited territory and to sketch in the topography roughly without trespassing. Sometimes that portion of the survey must be delayed until more friendly relations are established. In the case of a governmental agency or a public utility, when condemnation proceedings have been started, a bond covering possible damage to the owner may be posted and the surveys may then proceed.

The engineer's tact, good judgment, and ability to get along with property owners and other influential persons in the community will contribute largely to his progress to administrative responsibilities, while neglect of this important function is apt to handicap him severely.

The right of way agent needs even more diplomacy. In one instance it was necessary to obtain 78 signatures on one transaction, including those of heirs of the fourth generation located in seven states.

Getting a right of way on property owned by either a married man or woman requires the signature of both and this may turn out to be more difficult than rounding up 78 missing heirs. Getting some married couples to agree on anything calls for a degree of diplomacy beyond an engineer and rare even in a right of way agent.

The main objectives of both engineers and right of way agents is to maintain pleasant relations with the public, to serve the public, and to keep reasonable the costs which in the end are borne by the public.

CHAPTER XV

CONSTRUCTION

CONSTRUCTION PROCEDURE

123. General. The following three chapters will discuss America's largest industry, construction, which offers attractive careers in construction supervision, professional management, and contracting.

124. Re-establishing a Final Location and Ordering Materials. Many of the final location stakes may be knocked out and lost. The first step in construction is to check and re-reference sufficient points such as P.Is., T.Cs., C.Cs., and C.Ts. so that they may be easily and definitely re-established. At this time the elevations of all bench marks and other important points are checked. Frequently, discrepancies are found and these must be satisfactorily adjusted.

As soon as sufficient information is available from the surveys, the necessary materials should be ordered, so that the delay in delivery will be minimized. Table 124, pages 214 and 215, shows a data sheet for an electric transmission line from which the materials may be ordered. Similar tabulations may be prepared for other constructions.

125. Cross-Sectioning. The line must be cross-sectioned ahead of the grading operations, as mentioned in Chapter XII. Vertical curves are computed and the grade elevations of *all* stations are entered in the notebook *before* going into the field. Rights of way through timber should be cleared before cross-sectioning. It is desirable to clear off timber before the final location and essential to do so before cross-sectioning, usually with a bulldozer.

126. Staking Appurtenant Structures. Plans— sometimes standard, sometimes special—are furnished for all structures of importance. As the structure is staked in the field, the plan is redrawn in the masonry field note book, with the survey work clearly recorded.

For all structures, *it is essential that the reference stakes and/or "batter boards" be so set that the essential and controlling points of the structure may be reproduced on the ground, on 'he falsework or concrete forms, and on the finished structure at any time during the construction.* It should be remembered that most stakes will be destroyed or disturbed unless special precautions are taken to preserve them, and that piles of materials or other obstacles may make survey operations difficult during construction. Should the reference points be obliterated or inaccessible during construction, and should it therefore become necessary to relocate the structure from more remote survey points, difficulty, annoyance, and expense arise in reconciling the position of the partially completed construction and the position indicated by the second survey.

In setting stakes for construction, too many stakes are expensive and apt to be confusing to the construction men, while too few stakes require the foreman to set the missing ones, often not precisely or economically. A happy mean should be chosen between these extremes, preferably in consultation with the construction foreman.

Appurtenant structures are usually built before the main construction is completed and consequently they must be painstakingly staked out to correspond with the final location stakes. *It*

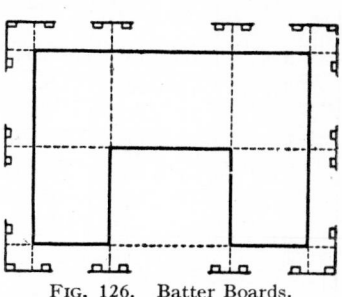

Fig. 126. Batter Boards.

is particularly necessary that the elevation data be correct since frequently there is no completed construction in the neighborhood to give assurance that the structure is at

Tower Number	Station Number	Angle	Tower		Foundation (U.S.G.S. Datum)	
			Type	Dwg. No.	Type	Elev. Pile Cut Off
829	604+94.4	90° 10′ Rt.	0–98	64562	Pile	−1.0′
830	597+05.8		AH	34449	Pile	−1.0′
831	588+67.6	1° 28½′ Lt.	AH	34449	Pile	−1.0′
832	582+14.7	59° 39′ Lt.	0–92	65562	Std.	—
833A	577+62.8		AH	34449	Std.	—
833	573+94.3	42° 54½′ Rt.	CH–DE	34451	Std.	—
834A	568+48.2		AH	34449	Std.	—
834	562+13.1	42° 43′ Lt.	CH–DE	34451	Std.	—
835	556+85.1	16° 00½′ Rt.	CH–DE	34451	Sp.	—
836	549+96		AH	34449	Sp.	—
837	541+97.4		AH	34449	Sp.	—
838	533+96.5		AH	34449	Sp.	—
839	525+93.6		AH	34449	Sp.	—
840	517+91.1		AH	34449	Sp.	—
841	509+87.7		AH	34449	Sp.	—
842	501+87.4		AH	34449	Sp.	—
843	495+25.0 495+52.6	0° 34¼′ Lt.	AH	34449	Sp.	—
844	487+71.9	15° 35′ Rt.	BH–DE	34450	Pile	0.0′
845	478+29	13° 50½′ Rt.	BH–DE	34450	Pile	−1.0′

FOUNDATION (U.S.G.S. DATUM)		EXTENSION		REMARKS
Elev. Top Concr.	Dwg. No.	Length	Dwg. No.	
4.0′	35403	10.0′		Sq. Cross Arms, Dwg. #24914 on S. Side of Tower. D.E. Take off to Substation.
4.0′	35401	10.0′	24625	
4.0′	35401	2½′	34914	BH Footing with AH Stub. Tele. Transp., Cir. #1
--	—	—	—	D.E., No Piles, Sq. Cross Arms, Existing Tower
—	—	—	—	D.E., No Piles, Sq. Cross Arms, Existing Tower
—	—	—	—	D.E., No Piles, Sq. Cross Arms, Existing Tower. Telephone Transposition, Circuit #2
—	—	—	—	D.E., No Piles, Sq. Cross Arms, Existing Tower
—	—	—	—	D.E., No Piles, Sq. Cross Arms, Existing Tower
+9.0′	35400			
+9.0′	35400	10.0′	24625	Telephone Transposition, Circuit #1
+9.0′	35400	10.0′	24625	
+9.0′	35400	10.0′	24625	Telephone Transposition, Circuit #2
+9.0′	35400	10.0′	24625	
+9.0′	35400	10.0′	24625	Telephone Transposition, Circuit #1
+9.0′	35400	10.0′	24625	
+9.0′	35400	10.0′	24625	Telephone Transposition, Circuit #2
+9.0′	35400			
5.0′	35401	21.0′	—	Telephone Transposition, Circuit #1
4.0′	35401	21.0′		

about the right elevation. Only carefully checked bench marks should be used, and one or two should be established near enough to each important structure so that one setup of the level will suffice to transfer elevations to any part of the structure.

Buildings. Buildings are staked in accordance with the plans of the architect or engineer or in line with the wishes of the owner, after the property lines are established. It is not possible to retain stakes set at the corners of structures since such stakes would be dug out in the excavation for foundations. Batterboards (Fig. 126) made of $2'' \times 4''$ posts driven into the ground across which are spiked horizontal $1'' \times 4''$ strips, are set some few feet outside of the structure lines. Heavier strips and posts are necessary for important structures. Nails are driven into these horizontal strips on the prolongation of the lines of the building, or notches are cut in the horizontal strips, so that a wire or chalk line stretched over the nails or notches will define the structure line throughout its length. It is sometimes convenient to set these batterboards at some even number of feet above or below the top of foundation or floor level, and in such case the tightly drawn wire or chalk line will give approximate elevation data. Sag prevents elevations from being exact except near the batterboards.

Culverts. The site should be checked with the plans. The stream bed or contour may have changed to such an extent that the location of the culvert must be shifted or the flow line raised or lowered. A flow-line gradient of from one to two per cent is desirable. Too flat a flow line may cause silting in the culvert, and too steep a flow line may cause scouring at the outlet.

It is best to set a hub at the intersection of the center lines of the route and of the culvert, and it is desirable, though not always possible, to make the angle between axis of culvert and center line of route 90 degrees, even if it is necessary to change the bed of the stream slightly to accomplish this. Construction stakes are then set at the ends of the culvert, and reference stakes are set sufficiently beyond, perhaps 25 to 50 feet, so that they are not likely to be disturbed.

The required capacities of culverts are discussed in § 140.

Bridges.   Figure 126a shows stakes necessary for a wing-wall type of bridge abutment.   The stakes must be set out far enough so as to avoid disturbance during rough excavation, pile driving, form setting, concreting, and so on, and in such position that the several more important points (in Fig. 126a the transit points, marked thus ○) may be reproduced on the ground, on the concrete forms, or on the concrete at any time during the construction.

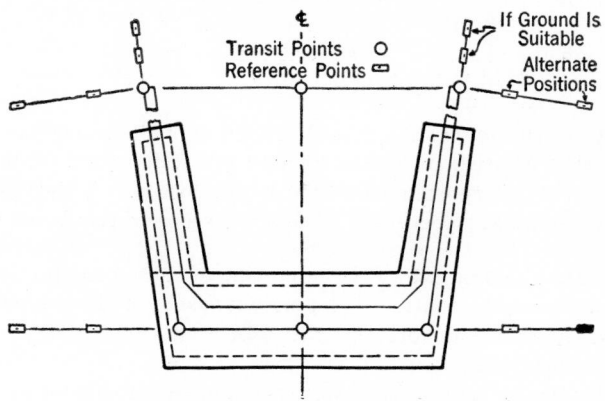

Fig. 126a.   Wingwall Abutment.

For larger bridges, which have piers in the stream, it is frequently necessary to stake out base lines on each shore and to locate the piers from these base lines by triangulation.

Canal Structures.   Checks, drops, inlets, outlets, flumes, inverted syphons, and so on, along canals are similar to other route structures.   They are staked in the same manner as are bridge abutments or culverts.   It is the duty of the field engineer to extend them into the bottom and banks in such a manner as to prevent percolation.

Tunnels. Tunnel work presents specialized problems in surveys and in construction, and the reader is therefore referred to books and periodicals on the subject. See Rubey, Lommel, and Todd, *Engineering Surveys—Elementary and Applied*.

127. "Change Orders." Following the final location survey and during construction, changes are often made in the location and profile and in appurtenant structures; and these changes must be recorded completely and systematically and reported to all concerned in writing, usually on a standard "change order" form. This frequently involves equations in the stationing along the final location.

It is usually necessary for the contractor, if there is one, to sign the change order so that the contract relation shall be maintained in legal form.

128. Inspection. It is the function of the inspector to see that a satisfactory construction job is done, and to act fairly in interpreting contract requirements. A detailed discussion of inspection is beyond the scope of this book.

129. Contracts. A large portion of route construction is done under contract. Numerous books and technical periodicals are devoted to this aspect of engineering and construction work.

Under the "unit price" contract, payment is made for each cubic yard or other unit comprised in the work; consequently much surveying is involved in computing these quantities for monthly estimates and at the completion of the job.

Under the "lump sum" contract, the complete job is paid for as a whole and less surveying and computation of quantities is needed.

Under the "cost plus" contract, the contractor is paid for the expenses which he incurs, plus a percentage to cover various overhead expenses and profit. Here a minimum of surveying and computation of quantities is necessary.

130. Monthly Estimates. Payments are usually made to the contractor each month during the progress of construction, and it is therefore necessary to estimate from measurement and observation the quantity of each class of work done to date. On this basis, he receives a partial or progress payment, usually with a "hold back" of ten or fifteen percent which is retained until after the entire work done under the contract has been satisfactorily completed and accepted by the owner.

The engineer in charge of construction must therefore prepare such monthly estimates, or he must have them prepared. Under many contracts, materials delivered on the ground and for which the contractor has paid, are allowed in the monthly estimate in part or in whole, except for the retained percentage mentioned above.

131. "Progress Reports," either in tabular or graphic form, are prepared from every monthly estimate of quantities. Photographs taken at various stages of the construction are frequently helpful.

Before work starts, it is customary on large projects to prepare a proposed construction schedule showing the several sub-divisions of the work (frequently in graphical form), on which schedule progress is entered as accomplished. This chart is the basis for periodically coordinating the inter-dependent sub-divisions through job conferences of the heads of the several sub-divisions.

132. Final Estimate. Following completion of the construction, the engineer prepares a final estimate of the quantities of the various items of construction and of the total money values of construction under the terms of the contract. Under a typical *unit cost contract*—the form of contract usual in route construction—this would include the number of acres of clearing and grubbing; cubic yards of excavation, loose rock, and solid rock; station-yards of overhaul; cubic yards of concrete of one or more classes;

pounds of steel; and so on.   Each of these is multiplied by the corresponding price per unit, as named in the contract, and the total amount is certified as due the contractor. The contractor is then paid the difference between this amount and the sum of all previous partial payments.   This closes the job and the contract is discharged.

133. Summary. It may be stated that supervision of construction requires (a) maintaining as many resident engineers and inspectors on the work as may be necessary to secure proper results; (b) giving all necessary lines and grades; (c) inspecting all material and workmanship; (d) checking all shop drawings and lists of materials furnished by the contractor; (e) preparing additional details as circumstances arising during the progress of the work may require; (f) preparing monthly estimates of work done as a basis of partial payments to the contractor; (g) maintaining contact between the home office and the resident engineers through weekly progress reports, mail and telephone or telegraph; (h) visits to the work by representatives of the home office at appropriate intervals of about once a month (once per week, once per 60 days, or any other period that may seem adequate under the circumstances); (i) preparing a set of "record" plans showing the work as actually completed; (j) preparing a final report containing a history of the work and general instructions for its maintenance and operation; (k) monumenting the survey for permanent reference.

134. Operation after Construction. The engineer is sometimes engaged to supervise the early period of operation of the project, following the completion of construction. This may involve monthly inspection, conferences, checking of drawings, maintaining general touch with the work through correspondence or telephone, and so on.   Further and more detailed duties may be involved, even to the extent of appointing the engineer as manager.

135. Management and Administration. After the early period of operation, it is not uncommon for the engineer to be engaged as manager of some department of the operating company, or even as general manager of the company. In this case he may later advance to the presidency, and after a period of time, to the highest corporate position, that of chairman of the board of directors. A large proportion of the higher operating officials are engineers.

CONSTRUCTION DATA

It is beyond the scope of this volume to give detailed discussion to all kinds of construction or to specifications or construction standards. Knowledge concerning these must come from engineering experience, or must be obtained from the construction standards of the organization doing the work, from books devoted to such details, from technical periodicals, and from the publications of technical societies. It is possible, however, to include in this chapter some information which is frequently needed for *emergency use* in the field. The data given here must not be assumed to be final and complete; rather, they are to be used *tentatively* until a more complete reference is available.

136. Allowable Bearing Power of Soils. It is impossible to give this information so that it may be used without question for any particular foundation. The engineer should check the records of foundations in the vicinity if such are available, and should use these records as a guide to his judgment. If the work is important, or if there is doubt as to the allowable bearing power of soils, actual tests should be made at the site. For particularly difficult foundations, a consultant who is an expert on local conditions should be retained.

With these qualifications in mind, Table 136 may be used to obtain a rough general idea of the allowable bearing power of soils.

TABLE 136

BEARING POWER OF SOILS

National Board of Fire Underwriters

TYPE OF SOIL	TONS PER SQUARE FOOT
Clay, firm, dry	3
firm, wet	2
hard	4
soft	1
Clay and sand, wet	2
Gravel	4
Hard pan	8–15
Rock	15–72
Sand, coarse	4
fine, f.rm, dry	3
fine, wet	2

It is inadvisable to rest important foundations on filled ground, on loam, or on soil containing organic matter. The material should be in relatively thick beds if full allowable bearing power is to be used; otherwise, if underlain by a softer material, the upper soils should be of sufficient thickness to distribute the load over the requisite area of underlying soil.

137. Bearing Power of Piles. It is possible to plan a safe and economical pile foundation only by observing the behavior of a few test piles driven at the site and loaded until they show distinct settlement. Such tests are usually not available except for important structures, and the engineer's judgment must be guided by his knowledge and experience and by such specifications as those of the Missouri Highway Commission (1955) which follow:

"*Hammers for Timber Piles.* Gravity hammers for driving timber piles shall weigh not less than two thousand (2,000) pounds and preferably shall weigh three thousand (3,000) pounds. The fall of the hammer shall be so regulated as to avoid injury to the piles and shall, in no case, exceed twenty (20) feet. The Contractor shall establish the true weight of the hammer used on the work to the satisfaction of the Engineer. Steam hammers used for driving timber piles shall develop an energy of not less than four thousand one hundred (4,100) foot pounds per blow at each full stroke of the piston.

"*Hammers for Precast Concrete Piles.* Precast concrete piles shall be driven with steam hammers. The steam hammers shall develop an energy per blow at each full stroke of the piston of not less than three thousand five hundred (3,500) foot pounds per cubic yard of concrete in the pile being driven. The total energy developed by the hammer shall be not less than eight thousand (8,000) foot pounds per blow. Gravity hammers, when permitted by the engineer to be used for this purpose, shall have a weight not less than that of the pile and the maximum drop shall not exceed eight (8) feet.

"*Hammers for Cast-in-Place Concrete Piles.* Shells driven without a mandrel shall be driven with a steam hammer which develops an energy per blow at each full stroke of the piston of not less than seven thousand (7,000) foot pounds. Shells driven with a core or mandrel shall be driven with a steam hammer which shall develop an energy per blow at each full stroke of the piston of not less than ten thousand (10,000) foot pounds.

"*Hammers for Steel Piles.* Steel piles, in general, shall be driven with steam hammers which shall develop an energy per blow at each full stroke of the piston of not less than seven thousand (7,000) foot pounds. Gravity hammers, when permitted by the Engineer for this purpose, shall have a weight equal to the weight of the pile, but in no case less than three thousand (3,000) pounds. . . .

"If loading tests are not required, the following formulas shall be used as a guide to determine the safe bearing values for piles driven in vertical position.

"For timber and steel piles, and shells driven without a mandrel for cast-in-place concrete piles:

$$P = \frac{2WH}{S + 10} \text{ for gravity hammers;}$$

$$P = \frac{2WH}{S + 0.1} \quad \text{for single acting steam hammers;}$$

$$P = \frac{2E}{S + 0.1} \quad \text{for double acting steam hammers.}$$

"For precast concrete piles, and shells for cast-in-place concrete piles driven with a mandrel:

$$P = \frac{2WH}{S + 0.1 \dfrac{w}{W}} \quad \text{for single acting steam hammers;}$$

$$P = \frac{2E}{S + 0.1 \dfrac{w}{W}} \quad \text{for double acting steam hammers.}$$

"For piles driven to a batter, the safe bearing value of the pile shall be taken as U times P, in which U is determined as follows:

$$U = \frac{.25(4 - m)}{1 + m^2} \quad \text{for gravity hammers;}$$

$$U = \frac{.1(10 - m)}{1 + m^2} \quad \text{for steam hammers.}$$

" P equals safe allowable bearing value of piles, in pounds, when driven vertically.

W equals weight of striking parts of hammer, in pounds.

w equals weight of pile, in pounds.

H equals height of fall, in feet.

E equals manufacturer's rated energy in foot pounds per blow at manufacturer's rated speed.

S equals average penetration, in inches per blow, for five (5) to ten (10) consecutive blows for gravity hammers, or ten (10) to twenty (20) consecutive blows for steam hammers.

m equals tangent of the angle of batter.

"The above formulas are applicable only when:

(*a*) The hammer has a free fall.

(*b*) The pile head is not broomed, crushed, or splintered.

(*c*) There is no appreciable bounce of the hammer after striking the pile.

(*d*) The penetration is at a uniform or uniformly decreasing rate.

(*e*) The fall of a gravity hammer is limited to fifteen (15) feet."

The safe bearing power of the piles shall not exceed their safe crushing strength.   In some cases it will be necessary to investigate the strength of the pile when it acts as a column.

The character of the soil penetrated; condition of driving; distribution, size and length of pile; and the computed load must all be given due consideration in determining the reliability of driven piles.   Special care is necessary where settlement is harmful.

138. Strength of Building Materials.   The following tables will give a rough idea of average unit stresses under average conditions of use.   They must be modified by judgment and according to the quality of the material and the particular use which the engineer has in mind.

TABLE 138

STRUCTURAL TIMBER—OCCASIONALLY WET
Safe Unit Working Stresses in Pounds per Square Inch

	TRANSVERSE BENDING STRESSES				HOR. SHEARING STRESS (PARALLEL TO GRAIN)		COMPRESSIVE STRESSES			
	Thickness 5 Inches and over		Thickness 4 Inches and under				Perpendicular to Grain	Parallel with Grain		
	Select	Common	Select	Common	Select	Common		Select	Common
Douglas Fir	1385	1040	1235	985	90	72	240	1065	800
Red Oak	1200	960	1070	910	125	100	375	900	720
Yellow Pine	....	1040	....	985	....	88	....	....	800
White Pine	....	800	640	710	600	85	68	150	750	600

TABLE 138a

STRENGTH OF METALS AND MASONRY IN POUNDS PER SQUARE INCH

	AVERAGE ULTIMATE STRENGTHS				SAFE WORKING STRESSES (PORTLAND CEMENT MORTAR)	
	Compression	Tension	Bending	Shear	Compression	Bearing
Structural Steel-Shapes, Plates, Bars	Same as tensile	60000	Same as tensile	¾ tensile	. . . .	. . . .
Cast Iron	80000	16000	30000	19000	. . . .	. . . .
Granite Masonry	. . . .	. . . .	. . . .	. . . .	420	600
Limestone Masonry	. . . .	. . . .	. . . .	. . . .	350	500

Concrete, P.C. (28 days)		Reinforced Concrete	
	Granite, trap rock	4500	Safe Working Stresses in Percent of Ultimate Compression
1 : 1 : 2	Furnace Slag	4300	Compression { Plain Concrete Piers, length 4 dia. — 22.5%
	Limestone and Sandstone, hard	4300	Reinforced Columns, length 12 dia. — 22.5%
	Limestone and Sandstone, soft	3500	Reinforced Beams — 40.0%
	Cinders	1500	Bearing — Surface twice the loaded area — 25.0%
1 : 2 : 4	Granite, trap rock	3800	Shear and Diag. Tension { Hor. Bars, no web reinforcement — 2.0%
	Furnace Slag	3500	Hor. Bars, vertical stirrups — 1.5%
	Limestone and Sandstone, hard	3500	Bent bars and vertical stirrups — 5.0%
	Limestone and Sandstone, soft	3000	Same, securely attached — 6.0%
	Cinders	1000	Drawn Wire — 2.0%
1 : 3 : 6	Granite, trap rock	2500	Bond Stress { Plain reinforcing Bars — 4.0%
	Furnace Slag	2200	Deformed Bars, best type — 5.0%
	Limestone and Sandstone, hard	2200	
	Limestone and Sandstone, soft	2000	
	Cinders	700	

Timber. The strength of structural timbers depends upon a number of factors: the species of wood and its age, the seasoning and resultant moisture content, and the influence of defects and variation in strength due to conditions of load and service. See Table 138, page 225.

The most recent studies of properties of timber have been made by the Forest Products Laboratory, U. S. Forest Service. The results of these studies have been embodied in the *Specifications for American Lumber Standards;* in the Specifications for Timber, 1927 Standards of the American Society for Testing Materials; in the *1937 Manual* of the American Railway Engineering Association; and in the *1926 Report of the Building Code Committee*, U. S. Bureau of Standards. These should be referred to in making a complete investigation of the strength of structural timber and other data pertaining to its uses.

Other Building Materials. The strength of building materials varies considerably, depending upon their constituent elements and quality of workmanship. The opposite table gives the average ultimate stress and safe working stress for the more commonly used building materials.

139. Concrete Data. Tables 139 and 139a, and Fig. 139 are given for emergency field reference and should be used only to refresh the memory, not as a complete basis for

TABLE 139

RECOMMENDED SLUMPS FOR CONCRETE*

TYPE OF CONSTRUCTION	SLUMP IN INCHES	
	Maximum	Minimum
Reinforced foundation walls and footings	5	2
Plain footings, caissons and substructure walls	4	1
Slabs, beams and reinforced walls.	6	3
Building columns.	6	3
Pavements	3	2
Heavy mass construction.	3	1

* Adapted from the 1940 Joint Committee Report on "Recommended Practice and Standard Specifications for Concrete and Reinforced Concrete." When high-frequency vibrators are used, the values given should be reduced about one-third.

TABLE 139a

Weight of Materials Required for Concrete

Max. Size of Coarse Agg., In.	Water, Gal. per Sack Cement	Using Rounded Coarse Aggregate									Using Angular Coarse Aggregate								
		Sand, per-cent of total	Per sack cement		Per cu. yd. of concrete					Yield, cu. ft. conc. per sack cement	Sand, per-cent of total	Per sack cement		Per cu. yd. of concrete					Yield, cu. ft. conc. per sack cement
			sand, lb.	gravel, lb.	water		cement, sacks	sand, lb.	gravel, lb.			sand, lb.	stone, lb.	water		cement, sacks	sand, lb.	stone, lb.	
					lb.	gal.								lb.	gal.				
With Medium Sand—Fineness Modulus 2.60–2.90																			
¾	5	43	180	235	310	37	7.4	1330	1740	3.65	48	175	190	335	40	8.0	1400	1520	3.38
1	5	38	165	270	300	36	7.2	1190	1945	3.75	43	165	220	325	39	7.8	1290	1715	3.46
1½	5	34	160	310	280	34	6.8	1090	2110	3.97	39	160	250	305	37	7.4	1185	1850	3.65
2	5	31	160	350	270	32	6.4	1025	2240	4.22	36	160	190	295	35	7.0	1120	2030	3.86
¾	5½	44	205	260	310	37	6.7	1370	1740	4.03	49	200	210	335	40	7.3	1460	1535	3.70
1	5½	39	190	300	300	36	6.5	1235	1950	4.15	44	190	240	325	39	7.1	1350	1705	3.80
1½	5½	35	180	340	280	34	6.2	1115	2115	4.36	40	185	280	305	37	6.7	1240	1875	4.03
2	5½	32	180	390	270	32	5.8	1045	2260	4.66	37	185	315	295	35	6.4	1185	2015	4.22
¾	6	45	230	280	310	37	6.2	1425	1735	4.36	50	230	230	335	40	6.7	1540	1540	4.03
1	6	40	215	320	300	36	6.0	1290	1920	4.50	45	215	260	325	39	6.5	1400	1690	4.15
1½	6	36	205	365	280	34	5.7	1170	2080	4.74	41	210	300	305	37	6.2	1300	1860	4.36
2	6	33	210	425	270	32	5.3	1110	2250	5.10	38	210	345	295	35	5.8	1220	2000	4.66
¾	6½	46	260	305	310	37	5.7	1480	1740	4.74	51	255	245	335	40	6.2	1580	1520	4.36
1	6½	41	240	350	300	36	5.5	1320	1925	4.91	46	240	280	325	39	6.0	1440	1680	4.50
1½	6½	37	235	400	280	34	5.2	1220	2080	5.19	42	235	325	305	37	5.7	1340	1850	4.74
2	6½	34	235	455	270	32	4.9	1150	2230	5.51	39	235	370	295	35	5.4	1270	2000	5.00
¾	7	47	285	325	310	37	5.3	1510	1725	5.10	52	285	265	335	40	5.7	1625	1510	4.74
1	7	42	270	370	300	36	5.1	1375	1890	5.30	47	265	300	325	39	5.6	1480	1680	4.82
1½	7	38	260	420	280	34	4.9	1275	2060	5.51	43	260	350	305	37	5.3	1380	1855	5.10
2	7	35	260	480	270	32	4.6	1195	2210	5.87	40	265	395	295	35	5.0	1325	1975	5.40
¾	7½	48	320	350	310	37	4.9	1570	1715	5.51	53	315	280	335	40	5.3	1670	1485	5.10
1	7½	43	295	390	300	36	4.8	1415	1875	5.63	48	295	320	325	39	5.2	1535	1665	5.19
1½	7½	39	290	455	280	34	4.5	1305	2050	6.00	44	295	370	305	37	4.9	1445	1810	5.51
2	7½	36	285	510	270	32	4.3	1225	2190	6.28	41	290	415	295	35	4.7	1360	1950	5.75
¾	8	49	350	365	310	37	4.6	1610	1680	5.87	54	345	290	335	40	5.0	1725	1450	5.40

proportioning concrete. They are taken from *Design and Control of Concrete Mixtures*, published every few years by the Portland Cement Association, where more complete data may be obtained. Table 139a is for dry aggregates and a three-inch slump.

All of the data given in this book are for the usual type of concrete and may not apply satisfactorily to air-entrained, high-early-strength, accelerated-set, water-tight, light-weight, or other special types of concrete.

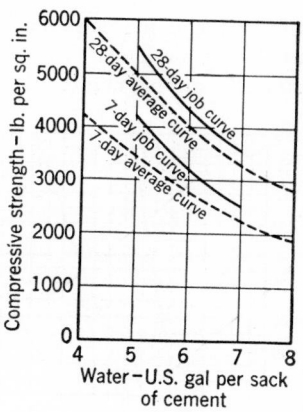

FIG. 139.

Table 139 is based on the *slump test* which should be made in accordance with the *Tentative Method of Test for Consistency of Portland Cement Concrete* of the American Society for Testing Materials.

In the absence of field tests, Fig. 139 may be used for design where the water-cement ratio is carefully controlled by accurate measurement of quantities of water, cement, and aggregate with proper correction for water carried by the aggregate. The job curve is a representative curve obtained from tests of the materials to be used on a specific project.

140. Waterway Size for Culverts or Bridges.

In cases of large and/or more important structures, the size of opening must be determined by careful investigation of the size of existing structures, from reliable information regarding high water elevations, and from hydrological studies. Where damage and inconvenience due to high water is slight, it is usually sufficient to provide for the ordinary, rather than the extraordinary, flood.

Empirical formulas are helpful in checking and estimating the size of waterway required, but should not be depended upon if the more direct information mentioned above is available, or if elaborate studies of maximum rainfall and run-off can be made. The empirical formula most com-

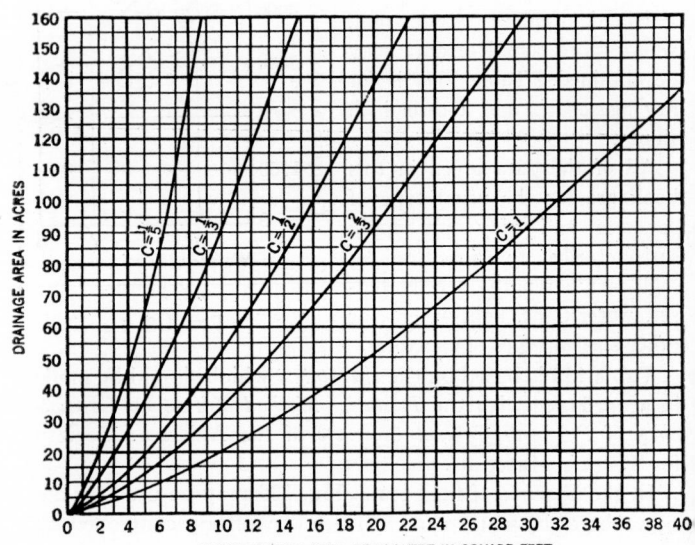

FIG. 140.   Area of Waterway = $C \sqrt[4]{(\text{Acres of drainage})^3}$.   The factor C depends upon the contour and character of the land drained.

$C = 1$ for steep and rocky ground with abrupt slopes,
$C = 2/3$ for rough hilly country of moderate slopes,
$C = 1/2$ for uneven valleys, wide as compared to length,
$C = 1/3$ for rolling agricultural country where the length of valley is
            three or four times the width,
$C = 1/5$ for level districts not affected by accumulated snow or severe
            floods.

For still milder conditions decrease C.   Increase C for steep side slopes, or where the upper part of the valley has greater fall than the channel through the culvert.

monly used is that of *Talbot*, diagrammed in Fig. 140.   It was developed for the Mississippi Valley, and should not be used in other sections of the country where conditions of rainfall and run-off are different.

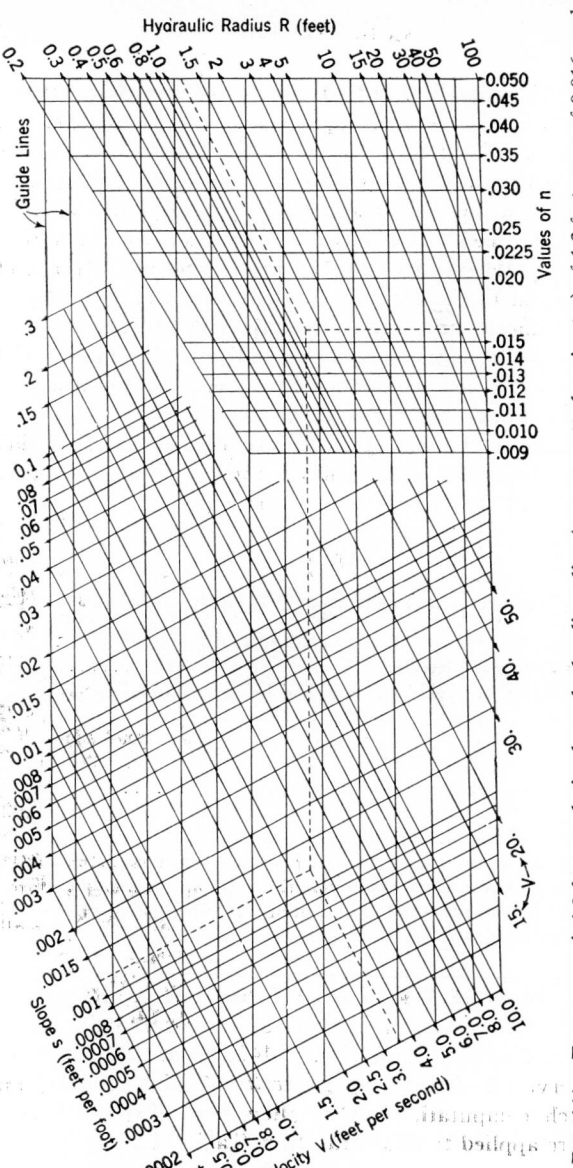

FIG. 141. EXAMPLE. A 4.8-foot steel pipe has a hydraulic radius (area ÷ wetted perimeter) of 1.2 feet, an n of 0.016, and a slope of 0.0012. By following the dotted lines downward the velocity is found to be 3.5 feet per second. (Reprinted by permission from Creager and Justin, *Hydro-Electric Handbook*, John Wiley and Sons, Inc., publishers.)

231

141. Flow of Water in Pipes and Open Channels.
The data in this section apply to pipes flowing either full
or partly full, and to open channels.   Figure 141 may be
used to estimate flow under all ordinary conditions with an
accuracy which is comparable to the accuracy with which n
may be assumed.   It is based on the Manning and Chezy
formulas as diagrammed by Mr. Fred C. Scobey, Bureau of
Agricultural Engineering, U. S. Department of Agriculture.

It is difficult, and frequently impossible, to estimate the
coefficient of roughness, n (Table 141), within 10 percent of
its true value and, consequently, V will vary inversely in
the same proportion from its true value.

In practice, values of n are usually somewhat larger
than in Table 141 since the channels or pipes are rarely
straight and the flow is usually disturbed.

TABLE 141

Values of n for Fairly Straight Channels

Planed timber, glazed or enameled surfaces, smooth clean
   cement, in perfect order............................. 0.010
Unplaned timber, newly and well laid brickwork, moderately
   clean iron pipe, and smoothest concrete.............. 0.012
Smooth stonework, iron, ordinary brickwork, and good con-
   crete and vitrified clay pipe........................ 0.013
Smooth fine gravel or tuberculated iron.................. 0.020
Corrugated metal....................................... 0.021
Earth in ordinary condition............................ 0.025
Earth in rather poor condition with stones or weeds...... 0.030
Earth in poor condition about one-third full of vegetation.. 0.035
Channels in exceptionally bad condition, two-thirds full of
   vegetation, up to.................................... 0.050

142. Flow of Water over Weirs.   It is often necessary roughly to estimate the flow of water over weirs, dams,
levees, and so on.   Tables 142 to 142c, from U. S. Reclamation Service *Hydraulic and Excavation Tables*, provide data
for such computation.   Multipliers from Tables 142a to
142c are applied to quantities from Table 142.

TABLE 142

DISCHARGE PER FOOT OF LENGTH OVER SHARP-CRESTED VERTICAL
WEIRS WITHOUT END CONTRACTIONS *

[Computed from the formula

$$Q = \left(0.405 + \frac{.00984}{h} \right) \left(1 + 0.55 \frac{h^2}{(p+h)^2} \right) Lh\sqrt{2gh}$$

(h = observed head, in feet; p = height of weir, in feet; L = length
of crest, in feet; Q = discharge in second-feet).]

p	2	4	6	8	10	20	30
h							
0.1	0.13	0.13	0.13	0.13	0.13	0.13	0.13
0.2	.33	.33	.33	.33	.33	.33	.33
0.4	.88	.88	.87	.87	.87	.87	.87
0.6	1.62	1.59	1.58	1.58	1.57	1.57	1.57
0.8	2.50	2.43	2.41	2.41	2.40	2.40	2.40
1.0	3.53	3.40	3.36	3.35	3.34	3.33	3.33
1.2	4.69	4.48	4.42	4.40	4.38	4.36	4.36
1.4	5.99	5.68	5.58	5.55	5.52	5.49	5.48
1.6	7.40	6.97	6.84	6.78	6.75	6.69	6.68
1.8	8.93	8.37	8.18	8.09	8.05	7.98	7.96
2.0	10.58	9.87	9.62	9.51	9.44	9.34	9.32
2.2	12.33	11.46	11.14	10.99	10.91	10.78	10.75
2.4	14.20	13.15	12.75	12.56	12.45	12.28	12.24
2.6	16.17	14.92	14.44	14.20	14.07	13.85	13.80
2.8	18.23	16.79	16.21	15.92	15.76	15.48	15.42
3.0	20.38	18.74	18.06	17.71	17.52	17.18	17.10
3.2	22.64	20.77	19.98	19.58	19.34	18.93	18.83
3.4	24.98	22.89	21.99	21.52	21.24	20.75	20.63
3.6	27.42	25.09	24.06	23.52	23.20	22.62	22.48
3.8	29.94	27.38	26.22	25.60	25.23	24.56	24.39

* This table should not be used where the weir is submerged, nor
unless the overfalling sheet is aerated on the downstream face of the
weir. If a vacuum forms under the falling sheet, the discharge may be
5 per cent greater than given in this table. This table is not accurate
for values of h greater than one-third L.

TABLE 142 (*Continued*)

DISCHARGE PER FOOT OF LENGTH OVER SHARP-CRESTED VERTICAL
WEIRS WITHOUT END CONTRACTIONS

p	2	4	6	8	10	20	30
h							
4.0	32.54	29.74	28.45	27.74	27.32	26.55	26.35
4.2	35.22	32.18	30.75	29.96	29.48	28.59	28.35
4.4	37.99	34.70	33.12	32.24	31.70	30.68	30.42
4.6	40.83	37.29	35.56	34.58	33.98	32.82	32.53
4.8	43.75	39.96	38.07	37.00	36.32	35.04	34.70
5.0	46.73	42.69	40.65	39.48	38.74	37.21	36.91
5.2	49.79	45.50	43.29	42.01	41.20	39.61	39.17
5.4	52.94	48.38	46.00	44.60	43.71	41.96	41.47
5.6	56.15	51.34	48.79	47.27	46.31	44.38	43.83
5.8	59.42	54.34	51.62	49.99	48.94	46.83	46.22
6.0	62.77	57.43	54.53	52.78	51.64	49.34	48.67
6.2	66.18	60.58	57.50	55.63	54.40	51.90	51.16
6.4	69.65	63.79	60.53	58.53	57.22	54.50	53.70
6.6	73.19	67.07	63.63	61.50	60.09	57.16	56.27
6.8	76.80	70.42	66.78	64.53	63.02	59.96	58.90
7.0	80.46	73.82	70.00	67.60	66.00	62.61	61.56
7.2	84.18	77.29	73.28	70.74	69.04	65.40	64.27
7.4	87.97	80.81	76.61	73.94	72.14	68.24	67.02
7.6	91.82	84.40	80.01	77.19	75.28	71.13	69.81
7.8	95.72	88.05	83.46	80.50	78.48	74.06	72.65
8.0	99.68	91.75	86.97	83.87	81.74	77.04	75.53
8.2	103.70	95.51	90.54	87.29	85.25	80.06	78.44
8.4	107.78	99.34	94.16	90.76	88.41	83.13	81.40
8.6	111.91	103.21	97.84	94.29	91.82	86.25	84.41
8.8	116.09	107.14	101.57	97.87	95.28	89.40	87.44
9.0	120.33	111.13	105.36	101.50	98.80	92.61	90.52
9.2	124.62	115.18	109.21	105.19	102.37	95.86	93.65
9.4	128.97	119.27	113.10	108.93	105.99	99.14	96.80
9.6	133.36	123.42	117.05	112.72	109.65	102.48	100.00
9.8	137.82	127.63	121.05	116.57	113.37	105.85	103.25
10.0	142.31	131.87	125.10	120.46	117.14	109.27	106.52

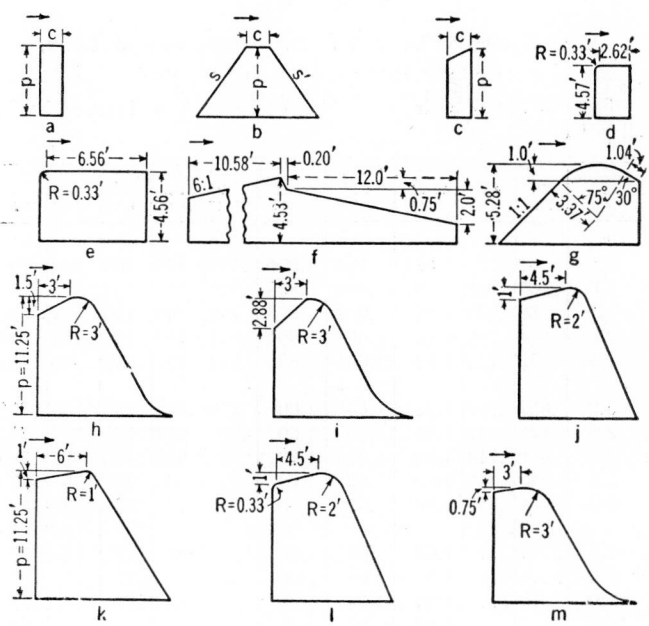

Fig. 142. Types of Weirs.

TABLE 142a

MULTIPLIERS OF DISCHARGE OVER RECTANGULAR WEIR, BROAD-CRESTED (TYPE *a*, FIG. 142)

[p = height of weir; c = width of crest; h = observed head; all in feet.]

p c	4.6 2.6	4.6 6.6	11.25 .48	11.25 .93	11.25 1.65	11.25 3.17	11.25 5.88	11.25 8.98	11.25 12.24	11.25 16.36
h										
0.5	....	....	.821	.792	.806	.792	.799	.801	.786	.790
1.0	.765	.708	.997	.899	.808	.795	.791	.794	.815	.790
1.5	.789	.709	1.00	.982	.878	.796	.796	.793	.814	.792
2.0	.814	.710	1.00	1.00	.906	.815	.797	.792	.797	.793
2.5	.835	.711	1.00	1.00	.985	.844	.797	.790	.796	.793
3.0	.857	.711	1.00	1.00	1.00	.870	.797	.788	.794	.791
3.5	.878	.712	1.00	1.00	1.00	.90	.812	.787	.794	.791
4.0	.899	.714	1.00	1.00	1.00	.93	.834	.786	.792	.789
5.0	.940	.716	1.00	1.00	1.00	.97	(*a*)	.78	.79	.78
6.0	.986	.718	1.00	1.00	1.00	.98	(*a*)	.78	.78	.78
7.0	....	....	1.00	1.00	1.00	(*a*)	(*a*)	.77	.78	.77
8.0	....	....	1.00	1.00	1.00	(*a*)	(*a*)	.77	.77	.77
9.0	....	....	1.00	1.00	1.00	(*a*)	(*a*)	.77	.77	.77
10.0	....	....	1.00	1.00	1.00	(*a*)	(*a*)	.77	.77	.77

a Value doubtful.

TABLE 142b

MULTIPLIERS OF DISCHARGE FOR TRAPEZOIDAL WEIRS
[p = height of weir, in feet; c = width of crest, in feet; s = upstream slope; s' = downstream slope; h = observed head, in feet.]

	TYPE b, FIG. 142							TYPE c, FIG. 142	
p c s s'	4.9 .33 2 : 1 0	4.9 .66 2 : 1 0	4.9 .66 3 : 1 0	4.9 .66 4 : 1 0	4.9 .66 5 : 1 0	4.9 .33 2 : 1 5 : 1	4.9 .66 2 : 1 2 : 1	4.65 7.00 4.67 : 1	11.25 6.00 6 : 1 ....
h									
1.0	1.137	1.048	1.066	1.039	1.009	1.095	1.071	1.042	1.060
1.5	1.131	1.068	1.066	1.039	1.009	1.071	1.066	1.033	1.069
2.0	1.120	1.080	1.061	1.033	1.005	1.044	1.053	1.024	1.054
2.5	1.106	1.085	1.052	1.026	.997	1.024	1.047	1.012	1.012
3.0	1.094	1.088	1.047	1.020	.991	1.009	1.047	.995	.985
3.5	1.085	1.087	1.043	1.017	.988	1.003	1.050	.983	.979
4.0	1.072	1.084	1.038	1.012	.984	1.014	1.052	.977	.976
4.5	1.064	1.081	1.035	1.009	.980	1.023	1.055	.974	.973
5.0	....	....	....	....	....	....	....	.97	.97
6.0	....	....	....	....	....	....	....	.97	.96
7.0	....	....	....	....	....	....	....	.97	.96
8.0	....	....	....	....	....	....	....	.96	.95
9.0	....	....	....	....	....	....	....	.96	.95
10.0	....	....	....	....	....	....	....	.96	.95

TABLE 142c

MULTIPLIERS OF DISCHARGE FOR COMPOUND WEIRS

[p = height of weir, in feet; h = observed head, in feet.]

p	4.57	4.56	4.53	5.28	11.25	11.25	11.25	11.25	11.25	11.25
Type, Fig. 142	d	e	f	g	h	i	j	k	l	m
h										
0.5	.....	.....	.....	.....	.941	.924	.933	.962	.971	.947
1.0	.842	.836	.929	.976	1.039	1.033	.988	1.045	1.033	1.000
1.5	.866	.834	.950	.979	1.087	1.093	1.018	1.066	1.042	1.036
2.0	.888	.831	.953	.988	1.109	1.133	1.033	1.063	1.035	1.063
2.5	.906	.826	.947	1.000	1.118	1.153	1.045	1.020	1.033	1.085
3.0	.927	.822	.942	1.016	1.120	1.163	1.054	.997	1.045	1.096
3.5	.945	.817	.936	1.032	1.127	1.169	1.060	.994	1.054	1.108
4.0	.965	.812	.931	1.044	1.123	1.165	1.060	.991	1.057	1.110
5.0	1.00	.80	.92	1.05	1.11	1.16	1.05	.98	1.05	1.10
6.0	.....	.....	.....	.....	1.11	1.15	1.04	.98	1.04	1.10
7.0	.....	.....	.....	.....	1.10	1.14	1.04	.97	1.04	1.09
8.0	.....	.....	.....	.....	1.10	1.14	1.04	.97	1.03	1.09
9.0	.....	.....	.....	.....	1.09	1.14	1.03	.97	1.03	1.08
10.0	.....	.....	.....	.....	1.09	1.13	1.03	.97	1.03	1.08

143. Conversion Factors.   Table 143 gives the conversion factors for the more useful units of measurement.

TABLE 143
CONVERSION FACTORS

MULTIPLY	BY	TO OBTAIN
Acres	43560	Square feet
Acres	10	Square chains
Acre-feet	43560	Cubic feet
" "	325851	Gallons
Atmospheric pressure	29.92	Inches of mercury
" "	33.90	Feet of water
" "	14.70	Lbs./sq. in.
Barrels—oil	42	Gallons—oil
" —cement	376	Pounds—cement
Bags or sacks—cement	94	Pounds— "
Board-feet	144 sq. in. $\times$ 1 in.	Cubic inches
British Thermal Units	777.5	Foot-lbs.
	2.928×10^{-4}	Kilowatt-hrs.
Centimeters	.3937	Inches
Cubic feet	1728	Cubic inches
" "	7.48052	Gallons
Cubic feet of water	62.4	Pounds
Cubic feet/second	.646317	Million gals./day
" " "	448.831	Gallons/min.
" " "	1.983	Acre feet/24 hours
Fathoms	6	Feet
Feet/second	.6818	Miles/hr.
Foot-pounds	1.286×10^{-3}	B. T. U.
	3.766×10^{-7}	Kilowatt-hrs.
Foot-pounds/min.	2.260×10^{-5}	Kilowatts
Gallons	.1337	Cubic feet
Gallons, Imperial	1.20095	U. S. gallons
" U. S.	.83267	Imperial gallons
Gallons water	8.35	Pounds of water
Hectares	2.471	Acres
Horse-power	33000	Foot-lbs./min.
" "	550	Foot-lbs./second
" "	.7457	Kilowatts
Inches	2.540	Centimeters
Kilograms	2.20462	Pounds
Kilometers	.6214	Miles
Links	7.92	Inches
Liters	1.0567	Quarts
$\dfrac{\text{Width (in.)} \times \text{Thickness (in.)}}{12}$	Length (ft.)	Board feet
Meters	1.094	Yards
Miles	5280	Feet
Miles	80	Chains
Miles/hr.	1.467	Feet/sec.
Miles/hr.	.8684	Knots
Miner's inches	1.5	Cubic feet/min.
Parts/million	.0584	Grains/U. S. gallon
Rod	16.5	Feet
Square miles	640	Acres
Temp. (° F.) + 460	1	Abs. temp. (° F.)
" " − 32	5/9	Temp. (° C.)
Tons (short)	2000	Pounds

144. Weights of Materials. Table 144 gives the specific gravity and weights of the more common building materials.

TABLE 144

SPECIFIC GRAVITIES AND WEIGHTS

SUBSTANCE	SPECIFIC GRAVITY	WEIGHT LBS. PER CU. FT.
Aluminum	2.55–2.75	165
Iron, cast, pig	7.2	450
Lead	11.28–11.35	706
Steel	7.8–7.9	490
Douglas Fir	0.54	34
Oak, red	0.71	44
Pine, white, yellow	0.43–0.45	27–28
Limestone, marble	. . . . . .	95
Cement, Portland, loose	. . . . . .	90
Clay, damp, plastic	. . . . . .	110
Earth, moist, loose	. . . . . .	78
" mud, flowing	. . . . . .	108
Sand, gravel, wet	. . . . . .	118–120
Concrete		
Cement, stone, sand	2.2–2.4	144
" slag, etc.	1.9–2.3	130
" cinder, etc.	1.5–1.7	100

145. Cost of Various Constructions. Construction and operating costs of various types of industrial operations are obtained from the experience and records of each industry. Construction and contracting companies make the best construction estimates in connection with their bids. Where such experience and records are not available, it is customary

(1) to estimate the total cost by comparing the proposed construction with other similar construction whose total cost is known, or

(2) to estimate the cost per unit, as for example per mile for railway or highway, or per cubic foot of space content for a building, or

(3) to prepare a bill of material for the project and estimate the cost per unit of each kind of material, in place in the construction. This is the most common form of an "engineer's estimate." The costs of the material, preferably delivered on the ground, may be obtained from manufacturing and supply companies. The labor and equipment costs must come from previous experience, largely from costs or from contract prices from similar completed work.

The preparation of estimates, both of first costs and of operating costs, is one of the most important responsibilities of professional engineers and executives. Poor estimates are often disastrous, particularly to contractors. Estimating is especially difficult and dangerous in times of increasing prices, wages, and shortages.

The Engineering News-Record Construction and Building Cost Index, Fig. 145, enables one to bring old estimates up to date. However, this is an overall Index in which the proportions of component items vary greatly. The Index shows 650% and 450% overall cost increases from 1913 to 1955. During this period some construction increased over 600%, common brick laid up in wall increased nearly 600%, common board sheathing nearly 500%, sheet metal roofing in place 300%, concrete wall in place 200%, and area excavation 40%. In the last two items, improved construction methods and equipment have largely offset tremendous increases in hourly labor rates.

It is therefore necessary in using this overall Index to alter the percentage taken from Fig. 145 according to the proportions of the constituents in the work involved. All new estimates should show the Index figure of that date. When referring to old estimates or costs, it is helpful if the Index figure for the old date has been shown, as on Figs. 146, 147, and 156.

Types 2 and 3 of the estimates mentioned previously in this section follow, and a contractor's bid is given toward the end of the following chapter.

146. Estimates by Cost per Complete Unit. The use of cost-per-mile estimates is illustrated in Fig. 146 which gives

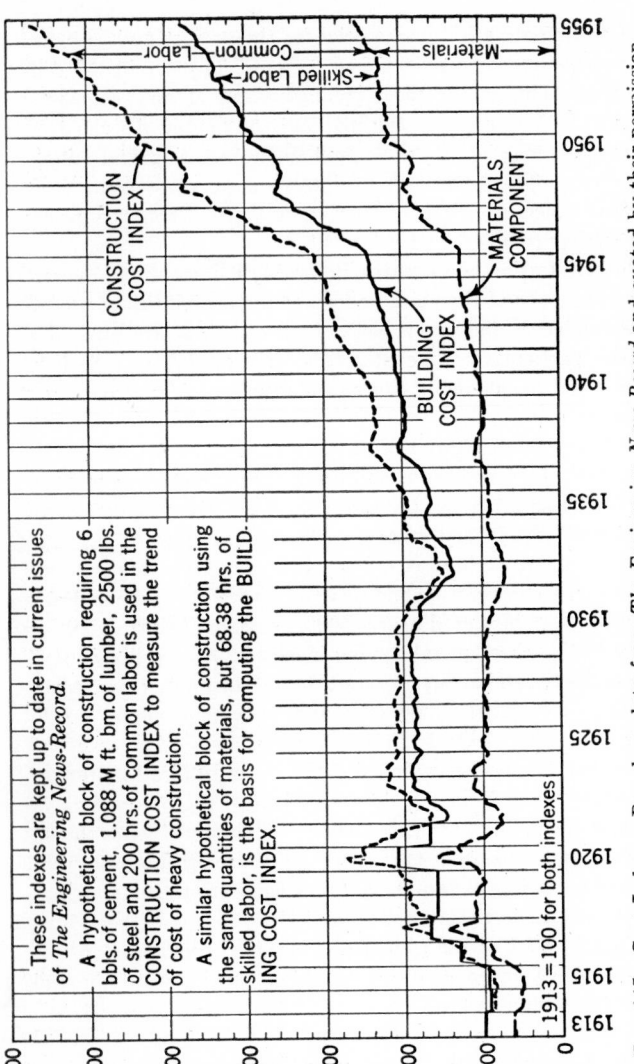

These indexes are kept up to date in current issues of *The Engineering News-Record*.

A hypothetical block of construction requiring 6 bbls. of cement, 1.088 M ft. bm. of lumber, 2500 lbs. of steel and 200 hrs. of common labor is used in the CONSTRUCTION COST INDEX to measure the trend of cost of heavy construction.

A similar hypothetical block of construction using the same quantities of materials, but 68.38 hrs. of skilled labor, is the basis for computing the BUILDING COST INDEX.

CONSTRUCTION COST INDEX

BUILDING COST INDEX

MATERIALS COMPONENT

Materials

Skilled Labor

Common Labor

1913 = 100 for both indexes

Fig. 145. Cost Indexes. Based on data from *The Engineering News-Record* and quoted by their permission. Copyright 1955 by McGraw-Hill Publishing Co., Inc.

the cost comparison accompanying a reconnaissance survey and report made to determine the cheapest method of transporting coal from a mine to either of two nearby railroads, the Wabash and the M.K.&T.   Four different means of transportation are considered and an alternative railroad spur was included for the M.K.&T.   The tabulation, estimating the costs per ton delivered to the railroad, results in a figure for each of the nine possible means and routes investigated.

Obviously such estimates are not precise, perhaps more than 10% from the actual final costs, but they are easily and quickly made in the early stages of planning for a project.   The lengths for each route may be scaled from a U.S.G.S. map or an aerial map, or secured from other sources.   The cost figures must come from previous experience, from specialists, or from manufacturers.

A similiar study could be made for transporting aggregates for mass concrete from their source to a construction job, or for other reconnaissance situations.

147. Estimates Made from Quantity Surveys.

Following the reconnaissance estimate of the preceding section, a preliminary ground or photogrammetric survey would provide a map like Fig. 16c on page 33, but much longer, on a scale of perhaps $1'' = 200'$.   Assuming that it has been decided to build a spur track from the mine to the M.K.&T. railroad, a paper location would be made on the map and a paper profile prepared. The required quantities for the construction are now taken from the map and profile and the "engineer's estimate" of Fig. 147 is prepared.   For the usual types of work, such an estimate should be within 10% of the actual final cost.

The more precise contractor's bid is given in Chapter XVII

It is difficult to secure cost and construction data in print.   A quite complete subject index of costs involved in chemical engineering economics occurs in *Chemical Engineering*, October 1954, pages 185 to 193.   This sort of data should be, but is not, generally available for other engineering costs.   A few of the better and more available cost sources are:

| ITEM | RAILROAD SPUR | | | HIGHWAY | | TRAMWAY | | BELTWAY | |
	Wabash	M.K.&T. Alternate #1	Alternate #2	Wabash	M.K.&T.	Wabash	M.K.&T.	Wabash	M.K.&T.
LENGTH									
Length in Miles	1.7	1.4	1.0	1.7	1.0	1.4	0.9	1.4	0.9
Cost per Mile	$70,000	$80,000	$100,000	$40,000	$60,000	$200,000	$200,000	$300,000	$300,000
FIRST COST									
Total Length Cost	119,000	112,000	100,000	68,000	60,000	280,000	180,000	420,000	270,000
Loading Facilities	0	0	0	28,000	28,000	10,000	10,000	10,000	10,000
Equipment	0	0	0	0	0	0	0	0	0
Total Construction Cost	119,000	112,000	100,000	96,000	88,000	290,000	190,000	430,000	280,000
Salvage Value	11,900	11,200	10,000	9,600	8,800	145,000	95,000	215,000	140,000
Total Net Cost	107,100	100,800	90,000	86,400	79,200	145,000	95,000	215,000	140,000

ANNUAL COST

Operation	12,000	12,000	12,000	61,200	36,000	15,000	15,000	15,000	15,000
Interest	3,270	3,080	2,750	2,640	2,420	10,875	7,375	16,725	10,500
Depreciation	10,710	10,080	9,000	8,640	7,920	14,500	9,500	21,500	14,000
Contingencies, 10% of above 3 items	2,598	2,516	2,375	7,248	4,634	4,038	3,188	5,323	3,950
Total Annual Cost	28,578	27,676	26,125	79,728	50,974	44,413	35,063	58,548	43,450

COST PER TON

Cost per Ton	$ 0.16	$ 0.15	$ 0.15	$ 0.44	$ 0.28	$ 0.25	$ 0.19	$ 0.33	$ 0.24

General Information: Mine life is 10 years and output is 600 tons daily or 180,000 tons annually.

On the principle of mass production, increasing the output will reduce costs per ton and decreasing output will increase costs per ton.

Straight line depreciation is 10% per annum on Total Net Cost. Interest per year on unpaid balance = $\left(\dfrac{\text{First Cost} + \text{Salvage}}{2}\right)$ (5%).

ENR Construction Cost Index = 600 for 1955.

Fig. 146. Reconnaissance Cost Comparison, Based on Costs per Mile.

245

ESTIMATE FOR CONSTRUCTION OF RAILROAD TRACK TO MINE

Item	Description	Amount	Unit Cost	Cost
Right of Way	Acres	16.07	$ 400.00	$ 6,428
Clearing	Acres	16.07	50.00	804
Grading	Cu. Yd., Earth	14,400	0.60	8,640
Grading	Cu. Yd., Rock	6,400	2.50	16,000
Overhaul	Sta. Cu. Yd.	47,800	0.07	3,346
Pipes, Corrugated	Lin. Ft, 18"	48	8.00	384
Culverts, Concrete	Lin. Ft, 4' x 8'	99	40.00	3,960
Timber, Trestle	Lin. Ft, Framed	64	40.00	2,560
Ties	1st Class, Untreated	5,500	2.50	13,750
Rail, 2nd hand, 70 lb. per yd.	Tons	163.3	80.00	13,064
Bolts, Spikes and Accessories	Track Feet	7,000	0.50	3,500
Ballast (in place), Clinkers	Cu. Yd.	3,000	2.00	6,000
Turnouts, Complete, 2nd hand		1	1,500.00	1,500
Derails, Complete		2	100.00	200
Cattle Guards	Metal	4	100.00	400
Road Crossing	Blacktop	1	200.00	200
Road Crossing Signs		2	150.00	300
Sewer Re-alignment	Lin. Ft	250	10.00	2,500
Labor Laying Track	Lin. Ft. of Track	7,000	.40	2,800

Total Field Cost	$ 86,336
Contingencies, 10% ±	8,832
Eng'r'g. & Sup'v'n., 10% ±	8,832

Other labor, freight, and handling are included in unit costs.

Grand Total Cost	$104,000

ENR Construction Cost Index = 600 for 1955.

Seelye, E. E. *Volume II, Specifications and Costs*, Wiley, 1951.
The Engineering News-Record—Cost data in the first issue every month
The Engineering News-Record, *The Annual Compilation of Construction Costs*.

See also those books listed at the ends of Chapters XVI and XVII.

CHAPTER XVI

THE CONSTRUCTION ENGINEER AND
PROFESSIONAL MANAGEMENT *

148. Introduction. Construction, replacement, and maintenance for industry and government in the United States has expanded steadily over the past several years to a $57 billion annual volume in 1955, and it promises to continue growing. This program comprises 15 percent of our national production, employs nearly 10 million workers, has become our largest industry, and offers unexcelled opportunities to civil engineers.

Most of our other industries that are necessary for prosperity and defense, including the scientific engineering fields, are in immediate danger of being held back and forced into idle waiting for places in which to work and to house their personnel, mainly because of the lack of competent construction engineers and managers.

The surveying and detailed computations of routes are of a sub-professional nature, they should be performed by young engineers-in-training or by experienced technicians without college training, and their principles should be learned in college so that the graduate may perform or supervise them.

When these techniques are used in the overall design and economic study of a complete project, the work becomes professional engineering and leads into actual construction, contracting, and professional management as explained in this, and the next, chapters. The contracting and management fields are the more remunerative for the civil engineer and satisfy a desire for accomplishment, that "constructive instinct" which often eludes the engineer who designs or researches only.

149. The Construction Engineer. The actual con-

* Harry Rubey, *Construction and Professional Management, Journal of Engineering Education,* November 1955.

struction work of the preceding chapter is usually accomplished under the direction of the construction engineer by contractors and by company forces.

The construction engineer represents the owner and is expected to secure good construction while enforcing contract provisions fairly. He also acts as liaison between the science of engineering (represented by the designing engineer) and the art of construction management (represented by the contractor or company construction superintendent). Providing he demonstrates the necessary interest and ability, his work gives him opportunity to become a professional manager for his industry or for a contractor, or to organize his own contracting company.

In a large organization, the construction engineer has responsibility for the construction of new facilities, for extensive replacement and reconstruction, and sometimes for maintenance and repairs. Often these are scattered over a wide area and over many separate plants or installations.

He assumes complete responsibility for seeing that construction work done by contractors or by company forces meets the standards of his organization and stays within budget limits. Even slight departures from these requirements can seldom be tolerated since they are like the camel pushing his nose under the tent; then soon his head and body. Enforcement of construction standards is easier when operated as a "taut ship," that is, by rather strict requirement of "good and workmanlike results." In fact no other attitude is practicable nor is it permanently helpful to contractors, construction forces, construction engineers, professional engineers, or the public.

His work includes cooperation with the engineering department on designing the project, organizing company forces for their part of the work, advertising and securing bids, letting contracts for the project, supervising execution of contracts by contractors or of work by company forces, making progress reports and monthly and final estimates, accepting the completed work for the owner, monumenting construction and perfecting construction records, operating for a brief period, and repeating all this on current and subsequent projects.

It also includes his participation in research by, and cooperation with, engineering designers, contractors, and others; all with a view to better, quicker, and cheaper construction.   Research will include improved design, materials, applications, procedures, transportation, mass production, automation, and operational analysis.

150. Organization of the Construction Management Department.   The construction engineer, or civil engineer with some similar title, heads the construction management division or department.   From here down the organization varies. With the smallest construction program there may be only one civil engineer.

In a large organization, project engineers recommend the outside contractors for construction work and then arrange for equipment purchases, release drawings to the construction field offices, maintain cost controls, and check construction schedules on all projects.

Resident engineers represent the company and follow construction progress at project sites.

Field project engineers make construction surveys, gather data, and have other field duties.

For manufacturing companies, resident industrial engineers in the field represent the company in planning operations and controlling costs.

The young engineer in construction management is often assigned initially as an assistant to a project manager or, for manufacturing companies, as a member of a construction-industrial group.   Later field assignments provide him with the training and experience to move eventually into either of those roles.

As the new man demonstrates his ability to handle both his engineering work and large groups of technically trained men, he is assigned full responsibility for construction projects.   It will be noted that these are mainly management responsibilities with only limited technical or sub-professional duties.

As indicated in the following section the foregoing experience and contacts lead naturally into the upper levels of corporate professional management, providing ambition and native ability are present.

151. Professional Management.   Because the construction engineer must be "future minded" and is planning and building for future operations, and because top management must be "future minded" rather than absorbed in the details of today's operating problems, the construction engineer rather than the operating engineer often is better fitted for promotion to top management.   This has happened in the past and should occur even more frequently in the future.

Young engineers should realize that already the 1950 census classifies half of professional civil engineers in construction, that management is now a profession requiring an educated professional viewpoint which is easily included in engineering curricula, that getting along with people is essential for both construction and management, and that even the technical engineer must know and conform to the aims and requirements of construction and management.   In line with modern trends and developments such terms as *engineer-contractor, engineered construction, construction management,* and *professional management* are used in this, and the next, chapters.   They should be publicized in order to enhance the engineer's prestige.

Construction (including suppliers of materials, equipment, bonds, and the like) provides many management openings.   In addition, there are excellent positions for civil engineers in the professional management of government such as in city managership and in highways; and in other industry besides construction such as the railway, aircraft, oil, steel, chemical, and public utility fields.   Fortunately, the civil engineer who is qualified in construction management can either remain in construction profitably or change over to upper level industrial management.

Because of rapid expansion, obsolescence, new products, bombing hazards, decentralization, and the like, the construction and betterment program today is often as important to an organization as its operations.   Thus former engineer-managers of construction now are becoming even more necessary and valuable as top professional managers for large industry than in the past, and this has always been the civil engineer's main approach to top management.

Many graduates will find satisfying careers intermediately between management and technology as staff officers, consulting engineers, marketing specialists, management and financial advisers, managers for associations, and the like where experience in construction and professional management is most valuable.

152. The Rise and Fall of Engineers as Managers.

Around the turn of the century, managers were strong entrepreneurs and lucky gamblers, rarely engineers, who established their own businesses and often lost them. The larger corporations were often in receiverships. Then followed a period of larger business managed mainly by lawyers, marketing men, financiers, and engineers who seldom had sought management positions; more often they were impressed into management. Failures still predominated.

Since the great depression the need has become recognized for professional managers, most frequently engineers; not those rugged individualists of the early period nor the capable specialists of the middle period, but men trained from the beginning to become conservative professional managers (almost trustees) for unbelievably large and stable organizations where even the thought of failure cannot be tolerated. They are skilled in government, corporate controls, tax laws, mergers, finance, public relations, and human relations with their eye on management at intermediate and broad policy levels, above management technicalities such as are taught in industrial engineering. This group must start early, for example in college, to direct their attention, at least in part, toward professional management rather than exclusively toward technical specialization.

Civil engineers are more broadly educated, have broader contacts with the public, and can better be encouraged in this direction while in college than can other kinds of engineers who are narrowed under increased specialization in science, technology, and gadgets. From the founding of our country under surveyor and civil engineer George Washington, managers have been men of judgment and balance who dealt with people, not gadgets. Even before this specialization, government and the larger corporations favored the broader civil engineers as managers, for example, half of the presidents of the larger railroads were civil engineers. And civil engineer executives predominated in the steel, oil, and other large and growing industries. Consulting engineer-management firms frequently were staffed with a major proportion of civil engineers.

The majority of the better positions held by civil engineers are primarily managerial.

In November 1952, an elaborate study in *Fortune* magazine showed nearly 45 percent of America's top industrial management to have engineering backgrounds. But it also showed that this percentage was greatly decreased (to 28 percent) for those under 50 years of age, in other words, that the proportion of engineers in top management has passed the peak and that younger engineers already were losing out to non-engineers who, although not so capable, have more aggressively prepared and sold themselves for management. New examples of engineers missing their management opportunities occur constantly.

There are those who will say that good engineers will become managers, but nowadays the odds are against them and the possibility in this direction is rapidly diminishing. Civil engineers in the past were drafted into management, sometimes unwillingly, and they seldom prepared for or sought it. But conditions have changed and, if educators do not point out this management opportunity and give introductory study leading to management, engineering graduates will largely remain technicians or modestly paid professional engineers.

Fortunately, many civil engineers now are needed to manage construction and so can rise again through construction to professional management. The pictures following this chapter show a dozen types of routes which are constructed, and often professionally managed, by civil engineers.

This chapter might be summarized as describing the activities of the construction engineer in supervising construction. It also points out that these duties may lead him into professional management.   His third outlet as an engineer-contractor, either employee or employer, is described in the following chapter.

Many corporations and governmental agencies publish specifications and manuals covering their construction operations. Perhaps the best general references for the construction engineer, in addition to those at the end of the next chapter, is the set of "Data Books for Civil Engineers," by E. E. Seelye, published by Wiley, as follows:

Vol. 1.   Design, 1951.
Vol. 2.   Specifications and Costs, 1951.
Vol. 3.   Field Practice, 1954.

Twelve-foot Wood Pipe, Sante Fe Tank and Tower Company, Los Angeles

Electrical Transmission Line, Union Electric Company, Saint Louis

Cableway or Tramway, John A. Roebling's Sons

Pennsylvania High Speed Steam Train

Burlington Diesel, Electric Zephyr

Canal, Metropolitan Water District of Southern California

Grade Separation, New York Department of Public Works

High Voltage Transmission Line, Southern California
Edison Company

Aqueduct, Metropolitan Water District of Southern California

Welded Steel Pipeline, United States Steel Corporation

A Missouri Highway

Goodyear Conveyor Belt

CHAPTER XVII

THE ENGINEER-CONTRACTOR

153. Introduction. For a consideration, the contractor engages to take the risks involved and to construct a project such as a route, a bridge, etc.

In contrast to the construction engineer of the preceding chapter, the engineer-contractor does relatively less engineering supervision and more actual professional management of construction. His work partakes less of the science of engineering and more of the art of management. However, his company will be increasingly engaged in research and design and he speaks of *engineered construction* and of the *profession of contracting.*

The engineer-contractor is motivated more keenly by profit than is the construction or professional engineer. He may prefer to remain with the contracting organization and assume upper management responsibilities there, but he also has entree into the construction divisions of those industrial corporations or governmental agencies with which he is in contact. From such a construction division he can progress into upper professional management in the same manner as was explained in the preceding chapter.

154. The Contractor's Equipment. Most of the improvement in contracting is due to the better equipment provided by manufacturers. In other respects progress has been slow and will continue slowly until the industry becomes professionally managed by the younger generation of engineers now entering the larger construction organizations. The improvements possible in both equipment and management are almost unlimited.

Construction equipment offers an attractive and remunerative field for the engineer who may design, produce, sell, or service it; or who may become a dealer or distributor with his own profitable business.

Many new and improved types of construction equipment are

being perfected and produced by strong and prosperous manufacturing companies, they can be seen everywhere, and they change and improve so rapidly that it would be useless to describe or illustrate them here.   The value of the machinery on a construction job sometimes approaches the total contract cost.

155. The Contractor's Organization.   So that the reader may consider his qualifications for the upper levels of contracting, the titles of the keen and capable officers running a typical multimillion-dollar income contracting business follow. It will be noted that many types of ability are represented and that some of the positions are filled by women.   The officers are president, first vice-president, second vice-president, treasurer and comptroller, secretary and administrative coordinator, chief engineer, general superintendent, equipment superintendent, office manager, production manager of readymix and aggregates, sales manager of readymix and aggregates, and manager of industrial relations.

For expansion, a contractor may spread geographically, or he may diversify locally into associated lines of business.   Either method tends to stabilize his business.   By expanding in both directions, his opportunity for growth is boundless.

156. The Contractor's Bid.   In essence, a bid is a "firm" or binding agreement to furnish certain things and services for the amount of the bid.   The most careful and precise estimates of cost are made by contractors or manufacturers who are bidding on some proposed project or job.   Poor estimates are disastrous to them, so they naturally give their best thought and effort to preparing the estimate.   If they bid too high they get no work to do, while too low a bid will cause them to lose money; in either case, many poor bids mean failure.

The preparation of bids is discussed in the books listed at the end of this chapter.   Much of their preparation must be learned in actual practice, and there is considerable variation in the procedures followed by different contracting companies.   Figure 156 indicates the detail of a bid for a highway overpass above a railway.   It will be noted that the field, or direct, expense is estimated separately from the overhead expense.   Each contracting company prepares its bids somewhat differently and keeps this form a secret from its competitors, in fact all bidding figures and procedures are preserved with strictest secrecy.

The greater precision of this "bid" type of estimate is possible because detailed plans and specifications are now available, because the estimate is subdivided more minutely, because better estimators prepare the figures, because of compensating errors, and because of the more immediate and greater penalty following a poor bid.   The contractor's total estimated (not his bid) cost on ordinary and repetitive work should be within a few percent of his actual final cost although individual items on the estimate may be 25 percent or more in error.   His actual bid may be quite different from what he thinks the work will cost him.   On hazardous or unusual work, the errors will be greater.

Figure 156 was prepared after the quantities had been taken from the plans and specifications, and it resulted in a total or "lump-sum" bid.   In contrast to Figs. 146 and 147 where the final total is "rounded off" to indicate the degree of precision of the estimates, it will be noted that the final total contractor's bid of Fig. 156 is an odd figure, to minimize the chance of two bids being identical and to secure the contract over a competitor who rounds off his total bid.

Bids are frequently asked on a unit-cost basis instead of the lump-sum total of Fig. 156.   The lump-sum bid is prepared first and then segregated into a unit-cost bid as shown on Fig. 156a. Considerable judgment is required in allocating the overhead. In this case overhead was directly proportioned to labor cost, and then modified to reflect the extent to which equipment was used on each item.   The mathematical unit costs resulting from simple division are increased or decreased as judgment dictates and then rounded off.   However, the lower right-hand total (which will be the owner's usual basis for awarding the contract) should still be an odd figure slightly below the anticipated bids of competitors.

The estimator continually must compare his estimates with the

Item No.	Division	Subject	Per Cu. Yd.	Labor	Materials	Total
1.	Class A 81.6 cu. yd.	Stone—0.9 cu. yd. = 2400# @ 1.40/ton	$ 1.68			
		Sand—0.5 cu. yd. = 1200# @ 1.60/ton	0.96			
		Cement—1.5 bbls. @ $4.00	6.00			

		Forms—Wall
		  7220 @ 0.42
		  $= \dfrac{\$3030.}{81.6} =$
			37.10			

		Finishing 3500 @ 8¢ $= \dfrac{\$280.}{81.6} =$	3.43			
		Mixing and Placing	5.00			
		Hauling and Misc.	1.83			
			$56.00	$ 3,218	$ 1,352	$ 4,570
2.	Class B Substruct. 477.5 cu. yd.	Stone—0.9 cu. yd.	$ 1.68			
		Sand—0.5 cu. yd.	0.96			
		Cement—1.25 bbls.	5.00			

		Forms , sq. ft.
		  Walls—8,000
		    @ 0.42 = $3,360
		  Supp.—1,300
		    @ 0.70 = 910
		  $= \dfrac{\$4,270}{477.5} =$
			8.93			

		Finish—4,600 @ 8¢ $= \dfrac{\$368.}{477.5} =$	0.77			
		Mixing and Placing	3.00			
		Hauling and Misc.	1.66			
			$22.00	5,736	4,769	10,505
3.	Class B Super-struct. 830.8 cu. yd.	Stone—0.9 cu. yd.	1.68			
		Sand—0.5 cu. yd.	0.96			
		Cement—1.25 bbls.	5.00			

		Forms
		  Walls—12,000
		    @ 0.42 = $ 5,040
		  Supp.—21,000
		    @ 0.70 = 14,700
		  $= \dfrac{\$19,740}{830.8} =$
			23.75			

		Finish—21,700 @ 0.08 $= \dfrac{\$1736}{830.8} =$	2.09			
		Mixing and Placing	4.00			
		Hauling and Misc.	1.52			
			$39.00	21,880	10,520	32,400

(ENR Construction Cost Index = 590 for 1954.)

Fig. 156. Contractor's Lump-Sum Bid, Highway-Railway Overpass.

Item No.	Division	Subject	Per Cu. Yd.	Cost Labor	Cost Materials	Cost Total
4.	Reinf. Steel 247,400#	F.O.B. Columbia 4¢/# Bending & Placing 2¢ Hauling & Handling 1¢ 7¢/#		7,422	9,896	17,318
5.	Excavation for Footings 425 cu. yd.	@ $2.00		850		850
6.	Sewer Relocation 65 lin. ft.	@ $3.00 (labor) 1.00 (material) 4.00/lin. ft.		195	65	260
7.	Bearing Plates			300	1,500	1,800
8.	Removal of Existing Structure			2,000	1,000	3,000
		Subcontracts				
9.	Lighting System				2,000	2,000
10.	2½" Telephone Conduit				500	500
		TOTAL FIELD COST		$41,601	$31,602	$ 73,203

Job Overhead

	Labor	Materials	Total
Superintendence and Timekeeping Watchmen, Waterboys and Tool House Men }	$ 2,800		$ 2,800
Plant Erection and Dismantling	2,000		2,000
Field Repairs	1,500	500	2,000
Use of Plant, 6% of Plant Value per Month		7,244	7,244
Taxes (income, social security, etc.)		4,000	4,000
Coal, Gasoline, Oil		500	500
Miscellaneous Supplies		500	500
Warehouse Labor	500		500
Bond, 1¼% of Bid		520	520
Liability Insurance, 7% of Payroll		2,910	2,910
Traveling Expenses		750	750
Job Interest, 6% of $18,000 for 6 Months		540	540
Contingencies, 5% of Bid		6,570	6,570
TOTAL JOB OVERHEAD	$ 6,800	$24,034	$ 30,834
GENERAL & OFFICE OVERHEAD			21,000
TOTAL COST			$125,037
PROFIT, 5% of Total Cost (Addition to Surplus)			6,252
BID			$131,289

Fig. 156. *Continued.*

Item	Description	Units	Field Costs			Over-Head	Total	Unit Costs		Total Bid
			Labor	Material	Total			Mathe-matical	Actual Bid	
1.	Excavation	425 cu. yd.	850		850	1,185	2,035	4.78	4.80	2,040.00
2.	Concrete, Class A	81.6 cu. yd.	3,218	1,352	4,570	4,490	9,060	111.10	109.00	8,894.40
3.	Concrete, Class B Superstructure	830.8 cu. yd.	21,879	10,522	32,401	30,600	63,001	75.75	76.00	63,140.80
4.	Concrete, Class B Substructure	477.5 cu. yd.	5,736	4,769	10,505	8,000	18,505	38.75	39.00	18,622.50
5.	Reinforcing Steel	247,400 lb.	7,422	9,896	17,318	10,000	27,318	0.1103	0.11	27,214.00
6.	Bearing Plates		300	1,500	1,800	300	2,100	- -	- -	2,100.00
7.	2½ Telephone Conduit	1		500	500	90	590	- -	- -	590.00
8.	Relocating Existing 18 in. V. C. P. Sewer	65 lin. ft.	195	65	260	270	530	8.16	8.00	520.00
9.	Lighting System	1		2,000	2,000	360	2,360	- -	- -	2,360.00
10.	Removing Existing Structure	1	2,000	1,000	3,000	2,790	5,790	- -	- -	5,790.00
	Totals	- - -	41,600	31,604	73,204	58,085	131,289	- -	- -	131,273.70

Fig. 156a.   Contractor's Unit-Price Bid for a Highway-Railroad Overpass, Computed from Lump-Sum Bid of Fig. 156.

bids of competitors and with the costs of his completed work so that he may correct his "personal equation." His employer also is vitally interested in the accuracy of these estimates. It is therefore commonly the practice, after a bid or estimate is accepted, to assign a cost-control number or letter to each item thereon. As the work progresses the costs are reported accordingly, and by this segregation a comparison between the actual costs and the estimated costs is made available as the work progresses and at its completion. These actual costs are of course available for subsequent bidding.

157. Contracting as a Career. The "gamble" in contracting is gradually being minimized as professional engineer-management replaces the uneducated older generation of "foreman to president" owners and managers. While the engineer-contractor must be experienced in the technical phases of engineering, it is even more important that he be a professional manager. As professional management has developed in the past 20 years, it has made business and government increasingly stable, and this stability is now being felt in contracting.

The interested and qualified young engineer will find here an interesting field of service and the highest financial rewards. Mr. Dwight W. Winkelman, member of the American Society of Civil Engineers, president of his own contracting company, past president of the Associated General Contractors of America, and past chairman of its Educational Committee has recently said:*

"Today, in our judgment, there are greater opportunities for civil engineers in construction than at any time in the history of our country.

"Also today there is probably a greater need for engineers in all phases of construction than there ever has been.

"Professor Rubey has just spoken to you forcefully and accurately on the need for engineers in construction management. I want to subscribe to what he has said. . . .

* Annual meeting of the American Society for Engineering Education, Pennsylvania State University, June 23, 1955.

"While I am sure that all of us can recognize the growing needs for engineers to do research, to design projects, and to administer construction programs, I would like to confine my discussion to the need for engineers in a management capacity in contracting organizations.

"*Importance for Construction.*   Construction has now become the largest single productive activity in the nation.   The output of the industry now surpasses the value of agricultural production.

"Last year when the construction industry established a new all-time record for the ninth consecutive year, about $1 in every $7 spent for goods and services throughout the country was spent for construction.   Directly and indirectly the industry accounts for jobs for 17 percent of the gainfully employed . . .

"*Need for Engineers in Management.*   There are other reasons why we believe that there are now greater opportunities for engineers in contracting management.

"In recent years great forward steps have been taken in engineering research, in the conception and design of projects to fit their purposes more exactly, in methods and machinery, and in many other ways which make the construction of projects more exacting.

"More than ever before, it is essential today that contractors have competent engineers on their staffs so that the operations can be carried out efficiently and economically.

"Also, the force of competition has become so keen that the contractor who cannot keep increasing his efficiency is in danger of going out of business.

"Today projects are being more boldly and brilliantly conceived.   Their designs have become more perfect and more complex.   But it takes the contractor with skill, imagination, courage, initiative, hard work, and a sound understanding of engineering to create a useful facility from the plans and specifications.

"In our work as contractors we must understand the owner and the designer so that we will construct a project which will accomplish what it is supposed to.   We must assemble, train and direct the operations of skilled workmen, and comply with a host of laws, rules, regulations, and customs while doing it.   We must secure and schedule the operations of machinery, which on some projects may have a value equal to the amount of the contract.

"At all kinds of locations and in all kinds of weather we must conduct our operations to provide for the safety of workmen and the public.   We must maintain good relations with the public so that we merit their respect and confidence.   We must pay our taxes.   And we must turn over to the owner a project of specified quality at the agreed upon time.   And we have taken the risk that the bid we made before starting the work will be adequate to pay our costs and return us, we hope, a modest profit.

"I think it should be obvious to you that we in contracting organizations have a great need for engineers with a sound technical education and the ability to get along with people and to plan and carry out the various complex operations which we must perform.

"*Contracting as a Profession.*   We in the A.G.C., as we gain a greater understanding of the importance of our industry to the national welfare, feel that we have a heavy responsibility for constructing those projects which are so essential to the progress of America.

"But as we carry out our work efficiently and economically and in such a manner that the public receives increasing value for its investment in construction, we can also take great satisfaction in accomplishing important work for society . . .

"My purpose is to stress what I believe is the necessity of thoroughly trained and competent men entering into the management of the construction firms which actually construct those facilities which are vital to the progress of the country . . .

"In closing, I would like to repeat that construction has now become the greatest single productive activity in the nation, and that the industry has a basic part to play in the growth, development and defense of the nation.

"Now there are greater opportunities than ever before for the civil engineer in the management field of general contracting.

"Contractors have an increasing need for engineers who not only have a sound technical education, but who have been exposed to the fundamentals of construction through optional courses while in college.

"The young engineer entering construction management has the opportunity not only to gain monetary rewards, but also the satisfaction of accomplishing important work for society."

158. The Contractor's Work.   The contractor, either a corporation or individual, who constructs routes is called a general, or heavy construction, contractor as contrasted with a building contractor.   He constructs highways, railways, pipe lines, airports, bridges, tunnels, canals, dams, transmission lines, flumes, cableways, beltways, industrial plants, and the like. Along with these he often constructs minor buildings, docks and piers, and most large constructions other than major buildings.

A few of the recent books that are most available and useful in contracting, in addition to those at the end of the preceding chapter, are:

Associated General Contractors of America, *Manual*, Munsey Building, Washington 4, D. C., 1953.
Kellogg, F. H., *Construction Methods and Machinery*, Prentice-Hall, 1954.
Puerifoy, R. L., *Construction Planning, Equipment, and Methods*, McGraw-Hill, 1956.
———, *Estimating Construction Costs*, McGraw-Hill, 1953.
Pulver, H. E., *Construction Estimates and Costs*, McGraw-Hill, 1947.
Walker, Frank R., *The Building Estimator's Reference Book*, 12th Edition, F. R. Walker Company, Chicago, 1954.

CHAPTER XVIII

COMPARISON OF VARIOUS DEFINITIONS OF DEGREE OF CURVE

159. General. Throughout the preceding pages and in the tables, the *arc definition* and the chord definition of degree of curve have been used since most organizations use one or the other of these types. References to the *arc definition* are *italicized* in this chapter. Sometimes it is found that a single organization uses both, the chord definition for flat curves and the *arc definition* for those of sharper degree than, say, 10. Often in the same organization one field engineer uses one definition, another field engineer another. The office men usually agree among themselves but vary from some of the field men's practice. Seldom do all of these men recognize what they are doing by its accepted title; rather, they follow some customary procedure without designating its name.

Of course, curves computed by one definition and staked in the field by another will not check nor will the values of one definition exactly check those of another. In such situations, long and loud argument is heard, often characterized more by heat than by light, as to what is the correct procedure and why the results do not check. An attempt will be made in this chapter to resolve such discussion.

Before proceeding further it will be necessary to describe definitions of degree of curve other than those of *arc* and chord. They are seldom used with conscious selection but some of their characteristics crop up because of the past field practice of the engineer or because of the field tables to which he is accustomed and which he uses.

160. Even-Radius Curves. By a few highway departments (notably in California), the United States Reclamation Service, many foreign countries, but rarely elsewhere, the conception of degree of curve is not used at all. Such organizations designate the sharpness by specifying the radius. Usually round numbers are used for this radius, for example, 5,000 feet, or 200 feet, or the like. Table V gives data for such "even-radius" curves and the data from this, or similar tables, will provide precise checks. As an objection to this method, it should be noted that the deflection angles and the chord lengths are usually odd values which add to the difficulty of computing and staking.

Table I (*italic figures*) and Table II give accurate values for even-radius curves, although fractional values of D will often be used.

161. Radius of 5730 Feet. Some books, and a few engineers, use the radius of a one degree curve as 5730 feet. They define the degree of curve as the angle at the center of the curve subtended by an arc of 100.0074 feet. In staking this curve, 100-foot chords are used up to D = 3°; 50-foot chords are used between D = 3° and D = 7°; 25-foot chords are used for sharper curves; and thus the staked chords approximate the arc.

The formulas of the *arc definition* are used, with R always being $\dfrac{5730}{D}$.

If Tables I and II of this text are to be used with this definition, Table I (*arc definition values*) is only approximately, although very closely, correct. Values from Table II should be increased by 0.007%, although this correction is usually negligible.

Results from this method are not exact, it has limited usage, and it is not recommended for precise work. Furthermore, 25- and 50-foot chords often are superfluous. While this definition gives satisfactory approximations for much work, one never knows just how much it is in error.

162. Metric Curves. In those rare cases (mostly abroad) where a 20-meter tape (65.617 feet) is used in laying out curves the metric degree of curve may be defined as the deflection angle for a 20-meter *arc* or chord.

The stations are actually 10-meter lengths along tangent *or arc*, but only every other station (the even numbered stations) are staked. Where the chord definition of degree of curve is used around curves, two stations are set, and defined, by one 20-meter chord.

A study of the geometric relations for the more conventional definitions of degree of curve will indicate how to calculate the necessary values. The usual tables can be used. For example, the tabular values from Table II divided by 10 give metric values for either *arc* or chord definitions.

As an example under the metric chord definition, a 1° metric curve has a radius of 572.99 meters, an arc length of 20.001 meters, and an equivalent U.S. degree of curve of 3° 3′. Where the metric system of measurement is used abroad, curvature is more frequently specified by the radius than by degree of curve. For example, the German superhighways often had a radius of 2,000 meters, or a degree of curve, as we would express it, of about 0° 52′.

163. Discrepancies. There are slight differences between the curve notes and values as computed variously according to the *arc*, chord, and 5730-foot definitions of degree of curve. Occasionally these discrepancies are large enough to cause trouble, but more frequently they are sufficiently accurate for field work and are annoying only when checks are attempted by another engineer in the field or office.

From the explanations of the *arc* and chord definitions given in Chapter V and in the Curve Tables, where chord data is in regular type and *arc data in italic type*, it is obvious where certain discrepancies may exist, and their amount.

One fertile source of error for all definitions arises where the length, L, of the curve is computed by formula 33e of page 61, namely, $L = \dfrac{(I)}{(D)} (100)$, as though it were to be staked by 100-foot *arcs* or chords; and then the curve is staked with short chords of exactly 50 feet or 25 feet without applying the corrections of Table IV.

When using the *arc* definition, if chords exactly 50 or 100 feet long are measured in staking, discrepancies will always result, although they may be negligible on flat curves. Such discrepancies can be eliminated by using the italic values in the right-hand column of Table I or the sub-chord values in Table IV.

In the even-radius definition, no discrepancies will occur if Table V or a similar extension of it is used. Note that this definition follows the *arc definition formulas and ideas* except that the radius (usually some even value) rather than the degree of curve, is the basic measure of the sharpness of the curve.

Greatest difficulty arises in explaining the discrepancies for the 5730-foot definition. Here neither the 100-foot arc nor the 100-foot chord subtend the degree of curve at the center of the curve, rather an arc of 100.0074 feet subtends the degree of curve at the center. This tends to give values checking closely with the *arc* definition; but only precisely so for a few values of D. For example, for a 1° curve, the radius 5730 feet differs 0.42 of a foot from the *5729.58 value of the arc definition*. The tangent, external, and length of curve will vary proportionately.

Bearing these possible discrepancies in mind, the engineer must thoroughly understand the Tables which he uses.

The Tables in this book have been prepared especially so that they may be used for all definitions. Explanations are given in the text and also accompany the Tables.

164. Comparison of Values Under Various Definitions. Table 164 is presented to show the different values for the curve (I = 97° 13', D = 16° 42', and P.I. = 185 + 04.3) under the two major conceptions, namely, the chord and *arc* definitions.

TABLE 164

FUNCTION	100-FOOT CHORD (RAILWAY) DEFINITION	100-FOOT ARC (HIGHWAY) DEFINITION
Radius	344.3	*343.1*
Tangent	390.6	*389.3*
External	176.4	*175.8*
T.C.	181+13.7	*181+15.0*
Length of curve	582.1 (around chords)	*582.1* (*around arc*)
C.T.	186+95.8	*186+97.1*
First chord	86.3	*84.8*
Last chord	95.8	*96.8*
Chord corresponding to 100-foot arc		*99.6*
Deflection angle for first chord	7° 12'	*7° 05'*
Deflection angle for final chord	8° 00'	*8° 05'*

Note that since the tangent lengths are different, the T.C. and the C.T. will fall at different stationing. As a result, the end subchords and the corresponding sub-deflection angles will differ, and as a further consequence all deflection angles in the field notes will vary, although these are not shown in Table 164.

The column of figures for the *arc* definition are properly computed on the assumption that the proper 99.6-foot chords, instead of 100-foot chords, were used in staking the full stations.

No columns are included in Table 164 for the 5730-foot, the even-radius, or the metric definitions.

The 5730-foot definition values would correspond very closely with the *arc* definition values since, by chance for this particular D = 16° 42', both definitions give the same radius. This would not always be precisely true.

The even-radius definition values would correspond exactly with the *arc* definition values, but note that the 16° 42′ curve would not have an even radius.

The metric definition could follow either the *arc* or chord definitions but the values will vary.

In conclusion, attention must be called to the effect of the definition of degree of curve on the transition spiral used. The A.R.E.A. spiral of Chapter IX in this text is precisely correct for and follows the chord definition.

The Barnett Transition Spiral mentioned on pages 105, 106, 137, and 138, often used in highway work, is precisely correct for and follows the *arc* definition.

Fortunately, the discrepancies between the values for the A.R.E.A. spiral and the Barnett spiral are negligible except as mentioned on pages 137–138, and as described in the explanations accompanying Tables VII and VIII.

CHAPTER XIX

HIGHWAY PRACTICE

165. Purpose of This Chapter. For those interested in highway work, modern methods in that field are authoritatively summarized in two publications issued in 1949, namely, "Manual of Highway Construction Practices and Methods," American Association of State Highway Officials; and "Highway Practice in the United States of America," Public Roads Administration. These several hundred pages of late material may be obtained for a nominal charge.

Those portions of the latter reference which are of a geometric nature and therefore suitable for a text of this nature are quoted herewith. The latter part of the chapter shows geometric data which is standard for a particular highway organization, The Missouri State Highway Commission.

166. Geometric Practice. "Geometric design as practiced by the several State highway departments and other designing agencies is not completely uniform. There remains a considerable variety in the laws of the States limiting the sizes and weights of vehicles, and the differences in these respects have an influence upon the decisions of highway designers. There are differences in the financing ability of the various governments and these too modify the standards of roads as built. Moreover, there are differences in the interpretation of experience and the evidence of research, and these are reflected in the variety of design practice.

"Within limits, this variety is accepted as unavoidable by the Public Roads Administration, and tolerated in its approval of plans developed by the initiating State agencies for Federal-aid improvements. The strongest force tending to level these differences is the standardizing influence of technical committees of the American Association of State Highway Officials. In this association, all State highway departments and the Public Roads Administration hold membership and join in the deliberations of its committees.

"Standards proposed and revised from time to time by these committees are recommended to the association and in turn submitted to the membership for adoption by letter ballot. Each member department, including the Public Roads Administration, is entitled to one vote. Upon approval by a required majority, a standard thus submitted is declared 'adopted' and becomes a standard of the association.

Maximum Sizes and Weights of Vehicles

"Following this process, the association has adopted a standard or policy concerning the maximum sizes and weights of vehicles that should be permitted to operate, and has recommended this policy for uniform adoption by law in the several States. While this policy takes into account the relatively low standards of a large part of the existing highway development as a condition modifying the present feasibility of accommodating the operation of vehicles, and is not, therefore, intended to constitute, unmodified, a basis for the design of new highways and structures, it nevertheless has an influence upon the design practices employed. It is appropriate, therefore, at this point, to introduce the various limits adopted.

" They are:

For the maximum height of vehicles, $12\frac{1}{2}$ feet.

For the maximum width of vehicles, 96 inches. (The policy includes a recommendation that this limit may be increased to 102 inches if and when the width of existing highways is sufficient to justify the change.)

For the maximum length of—

Single trucks and two-axle busses, 35 feet.

Three-axle busses, 40 feet.

Tractor-semitrailer combinations, 50 feet.

Other combinations of vehicles (not more than two units), 60 feet.

For the maximum load on one axle, 18,000 pounds.

For the maximum gross weight of vehicles and combinations, and the weight permissible upon any group of axles of the vehicles or combinations, various amounts as given in a table relating permissible weight to the spacing of axles, measured in feet, as follows:

DISTANCE BETWEEN THE EXTREME AXLES OF ANY GROUP OF AXLES (FEET)	MAXIMUM WEIGHT PERMISSIBLE ON ALL AXLES OF THE GROUP (POUNDS)	DISTANCE BETWEEN THE EXTREME AXLES OF ANY GROUP OF AXLES (FEET)	MAXIMUM WEIGHT PERMISSIBLE ON ALL AXLES OF THE GROUP (POUNDS)	DISTANCE BETWEEN THE EXTREME AXLES OF ANY GROUP OF AXLES (FEET)	MAXIMUM WEIGHT PERMISSIBLE ON ALL AXLES OF THE GROUP (POUNDS)
4	32,000	22	45,700	40	60,800
5	32,000	23	46,590	41	61,580
6	32,000	24	47,470	42	62,360
7	32,000	25	48,350	43	63,130
8	32,610	26	49,220	44	63,890
9	33,580	27	50,090	45	64,650
10	34,550	28	50,950	46	65,400
11	35,510	29	51,800	47	66,150
12	36,470	30	52,650	48	66,890
13	37,420	31	53,490	49	67,620
14	38,360	32	54,330	50	68,350
15	39,300	33	55,160	51	69,070
16	40,230	34	55,980	52	69,790
17	41,160	35	56,800	53	70,500
18	42,080	36	57,610	54	71,200
19	42,990	37	58,420	55	71,900
20	43,900	38	59,220	56	72,590
21	44,800	39	60,010	57	73,280

CLASSIFICATION OF TRAFFIC

"With these proposed limits of the size and weight of vehicles in mind, and with due regard to the reservations expressed as to their bearing upon highway design, we may

now proceed to a consideration of some of the standards
of geometric design.

"Basic to the consideration are certain broad definitions
of the type, volume, and speed of traffic contemplated and
differentiated in the standards.

"These definitions are contained in the *Policy on Highway
Classification* of the American Association of State Highway
Officials.   They include type of traffic, traffic density, and
design speed.

"*Type.*   The type of traffic is classified by the percentage
of passenger cars and commercial vehicles and affects such
elements involved in the geometric design as traffic lane
widths, capacity of the traffic lanes, maximum radius of
curvature, especially at intersections and on ramps, and
maximum gradients.

"*Density.*   The traffic density assumed for purposes of
design is that hourly traffic volume that is expected to be
the thirtieth highest hourly volume during the year for
which the road is designed.

"*Speed.*   The design speed is the maximum approximately
uniform speed which can be adopted safely by the faster
group of drivers during periods of low traffic volume, ex-
cluding the small percentage of reckless drivers.   The
standards are differentiated for design speeds of 30, 40, 50,
60, and 70 miles per hour.   The design speed is selected for
correlation of those geometric features such as curvature,
superelevation, and sight distance, upon which the safe
operation of vehicles is dependent.

"Closely related to the design speed, although not included in the association's policies but rapidly coming into
general use, is the term operating speed.   It is the highest
average speed, exclusive of stops, at which a driver can
travel on a roadway under prevailing traffic conditions without at any time exceeding the design speed.   Operating
speed varies for any given road, being low when traffic is
heavy and approaching design speed when traffic is light.

"Modified as necessary by these basic definitions of traffic conditions, the principal geometric design standards are described in the following sections.

ALINEMENT

"The alinement that is selected for a highway determines how effectively and safely the completed facility will meet the demands of traffic. Alinement between control points should be of as high standard as is commensurate with the topography and the existing traffic, in order that future improvements may be made with a minimum of investment loss due to obsolescence. Sudden changes between curves of widely different radii or between long tangents and sharp curves should be avoided by use of curves of gradually increasing or decreasing radii; avoiding, however, an appearance of forced alinement. A curve at the end of a long tangent is definitely more hazardous than the same degree of curvature associated with a series of curves. It is essential to select an alinement free from sudden changes that come as a surprise to the operator. In relatively level topography, the use of long curves of large radii should be preferred to long tangents connected by relatively sharp curves. Where horizontal curves occur on grade summits, the vertical sight distance should exceed the horizontal sight distance.

"*Superelevation*. Maximum superelevation of 0.12 foot per foot is recommended by the American Association of State Highway Officials. Where snow and ice conditions prevail, 0.08 foot per foot is the maximum that should be used. In recent practice, superelevations of 0.16 foot per foot have been found to be very satisfactory on ramps at interchanges, especially on the down ramps where design must generally provide for higher speeds than on up ramps.

In obtaining superelevation, it is desirable that the slope of the outer edge of pavement with respect to the profile of the center line should not be greater than 1 in 200.

"*Curvature*. Wherever feasible the flattest curvature possible should be used. Design policies of the American

Association of State Highway Officials provide that the minimum radius of curvature shall be as shown in Table 166.

TABLE 166

MINIMUM RADIUS OF CURVATURE

ASSUMED DESIGN SPEED	RADIUS OF CURVATURE	
	Desirable Minimum	Absolute Minimum
M.p.h.	Feet	Feet
30	290	230
40	520	410
50	820	640
60	1,150	960
70	1,910	1,430

"The absolute minimum radius is based upon a practical maximum superelevation, and a safe value for the side friction factor of 0.16 for speeds up to 60 miles per hour and 0.14 for a speed of 70 miles per hour. The desirable minimum radius is based on the same friction factors but approximately half the maximum superelevation.

"It should be recognized that the stated minimum radii are safe for the indicated speeds only when the curves are superelevated to the maximum and approached with adequate transitions. Larger radii, perhaps as large as those for the next higher 10 miles per hour, should be adopted as a minimum for entirely safe and comfortable operation.

"*Transitions.* Transitions should be applied to all curves of such radii that the offset from the circular arc is greater than 1 foot for a transition of the required length L_s, as determined by the formula

$$L_s = \frac{1.6v^3}{R}$$

"In this formula, v is the assumed design speed in miles per hour and R, the radius in feet.

"Where possible, superelevation should be attained within the limits of the transition, which should be of such length that the slope of the outer edge of pavement with respect to the profile of the center line is no greater than 1 in 200.

"*Minimum Length of Curve.* For small deflection angles the curve should be long enough to avoid the appearance of a kink. The curve should be at least 500 feet long for a deflection angle of 5 degrees and should increase 100 feet in length for each decrease of 1 degree in the deflection angle.

GRADES

"Agreement has not been reached on the maximum grade or the length of sustained grade to be used for various combinations of terrain and traffic density. The information shown [elsewhere in this bulletin] is, however, useful in determining the maximum length of grade that will reduce truck speeds to values that are objectionable to the operators of passenger cars. These data are also useful in determining when added lanes should be provided on long grades.

"On long grades, it is preferable to break the sustained grade by short sections of lesser grade, rather than to lay a uniform sustained grade that may be only slightly below the allowable maximum, provided the break in grade will not affect the length of highway on which passing maneuvers can be performed safely. Secondary dips in the profile, in which vehicles may be hidden from view, should be avoided. Where it is found that grades less than the maximum may be obtained over a considerable length of a project, but there are maximum grades of sufficient length to slow down loaded vehicles to a crawl speed at certain places, provision of additional lanes for slow-moving vehicles should be considered.

"While the association policy does not particularize, it is known that trucks and combination units with their normal loadings are appreciably slowed down by gradients, of sufficient length, as low as 3 percent. [A table of this bulletin]

shows that trucks are reduced to speeds so low as to prevent
satisfactory passenger-car operation even when the steeper
grades are short in length.

SIGHT DISTANCE

"Sight distance is the length of roadway visible to the
driver of a passenger vehicle at any given point on the roadway when the view is unobstructed by traffic. For purposes
of design and to determine operating conditions on a highway, sight distance is divided into two categories—stopping
sight distance and passing sight distance.

"*Stopping Sight Distance.* Stopping sight distance is
the distance required by the driver of a vehicle, traveling at
a given speed, to bring his vehicle to a stop after an object
on the roadway becomes visible. The driver should have
such sight distance at all times. The American Association
of State Highway Officials uses a height of 4 inches for the
object on the roadway, on the assumption that any object
lower than 4 inches will not be a serious obstruction if it is
hit. Stopping sight distance is therefore measured from
the driver's eyes, which are assumed to be $4\frac{1}{2}$ feet above the
pavement surface, to an object 4 inches high on the road.

"*Passing Sight Distance.* Passing sight distance is the
minimum sight distance that must be available to enable the
driver of one vehicle to pass another vehicle safely and comfortably, without interfering with the speed of an oncoming
vehicle traveling at the design speed should it come into view
after the overtaking maneuver is started. According to the
American Association of State Highway Officials, the sight
distance available for passing at any place is the longest
distance at which a driver whose eyes are $4\frac{1}{2}$ feet above the
pavement surface can see the top of an object $4\frac{1}{2}$ feet high
on the road.

"While stopping distance is necessary continuously on
all types of highways, passing sight distance is necessary
only on two-way roadways with two or three lanes.

"Minimum sight distances recommended by the American Association of State Highway Officials are shown in Table 167.

TABLE 167

Minimum Sight Distances

DESIGN SPEED	STOPPING: 2-, 3-, AND 4-LANE HIGHWAYS	SIGHT DISTANCES			
		PASSING			
		2-LANE HIGHWAYS		3-LANE HIGHWAYS	
		Desirable	Absolute	Desirable	Absolute
M.p.h.	Feet	Feet	Feet	Feet	Feet
30	200	600	500	.....	.....
40	275	1,100	900	.....	.....
50	350	1,600	1,400	1,100	900
60	475	2,300	2,100	1,500	1,300
70	600	3,200	2,900	2,000	1,800

"*Recent Studies.*   Recent studies have shown that the stopping sight distances listed in Table 167 are not adequate for many vehicles in actual use at the present time.   If adequate stopping distances are to be provided for all passenger cars, other than the 10 or 15 percent with brakes in very poor condition, stopping sight distances 20 to 30 percent higher than those in Table 167 must be provided. Trucks and combination units require much longer distances in·stopping than do passenger cars at corresponding speeds. A stopping sight distance which is adequate for a passenger car traveling 70 miles an hour is not adequate for combination units, with normal loads, above about 50 miles per hour.

"Results of recent studies of the manner in which drivers perform passing maneuvers on two-lane roads show that most drivers base the decision to begin passing on the distance they can see the road surface ahead rather than the distance to a point $4\frac{1}{2}$ feet above the road surface.   Unless a driver is completely familiar with the profile of a route, he cannot be sure that there is no approaching vehicle on the road surface that is not visible in a short dip in the road ahead.   It is only when a vehicle is in view that he has any idea as to how far it is to a point $4\frac{1}{2}$ feet above the road surface on a vertical curve.

"At any given point on a highway, a driver is not aided greatly by sight distance in excess of 2,000 feet.   For this reason and also because a large majority of passed vehicles move at slow speed and may be passed in a short distance, the percentage of highway on which a sight distance of 1,500 feet or more is available can be used as a criterion of the sight distance adequacy of two- and three-lane highways. A more complete discussion of sight-distance requirements as related to traffic volume is presented [elsewhere in this bulletin].

"In rough terrain requiring large expenditures to produce the required percentage of passing sight distance, construction of a four-lane highway is sometimes the best solution. In modernization of old two- and three-lane roads, widening to four lanes is often preferable to extensive work in lengthening sight distance to required standards.

"Many of our early highways were designed using a maximum grade, a maximum curvature, and other fixed standards.   To avoid exceeding fixed maximum grade, it has sometimes been necessary to introduce added distance and curvature which has resulted in a highway that would not accommodate traffic as effectively as one with somewhat steeper grades but better alinement.   It is not sufficient to consider various elements of design, such as gradient, curvature, and sight distance, independently.   They must be considered in combination to obtain the alinement and profile over which vehicles can operate most efficiently and safely."

167. Location and Design.   "We now turn to matters concerned with the specific location of highways within the determined systems and the design of the physical features of the highways, including their drainage, foundations, and surfaces.   In these respects the guiding purposes are:

"1. To place the highway in optimum conformity with its terrain and adjoining land uses;

"2. To protect the highways and bridges against the destructive action of water; and

"3. To provide foundations, structures, and surfaces which, at an optimum combination of construction and maintenance cost, economically related to the value of the transportation service to be afforded, will have the strength to resist anticipated traffic and natural forces.

"In approaching these phases of the discussion it is logical to begin with a consideration of the objectives and methods of location as they are viewed and practiced in the United States.

"First, it should be borne in mind that many miles of highways, especially in the more fully developed areas of the country, are now substantially fixed in their existing locations.   Reconstruction of these highways occurs periodically in projects a few miles in length, with no choice of new location at all.   When short sections of such highways are relocated to correct local deficiencies of alinement, the objectives are the same as those which are sought in more extended new location or relocation, but the methods are, generally, the familiar methods of ground surveying.

Location Objectives

"Modern American highways, in contrast with those in some other countries, are designed almost exclusively for motor vehicles.   Our main reason for relocating and reconstructing the average primary highway is the fact that it has become obsolete for use by existing volumes and types of motor traffic.   The main objectives of new highway location include the following, among others:

"1. A location is desired which will, as far as possible,

provide at lowest possible cost permanently optimum operating conditions for a gradually developing stream of composite traffic.

"2. This means a location which meets standards of grade, alinement, and sight distance based on actual existing and probable future traffic over a period of at least 25 years.

"3. A location to standards which will permit operation of vehicles at a constant average design speed, without gear shifting in ascent or braking in descent.

"These objectives and others of equal importance require complete topographic and land use information between the terminal points selected before the highway location survey begins. The final objective of such a survey will be the use of such complete information in obtaining the best possible permanent location of the highway, considering the standards of construction believed justified by future traffic.

"Modern American practice in highway location involves four typical stages which may be briefly described as:

"1. Reconnaissance of the region or general area through which a proposed new or relocated highway is to pass.

"2. Reconnaissance of possible alternate routes indicated by existing regional maps and supplementary regional surveys. In this second step best locations are selected for:

"3. Preliminary location surveys.

"4. Final location surveys and preparation of plans are the culmination of the highway location process."

(See pages 20–23 for Aerial Reconnaissance.)

Preliminary Location Surveys

"Let it now be assumed that three or more alternate routes have been selected and mapped for study. Assume, also, that there are overlapping strip photographs at a 500-foot per inch scale (1 : 6,000) and a photogrammetric contour map at this same scale with 10-foot contour interval. A trial line can now be laid down on the map, with a spline, which will follow in very close approximation such a line staked on the ground. Such a line will readily avoid badly drained ground, impassable rough topography, valuable buildings, or other obstacles. The line will cross streams at points seen to be reasonably practicable as bridge sites. In cases of doubt, questioned points can be identified on paired photographs under the stereoscope and examined in detail on the ground. Finally, from such photographs and maps, rough estimates of excavation yardage, bridge and culvert construction costs, and the like can be made. The usual result of such calculations in open undeveloped country will be to make possible selection of a single, best, and most economical line location on the contour map. This selected preliminary location will then be ready for preliminary survey.

"The preliminary location survey will usually require aerial photography on a strip $\frac{1}{4}$ to 1 mile wide. Details such as fence lines and property line corners must be identifiable, and accurate estimation of excavation yardage will be necessary at this stage. Location of points of curvature and points of tangency on the map will be required. These details will require contour map scales of from 200 to 100 feet per inch, although only in built-up suburban areas will the larger of the two scales be required. The 200 feet per inch contour map can be prepared from the 500 feet per inch photographs taken for stage 2.

"*Value of Aerial Photography.* Important points to be emphasized in the preliminary location stage are these:

"1. Previous reconnaissance stages of survey have covered wide bands or zones of ground area. The preliminary survey stage brings the zone of coverage to a strip from $\frac{1}{4}$ to 1 mile wide, on which contour lines will be obtained.

"2. At the usual scale of 200 feet per inch, a line can be laid down, on the map and photographs, which can be located on the ground and, when desired, staked out.

"3. At the scale of 200 feet per inch, estimates of yardage of excavation can be made for the selected line. Such estimates, when checked by cross sectioning and computation, have been within 5 percent of the actual excavation quantities.

"4. Field stake-out and trial-and-error location of a series of alternate preliminary lines on the ground can be avoided by the aerial survey methods outlined.

"5. By avoiding actual staking out of preliminary lines, private property owners are not unduly alarmed as they always are by ground surveys. Values of land to be acquired are not increased as they are by the usual discussion with property owners which follows the staking out of a survey line.

"6. At the map scale of 200 feet per inch, the value of buildings may be appraised, property lines may be laid out from the photography, and property maps prepared.

"7. On such contour maps, supplemented by stereoscopic examination of paired photographs, the road alinement can be fitted to the topography with the least possible cut and fill permitted by assumed controls of curvature, profile, and sight distance. All serious obstacles, such as rock cliffs, marshes, and bad stream crossings can be avoided before any lines are staked out on the ground.

FINAL LOCATION SURVEYS

"The final location of the preliminary line, selected either by trial and error on the ground, or by means of aerial photographs and photogrammetric maps, is a process well understood by all experienced highway engineers. The obtaining of cross-section information, the layout of sections of tangents and curves, the estimation of yardage by end-area methods—all these are familiar. The use of aerial survey methods, as now practiced by American engineers, normally terminates when the best preliminary line available between selected terminal points, and passing through selected control points, has been laid down on the ground. This best preliminary location line, with necessary minor adjustments during the stake-out process, becomes the final location line."

168. An Overall Transportation Policy.* Our whole elaborate transportation system of highways, railways, airways, waterways, pipe and transmission lines, and so on has grown haphazardly and must be coordinated under a general program that will give increased effectiveness for peace or war. If this is not accomplished in peacetime, worse transportation will be suffered in wartime with greater embargoes, disruptions, conflicts, inefficiencies, and logistic difficulties of all kinds.

The capacity, convenience, safety, cost, and speed of transportation can be greatly improved with little expense by an adequate overall policy designed intelligently for a greatly expanding future. The only comprehensive solution is the appointment of a non-political Presidential Commission to study and hold hearings covering the entire transportation field, then to devise means for allocating fairly the services to be performed among the agencies that can handle them best. This will secure political support from all parties and minimize the difficulties that frustrated the 1955 Congress in highway legislation, prevent waste, reduce congestion and casualties, foster cooperation and eliminate needless competition, and stabilize the situation so that each transportation agency can function most effectively.

168a. Present Highway Standards. Some standards of the Missouri Highway Commission are shown on the pages immediately following as Figures 168 to 168h. Standards are improving constantly, as for example, in wider pavements, wider roadbeds, and wider rights of way.

The Missouri Highway Commission, and many other state commissions, publish survey manuals and construction manuals which set forth their practices in detail.

An extensive publication on "Roads and Airfields" was issued in 1951 by the U. S. Army Engineer School, Ft. Belvoir, Virginia, as "Engineer School Special Text, ST-5-250-1."

* Harry Rubey, *How to Plan and Pay for the Safe and Adequate Highways We Need*, General Motors Better Highway Awards, 1953.

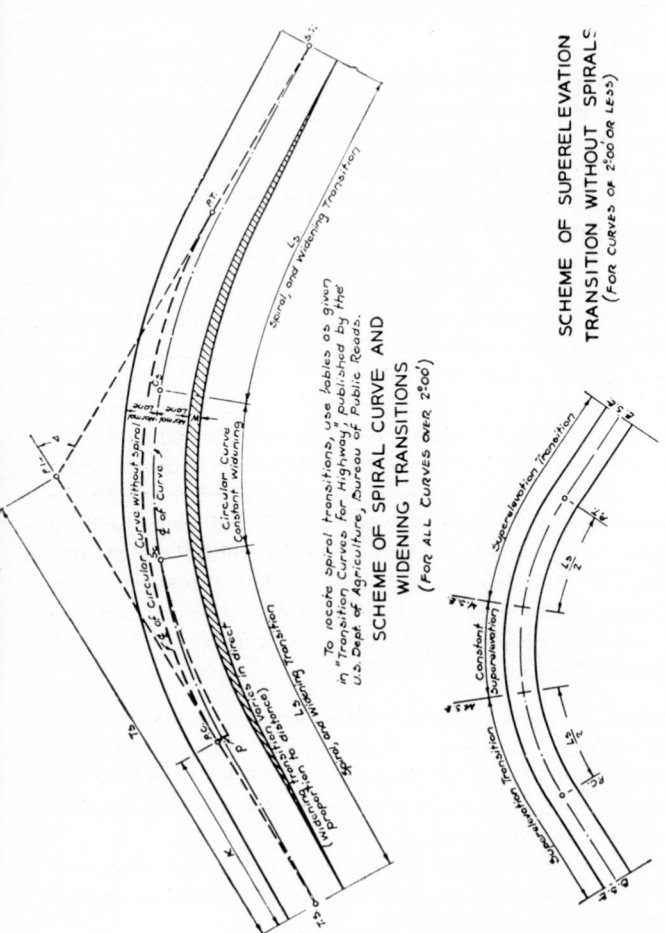

To locate spiral transitions, use tables as given in "Transition Curves for Highways," published by the U.S. Dept. of Agriculture, Bureau of Public Roads.

SCHEME OF SPIRAL CURVE AND WIDENING TRANSITIONS

(For all curves over 2°00')

SCHEME OF SUPERELEVATION TRANSITION WITHOUT SPIRALS

(For curves of 2°00' or less)

Fig. 168. Spiraling, Widening, and Superelevating.

SUPERELEVATION AND WIDENING DATA

Design Speed →	30 M.P.H. or Less				40 M.P.H.						50 M.P.H.						60 M.P.H.						70 M.P.H.				
Normal Surface Width →			20'	22'			20'	22'	24'	44'			20'	22'	24'	44'			20'	22'	24'	44'			22'	24'	44'
Degree of Curve Dc ↓	e	L_s	W'	W'	e	L_s	W'	W'	W'	W'	e	L_s	W'	W'	W'	W'	e	L_s	W'	W'	W'	W'	e	L_s	W'	W'	W'
0° to 1°00'	0	0	0	0	0	0	0	0	0	0	0	0	0	0	0	0	0	0	0	0	0	0	0	0	0	0	0
1°01' to 1°30'	.01	150	0	0	.01	150	0	0	0	0	.02	150	0	0	0	0	.04	150	0	0	0	0	.05	150	0	0	0
2°00'	.01	150	0	0	.02	150	0	0	0	0	.03	150	0	0	0	0	.05	150	0	0	0	0	.06	200	0	0	0
2°30'	.01	150	0	0	.02	150	0	0	0	0	.04	150	0	0	0	0	.06	150	0	0	0	0	.08	250	0	0	0
3°00'	.02	150	0	0	.03	150	0	0	0	0	.05	150	0	0	0	0	.07	200	0	0	0	0	.08	300	0	0	0
3°30'	.02	150	0	0	.03	150	0	0	0	0	.06	150	0	0	0	0	.08	200	0	0	0	0	.08	350	0	0	0
4°	.02	150	0	0	.04	150	0	0	0	0	.06	150	0	0	0	0	.08	250	0	0	0	2.0	.08	400	2.0	0	2.0
5°	.03	150	0	0	.05	150	0	0	0	0	.08	150	2.0	0	0	0	.08	300	2.0	0	0	2.0			Max. Curve 4°00'		
6°	.03	150	0	0	.06	150	0	0	0	0	.08	200	4.0	2.0	0	0	.08	350	2.0	0	0	3.0					
7°	.04	150	0	0	.07	150	2.0	0	0	0	.08	250	4.0	2.0	0	3.0			Max. Curve 6°00'								
8°	.05	150	2.0	0	.08	150	4.0	2.0	0	0	.08	300	4.0	2.0	0	3.0											
9°	.05	150	2.0	0	.08	150	4.0	2.0	0	3.0	.08	300	5.0	3.0	2.0	3.0											
10°	.06	150	4.0	2.0	.08	150	4.0	2.0	0	3.0			Max. Curve 9°00'														
11°	.06	150	4.0	2.0	.08	200	4.0	2.0	0	3.0																	
12°	.07	150	4.0	2.0	.08	200	5.0	3.0	2.0	4.0																	
13°	.07	150	4.0	2.0	.08	250	5.0	3.0	2.0	4.0																	
14°	.08	150	4.0	2.0	.08	250	5.0	3.0	2.0	4.0																	
15°00' to 22°59'	.08	150	5.0	3.0			Max. Curve 14°00'																			
23°00' to 23°59'	.08	150	6.0	4.0																						
24°00' to 25°00'	.08	200	6.0	4.0																						
		Max Curve 25°00'																								

NOTES:— Curves of 2°00' or less are not to be spiraled.
On dual lane projects, consider each roadbed separately.
"S" denotes the superelevation in Ft. per Ft.; L_s is the minimum length in feet of the spiral and widening transition; "W" the widening in feet for surfacing and inside shoulder.
Values for degrees of curve not shown in above table shall be identical with those for the nearest tabulated curve. In case of tie, use values for next higher degree curve.
See Curve data on Plan sheet for "L_s" to be used on each curve.

FIG. 168a. Superelevating and Widening.

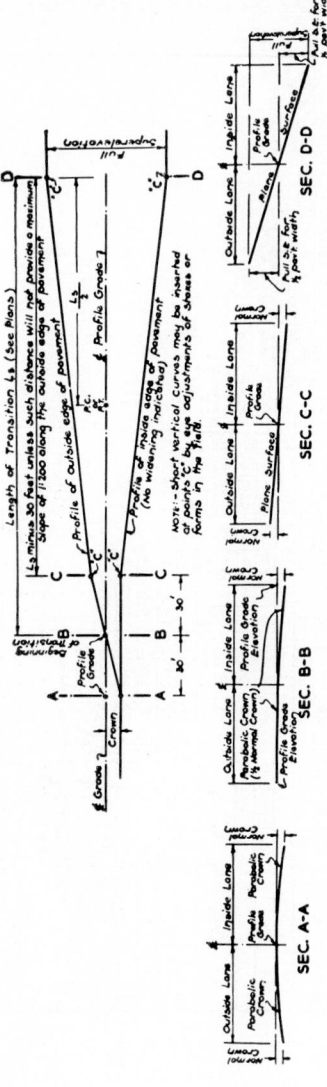

CASE NO. 1 —— Where High Point of Pavement is at ℄ on Tangent Section
(Note—Use for 2-lane traffic roads only. Pavement revolved about its ℄)

FIG. 168b. Straight Line Methods of Attaining Superelevation, Case No. 1.

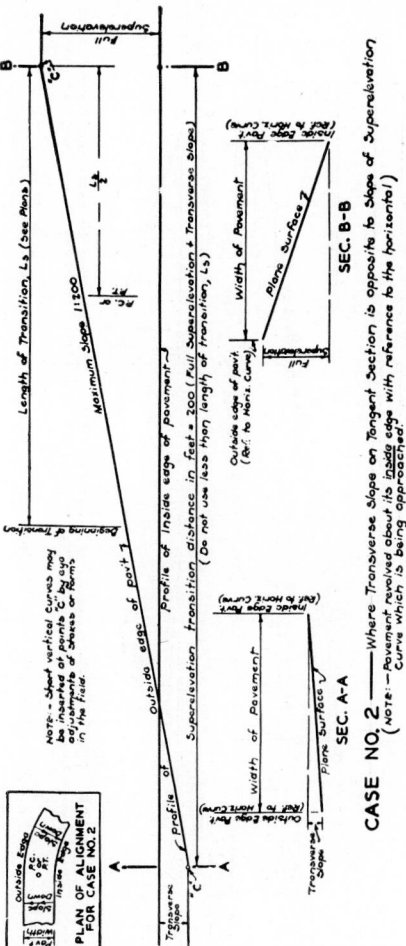

CASE NO. 2 — Where Transverse Slope on Tangent Section is opposite to Slope of Superelevation
(NOTE:—Pavement revolved about its inside edge with reference to the horizontal)
Curve which is being approached.)

Fig. 168c. Straight Line Methods of Attaining Superelevation, Case No. 2.

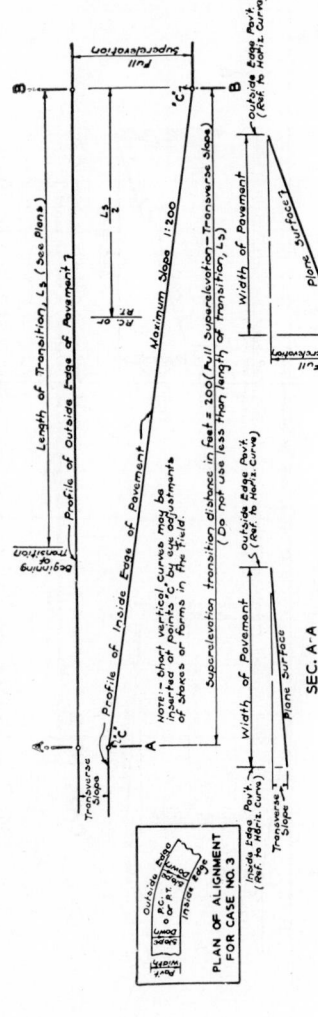

CASE NO. 3 — Where Transverse Slope on Tangent Section is in same Direction as Slope of Superelevation
(NOTE:- Pavement revolved about its outside edge with reference to horizontal curve which is being approached)

FIG. 168d. Straight Line Methods of Attaining Superelevation, Case No. 3.

Average daily traffic at the time of construction		SUPPLEMENTARY		
		Under 100 Vehicles	100 to 400 Vehicles	
Minimum & Desirable Speed			N	D
Design Speed in M.P.H.	Flat	40	45	55
	Rolling	30	35	45
	Mountainous	20	25	35
Non-Passing Sight Dist. (4.5Ft. & 4 inch)	Flat		315	415
	Rolling		240	315
	Mountainous		165	240
Passing Sight Dist. (4.5 Ft.& 4.5 Ft.; provide at least once every 2 miles)	Flat		1150	1750
	Rolling		700	1150
	Mountainous		500	700
Gradients	Flat	8 5	8	5
	Rolling	12 7	10	7
	Mountainous	15 10	12	9
Curvature	Flat	14°	11	7
	Rolling	25°	18	11
	Mountainous	56	36	18
Surface Width (Min.& Range)		12 - 20	16 - 20	
Roadbed Width (Min.& Range)		20	24	
Right of Way Width (Min.& Range)		60	60	
Cut Slopes (Not Steeper than)		$1\frac{1}{2}$:1	$1\frac{1}{4}$:1	
Fill Slopes (Not Steeper than)		$1\frac{1}{2}$:1	$1\frac{1}{4}$:1	
In Slopes (Not Steeper than)		2:1	2:1	
Depth of Ditch (Min. below Shoulder)		1	1	
Spiral Curves		None	None	
Bridges (New)	Width	14	22	
	Loading	H-10	H-15	
Bridges (Use in place)	Width		15	
	Loading		6 T	
Box Culvert Standards		C-531 (5'-12' Spans) C-532 (2'-4' Spans) C-31 (Skew)		
Pipe Culverts	For Cross-Road Struct.	12" to 180° Incl. No Hdwls.		
	For Struct. under Appr's.	12" to 180° Incl. No Hdwls.		
Typical Section Dwg.#		1 AC	1 AC	

Fig. 168e. General Design Data.

			MAJOR SYSTEM			
Average daily traffic at the time of construction			Under 400 Vehicles		400 to 1000 Vehicles	
Minimum & Desirable Speed			M	D	M	D
Design Speed in M.P.H.		Flat	45	55	50	60
		Rolling	35	45	40	50
		Mountainous	25	35	30	40
Non-Passing Sight Dist. (4.5 Ft. & 4 inch)		Flat	315	415	350	475
		Rolling	240	315	275	350
		Mountainous	165	240	200	275
Passing Sight Dist. (4.5 Ft.& 4.5 Ft.; provide at least once every 2 miles)		Flat	1150	1750	1400	2100
		Rolling	700	1150	900	1400
		Mountainous	500	700	500	900
Gradients		Flat	8	5	7	5
		Rolling	10	6	8	6
		Mountainous	12	7	10	7
Curvature		Flat	11	7	9	5
		Rolling	18	11	14	7
		Mountainous	36	18	25	11
Surface Width (Min.& Range)			18 - 20		18 - 22	
Roadbed Width (Min.& Range)			26 - 30		26 - 38	
Right of Way Width (Min.& Range)			80		80 - 100	
Cut Slopes (Not Steeper than)			1½:1		3:1 under 10'Ⓡ	
					2:1 over 10'Ⓡ	
Fill Slopes (Not Steeper than)			1½:1		3:1 under 10'Ⓡ	
					2:1 over 10' Ⓜ	
In Slopes (Not Steeper than)			2:1		3:1	
Depth of Ditch (Min. below Shoulder)			2		2	
Spiral Curves			On all Curves over 2°-00'			
Bridges (New)		Width	To be determined by Bridge Bureau			
		Loading				
Bridges (Use in place)		Width	To be determined by Bridge Bureau			
		Loading				
Box Culvert Standards			C-528 (5'-12' Spans) C-530 (2'-4' Spans) C-27 (Skew)			
Pipe Culverts	For Cross-Road Struct.		15" to 48" Incl. with Hdwls.			
	For Struct. under Appr's.		12" to 180" Incl. No Hdwls.			
Typical Section Dwg.#			1 AB		1 AB or 1 AA	

FIG. 168f. General Design Data.

MAJOR AND INTERSTATE SYSTEMS							
1000 to 2000 Vehicles		2000 to 3000 Vehicles		3000 to 5000 Vehicles		Over 5000 Vehicles	
M	D	M	D	M	D	M	D
60	65	65	70	65	70	65	70
50	55	55	60	55	60	55	60
40	45	40	50	40	50	40	50
475	540	540	600	540	600	540	600
350	415	415	475	415	475	415	475
275	315	275	350	275	350	275	350
2100	2500	2500	2900	2500	2900	2500	2900
1400	1750	1750	2100	1750	2100	1750	2100
900	1150	900	1400	900	1400	900	1400
5	5	5	5	5	5	5	5
6	6	6	6	6	6	6	6
6	6	6	6	6	6	6	6
5	5	5	4	5	4	5	4
7	7	7	6	7	6	7	6
11	9	11	9	11	9	11	9
22		22 - 24		24		44	
‡38 - 42		42 - 44		44		80 - 108	
120 - 220		120 - 220		120 - 250		150 - 250	
3:1 under 10'		3:1 under 10'		3:1 under 10'		3:1 under 10'	
2:1 over 10'		2:1 over 10'		2:1 over 10'		2:1 over 10'	
‡3:1 under 10'		4:1 under 10'		4:1 under 10'		4:1 under 10'	
2:1 over 10'		2:1 over 10'		2:1 over 10'		2:1 over 10'	
4:1		4:1		4:1		4:1	
2		2		2		2	
On all Curves over 2°-00'							
To be determined by Bridge Bureau							
To be determined by Bridge Bureau							
C-529 (5'-12' Spans) C-530 (2'-4' Spans) C-27 (Skew)							
15° to 48° Incl. with Hdwls.							
12° to 180° Incl. No Hdwls.							
I AB or I AA		I AA		I AA or Spec. for Dual Lane		Spec. for Dual	

Fig. 168g. General Design Data. (*Continued.*)

GENERAL NOTES

Minimum and desirable standards as listed apply to design speed only. After design speed is determined other standards listed under design speed are minimum and should be considered for use when they make possible an appreciable reduction in construction cost. In general more desirable standards should be used.

It is permissible to change design speed within a single project if topography indicates such proceedure will result in economy in construction.

For supplementary roads carrying over 400 vehicles per day use major system standards.

On major and interstate systems gradients of 7% may be used in short lengths only.

Cut and fill slopes are to be modified in stable and semi-stable materials. (See typical sections.)

*In special cases such as school house or cemetery in section corner, shorter radius may be used.

≠On interstate system fill slopes shall not be steeper than 4:1, and minimum 10' shoulder widths are required.

Dual Roads:- When average daily traffic at time of construction exceeds 3000 vehicles per day, secure R/W for dual construction. When traffic exceeds 5000 vehicles per day, consider initial dual construction.

Median Strip Widths:-
        Min. 15'; Desirable 40'. (Rural)
        Min. 4'; Desirable 12'. (Urban)

Urban Area Standards:-
        Min. Design speed 40 M.P.H.; Desirable 50 M.P.H.
        Max. Curvature 14°
        Min. Non-Passing Sight Distance 275'
        Min. Passing Sight Distance 900'
        Min. Lane Width 12'

"Rounding of slopes" and "Compacting by Rolling" required only when using major system standards. "Machine Grading" and "Reconditioning Roadway" generally permitted only when using supplementary standards.

⊕These slopes apply for Major System roads only. Steeper slopes permitted for supplementary roads.

In establishing culvert lengths normal roadbed width and normal slopes shall be used.

Fɪɢ. 168h. General Design Data.

294

CHAPTER XX

AERIAL PHOTOGRAPHY IN
ROUTE SURVEYING

By Talbert Abrams, President

Abrams Aerial Survey Corporation—Abrams Instrument Corporation
Lansing, Michigan

[This chapter was a pioneering address before the American Society for Engineering Education. It remains adequate and comprehensive although some of the older equipment such as the contour finder is now obsolete. Recent technical progress is indicated in the Addendum at the end of the chapter, added in 1956.]

169. General Considerations. Route surveying is thought of by many in connection with highways and railways only, but the very definition, the course or way which is to be traveled, alone indicates it refers to any method of transportation or transmission on the ground or in the air. Among the most common routes are airways, highways, railways, pipelines, transmission lines, cableways, beltways, drainage and intercoastal canals, river routes, and the like.

The usual ground methods of route surveying are accompanied by

(1) a sudden rise in real estate values along the route, resulting in higher costs of right-of-way, injunctions, and lawsuits.

(2) delays in preparing preliminary plans due to time required for preliminary ground surveys.

(3) a lack of visual evidence of the problems involved in locating the preliminary route.

(4) an indeterminate amount of study of several routes plus much field inspection to permit selection of best possible route for final location.

The traditional ground methods are rapidly being replaced by aerial photography and subsequent photo interpretation and photo measurements from

(1) contact prints.

(2) photographic enlargements.

(3) mosaics.

The planning of an aerial route survey will be centered around the choice of the

(1) photographic negative scale.

(2) width of area to be covered by flight.

(3) kind and accuracy of data to be acquired through the survey.

(4) equipment available.

The photographic mission for the aerial route survey will be planned in accordance with the

(1) best directions of flight.

(2) availability of bases.

(3) prevailing climatic conditions.

The engineering data available from an aerial route survey consists of

(1) a birdseye view of the entire project area from a mosaic.

(2) the qualitative facts through stereoscopic study of contact prints.

(3) the quantitative facts through parallax measurements with the Contour Finder, Height Finder and Stereoscopic Projection Mapping Machines.

Stereoscopic studies of contact prints provide

(1) qualitative data such as

(*a*) soil types.

(*b*) drainage.

(*c*) general information on the "lay of the land" for route selection.

(*d*) cultural features.

(2) quantitative parallax measurements with photogrammetric instruments for

(*a*) general differential leveling.

(*b*) profile leveling.

(*c*) cross sections for earthwork.

(*d*) borrow pit computations.

Mosaics are of several kinds

(1) uncontrolled, semi-controlled, and controlled.

(2) sectional or in one piece depending on size of job and scale of mosaic.

Some of the uses of the aerial route survey are that

(1) the entire right of way can be delineated.

(2) governmental land subdivision lines can be shown and used to describe right-of-way acquisition.

(3) individual property descriptions can be plotted.

(4) various types of work can be carried on at one time and progress of all jobs can be easily charted.

(5) one hundred per cent planimetric detail over or through which route might go can be seen at a glance.

(6) more logical comparison of routes can be made.

Highway and railway route surveys are of many kinds, among them being

(1) entirely new location.

(2) new location over part of route.

(3) straightening old route.

(4) access roads and railway sidings.

A suggested aerial program for these purposes would include

(1) a photo scale of 1 : 2,400, 1 : 4,800, 1 : 12,000, 1 : 60,000.

(2) a width of project of one flight along a center line or a blocking up of an area or region.

(3) a choice of scale which is a factor in the scope of parallax measurements. A practical contour interval would be between 1/600 and 1/1200 of flight altitude, depending on the stereo-photogrammetric instrument to be used. A low altitude flight might be desirable for earthwork computation.

(4) The use of photo enlargements for the plan part of the plan and profile would eliminate all of topographic survey-ing other than pure traverse work and spot elevations.

A suggested program for an oil, gas, or water pipeline would include

(1) a photo scale of 1 : 5,000, 1 : 10,000, 1 : 20,000.

(2) one flight width for long lines.

(3) less interest in earthwork than in overall gradient, as pipeline may be laid near top of ground.

(4) a stereoscopic study for location of best gradient. Differential leveling with the Contour Finder can give actual gradient. A pipeline transports material under pressure and thus must use boosters along the line. As straight an alignment as possible is therefore desired. It would probably be better to increase gradient and use boosters over a shorter route than to use a longer route with flatter grades.

A suggested program for an overhead transmission line would include

(1) large scale photos and low altitude flight.

(2) no earthwork involved.

(3) use of parallax measurements to spot tower locations and compute maximum wire or cable sag allowable and, therefore, low altitude photos are necessary for measuring accuracy.

(4) one flight wide.

Once a route is established it will remain an artery of life and commerce until it is no longer needed, or until it has become an obstacle in the way of progress, so its location must be chosen with great care and engineering ability. Every scientific instrument that could contribute to a better location should be employed and the more information used wisely the less the cost and the more useful the route will be.

There is now described step by step the usual method of making an air survey for route locations here in the United States.

170. Example Number I. The project is a Super-Highway, Detroit to Willow Run, a distance of 25 miles.

1st Step. All information available was gathered together, which in this case was the following:

State Highway Maps

Regional Highway Maps
County Road Maps
Township Road Maps
City Maps
Aerial Photographs, scale 1 : 20,000, 5 years old
Aerial Photographs, scale 1 : 10,000, 10 years old

2nd Step. Study was made in the office of all maps and aerial photos and it was decided that a reconnaissance flight was necessary with all project engineers flown over the area. [Today all of this study would be made in the office from photogrammetric plan and topographic maps, thus saving time and money.]

3rd Step. A conference was held and the several possible locations were sketched, thus narrowing the location down to a minimum for the aerial survey.

4th Step. A set of air photos was made, at a scale of $1'' = 800'$, of the reduced area and studied stereoscopically, to note any unusual obstructions that would interfere with a road location.

5th Step. The tentative road location was plotted on the office pictures which were enlarged to a scale of approximately $1'' = 200'$ without ever having had a man on the ground in the field.

6th Step. The land buyers were now given a set of pictures, scale $1'' = 400'$, without the road location, but just the outline of the pieces of property which they were to buy.

7th Step. The center line of the highway having now been tentatively decided and the future location narrowed down to the bare minimum necessary, it was decided to have still larger pictures made of the restricted areas.

8th Step. Stereoscopic aerial photos, scale $1'' = 200'$ with enlargements at the scale of $1'' = 40'$, were made on which to plot all grade separations, crossovers, under-passes and drainage structures, and with the land layout in visual form to show the location of all trees, shrubs, surface stones, buildings, existing drainage, and structures. Practically all questions could be answered in the office and a final align-

ment and road layout was designed onto the photos. As
property lines were being surveyed and monumented in the
field, the ground control was secured to make our enlargements as accurate as the ground control could be plotted.

9th Step.   Many hand-drawn line maps were made from
the aerial photos as follows:

Maps were traced directly from the enlargements.

Maps were plotted with the sketchmasters.

Maps were drawn off at varying scales with the Panta-
graph.

Maps showing contours were made with the Contour
Finder.

Road maps were made showing first, second, and third
class roads; trails; paths and bridges; farm lanes; railroads;
and conditions of roads and materials used and available.

Maps showing legal property descriptions and buildings
and fences were made by the legal department.

Comparative tax values were plotted on the photos.

It must be kept in mind that this route map made by the
aerial survey was in a suburban area adjacent to the fourth
largest city in the United States.   The area was relatively
flat and had been mapped and re-mapped many times for
almost every imaginable purpose, but still when a new
project such as the Willow Run Super-Highway was conceived, the very latest information was necessary and could
best be gotten by the aerial method.

171. Example Number II.   The opposite of this condition is a road to be built through poorly wooded, rugged
north country.   The project is in the planning stage, the
route is to connect existing trunk lines along a better and
shorter route, but money is not available for the shorter
route if it costs too much.

Timber cruisers have a good general idea of the country
and recommend the old logging routes be improved.   No
good existing map is available.   The area is 100 miles long
by 25 miles wide.

1st Step.   The area is photographed at a scale of 1 : 40,000 and the stereoscopic pictures studied to get a better idea of the country.   A photo index gave us the first reasonably accurate map of the area showing rivers, lakes, trails, hills, swamps, and mountains.

2nd Step.   Monumented ground control established around the perimeter of the area by the U.S.G.S. was re-covered and plotted on a new base, scale 1 : 20,000 and new astronomical positions were established for additional con-trol at about one point for every 50 square miles or one fix as near the center as possible of every 7.5 minute quadrangle.

3rd Step.   A Lazy Daisy Mechanical Triangulator lay down was built up and a new map projected and with this control a mosaic was made at the scale of 1 : 20,000, thus giving us the first map of the area with a relatively high degree of accuracy.

4th Step.   The appearance of the mosaic and the shadows gave a general appearance of relief; however, this could not be depended upon for locating a highway route so the Con-tour Finder was used without any vertical ground control. By using just the height of the airplane and the measured distance between print centers and the Photogrammetric Computer we gained a factor suitable for a preliminary check of the relief in the area.

We laid out several prospective center lines for the new route and then with the Contour Finder, checked the vary-ing elevations along the routes and for a distance of about 2000 feet both sides of the route.   With this information we were able to estimate the cost of cuts and fills, the number of culverts and bridges required and also the scenic value of comparable routes.   Finally, having established the relative cost, utility to the best parts of the area, and the scenic values, a choice of many routes was narrowed down to several possibilities fairly close to each other.

5th Step.   Now with a good air map at hand that could be used as a flight map for low altitude picture, we went back and flew a single flight strip at a scale of 1 : 4800 along the center line of the area best adapted to the route. This flight strip was 3600 feet wide and covered the best possibilities. The flight at low altitude was made in the early spring before the leaves came out on the trees.

6th Step. The air photos, scale 1 : 4800, were studied stereoscopically and, with the Contour Finder to check spot elevations, a final line was picked along the easiest grades avoiding swamps and difficult areas.

Air photo enlargements, scale 1 : 1200, were made for use as plane table sheets.

The proposed center line was marked on these sheets and the survey crew went into the field to accurately measure the horizontal and vertical distances and stake out the route. With a protractor in the drafting room, compass bearings were measured and plotted on the photographic plane table sheets, and distances were scaled off to points of intersection where the route turned to a new tangent.

In the heavily wooded areas, transits were set up to the pre-determined angles and lines were cut through the woods for several miles at a time, the only check being the information available on the aerial photographs. The 110-mile line was staked in the field without any off-line survey. Points of beginning and ending were the same as originally planned.

7th Step. With the vertical control established along the center line, the Contour Finder completed the necessary contouring on both sides of the center line for a distance of 200 feet where necessary. In some places a watershed line was extended around a basin, the drainage of which had to be accommodated by bridge or culvert. In areas like this, no other contouring was necessary.

Going back over this project one will see that we took a look at 2500 square miles. The high altitude photography required about 250 pictures. For the low altitude maximum information pictures only 400 were required. The field survey was limited to 10 "astronomical fixes" and about 110 miles of transit traverse and leveling. Most of

Fig. 172. Galileo-Santoni Stereocartograph, Model IV, in the Abrams Laboratory.

Fig. 172a. Abrams Laboratory Technicians Check the Scale of a Large Stapled Mosaic of Fort Wayne.

the engineering was done on the photos in the office under good supervision and control. The engineers were worth more to the job interpreting photos, contouring, and mosaicking than they would have been as draftsmen plotting field notes and were paid more because of their specialty as photogrammetrists.

172. Addendum.   There have been described briefly the steps necessary for the earlier surveys.   We have since, to 1956, completed a great many other types of surveys for river projects, railway terminals, pipe lines, power transmission lines, and many other kinds of routes as well as a great variety of surveys for other purposes.   Our highway work now is mostly one-foot or two-foot contour maps made directly from photographs with little ground control.   The newer techniques for highways are quite improved over a few years ago.

Techniques and equipment are constantly improving.   Our laboratories are equipped with Italian Santoñi Stereocartographs, Fig. 172, and this first order plotting equipment for photogrammetric work is without doubt the finest in the world for making contour maps directly from photographs and extending the ground control by aerial triangulation.   We also have Kelch type plotters, the Multiplex, Stereoscopes and Height Finders.

The Detroit area, typical of many cities, has been photographed at least ten times to my knowledge in the past thirty years, often for route location and construction.   Photogrammetry is not just aerial photography.   It is the science of making vertical measurements from stereophotographs and that includes microphotography and microscopic photography, Stereoscopic X-ray, Optical Comparators, and the newer measurements of electronic images such as Radar and Television.

Selected references follow:

Abrams, Talbert, *Essentials of Aerial Surveying and Photo Interpretation*, McGraw-Hill Book Company, New York, 1944.
American Society of Photogrammetry, *Manual of Photogrammetry*, Pitman Publishing Corp., New York, 1950.
Sharp, H. O., *Practical Photogrammetry*, The Macmillan Company, 1951.

PROBLEMS

The answers for curve problems are based on the chord definition of degree of curve. *Arc definition* answers vary slightly.

Begin sketches for curves at the left of the sheet and turn all intersection angles to the right.

CHAPTER I

1. List all of the types of industry you can think of that require route surveys.

2. State the factors that influence route selection.

CHAPTER II

1. Make a map reconnaissance on a United States Geological Survey topographic sheet, or sheets, for a type of route in which you are interested, preferably in some territory with which you are familiar and which you can easily reach for field work. It is desirable to choose a type of route which involves the more difficult field and office work. If available, use aerial photographs or maps.

2. Following the foregoing map reconnaissance, take a short set of barometric field notes similar to those in the text. It is preferable that the elevation of the points be unknown and that they be computed according to the methods given in the text. They should then be checked against the true elevations.

3. Make a map reconnaissance, a field reconnaissance, and a reconnaissance report for a small project, preferably covering that of the two preceding problems. Consider various alternative methods of serving the needs: for example, consider whether a trucking road, or an industrial railroad, or a tramway, or a waterway would be the most economical and best means of moving coal from a mine.

CHAPTER III

1. Make a preliminary survey of the most desirable route indicated by the preceding reconnaissance. It is desirable that each of several parties use a different one of the methods described in the text for making the preliminary survey and that the various methods be discussed with the other parties, thus familiarizing all with the several methods. Complete the preliminary map including contours. The preliminary map may be made by aerial methods.

2. Make a bill of the cost of the preliminary survey just completed using current normal salary scales for engineering work of this type.

CHAPTER IV

1. Make a location survey over the preceding preliminary survey, first making a paper location on the preliminary map and taking a profile from this paper location. If part of the location demands a long uniform grade, use a grade contour in projecting this portion of the map. In important work, or for flat-grade hydraulic work, it is frequently desirable to survey the grade contour on the ground before staking the final location.

2. Make a bill of the cost of the location survey using normal engineering salaries.

3. Prepare an engineers' estimate of the cost of the project.

CHAPTER V

1. (a) Given $I = 39° 24'$, $D = 3° 30'$ and P.I. $= 37 + 43.8$. Compute field note for staking this curve, including two setups at intermediate full stations on the curve. Solve by formulas and check by tables. Ans. $T = 586.2$, $L = 1125.7$, $E = 101.8$, T.C. $= 31 + 57.6$

(b) Same for $D = 4°$.

(c) Same for $D = 4° 30'$.

2. (a) How can a simple curve be run in and checked if either the T.C. or the C.T. is inaccessible?

(b) Same with P.I. inaccessible.

(c) Same with an obstruction on the curve about one-third of the way around the curve.

3. (a) A $3°$ curve begins at station $373 + 20$. Find the tangent offset at station 376. What is the approximate distance at 376 between this curve and a curve which is $1°$ sharper beginning at the same T.C.? Ans. 6.9 feet, 20.5 feet

(b) Same for a $4°$ curve.

(c) Same for a $2°$ curve.

4. (a) For the curve of problem 3a with $I = 12° 18'$, compute the offsets from the tangent to all stations using geometric and trigonometric methods. Check offset to C.T. by R vers I. Ans. 43.84 feet

(b) Same for a $4°$ curve.

(c) Same for a $2°$ curve.

5. Again refer to 3. Show on a sketch how you would pass an obstruction at station 375 on the curve by a method or methods other than offsets from the long chord, assuming that most of the curve could be staked by deflection angles.

6. (a) A 300-foot chord of a simple curve makes an angle of 5° 30′ with an adjacent 200-foot chord produced. Find D. Ans. D = 2° 12′

(b) Same with 250-foot and 150-foot chords intersecting at an angle of 4°.

(c) Same for 350-foot and 250-foot chords intersecting at an angle of 6°.

7. Prove that for a 1° curve the chord offset in feet is very closely one and three-quarters times D for each 100-foot station.

8. Find the length of chord whose middle ordinate in inches will equal the degree of curve. Show the derivation.

9. (a) If four equal chords are used instead of one 100-foot chord in laying out the 20° curve, how long should they be?

(b) Same for 15° curve.

(c) Same for 25° curve.

10. (a) The alignment of a route survey is as follows: Beginning at station 39 + 89, thence N 8° 40′ W to station 42 + 80, thence around a 3° curve right (central angle = 28° 12′), thence along the tangent to station 60 + 12, thence around a 4° curve left (central angle = 43° 28′). The coordinates of 39 + 89 are N 6483.0 and E 8645.0. Find the coordinates of the center of the arc of the final curve. Ans. N 8977.7, E 9035.6

(b) Same with D = 2° on first curve and 3° on second curve.

(c) Same with D = 4° on first curve and 5° on second curve.

11. (a) Two tangents intersect at station 10 + 40 at an angle of 38° 24′. What degree of curve will pass through a point 23.7 feet to the right of station 8 + 75 on the back tangent? Ans. D = 5° 43′

(b) Same with offset of 18.4 feet.

(c) Same with offset of 28.9 feet.

12. (a) A 3° curve with I = 14° 46′ has been staked on the ground, the T.C. falling at station 14 + 27.0. Excessive earthwork on this location requires that the curve be sharpened so as to move the center of the arc radially for 6.0 feet. What degree of curve is required and what is the station of the new T.C.? Ans. 4° 48′, 15 + 19.7

(b) Same with the curve flattened to move the center of the arc a distance of 6.0 feet.

(c) Same with the curve sharpened to move the center of the arc a distance of 3.0 feet.

13. (a) A 3° curve right with I = 38° 10′ has been run in the field and it is found that the C.T. is three feet too far to the left of, and the tangent is parallel to, the required forward tangent. How much and in what direction must the T.C. be moved in order that the C.T. shall correspond with the required forward tangent? Ans. 4.9 feet

(b) Same but three feet to the right.

(c) Same but five feet to the left.

CHAPTER VI

1. (a) Two tangents intersecting at an angle of $32°\ 0'$ are to be connected with a compound curve $D = 3°$ and $D = 6°$. $I_L = 19°\ 22'$. Find the intersection angle, I_S, and the tangent lengths of the compound curve. Ans. $I_S = 12°\ 38'$, $T_S = 375.9$, $T_L = 504.1$

(b) Same with $I = 28°$.

(c) Same with $I = 24°$.

2. In problem 1 using $T_S = 309.30$ but not having I_L given; find I_S, I_L, and T_L for the same intersecting tangents. Ans. $I_S = 20°\ 38'$, $I_L = 11°\ 22'$, $T_L = 478.58$

3. (a) Given $I = 58°\ 42'$, $I_L = 32°\ 30'$, $D_S = 6°$, and $D_L = 3°$. Compute I_S and T_S. Find the station of T.C., C.C., and C.T.; with the P.I. at station $29 + 83.3$. Set up the field notes for the compound curve. The long radius is adjacent to the C.T. Ans. $I_S = 26°\ 12'$, $T_S = 712.00'$, $T_L = 959.13'$

(b) Same with $D_S = 4°$ and $D_L = 2°$.

(c) Same with $D_S = 5°$ and $D_L = 1°$.

4. (a) Given $I = 46°\ 18'$ at station $88 + 79.3$, $D_L = 3°\ 30'$, $I_L = 22°\ 18'$, $D_S = 6°$, $I_S = 24°\ 0'$. Without changing the radii, compute the new value of I_L so that the curve will end in a parallel tangent five feet outside of the T.C. that is adjacent to the long radius curve. Place R_L and T.C. at left. Ans. $I_L = 23°\ 23'$

(b) Same but five feet inside of the T.C.

(c) Same but ten feet outside of the C.C.

5. (a) Given $I = 36°\ 42'$, $D = 3°$, T.C. $= 18 + 17.0$, and at station 27 a line AB which makes an angle of $20°$ right with the forward tangent. When the $3°$ curve and the line AB are connected by an $8°$ curve, find T_L by solving triangles along the forward tangents. Ans. $T_L = 754.0'$

(b) Same with a $7°$ connecting curve.

(c) Same with a $6°$ connecting curve.

6. (a) A $4°$ curve, T.C. $= 37 + 42.0$, is staked for a $16°\ 8'$ central angle where it is desired to offset 20-feet right inwardly along the radius to a point B. It is desired to run a curve from the old T.C. through B. Find the degree of the required curve. Also com-

pound this required curve at B to end on the final tangent of the
4° curve, where $I = 40° 11'$.   *Ans.* 5° 28'

(*b*) Same but 25-feet right.

(*c*) Same but 30-feet right.

7. (*a*) Given a simple curve with $D = 3°$, $I = 27° 36'$, and
T.C. = 781 + 47.0. Substitute a 5° curve for the 3° curve and
flatten the ends using $I_L = 3°$. What will be the degree of two
equal flat curves which end at the same T.C. and C.T.? *Ans.* Approximately, from lengths of curves, 1° 14'

(*b*) Same, substituting a 4° curve.

(*c*) Same, substituting a 6° curve.

8. (*a*) A railroad industrial track leaves a straight main line
with a No. 8 turnout. From the heel of the frog a 12° reverse
curve becomes parallel (at point A) to the main line at a right
angle distance therefrom of 192 feet. What is the distance (measured parallel to the main line) from A to the $\frac{1}{2}$-inch point of frog?
Ans. 520.35 feet

(*b*) Same with No. 10 frog.

(*c*) Same with No. 12 frog and reversed curves with $D = 8°$.

NOTE. Use §§ 43 and 72. If room permits, tangents would
be inserted.

CHAPTER VII

1. Work some of the problems of Chapter VI by solving a
traverse.

CHAPTER VIII

1. (*a*) Compute by the first method and check by the second
method of § 48 a vertical curve 600 feet long connecting a $+ 0.2$
percent grade with a $- 0.6$ percent grade, proceeding to the right.
The grades intersect at station 100 with an elevation of 721.42 feet.

(*b*) Same, but with a $+ 0.4$ percent grade meeting a $+ 0.2$
percent grade.

(*c*) Same, but with a $- 0.6$ percent grade meeting a $+ 0.4$
percent grade.

2. In problem 1, how long a vertical curve would be needed for
a first class railroad? (*a*) *Ans.* 8 stations

3. How long a vertical curve would be needed for a first class highway with $g = +2$ percent, $g' = -4$ percent, and sight distance
= 1000 feet. *Ans.* 16 stations

4. (*a*) Find the maximum degree of curve, also the maximum r
(rate of change of gradient), around which it would be possible
to lay a 12-inch bell-joint concrete pipe, if the pipe comes in 16-foot
lengths. Assume the bell to be 4 inches long, with an available
total clearance of one-fourth inch. Check your conclusions by

means of a manufacturer's catalog. *Ans.* 22½°. Use smaller value

(*b*) Same but for 12-foot lengths of 36-inch cast-iron pipe.

(*c*) Same but for 3-foot lengths of 24-inch vitrified sewer pipe.

5. Derive formulas 51 and 51a.

6. Plot a 1500-foot sight distance on Fig. 51.

CHAPTER IX

1. Discuss unbalanced superelevation and minimum length of spirals.

2. (*a*) On a railroad where the maximum curvature is 3°, what maximum speed is permissible? Assuming that there is no limitation on the expense involved in lengthening a spiral, what length of spiral would you recommend?

(*b*) Same with 5°.

(*c*) Same with 7°.

3. (*a*) A D. & R. G. Railway passenger train makes a 75-mile run from Colorado Springs to Denver in one hour and fifteen minutes. Around 5° curves on this territory, what would be your recommendation regarding maximum speed, actual superelevation, unbalanced superelevation and desirable length of spiral? Discuss.

(*b*) Same with a 6° curve.

(*c*) Same with a 4° curve.

4. (*a*) Given $D = 2°$, $I = 14° 10'$, T.S. $= 39 + 43.6$ and $L = 500$ feet. Set up a complete set of field notes for laying out this curve with identical spirals. *Ans.* $T = 606.4$ feet, S.T. $= 51 + 51.9$

(*b*) Same with $D = 1° 30'$ and $L = 200$ feet.

(*c*) Same with $D = 3°$ and $L = 300$ feet.

5. (*a*) A 6° curve. $I = 36° 24'$, is spiraled with $L = 195$ feet on one end and $L = 260$ feet on the opposite end. Compute the tangent distances. *Ans.* $Ts_S = 414.24$ $Ts_L = 442.76'$

(*b*) Same with 5° curve and with each spiral 15 feet shorter than in (*a*).

(*c*) Same with 4° curve and with each spiral 30 feet shorter than in (*a*).

6. With the data of problem 4 compute the spiral deflection angles for running in the spiral with the transit at the sharper end of the spiral. Check by Table X.

7. With the data of problem 4 compute the spiral deflection angles for running in the spiral with the transit at point 7 (7/10 of the way around the spiral).

8. With the data of problem 4 compute the coordinates for staking the spiral with the T.S. as origin.

9. With the data of problem 4, station $39 + 52$ is the beginning of a pile trestle consisting of twelve 16-foot spans. Compute the spiral deflection angles for locating the centers of the last two pile caps. *Ans.* $14'$ and $16'$

10. Given a compound curve of $3°$ and $7°$ with $I = 46° 12'$ and $I_L = 20° 15'$. Use 150 feet of spiral on the $3°$ curve, 280 feet of spiral on the $7°$ curve, and 200 feet of spiral between the curves. Compute the two tangent lengths and the deflection angles for the 200-ft. spiral between the curves. *Ans.* $T_L = 740.91'$, $T_S = 580.92'$

11. With the data of problem 4, compute Es.

12. Derive the formulas in Fig. 66a.

CHAPTER X

1. (a) Draw the sketch and dimension it for a No. 8 turnout with straight switch rails from straight track. Show on the sketch how you would determine the frog angle of an existing frog which you ran across in stock. Compute the radius of the turnout curve.

(b) Same for No. 10 turnout.

(c) Same for No. 12 turnout.

2. (a) Compute the minimum distance between $\frac{1}{2}$-inch frog points (parallel to the main track) for a crossover between parallel straight tracks on 16 foot centers, using a No. 8 turnout with straight switch rails in one track and a No. 10 turnout with straight switch rails in the other. What is the degree of connecting curve between frogs. *Ans.* 58.2 feet, $3° 31'$

(b) Same for No. 10 frog and No. 12 frog.

(c) Same for No. 12 frog and No. 16 frog.

3. (a) Find the minimum degree of curve necessary to connect a No. 8 turnout with a parallel siding on 14-foot centers. *Ans.* $5° 24'$

(b) Same for a No. 10 turnout from a $4°$ main line curve.

(c) Same for a No. 12 turnout from a $3°$ main line curve.

4. In problem 2, with straight track between frogs and with identical frogs having the number first given, find the distance parallel to the main tract between points A and A' as indicated on Fig. 70a. *Ans.* 127.5 feet

5. (a) Two parallel straight tracks on 16-foot centers are connected by a reverse curve crossover of 521.7 radius, using No. 8 turnouts, with straight switch rails. What is the distance between $\frac{1}{2}$-inch points of frog, parallel to the main line. *Ans.* 47.59 feet

(b) Same with No. 10 turnouts.

(c) Same with No. 12 turnouts and $4°$ reverse curve.

6. (a) Sketch and dimension for staking a turnout from single to double track on 16-foot centers (center line of single track produced to lie midway between double tracks) using a No. 10 frog.

(b) Same for No. 16 frog.

(c) Same for No. 20 frog.

7. (a) A No. 8 turnout (straight switch rails) is located with $\frac{1}{2}$-inch P.F. 100 feet from the intersection of the tangent produced of a mine spur. The angle between the tangent produced and the main line is 15°. What minimum degree of curve and what central angle of curve will be needed for the connection? *Ans.* 1° 39′, 7° 51′

(b) Same for No. 10 turnout.

(c) Same for No. 12 turnout.

8. (a) The tangent, produced, of a new industrial track makes a deflection angle of 40° 32′ with a straight main line. The connecting curve, beginning at the heel of a No. 10 frog in the main line, is to be a 12° curve. What is the distance from the intersection of the straight center lines to a point opposite to the $\frac{1}{2}$-inch P.F., measures along the center of the main line? *Ans.* 134.78 ft.

(b) Same with angle of 60° 18′ and a 10° curve.

(c) Same with an angle of 113° 23′ and a 7° curve.

9. In the preceding problem, it is necessary to move the frog backward (away from the intersection of the tangents) 4.3 feet so that the heel of the frog may come at a rail joint. What is the degree of the connecting curve? *Ans.* 11° 40′

10. (a) A Y track is to be located with a stem, produced, making an angle of 86° 41′ with a main line and connected thereto with an 8° curve. The other branch of the Y is to be a 10° curve. No. 8 turnouts with straight switch rails are to be used. Give data for staking, omitting curve notes. The 10° curve has the larger I.

(b) Same with an angle of 109° 13.

(c) Same with an angle of 102° 46′.

11. (a) Two main lines cross at an angle of 68° 11′. Using two No. 10 turnouts, compute the distance from the intersection of the main line center lines to each of the $\frac{1}{2}$-inch P.F.s. $D = 7°$. *Ans.* 483.56 ft.

(b) Same with angle of 78° 35′. $D = 9°$.

(c) Same with angle of 114° 56′. $D = 12°$.

12. (a) Sketch a yard ladder track layout using No. 8 turnouts with straight switch rails and with four tracks on 14-foot centers. State how you would proceed to stake it.

(b) Same with No. 8 turnout from main track and No. 10 turnouts from ladder track.

(c) Same with the ladder track making twice the angle of a No. 8 frog with the main line, with the second track taking out of the main line, and with the third and fourth yard tracks and the fifth and sixth yard tracks (six tracks in this case) being arranged in pairs. One track of each pair turns out from the ladder track and the other track of that pair turns out from the first track of that pair. The purpose here is to shorten the yard.

CHAPTER XI

1. Stringlining is best learned by measuring and tabulating ordinates on an existing railroad curve and computing its revised alignment ordinates. Here practical difficulties are encountered and judgment is needed as well as theory.

CHAPTER XII

1. (*a*) Following a field reconnaissance survey, how would you make an estimate of excavation and embankment, including classification, for a main line railway?

(*b*) Same, but for a main highway.

(*c*) Same, but for a large canal.

2. (*a*) Following a preliminary survey, how would you make an estimate of excavation and embankment, including classification, for a main line railway?

(*b*) Same, but for a main highway.

(*c*) Same, but for a large canal.

3. (*a*) Following a final location survey which included cross-sections, answer the same questions as in 2.

4. (*a*) Make a preliminary estimate of the yardage in cut and fill, separately, from station 4 + 00 to 5 + 00, inclusive, on the profile of Fig. 85a, using Table XXII. *Ans.* 370 cu. yds.

(*b*) Same, but for stations 0 + 00 to 1 + 00.

(*c*) Same, but for stations 1 + 64 to 3 + 00.

5. Same as problem 4 except assume the ground slopes 20 percent transversely, and use Tables XIX and XX. *Ans.* 450 cu. yds.

6. (*a*) Using the field cross-section notes of Fig. 85b, compute by formulas and check by diagram of Table XXI, the yardage for a final estimate between stations 0 + 0 and 0 + 46, omitting the prismoidal and curvature corrections, as is the common practice. *Ans.* 201 cu. yds.

(*b*) Same, but for stations 0 + 46 to 1 + 00.

(*c*) Same, but for stations 1 + 00 to 1 + 64.

7. (*a*) Same as problem 6 except for stations 1 + 64 to 2 + 00.

(*b*) Same as problem 6 except for stations 2 + 00 to 2 + 28.

(*c*) Same as problem 6 except for stations 2 + 28 to 2 + 87.4.

8. (*a*) Using the cross-section notes between station 3 and station 4 of Fig. 85b, plat on cross-section paper (scale 1″ = 10′), planimeter the cross-sections, and take the yardage from Table XXIII. *Ans.* 376 cu. yds.

(*b*) Same but using station 4 to station 4 + 48.

(*c*) Same but using station 4 + 48 to station 5.

9. (*a*) Compute the yardage between station 3 and station 4 of Fig. 85b by the method of § 90. *Ans.* 376 cu. yds.

(*b*) Same, but using station 4 to 4 + 48.

(*c*) Same, but using station 4 + 48 to station 5.

10. (*a*) Compute by formula the prismoidal volume between station 1 to station 1 + 64, and check by using Table XXI to get end area volume and to apply prismoidal correction. Check by grade triangle method. *Ans.* 332.7 cu. yds.

(*b*) Same, but from station 0 + 46 and station 1.

(*c*) Same, but from station 3 to station 4, noting that station 4 is *not* a three-level section.

11. Prove that $\dfrac{2}{3}\left(\dfrac{d_L + d_R}{2}\right)$ is the correct expression for that distance as shown on Fig. 100.

12. (*a*) Determine the curvature correction at station 1 on Fig. 85b, assuming that the alignment is on a ten-degree curve to the right. Is the correction to be added to, or subtracted from, the volume computed by averaging end areas? *Ans.* 2.8 cu. yds., subtracted, per station

(*b*) Same, but at station 0 + 46.

(*c*) Same, but at station 0, considering only the cut for which payment is made.

CHAPTER XIII

1. From the profile, or (preferably) from the cross-section notes taken on the location survey or later prepare a mass diagram: assume unit costs for Class A excavation, Class C excavation, borrow, and overhaul (including an assumed free haul limit); compute the economic limit of haul; establish economic balances on the diagram; establish the free haul limits on the diagram; compute the amount of overhaul; and make an estimate of the cost. Assume the usual case in which the contractor is paid for excavation, borrow and overhaul but is not paid for embankment.

CHAPTER XIV

1. A right of way description reads as follows: Beginning at the Northwest corner of Section 25, Township 10 North, Range 3 East of the Willamette Meridian, Salem County, Oregon; thence N 37° 47' W 287.6 feet to a point of tangency; thence northerly along the arc of a simple curve to the right of 2864.9 feet radius for a distance of 1830.0 feet to a point of tangency; thence 2000.0 feet along a line AB, etc. Without changing the radius, amend the description so that the line AB shall be 20 feet to the right of its former location. Rewrite the description to conform to the new location.

2. Prepare right of way descriptions for various types of routes repeating the figures in words and otherwise making the description as error proof as possible.

ASTRONOMIC PROBLEMS

1. (*a*) Compute from the Ephemeris the declination of the sun for your location, for the current year, at 4:00 P.M. (Standard time), August 3. (*b*) For 10:00 A.M. December 6. (*c*) For 2:30 P.M. March 21. (*d*) For 9:30 A.M. September 23.

2. (*a*) Compute from formula (148) the bearing of Polaris at elongation for your locality and for the current year, for that date on which the bearing is a maximum. Check by the Ephemeris table. (*b*) For the date on which the bearing is a minimum. (*c*) For the current date. (*d*) For March 7.

3. (*a*) For your locality and for the current year, compute from the Ephemeris the watch time for a night elongation of Polaris on January 16. Is Polaris east or west of the meridian? (*b*) June 21. (*c*) October 16. (*d*) December 4.

4. (*a*) From the following notes, compute the watch time of a night elongation of Polaris for the current date, and for your locality. Is that elongation east or west of the meridian? Compute the angle of formula (148) and check by the Ephemeris table. Compute the azimuth from the transit to the reference point. (*b*) For February 22, of the current year. (*c*) For July 7, of the current year. (*d*) For November 29, of the current year.

OBSER-VATION	BUBBLE	PLATE VERNIERS			REMARKS
		A	B	Mean	
	Down	0° 00′	180° 00′		On reference stake
1	"	18° 49′	198° 50′		Clockwise, to Polaris at elongation
2	Up	198° 51′	18° 50′		On Polaris at elonga-tion
	"	180° 01′	0° 00′		On reference stake

5. (*a*) For the current date and your locality, compute the azimuth of a line from the transit to the reference point, for the following set of direct solar observations. While this is not a bona fide set of data for various localities and times, yet the computations may be carried through satisfactorily. (*b*) For Latitude 47° 25′ north, Longitude 122° 18′ west. (*c*) For Latitude 29° 11′

north, Longitude 82° 07′ west.   (d) For Latitude 27° 49′ north, Longitude 97° 52′ west.

| Object | Plate Verniers | | | Vertical Angle | Watch (Standard) Time |
	A	B	Mean		
	Telescope Normal				
Ref. stake	0° 00′	180° 00′			
Sun $\underline{0}$|-	23° 18′	203° 18′		34° 03′	9:16
	(clockwise)				
	Telescope Inverted				
Sun -|$\overline{0}$	203° 25′	23° 25′		35° 01′	9:19
Ref. stake	180° 01′	0° 01′			

CHAPTER XVIII

1. (a) Given D = 18° 32′, I = 93° 14′, and the P.I. at station 137 + 41.2, fill in a tabulation similar to the following which compares the curves as computed by the chord definition and by the arc definition.   No entries can be made in the blanks which contain the short horizontal line. c_1, c_2, d_1, and d_2 are the first and final chords and the corresponding deflection angles.

| | 100-Foot Chord Definition | | | | 100-Foot Arc Definition | | | |
| | From Formula | | From Tables | | From Formula | | From Tables | |
	Exact	Approx.	Exact	Approx.	Exact	Approx.	Exact	Approx.
R			—			—		—
T		—				—		—
E		—				—		—
L			—			—		—
C.T.			—			—		—
c_1		—		—				—
c_2		—		—				—
d_1			—			—		—
d_2			—			—		—

(b) Same but with D = 21° 18′ and I = 87° 43′.
(c) Same but with D = 17° 47′ and I = 90° 18′.

TABLES

PREFACE TO TABLES, THIRD EDITION

These tables are the outgrowth of some 50 years of engineering practice and teaching in the field of transportation. They have been arranged to facilitate use and to cover the wide range of requirements of the civil engineer in a rapidly changing world; they are modern and complete. Where explanation is needed, it has been given at the end of each table.

Tables I, II, III, and IIIA are carefully arranged so that data for the usual circular curve may be secured therefrom with the least effort and chance of error. Tables IV and V give data on circular curves for occasional use.

The spiral tables, VI to XI, inclusive, are largely those of the American Railway Engineering Association, with some modifications to facilitate their use. *They also may be used for the Barnett Highway Spiral (arc definition) as explained on page 79 of the Tables.* Table VIII, Selected Spirals, was set up in this form and extended to include the longer spirals for modern high speeds after consultation with leading authorities of the country.

Tables XIII, XIV, XV, XVII, and XVIII are the long-used 5-place *Macmillan Mathematical Tables*, reduced to pocket size. Table XXXIV gives 8-place sines and cosines.

Tables XIX to XXIV, inclusive, provide for a wide range of earthwork computations. Selections from the *United States Reclamation Service Tables* have been included. The Triangular Prism Diagram of Table XXI is sufficiently large for practical use and provides for a limitless variety of earthwork computations, including the rarely used prismoidal correction. Table XXIV is useful in canal work.

Table XXXIII should aid in extending the use of the improved barometric method of securing elevation data.

The other tables are similar to those in general use, or are modified so as to add to their usefulness. The author will greatly appreciate suggestions for improving the tables.

HARRY RUBEY

COLUMBIA, MO.
1956

TABLES

PAGES

I. Radii, Degrees of Curve, Deflections, Tangent Offsets Mid Ordinates, and Chords 1

II. Lengths, Tangents, and Externals for a 1° Curve. 19

III. Tangent and External Corrections 52

IIIa. Tangent Offsets 53

IV. Arc Excess and True Subchords for Fractional Stations 54

V. Deflections and Chords for 25-, 50-, and 100-Foot Arcs 55

VI. Lengths of Long Chords 56

VII. Functions of the Ten-Chord Spiral 57

VIII. Selected Spirals 76

IX. Spiral Deflections 93

X. Intermediate Setup on Spiral 95

XI. Correction to Spiral Deflection Angles (diagram) . . . 96

XII. Theoretical or Balanced Superelevation 97

XIII. Logarithms of Numbers 98

XIVa. Values of S and T for Interpolation 117

XIV. Logarithms of Trigonometric Functions 118

XV. Values of Trigonometric Functions 163

XVI. Natural Versines and Exsecs 186

XVII. Powers, Roots, and Reciprocals 209

XVIII. Arc Lengths for Radius of 1 227

XIX. Cubic Yards per 100 Lineal Feet of Level Triangular Section 228

XX. Multiplying Factor to Determine Additional Yardage for Various Transverse Slopes 232

XXI. Triangular Prisms (diagrams) . . . . *facing* 232

XXII. Cubic Yards per 100-Foot Station 233

XXIII. Yardage per 100-Foot Station—From Double End Areas 236

XXIV. Canal Sections—Balanced Center Cut 238

XXV. Turnouts and Crossover Data 239

XXVI. Ordinates for Staking Curves with Tape 241

XXVII. Stadia Coefficients. Vertical Rod 242

XXVIII. Convergence of Meridians 249

XXIX. Grades and Grade Angles 250

XXX. Slope Taping Corrections 252

XXXI. Right of Way Acreages 100 Feet Wide 253

XXXII. Inches in Decimals of a Foot 254

XXXIII. Average Air Temperature Correction for Barometric Leveling 255

XXXIV. Natural Sines and Cosines (Eight-place) 259

XXXV. Numbers and Formulas 274

Degree of Curve, D		Defl. Min. Per Ft.	Chord Definition			Arc Definition	
Min.	Deci-mal		Radius R	Log. R	Tan. Off. 100-Ft. Ch.	Radius R	Chord
0°		0.000	infin.	infin.	.000	infin.	100.00
1	.0167	0.005	343774.68	5.536274	.015	343774.68	100.00
2	.0333	0.010	171887.34	5.235244	.029	171887.34	100.00
3	.0500	0.015	114591.56	5.059153	.044	114591.56	100.00
4	.0667	0.020	85943.67	4.934214	.058	85943.67	100.00
5	.0833	0.025	68754.94	4.837304	.073	68754.94	100.00
6	.1000	0.030	57295.79	4.758123	.087	57295.78	100.00
7	.1167	0.035	49110.68	4.691176	.102	49110.67	100.00
8	.1333	0.040	42971.84	4.633184	.116	42971.84	100.00
9	.1500	0.045	38197.20	4.582031	.131	38197.19	100.00
10	.1667	0.050	34377.48	4.536274	.145	34377.47	100.00
11	.1833	0.055	31252.26	4.494881	.160	31252.24	100.00
12	.2000	0.060	28647.90	4.457093	.175	28647.89	100.00
13	.2167	0.065	26444.22	4.422331	.189	26444.21	100.00
14	.2333	0.070	24555.35	4.390146	.204	24555.33	100.00
15	.2500	0.075	22918.33	4.360183	218	22918.31	100.00
16	.2667	0.080	21485.94	4.332154	233	21435.92	100.00
17	.2833	0.085	20222.06	4.305825	.247	20222.04	100.00
18	.3000	0.090	19098.61	4.281002	.262	19098.59	100.00
19	.3167	0.095	18093.43	4.257521	.276	18093.40	100.00
20	.3333	0.100	17188.76	4.235244	.291	17188.73	100.00
21	.3500	0.105	16370.25	4.214055	.305	16370.22	100.00
22	.3667	0.110	15626.15	4.193852	.320	15626.12	100.00
23	.3833	0.115	14946.75	4.174547	.335	14946.73	100.00
24	.4000	0.120	14323.97	4.156064	.349	14323.95	100.00
25	.4167	0.125	13751.02	4.138335	.364	13750.99	100.00
26	.4333	0.130	13222.13	4.121302	.378	13222.10	100.00
27	.4500	0.135	12732.43	4.104911	.393	12732.40	100.00
28	.4667	0.140	12277.70	4.089117	.407	12277.67	100.00
29	.4833	0.145	11854.33	4.073877	.422	11854.30	100.00
30	.5000	0.150	11459.19	4.059154	.436	11459.15	100.00
31	.5167	0.155	11089.54	4.044914	.451	11089.50	100.00
32	.5333	0.160	10743.00	4.031125	.465	10742.96	100.00
33	.5500	0.165	10417.45	4.017762	.480	10417.41	100.00
34	.5667	0.170	10111.06	4.004797	.495	10111.02	100.00
35	.5833	0.175	9822.18	3.992208	.509	9822.13	100.00
36	.6000	0.180	9549.34	3.979973	.524	9549.29	100.00
37	.6167	0.185	9291.25	3.968074	.538	9291.21	100.00
38	.6333	0.190	9046.75	3.956492	.553	9046.70	100.00
39	.6500	0.195	8814.78	3.945212	.567	8814.73	100.00
40	.6667	0.200	8594.42	3.934216	.582	8594.37	100.00
41	.6833	0.205	8384.80	3.923493	.596	8384.75	100.00
42	.7000	0.210	8185.16	3.913027	.611	8185.11	100.00
43	.7167	0.215	7994.81	3.902808	.625	7994.76	100.00
44	.7333	0.220	7813.11	3.892824	.640	7813.06	100.00
45	.7500	0.225	7639.49	3.883064	.654	7639.44	100.00
46	.7667	0.230	7473.42	3.873519	.669	7473.36	100.00
47	.7833	0.235	7314.41	3.864179	.684	7314.35	100.00
48	.8000	0.240	7162.03	3.855036	.698	7161.97	100.00
49	.8167	0.245	7015.87	3.846081	.713	7015.81	100.00
50	.8333	0.250	6875.55	3.837308	.727	6875.49	100.00
51	.8500	0.255	6740.74	3.828708	.742	6740.68	100.00
52	.8667	0.260	6611.12	3.820275	.756	6611.05	100.00
53	.8833	0.265	6486.38	3.812002	.771	6486.31	100.00
54	.9000	0.270	6366.26	3.803885	.785	6366.20	100.00
55	.9167	0.275	6250.51	3.795916	.800	6250.45	100.00
56	.9333	0.280	6138.90	3.788090	.814	6138.83	100.00
57	.9500	0.285	6031.20	3.780404	.829	6031.14	100.00
58	.9667	0.290	5927.22	3.772851	.844	5927.15	100.00
59	.9833	0.295	5826.76	3.765427	.858	5826.69	100.00

Degree of Curve, D		Defl. Min. Per Ft.	Chord Definition			Arc Definition	
Min.	Deci- mal		Radius R	Log. R	Tan. Off. 100-Ft. Ch.	Radius R	Chord
1°		.300	5729.65	3.758128	.873	*5729.58*	*100.00*
1	.0167	.305	5335.72	3.750950	.887	*5635.65*	*100.00*
2	.0333	.310	5544.83	3.743888	.902	*5544.75*	*100.00*
3	.0500	.315	5456.82	3.736939	.916	*5456.74*	*100.00*
4	.0667	.320	5371.56	3.730100	.931	*5371.48*	*100.00*
5	.0833	.325	5288.92	3.723367	.945	*5288.84*	*100.00*
6	.1000	.330	5208.79	3.716737	.960	*5208.71*	*100.00*
7	.1167	.335	5131.05	3.710206	.974	*5130.97*	*100.00*
8	.1333	.340	5055.59	3.703772	.989	*5055.51*	*100.00*
9	.1500	.345	4982.33	3.697432	1.004	*4982.24*	*100.00*
10	.1667	.350	4911.15	3.691183	1.018	*4911.07*	*100.00*
11	.1833	.355	4841.99	3.685023	1.033	*4841.90*	*100.00*
12	.2000	.360	4774.74	3.678949	1.047	*4774.65*	*100.00*
13	.2167	.365	4709.33	3.672959	1.062	*4709.24*	*100.00*
14	.2333	.370	4645.69	3.667051	1.076	*4645.60*	*100.00*
15	.2500	.375	4583.75	3.661221	1.091	*4583.66*	*100.00*
16	.2667	.380	4523.44	3.655469	1.105	*4523.35*	*100.00*
17	.2833	.385	4464.70	3.649792	1.120	*4464.61*	*100.00*
18	.3000	.390	4407.46	3.644189	1.134	*4407.37*	*100.00*
19	.3167	.395	4351.67	3.638656	1.149	*4351.58*	*100.00*
20	.3333	.400	4297.28	3.633194	1.164	*4297.18*	*100.00*
21	.3500	.405	4244.23	3.627799	1.178	*4244.13*	*100.00*
22	.3667	.410	4192.47	3.622470	1.193	*4192.37*	*100.00*
23	.3833	.415	4141.96	3.617206	1.207	*4141.86*	*100.00*
24	.4000	.420	4092.66	3.612005	1.222	*4092.56*	*100.00*
25	.4167	.425	4044.51	3.606866	1.236	*4044.41*	*100.00*
26	.4333	.430	3997.48	3.601787	1.251	*3997.38*	*100.00*
27	.4500	.435	3951.54	3.596766	1.265	*3951.43*	*100.00*
28	.4667	.440	3906.64	3.591803	1.280	*3906.53*	*100.00*
29	.4833	.445	3862.74	3.586896	1.294	*3862.64*	*100.00*
30	.5000	.450	3819.83	3.582044	1.309	*3819.71*	*100.00*
31	.5167	.455	3777.85	3.577245	1.324	*3777.74*	*100.00*
32	.5333	.460	3736.79	3.572499	1.338	*3736.68*	*100.00*
33	.5500	.465	3696.61	3.567804	1.353	*3696.50*	*100.00*
34	.5667	.470	3657.29	3.563160	1.367	*3657.18*	*100.00*
35	.5833	.475	3618.80	3.558564	1.382	*3618.68*	*100.00*
36	.6000	.480	3581.10	3.554017	1.396	*3580.99*	*100.00*
37	.6167	.485	3544.19	3.549517	1.411	*3544.07*	*100.00*
38	.6333	.490	3508.02	3.545063	1.425	*3507.91*	*100.00*
39	.6500	.495	3472.59	3.540654	1.440	*3472.47*	*100.00*
40	.6667	.500	3437.87	3.536289	1.454	*3437.75*	*100.00*
41	.6833	.505	3403.83	3.531968	1.469	*3403.71*	*100.00*
42	.7000	.510	3370.46	3.527690	1.483	*3370.34*	*100.00*
43	.7167	.515	3337.74	3.523453	1.498	*3337.62*	*100.00*
44	.7333	.520	3305.65	3.519257	1.513	*3305.53*	*100.00*
45	.7500	.525	3274.18	3.515101	1.527	*3274.05*	*100.00*
46	.7667	.530	3243.29	3.510985	1.542	*3243.16*	*100.00*
47	.7833	.535	3212.98	3.506908	1.556	*3212.85*	*100.00*
48	.8000	.540	3183.23	3.502868	1.571	*3183.10*	*100.00*
49	.8167	.545	3154.03	3.498866	1.585	*3153.90*	*100.00*
59	.8333	.550	3125.36	3.494900	1.600	*3125.22*	*100.00*
51	.8500	.555	3097.20	3.490970	1.614	*3097.07*	*100.00*
52	.8667	.560	3069.55	3.487075	1.629	*3069.42*	*100.00*
53	.8833	.565	3042.39	3.483215	1.643	*3042.25*	*100.00*
54	.9000	.570	3015.71	3.479389	1.658	*3015.57*	*100.00*
55	.9167	.575	2989.48	3.475596	1.673	*2989.35*	*100.00*
56	.9333	.580	2963.72	3.471836	1.687	*2963.58*	*100.00*
57	.9500	.585	2938.39	3.468109	1.702	*2938.25*	*100.00*
58	.9667	.590	2913.49	3.464413	1.716	*2913.34*	*100.00*
59	.9833	.595	2889.01	3.460749	1.731	*2888.86*	*100.00*

Degree of Curve, D		Defl. Min. Per Ft.	Chord Definition			Arc Definition	
Min.	Decimal		Radius R	Log. R	Tan. Off. 100-Ft. Ch.	Radius R	Chord
2°		.600	2864.93	3.457115	1.745	2864.79	99.99
1	.0167	.605	2841.26	3.453511	1.760	2841.11	99.99
2	.0333	.610	2817.97	3.449937	1.774	2817.83	99.99
3	.0500	.615	2795.06	3.446392	1.789	2794.92	99.99
4	.0667	.620	2772.53	3.442876	1.803	2772.38	99.99
5	.0833	.625	2750.35	3.439388	1.818	2750.20	99.99
6	.1000	.630	2728.52	3.435928	1.832	2728.37	99.99
7	.1167	.635	2707.04	3.432495	1.847	2706.89	99.99
8	.1333	.640	2385.89	3.429089	1.862	2385.74	99.99
9	.1500	.645	2665.08	3.425710	1.876	2364.92	99.99
10	.1667	.650	2644.58	3.422356	1.891	2644.42	99.99
11	.1833	.655	2624.39	3.419029	1.905	2624.23	99.99
12	.2000	.660	2604.51	3.415727	1.920	2604.35	99.99
13	.2167	.665	2584.93	3.412449	1.934	2584.77	99.99
14	.2333	.670	2565.65	3.409197	1.949	2565.48	99.99
15	.2500	.675	2546.64	3.405968	1.963	2546.48	99.99
16	.2667	.680	2527.92	3.402763	1.978	2527.76	99.99
17	.2833	.685	2509.47	3.399582	1.992	2509.30	99.99
18	.3000	.690	2491.29	3.396424	2.007	2491.12	99.99
19	.3167	.695	2473.36	3.393289	2.022	2473.20	99.99
20	.3333	.700	2455.70	3.390176	2.036	2455.53	99.99
21	.3500	.705	2438.28	3.387085	2.051	2438.12	99.99
22	.3667	.710	2421.12	3.384016	2.065	2420.95	99.99
23	.3833	.715	2404.19	3.380969	2.080	2404.02	99.99
24	.4000	.720	2387.50	3.377943	2.094	2387.32	99.99
25	.4167	.725	2371.04	3.374938	2.109	2370.86	99.99
26	.4333	.730	2354.80	3.371954	2.123	2354.62	99.99
27	.4500	.735	2338.78	3.368990	2.138	2338.60	99.99
28	.4667	.740	2322.98	3.366046	2.152	2322.80	99.99
29	.4833	.745	2307.39	3.363122	2.167	2307.21	99.99
30	.5000	.750	2292.01	3.360217	2.181	2291.83	99.99
31	.5167	.755	2276.84	3.357332	2.196	2276.65	99.99
32	.5333	.760	2261.86	3.354466	2.211	2261.68	99.99
33	.5500	.765	2247.08	3.351618	2.225	2246.89	99.99
34	.5667	.770	2232.49	3.348789	2.240	2232.30	99.99
35	.5833	.775	2218.09	3.345979	2.254	2217.90	99.99
36	.6000	.780	2203.87	3.343187	2.269	2203.68	99.99
37	.6167	.785	2189.84	3.340412	2.283	2189.65	99.99
38	.6333	.790	2175.98	3.337655	2.298	2175.79	99.99
39	.6500	.795	2162.30	3.334915	2.312	2162.10	99.99
40	.6667	.800	2148.79	3.332193	2.327	2148.59	99.99
41	.6833	.805	2135.43	3.329488	2.341	2135.25	99.99
42	.7000	.810	2122.26	3.326799	2.356	2122.07	99.99
43	.7167	.815	2109.24	3.324127	2.371	2109.05	99.99
44	.7333	.820	2096.39	3.321471	2.385	2096.19	99.99
45	.7500	.825	2083.68	3.318832	2.400	2083.48	99.99
46	.7667	.830	2071.13	3.316208	2.414	2070.93	99.99
47	.7833	.835	2058.73	3.313600	2.429	2058.53	99.99
48	.8000	.840	2046.48	3.311008	2.443	2046.28	99.99
49	.8167	.845	2034.37	3.308431	2.458	2034.17	99.99
50	.8333	.850	2022.41	3.305869	2.472	2022.20	99.99
51	.8500	.855	2010.58	3.303323	2.487	2010.38	99.99
52	.8367	.860	1998.90	3.300791	2.501	1998.69	99.99
53	.8833	.835	1987.35	3.298274	2.516	1987.14	99.99
54	.9000	.870	1975.93	3.295771	2.530	1975.71	99.99
55	.9167	.875	1964.64	3.293283	2.545	1964.43	99.99
56	.9333	.880	1953.48	3.290809	2.560	1953.27	99.99
57	.9500	.885	1942.44	3.288349	2.574	1942.23	99.99
58	.9667	.890	1931.53	3.285902	2.589	1931.32	99.99
59	.9833	.895	1920.75	3.283470	2.603	1920.53	99.99

Degree of Curve, D		Defl. Min. Per Ft.	Chord Definition			Arc Definition	
Min.	Deci-mal		Radius R	Log. R	Tan. Off. 100-Ft. Ch.	Radius R	Chord
3°		.900	1910.08	3.281051	2.618	*1909.86*	*99.99*
1	.0167	.905	1899.53	3.278645	2.632	*1899.31*	*99.99*
2	.0333	.910	1889.09	3.276253	2.647	*1888.86*	*99.99*
3	.0500	.915	1878.77	3.273874	2.661	*1878.55*	*99.99*
4	.0667	.920	1868.56	3.271508	2.676	*1868.33*	*99.99*
5	.0833	.925	1858.47	3.269155	2.690	*1858.24*	*99.99*
6	.1000	.930	1848.48	3.266814	2.705	*1848.25*	*99.99*
7	.1167	.935	1838.59	3.264486	2.719	*1838.37*	*99.99*
8	.1333	.940	1828.82	3.262170	2.734	*1828.59*	*99.99*
9	.1500	.945	1819.14	3.259867	2.749	*1818.91*	*99.99*
10	.1667	.950	1809.57	3.257576	2.763	*1809.34*	*99.99*
11	.1833	.955	1800.10	3.255296	2.778	*1799.87*	*99.99*
12	.2000	.960	1790.73	3.253029	2.792	*1790.49*	*99.99*
13	.2167	.965	1781.45	3.250774	2.807	*1781.22*	*99.99*
14	.2333	.970	1772.27	3.248530	2.821	*1772.03*	*99.99*
15	.2500	.975	1763.18	3.246297	2.836	*1762.95*	*99.99*
16	.2667	.980	1754.19	3.244077	2.850	*1753.95*	*99.99*
17	.2833	.985	1745.29	3.241867	2.865	*1745.05*	*99.99*
18	.3000	.990	1736.48	3.239669	2.879	*1736.24*	*99.99*
19	.3167	.995	1727.75	3.237481	2.894	*1727.51*	*99.99*
20	.3333	1.000	1719.12	3.235305	2.908	*1718.87*	*99.99*
21	.3500	1.005	1710.57	3.233140	2.923	*1710.32*	*99.99*
22	.3667	1.010	1702.10	3.230985	2.938	*1701.86*	*99.99*
23	.3833	1.015	1693.72	3.228841	2.952	*1693.47*	*99.99*
24	.4000	1.020	1685.42	3.226707	2.967	*1685.17*	*99.99*
25	.4167	1.025	1677.20	3.224584	2.981	*1676.95*	*99.99*
26	.4333	1.030	1669.06	3.222472	2.996	*1668.81*	*99.99*
27	.4500	1.035	1661.00	3.220369	3.010	*1660.75*	*99.99*
28	.4667	1.040	1653.02	3.218277	3.025	*1652.76*	*99.99*
29	.4833	1.045	1645.11	3.216194	3.039	*1644.85*	*99.99*
30	.5000	1.050	1637.28	3.214122	3.054	*1637.02*	*99.98*
31	.5167	1.055	1629.52	3.212060	3.068	*1629.36*	*99.98*
32	.5333	1.060	1621.84	3.210007	3.083	*1621.58*	*99.98*
33	.5500	1.065	1614.22	3.207964	3.097	*1613.94*	*99.98*
34	.5667	1.070	1606.68	3.205930	3.112	*1606.42*	*99.98*
35	.5833	1.075	1599.21	3.203906	3.127	*1598.95*	*99.98*
36	.6000	1.080	1591.81	3.201892	3.141	*1591.55*	*99.98*
37	.6167	1.085	1584.48	3.199886	3.156	*1584.22*	*99.98*
38	.6333	1.090	1577.21	3.197890	3.170	*1576.95*	*99.98*
39	.6500	1.095	1570.01	3.195903	3.185	*1569.75*	*99.98*
40	.6667	1.100	1562.88	3.193925	3.199	*1562.61*	*99.98*
41	.6833	1.105	1555.81	3.191956	3.214	*1555.54*	*99.98*
42	.7000	1.110	1548.80	3.189996	3.228	*1548.53*	*99.98*
43	.7167	1.115	1541.86	3.188045	3.243	*1541.59*	*99.98*
44	.7333	1.120	1534.98	3.186103	3.257	*1534.71*	*99.98*
45	.7500	1.125	1528.16	3.184169	3.272	*1527.89*	*99.98*
46	.7667	1.130	1521.40	3.182244	3.286	*1521.13*	*99.98*
47	.7833	1.135	1514.70	3.180327	3.301	*1514.43*	*99.98*
48	.8000	1.140	1508.06	3.178419	3.316	*1507.78*	*99.98*
49	.8167	1.145	1501.48	3.176519	3.330	*1501.20*	*99.98*
50	.8333	1.150	1494.95	3.174627	3.345	*1494.67*	*99.98*
51	.8500	1.155	1488.48	3.172744	3.359	*1488.20*	*99.98*
52	.8667	1.160	1482.07	3.170868	3.374	*1481.79*	*99.98*
53	.8833	1.165	1475.71	3.169001	3.388	*1475.43*	*99.98*
54	.9000	1.170	1469.41	3.167142	3.403	*1469.12*	*99.98*
55	.9167	1.175	1463.16	3.165291	3.417	*1462.87*	*99.98*
56	.9333	1.180	1456.96	3.163447	3.432	*1456.67*	*99.98*
57	.9500	1.185	1450.81	3.161612	3.446	*1450.53*	*99.98*
58	.9667	1.190	1444.72	3.159784	3.461	*1444.43*	*99.98*
59	.9833	1.195	1438.68	3.157963	3.475	*1438.39*	*99.98*

Degree of Curve, D		Defl. Min. Per Ft.	Chord Definition			Arc Definition	
Min.	Decimal		Radius R	Log. R	Tan. Off. 100-Ft. Ch.	Radius R	Chord
4°		1.200	1432.69	3.156151	3.490	*1432.39*	*99.98*
1	.0167	1.205	1426.74	3.154346	3.505	*1426.45*	*99.98*
2	.0333	1.210	1420.85	3.152548	3.519	*1420.56*	*99.98*
3	.0500	1.215	1415.01	3.150758	3.534	*1414.71*	*99.98*
4	.0667	1.220	1409.21	3.148975	3.548	*1408.91*	*99.98*
5	.0833	1.225	1403.46	3.147200	3.563	*1403.16*	*99.98*
6	.1000	1.230	1397.76	3.145431	3.577	*1397.46*	*99.98*
7	.1167	1.235	1392.10	3.143670	3.592	*1391.80*	*99.98*
8	.1333	1.240	1386.49	3.141916	3.606	*1386.19*	*99.98*
9	.1500	1.245	1380.92	3.140169	3.621	*1380.62*	*99.98*
10	.1667	1.250	1375.40	3.138430	3.635	*1375.10*	*99.98*
11	.1833	1.255	1369.92	3.136697	3.650	*1369.62*	*99.98*
12	.2000	1.260	1364.49	3.134971	3.664	*1364.19*	*99.98*
13	.2167	1.265	1359.10	3.133251	3.679	*1358.79*	*99.98*
14	.2333	1.270	1353.75	3.131539	3.693	*1353.44*	*99.98*
15	.2500	1.275	1348.45	3.129833	3.708	*1348.14*	*99.98*
16	.2667	1.280	1343.18	3.128134	3.723	*1342.87*	*99.98*
17	.2833	1.285	1337.96	3.126442	3.737	*1337.65*	*99.98*
18	.3000	1.290	1332.77	3.124756	3.752	*1332.46*	*99.98*
19	.3167	1.295	1327.63	3.123077	3.766	*1327.32*	*99.98*
20	.3333	1.300	1322.53	3.121404	3.781	*1322.21*	*99.98*
21	.3500	1.305	1317.46	3.119738	3.795	*1317.14*	*99.98*
22	.3367	1.310	1312.43	3.118078	3.810	*1312.12*	*99.98*
23	.3833	1.315	1307.45	3.116424	3.824	*1307.13*	*99.98*
24	.4000	1.320	1302.50	3.114777	3.839	*1302.18*	*99.98*
25	.4167	1.325	1297.58	3.113136	3.853	*1297.26*	*99.98*
26	.4333	1.330	1292.71	3.111501	3.868	*1292.39*	*99.98*
27	.4500	1.335	1287.87	3.109872	3.882	*1287.55*	*99.98*
28	.4667	1.340	1283.07	3.108249	3.897	*1282.74*	*99.98*
29	.4833	1.345	1278.30	3.106632	3.911	*1277.97*	*99.98*
30	.5000	1.350	1273.57	3.105022	3.926	*1273.24*	*99.97*
31	.5167	1.355	1268.87	3.103417	3.941	*1268.45*	*99.97*
32	.5333	1.360	1264.21	3.101818	3.955	*1263.88*	*99.97*
33	.5500	1.365	1259.58	3.100225	3.970	*1259.25*	*99.97*
34	.5667	1.370	1254.98	3.098638	3.984	*1254.65*	*99.97*
35	.5833	1.375	1250.42	3.097057	3.999	*1250.09*	*99.97*
36	.6000	1.380	1245.89	3.095481	4.013	*1245.56*	*99.97*
37	.6167	1.385	1241.40	3.093912	4.028	*1241.06*	*99.97*
38	.6333	1.390	1236.94	3.092347	4.042	*1236.60*	*99.97*
39	.6500	1.395	1232.51	3.090789	4.057	*1232.17*	*99.97*
40	.6667	1.400	1228.11	3.089236	4.071	*1227.77*	*99.97*
41	.6833	1.405	1223.74	3.087689	4.086	*1223.40*	*99.97*
42	.7000	1.410	1219.40	3.086147	4.100	*1219.06*	*99.97*
43	.7167	1.415	1215.09	3.084610	4.115	*1214.75*	*99.97*
44	.7333	1.420	1210.82	3.083079	4.129	*1210.47*	*99.97*
45	.7500	1.425	1206.57	3.081553	4.144	*1206.23*	*99.97*
46	.7667	1.430	1202.36	3.080033	4.159	*1202.01*	*99.97*
47	.7833	1.435	1198.17	3.078518	4.173	*1197.82*	*99.97*
48	.8000	1.440	1194.01	3.077008	4.188	*1193.66*	*99.97*
49	.8167	1.445	1189.88	3.075504	4.202	*1189.53*	*99.97*
50	.8333	1.450	1185.78	3.074005	4.217	*1185.43*	*99.97*
51	.8500	1.455	1181.71	3.072511	4.231	*1181.36*	*99.97*
52	.8667	1.460	1177.66	3.071022	4.246	*1177.31*	*99.97*
53	.8833	1.465	1173.65	3.069538	4.260	*1173.29*	*99.97*
54	.9000	1.470	1169.66	3.068059	4.275	*1169.30*	*99.97*
55	.9167	1.475	1165.70	3.066585	4.289	*1165.34*	*99.97*
56	.9333	1.480	1161.76	3.065116	4.304	*1161.40*	*99.97*
57	.9500	1.485	1157.85	3.063653	4.318	*1157.49*	*99.97*
58	.9667	1.490	1153.97	3.062194	4.333	*1153.61*	*99.97*
59	.9833	1.495	1150.11	3.060740	4.347	*1149.75*	*99.97*

| Degree of Curve, D | | Defl. Min. Per Ft. | Chord Definition | | | Arc Definition | |
Min.	Deci-mal		Radius R	Log. R	Tan. Off. 100-Ft. Ch.	Radius R	Chord
5°		1.500	1146.28	3.059290	4.362	1145.92	99.97
1	.0167	1.505	1142.47	3.057846	4.376	1142.11	99.97
2	.0333	1.510	1138.69	3.056407	4.391	1138.31	99.97
3	.0500	1.515	1134.94	3.054972	4.405	1134.57	99.97
4	.0667	1.520	1131.21	3.053542	4.420	1130.84	99.97
5	.0833	1.525	1127.50	3.052116	4.435	1127.13	99.97
6	.1000	1.530	1123.82	3.050696	4.449	1123.45	99.97
7	.1167	1.535	1120.16	3.049280	4.464	1119.79	99.97
8	.1333	1.540	1116.52	3.047868	4.478	1116.15	99.97
9	.1500	1.545	1112.91	3.046462	4.493	1112.54	99.97
10	.1667	1.550	1109.33	3.045059	4.507	1108.95	99.97
11	.1833	1.555	1105.76	3.043662	4.522	1105.39	99.97
12	.2000	1.560	1102.22	3.042268	4.536	1101.84	99.97
13	.2167	1.565	1098.70	3.040880	4.551	1098.32	99.97
14	.2333	1.570	1095.20	3.039495	4.565	1094.82	99.97
15	.2500	1.575	1091.73	3.038115	4.580	1091.35	99.97
16	.2367	1.580	1088.28	3.036740	4.594	1087.89	99.97
17	.2833	1.585	1084.85	3.035368	4.609	1084.46	99.97
18	.3000	1.590	1081.44	3.034002	4.623	1081.05	99.97
19	.3167	1.595	1078.05	3.032639	4.638	1077.66	99.97
20	.3333	1.600	1074.68	3.031281	4.653	1074.30	99.96
21	.3500	1.605	1071.34	3.029927	4.667	1070.95	99.96
22	.3367	1.610	1068.01	3.028577	4.682	1067.62	99.96
23	.3833	1.615	1064.71	3.027231	4.696	1064.32	99.96
24	.4000	1.620	1061.43	3.025890	4.711	1061.03	99.96
25	.4167	1.625	1058.16	3.024552	4.725	1057.77	99.96
26	.4333	1.630	1054.92	3.023219	4.740	1054.52	99.96
27	.4500	1.635	1051.70	3.021890	4.754	1051.30	99.96
28	.4667	1.640	1048.49	3.020565	4.769	1048.09	99.96
29	.4833	1.645	1045.31	3.019244	4.783	1044.91	99.96
30	.5000	1.650	1042.14	3.017927	4.798	1041.74	99.96
31	.5167	1.655	1039.00	3.016614	4.812	1038.59	99.96
32	.5333	1.660	1035.87	3.015305	4.827	1035.47	99.96
33	.5500	1.665	1032.76	3.013999	4.841	1032.36	99.96
34	.5667	1.670	1029.67	3.012698	4.856	1029.27	99.96
35	.5833	1.675	1026.60	3.011401	4.870	1026.19	99.96
36	.6000	1.680	1023.55	3.010107	4.885	1023.14	99.96
37	.6167	1.685	1020.51	3.008818	4.900	1020.10	99.96
38	.6333	1.690	1017.49	3.007532	4.914	1017.09	99.96
39	.6500	1.695	1014.50	3.006250	4.929	1014.08	99.96
40	.6667	1.700	1011.51	3.004972	4.943	1011.10	99.96
41	.6833	1.705	1008.55	3.003698	4.958	1008.14	99.96
42	.7000	1.710	1005.60	3.002427	4.972	1005.19	99.96
43	.7167	1.715	1002.67	3.001160	4.987	1002.26	99.96
44	.7333	1.720	999.76	2.999897	5.001	999.35	99.96
45	.7500	1.725	996.87	2.998637	5.016	996.45	99.96
46	.7667	1.730	993.99	2.997381	5.030	993.57	99.96
47	.7833	1.735	991.13	2.996129	5.045	990.71	99.96
48	.8000	1.740	988.28	2.994880	5.059	987.86	99.96
49	.8167	1.745	985.45	2.993635	5.074	985.03	99.96
50	.8333	1.750	982.64	2.992393	5.088	982.21	99.96
51	.8500	1.755	979.84	2.991155	5.103	979.42	99.96
52	.8667	1.760	977.06	2.989921	5.117	976.63	99.96
53	.8833	1.765	974.29	2.988690	5.132	973.87	99.96
54	.9000	1.770	971.54	2.987463	5.146	971.12	99.96
55	.9167	1.775	968.81	2.986239	5.161	968.38	99.96
56	.9333	1.780	966.09	2.985018	5.175	965.66	99.96
57	.9500	1.785	963.39	2.983801	5.190	962.95	99.96
58	.9667	1.790	960.70	2.982587	5.205	960.26	99.96
59	.9833	1.795	958.02	2.981377	5.219	957.59	99.96

Degree of Curve, D		Defl. Min. Per Ft.	Chord Definition			Arc Definition	
Min.	Decimal		Radius R	Log. R	Tan. Off. 100-Ft. Ch.	Radius R	Chord
6°		1.800	955.37	2.980170	5.234	954.93	99.95
1	.0167	1.805	952.72	2.978966	5.248	952.28	99.95
2	.0333	1.810	950.09	2.977766	5.263	949.65	99.95
3	.0500	1.815	947.48	2.976569	5.277	947.04	99.95
4	.0667	1.820	944.88	2.975375	5.292	944.44	99.95
5	.0833	1.825	942.29	2.974185	5.306	941.85	99.95
6	.1000	1.830	939.72	2.972998	5.321	939.28	99.95
7	.1167	1.835	937.16	2.971814	5.335	936.72	99.95
8	.1333	1.840	934.62	2.970633	5.350	934.17	99.95
9	.1500	1.845	932.09	2.969456	5.364	931.64	99.95
10	.1667	1.850	929.57	2.968282	5.379	929.12	99.95
11	.1833	1.855	927.07	2.967111	5.393	926.62	99.95
12	.2000	1.860	924.58	2.965943	5.408	924.13	99.95
13	.2167	1.865	922.10	2.964778	5.422	921.65	99.95
14	.2333	1.870	919.64	2.963616	5.437	919.18	99.95
15	.2500	1.875	917.19	2.962458	5.451	916.73	99.95
16	.2667	1.880	914.75	2.961303	5.466	914.29	99.95
17	.2833	1.885	912.33	2.960150	5.480	911.87	99.95
18	.3000	1.890	909.92	2.959001	5.495	909.46	99.95
19	.3167	1.895	907.52	2.957855	5.510	907.06	99.95
20	.3333	1.900	905.13	2.956711	5.524	904.67	99.95
21	.3500	1.905	902.76	2.955571	5.539	902.30	99.95
22	.3667	1.910	900.40	2.954434	5.553	899.93	99.95
23	.3833	1.915	898.05	2.953300	5.568	897.58	99.95
24	.4000	1.920	895.71	2.952168	5.582	895.25	99.95
25	.4167	1.925	893.39	2.951040	5.597	892.92	99.95
26	.4333	1.930	891.08	2.949915	5.611	890.61	99.95
27	.4500	1.935	888.78	2.948792	5.626	888.31	99.95
28	.4667	1.940	886.49	2.947673	5.640	886.02	99.95
29	.4833	1.945	884.21	2.946556	5.655	883.74	99.95
30	.5000	1.950	881.95	2.945442	5.669	881.47	99.95
31	.5167	1.955	879.69	2.944331	5.684	879.22	99.95
32	.5333	1.960	877.45	2.943223	5.698	876.98	99.95
33	.5500	1.965	875.22	2.942118	5.713	874.75	99.95
34	.5667	1.970	873.00	2.941015	5.727	872.52	99.95
35	.5833	1.975	870.79	2.939916	5.742	870.32	99.95
36	.6000	1.980	868.60	2.938819	5.756	868.12	99.95
37	.6167	1.985	866.41	2.937725	5.771	865.93	99.95
38	.6333	1.990	864.24	2.936633	5.785	863.76	99.95
39	.6500	1.995	862.07	2.935545	5.800	861.59	99.95
40	.6667	2.000	859.92	2.934459	5.814	859.44	99.94
41	.6833	2.005	857.78	2.933376	5.829	857.29	99.94
42	.7000	2.010	855.65	2.932295	5.844	855.16	99.94
43	.7167	2.015	853.53	2.931218	5.858	853.04	99.94
44	.7333	2.020	851.42	2.930142	5.873	850.93	99.94
45	.7500	2.025	849.32	2.929070	5.887	848.83	99.94
46	.7667	2.030	847.23	2.928000	5.902	846.74	99.94
47	.7833	2.035	845.15	2.926933	5.916	844.66	99.94
48	.8000	2.040	843.08	2.925869	5.931	842.59	99.94
49	.8167	2.045	841.02	2.924807	5.945	840.52	99.94
50	.8333	2.050	838.97	2.923747	5.960	838.47	99.94
51	.8500	2.055	836.93	2.922691	5.974	836.43	99.94
52	.8667	2.060	834.90	2.921637	5.989	834.40	99.94
53	.8833	2.065	832.88	2.920585	6.003	832.38	99.94
54	.9000	2.070	830.88	2.919536	6.018	830.37	99.94
55	.9167	2.075	828.88	2.918490	6.032	828.37	99.94
56	.9333	2.080	826.89	2.917446	6.047	826.38	99.94
57	.9500	2.085	824.91	2.916404	6.061	824.40	99.94
58	.9667	2.090	822.93	2.915365	6.076	822.43	99.94
59	.9833	2.095	820.97	2.914329	6.090	820.48	99.94

| Degree of Curve, D | | Defl. Min. Per Ft. | Chord Definition | | | Arc Definition | |
Min.	Decimal		Radius R	Log. R	Tan. Off. 100-Ft. Ch.	Radius R	Chord
7°		2.100	819.02	2.913295	6.105	818.51	99.94
1	.0167	2.105	817.08	2.912263	6.119	816.57	99.94
2	.0333	2.110	815.14	2.911234	6.134	814.63	99.94
3	.0500	2.115	813.22	2.910208	6.148	812.70	99.94
4	.0667	2.120	811.30	2.909183	6.163	810.79	99.94
5	.0833	2.125	809.40	2.908162	6.177	808.88	99.94
6	.1000	2.130	807.50	2.907142	6.192	806.98	99.94
7	.1167	2.135	805.61	2.906125	6.206	805.09	99.94
8	.1333	2.140	803.73	2.905111	6.221	803.21	99.94
9	.1500	2.145	801.86	2.904098	6.236	801.34	99.94
10	.1667	2.150	800.00	2.903089	6.250	799.48	99.93
11	.1833	2.155	798.14	2.902081	6.265	797.62	99.93
12	.2000	2.160	796.30	2.901076	6.279	795.78	99.93
13	.2167	2.165	794.46	2.900073	6.294	793.94	99.93
14	.2333	2.170	792.63	2.899073	6.308	792.11	99.93
15	.2500	2.175	790.81	2.898074	6.323	790.29	99.93
16	.2667	2.180	789.00	2.897079	6.337	788.47	99.93
17	.2833	2.185	787.20	2.896085	6.352	786.67	99.93
18	.3000	2.190	785.40	2.895094	6.366	784.87	99.93
19	.3167	2.195	783.62	2.894104	6.381	783.09	99.93
20	.3333	2.200	781.84	2.893118	6.395	781.31	99.93
21	.3500	2.205	780.07	2.892133	6.410	779.53	99.93
22	.3667	2.210	778.31	2.891151	6.424	777.77	99.93
23	.3833	2.215	776.55	2.890171	6.439	776.02	99.93
24	.4000	2.220	774.81	2.889193	6.453	774.27	99.93
25	.4167	2.225	773.07	2.888217	6.468	772.53	99.93
26	.4333	2.230	771.34	2.887244	6.482	770.80	99.93
27	.4500	2.235	769.61	2.886272	6.497	769.07	99.93
28	.4667	2.240	767.90	2.885303	6.511	767.35	99.93
29	.4833	2.245	766.19	2.884336	6.526	765.65	99.93
30	.5000	2.250	764.49	2.883371	6.540	763.94	99.93
31	.5167	2.255	762.80	2.882409	6.555	762.25	99.93
32	.5333	2.260	761.11	2.881448	6.569	760.56	99.93
33	.5500	2.265	759.43	2.880490	6.584	758.88	99.93
34	.5667	2.270	757.76	2.879534	6.598	757.21	99.93
35	.5833	2.275	756.10	2.878580	6.613	755.55	99.93
36	.6000	2.280	754.44	2.877627	6.627	753.89	99.93
37	.6167	2.285	752.80	2.876678	6.642	752.24	99.93
38	.6333	2.290	751.16	2.875730	6.656	750.60	99.93
39	.6500	2.295	749.52	2.874784	6.671	748.96	99.93
40	.6667	2.300	747.89	2.873840	6.685	747.34	99.92
41	.6833	2.305	746.27	2.872898	6.700	745.72	99.92
42	.7000	2.310	744.66	2.871959	6.714	744.10	99.92
43	.7167	2.315	743.06	2.871021	6.729	742.49	99.92
44	.7333	2.320	741.46	2.870086	6.743	740.89	99.92
45	.7500	2.325	739.87	2.869152	6.758	739.30	99.92
46	.7667	2.330	738.28	2.868221	6.773	737.71	99.92
47	.7833	2.335	736.70	2.867291	6.787	736.13	99.92
48	.8000	2.340	735.13	2.866363	6.802	734.56	99.92
49	.8167	2.345	733.56	2.865438	6.816	733.00	99.92
50	.8333	2.350	732.01	2.864514	6.831	731.44	99.92
51	.8500	2.355	730.45	2.863593	6.845	729.88	99.92
52	.8667	2.360	728.91	2.862673	6.860	728.34	99.92
53	.8833	2.365	727.37	2.861755	6.874	726.80	99.92
54	.9000	2.370	725.84	2.860840	6.889	725.26	99.92
55	.9167	2.375	724.31	2.859926	6.903	723.74	99.92
56	.9333	2.380	722.79	2.859014	6.918	722.23	99.92
57	.9500	2.385	721.28	2.858104	6.932	720.70	99.92
58	.9667	2.390	719.77	2.857196	6.947	719.19	99.92
59	.9833	2.395	718.27	2.856290	6.961	717.69	99.92

Degree of Curve, D		Defl. Min. Per Ft.	Chord Definition			Arc Definition	
Min.	Deci-mal		Radius R	Log. R	Tan. Off. 100-Ft. Ch.	Radius R	Chord
8°		2.400	716.78	2.855385	6.976	*716.20*	*99.93*
1	.0167	2.405	715.29	2.854483	6.990	*714.71*	*99.92*
2	.0333	2.410	713.81	2.853583	7.005	*713.23*	*99.92*
3	.0500	2.415	712.33	2.852684	7.019	*711.75*	*99.92*
4	.0667	2.420	710.87	2.851787	7.034	*710.28*	*99.92*
5	.0833	2.425	709.40	2.850892	7.048	*708.81*	*99.92*
6	.1000	2.430	707.94	2.849999	7.063	*707.35*	*99.92*
7	.1167	2.435	706.49	2.849108	7.077	*705.90*	*99.92*
8	.1333	2.440	705.05	2.848219	7.092	*704.46*	*99.92*
9	.1500	2.445	703.61	2.847331	7.106	*703.02*	*99.92*
10	.1667	2.450	702.18	2.846446	7.121	*701.58*	*99.91*
11	.1833	2.455	700.75	2.845562	7.135	*700.16*	*99.91*
12	.2000	2.460	699.33	2.844679	7.150	*698.73*	*99.91*
13	.2167	2.465	697.91	2.843799	7.164	*697.31*	*99.91*
14	.2333	2.470	696.50	2.842921	7.179	*695.90*	*99.91*
15	.2500	2.475	695.09	2.842044	7.193	*694.49*	*99.91*
16	.2667	2.480	693.70	2.841169	7.208	*693.09*	*99.91*
17	.2833	2.485	692.30	2.840296	7.222	*691.70*	*99.91*
18	.3000	2.490	690.91	2.839424	7.237	*690.31*	*99.91*
19	.3167	2.495	689.53	2.838555	7.251	*688.92*	*99.91*
20	.3333	2.500	688.16	2.837687	7.266	*687.55*	*99.91*
21	.3500	2.505	686.78	2.836821	7.280	*686.18*	*99.91*
22	.3667	2.510	685.42	2.835956	7.295	*684.81*	*99.91*
23	.3833	2.515	684.06	2.835093	7.309	*683.45*	*99.91*
24	.4000	2.520	682.70	2.834232	7.324	*682.09*	*99.91*
25	.4167	2.525	681.35	2.833373	7.338	*680.74*	*99.91*
26	.4333	2.530	680.01	2.832515	7.353	*679.40*	*99.91*
27	.4500	2.535	678.67	2.831660	7.367	*678.06*	*99.91*
28	.4667	2.540	677.34	2.830805	7.382	*676.72*	*99.91*
29	.4833	2.545	676.01	2.829953	7.396	*675.39*	*99.91*
30	.5000	2.550	674.69	2.829102	7.411	*674.07*	*99.91*
31	.5167	2.555	673.37	2.828253	7.425	*672.75*	*99.91*
32	.5333	2.560	672.06	2.827405	7.440	*671.43*	*99.91*
33	.5500	2.565	670.75	2.826560	7.454	*670.13*	*99.91*
34	.5667	2.570	669.45	2.825715	7.469	*668.82*	*99.91*
35	.5833	2.575	668.15	2.824873	7.483	*667.52*	*99.91*
36	.6000	2.580	666.86	2.824032	7.498	*666.23*	*99.91*
37	.6167	2.585	665.57	2.823193	7.512	*664.94*	*99.91*
38	.6333	2.590	664.29	2.822355	7.527	*663.66*	*99.91*
39	.6500	2.595	663.01	2.821519	7.541	*662.38*	*99.91*
40	.6667	2.600	661.74	2.820685	7.556	*661.11*	*99.90*
41	.6833	2.605	660.47	2.819852	7.570	*659.84*	*99.90*
42	.7000	2.610	659.21	2.819021	7.585	*658.57*	*99.90*
43	.7167	2.615	657.95	2.818191	7.599	*657.31*	*99.90*
44	.7333	2.620	656.69	2.817363	7.614	*656.06*	*99.90*
45	.7500	2.625	655.45	2.816537	7.628	*654.81*	*99.90*
46	.7676	2.630	654.20	2.815712	7.643	*653.56*	*99.90*
47	.7833	2.635	652.96	2.814889	7.657	*652.32*	*99.90*
48	.8000	2.640	651.73	2.814067	7.672	*651.09*	*99.90*
49	.8167	2.645	650.50	2.813247	7.686	*649.86*	*99.90*
50	.8333	2.650	649.27	2.812428	7.701	*648.63*	*99.90*
51	.8500	2.655	648.05	2.811611	7.715	*647.41*	*99.90*
52	.8667	2.660	646.84	2.810796	7.730	*646.19*	*99.90*
53	.8833	2.665	645.63	2.809982	7.744	*644.98*	*99.90*
54	.9000	2.670	644.42	2.809169	7.759	*643.77*	*99.90*
55	.9167	2.675	643.22	2.808358	7.773	*642.57*	*99.90*
56	.9333	2.680	642.02	2.807549	7.788	*641.37*	*99.90*
57	.9500	2.685	640.83	2.806741	7.802	*640.18*	*99.90*
58	.9667	2.690	639.64	2.805935	7.817	*638.99*	*99.90*
59	.9833	2.695	638.45	2.805130	7.831	*637.80*	*99.90*

| Degree of Curve, D | | Defl. Min. Per Ft. | Chord Definition | | | Arc Definition | |
Min.	Deci-mal		Radius R	Log. R	Tan. Off. 100-Ft. Ch.	Radius R	Chord
9°		2.700	637.27	2.804327	7.846	636.62	99.90
2	.0333	2.710	634.93	2.802724	7.875	634.27	99.90
4	.0667	2.720	632.60	2.801128	7.904	631.94	99.90
6	.1000	2.730	630.29	2.799538	7.933	629.62	99.90
8	.1333	2.740	627.99	2.797953	7.962	627.33	99.90
10	.1667	2.750	625.71	2.796374	7.991	625.04	99.89
12	.2000	2.760	623.45	2.794801	8.020	622.78	99.89
14	.2333	2.770	621.20	2.793234	8.049	620.53	99.89
16	.2667	2.780	618.97	2.791673	8.078	618.30	99.89
18	.3000	2.790	616.76	2.790117	8.107	616.08	99.89
20	.3333	2.800	614.56	2.788566	8.136	613.88	99.89
22	.3667	2.810	612.38	2.787021	8.165	611.70	99.89
24	.4000	2.820	610.21	2.785482	8.194	609.53	99.89
26	.4333	2.830	608.06	2.783948	8.223	607.38	99.89
28	.4667	2.840	605.93	2.782420	8.252	605.24	99.89
30	.5000	2.850	603.80	2.780897	8.281	603.11	99.88
32	.5333	2.860	601.70	2.779379	8.310	601.00	99.88
34	.5667	2.870	599.61	2.777867	8.339	598.91	99.88
36	.6000	2.880	597.53	2.776360	8.368	596.83	99.88
38	.6333	2.890	595.47	2.774858	8.397	594.77	99.88
40	.6667	2.900	593.42	2.773361	8.426	592.72	99.88
42	.7000	2.910	591.38	2.771870	8.455	590.68	99.88
44	.7333	2.920	589.36	2.770383	8.484	588.67	99.88
46	.7667	2.930	587.36	2.768902	8.513	586.65	99.88
48	.8000	2.940	585.36	2.767426	8.542	584.66	99.88
50	.8333	2.950	583.38	2.765955	8.571	582.67	99.88
52	.8667	2.960	581.42	2.764489	8.600	580.70	99.88
54	.9000	2.970	579.46	2.763028	8.629	578.75	99.88
56	.9333	2.980	577.53	2.761572	8.658	576.80	99.88
58	.9667	2.990	575.60	2.760120	8.687	574.87	99.88
10°		3.000	573.69	2.758674	8.716	572.96	99.87
2	.0333	3.010	571.79	2.757232	8.745	571.05	99.87
4	.0667	3.020	569.90	2.755796	8.774	569.16	99.87
6	.1000	3.030	568.02	2.754364	8.803	567.29	99.87
8	.1333	3.040	566.16	2.752937	8.831	565.42	99.87
10	.1667	3.050	564.31	2.751514	8.860	563.56	99.87
12	.2000	3.060	562.47	2.750096	8.889	561.72	99.87
14	.2333	3.070	560.64	2.748683	8.918	559.89	99.87
16	.2667	3.080	558.82	2.747274	8.947	558.08	99.87
18	.3000	3.090	557.02	2.745870	8.976	556.27	99.87
20	.3333	3.100	555.23	2.744471	9.005	554.48	99.86
22	.3667	3.110	553.45	2.743076	9.034	552.69	99.86
24	.4000	3.120	551.68	2.741686	9.063	550.92	99.86
26	.4333	3.130	549.92	2.740300	9.092	549.16	99.86
28	.4667	3.140	548.17	2.738918	9.121	547.41	99.86
30	.5000	3.150	546.44	2.737541	9.150	545.67	99.86
32	.5333	3.160	544.71	2.736169	9.179	543.95	99.86
34	.5667	3.170	543.00	2.734800	9.208	542.23	99.86
36	.6000	3.180	541.30	2.733436	9.237	540.53	99.86
38	.6333	3.190	539.61	2.732077	9.266	538.83	99.86
40	.6667	3.200	537.92	2.730721	9.295	537.15	99.85
42	.7000	3.210	536.25	2.729370	9.324	535.47	99.85
44	.7333	3.220	534.59	2.728023	9.353	533.81	99.85
46	.7667	3.230	532.94	2.726681	9.382	532.16	99.85
48	.8000	3.240	531.30	2.725342	9.411	530.52	99.85
50	.8333	3.250	529.67	2.724008	9.440	528.88	99.85
52	.8667	3.260	528.05	2.722677	9.469	527.26	99.85
54	.9000	3.270	526.44	2.721351	9.498	525.65	99.85
56	.9333	3.280	524.84	2.720029	9.527	524.05	99.85
58	.9667	3.290	523.25	2.718711	9.556	522.45	99.85

| Degree of Curve, D | | Defl. Min. Per Ft. | Chord Definition | | | | Arc Definition | |
Min.	Decimal		Radius R	Log. R	Tan. Off. 100-Ft. Ch.	Mid. Ord. 100-Ft. Ch.	Radius R	Chord
11°		3.300	521.67	2.717397	9.585	2.402	520.87	99.85
2	.0333	3.310	520.10	2.716087	9.614	2.409	519.30	99.85
4	.0667	3.320	518.54	2.714781	9.642	2.416	517.73	99.85
6	.1000	3.330	516.99	2.713479	9.671	2.423	516.18	99.85
8	.1333	3.340	515.44	2.712181	9.700	2.431	514.63	99.85
10	.1667	3.350	513.91	2.710887	9.729	2.438	513.10	99.84
12	.2000	3.360	512.38	2.709596	9.758	2.445	511.57	99.84
14	.2333	3.370	510.87	2.708310	9.787	2.453	510.05	99.84
16	.2667	3.380	509.36	2.707027	9.816	2.460	508.54	99.84
18	.3000	3.390	507.86	2.705748	9.845	2.467	507.04	99.84
20	.3333	3.400	506.38	2.704473	9.874	2.475	505.55	99.84
22	.3667	3.410	504.90	2.703202	9.903	2.482	504.07	99.84
24	.4000	3.420	503.42	2.701934	9.932	2.489	502.59	99.84
26	.4333	3.430	501.96	2.700671	9.961	2.496	501.13	99.84
28	.4667	3.440	500.51	2.699410	9.990	2.504	499.67	99.84
30	.5000	3.450	499.06	2.698154	10.019	2.511	498.22	99.83
32	.5333	3.460	497.62	2.696901	10.048	2.518	496.78	99.83
34	.5667	3.470	496.19	2.695652	10.077	2.526	495.35	99.83
36	.6000	3.480	494.77	2.694407	10.106	2.533	493.93	99.83
38	.6333	3.490	493.36	2.693165	10.135	2.540	492.51	99.83
40	.6667	3.500	491.96	2.691926	10.164	2.547	491.11	99.83
42	.7000	3.510	490.56	2.690692	10.192	2.555	489.71	99.83
44	.7333	3.520	489.17	2.689460	10.221	2.562	488.32	99.83
46	.7667	3.530	487.79	2.688233	10.250	2.569	486.93	99.83
48	.8000	3.540	486.42	2.687008	10.279	2.577	485.56	99.83
50	.8333	3.550	485.05	2.685788	10.308	2.584	484.19	99.82
52	.8367	3.560	483.69	2.684570	10.337	2.591	482.83	99.82
54	.9000	3.570	482.34	2.683357	10.366	2.598	481.48	99.82
56	.9333	3.580	481.00	2.682146	10.395	2.606	480.13	99.82
58	.9667	3.590	479.67	2.680939	10.424	2.613	478.79	99.82
12°		3.600	478.34	2.679735	10.453	2.620	477.46	99.82
2	.0333	3.610	477.02	2.678535	10.482	2.628	476.14	99.82
4	.0667	3.620	475.71	2.677338	10.511	2.635	474.83	99.82
6	.1000	3.630	474.40	2.676145	10.540	2.642	473.52	99.82
8	.1333	3.640	473.10	2.674954	10.569	2.650	472.22	99.82
10	.1667	3.650	471.81	2.673767	10.597	2.657	470.92	99.81
12	.2000	3.660	470.53	2.672584	10.626	2.664	469.64	99.81
14	.2333	3.670	469.25	2.671403	10.655	2.671	468.36	99.81
16	.2667	3.680	467.98	2.670226	10.684	2.679	467.09	99.81
18	.3000	3.690	466.72	2.669052	10.713	2.686	465.82	99.81
20	.3333	3.700	465.46	2.667881	10.742	2.693	464.56	99.81
22	.3667	3.710	464.21	2.666713	10.771	2.701	463.31	99.81
24	.4000	3.720	462.96	2.665549	10.800	2.708	462.06	99.81
26	.4333	3.730	461.73	2.664388	10.829	2.715	460.82	99.81
28	.4367	3.740	460.50	2.663229	10.858	2.722	459.59	99.81
30	.5000	3.750	459.28	2.662074	10.887	2.730	458.37	99.80
32	.5333	3.760	458.06	2.660922	10.916	2.737	457.15	99.80
34	.5667	3.770	456.85	2.659773	10.945	2.744	455.93	99.80
36	.6000	3.780	455.65	2.658628	10.973	2.752	454.73	99.80
38	.6333	3.790	454.45	2.657485	11.002	2.759	453.53	99.80
40	.6667	3.800	453.26	2.656345	11.031	2.766	452.34	99.80
42	.7000	3.810	452.07	2.655208	11.060	2.774	451.15	99.80
44	.7333	3.820	450.89	2.654075	11.089	2.781	449.97	99.80
46	.7667	3.830	449.72	2.652944	11.118	2.788	448.79	99.80
48	.8000	3.840	448.56	2.651816	11.147	2.795	447.62	99.80
50	.8333	3.850	447.40	2.650691	11.176	2.803	446.46	99.79
52	.8667	3.860	446.24	2.649570	11.205	2.810	445.30	99.79
54	.9000	3.870	445.09	2.648451	11.234	2.817	444.15	99.79
56	.9333	3.880	443.95	2.647335	11.263	2.825	443.01	99.79
58	.9667	3.890	442.81	2.646221	11.291	2.832	441.87	99.79

Degree of Curve, D		Defl. Min. Per Ft.	Chord Definition				Arc Definition	
Min.	Deci-mal		Radius R	Log. R	Tan. Off. 100-Ft. Ch.	Mid. Ord. 100-Ft. Ch.	Radius R	Chord
13°		3.900	441.68	2.645111	11.320	2.839	*440.74*	*99.78*
2	.0333	3.910	440.56	2.644004	11.349	2.839	*439.61*	*99.78*
4	.0667	3.920	439.44	2.642899	11.378	2.854	*438.49*	*99.78*
6	.1000	3.930	438.33	2.641798	11.407	2.861	*437.37*	*99.78*
8	.1337	3.940	437.22	2.640699	11.436	2.868	*436.26*	*99.78*
10	.1667	3.950	436.12	2.639603	11.465	2.876	*435.16*	*99.78*
12	.2000	3.960	435.02	2.638510	11.494	2.883	*434.06*	*99.78*
14	.2333	3.970	433.93	2.637419	11.523	2.890	*432.97*	*99.78*
16	.2667	3.980	432.84	2.636331	11.552	2.898	*431.88*	*99.78*
18	.3000	3.990	431.76	2.635246	11.580	2.905	*430.79*	*99.78*
20	.3333	4.000	430.69	2.634164	11.609	2.912	*429.72*	*99.77*
22	.3667	4.010	429.62	2.633085	11.638	2.919	*428.65*	*99.77*
24	.4000	4.020	428.56	2.632008	11.667	2.927	*427.58*	*99.77*
26	.4333	4.030	427.50	2.630934	11.696	2.934	*426.52*	*99.77*
28	.4667	4.040	426.44	2.629863	11.725	2.941	*425.46*	*99.77*
30	.5000	4.050	425.40	2.628794	11.754	2.949	*424.41*	*99.77*
32	.5333	4.060	424.35	2.627728	11.783	2.956	*423.37*	*99.77*
34	.5667	4.070	423.32	2.626665	11.812	2.963	*422.33*	*99.77*
36	.6000	4.080	422.28	2.625604	11.840	2.971	*421.29*	*99.77*
38	.6333	4.090	421.26	2.624546	11.869	2.978	*420.26*	*99.77*
40	.6667	4.100	420.23	2.623490	11.898	2.985	*419.24*	*99.76*
42	.7000	4.110	419.22	2.622437	11.927	2.992	*418.22*	*99.76*
44	.7333	4.120	418.20	2.621387	11.956	3.000	*417.20*	*99.76*
46	.7667	4.130	417.19	2.620339	11.985	3.007	*416.19*	*99.76*
48	.8000	4.140	416.19	2.619294	12.014	3.014	*415.19*	*99.76*
50	.8333	4.150	415.19	2.618251	12.043	3.022	*414.19*	*99.76*
52	.8667	4.160	414.20	2.617211	12.071	3.029	*413.20*	*99.76*
54	.9000	4.170	413.21	2.616173	12.100	3.036	*412.20*	*99.76*
56	.9333	4.180	412.23	2.615138	12.129	3.044	*411.21*	*99.76*
58	.9667	4.190	411.25	2.614106	12.158	3.051	*410.23*	*99.76*
14°		4.200	410.28	2.613075	12.187	3.058	*409.26*	*99.75*
2	.0333	4.210	409.31	2.612048	12.216	3.065	*408.28*	*99.75*
4	.0367	4.220	408.34	2.611023	12.245	3.073	*407.32*	*99.75*
6	.1000	4.230	407.38	2.610000	12.274	3.080	*406.35*	*99.75*
8	.1333	4.240	406.42	2.608980	12.302	3.087	*405.39*	*99.75*
10	.1667	4.250	405.47	2.607962	12.331	3.095	*404.44*	*99.74*
12	.2000	4.260	404.53	2.606946	12.360	3.102	*403.49*	*99.74*
14	.2333	4.270	403.58	2.605933	12.389	3.109	*402.55*	*99.74*
16	.2667	4.280	402.65	2.604923	12.418	3.117	*401.61*	*99.74*
18	.3000	4.290	401.71	2.603914	12.447	3.124	*400.66*	*99.74*
20	.3333	4.300	400.78	2.602908	12.476	3.131	*399.74*	*99.74*
22	.3667	4.310	399.86	2.601905	12.504	3.138	*398.81*	*99.74*
24	.4000	4.320	398.94	2.600904	12.533	3.146	*397.89*	*99.74*
26	.4333	4.330	398.02	2.599905	12.562	3.153	*396.97*	*99.74*
28	.4667	4.340	397.11	2.598908	12.591	3.160	*396.05*	*99.74*
30	.5000	4.350	396.20	2.597914	12.620	3.168	*395.14*	*99.73*
32	.5333	4.360	395.30	2.596922	12.649	3.175	*394.24*	*99.73*
34	.5667	4.370	394.40	2.595933	12.678	3.182	*393.33*	*99.73*
36	.6000	4.380	393.50	2.594945	12.706	3.190	*392.44*	*99.73*
38	.6333	4.390	332.61	2.593960	12.735	3.197	*391.54*	*99.73*
40	.6667	4.400	391.72	2.592978	12.764	3.204	*390.65*	*99.73*
42	.7000	4.410	390.84	2.591997	12.793	3.211	*389.77*	*99.73*
44	.7333	4.420	389.96	2.591019	12.822	3.219	*388.89*	*99.73*
46	.7667	4.430	389.08	2.590043	12.851	3.226	*388.01*	*99.73*
48	.8000	4.440	388.21	2.589069	12.880	3.233	*387.13*	*99.73*
50	.8333	4.450	387.34	2.588097	12.908	3.241	*386.26*	*99.72*
52	.8667	4.460	386.48	2.587128	12.937	3.248	*385.40*	*99.72*
54	.9000	4.470	385.62	2.586161	12.966	3.255	*384.54*	*99.72*
56	.9333	4.480	384.77	2.585196	12.995	3.263	*583.68*	*99.72*
58	.9667	4.490	383.91	2.584233	13.024	3.270	*382.82*	*99.72*

Degree of Curve, D		Defl. Min. Per Ft.	Chord Definition				Arc Definition	
Min.	Deci- mal		Radius R	Log. R	Tan. Off. 100-Ft. Ch.	Mid. Ord. 100-Ft. Ch.	Radius R	Chord
15°		4.500	383.06	2.583272	13.053	3.277	381.97	99.71
2	.0333	4.510	382.22	2.582314	13.081	3.284	381.12	99.71
4	.0667	4.520	381.38	2.581358	13.110	3.292	380.28	99.71
6	.1000	4.530	380.54	2.580403	13.139	3.299	379.44	99.71
8	.1333	4.540	379.71	2.579451	13.168	3.306	378.61	99.71
10	.1667	4.550	378.88	2.578501	13.197	3.314	377.77	99.71
12	.2000	4.560	378.05	2.577553	13.226	3.321	376.95	99.71
14	.2333	4.570	377.23	2.576608	13.254	3.328	376.12	99.71
16	.2667	4.580	376.41	2.575664	13.283	3.336	375.30	99.71
18	.3000	4.590	375.60	2.574722	13.312	3.343	374.48	99.71
20	.3333	4.600	374.79	2.573783	13.341	3.350	373.67	99.70
22	.3667	4.610	373.98	2.572845	13.370	3.358	372.86	99.70
24	.4000	4.620	373.17	2.571910	13.399	3.365	372.05	99.70
26	.4333	4.630	372.37	2.570977	13.427	3.372	371.25	99.70
28	.4667	4.640	371.57	2.570045	13.456	3.379	370.45	99.70
30	.5000	4.650	370.78	2.569116	13.485	3.387	369.66	99.69
32	.5333	4.660	369.99	2.568189	13.514	3.394	368.86	99.69
34	.5667	4.670	369.20	2.567264	13.543	3.401	368.07	99.69
36	.6000	4.680	368.42	2.566340	13.572	3.409	367.28	99.69
38	.6333	4.690	367.64	2.565419	13.600	3.416	366.50	99.69
40	.6667	4.700	366.86	2.564500	13.629	3.423	365.72	99.69
42	.7000	4.710	366.09	2.563582	13.658	3.431	364.94	99.69
44	.7333	4.720	365.32	2.562667	13.687	3.438	364.17	99.69
46	.7667	4.730	364.55	2.561754	13.716	3.445	363.40	99.69
48	.8000	4.740	363.78	2.560843	13.744	3.452	362.63	99.69
50	.8333	4.750	363.02	2.559933	13.773	3.460	361.87	99.68
52	.8667	4.760	362.26	2.559026	13.802	3.467	361.11	99.68
54	.9000	4.770	361.51	2.558120	13.831	3.474	360.35	99.68
56	.9333	4.780	360.76	2.557216	13.860	3.482	359.59	99.68
58	.9667	4.790	360.01	2.556315	13.889	3.489	358.85	99.68
16°		4.800	359.27	2.555415	13.917	3.496	358.10	99.67
2	.0333	4.810	358.52	2.554517	13.946	3.504	357.35	99.67
4	.0667	4.820	357.78	2.553621	13.975	3.511	356.61	99.67
6	.1000	4.830	357.05	2.552727	14.004	3.518	355.87	99.67
8	.1333	4.840	356.32	2.551834	14.033	3.526	355.14	99.67
10	.1667	4.850	355.59	2.550944	14.061	3.533	354.41	99.67
12	.2000	4.860	354.86	2.550055	14.090	3.540	353.68	99.67
14	.2333	4.870	354.14	2.549169	14.119	3.547	352.95	99.67
16	.2667	4.880	353.41	2.548284	14.148	3.555	352.23	99.67
18	.3000	4.890	352.70	2.547401	14.177	3.562	351.51	99.67
20	.3333	4.900	351.98	2.546519	14.205	3.569	350.79	99.66
22	.3667	4.910	351.27	2.545640	14.234	3.577	350.08	99.66
24	.4000	4.920	350.56	2.544762	14.263	3.584	349.36	99.66
26	.4333	4.930	349.85	2.543887	14.292	3.591	348.66	99.66
28	.4667	4.940	349.15	2.543013	14.320	3.599	347.95	99.66
30	.5000	4.950	348.45	2.542140	14.349	3.606	347.25	99.65
32	.5333	4.960	347.75	2.541270	14.378	3.613	346.55	99.65
34	.5667	4.970	347.06	2.540401	14.407	3.621	345.85	99.65
36	.6000	4.980	346.37	2.539535	14.436	3.628	345.16	99.65
38	.6333	4.990	345.68	2.538670	14.464	3.635	344.46	99.65
40	.6667	5.000	344.99	2.537806	14.493	3.643	343.77	99.65
42	.7000	5.010	344.31	2.536945	14.522	3.650	343.09	99.65
44	.7333	5.020	343.63	2.536085	14.551	3.657	342.41	99.65
46	.7667	5.030	342.95	2.535227	14.580	3.664	341.72	99.65
48	.8000	5.040	342.27	2.534370	14.608	3.672	341.05	99.65
50	.8333	5.050	341.60	2.533516	14.637	3.679	340.37	99.64
52	.8667	5.060	340.93	2.532663	14.666	3.686	339.70	99.64
54	.9000	5.070	340.26	2.531811	14.695	3.694	339.03	99.64
56	.9333	5.080	339.60	2.530962	14.723	3.701	338.36	99.64
58	.9667	5.090	338.93	2.530114	14.752	3.708	337.70	99.64

14 — Table I. Radii, Etc. [I

Degree of Curve, D		Deff. Min. Per Ft.	Chord Definition				Arc Definition	
Min.	Decimal		Radius R	Log. R	Tan. Off. 100-Ft. Ch.	Mid. Ord. 100-Ft. Ch.	Radius R	Chord
17°		5.100	338.27	2.529268	14.781	3.716	337.03	99.63
2	.0333	5.110	337.62	2.528424	14.810	3.723	336.38	99.63
4	.0667	5.120	336.96	2.527581	14.838	3.730	335.72	99.63
6	.1000	5.130	336.31	2.526740	14.867	3.738	335.06	99.63
8	.1333	5.140	335.66	2.525900	14.896	3.745	334.41	99.63
19	.1667	5.150	335.01	2.525062	14.925	3.752	333.76	99.62
12	.2000	5.160	334.37	2.524226	14.954	3.760	333.12	99.62
14	.2333	5.170	333.73	2.523392	14.982	3.767	332.47	99.62
16	.2667	5.180	333.09	2.522559	15.011	3.774	331.83	99.62
18	.3000	5.190	332.45	2.521728	15.040	3.781	331.19	99.62
20	.3333	5.200	331.82	2.520898	15.069	3.789	330.55	99.62
22	.3367	5.210	331.18	2.520070	15.097	3.796	329.92	99.62
24	.4000	5.220	330.56	2.519244	15.126	3.803	329.29	99.62
26	.4333	5.230	329.93	2.518419	15.155	3.811	328.66	99.62
28	.4667	5.240	329.30	2.517596	15.184	3.818	328.03	99.62
30	.5000	5.250	328.69	2.516774	15.212	3.825	327.40	99.61
32	.5333	5.260	328.06	2.515954	15.241	3.833	326.78	99.61
34	.5667	5.270	327.44	2.515136	15.270	3.840	326.16	99.61
36	.6000	5.280	326.83	2.514319	15.299	3.847	325.54	99.61
38	.6333	5.290	326.22	2.513504	15.327	3.855	324.93	99.61
40	.6667	5.300	325.60	2.512690	15.356	3.862	324.32	99.60
42	.7000	5.310	325.00	2.511878	15.385	3.869	323.70	99.60
44	.7333	5.320	324.39	2.511067	15.414	3.877	323.09	99.60
46	.7667	5.330	323.79	2.510258	15.442	3.884	322.49	99.60
48	.8000	5.340	323.18	2.509451	15.471	3.891	321.89	99.60
50	.8333	5.350	322.59	2.508645	15.500	3.899	321.28	99.59
52	.8667	5.360	321.99	2.507840	15.529	3.906	320.69	99.59
54	.9000	5.370	321.39	2.507037	15.557	3.913	320.09	99.59
56	.9333	5.380	320.80	2.506236	15.586	3.920	319.49	99.59
58	.9667	5.390	320.21	2.505436	15.615	3.928	318.90	99.59
18°		5.400	319.62	2.504638	15.643	3.935	318.31	99.59
2	.0333	5.410	319.04	2.503841	15.672	3.942	317.72	99.59
4	.0667	5.420	318.45	2.503045	15.701	3.950	317.14	99.59
6	.1000	5.430	317.87	2.502251	15.730	3.957	316.55	99.59
8	.1333	5.440	317.29	2.501459	15.758	3.964	315.97	99.59
10	.1667	5.450	316.72	2.500668	15.787	3.972	315.39	99.58
12	.2000	5.460	316.14	2.499879	15.816	3.979	314.81	99.58
14	.2333	5.470	315.57	2.499091	15.845	3.986	314.24	99.58
16	.2667	5.480	314.99	2.498304	15.873	3.994	313.66	99.58
18	.3000	5.490	314.43	2.497519	15.902	4.001	313.09	99.58
20	.3333	5.500	313.86	2.496736	15.931	4.008	312.52	99.57
22	.3667	5.510	313.30	2.495953	15.959	4.016	311.96	99.57
24	.4000	5.520	312.73	2.495173	15.988	4.023	311.39	99.57
26	.4333	5.530	312.17	2.494393	16.017	4.030	310.83	99.57
28	.4667	5.540	311.61	2.493616	16.046	4.038	310.27	99.57
30	.5000	5.550	311.06	2.492839	16.074	4.045	309.71	99.56
32	.5333	5.560	310.50	2.492064	16.103	4.052	309.15	99.56
34	.5667	5.570	309.95	2.491291	16.132	4.060	308.59	99.56
36	.6000	5.580	309.40	2.490518	16.160	4.067	308.04	99.56
38	.6333	5.590	308.85	2.489748	16.189	4.074	307.49	99.56
40	.6667	5.600	308.30	2.488978	16.218	4.081	306.94	99.56
42	.7000	5.610	307.76	2.488210	16.246	4.089	306.39	99.56
44	.7333	5.620	307.22	2.487444	16.275	4.096	305.85	99.56
46	.7667	5.630	306.68	2.486679	16.304	4.103	305.31	99.56
48	.8000	5.640	306.14	2.485915	16.333	4.111	304.76	99.56
50	.8333	5.650	305.60	2.485152	16.361	4.118	304.22	99.55
52	.8667	5.660	305.06	2.484391	16.390	4.125	303.69	99.55
54	.9000	5.670	304.53	2.483632	16.419	4.133	303.15	99.55
56	.9333	5.680	304.00	2.482873	16.447	4.140	302.62	99.55
58	.9667	5.690	303.47	2.482116	16.476	4.147	302.09	99.55

| Degree of Curve, D | | Defl. Min. Per Ft. | Chord Definition | | | | Arc Definition | |
Min.	Deci-mal		Radius R	Log. R	Tan. Off. 100-Ft. Ch.	Mid. Ord. 100-Ft. Ch.	Radius R	Chord
19°		5.700	302.94	2.481361	16.505	4.155	*301.56*	*99.54*
2	.0333	5.710	302.42	2.480667	16.533	4.162	*301.03*	*99.54*
4	.0667	5.720	301.89	2.479854	16.562	4.169	*300.50*	*99.54*
6	.1C00	5.730	301.37	2.479102	16.591	4.177	*299.98*	*99.54*
8	.1333	5.740	300.85	2.478352	16.620	4.184	*299.46*	*99.54*
10	.1667	5.750	300.33	2.477603	16.648	4.191	*298.93*	*99.53*
12	.2000	5.760	299.82	2.476855	16.677	4.199	*298.42*	*99.53*
14	.2333	5.770	299.30	2.476109	16.706	4.206	*297.90*	*99.53*
16	.2667	5.780	298.79	2.475364	16.734	4.213	*297.38*	*99.53*
18	.3000	5.790	298.28	2.474621	16.763	4.221	*296.87*	*99.53*
20	.3333	5.800	297.77	2.473878	16.792	4.228	*296.36*	*99.52*
22	.3667	5.810	297.26	2.473137	16.820	4.235	*295.85*	*99.52*
24	.4000	5.820	296.76	2.472398	16.849	4.243	*295.34*	*99.52*
26	.4333	5.830	296.25	2.471659	16.878	4.250	*294.83*	*99.52*
28	.4667	5.840	295.75	2.470922	16.906	4.257	*294.33*	*99.52*
30	.5000	5.850	295.25	2.470186	16.935	4.265	*293.82*	*99.52*
32	.5333	5.860	294.75	2.469452	16.964	4.272	*293.32*	*99.52*
34	.5667	5.870	294.25	2.468718	16.992	4.279	*292.82*	*99.52*
36	.6000	5.880	293.76	2.467986	17.021	4.287	*292.33*	*99.52*
38	.6333	5.890	293.26	2.467256	17.050	4.294	*291.83*	*99.52*
40	.6667	5.900	292.77	2.466526	17.078	4.301	*291.33*	*99.51*
42	.7000	5.910	292.28	2.465798	17.107	4.308	*290.84*	*99.51*
44	.7333	5.920	291.79	2.465071	17.136	4.316	*290.35*	*99.51*
46	.7667	5.930	291.30	2.464345	17.164	4.323	*289.86*	*99.51*
48	.8000	5.940	290.82	2.463621	17.193	4.330	*289.37*	*99.51*
50	.8333	5.950	290.33	2.462897	17.222	4.338	*288.89*	*99.50*
52	.8667	5.960	289.85	2.462175	17.250	4.345	*288.40*	*99.50*
54	.9000	5.970	289.37	2.461455	17.279	4.352	*287.92*	*99.50*
56	.9333	5.980	288.89	2.460735	17.308	4.360	*287.43*	*99.50*
58	.9667	5.990	288.41	2.460017	17.336	4.367	*286.96*	*99.50*
20°		6.000	287.94	2.459300	17.365	4.374	*286.48*	*99.49*
10	.1667	6.050	285.58	2.455733	17.508	4.411	*284.11*	*99.48*
20	.3333	6.100	283.27	2.452195	17.651	4.448	*281.78*	*99.48*
30	.5000	6.150	280.99	2.448688	17.794	4.484	*279.49*	*99.47*
40	.6667	6.200	278.75	2.445209	17.937	4.521	*277.24*	*99.46*
50	.8333	6.250	276.54	2.441759	18.081	4.558	*275.02*	*99.45*
21°		6.300	274.37	2.438337	18.224	4.594	*272.84*	*99.44*
10	.1667	6.350	272.23	2.434943	18.367	4.631	*270.69*	*99.43*
20	.3333	6.400	270.13	2.431576	18.509	4.668	*268.57*	*99.42*
30	.5000	6.450	268.06	2.428235	18.652	4.704	*266.49*	*99.41*
40	.6667	6.500	266.02	2.424921	18.795	4.741	*264.44*	*99.41*
50	.8333	6.550	264.02	2.421633	18.938	4.778	*262.42*	*99.40*
22°		6.600	262.04	2.418371	19.081	4.814	*260.44*	*99.39*
10	.1667	6.650	260.10	2.415134	19.224	4.851	*258.48*	*99.38*
20	.3333	6.700	258.18	2.411922	19.366	4.888	*256.55*	*99.37*
30	.5000	6.750	256.29	2.408734	19.509	4.925	*254.65*	*99.36*
40	.6667	6.800	254.43	2.405571	19.652	4.961	*252.78*	*99.35*
50	.8333	6.850	252.60	2.402431	19.794	4.998	*250.93*	*99.34*
23°		6.900	250.79	2.399315	19.937	5.035	*249.11*	*99.33*
10	.1667	6.950	249.01	2.396222	20.079	5.071	*247.32*	*99.32*
20	.3333	7.000	247.26	2.393151	20.222	5.108	*245.55*	*99.31*
30	.5000	7.050	245.53	2.390103	20.364	5.145	*243.81*	*99.30*
40	.6667	7.100	243.82	2.387077	20.507	5.182	*242.09*	*99.29*
50	.8333	7.150	242.14	2.384074	20.649	5.218	*240.40*	*99.28*
24°		7.200	240.49	2.381091	20.791	5.255	*238.73*	*99.27*
10	.1667	7.250	238.85	2.378130	20.933	5.292	*237.09*	*99.26*
20	.3333	7.300	237.24	2.375190	21.076	5.329	*235.46*	*99.25*
30	.5000	7.350	235.65	2.372270	21.218	5.366	*233.86*	*99.24*
40	.6667	7.400	234.08	2.369371	21.360	5.402	*232.28*	*99.23*
50	.8333	7.450	232.54	2.366492	21.502	5.439	*230.72*	*99.22*

Degree of Curve, D		Defl. Min. Per Ft.	Chord Definition				Arc Definition	
Min.	Deci- mal		Radius R	Log. R	Tan. Off. 100-Ft. Ch.	Mid. Ord. 100-Ft. Ch.	Radius R	Chord
25°		7.500	231.01	2.363633	21.644	5.476	229.18	99.21
10	.1667	7.550	229.51	2.360794	21.786	5.513	227.66	99.20
20	.3333	7.600	228.02	2.357974	21.928	5.549	226.17	99.19
30	.5000	7.650	226.55	2.355173	22.070	5.586	224.69	99.18
40	.6667	7.700	225.11	2.352391	22.212	5.623	223.23	99.17
50	.8333	7.750	223.68	2.349627	22.353	5.660	221.79	99.16
26°		7.800	222.27	2.346882	22.495	5.697	220.37	99.14
10	.1667	7.850	220.88	2.344155	22.637	5.734	218.96	99.13
20	.3333	7.900	219.51	2.341446	22.778	5.770	217.58	99.12
30	.5000	7.950	218.15	2.338755	22.920	5.807	216.21	99.11
40	.6667	8.000	216.81	2.336081	23.062	5.844	214.86	99.10
50	.8333	8.050	215.49	2.333424	23.203	5.881	213.52	99.09
27°		8.100	214.18	2.330785	23.345	5.918	212.21	99.08
10	.1667	8.150	212.89	2.328162	23.486	5.955	210.90	99.07
20	.3333	8.200	211.62	2.325556	23.627	5.992	209.62	99.05
30	.5000	8.250	210.36	2.322967	23.769	6.029	208.35	99.04
40	.6667	8.300	209.12	2.320393	23.910	6.065	207.09	99.03
50	.8333	8.350	207.89	2.317836	24.051	6.102	205.85	99.02
28°		8.400	206.68	2.315295	24.192	6.139	204.63	99.01
10	.1667	8.450	205.48	2.312769	24.333	6.176	203.42	99.00
20	.3333	8.500	204.30	2.310259	24.474	6.213	202.22	98.98
30	.5000	8.550	203.13	2.307764	24.615	6.250	201.04	98.97
40	.6667	8.600	201.97	2.305285	24.756	6.287	199.87	98.96
50	.8333	8.650	200.83	2.302820	24.897	6.324	198.71	98.95
29°		8.700	199.70	2.300370	25.038	6.360	197.57	98.94
10	.1667	8.750	198.58	2.297935	25.179	6.398	196.44	98.92
20	.3333	8.800	197.48	2.295515	25.320	6.435	195.33	98.92
30	.5000	8.850	196.38	2.293108	25.460	6.472	194.22	98.90
40	.6667	8.900	195.31	2.290716	25.601	6.509	193.13	98.89
50	.8333	8.950	194.24	2.288338	25.741	6.545	192.05	98.87
30°		9.000	193.19	2.285974	25.882	6.583	190.98	98.86
10	.1667	9.050	192.14	2.283623	26.022	6.620	189.93	98.85
20	.3333	9.100	191.11	2.281286	26.163	6.657	188.89	98.84
30	.5000	9.150	190.09	2.278963	26.303	6.694	187.86	98.83
40	.6667	9.200	189.08	2.276652	26.443	6.731	186.83	98.81
50	.8333	9.250	188.09	2.274355	26.584	6.768	185.82	98.80
31°		9.300	187.10	2.272071	26.724	6.805	184.82	98.79
10	.1667	9.350	186.12	2.269800	26.864	6.842	183.84	98.77
20	.3333	9.400	185.16	2.267541	27.004	6.879	182.86	98.76
30	.5000	9.450	184.20	2.265295	27.144	6.916	181.89	98.74
40	.6667	9.500	183.26	2.263062	27.284	6.953	180.93	98.73
50	.8333	9.550	182.32	2.260841	27.424	6.990	179.99	98.72
32°		9.600	181.40	2.258632	27.564	7.027	179.05	98.71
10	.1667	9.650	180.48	2.256435	27.704	7.064	178.12	98.70
20	.3333	9.700	179.58	2.254250	27.843	7.101	177.20	98.68
30	.5000	9.750	178.68	2.252077	27.983	7.138	176.29	98.66
40	.6667	9.800	177.79	2.249916	28.123	7.175	175.40	98.66
50	.8333	9.850	176.92	2.247766	28.263	7.213	174.50	98.63
33°		9.900	176.05	2.245628	28.402	7.250	173.62	98.62
10	.1667	9.950	175.19	2.243501	28.541	7.287	172.75	98.61
20	.3333	10.000	174.34	2.241386	28.680	7.324	171.89	98.60
30	.5000	10.050	173.49	2.239282	28.820	7.361	171.03	98.58
40	.6667	10.100	172.66	2.237188	28.959	7.398	170.18	98.56
50	.8333	10.150	171.83	2.235106	29.098	7.436	169.35	98.55
34°		10.200	171.02	2.233035	29.237	7.473	168.52	98.54
10	.1667	10.250	170.21	2.230974	29.376	7.510	167.70	98.53
20	.3333	10.300	169.40	2.228924	29.515	7.547	166.88	98.51
30	.5000	10.350	168.61	2.226884	29.654	7.584	166.07	98.49
40	.6667	10.400	167.82	2.224855	29.793	7.621	165.28	98.48
50	.8333	10.450	167.05	2.222837	29.932	7.659	164.48	98.46

| Degree of Curve, D | | Defl. Min. Per Ft. | Chord Definition | | | | Arc Definition | |
Min.	Deci-mal		Radius R	Log. R	Tan. Off. 100-Ft. Ch.	Mid. Ord. 100-Ft. Ch.	Radius R	Chord
35°		10.500	166.28	2.220828	30.071	7.696	*163.70*	*98.45*
10	.1667	10.550	165.51	2.218830	30.210	7.733	*162.93*	*98.44*
20	.3333	10.600	164.76	2.216842	30.348	7.770	*162.16*	*98.42*
30	.5000	10.650	164.01	2.214863	30.487	7.808	*161.40*	*98.41*
40	.6667	10.700	163.27	2.212895	30.625	7.845	*160.64*	*98.39*
50	.8333	10.750	162.53	2.210937	30.764	7.882	*159.90*	*98.38*
36°		10.800	161.80	2.208988	30.902	7.919	*159.15*	*98.36*
10	.1667	10.850	161.08	2.207048	31.040	7.957	*158.42*	*98.34*
20	.3333	10.900	160.37	2.205119	31.178	7.994	*157.69*	*98.33*
30	.5000	10.950	159.66	2.203198	31.316	8.031	*156.97*	*98.31*
40	.6667	11.000	158.96	2.201288	31.454	8.068	*156.26*	*98.30*
50	.8333	11.050	158.27	2.199386	31.592	8.106	*155.55*	*98.29*
37°		11.100	157.58	2.197494	31.730	8.143	*154.85*	*98.27*
10	.1667	11.150	156.90	2.195610	31.868	8.181	*154.16*	*98.26*
20	.3333	11.200	156.22	2.193736	32.006	8.218	*153.47*	*98.24*
30	.5000	11.250	155.55	2.191871	32.144	8.255	*152.79*	*98.23*
40	.6667	11.300	154.89	2.190014	32.282	8.292	*152.11*	*98.21*
50	.8333	11.350	154.23	2.188167	32.420	8.330	*151.44*	*98.19*
38°		11.400	153.58	2.186328	32.557	8.367	*150.78*	*98.18*
10	.1667	11.450	152.93	2.184498	32.695	8.405	*150.12*	*98.16*
20	.3333	11.500	152.29	2.182676	32.832	8.442	*149.47*	*98.15*
30	.5000	11.550	151.66	2.180863	32.969	8.480	*148.82*	*98.13*
40	.6667	11.600	151.03	2.179059	33.106	8.517	*148.18*	*98.11*
50	.8333	11.650	150.41	2.177263	33.244	8.555	*147.54*	*98.10*
39°		11.700	149.79	2.175475	33.381	8.592	*143.91*	*98.08*
10	.1667	11.750	149.17	2.173695	33.518	8.630	*146.29*	*98.07*
20	.3333	11.800	148.57	2.171924	33.655	8.667	*145.67*	*98.05*
30	.5000	11.850	147.97	2.170160	33.792	8.704	*145.05*	*98.03*
40	.6667	11.900	147.37	2.168405	33.929	8.741	*144.44*	*98.01*
50	.8333	11.950	146.78	2.166658	34.066	8.779	*143.84*	*98.00*
40°		12.000	146.19	2.164918	34.202	8.817	*143.24*	*97.98*
30	.5000	12.150	144.46	2.159748	34.612	8.929	*141.47*	*97.94*
41°		12.300	142.77	2.154645	35.021	9.042	*139.74*	*97.88*
30	.5000	12.450	141.13	2.149610	35.429	9.154	*138.06*	*97.82*
42°		12.600	139.52	2.144641	35.837	9.267	*136.42*	*97.78*
30	.5000	12.750	137.95	2.139736	36.244	9.379	*134.81*	*97.72*
43°		12.900	136.43	2.134895	36.650	9.493	*133.25*	*97.68*
30	.5000	13.050	134.93	2.130114	37.056	9.606	*131.71*	*97.62*
44°		13.200	133.47	2.125395	37.461	9.719	*130.22*	*97.56*
30	.5000	13.350	132.35	2.120734	37.865	9.832	*128.75*	*97.50*
45°		13.500	130.66	2.116130	38.268	9.946	*127.32*	*97.44*
30	.5000	13.650	129.30	2.111584	38.671	10.060	*125.92*	*97.38*
46°		13.800	127.97	2.107092	39.073	10.170	*124.56*	*97.34*
30	.5000	13.950	126.66	2.102655	39.474	10.290	*123.22*	*97.28*
47°		14.100	125.39	2.098270	39.875	10.400	*121.91*	*97.22*
30	.5000	14.250	124.15	2.093938	40.275	10.510	*120.62*	*97.16*
48°		14.400	122.93	2.089657	40.674	10.630	*119.37*	*97.10*
30	.5000	14.550	121.74	2.085425	41.072	10.740	*118.14*	*97.04*
49°		14.700	120.57	2.081243	41.469	10.860	*116.93*	*96.98*
30	.5000	14.850	119.43	2.077109	41.866	10.970	*115.75*	*96.92*
50°		15.000	118.31	2.073022	42.262	11.080	*114.59*	*96.86*
30	.5000	15.150	117.21	2.068981	42.657	11.200	*113.46*	*96.80*

| Degree of Curve, D | | Defl. Min. Per Ft. | Chord Definition | | | | Arc Definition | |
Min.	Decimal		Radius R	Log. R	Tan. Off. 100-Ft. Ch.	Mid. Ord. 100-Ft. Ch.	Radius R	Chord
51°		15.300	116.14	2.064986	43.051	11.310	*112.34*	*96.72*
30	.5000	15.450	115.09	2.061035	43.445	11.430	*111.25*	*96.66*
52°		15.600	114.06	2.057128	43.837	11.540	*110.18*	*96.60*
30	.5000	15.750	113.05	2.053264	44.229	11.660	*109.13*	*96.54*
53°		15.900	112.06	2.049443	44.620	11.770	*108.11*	*96.48*
30	.5000	16.050	111.09	2.045663	45.010	11.890	*107.09*	*96.40*
54°		16.200	110.13	2.041923	45.399	12.000	*106.10*	*96.34*
30	.5000	16.350	109.20	2.038224	45.787	12.120	*105.13*	*96.28*
55°		16.500	108.28	2.034564	46.175	12.240	*104.17*	*96.20*
30	.5000	16.650	107.38	2.030943	46.561	12.350	*103.24*	*96.14*
56°		16.800	106.50	2.027361	46.947	12.470	*102.31*	*96.06*
30	.5000	16.950	105.64	2.023815	47.332	12.580	*101.41*	*96.00*
57°		17.100	104.79	2.020307	47.716	12.700	*100.52*	*95.92*
30	.5000	17.250	103.95	2.016835	48.099	12.810	*99.64*	*95.86*
58°		17.400	103.13	2.013398	48.481	12.930	*98.78*	*95.78*
30	.5000	17.550	102.33	2.009998	48.862	13.050	*97.94*	*95.72*
59°		17.700	101.54	2.006631	49.242	13.170	*97.11*	*95.64*
30	.5000	17.850	100.76	2.003299	49.622	13.280	*96.30*	*95.58*
60°		18.000	100.00	2.000000	50.000	13.400	*95.49*	*95.49*

EXAMPLE.   Given a 12° 40′ (12.6667°) curve:

deflection per foot of chord = 3.8 minutes (exact for arc, approximate for chord definition)

radius for chord definition = 453.26 feet

log. radius for chord definition = 2.656345

tangent offset for a 100-ft. chord = 11.031 feet (exact for chord definition, approximate for arc definition)

middle ordinate for a 100-ft. chord = 2.766 feet (exact for chord definition, approximate for arc definition)

radius for arc definition = 452.34 feet

length of chord for a 100-foot arc = 99.80 feet

An approximate value for the middle ordinate may be obtained by dividing the tangent offset by four (4).   Above 11° the approximation is not sufficiently precise and values for middle ordinates may be obtained directly from the Table.

For chords other than 100 feet in length, the tangent offset and middle ordinates may be obtained by multiplying the values given in the Table by the square of the ratio of the two chords (or arcs), for instance, for a 47.3-foot chord (or arc):

tangent offset = 11.031 × (47.3/100)² = 2.468 feet (exact for chord definition, approximate for arc definition)

middle ordinate = 2.766 × (47.3/100)² = 0.619 feet (approximate for both definitions)

(All Definitions of Degree of Curve)

Min-utes	0° Length L	0° Tan. T	0° Ext. E	1° Length L	1° Tan. T	1° Ext. E	2° Length L	2° Tan. T	2° Ext. E
0	0.00	0.0	0	100.00	50.0	.2	200.00	100.0	.9
1	1.67	0.8	0	101.67	50.8	.2	201.67	100.8	.9
2	3.33	1.7	0	103.33	51.7	.2	203.33	101.7	.9
3	5.00	2.5	0	105.00	52.5	.2	205.00	102.5	.9
4	6.67	3.3	0	106.67	53.3	.2	206.67	103.3	.9
5	8.33	4.2	0	108.33	54.2	.3	208.33	104.2	.9
6	10.00	5.0	0	110.00	55.0	.3	210.00	105.0	1.0
7	11.67	5.8	0	111.67	55.8	.3	211.67	105.8	1.0
8	13.33	6.7	0	113.33	56.7	.3	213.33	106.7	1.0
9	15.00	7.5	0	115.00	57.5	.3	215.00	107.5	1.0
10	16.67	8.3	0	116.67	58.3	.3	216.67	108.3	1 0
11	18.33	9.2	0	118.33	59.2	.3	218.33	109.2	1.0
12	20.00	10.0	0	120.00	60.0	.3	220.00	110.0	1.1
13	21.67	10.8	0	121.67	60.8	.3	221.67	110.8	1.1
14	23.33	11.7	0	123.33	61.7	.3	223.33	111.7	1.1
15	25.00	12.5	0	125.00	62.5	.3	225.00	112.5	1.1
16	26.67	13.3	0	126.67	63.3	.4	226.67	113.3	1.1
17	28.33	14.2	0	128.33	64.2	.4	228.33	114.2	1.1
18	30.00	15.0	0	130.00	65.0	.4	230.00	115.0	1.2
19	31.67	15.8	0	131.67	65.8	.4	231.67	115.8	1.2
20	33.33	16.7	0	133.33	66.7	.4	233.33	116.7	1.2
21	35.00	17.5	0	135.00	67.5	.4	235.00	117.5	1.2
22	36.67	18.3	0	136.67	68.3	.4	236.67	118.4	1.2
23	38.33	19.2	0	138.33	69.2	.4	238.33	119.2	1.2
24	40.00	20.0	0	140.00	70.0	.4	240.00	120.0	1.3
25	41.67	20.8	0	141.67	70.8	.4	241.67	120.9	1.3
26	43.33	21.7	0	143.33	71.7	.4	243.33	121.7	1.3
27	45.00	22.5	0	145.00	72.5	.5	245.00	122.5	1.3
28	46.67	23.3	0	146.67	73.3	.5	246.67	123.4	1.3
29	48.33	24.2	.1	148.33	74.2	.5	248.33	124.2	1.3
30	50.00	25.0	.1	150.00	75.0	.5	250.00	125.0	1.4
31	51.67	25.8	.1	151.67	75.8	.5	251.67	125.9	1.4
32	53.33	26.7	.1	153.33	76.7	.5	253.33	126.7	1.4
33	55.00	27.5	.1	155.00	77.5	.5	255.00	127.5	1.4
34	56.67	28.3	.1	156.67	78.3	.5	256.67	128.4	1.4
35	58.33	29.2	.1	158.33	79.2	.5	258.33	129 2	1.5
36	60.00	30.0	.1	160.00	80.0	.6	260.00	130.0	1.5
37	61.67	30.8	.1	161.67	80.8	.6	261.67	130.9	1.5
38	63.33	31.7	.1	163.33	81.7	.6	263.33	131.7	1.5
39	65.00	32.5	.1	165.00	82.5	.6	265.00	132.5	1.5
40	66.67	33.3	.1	166.67	83.3	.6	266.67	133.4	1.6
41	68.33	34.2	.1	168.33	84.2	.6	268.33	134.2	1.6
42	70.00	35.0	.1	170.00	85.0	.6	270.00	135.0	1.6
43	71.67	35.8	.1	171.67	85.8	.6	271.67	135.9	1.6
44	73.33	36.7	.1	173.33	86.7	.7	273.33	136.7	1.6
45	75.00	37.5	.1	175.00	87.5	.7	275.00	137.5	1.7
46	76.67	38.3	.1	176.67	88.3	.7	276.67	138.4	1.7
47	78.33	39.2	.1	178.33	89.2	.7	278.33	139.2	1.7
48	80.00	40.0	.1	180.00	90.0	.7	280.00	140.0	1.7
49	81.67	40.8	.1	181.67	90.8	.7	281.67	140.9	1.7
50	83.33	41.7	.2	183.33	91.7	.7	283.33	141.7	1.8
51	85.00	42.5	.2	185.00	92.5	.7	285.00	142.5	1.8
52	86.67	43.3	.2	186.67	93.3	.8	286.67	143.4	1.8
53	88.33	44.2	.2	188.33	94.2	.8	288.33	144.2	1.8
54	90.00	45.0	.2	190.00	95.0	.8	290.00	145.0	1.8
55	91.67	45.8	.2	191.67	95.8	.8	291.67	145.9	1.9
56	93.33	46.7	.2	193.33	96.7	.8	293.33	146.7	1.9
57	95.00	47.5	.2	195.00	97.5	.8	295.00	147.5	1.9
58	96.67	48.3	.2	196.67	98.3	.8	296.67	148.4	1.9
59	98.33	49.2	.2	198.33	99.2	.9	298.33	149.2	1.9

(All Definitions of Degree of Curve)

Min-utes	3° Length L	3° Tan. T	3° Ext. E	4° Length L	4° Tan. T	4° Ext. E	5° Length L	5° Tan. T	5° Ext. E
0	300.00	150.0	2.0	400.00	200.1	3.5	500.00	250.2	5.5
1	301.67	150.9	2.0	401.67	200.9	3.5	501.67	251.0	5.5
2	303.33	151.7	2.0	403.33	201.8	3.6	503.33	251.8	5.5
3	305.00	152.5	2.0	405.00	202.6	3.6	505.00	252.7	5.6
4	306.67	153.4	2.1	406.67	203.4	3.6	506.67	253.5	5.6
5	308.33	154.2	2.1	408.33	204.3	3.7	508.33	254.3	5.6
6	310.00	155.0	2.1	410.00	205.1	3.7	510.00	255.2	5.7
7	311.67	155.9	2.1	411.67	205.9	3.7	511.67	256.0	5.7
8	313.33	156.7	2.1	413.33	206.8	3.7	513.33	256.8	5.8
9	315.00	157.5	2.2	415.00	207.6	3.8	515.00	257.7	5.8
10	316.67	158.4	2.2	416.67	208.4	3.8	516.67	258.5	5.8
11	318.33	159.2	2.2	418.33	209.3	3.8	518.33	259.3	5.9
12	320.00	160.0	2.2	420.00	210.1	3.9	520.00	260.2	5.9
13	321.67	160.9	2.3	421.67	210.9	3.9	521.67	261.0	5.9
14	323.33	161.7	2.3	423.33	211.8	3.9	523.33	261.9	6.0
15	325.00	162.5	2.3	425.00	212.6	3.9	525.00	262.7	6.0
16	326.67	163.4	2.3	426.67	213.4	4.0	526.67	263.5	6.1
17	328.33	164.2	2.4	428.33	214.3	4.0	528.33	264.4	6.1
18	330.00	165.0	2.4	430.00	215.1	4.0	530.00	265.2	6.1
19	331.67	165.9	2.4	431.67	215.9	4.1	531.67	266.0	6.2
20	333.33	166.7	2.4	433.33	216.8	4.1	533.33	266.9	6.2
21	335.00	167.6	2.4	435.00	217.6	4.1	535.00	267.7	6.3
22	336.67	168.4	2.5	436.67	218.4	4.2	536.67	268.5	6.3
23	338.33	169.2	2.5	438.33	219.3	4.2	538.33	269.4	6.3
24	340.00	170.1	2.5	440.00	220.1	4.2	540.00	270.2	6.4
25	341.67	170.9	2.5	441.67	220.9	4.3	541.67	271.0	6.4
26	343.33	171.7	2.6	443.33	221.8	4.3	543.33	271.9	6.4
27	345.00	172.6	2.6	445.00	222.6	4.3	545.00	272.7	6.5
28	346.67	173.4	2.6	446.67	223.4	4.4	546.67	273.5	6.5
29	348.33	174.2	2.6	448.33	224.3	4.4	548.33	274.4	6.6
30	350.00	175.1	2.7	450.00	225.1	4.4	550.00	275.2	6.6
31	351.67	175.9	2.7	451.67	226.0	4.5	551.67	276.1	6.6
32	353.33	176.7	2.7	453.33	226.8	4.5	553.33	276.9	6.7
33	355.00	177.6	2.8	455.00	227.6	4.5	555.00	277.7	6.7
34	356.67	178.4	2.8	456.67	228.5	4.6	556.67	278.6	6.8
35	358.33	179.2	2.8	458.33	229.3	4.6	558.33	279.4	6.8
36	360.00	180.1	2.8	460.00	230.1	4.6	560.00	280.2	6.9
37	361.67	180.9	2.9	461.67	231.0	4.7	561.67	281.1	6.9
38	363.33	181.7	2.9	463.33	231.8	4.7	563.33	281.9	6.9
39	365.00	182.6	2.9	465.00	232.6	4.7	565.00	282.7	7.0
40	366.67	183.4	2.9	466.67	233.5	4.8	566.67	283.6	7.0
41	368.33	184.2	3.0	468.33	234.3	4.8	568.33	284.4	7.1
42	370.00	185.1	3.0	470.00	235.1	4.8	570.00	285.2	7.1
43	371.67	185.9	3.0	471.67	236.0	4.9	571.67	286.1	7.1
44	373.33	186.7	3.0	473.33	236.8	4.9	573.33	286.9	7.2
45	375.00	187.6	3.1	475.00	237.6	4.9	575.00	287.7	7.2
46	376.67	188.4	3.1	476.67	238.5	5.0	576.67	288.6	7.3
47	378.33	189.2	3.1	478.33	239.3	5.0	578.33	289.4	7.3
48	380.00	190.1	3.2	480.00	240.1	5.0	580.00	290.3	7.3
49	381.67	190.9	3.2	481.67	241.0	5.1	581.67	291.1	7.4
50	383.33	191.7	3.2	483.33	241.8	5.1	583.33	291.9	7.4
51	385.00	192.6	3.2	485.00	242.6	5.1	585.00	292.8	7.5
52	386.67	193.4	3.3	486.67	243.5	5.2	586.67	293.6	7.5
53	388.33	194.2	3.3	488.33	244.3	5.2	588.33	294.4	7.6
54	390.00	195.1	3.3	490.00	245.2	5.2	590.00	295.3	7.6
55	391.67	195.9	3.3	491.67	246.0	5.3	591.67	296.1	7.6
56	393.33	196.7	3.4	493.33	246.8	5.3	593.33	296.9	7.7
57	395.00	197.6	3.4	495.00	247.7	5.3	595.00	297.8	7.7
58	396.67	198.4	3.4	496.67	248.5	5.4	596.67	298.6	7.8
59	398.33	199.2	3.5	498.33	249.3	5.4	598.33	299.4	7.8

(All Definitions of Degree of Curve)

Min-utes	6°			7°			8°		
	Length L	Tan. T	Ext. E	Length L	Tan. T	Ext. E	Length L	Tan. T	Ext. E
0	600.00	300.0	7.9	700.00	350.4	10.7	800.00	400.7	14.0
1	601.67	301.1	7.9	701.67	351.3	10.8	801.67	401.5	14.1
2	603.33	301.9	8.0	703.33	352.1	10.8	803.33	402.3	14.1
3	605.00	302.8	8.0	705.00	352.9	10.9	805.00	403.2	14.2
4	606.67	303.6	8.0	706.67	353.8	11.0	806.67	404.0	14.2
5	608.33	304.5	8.1	708.33	354.6	11.0	808.33	404.8	14.3
6	610.00	305.3	8.1	710.00	355.5	11.0	810.00	405.7	14.3
7	611.67	306.1	8.2	711.67	356.3	11.1	811.67	406.5	14.4
8	613.33	307.0	8.2	713.33	357.1	11.1	813.33	407.4	14.5
9	615.00	307.8	8.3	715.00	358.0	11.2	815.00	408.2	14.5
10	616.67	308.6	8.3	716.67	358.8	11.2	816.67	409.0	14.6
11	618.33	309.5	8.4	718.33	359.6	11.3	818.33	409.9	14.6
12	620.00	310.3	8.4	720.00	360.5	11.3	820.00	410.7	14.7
13	621.67	311.1	8.4	721.67	361.3	11.4	821.67	411.5	14.8
14	623.33	312.0	8.5	723.33	362.2	11.4	823.33	412.4	14.8
15	625.00	312.8	8.5	725.00	363.0	11.5	825.00	413.2	14.9
16	626.67	313.7	8.6	726.67	363.8	11.5	826.67	414.1	14.9
17	628.33	314.5	8.6	728.33	364.7	11.6	828.33	414.9	15.0
18	630.00	315.3	8.7	730.00	365.5	11.6	830.00	415.7	15.1
19	631.67	316.2	8.7	731.67	366.3	11.7	831.67	416.6	15.1
20	633.33	317.0	8.8	733.33	367.2	11.8	833.33	417.4	15.2
21	635.00	317.8	8.8	735.00	368.0	11.8	835.00	418.2	15.2
22	636.67	318.7	8.9	736.67	368.8	11.9	836.67	419.1	15.3
23	638.33	319.5	8.9	738.33	369.7	11.9	838.33	419.9	15.4
24	640.00	320.3	8.9	740.00	370.5	12.0	840.00	420.8	15.4
25	641.67	321.2	9.0	741.67	371.4	12.0	841.67	421.6	15.5
26	643.33	322.0	9.0	743.33	372.2	12.1	843.33	422.4	15.6
27	645.00	322.8	9.1	745.00	373.0	12.1	845.00	423.3	15.6
28	646.67	323.7	9.1	746.67	373.9	12.2	846.67	424.1	15.7
29	648.33	324.5	9.2	748.33	374.7	12.2	848.33	424.9	15.7
30	650.00	325.4	9.2	750.00	375.5	12.3	850.00	425.8	15.8
31	651.67	326.2	9.3	751.67	376.4	12.3	851.67	426.6	15.9
32	653.33	327.0	9.3	753.33	377.2	12.4	853.33	427.5	15.9
33	655.00	327.9	9.4	755.00	378.1	12.5	855.00	428.3	16.0
34	656.67	328.7	9.4	756.67	378.9	12.5	856.67	429.1	16.0
35	658.33	329.5	9.5	758.33	379.7	12.6	858.33	430.0	16.1
36	660.00	330.4	9.5	760.00	380.6	12.6	860.00	430.8	16.2
37	661.67	331.2	9.6	761.67	381.4	12.7	861.67	431.7	16.2
38	663.33	332.0	9.6	763.33	382.2	12.7	863.33	432.5	16.3
39	665.00	332.9	9.7	765.00	383.1	12.8	865.00	433.3	16.4
40	666.67	333.7	9.7	766.67	383.9	12.8	866.67	434.2	16.4
41	668.33	334.6	9.8	768.33	384.7	12.9	868.33	435.0	16.5
42	670.00	335.4	9.8	770.00	385.6	13.0	870.00	435.8	16.6
43	671.67	336.2	9.9	771.67	386.4	13.0	871.67	436.7	16.6
44	673.33	337.1	9.9	773.33	387.3	13.1	873.33	437.5	16.7
45	675.00	337.9	10.0	775.00	388.1	13.1	875.00	438.4	16.7
46	676.67	338.7	10.0	776.67	388.9	13.2	876.67	439.2	16.8
47	678.33	339.6	10.1	778.33	389.8	13.2	878.33	440.0	16.9
48	680.00	340.4	10.1	780.00	390.6	13.3	880.00	440.9	17.0
49	681.67	341.2	10.2	781.67	391.4	13.4	881.67	441.7	17.0
50	683.33	342.1	10.2	783.33	392.3	13.4	883.33	442.5	17.1
51	685.00	342.9	10.3	785.00	393.1	13.5	885.00	443.4	17.1
52	686.67	343.7	10.3	786.67	394.0	13.5	886.67	444.2	17.2
53	688.33	344.6	10.4	788.33	394.8	13.6	888.33	445.1	17.3
54	690.00	345.4	10.4	790.00	395.6	13.6	890.00	445.9	17.3
55	691.67	346.3	10.5	791.67	396.5	13.7	891.67	446.7	17.4
56	693.33	347.1	10.5	793.33	397.3	13.8	893.33	447.6	17.5
57	695.00	347.9	10.6	795.00	398.1	13.8	895.00	448.4	17.5
58	696.67	348.8	10.6	796.67	399.0	13.9	896.67	449.3	17.6
59	698.33	349.6	10.7	798.33	399.8	13.9	898.33	450.1	17.7

(All Definitions of Degree of Curve)

Min-utes	9° Length L	9° Tan. T	9° Ext. E	10° Length L	10° Tan. T	10° Ext. E	11° Length L	11° Tan. T	11° Ext. E
0	900.00	450.9	17.7	1000.00	501.2	21.9	1100.00	551.7	26.5
1	901.67	451.8	17.8	1001.67	502.1	22.0	1101.67	552.5	26.6
2	903.33	452.6	17.8	1003.33	503.0	22.0	1103.33	553.4	26.7
3	905.00	453.4	17.9	1005.00	503.8	22.1	1105.00	554.2	26.7
4	906.67	454.3	18.0	1006.67	504.6	22.2	1106.67	555.1	26.8
5	908.33	455.1	18.0	1008.33	505.5	22.3	1108.33	555.9	26.9
6	910.00	456.0	18.1	1010.00	506.3	22.3	1110.00	556.7	27.0
7	911.67	453.8	18.2	1011.67	507.2	22.4	1111.67	557.6	27.1
8	913.33	457.6	18.2	1013.33	508.0	22.5	1113.33	558.4	27.2
9	915.00	458.5	18.3	1015.00	508.8	22.6	1115.00	559.3	27.2
10	916.67	459.3	18.4	1016.67	509.7	22.6	1116.67	560.1	27.3
11	918.33	460.2	18.4	1018.33	510.5	22.7	1118.33	561.0	27.4
12	920.00	461.0	18.5	1020.00	511.4	22.8	1120.00	561.8	27.5
13	921.67	461.8	18.6	1021.67	512.2	22.8	1121.67	562.6	27.6
14	923.33	462.7	18.7	1023.33	513.0	22.9	1123.33	563.5	27.6
15	925.00	463.5	18.7	1025.00	513.9	23.0	1125.00	564.3	27.7
16	926.67	464.4	18.8	1026.67	514.7	23.1	1126.67	565.2	27.8
17	928.33	465.2	18.9	1028.33	515.6	23.1	1128.33	566.0	27.9
18	930.00	466.0	18.9	1030.00	516.4	23.2	1130.00	566.8	28.0
19	931.67	466.9	19.0	1031.67	517.2	23.3	1131.67	567.7	28.1
20	933.33	467.7	19.1	1033.33	518.1	23.4	1133.33	568.5	28.1
21	935.00	468.5	19.1	1035.00	518.9	23.5	1135.00	569.4	28.2
22	936.67	469.4	19.2	1036.67	519.8	23.5	1136.67	570.2	28.3
23	938.33	470.2	19.3	1038.33	520.6	23.6	1138.33	571.1	28.4
24	940.00	471.1	19.3	1040.00	521.4	23.7	1140.00	571.9	28.5
25	941.67	471.9	19.4	1041.67	522.3	23.8	1141.67	572.7	28.6
26	943.33	472.7	19.5	1043.33	523.1	23.8	1143.33	573.6	28.6
27	945.00	473.6	19.5	1045.00	524.0	23.9	1145.00	574.4	28.7
28	946.67	474.4	19.6	1046.67	524.8	24.0	1146.67	575.3	28.8
29	948.33	475.3	19.7	1048.33	525.6	24.1	1148.33	576.1	28.9
30	950.00	476.1	19.7	1050.00	526.5	24.1	1150.00	576.9	29.0
31	951.67	476.9	19.8	1051.67	527.3	24.2	1151.67	577.8	29.1
32	953.33	477.8	19.9	1053.33	528.2	24.3	1153.33	578.6	29.1
33	955.00	478.6	20.0	1055.00	529.0	24.4	1155.00	579.5	29.2
34	956.67	479.5	20.0	1056.67	529.8	24.4	1156.67	580.3	29.3
35	958.33	480.3	20.1	1058.33	530.7	24.5	1158.33	581.2	29.4
36	930.00	481.1	20.2	1060.00	531.5	24.6	1160.00	582.0	29.5
37	931.67	482.0	20.2	1061.67	532.4	24.7	1161.67	582.8	29.6
38	963.33	482.8	20.3	1063.33	533.2	24.8	1163.33	583.7	29.7
39	965.00	483.6	20.4	1035.00	534.0	24.8	1165.00	584.5	29.7
40	966.67	484.5	20.4	1036.67	534.9	24.9	1166.67	585.4	29.8
41	968.33	485.3	20.5	1068.33	535.7	25.0	1168.33	586.2	29.9
42	970.00	486.2	20.6	1070.00	536.6	25.1	1170.00	587.0	30.0
43	971.67	487.0	20.7	1071.67	537.4	25.1	1171.67	587.9	30.1
44	973.33	487.8	20.7	1073.33	538.2	25.2	1173.33	588.7	30.2
45	975.00	488.7	20.8	1075.00	539.1	25.3	1175.00	589.6	30.3
46	976.67	489.5	20.9	1076.67	539.9	25.4	1176.67	590.4	30.3
47	978.33	490.4	20.9	1078.33	540.8	25.5	1178.33	591.3	30.4
48	980.00	491.2	21.0	1080.00	541.6	25.5	1180.00	592.1	30.5
49	981.67	492.0	21.1	1081.67	542.5	25.6	1181.67	592.9	30.6
50	983.33	492.9	21.2	1083.33	543.3	25.7	1183.33	593.8	30.7
51	985.00	493.7	21.2	1085.00	544.1	25.8	1185.00	594.6	30.8
52	986.67	494.6	21.3	1086.67	545.0	25.9	1186.67	595.5	30.9
53	988.33	495.4	21.4	1088.33	545.8	25.9	1188.33	596.3	30.9
54	990.00	496.2	21.5	1090.00	546.7	26.0	1190.00	597.2	31.0
55	991.67	497.1	21.5	1091.67	547.5	26.1	1191.67	598.0	31.1
56	993.33	497.9	21.6	1093.33	548.3	26.2	1193.33	598.8	31.2
57	995.00	498.8	21.7	1095.00	549.2	26.3	1195.00	599.7	31.3
58	996.67	499.6	21.7	1096.67	550.0	26.3	1196.67	600.5	31.4
59	998.33	500.4	21.8	1098.33	550.9	26.4	1198.33	601.4	31.5

Min-utes	12°			13°			14°		
	Length L	Tan. T	Ext. E	Length L	Tan. T	Ext. E	Length L	Tan. T	Ext. E
0	1200.00	602.2	31.6	1300.00	652.8	37.1	1400.00	703.5	43.0
1	1201.67	603.1	31.6	1301.67	653.7	37.2	1401.67	704.4	43.1
2	1203.33	603.9	31.7	1303.33	654.5	37.3	1403.33	705.2	43.2
3	1205.00	604.7	31.8	1305.00	655.3	37.4	1405.00	706.1	43.3
4	1206.67	605.6	31.9	1306.67	656.2	37.5	1406.67	706.9	43.4
5	1208.33	606.4	32.0	1308.33	657.0	37.6	1408.33	707.7	43.5
6	1210.00	607.3	32.1	1310.00	657.9	37.6	1410.00	708.6	43.7
7	1211.67	608.1	32.2	1311.67	658.7	37.7	1411.67	709.4	43.8
8	1213.33	609.0	32.3	1313.33	659.6	37.8	1413.33	710.3	43.9
9	1215.00	609.8	32.4	1315.00	660.4	37.9	1415.00	711.1	44.0
10	1216.67	610.7	32.4	1316.67	661.3	38.0	1416.67	712.0	44.1
11	1218.33	611.5	32.5	1318.33	662.1	38.1	1418.33	712.8	44.2
12	1220.00	612.3	32.6	1320.00	662.9	38.2	1420.00	713.7	44.3
13	1221.67	613.2	32.7	1321.67	663.8	38.3	1421.67	714.5	44.4
14	1223.33	614.0	32.8	1323.33	664.6	38.4	1423.33	715.4	44.5
15	1225.00	614.9	32.9	1325.00	665.5	38.5	1425.00	716.2	44.6
16	1226.67	615.7	33.0	1326.67	666.3	38.6	1426.67	717.1	44.7
17	1228.33	616.5	33.1	1328.33	667.2	38.7	1428.33	717.9	44.8
18	1230.00	617.4	33.2	1330.00	668.0	38.8	1430.00	718.7	44.9
19	1231.67	618.2	33.3	1331.67	668.9	38.9	1431.67	719.6	45.0
20	1233.33	619.1	33.3	1333.33	669.7	39.0	1433.33	720.4	45.1
21	1235.00	619.9	33.4	1335.00	670.5	39.1	1435.00	721.3	45.2
22	1236.67	620.8	33.5	1336.67	671.4	39.2	1436.67	722.1	45.3
23	1238.33	621.6	33.6	1338.33	672.2	39.3	1438.33	723.0	45.4
24	1240.00	622.4	33.7	1340.00	673.1	39.4	1440.00	723.8	45.5
25	1241.67	623.3	33.8	1341.67	673.9	39.5	1441.67	724.7	45.6
26	1243.33	624.1	33.9	1343.33	674.8	39.6	1443.33	725.5	45.8
27	1245.00	625.0	34.0	1345.00	675.6	39.7	1445.00	726.4	45.9
28	1246.67	625.8	34.1	1346.67	676.5	39.8	1446.67	727.2	46.0
29	1248.33	626.7	34.2	1348.33	677.3	39.9	1448.33	728.1	46.1
30	1250.00	627.5	34.3	1350.00	678.1	40.0	1450.00	728.9	46.2
31	1251.67	628.3	34.4	1351.67	679.0	40.1	1451.67	729.8	46.3
32	1253.33	629.2	34.4	1353.33	679.8	40.2	1453.33	730.6	46.4
33	1255.00	630.0	34.5	1355.00	680.7	40.3	1455.00	731.4	46.5
34	1256.67	630.9	34.6	1356.67	681.5	40.4	1456.67	732.3	46.6
35	1258.33	631.7	34.7	1358.33	682.4	40.5	1458.33	733.1	46.7
36	1260.00	632.6	34.8	1360.00	683.2	40.6	1460.00	734.0	46.8
37	1261.67	633.4	34.9	1361.67	684.1	40.7	1461.67	734.8	46.9
38	1263.33	634.2	35.0	1363.33	684.9	40.8	1463.33	735.7	47.0
39	1265.00	635.1	35.1	1365.00	685.8	40.9	1465.00	736.5	47.1
40	1266.67	635 9	35.2	1366.67	686.6	41.0	1466.67	737.4	47.3
41	1268.33	636.8	35.3	1368.33	687.4	41.1	1468.33	738.2	47.4
42	1270.00	637.6	35.4	1370.00	688.3	41.2	1470.00	739.1	47.5
43	1271.67	638.5	35.5	1371.67	689.1	41.3	1471.67	739.9	47.6
44	1273.33	639.3	35.6	1373.33	690.0	41.4	1473.33	740.8	47.7
45	1275.00	640.2	35.7	1375.00	690.8	41.5	1475.00	741.6	47.8
46	1276.67	641.0	35.7	1376.67	691.7	41.6	1476.67	742.5	47.9
47	1278.33	641.8	35.8	1378.33	692.5	41.7	1478.33	743.3	48.0
48	1280.00	642.7	35.9	1380.00	693.4	41.8	1480.00	744.2	48.1
49	1281.67	643.5	36.0	1381.67	694.2	41.9	1481.67	745.0	48.2
50	1283.33	644.4	36.1	1383.33	695.1	42.0	1483.33	745.8	48.3
51	1285.00	645.2	36.2	1385.00	695.9	42.1	1485.00	746.7	48.5
52	1286.67	646.1	36.3	1386.67	696.7	42.2	1486.67	747.5	48.6
53	1288.33	646.9	36.4	1388.33	697.6	42.3	1488.33	748.4	48.7
54	1290.00	647.7	36.5	1390.00	698.4	42.4	1490.00	749.2	48.8
55	1291.67	648.6	36.6	1391.67	699.3	42.5	1491.67	750.1	48.9
56	1293.33	649.4	36.7	1393.33	700.1	42.6	1493.33	750.9	49.0
57	1295.00	650.3	36.8	1395.00	701.0	42.7	1495.00	751.8	49.1
58	1296.67	651.1	36.9	1396.67	701.8	42.8	1496.67	752.6	49.2
59	1298.33	652.0	37.0	1398.33	702.7	42.9	1498.33	753.5	49.3

(All Definitions of Degree of Curve)

Min-utes	15°			16°			17°		
	Length L	Tan. T	Ext. E	Length L	Tan. T	Ext. E	Length L	Tan. T	Ext. E
0	1500.00	754.3	49.4	1600.00	805.2	56.3	1700.00	856.3	63.6
1	1501.67	755.2	49.6	1601.67	806.1	56.4	1701.67	857.2	63.8
2	1503.33	756.0	49.7	1603.33	806.9	56.5	1703.33	858.0	63.9
3	1505.00	756.9	49.8	1605.00	807.8	56.7	1705.00	858.9	64.0
4	1506.67	757.7	49.9	1606.67	808.6	56.8	1706.67	859.7	64.1
5	1508.33	758.6	50.0	1608.33	809.5	56.9	1708.33	860.6	64.3
6	1510.00	759.4	50.1	1610.00	810.3	57.0	1710.00	861.4	64.4
7	1511.67	760.3	50.2	1611.67	811.2	57.1	1711.67	862.3	64.5
8	1513.33	761.1	50.3	1613.33	812.0	57.3	1713.33	863.1	64.6
9	1515.00	762.0	50.4	1615.00	812.9	57.4	1715.00	864.0	64.8
10	1516.67	762.8	50.6	1616.67	813.7	57.5	1716.67	864.8	64.9
11	1518.33	763.7	50.7	1618.33	814.6	57.6	1718.33	865.7	65.0
12	1520.00	764.5	50.8	1620.00	815.5	57.7	1720.00	866.5	65.2
13	1521.67	765.3	50.9	1621.67	816.3	57.9	1721.67	867.4	65.3
14	1523.33	766.2	51.0	1623.33	817.2	58.0	1723.33	868.2	65.4
15	1525.00	767.0	51.1	1625.00	818.0	58.1	1725.00	869.1	65.5
16	1526.67	767.9	51.2	1626.67	818.9	58.2	1726.67	869.9	65.7
17	1528.33	768.7	51.3	1628.33	819.7	58.3	1728.33	870.8	65.8
18	1530.00	769.6	51.5	1630.00	820.6	58.5	1730.00	871.6	65.9
19	1531.67	770.4	51.6	1631.67	821.4	58.6	1731.67	872.5	66.1
20	1533.33	771.3	51.7	1633.33	822.3	58.7	1733.33	873.3	66.2
21	1535.00	772.1	51.8	1635.00	823.1	58.8	1735.00	874.2	66.3
22	1536.67	773.0	51.9	1636.67	824.0	58.9	1736.67	875.1	66.4
23	1538.33	773.8	52.0	1638.33	824.8	59.1	1738.33	875.9	66.6
24	1540.00	774.7	52.1	1640.00	825.7	59.2	1740.00	876.8	66.7
25	1541.67	775.5	52.2	1641.67	826.5	59.3	1741.67	877.6	66.8
26	1543.33	776.4	52.4	1643.33	827.4	59.4	1743.33	878.5	67.0
27	1545.00	777.2	52.5	1645.00	828.2	59.5	1745.00	879.3	67.1
28	1546.67	778.1	52.6	1646.67	829.1	59.7	1746.67	880.2	67.2
29	1548.33	778.9	52.7	1648.33	829.9	59.8	1748.33	881.0	67.3
30	1550.00	779.8	52.8	1650.00	830.8	59.9	1750.00	881.9	67.5
31	1551.67	780.6	52.9	1651.67	831.6	60.0	1751.67	882.7	67.6
32	1553.33	781.5	53.0	1653.33	832.5	60.2	1753.33	883.6	67.7
33	1555.00	782.3	53.2	1655.00	833.3	60.3	1755.00	884.4	67.9
34	1556.67	783.2	53.3	1656.67	834.2	60.4	1756.67	885.3	68.0
35	1558.33	784.0	53.4	1658.33	835.0	60.5	1758.33	886.1	68.1
36	1560.00	784.9	53.5	1660.00	835.9	60.7	1760.00	887.0	68.3
37	1561.67	785.7	53.6	1661.67	836.7	60.8	1761.67	887.9	68.4
38	1563.33	786.6	53.7	1663.33	837.6	60.9	1763.33	888.7	68.5
39	1565.00	787.4	53.9	1665.00	838.4	61.0	1765.00	889.6	68.6
40	1566.67	788.3	54.0	1666.67	839.3	61.1	1766.67	890.4	68.8
41	1568.33	789.1	54.1	1668.33	840.1	61.3	1768.33	891.3	68.9
42	1570.00	790.0	54.2	1670.00	841.0	61.4	1770.00	892.1	69.0
43	1571.67	790.8	54.3	1671.67	841.8	61.5	1771.67	893.0	69.2
44	1573.33	791.7	54.4	1673.33	842.7	61.6	1773.33	893.8	69.3
45	1575.00	792.5	54.6	1675.00	843.5	61.8	1775.00	894.7	69.4
46	1576.67	793.4	54.7	1676.67	844.4	61.9	1776.67	895.5	69.6
47	1578.33	794.2	54.8	1678.33	845.2	62.0	1778.33	896.4	69.7
48	1580.00	795.1	54.9	1680.00	846.1	62.1	1780.00	897.2	69.8
49	1581.67	795.9	55.0	1681.67	846.9	62.3	1781.67	898.1	70.0
50	1583.33	796.8	55.1	1683.33	847.8	62.4	1783.33	898.9	70.1
51	1585.00	797.6	55.2	1685.00	848.6	62.5	1785.00	899.8	70.2
52	1586.67	798.5	55.4	1686.67	849.5	62.6	1786.67	900.7	70.4
53	1588.33	799.3	55.5	1688.33	850.3	62.8	1788.33	901.5	70.5
54	1590.00	800.2	55.6	1690.00	851.2	62.9	1790.00	902.4	70.6
55	1591.67	801.0	55.7	1691.67	852.0	63.0	1791.67	903.2	70.8
56	1593.33	801.9	55.8	1693.33	852.9	63.1	1793.33	904.1	70.9
57	1595.00	802.7	56.0	1695.00	853.7	63.3	1795.00	904.9	71.0
58	1596.67	803.6	56.1	1696.67	854.6	63.4	1796.67	905.8	71.2
59	1598.33	804.4	56.2	1698.33	855.5	63.5	1798.33	906.6	71.3

(All Definitions of Degree of Curve)

Min-utes	18° Length L	Tan. T	Ext. E	19° Length L	Tan. T	Ext. E	20° Length L	Tan. T	Ext. E
0	1800.00	907.5	71.4	1900.00	958.8	79.7	2000.00	1010.3	88.4
1	1801.67	908.3	71.6	1901.67	959.7	79.8	2001.67	1011.2	88.5
2	1803.33	909.2	71.7	1903.33	960.5	80.0	2003.33	1012.0	88.7
3	1805.00	910.1	71.8	1905.00	961.4	80.1	2005.00	1012.9	88.8
4	1806.67	910.9	72.0	1906.67	962.2	80.2	2006.67	1013.7	89.0
5	1808.33	911.8	72.1	1908.33	963.1	80.4	2008.33	1014.6	89.1
6	1810.00	912.6	72.2	1910.00	964.0	80.5	2010.00	1015.4	89.3
7	1811.67	913.5	72.4	1911.67	964.8	80.7	2011.67	1016.3	89.4
8	1813.33	914.3	72.5	1913.33	965.7	80.8	2013.33	1017.2	89.6
9	1815.00	915.2	72.6	1915.00	966.5	80.9	2015.00	1018.0	89.7
10	1816.67	916.0	72.8	1916.67	967.4	81.1	2016.67	1018.9	89.9
11	1818.33	916.9	72.9	1918.33	968.2	81.2	2018.33	1019.8	90.0
12	1820.00	917.7	73.0	1920.00	969.1	81.4	2020.00	1020.6	90.2
13	1821.67	918.6	73.2	1921.67	970.0	81.5	2021.67	1021.5	90.3
14	1823.33	919.5	73.3	1923.33	970.8	81.7	2023.33	1022.3	90.5
15	1825.00	920.3	73 4	1925.00	971.7	81.8	2025.00	1023.2	90.6
16	1826.67	921.2	73.6	1926.67	972.5	82.0	2026.67	1024.0	90.8
17	1828.33	922.0	73.7	1928.33	973.4	82.1	2028.33	1024.9	90.9
18	1830.00	922.9	73.8	1930.00	974.2	82.2	2030.00	1025.8	91.1
19	1831.67	923.7	74.0	1931.67	975.1	82.4	2031.67	1026.6	91.2
20	1833.33	924.6	74.1	1933.33	976.0	82.5	2033.33	1027.5	91.4
21	1835.00	925.4	74.3	1935.00	976.8	82.7	2035.00	1028.3	91.6
22	1836.67	926.3	74.4	1936.67	977.7	82.8	2036.67	1029.2	91.7
23	1838.33	927.1	74.5	1938.33	978.5	83.0	2038.33	1030.1	91.9
24	1840.00	928.0	74.7	1940.00	979.4	83.1	2040.00	1030.9	92.0
25	1841.67	928.9	74.8	1941.67	980.2	83.2	2041.67	1031.8	92.2
26	1843.33	929.7	74.9	1943.33	981.1	83.4	2043.33	1032.6	92.3
27	1845.00	930.6	75.1	1945.00	982.0	83.5	2045.00	1033.5	92.5
28	1846.67	931.4	75.2	1946.67	982.8	83.7	2046.67	1034.4	92.6
29	1848.33	932.3	75.4	1948.33	983.7	83.8	2048.33	1035.2	92.8
30	1850.00	933.1	75.5	1950.00	984.5	84.0	2050.00	1036.1	92.9
31	1851.67	934.0	75.6	1951.67	985.4	84.1	2051.67	1037.0	93.1
32	1853.33	934.8	75.8	1953.33	986.3	84.3	2053.33	1037.8	93.2
33	1855.00	935.7	75.9	1955.00	987.1	84.4	2055.00	1038.7	93.4
34	1856.67	936.6	76.0	1956.67	988.0	84.6	2056.67	1039.5	93.5
35	1858.33	937.4	76.2	1958.33	988.8	84.7	2058.33	1040.4	93.7
36	1860.00	938.3	76.3	1960.00	989.7	84.8	2060.00	1041.3	93.8
37	1861.67	939.1	76.5	1961.67	990.5	85.0	2061.67	1042.1	94.0
38	1863.33	940.0	76.6	1963.33	991.4	85.1	2063.33	1043.0	94.2
39	1865.00	940.8	76.7	1965.00	992.3	85.3	2065.00	1043.8	94.3
40	1866.67	941.7	76.9	1966.67	993.1	85.4	2066.67	1044.7	94.5
41	1868.33	942.5	77.0	1968.33	994.0	85.6	2068.33	1045.6	94.6
42	1870.00	943.4	77.1	1970.00	994.8	85.7	2070.00	1046.4	94.8
43	1871.67	944.3	77.3	1971.67	995.7	85.9	2071.67	1047.3	94.9
44	1873.33	945.1	77.4	1973.33	996.5	86.0	2073.33	1048.1	95.1
45	1875.00	946.0	77.6	1975.00	997.4	86.2	2075.00	1049.0	95.2
46	1876.67	946.8	77.7	1976.67	998.3	86.3	2076.67	1049.9	95.4
47	1878.33	947.7	77.8	1978.33	999.1	86.5	2078.33	1050.7	95.5
48	1880.00	948.5	78.0	1980.00	1000.0	86.6	2080.00	1051.6	95.7
49	1881.67	949.4	78.1	1981.67	1000.8	86.8	2081.67	1052.4	95.9
50	1883.33	950.3	78.3	1983.33	1001.7	86.9	2083.33	1053.3	96.0
51	1885.00	951.1	78.4	1985.00	1002.6	87.1	2085.00	1054.2	96.2
52	1886.67	952.0	78.5	1986.67	1003.4	87.2	2086.67	1055.0	96.3
53	1888.33	952.8	78.7	1988.33	1004.3	87.3	2088.33	1055.9	96.5
54	1890.00	953.7	78.8	1990.00	1005.1	87.5	2090.00	1056.8	96.6
55	1891.67	954.5	79.0	1991.67	1006.0	87.6	2091.67	1057.6	96.8
56	1893.33	955.4	79.1	1993.33	1006.9	87.8	2093.33	1058.5	97.0
57	1895.00	956.2	79.2	1995.00	1007.7	87.9	2095.00	1059.3	97.1
58	1896.67	957.1	79.4	1996.67	1008.6	88.1	2096.67	1060.2	97.3
59	1898.33	958.0	79.5	1998.33	1009.4	88.2	2098.33	1061.1	97.4

(All Definitions of Degree of Curve)

Min-utes	21°			22°			23°		
	Length L	Tan. T	Ext. E	Length L	Tan. T	Ext. E	Length L	Tan. T	Ext. E
0	2100.00	1061.9	97.6	2200.00	1113.7	107.2	2300.00	1165.7	117.4
1	2101.67	1062.8	97.7	2201.67	1114.6	107.4	2301.67	1166.6	117.6
2	2103.33	1063.7	97.9	2203.33	1115.5	107.6	2303.33	1167.4	117.7
3	2105.00	1064.5	98.1	2205.00	1116.3	107.7	2305.00	1168.3	117.9
4	2106.67	1065.4	98.2	2206.67	1117.2	107.9	2306.67	1169.2	118.1
5	2108.33	1066.2	98.4	2208.33	1118.1	108.1	2308.33	1170.1	118.3
6	2110.00	1067.1	98.5	2210.00	1118.9	108.2	2310.00	1170.9	118.4
7	2111.67	1068.0	98.7	2211.67	1119.8	108.4	2311.67	1171.8	118.6
8	2113.33	1068.8	98.8	2213.33	1120.7	108.6	2313.33	1172.7	118.8
9	2115.00	1069.7	99.0	2215.00	1121.5	108.7	2315.00	1173.5	118.9
10	2116.67	1070.6	99.2	2216.67	1122.4	108.9	2316.67	1174.4	119.1
11	2118.33	1071.4	99.3	2218.33	1123.2	109.1	2318.33	1175.3	119.3
12	2120.00	1072.3	99.5	2220.00	1124.1	109.2	2320.00	1176.1	119.5
13	2121.67	1073.1	99.6	2221.67	1125.0	109.4	2321.67	1177.0	119.6
14	2123.33	1074.0	99.8	2223.33	1125.8	109.6	2323.33	1177.9	119.8
15	2125.00	1074.9	100.0	2225.00	1126.7	109.7	2325.00	1178.7	120.0
16	2126.67	1075.7	100.1	2226.67	1127.6	109.9	2326.67	1179.6	120.2
17	2128.33	1076.6	100.3	2228.33	1128.4	110.1	2328.33	1180.5	120.3
18	2130.00	1077.5	100.4	2230.00	1129.3	110.2	2330.00	1181.3	120.5
19	2131.67	1078.3	100.6	2231.67	1130.2	110.4	2331.67	1182.2	120.7
20	2133.33	1079.2	100.8	2233.33	1131.0	110.6	2333.33	1183.1	120.9
21	2135.00	1080.0	100.9	2235.00	1131.9	110.7	2335.00	1183.9	121.0
22	2136.67	1080.9	101.1	2236.67	1132.8	110.9	2336.67	1184.8	121.2
23	2138.33	1081.8	101.2	2238.33	1133.6	111.1	2338.33	1185.7	121.4
24	2140.00	1082.6	101.4	2240.00	1134.5	111.2	2340.00	1186.6	121.6
25	2141.67	1083.5	101.6	2241.67	1135.4	111.4	2341.67	1187.4	121.8
26	2143.33	1084.4	101.7	2243.33	1136.2	111.6	2343.33	1188.3	121.9
27	2145.00	1085.2	101.9	2245.00	1137.1	111.8	2345.00	1189.2	122.1
28	2146.67	1086.1	102.0	2246.67	1138.0	111.9	2346.67	1190.0	122.3
29	2148.33	1086.9	102.2	2248.33	1138.8	112.1	2348.33	1190.9	122.5
30	2150.00	1087.8	102.4	2250.00	1139.7	112.3	2350.00	1191.8	122.6
31	2151.67	1088.7	102.5	2251.67	1140.6	112.4	2351.67	1192.6	122.8
32	2153.33	1089.5	102.7	2253.33	1141.4	112.6	2353.33	1193.5	123.0
33	2155.00	1090.4	102.8	2255.00	1142.3	112.8	2355.00	1194.4	123.2
34	2156.67	1091.3	103.0	2256.67	1143.2	112.9	2356.67	1195.2	123.3
35	2158.33	1092.1	103.2	2258.33	1144.0	113.1	2358.33	1196.1	123.5
36	2160.00	1093.0	103.3	2260.00	1144.9	113.3	2360.00	1197.0	123.7
37	2161.67	1093.9	103.5	2261.67	1145.8	113.4	2361.67	1197.9	123.9
38	2163.33	1094.7	103.6	2263.33	1146.6	113.6	2363.33	1198.7	124.1
39	2165.00	1095.6	103.8	2265.00	1147.5	113.8	2365.00	1199.6	124.2
40	2166.67	1096.4	104.0	2266.67	1148.4	114.0	2366.67	1200.5	124.4
41	2168.33	1097.3	104.1	2268.33	1149.2	114.1	2368.33	1201.3	124.6
42	2170.00	1098.2	104.3	2270.00	1150.1	114.3	2370.00	1202.2	124.8
43	2171.67	1099.0	104.5	2271.67	1151.0	114.5	2371.67	1203.1	124.9
44	2173.33	1099.9	104.6	2273.33	1151.8	114.6	2373.33	1203.9	125.1
45	2175.00	1100.8	104.8	2275.00	1152.7	114.8	2375.00	1204.8	125.3
46	2176.67	1101.6	104.9	2276.67	1153.6	115.0	2376.67	1205.7	125.5
47	2178.33	1102.5	105.1	2278.33	1154.4	115.1	2378.33	1206.6	125.7
48	2180.00	1103.4	105.3	2280.00	1155.3	115.3	2380.00	1207.4	125.8
49	2181.67	1104.2	105.4	2281.67	1156.2	115.5	2381.67	1208.3	126.0
50	2183.33	1105.1	105.6	2283.33	1157.0	115.7	2383.33	1209.2	126.2
51	2185.00	1105.9	105.8	2285.00	1157.9	115.8	2385.00	1210.0	126.4
52	2186.67	1106.8	105.9	2286.67	1158.8	116.0	2386.67	1210.9	126.6
53	2188.33	1107.7	106.1	2288.32	1159.6	116.2	2388.33	1211.8	126.7
54	2190.00	1108.5	106.3	2290.00	1160.5	116.3	2390.00	1212.6	126.9
55	2191.67	1109.4	106.4	2291.67	1161.4	116.5	2391.67	1213.5	127.1
56	2193.33	1110.3	106.6	2293.33	1162.2	116.7	2393.33	1214.4	127.3
57	2195.00	1111.1	106.7	2295.00	1163.1	116.9	2395.00	1215.3	127.5
58	2196.67	1112.0	106.9	2296.67	1164.0	117.0	2396.67	1216.1	127.6
59	2198.33	1112.9	107.1	2298.33	1164.8	117.2	2398.33	1217.0	127.8

(All Definitions of Degree of Curve)

Min-utes	24°			25°			26°		
	Length L	Tan. T	Ext. E	Length L	Tan. T	Ext. E	Length L	Tan. T	Ext. E
0	2400.00	1217.9	128.0	2500.00	1270.2	139.1	2600.00	1322.8	150.7
1	2401.67	1218.7	128.2	2501.67	1271.1	139.3	2601.67	1323.7	150.9
2	2403.33	1219.6	128.4	2503.33	1272.0	139.5	2603.33	1324.5	151.1
3	2405.00	1220.5	128.5	2505.00	1272.9	139.7	2605.00	1325.4	151.3
4	2406.67	1221.4	128.7	2506.67	1273.7	139.9	2606.67	1326.3	151.5
5	2408.33	1222.2	128.9	2508.33	1274.6	140.1	2608.33	1327.2	151.7
6	2410.00	1223.1	129.1	2510.00	1275.5	140.3	2610.00	1328.1	151.9
7	2411.67	1224.0	129.3	2511.67	1276.4	140.4	2611.67	1328.9	152.1
8	2413.33	1224.8	129.5	2513.33	1277.2	140.6	2613.33	1329.8	152.3
9	2415.00	1225.7	129.6	2515.00	1278.1	140.8	2615.00	1330.7	152.5
10	2416.67	1226.6	129.8	2516.67	1279.0	141.0	2616.67	1331.6	152.7
11	2418.33	1227.5	130.0	2518.33	1279.9	141.2	2618.33	1332.5	152.9
12	2420.00	1228.3	130.2	2520.00	1280.7	141.4	2620.00	1333.3	153.1
13	2421.67	1229.2	130.4	2521.67	1281.6	141.6	2621.67	1334.2	153.3
14	2423.33	1230.1	130.6	2523.33	1282.5	141.8	2623.33	1335.1	153.5
15	2425.00	1230.9	130.7	2525.00	1283.4	142.0	2625.00	1336.0	153.7
16	2426.67	1231.8	130.9	2526.67	1284.2	142.2	2626.67	1336.8	153.9
17	2428.33	1232.7	131.1	2528.33	1285.1	142.4	2628.33	1337.7	154.1
18	2430.00	1233.6	131.3	2530.00	1286.0	142.5	2630.00	1338.6	154.3
19	2431.67	1234.4	131.5	2531.67	1286.9	142.7	2631.67	1339.5	154.5
20	2433.33	1235.3	131.7	2533.33	1287.7	142.9	2633.33	1340.4	154.7
21	2435.00	1236.2	131.8	2535.00	1288.6	143.1	2635.00	1341.2	154.9
22	2436.67	1237.0	132.0	2536.67	1289.5	143.3	2636.67	1342.1	155.1
23	2438.33	1237.9	132.2	2538.33	1290.4	143.5	2638.33	1343.0	155.3
24	2440.00	1238.8	132.4	2540.00	1291.2	143.7	2640.00	1343.9	155.5
25	2441.67	1239.7	132.6	2541.67	1292.1	143.9	2641.67	1344.8	155.7
26	2443.33	1240.5	132.8	2543.33	1293.0	144.1	2643.33	1345.6	155.9
27	2445.00	1241.4	132.9	2545.00	1293.9	144.3	2645.00	1346.5	156.1
28	2446.67	1242.3	133.1	2546.67	1294.7	144.5	2646.67	1347.4	156.3
29	2448.33	1243.2	133.3	2548.33	1295.6	144.7	2648.33	1348.3	156.5
30	2450.00	1244.0	133.5	2550.00	1296.5	144.9	2650.00	1349.2	156.7
31	2451.67	1244.9	133.7	2551.67	1297.4	145.0	2651.67	1350.0	156.9
32	2453.33	1245.8	133.9	2553.33	1298.2	145.2	2653.33	1350.9	157.1
33	2455.00	1246.6	134.1	2555.00	1299.1	145.4	2655.00	1351.8	157.3
34	2456.67	1247.5	134.2	2556.67	1300.0	145.6	2656.67	1352.7	157.5
35	2458.33	1248.4	134.4	2558.33	1300.9	145.8	2658.33	1353.6	157.7
36	2460.00	1249.3	134.6	2560.00	1301.7	146.0	2660.00	1354.4	157.9
37	2461.67	1250.1	134.8	2561.67	1302.6	146.2	2661.67	1355.3	158.1
38	2463.33	1251.0	135.0	2563.33	1303.5	146.4	2663.33	1356.2	158.3
39	2465.00	1251.9	135.2	2565.00	1304.4	146.6	2665.00	1357.1	158.5
40	2466.67	1252.8	135.4	2566.67	1305.3	146.8	2666.67	1358.0	158.7
41	2468.33	1253.6	135.5	2568.33	1306.1	147.0	2668.33	1358.8	158.9
42	2470.00	1254.5	135.7	2570.00	1307.0	147.2	2670.00	1359.7	159.1
43	2471.67	1255.4	135.9	2571.67	1307.9	147.4	2671.67	1360.6	159.3
44	2473.33	1256.3	136.1	2573.33	1308.8	147.6	2673.33	1361.5	159.5
45	2475.00	1257.1	136.3	2575.00	1309.6	147.8	2675.00	1362.4	159.7
46	2476.67	1258.0	136.5	2576.67	1310.5	148.0	2676.67	1363.2	159.9
47	2478.33	1258.9	136.7	2578.33	1311.4	148.2	2678.33	1364.1	160.1
48	2480.00	1259.7	136.9	2580.00	1312.3	148.4	2680.00	1365.0	160.4
49	2481.67	1260.6	137.0	2581.67	1313.1	148.6	2681.67	1365.9	160.6
50	2483.33	1261.5	137.2	2583.33	1314.0	148.8	2683.33	1366.8	160.8
51	2485.00	1262.4	137.4	2585.00	1314.9	148.9	2685.00	1367.6	161.0
52	2486.67	1263.2	137.6	2586.67	1315.8	149.1	2686.67	1368.5	161.2
53	2488.33	1264.1	137.8	2588.33	1316.7	149.3	2688.33	1369.4	161.4
54	2490.00	1265.0	138.0	2590.00	1317.5	149.5	2690.00	1370.3	161.6
55	2491.67	1265.9	138.2	2591.67	1318.4	149.7	2691.67	1371.2	161.8
56	2493.33	1266.7	138.4	2593.33	1319.3	149.9	2693.33	1372.0	162.0
57	2495.00	1267.6	138.5	2595.00	1320.2	150.1	2695.00	1372.9	162.2
58	2496.67	1268.5	138.7	2596.67	1321.0	150.3	2696.67	1373.8	162.4
59	2498.33	1269.4	138.9	2598.33	1321.9	150.5	2698.33	1374.7	162.6

(All Definitions of Degree of Curve)

Min-utes	27° Length L	27° Tan. T	27° Ext. E	28° Length L	28° Tan. T	28° Ext. E	29° Length L	29° Tan. T	29° Ext. E
0	2700.00	1375.6	162.8	2800.00	1428.6	175.4	2900.00	1481.8	188.5
1	2701.67	1376.4	163.0	2801.67	1429.4	175.6	2901.67	1482.7	188.7
2	2703.33	1377.3	163.2	2803.33	1430.3	175.8	2903.33	1483.6	189.0
3	2705.00	1378.2	163.4	2805.00	1431.2	176.1	2905.00	1484.5	189.2
4	2706.67	1379.1	163.6	2806.67	1432.1	176.3	2906.67	1485.3	189.4
5	2708.33	1380.0	163.8	2808.33	1433.0	176.5	2908.33	1486.2	189.6
6	2710.00	1380.9	164.0	2810.00	1433.9	176.7	2910.00	1487.1	189.8
7	2711.67	1381.7	164.2	2811.67	1434.8	176.9	2911.67	1488.0	190.1
8	2713.33	1382.6	164.5	2813.33	1435.6	177.1	2913.33	1488.9	190.3
9	2715.00	1383.5	164.7	2815.00	1436.5	177.3	2915.00	1489.8	190.5
10	2716.67	1384.4	164.9	2816.67	1437.4	177.6	2916.67	1490.7	190.7
11	2718.33	1385.3	165.1	2818.33	1438.3	177.8	2918.33	1491.6	191.0
12	2720.00	1386.1	165.3	2820.00	1439.2	178.0	2920.00	1492.5	191.2
13	2721.67	1387.0	165.5	2821.67	1440.1	178.2	2921.67	1493.4	191.4
14	2723.33	1387.9	165.7	2823.33	1441.0	178.4	2923.33	1494.2	191.6
15	2725.00	1388.8	165.9	2825.00	1441.8	178.6	2925.00	1495.1	191.9
16	2726.67	1389.7	166.1	2826.67	1442.7	178.9	2926.67	1496.0	192.1
17	2728.33	1390.6	166.3	2828.33	1443.6	179.1	2928.33	1496.9	192.3
18	2730.00	1391.4	166.5	2830.00	1444.5	179.3	2930.00	1497.8	192.5
19	2731.67	1392.3	166.7	2831.67	1445.4	179.5	2931.67	1498.7	192.8
20	2733.33	1393.2	167.0	2833.33	1446.3	179.7	2933.33	1499.6	193.0
21	2735.00	1394.1	167.2	2835.00	1447.2	180.0	2935.00	1500.5	193.2
22	2736.67	1395.0	167.4	2836.67	1448.1	180.2	2936.67	1501.4	193.4
23	2738.33	1395.9	167.6	2838.33	1448.9	180.4	2938.33	1502.3	193.7
24	2740.00	1396.7	167.8	2840.00	1449.8	180.6	2940.00	1503.1	193.9
25	2741.67	1397.6	168.0	2841.67	1450.7	180.8	2941.67	1504.0	194.1
26	2743.33	1398.5	168.2	2843.33	1451.6	181.0	2943.33	1504.9	194.3
27	2745.00	1399.4	168.4	2845.00	1452.5	181.2	2945.00	1505.8	194.6
28	2746.67	1400.3	168.6	2846.67	1453.4	181.5	2946.67	1506.7	194.8
29	2748.33	1401.2	168.8	2848.33	1454.3	181.7	2948.33	1507.6	195.0
30	2750.00	1402.0	169.0	2850.00	1455.1	181.9	2950.00	1508.5	195.3
31	2751.67	1402.9	169.3	2851.67	1456.0	182.1	2951.67	1509.4	195.5
32	2753.33	1403.8	169.5	2853.33	1456.9	182.3	2953.33	1510.3	195.7
33	2755.00	1404.7	169.7	2855.00	1457.8	182.5	2955.00	1511.2	195.9
34	2756.67	1405.6	169.9	2856.67	1458.7	182.8	2956.67	1512.1	196.2
35	2758.33	1406.5	170.1	2858.33	1459.6	183.0	2958.33	1512.9	196.4
36	2760.00	1407.3	170.3	2860.00	1460.5	183.2	2960.00	1513.8	196.6
37	2761.67	1408.2	170.5	2861.67	1461.4	183.4	2961.67	1514.7	196.8
38	2763.33	1409.1	170.7	2863.33	1462.2	183.6	2963.33	1515.6	197.1
39	2765.00	1410.0	170.9	2865.00	1463.1	183.9	2965.00	1516.5	197.3
40	2766.67	1410.9	171.2	2866.67	1464.0	184.1	2966.67	1517.4	197.5
41	2768.33	1411.8	171.4	2868.33	1464.9	184.3	2968.33	1518.3	197.8
42	2770.00	1412.6	171.6	2870.00	1465.8	184.5	2970.00	1519.2	198.0
43	2771.67	1413.5	171.8	2871.67	1466.7	184.7	2971.67	1520.1	198.2
44	2773.33	1414.4	172.0	2873.33	1467.6	185.0	2973.33	1521.0	198.4
45	2775.00	1415.3	172.2	2875.00	1468.5	185.2	2975.00	1521.9	198.7
46	2776.67	1416.2	172.4	2876.67	1469.3	185.4	2976.67	1522.8	198.9
47	2778.33	1417.1	172.6	2878.33	1470.2	185.6	2978.33	1523.6	199.1
48	2780.00	1417.9	172.8	2880.00	1471.1	185.8	2980.00	1524.5	199.4
49	2781.67	1418.8	173.1	2881.67	1472.0	186.1	2981.67	1525.4	199.6
50	2783.33	1419.7	173.3	2883.33	1472.9	186.3	2983.33	1526.3	199.8
51	2785.00	1420.6	173.5	2885.00	1473.8	186.5	2985.00	1527.2	200.1
52	2786.67	1421.5	173.7	2886.67	1474.7	186.7	2986.67	1528.1	200.3
53	2788.33	1422.4	173.9	2888.33	1475.6	187.0	2988.33	1529.0	200.5
54	2790.00	1423.3	174.1	2890.00	1476.5	187.2	2990.00	1529.9	200.7
55	2791.67	1424.1	174.3	2891.67	1477.3	187.4	2991.67	1530.8	201.0
56	2793.33	1425.0	174.6	2893.33	1478.2	187.6	2993.33	1531.7	201.2
57	2795.00	1425.9	174.8	2895.00	1479.1	187.8	2995.00	1532.6	201.4
58	2796.67	1426.8	175.0	2896.67	1480.0	188.1	2996.67	1533.5	201.7
59	2798.33	1427.7	175.2	2898.33	1480.9	188.3	2998.33	1534.4	201.9

(All Definitions of Degree of Curve)

Min-utes	30°			31°			32°		
	Length L	Tan. T	Ext. E	Length L	Tan. T	Ext. E	Length L	Tan. T	Ext. E
0	3000.00	1535.3	202.1	3100.00	1589.0	216.3	3200.00	1643.0	230.9
1	3001.67	1536.1	202.4	3101.67	1589.9	216.5	3201.67	1643.9	231.1
2	3003.33	1537.0	202.6	3103.33	1590.8	216.7	3203.33	1644.8	231.4
3	3005.00	1537.9	202.8	3105.00	1591.7	217.0	3205.00	1645.7	231.6
4	3006.67	1538.8	203.0	3106.67	1592.6	217.2	3206.67	1646.6	231.9
5	3008.33	1539.7	203.3	3108.33	1593.5	217.5	3208.33	1647.5	232.1
6	3010.00	1540.6	203.5	3110.00	1594.4	217.7	3210.00	1648.4	232.4
7	3011.67	1541.5	203.7	3111.67	1595.3	217.9	3211.67	1649.3	232.6
8	3013.33	1542.4	204.0	3113.00	1596.2	218.2	3213.33	1650.2	232.9
9	3015.00	1543.3	204.2	3115.00	1597.1	218.4	3215.00	1651.1	233.1
10	3016.67	1544.2	204.4	3116.67	1598.0	218.7	3216.67	1652.0	233.4
11	3018.33	1545.1	204.7	3118.33	1598.8	218.9	3218.33	1652.9	233.6
12	3020.00	1546.0	204.9	2120.00	1599.7	219.1	3220.00	1653.8	233.9
13	3021.67	1546.9	205.1	3121.67	1600.6	219.4	3221.67	1654.7	234.1
14	3023.33	1547.8	205.4	3123.33	1601.5	219.6	3223.33	1655.6	234.4
15	3025.00	1548.7	205.6	3125.00	1602.4	219.9	3225.00	1656.5	234.6
16	3026.67	1549.6	205.8	3126.67	1603.3	220.1	3226.67	1657.4	234.9
17	3028.33	1550.4	206.1	3128.33	1604.2	220.4	3228.33	1658.3	235.1
18	3030.00	1551.3	206.3	3130.00	1605.1	220.6	3230.00	1659.2	235.4
19	3031.67	1552.2	206.5	3131.67	1606.0	220.8	3231.67	1660.1	235.6
20	3033.33	1553.1	206.8	3133.33	1606.9	221.1	3233.33	1661.0	235.9
21	3035.00	1554.0	207.0	3135.00	1607.8	221.3	3235.00	1661.9	236.2
22	3036.67	1554.9	207.2	3136.67	1608.7	221.6	3236.67	1662.8	236.4
23	3038.33	1555.8	207.5	3138.33	1609.6	221.8	3238.33	1663.7	236.7
24	3040.00	1556.7	207.7	3140.00	1610.5	222.1	3240.00	1664.6	236.9
25	3041.67	1557.6	207.9	3141.67	1611.4	222.3	3241.67	1665.5	237.2
26	3043.33	1558.5	208.2	3143.33	1612.3	222.5	3243.33	1666.4	237.4
27	3045.00	1559.4	208.4	3145.00	1613.2	222.8	3245.00	1667.3	237.7
28	3046.67	1560.3	208.7	3146.67	1614.1	223.0	3246.67	1668.2	237.9
29	3048.33	1561.2	208.9	3148.33	1615.0	223.3	3248.33	1669.1	238.2
30	3050.00	1562.1	209.1	3150.00	1615.9	223.5	3250.00	1670.0	238.4
31	3051.67	1563.0	209.4	3151.67	1616.8	223.8	3251.67	1670.9	238.7
32	3053.33	1563.9	209.6	3153.33	1617.7	224.0	3253.33	1671.8	238.9
33	3055.00	1564.8	209.8	3155.00	1618.6	224.2	3255.00	1672.8	239.2
34	3056.67	1565.7	210.1	3156.67	1619.5	224.5	3256.67	1673.7	239.4
35	3058.33	1566.6	210.3	3158.33	1620.4	224.7	3258.33	1674.6	239.7
36	3960.00	1567.5	210.5	3160.00	1621.3	225.0	3260.00	1675.5	239.9
37	3061.67	1568.4	210.8	3161.67	1622.2	225.2	3261.67	1676.4	240.2
38	3063.33	1569.2	211.0	3163.33	1623.1	225.5	3263.33	1677.3	240.5
39	3065.00	1570.1	211.2	3165.00	1624.0	225.7	3265.00	1678.2	240.7
40	3066.67	1571.0	211.5	3166.67	1624.9	226.0	3266.67	1679.1	241.0
41	3068.33	1571.9	211.7	3168.33	1625.8	226.2	3268.33	1680.0	241.2
42	3070.00	1572.8	212.0	3170.00	1626.7	226.5	3270.00	1680.9	241.5
43	3071.67	1573.7	212.2	3171.67	1627.6	226.7	3271.67	1681.8	241.7
44	3073.33	1574.6	212.4	3173.33	1628.5	226.9	3273.33	1682.7	242.0
45	3075.00	1575.5	212.7	3175.00	1629.4	227.2	3275.00	1683.6	242.2
46	3076.67	1576.4	212.9	3176.67	1630.3	227.4	3276.67	1684.5	242.5
47	3078.33	1577.3	213.1	3178.33	1631.2	227.7	3278.33	1685.4	242.8
48	3080.00	1578.2	213.4	3180.00	1632.1	227.9	3280.00	1686.3	243.0
49	3081.67	1579.1	213.6	3181.67	1633.0	228.2	3281.67	1687.2	243.3
50	3083.33	1580.0	213.9	3183.33	1633.9	228.4	3283.33	1688.1	243.5
51	3085.00	1580.9	214.1	3185.00	1634.8	228.7	3285.00	1689.0	243.8
52	3086.67	1581.8	214.3	3186.67	1635.7	228.9	3286.67	1690.0	244.0
53	3088.33	1582.7	214.6	3188.33	1636.6	229.2	3288.33	1690.9	244.3
54	3090.00	1583.6	214.8	3190.00	1637.5	229.4	3290.00	1691.8	244.5
55	3091.67	1584.5	215.1	3191.67	1638.4	229.7	3291.67	1692.7	244.8
56	3093.33	1585.4	215.3	3193.33	1639.3	229.9	3293.33	1693.6	245.1
57	3095.00	1586.3	215.5	3195.00	1640.2	230.2	3295.00	1694.5	245.3
58	3096.67	1587.2	215.8	3196.67	1641.1	230.4	3296.67	1695.4	245.6
59	3098.33	1588.1	216.0	3198.33	1642.0	230.7	3298.33	1696.3	245.8

(All Definitions of Degree of Curve)

Min-utes	33°			34°			35°		
	Length L	Tan. T	Ext. E	Length L	Tan. T	Ext. E	Length L	Tan. T	Ext. E
0	3300.00	1697.2	246.1	3400.00	1751.7	261.8	3500.00	1806.6	278.1
1	3301.67	1698.1	246.3	3401.67	1752.6	262.1	3501.67	1807.5	278.3
2	3303.33	1699.0	246.6	3403.33	1753.6	262.3	3503.33	1808.4	278.6
3	3305.00	1699.9	246.9	3405.00	1754.5	262.6	3505.00	1809.3	278.9
4	3306.67	1700.8	247.1	3406.67	1755.4	262.9	3506.67	1810.2	279.2
5	3308.33	1701.7	247.4	3408.33	1756.3	263.1	3508.33	1811.1	279.4
6	3310.00	1702.6	247.6	3410.00	1757.2	263.4	3510.00	1812.1	279.7
7	3311.67	1703.5	247.9	3411.67	1758.1	263.7	3511.67	1813.0	280.0
8	3313.33	1704.5	248.1	3413.33	1759.0	263.9	3513.33	1813.9	280.3
9	3315.00	1705.4	248.4	3415.00	1759.9	264.4	3515.00	1814.8	280.5
10	3316.67	1706.3	248.7	3416.67	1760.8	264.5	3516.67	1815.7	280.8
11	3318.33	1707.2	248.9	3418.33	1761.8	264.7	3518.33	1816.6	281.1
12	3320.00	1708.1	249.2	3420.00	1762.7	265.0	3520.00	1817.6	281.4
13	3321.67	1709.0	249.4	3421.67	1763.6	265.3	3521.67	1818.5	281.7
14	3323.33	1709.9	249.7	3423.33	1764.5	265.5	3523.33	1819.4	281.9
15	3325.00	1710.8	250.0	3425.00	1765.4	265.8	3525.00	1820.3	282.2
16	3326.67	1711.7	250.2	3426.67	1766.3	266.1	3526.67	1821.2	282.5
17	3328.33	1712.6	250.5	3428.33	1767.2	266.4	3528.33	1822.1	282.8
18	3330.00	1713.5	250.7	3430.00	1768.1	266.6	3530.00	1823.1	283.0
19	3331.67	1714.4	251.0	3431.67	1769.1	266.9	3531.67	1824.0	283.3
20	3333.33	1715.3	251.3	3433.33	1770.0	267.2	3533.33	1824.9	283.6
21	3335.00	1716.3	251.5	3435.00	1770.9	267.4	3535.00	1825.8	283.9
22	3336.67	1717.2	251.8	3436.67	1771.8	267.7	3536.67	1826.7	284.2
23	3338.33	1718.1	252.0	3438.33	1772.7	268.0	3538.33	1827.6	284.4
24	3340.00	1719.0	252.3	3440.00	1773.6	268.2	3540.00	1828.6	284.7
25	3341.67	1719.9	252.6	3441.67	1774.5	268.5	3541.67	1829.5	285.0
26	3343.33	1720.8	252.8	3443.33	1775.4	268.8	3543.33	1830.4	285.3
27	3345.00	1721.7	253.1	3445.00	1776.4	269.1	3545.00	1831.3	285.6
28	3346.67	1722.6	253.3	3446.67	1777.3	269.3	3546.67	1832.2	285.8
29	3348.33	1723.5	253.6	3448.33	1778.2	269.6	3548.33	1833.2	286.1
30	3350.00	1724.4	253.9	3450.00	1779.1	269.9	3550.00	1834.1	286.4
31	3351.67	1725.3	254.1	3451.67	1780.0	270.1	3551.67	1835.0	286.7
32	3353.33	1726.2	254.4	3453.33	1780.9	270.4	3553.33	1835.9	287.0
33	3355.00	1727.2	254.7	3455.00	1781.8	270.7	3555.00	1836.8	287.2
34	3356.67	1728.1	254.9	3456.67	1782.8	270.9	3556.67	1837.8	287.5
35	3358.33	1729.0	255.2	3458.33	1783.7	271.2	3558.33	1838.7	287.8
36	3360.00	1729.9	255.4	3460.00	1784.6	271.5	3560.00	1839.6	288.1
37	3361.67	1730.8	255.7	3461.67	1785.5	271.8	3561.67	1840.5	288.4
38	3363.33	1731.7	256.0	3463.33	1786.4	272.0	3563.33	1841.4	288.6
39	3365.00	1732.6	256.2	3465.00	1787.3	272.3	3565.00	1842.4	288.9
40	3366.67	1733.5	256.5	3466.67	1788.2	272.6	3566.67	1843.3	289.2
41	3368.33	1734.4	256.8	3468.33	1789.2	272.9	3568.33	1844.2	289.5
42	3370.00	1735.3	257.0	3470.00	1790.1	273.1	3570.00	1845.1	289.8
43	3371.67	1736.3	257.3	3471.67	1791.0	273.4	3571.67	1846.0	290.0
44	3373.33	1737.2	257.6	3473.33	1791.9	273.7	3573.33	1847.0	290.3
45	3375.00	1738.1	257.8	3475.00	1792.8	273.9	3575.00	1847.9	290.6
46	3376.67	1739.0	258.1	3476.67	1793.7	274.2	3576.67	1848.8	290.9
47	3378.33	1739.9	258.3	3478.33	1794.6	274.5	3578.33	1849.7	291.2
48	3380.00	1740.8	258.6	3480.00	1795.6	274.8	3580.00	1850.6	291.5
49	3381.67	1741.7	258.9	3481.67	1796.5	275.0	3581.67	1851.5	291.7
50	3383.33	1742.6	259.1	3483.33	1797.4	275.3	3583.33	1852.5	292.0
51	3385.00	1743.5	259.4	3485.00	1798.3	275.6	3585.00	1853.4	292.3
52	3386.67	1744.4	259.7	3486.67	1799.2	275.9	3586.67	1854.3	292.6
53	3388.33	1745.4	259.9	3488.33	1800.1	276.1	3588.33	1855.2	292.9
54	3390.00	1746.3	260.2	3490.00	1801.1	276.4	3590.00	1856.2	293.2
55	3391.67	1747.2	260.5	3491.67	1802.0	276.7	3591.67	1857.1	293.4
56	3393.33	1748.1	260.7	3493.33	1802.9	277.0	3593.33	1858.0	293.7
57	3395.00	1749.0	261.0	3495.00	1803.8	277.2	3595.00	1858.9	294.0
58	3396.67	1749.9	261.3	3496.67	1804.7	277.5	3596.67	1859.8	294.3
59	3398.33	1750.8	261.5	3498.33	1805.6	277.8	3598.33	1860.8	294.6

(All Definitions of Degree of Curve)

Min-utes	36° Length L	36° Tan. T	36° Ext. E	37° Length L	37° Tan. T	37° Ext. E	38° Length L	38° Tan. T	38° Ext. E
0	3600.00	1831.7	294.9	3700.00	1917.1	312.2	3800.00	1972.9	330.1
1	3601.67	1832.6	295.1	3701.57	1918.0	312.5	3801.67	1973.8	330.5
2	3603.33	1863.5	295.4	3703.33	1919.0	312.8	3803.33	1974.7	330.8
3	3605.00	1834.4	295.7	3705.00	1919.9	313.1	3805.00	1975.7	331.1
4	3606.67	1865.4	296.0	3706.67	1920.8	313.4	3806.67	1976.6	331.4
5	3608.33	1836.3	296.3	3708.33	1921.7	313.7	3808.33	1977.5	331.7
6	3610.00	1867.2	296.6	3710.00	1922.7	314.0	3810.00	1978.5	332.0
7	3611.67	1838.1	296.9	3711.67	1923.6	314.3	3811.67	1979.4	332.3
8	3613.33	1839.0	297.1	3713.33	1924.5	314.6	3813.33	1980.3	332.6
9	3615.00	1870.0	297.4	3715.00	1925.5	314.9	3815.00	1981.3	332.9
10	3616.67	1870.9	297.7	3716.67	1926.4	315.2	3816.67	1982.2	333.2
11	3618.33	1871.8	298.0	3718.33	1927.3	315.5	3818.33	1983.1	333.5
12	3620.00	1872.7	298.3	3720.00	1928.2	315.8	3820.00	1984.1	333.8
13	3621.67	1873.7	298.6	3721.67	1929.2	316.1	3821.67	1985.0	334.1
14	3623.33	1874.6	298.9	3723.33	1930.1	316.4	3823.33	1985.9	334.4
15	3625.00	1875.5	299.2	3725.00	1931.0	316.7	3825.00	1986.9	334.7
16	3626.67	1876.4	299.4	3726.67	1932.0	316.9	3826.67	1987.8	335.0
17	3628.33	1877.4	299.7	3728.33	1932.9	317.2	3828.33	1988.7	335.3
18	3630.00	1878.3	300.0	3730.00	1933.8	317.5	3830.00	1989.7	335.6
19	3631.67	1879.2	300.3	3731.67	1934.7	317.8	3831.67	1990.6	335.9
20	3633.33	1880.1	300.6	3733.33	1935.7	318.1	3833.33	1991.5	336.3
21	3635.00	1881.0	300.9	3735.00	1936.6	318.4	3835.00	1992.5	336.6
22	3636.67	1882.0	301.2	3736.67	1937.5	318.7	3836.67	1993.4	336.9
23	3638.33	1882.9	301.5	3738.33	1938.5	319.0	3838.33	1994.3	337.2
24	3640.00	1883.8	301.7	3740.00	1939.4	319.3	3840.00	1995.3	337.5
25	3641.67	1884.7	302.0	3741.67	1940.3	319.6	3841.67	1996.2	337.8
26	3643.33	1885.7	302.3	3743.33	1941.2	319.9	3843.33	1997.1	338.1
27	3645.00	1886.6	302.6	3745.00	1942.2	320.2	3845.00	1998.1	338.4
28	3646.67	1887.5	302.9	3746.67	1943.1	320.5	3846.67	1999.0	338.7
29	3648.33	1888.4	303.2	3748.33	1944.0	320.8	3848.33	1999.9	339.0
30	3650.00	1889.4	303.5	3750.00	1945.0	321.1	3850.00	2000.9	339.3
31	3651.67	1890.3	303.8	3751.67	1945.9	321.4	3851.67	2001.8	339.6
32	3653.33	1891.2	304.1	3753.33	1946.8	321.7	3853.33	2002.8	339.9
33	3655.00	1892.1	304.3	3755.00	1947.7	322.0	3855.00	2003.7	340.2
34	3656.67	1893.1	304.6	3756.67	1948.7	322.3	3856.67	2004.6	340.6
35	3658.33	1894.0	304.9	3758.33	1949.6	322.6	3858.33	2005.6	340.9
36	3660.00	1894.9	305.2	3760.00	1950.5	322.9	3860.00	2006.5	341.2
37	3661.67	1895.8	305.5	3761.67	1951.5	323.2	3861.67	2007.4	341.5
38	3663.33	1896.7	305.8	3763.33	1952.4	323.5	3863.33	2008.4	341.8
39	3665.00	1897.7	306.1	3765.00	1953.3	323.8	3865.00	2009.3	342.1
40	3666.67	1898.6	306.4	3766.67	1954.3	324.1	3866.67	2010.2	342.4
41	3668.33	1899.5	306.7	3768.33	1955.2	324.4	3868.33	2011.2	342.7
42	3670.00	1900.4	307.0	3770.00	1956.1	324.7	3870.00	2012.1	343.0
43	3671.67	1901.4	307.2	3771.67	1957.0	325.0	3871.67	2013.0	343.3
44	3673.33	1902.3	307.5	3773.33	1958.0	325.3	3873.33	2014.0	343.7
45	3675.00	1903.2	307.8	3775.00	1958.9	325.6	3875.00	2014.9	344.0
46	3676.67	1904.1	308.1	3776.67	1959.8	325.9	3876.67	2015.9	344.3
47	3678.33	1905.1	308.4	3778.33	1960.8	326.2	3878.33	2016.8	344.6
48	3680.00	1906.0	308.7	3780.00	1961.7	326.5	3880.00	2017.7	344.9
49	3681.67	1906.9	309.0	3781.67	1962.6	326.8	3881.67	2018.7	345.2
50	3683.33	1907.9	309.3	3783.33	1963.6	327.1	3882.33	2019.6	345.5
51	3685.00	1908.8	309.6	3785.00	1964.5	327.4	3885.00	2020.5	345.8
52	3686.67	1909.7	309.9	3786.67	1965.4	327.7	3886.67	2021.5	346.1
53	3688.33	1910.6	310.2	3788.33	1966.4	328.0	3888.33	2022.4	346.5
54	3690.00	1911.6	310.5	3790.00	1967.3	328.3	3890.00	2023.4	346.8
55	3691.67	1912.5	310.8	3791.67	1968.2	328.6	3891.67	2024.3	347.1
56	3693.33	1913.4	311.0	3793.33	1969.1	328.9	3893.33	2025.2	347.4
57	3695.00	1914.3	311.3	3795.00	1970.1	329.2	3895.00	2026.2	347.7
58	3696.67	1915.3	311.6	3796.67	1971.0	329.5	3896.67	2027.1	348.0
59	3698.33	1916.2	311.9	3798.33	1971.9	329.8	3898.33	2028.0	348.3

(All Definitions of Degree of Curve)

Min-utes	39° Length L	39° Tan. T	39° Ext. E	40° Length L	40° Tan. T	40° Ext. E	41° Length L	41° Tan. T	41° Ext. E
0	3900.00	2029.0	348.6	4000.00	2085.4	367.7	4100.00	2142.2	387.4
1	3901.67	2029.9	349.0	4001.67	2086.4	368.0	4101.67	2143.2	387.7
2	3903.33	2030.9	349.3	4003.33	2087.3	368.4	4103.33	2144.1	388.0
3	3905.00	2031.8	349.6	4005.00	2088.3	368.7	4105.00	2145.1	388.4
4	3906.67	2032.7	349.9	4006.67	2089.2	369.0	4106.67	2146.0	388.7
5	3908.33	2033.7	350.2	4008.33	2090.1	369.3	4108.33	2147.0	389.0
6	3910.00	2034.6	350.5	4010.00	2091.1	369.7	4110.00	2147.9	389.4
7	3911.67	2035.5	350.8	4011.67	2092.0	370.0	4111.67	2148.9	389.7
8	3913.33	2036.5	351.2	4013.33	2093.0	370.3	4113.33	2149.8	390.0
9	3915.00	2037.4	351.5	4015.00	2093.9	370.6	4115.00	2150.8	390.4
10	3916.67	2038.4	351.8	4016.67	2094.9	371.0	4116.67	2151.7	390.7
11	3918.33	2039.3	352.1	4018.33	2095.8	371.3	4118.33	2152.7	391.0
12	3920.00	2040.2	352.4	4020.00	2096.8	371.6	4120.00	2153.6	391.4
13	3921.67	2041.2	352.7	4021.67	2097.7	371.9	4121.67	2154.6	391.7
14	3923.33	2042.1	353.0	4023.33	2098.6	372.3	4123.33	2155.5	392.1
15	3925.00	2043.1	353.4	4025.00	2099.6	372.6	4125.00	2156.5	392.4
16	3926.67	2044.0	353.7	4026.67	2100.5	372.9	4126.67	2157.4	392.7
17	3928.33	2044.9	354.0	4028.33	2101.5	373.2	4128.33	2158.4	393.1
18	3930.00	2045.9	354.3	4030.00	2102.4	373.6	4130.00	2159.3	393.4
19	3931.67	2046.8	354.6	4031.67	2103.4	373.9	4131.67	2160.3	393.7
20	3933.33	2047.8	354.9	4033.33	2104.3	374.2	4133.33	2161.2	394.1
21	3935.00	2048.7	355.3	4035.00	2105.3	374.5	4135.00	2162.2	394.4
22	3936.67	2049.6	355.6	4036.67	2106.2	374.9	4136.67	2163.2	394.7
23	3938.33	2050.6	355.9	4038.33	2107.2	375.2	4138.33	2164.1	395.1
24	3940.00	2051.5	356.2	4040.00	2108.1	375.5	4140.00	2165.1	395.4
25	3941.67	2052.5	356.5	4041.67	2109.0	375.8	4141.67	2166.0	395.7
26	3943.33	2053.4	356.8	4043.33	2110.0	376.2	4143.33	2167.0	396.1
27	3945.00	2054.3	357.2	4045.00	2110.9	376.5	4145.00	2167.9	396.4
28	3946.67	2055.3	357.5	4046.67	2111.9	376.8	4146.67	2168.9	396.8
29	3948.33	2056.2	357.8	4048.33	2112.8	377.1	4148.33	2169.8	397.1
30	3950.00	2057.2	358.1	4050.00	2113.8	377.5	4150.00	2170.8	397.4
31	3951.67	2058.1	358.4	4051.67	2114.7	377.8	4151.67	2171.7	397.8
32	3953.33	2059.0	358.7	4053.33	2115.7	378.1	4153.33	2172.7	398.1
33	3955.00	2060.0	359.1	4055.00	2116.6	378.5	4155.00	2173.6	398.4
34	3956.67	2060.9	359.4	4056.67	2117.6	378.8	4156.67	2174.6	398.8
35	3958.33	2061.9	359.7	4058.33	2118.5	379.1	4158.33	2175.5	399.1
36	3960.00	2062.8	360.0	4060.00	2119.5	379.4	4160.00	2176.5	399.5
37	3961.67	2063.7	360.3	4061.67	2120.4	379.8	4161.67	2177.4	399.8
38	3963.33	2064.7	360.7	4063.33	2121.4	380.1	4163.33	2178.4	400.1
39	3965.00	2065.6	361.0	4065.00	2122.3	380.4	4165.00	2179.4	400.5
40	3966.67	2066.6	361.3	4066.67	2123.2	380.8	4166.67	2180.3	400.8
41	3968.33	2067.5	361.6	4068.33	2124.2	381.1	4168.33	2181.3	401.2
42	3970.00	2068.5	361.9	4070.00	2125.1	381.4	4170.00	2182.2	401.5
43	3971.67	2069.4	362.3	4071.67	2126.1	381.8	4171.67	2183.2	401.8
44	3973.33	2070.3	362.6	4073.33	2127.0	382.1	4173.33	2184.1	402.2
45	3975.00	2071.3	362.9	4075.00	2128.0	382.4	4175.00	2185.1	402.5
46	3976.67	2072.2	363.2	4076.67	2128.9	382.7	4176.67	2186.0	402.9
47	3978.33	2073.2	363.5	4078.33	2129.9	383.1	4178.33	2187.0	403.2
48	3980.00	2074.1	363.9	4080.00	2130.8	383.4	4180.00	2187.9	403.5
49	3981.67	2075.0	364.2	4081.67	2131.8	383.7	4181.67	2188.9	403.9
50	3983.33	2076.0	364.5	4083.33	2132.7	384.1	4183.33	2189.9	404.2
51	3985.00	2076.9	364.8	4085.00	2133.7	384.4	4185.00	2190.8	404.6
52	3986.67	2077.9	365.1	4086.67	2134.6	384.8	4186.67	2191.8	404.9
53	3988.33	2078.8	365.5	4088.33	2135.6	385.1	4188.33	2192.7	405.2
54	3990.00	2079.8	365.8	4030.00	2136.5	385.4	4190.00	2193.7	405.6
55	3991.67	2080.7	366.1	4091.67	2137.5	385.7	4191.67	2194.6	405.9
56	3993.33	2081.6	366.4	4093.33	2138.4	386.1	4193.33	2195.6	406.3
57	3995.00	2082.6	366.8	4095.00	2139.4	386.4	4195.00	2196.5	406.6
58	3996.67	2083.5	367.1	4096.67	2140.3	386.7	4196.67	2197.5	407.0
59	3998.33	2084.5	367.4	4098.33	2141.3	387.0	4198.33	2198.5	407.3

(All Definitions of Degree of Curve)

Min-utes	42° Length L	42° Tan. T	42° Ext. E	43° Length L	43° Tan. T	43° Ext. E	44° Length L	44° Tan. T	44° Ext. E
0	4200.00	2199.4	407.6	4300.00	2257.0	428.5	4400.00	2314.9	450.0
1	4201.67	2200.4	408.0	4301.67	2257.9	428.9	4401.67	2315.9	450.3
2	4203.33	2201.3	408.3	4303.33	2258.9	429.2	4403.03	2316.9	450.7
3	4205.00	2202.3	408.7	4305.00	2259.9	429.6	4405.00	2317.8	451.1
4	4206.67	2203.2	409.0	4306.67	2260.8	429.9	4406.67	2318.8	451.4
5	4208.33	2204.2	409.4	4308.33	2261.8	430.3	4408.33	2319.8	451.8
6	4210.33	2205.1	409.7	4310.00	2262.7	430.6	4410.00	2320.7	452.2
7	4211.67	2206.1	410.0	4311.67	2263.7	431.1	4411.67	2321.7	452.5
8	4213.33	2207.1	410.4	4313.33	2264.7	431.3	4413.33	2322.7	452.9
9	4215.00	2208.0	410.7	4315.00	2265.6	431.7	4415.00	2323.7	453.3
10	4216.67	2209.0	411.1	4316.67	2266.6	432.0	4416.67	2324.6	453.6
11	4218.33	2209.9	411.4	4318.33	2267.6	432.4	4418.33	2325.6	454.0
12	4220.00	2210.9	411.8	4320.00	2268.5	432.8	4420.00	2326.6	454.4
13	4221.67	2211.8	412.1	4321.67	2269.5	433.1	4421.67	2327.5	454.7
14	4223.33	2212.8	412.5	4323.33	2270.5	433.5	4423.33	2328.5	455.1
15	4225.00	2213.8	412.8	4325.00	2271.4	433.8	4425.00	2329.5	455.4
16	4226.67	2214.7	413.1	4326.67	2272.4	434.2	4426.67	2330.5	455.8
17	4228.33	2215.7	413.5	4338.33	2273.4	434.5	4428.33	2331.4	456.2
18	4230.00	2216.6	413.8	4330.00	2274.3	434.9	4430.00	2332.4	456.5
19	4231.67	2217.6	414.2	4331.67	2275.3	435.2	4431.67	2333.4	456.9
20	4233.33	2218.6	414.5	4333.33	2276.2	435.6	4433.33	2334.3	457.3
21	4235.00	2219.5	414.9	4335.00	2277.2	435.9	4435.00	2335.3	457.6
22	4236.67	2220.5	415.2	4336.67	2278.2	436.3	4436.67	2336.3	458.0
23	4238.33	2221.4	415.6	4338.33	2279.1	436.7	4438.33	2337.3	458.4
24	4240.00	2222.4	415.9	4340.00	2280.1	437.0	4440.00	2338.2	458.7
25	4241.67	2223.3	416.3	4341.67	2281.1	437.4	4441.67	2339.2	459.1
26	4243.33	2224.3	416.6	4343.33	2282.0	437.7	4443.33	2340.2	459.5
27	4245.00	2225.3	416.9	4345.00	2283.0	438.1	4445.00	2341.1	459.8
28	4246.67	2226.2	417.3	4346.67	2284.0	438.4	4446.67	2342.1	460.2
29	4248.33	2227.2	417.6	4348.33	2284.9	438.8	4448.33	2343.1	460.6
30	4250.00	2228.1	418.0	4350.00	2285.9	439.2	4450.00	2344.1	461.0
31	4251.67	2229.1	418.3	4351.67	2286.9	439.5	4451.67	2345.0	461.3
32	4253.33	2230.1	418.7	4353.33	2287.8	439.9	4453.33	2346.0	461.7
33	4255.00	2231.0	419.0	4355.00	2288.8	440.2	4455.00	2347.0	462.1
34	4256.67	2232.0	419.4	4356.67	2289.8	440.6	4456.67	2348.0	462.4
35	4258.33	2232.9	419.7	4358.33	2290.7	441.0	4458.33	2348.9	462.8
36	4260.00	2233.9	420.1	4360.00	2291.7	441.3	4460.00	2349.9	463.2
37	4261.67	2234.9	420.4	4361.67	2292.7	441.7	4461.67	2350.9	463.5
38	4263.33	2235.8	420.8	4363.33	2293.6	442.0	4463.33	2351.8	463.9
39	4265.00	2236.8	421.1	4365.00	2294.6	442.4	4465.00	2352.8	464.3
40	4266.67	2237.7	421.5	4366.67	2295.6	442.8	4466.67	2353.8	464.6
41	4268.33	2238.7	421.8	4338.33	2296.5	443.1	4468.33	2354.8	465.0
42	4270.00	2239.7	422.2	4370.00	2297.5	443.5	4470.00	2355.7	465.4
43	4271.67	2240.6	422.5	4371.67	2298.5	443.8	4471.67	2356.7	465.8
44	4273.33	2241.6	422.9	4373.33	2299.4	444.2	4473.33	2357.7	466.1
45	4275.00	2242.5	423.2	4375.00	2300.4	444.6	4475.00	2358.7	466.5
46	4276.67	2243.5	423.6	4376.67	2301.4	444.9	4476.67	2359.6	466.9
47	4278.33	2244.5	423.9	4378.33	2302.3	445.3	4478.33	2360.6	467.2
48	4280.00	2245.4	424.3	4380.00	2303.3	445.6	4480.00	2361.6	467.6
49	4281.67	2246.4	424.6	4381.67	2304.3	446.0	4481.67	2362.6	468.0
50	4283.33	2247.3	425.0	4383.33	2305.2	446.4	4483.33	2363.5	468.4
51	4285.00	2248.3	425.3	4385.00	2306.2	446.7	4485.00	2364.5	468.7
52	4286.67	2249.3	425.7	4386.67	2307.2	447.1	4486.67	2365.5	469.1
53	4288.33	2250.2	426.0	4388.33	2308.1	447.4	4488.33	2366.5	469.5
54	4290.00	2251.2	426.4	4390.00	2309.1	447.8	4490.00	2367.4	469.8
55	4291.67	2252.2	426.7	4391.67	2310.1	448.2	4491.67	2368.4	470.2
56	4293.33	2253.1	427.1	4393.33	2311.1	448.5	4493.33	2369.4	470.6
57	4295.00	2254.1	427.4	4395.00	2312.0	448.9	4495.00	2370.4	471.0
58	4296.67	2255.0	427.8	4396.67	2313.0	449.3	4496.67	2371.3	471.3
59	4298.33	2256.0	428.1	4398.33	2314.0	449.6	4498.33	2372.3	471.7

(All Definitions of Degree of Curve)

Min-utes	45°			46°			47°		
	Length L	Tan. T	Ext. E	Length L	Tan. T	Ext. E	Length L	Tan. T	Ext. E
0	4500.00	2373.3	472.1	4600.00	2432.1	494.8	4700.00	2491.3	518.2
1	4501.67	2374.3	472.5	4601.67	2433.1	495.2	4701.67	2492.3	518.6
2	4503.33	2375.3	472.8	4603.33	2434.1	495.6	4703.33	2493.3	519.0
3	4505.00	2376.2	473.2	4605.00	2435.0	496.0	4705.00	2494.3	519.4
4	4506.67	2377.2	473.6	4606.67	2434.30	496.4	4706.67	2495.3	519.8
5	4508.33	2378.2	474.0	4608.33	2437.0	496.7	4708.33	2496.3	520.2
6	4510.00	2379.2	474.3	4610.00	2438.0	497.1	4710.00	2497.3	520.6
7	4511.67	2380.1	474.7	4611.67	2439.0	497.5	4711.67	2498.3	521.0
8	4513.33	2381.1	475.1	4613.33	2440.0	497.9	4713.33	2499.3	521.4
9	4515.00	2382.1	475.4	4615.00	2440.9	498.3	4715.00	2500.2	521.8
10	4516.67	2383.1	475.8	4616.67	2441.9	498.7	4716.67	2501.2	522.2
11	4518.33	2384.0	476.2	4618.33	2442.9	499.1	4718.33	2502.2	522.6
12	4520.00	2385.0	476.6	4620.00	2443.9	499.4	4720.00	2503.2	523.0
13	4521.67	2386.0	477.0	4621.67	2444.9	499.8	4721.67	2504.2	523.4
14	4523.33	2387.0	477.3	4623.33	2445.9	500.2	4723.33	2505.2	523.7
15	4525.00	2388.0	477.7	4635.00	2446.9	500.6	4725.00	2506.2	524.1
16	4526.67	2388.9	478.1	4626.67	2447.8	501.0	4726.67	2507.2	524.5
17	4528.33	2389.9	478.5	4628.33	2448.8	501.4	4728.33	2508.2	524.9
18	4530.00	2390.9	478.8	4630.00	2449.8	501.8	4730.00	2509.2	525.3
19	4531.67	2391.9	479.2	4631.67	2450.8	502.2	4731.67	2510.2	525.7
20	4533.33	2392.8	479.6	4633.33	2451.8	502.5	4733.33	2511.2	526.1
21	4535.00	2393.8	480.0	4635.00	2452.8	502.9	4735.00	2512.2	526.5
22	4536.67	2394.8	480.3	4636.67	2453.8	503.3	4736.67	2513.2	526.9
23	4538.33	2395.8	480.7	4638.33	2454.7	503.7	4738.33	2514.1	527.3
24	4540.00	2396.8	481.1	4640.00	2455.7	504.1	4740.00	2515.1	527.7
25	4541.67	2397.7	481.5	4641.67	2456.7	504.5	4741.67	2516.1	528.1
26	4543.33	2398.7	481.9	4643.33	2457.7	504.9	4743.33	2517.1	528.5
27	4545.00	2399.7	482.2	4645.00	2458.7	505.3	4745.00	2518.1	528.9
28	4546.67	2400.7	482.6	4646.67	2459.7	505.6	4746.67	2519.1	529.3
29	4548.33	2401.7	483.0	4648.33	2460.7	506.0	4748.33	2520.1	529.7
30	4550.00	2402.6	483.4	4650.00	2461.7	506.4	4750.00	2521.1	530.1
31	4551.67	2403.6	483.8	4651.67	2462.6	506.8	4751.67	2522.1	530.5
32	4553.33	2404.6	484.1	4653.33	2463.6	507.2	4753.33	2523.1	530.9
33	4555.00	2405.6	484.5	4655.00	2464.6	507.6	4755.00	2524.1	531.3
34	4556.67	2406.6	484.9	4656.67	2465.6	508.0	4756.67	2525.1	531.7
35	4558.33	2407.5	485.3	4658.33	2466.6	508.4	4758.33	2526.1	532.1
36	4560.00	2408.5	485.7	4660.00	2467.6	508.8	4760.00	2527.1	532.5
37	4561.67	2409.5	486.0	4661.67	2468.6	509.2	4761.67	2528.1	532.9
38	4563.33	2410.5	486.4	4663.33	2469.6	509.5	4763.33	2529.1	533.3
39	4565.00	2411.5	486.8	4665.00	2470.5	509.9	4765.00	2530.1	533.7
40	4566.67	2412.4	487.2	4666.67	2471.5	510.3	4766.67	2531.1	534.2
41	4568.33	2413.4	487.6	4668.33	2472.5	510.7	4768.33	2532.1	534.6
42	4570.00	2414.4	487.9	4670.00	2473.5	511.1	4770.00	2532.1	535.0
43	4571.67	2415.4	488.3	4671.67	2474.5	511.5	4771.67	2534.1	535.4
44	4573.33	2416.4	488.7	4673.33	2475.5	511.9	4773.33	2535.0	535.8
45	4575.00	2417.4	489.1	4675.00	2476.5	512.3	4775.00	2536.0	536.2
46	4576.67	2418.3	489.5	4676.67	2477.5	512.7	4776.67	2537.0	536.6
47	4578.33	2419.3	489.8	4678.33	2478.5	513.1	4778.00	2538.0	537.0
48	4580.00	2420.3	490.2	4680.00	2479.4	513.5	4780.00	2539.0	537.4
49	4581.67	2421.3	490.6	4681.67	2480.4	513.9	4781.67	2540.0	537.8
50	4583.33	2422.3	491.0	4683.33	2481.4	514.3	4783.33	2541.0	538.2
51	4585.00	2423.2	491.4	4685.00	2482.4	514.6	4785.00	2542.0	538.6
52	4586.67	2424.2	491.7	4686.67	2483.4	515.0	4786.67	2543.0	539.0
53	4588.33	2425.2	492.1	4688.33	2484.4	515.4	4788.33	2544.0	539.4
54	4590.00	2426.2	492.5	4690.00	2485.4	515.8	4790.00	2545.0	539.8
55	4591.67	2427.2	492.9	4691.67	2486.4	516.2	4791.67	2546.0	540.2
56	4593.33	2428.2	493.3	4693.33	2487.4	516.6	4793.33	2547.0	540.6
57	4595.00	2429.1	493.7	4695.00	2488.4	517.0	4795.00	2548.0	541.0
58	4596.67	2430.1	494.1	4696.67	2489.3	517.4	4796.67	2549.0	541.4
59	4598.33	2431.1	494.4	4698.33	2490.3	517.8	4798.33	2550.0	541.8

(All Definitions of Degree of Curve)

Min-utes	48°			49°			50°		
	Length L	Tan. T	Ext. E	Length L	Tan. T	Ext. E	Length L	Tan. T	Ext. E
0	4800.00	2551.0	542.2	4900.00	2311.2	566.9	5000.00	2371.8	592.3
1	4801.67	2552.0	542.6	4901.67	2312.2	567.4	5001.67	2372.8	592.8
2	4803.33	2553.0	543.0	4903.33	2613.2	567.8	5003.33	2673.8	593.2
3	4805.00	2554.0	543.5	4905.00	2614.2	568.2	5005.00	2674.8	593.6
4	4806.67	2555.0	543.9	4906.67	2615.2	568.6	5006.67	2675.8	594.0
5	4808.33	2556.0	544.3	4908.33	2616.2	569.0	5008.33	2676.9	594.5
6	4810.00	2557.0	544.7	4910.00	2617.2	569.4	5010.00	2377.9	594.9
7	4811.67	2558.0	545.1	4911.67	2618.2	569.9	5011.33	2678.9	595.3
8	4813.33	2559.0	545.5	4913.33	2619.2	570.3	5013.33	2679.9	595.8
9	4815.00	2560.0	545.9	4915.00	2620.2	570.7	5015.00	2680.9	596.2
10	4816.67	2561.0	546.3	4916.67	2621.2	571.1	5016.67	2681.9	596.6
11	4818.33	2562.0	546.7	4918.33	2622.2	571.5	5018.33	2682.9	597.1
12	4820.00	2563.0	547.1	4920.00	2623.2	572.0	5020.00	2384.0	597.5
13	4821.67	2364.0	547.5	4921.67	2624.2	572.4	5021.67	2385.0	597.9
14	4823.33	2565.0	547.8	4923.33	2625.3	572.8	5023.33	2686.0	598.3
15	4825.00	2566.0	548.3	4925.00	2626.3	573.2	5025.00	2687.0	598.8
16	4826.67	2567.0	548.8	4926.67	2627.3	573.6	5026.67	2688.0	599.2
17	4828.33	2568.0	549.2	4928.33	2628.3	574.1	5028.33	2389.0	599.6
18	4830.00	2569.0	549.6	4830.00	2629.3	574.5	5030.00	2690.1	600.1
19	4831.67	2570.0	550.0	4931.67	2630.3	574.9	5031.67	2691.1	600.5
20	4833.33	2571.0	550.4	4933.33	2631.3	575.3	5033.33	2692.1	600.9
21	4835.00	2572.0	550.8	4935.00	2632.3	575.7	5035.00	2693.1	601.4
22	4836.67	2573.0	551.2	4936.67	2633.3	576.2	5036.67	2694.1	601.8
23	4838.33	2574.0	551.6	4938.33	2634.3	576.6	5038.33	2695.2	602.2
24	1840.00	2575.0	552.0	4940.00	2635.3	577.0	5040.00	2696.2	602.7
25	4841.67	2576.0	552.4	4941.67	2636.4	577.4	5041.67	2697.2	603.1
26	4843.33	2577.0	552.9	4943.33	2637.4	577.9	5043.33	2698.2	603.5
27	4845.00	2578.0	553.3	4945.00	2638.4	578.3	5045.00	2699.2	604.0
28	4846.67	2579.0	553.7	4946.67	2339.4	578.7	5046.67	2700.2	604.4
29	4848.33	2580.0	554.1	4948.33	2640.4	579.1	5048.33	2701.3	604.8
30	4850.00	2581.0	554.5	4950.00	2641.4	579.5	5050.00	2702.3	605.3
31	4351.67	2582.0	554.9	4951.67	2642.4	580.0	5051.67	2703.3	605.7
32	4853.33	2583.0	555.3	4953.33	2643.4	580.4	5053.33	2704.3	606.1
33	4855.00	2584.0	555.7	4955.00	2644.4	580.8	5055.00	2705.3	606.6
34	4856.67	2585.0	556.2	4956.67	2645.4	581.2	5056.67	2706.4	607.0
35	4858.33	2586.0	556.6	4958.33	2646.5	581.7	5058.33	2707.4	607.4
36	4860.00	2587.0	557.0	4960.00	2647.5	582.1	5060.00	2708.4	607.9
37	4861.67	2588.0	557.4	4961.67	2648.5	582.5	5061.67	2709.4	608.3
38	4863.33	2589.0	557.8	4963.33	2649.5	582.9	5063.33	2710.4	608.8
39	4865.00	2590.0	558.2	4965.00	2650.5	583.4	5065.00	2711.5	609.2
40	4866.67	2591.1	558.6	4966.67	2651.5	583.8	5066.67	2712.5	609.6
41	4868.33	2592.1	559.0	4968.33	2652.5	584.2	5068.33	2713.5	610.1
42	4870.00	2593.1	559.5	4970.00	2653.5	584.6	5070.00	2714.5	610.5
43	4871.67	2594.1	559.9	4971.67	2654.6	585.1	5071.67	2715.5	610.9
44	4873.33	2595.1	560.3	4973.33	2655.6	585.5	5063.33	2716.6	611.4
45	4875.00	2596.1	560.7	4975.00	2656.6	585.9	5075.00	2717.6	611.8
46	4876.67	2597.1	561.1	4976.67	2557.6	586.3	5076.67	2718.6	612.2
47	4878.33	2598.1	531.5	4978.33	2658.6	586.8	5078.33	2719.6	612.7
48	4880.00	2599.1	531.9	4980.00	2659.6	587.2	5080.00	2720.6	613.1
49	4881.67	2600.1	562.4	4981.67	2660.6	587.6	5081.67	2721.7	613.6
50	4883.33	2501.1	562.8	4983.33	2661.6	588.0	5083.33	2722.7	614.0
51	4885.00	2302.1	563.2	4985.00	2662.6	588.5	5085.00	2723.7	614.4
52	4886.67	2303.1	563.6	4986.67	2663.7	588.9	5086.67	2724.7	614.9
53	4888.33	2304.1	564.0	4988.33	2664.7	589.3	5088.33	2725.7	615.3
54	4890.00	2305.1	564.4	4990.00	2665.7	589.8	5090.00	2726.8	615.8
55	4891.67	2606.1	564.9	4991.67	2666.7	590.2	5091.67	2727.8	616.2
56	4893.33	2307.1	565.3	4993.33	2667.7	590.6	5093.33	2728.8	616.6
57	4895.00	2608.1	565.7	4995.00	2668.7	591.0	5095.00	2729.8	617.1
58	4896.67	2609.1	566.1	4996.67	2669.8	591.5	5096.67	2730.9	617.5
59	4898.33	2610.1	566.5	4998.33	2670.8	591.9	5098.33	2731.9	618.0

(All Definitions of Degree of Curve)

Min-utes	51° Length L	51° Tan. T	51° Ext. E	52° Length L	52° Tan. T	52° Ext. E	53° Length L	53° Tan. T	53° Ext. E
0	5100.00	2732.9	618.4	5200.00	2794.5	645.2	5300.00	2856.7	672.7
1	5101.67	2733.9	618 8	5201.67	2795.6	645.6	5301.67	2357.7	673.1
2	5103.33	2734.9	619.3	5203.33	2796.6	646.1	5333.33	2358.8	673.6
3	5105.00	2736.0	619.7	5205.00	2797.6	646.5	5305.00	2359.8	674.1
4	5106.67	2737.0	620.2	5206.67	2798.7	647.0	5306.67	2360.9	674.5
5	5108.33	2738.0	620.6	5208.33	2799.7	647.4	5308.33	2361.9	675.0
6	5110.00	2739.0	621.0	5210.00	2300.7	647.9	5310.00	2862.9	675.5
7	5111.67	2740.1	621.5	5211.67	2801.8	648.3	5311.67	2864.0	675.9
8	5113.33	2741.1	621.9	5213.33	2802.8	648.8	5313.33	2865.0	676.4
9	5115.00	2742.1	622.4	5215.00	2803.8	649.2	5315.00	2866.1	676.9
10	5116.67	2743.1	622.8	5216.67	2804.9	649.7	5316.67	2867.1	677.3
11	5118.33	2744.2	623.3	5218.33	2805.9	650.2	5318.33	2868.2	677.8
12	5120.00	2745.2	623.7	5220.00	2806.9	650.6	5320.00	2869.2	678.3
13	5121.67	2746.2	624.1	5221.67	2808.0	651.1	5321.67	2870.2	678.7
14	5123.33	2747.2	624.6	5223.33	2809.0	651.5	5323.33	2871.3	679.2
15	5125.00	2748.3	625.0	5225.00	2810.0	652.0	5325.00	2872.3	679.7
16	5126.67	2749.3	625.4	5226.67	2811.1	652.4	5326.67	2873.4	680.1
17	5128.33	2750.3	625.9	5228.33	2812.1	652.9	5328.33	2874.4	680.6
18	5130.00	2751.3	626.4	5230.00	2813.1	653.3	5330.00	2875.5	681.1
19	5131.67	2752.4	626.8	5231.67	2814.2	653.8	5331.67	2876.5	681.5
20	5133.33	2753.4	627.2	5233.33	2815.2	654.3	5333.33	2877.5	682.0
21	5135.00	2754.4	627.7	5235.00	2316.2	654.7	5335.00	2378.6	682.5
22	5136.67	2755.4	628.1	5236.67	2817.3	655.2	5336.67	2879.6	682.9
23	5138.33	2756.5	628.6	5238.33	2818.3	655.6	5338.33	2880.7	683.4
24	5140.00	2757.5	629.0	5240.00	2819.3	656.1	5340.00	2881.7	683.9
25	5141.67	2758.5	629.5	5241.67	2820.4	656.5	5341.67	2882.8	684.3
26	5143.33	2759.5	629.9	5243.33	2821.4	657.0	5343.33	2883.8	684.8
27	5145.00	2760.6	630.4	5245.00	2822.4	657.5	5345.00	2884.8	685.3
28	5146.67	2761.6	630.8	5246.67	2823.5	657.9	5346.67	2885.9	685.7
29	5148.33	2762.6	631.2	5248.33	2824.5	658.4	5348.33	2886.9	686.2
30	5150.00	2763.7	631.7	5250.00	2825.6	658.8	5350.00	2888.0	686.7
31	5151.67	2764.7	632.1	5251.67	2826.6	659.3	5351.67	2889.0	687.2
32	5153.33	2765.7	632.6	5253.33	2827.6	659.7	5353.33	2890.1	687.6
33	5155.00	2766.7	633.0	5255.00	2828.7	660.2	5355.00	2891.1	688.1
34	5156.67	2767.8	633.5	5256.67	2829.7	660.7	5356.67	2892.2	688.6
35	5158.33	2768.8	633.9	5258.33	2830.7	661.1	5358.33	2893.2	689.0
36	5160.00	2769.8	634.4	5260.00	2831.8	661.6	5360.00	2894.3	689.5
37	5161.67	2770.8	634.8	5261.67	2832.8	662.0	5361.67	2895.3	690.0
38	5163.33	2771.9	635.3	5263.33	2833.8	662.5	5363.33	2896.3	690.5
39	5165.00	2772.9	635.7	5265.00	2834.9	663.0	5365.00	2897.4	690.9
40	5166.67	2773.9	636.2	5266.67	2855.9	663.4	5366.67	2898.4	691.4
41	5168.33	2775.0	636.6	5268.33	2837.0	663.9	5368.33	2899.5	691.9
42	5170.00	2776.0	637.1	5270.00	2838.0	664.3	5370.00	2900.5	692.3
43	5171.67	2777.0	637.5	5271.67	2839.0	664.8	5371.67	2901.6	692.8
44	5173.33	2778.1	638.0	5273.33	2840.1	665.3	5373.33	2902.6	693.3
45	5175.00	2779.1	638.4	5275.00	2841.1	665.7	5375.00	2903.7	693.8
46	5176.67	2780.1	638.9	5276.67	2842.1	666.2	5376.67	2904.7	694.2
47	5178.33	2781.1	639.3	5278.33	2843.2	666.6	5378.33	2905.8	694.7
48	5180.00	2782.2	639.8	5280.00	2844.2	667.1	5380.00	2906.8	695.2
49	5181.67	2783.2	640.2	5281.67	2845.3	667.6	5381.67	2907.9	695.7
50	5183.33	2784.2	640.7	5283.33	2846.3	668.0	5383.33	2908.9	696.1
51	5185.00	2785.3	641.1	5285.00	2847.3	668.5	5385.00	2910.0	696.6
52	5186.67	2786.3	641.6	5286.67	2848.4	669.0	5386.67	2911.0	697.1
53	5188.33	2787.3	642.0	5288.33	2849.4	669.4	5388.33	2912.1	697.6
54	5190.00	2788.3	642.5	5290.00	2850.5	669.9	5390.00	2913.1	698.0
55	5191.67	2789.4	642.9	5291.67	2851.5	670.3	5391.67	2914.2	698.5
56	5193.33	2790.4	643.4	5293.33	2852.5	670.8	5393.33	2915.2	699.0
57	5195.00	2791.4	643.8	5295.00	2853.6	671.3	5395.00	2916.3	699.5
58	5196.67	2792.5	644.3	5296.67	2854.6	671.7	5396.67	2917.3	699.9
59	5198.33	2793.5	644.7	5298.33	2855.7	672.2	5398.33	2918.4	700.4

(All Definitions of Degree of Curve)

Min-	54°			55°			56°		
utes	Length L	Tan. T	Ext. E	Length L	Tan. T	Ext. E	Length L	Tan. T	Ext. E
0	5400.00	2919.4	700.9	5500.00	2982.7	729.9	5600.00	3046.5	759.6
1	5401.67	2920.5	701.4	5501.67	2983.7	730.3	5601.67	3047.6	760.1
2	5403.33	2921.5	701.8	5503.33	2984.8	730.8	5603.33	3048.6	760.6
3	5405.00	2922.6	702.3	5505.00	2985.8	731.3	5605.00	3049.7	761.1
4	5406.67	2923.6	702.8	5506.67	2986.9	731.8	5606.67	3050.8	761.6
5	5408.33	2924.7	703.3	5508.33	2988.0	732.3	5608.33	3051.9	762.1
6	5410.00	2925.7	703.8	5510.00	2989.0	732.8	5610.00	3052.9	762.6
7	5411.67	2926.8	704.2	5511.67	2990.1	733.3	5611.67	3054.0	763.1
8	5413.33	2927.8	704.7	5513.33	2991.1	733.8	5613.33	3055.1	763.6
9	5415.00	2928.9	705.2	5515.00	2992.2	734.3	5615.00	3056.1	764.1
10	5416.67	2929.9	705.7	5516.67	2993.3	734.8	5616.67	3057.2	764.6
11	5418.33	2931.0	706.1	5518.33	2994.3	735.3	5618.33	3058.3	765.1
12	5420.00	2932.0	706.6	5520.00	2995.4	735.7	5620.00	3059.3	765.6
13	5421.67	2933.1	707.1	5521.67	2996.5	736.2	5621.57	3060.4	766.1
14	5423.33	2934.1	707.6	5523.33	2997.5	736.7	5623.33	3061.5	766.6
15	5425.00	2935.2	708.1	5525.00	2998.6	737.2	5625.00	3062.6	767.1
16	5426.67	2936.2	708.6	5526.67	2999.6	737.7	5626.67	3063.6	767.6
17	5428.33	2937.3	709.0	5528.33	3000.7	738.2	5628.33	3064.7	768.1
18	5430.00	2938.3	709.5	5530.00	3001.8	738.7	5630.00	3065.8	768.6
19	5431.67	2939.4	710.0	5531.67	3002.8	739.2	5631.67	3066.8	769.2
20	5433.00	2940.4	710.5	5533.33	3003.9	739.7	5633.33	3067.9	769.7
21	5435.00	2941.5	710.9	5535.00	3004.9	740.2	5635.00	3069.0	770.2
22	5436.67	2942.5	711.4	5536.67	3006.0	740.7	5636.67	3070.1	770.7
23	5438.33	2943.6	711.9	5538.33	3007.1	741.2	5638.33	3071.1	771.2
24	5440.00	2944.6	712.4	5540.00	3008.1	741.7	5640.00	3072.2	771.7
25	5441.67	2945.7	712.9	5541.67	3009.2	742.1	5641.67	3073.3	772.2
26	5443.33	2946.8	713.4	5543.33	3010.3	742.6	5643.33	3074.4	772.7
27	5445.00	2947.8	713.8	5545.00	3011.3	743.1	5645.00	3075.4	773.2
28	5446.67	2948.9	714.3	5546.67	3012.4	743.6	5646.67	3076.5	773.7
29	5448.33	2949.9	714.8	5548.33	3013.5	744.1	5648.33	3077.6	774.2
30	5450.00	2951.0	715.3	5550.00	3014.5	744.6	5650.00	3078.7	774.7
31	5451.67	2952.0	715.8	5551.67	3015.6	745.1	5651.67	3079.7	775.2
32	5453.33	2953.1	716.2	5553.33	3016.6	745.6	5653.33	3080.8	775.7
33	5455.00	2954.1	716.7	5555.00	3017.7	746.1	5655.00	3081.9	776.3
34	5456.67	2955.2	717.2	5556.67	3018.8	746.6	5656.67	3082.9	776.8
35	5458.33	2956.2	717.8	5558.33	3019.8	747.1	5658.33	3084.0	777.3
36	5460.00	2957.3	718.2	5560.00	3020.9	747.6	5660.00	3085.1	777.8
37	5461.67	2958.3	718.7	5561.67	3022.0	748.1	5661.67	3086.2	778.3
38	5463.33	2959.4	719.1	5563.33	3023.0	748.6	5663.33	3087.2	778.8
39	5465.00	2960.5	719.6	5565.00	3024.1	749.1	5665.00	3088.3	779.3
40	5466.67	2961.5	720.1	5566.67	3025.2	749.6	5666.67	3089.4	779.8
41	5468.33	2962.6	720.6	5568.33	3026.2	750.1	5668.33	3090.5	780.3
42	5470.00	2963.6	721.1	5570.00	3027.3	750.6	5670.00	3091.6	780.9
43	5471.67	2964.7	721.6	5571.67	3028.4	751.1	5671.67	3092.6	781.4
44	5473.33	2965.7	722.1	5573.33	3029.4	751.6	5673.33	3093.7	781.9
45	5475.00	2966.8	722.5	5575.00	3030.5	752.1	5675.00	3094.8	782.4
46	5476.67	2967.9	723.0	5576.67	3031.6	752.6	5676.67	3095.9	782.9
47	5478.33	2968.9	723.5	5578.33	3032.6	753.1	5678.33	3096.9	783.4
48	5480.00	2970.0	724.0	5580.00	3033.7	753.6	5680.00	3098.0	783.9
49	5481.67	2971.0	724.5	5581.67	3034.8	754.1	5681.67	3099.1	784.4
50	5483.33	2972.1	725.0	5583.33	3035.8	754.6	5683.33	3100.2	784.9
51	5485.00	2973.1	725.5	5585.00	3036.9	755.1	5685.00	3101.2	785.5
52	5486.67	2974.2	725.9	5586.67	3038.0	755.6	5686.67	3102.3	786.0
53	5488.33	2975.3	726.4	5588.33	3039.0	756.1	5688.33	3103.4	786.5
54	5490.00	2976.3	726.9	5590.00	3040.1	756.6	5690.00	3104.5	787.0
55	5491.67	2977.4	727.4	5591.67	3041.2	757.1	5691.67	3105.6	787.5
56	5493.33	2978.4	727.9	5593.33	3042.2	757.6	5693.33	3106.6	788.0
57	5495.00	2979.5	728.4	5595.00	3043.3	758.1	5695.00	3107.7	788.5
58	5496.67	2980.5	728.9	5596.67	3044.4	758.6	5696.67	3108.8	789.1
59	5498.33	2981.6	729.4	5598.33	3045.4	759.1	5698.33	3109.9	789.6

(All Definitions of Degree of Curve)

Min-utes	57°			58°			59°		
	Length L	Tan. T	Ext. E	Length L	Tan. T	Ext. E	Length L	Tan. T	Ext. E
0	5700.00	3110.9	790.1	5800.00	3176.0	821.4	5900.00	3241.7	853.5
1	5701.67	3112.0	790.6	5801.67	3177.1	821.9	5901.67	3242.8	854.0
2	5703.33	3113.1	791.1	5803.33	3178.2	822.4	5903.33	3243.9	854.5
3	5705.00	3114.2	791.6	5805.00	3179.3	823.0	5905.00	3245.0	855.1
4	5706.67	3115.3	792.1	5806.67	3180.4	823.5	5906.67	3246.1	855.6
5	5708.33	3116.3	792.7	5808.33	3181.4	824.0	5908.33	3247.2	856.2
6	5710.00	3117.4	793.2	5810.00	3182.5	824.5	5910.00	3248.3	856.7
7	5711.67	3118.5	793.7	5811.67	3183.6	825.1	5911.67	3249.4	857.3
8	5713.33	3119.6	794.2	5813.33	3184.7	825.6	5913.33	3250.5	857.8
9	5715.00	3120.7	794.7	5815.00	3185.8	826.1	5915.00	3251.6	858.3
10	5716.67	3121.7	795.2	5816.67	3186.9	826.7	5916.67	3252.7	858.9
11	5718.33	3122.8	795.8	5818.33	3188.0	827.2	5918.33	3253.8	859.4
12	5720.00	3123.9	796.3	5820.00	3189.1	827.7	5920.00	3254.9	860.0
13	5721.67	3125.0	796.8	5821.67	3190.2	828.3	5921.67	3256.0	860.5
14	5723.33	3126.1	797.3	5823.33	3191.3	828.8	5923.33	3257.1	861.1
15	5725.00	3127.2	797.8	5825.00	3192.4	829.3	5925.00	3258.2	861.6
16	5726.67	3128.2	798.3	5826.67	3193.5	829.9	5926.67	3259.3	862.2
17	5728.33	3129.3	798.9	5828.33	3194.5	830.4	5928.33	3260.4	862.7
18	5730.00	3130.4	799.4	5830.00	3195.6	830.9	5930.00	3261.5	863.2
19	5731.67	3131.5	799.9	5831.67	3196.7	831.4	5931.67	3262.6	863.8
20	5733.33	3132.6	800.4	5833.33	3197.8	832.0	5933.33	3263.7	864.3
21	5735.00	3133.6	800.9	5835.00	3198.9	832.5	5935.00	3264.8	864.9
22	5736.67	3134.7	801.5	5836.67	3200.0	833.0	5936.67	3265.9	865.4
23	5738.33	3135.8	802.0	5838.33	3201.1	833.6	5938.33	3267.0	866.0
24	5740.00	3136.9	802.5	5840.00	3202.2	834.1	5940.00	3268.1	866.5
25	5741.67	3138.0	803.0	5841.67	3203.3	834.6	5941.67	3269.2	867.1
26	5743.33	3139.1	803.5	5843.33	3204.4	835.2	5943.33	3270.3	867.6
27	5745.00	3140.1	804.1	5845.00	3205.5	835.7	5945.00	3271.4	868.2
28	5746.67	3141.2	804.6	5846.67	3206.6	836.2	5946.67	3272.6	868.7
29	5748.33	3142.3	805.1	5848.33	3207.7	836.8	5948.33	3273.7	869.3
30	5750.00	3143.4	805.6	5850.00	3208.8	837.3	5950.00	3274.8	869.8
31	5751.67	3144.5	806.1	5851.67	3209.9	837.8	5951.67	3275.9	870.4
32	5753.33	3145.6	806.7	5853.33	3210.9	838.4	5953.33	3277.0	870.9
33	5755.00	3146.6	807.2	5855.00	3212.0	838.9	5955.00	3278.1	871.5
34	5756.67	3147.7	807.7	5856.67	3213.1	839.5	5956.67	3279.2	872.0
35	5758.33	3148.8	808.2	5858.33	3214.2	840.0	5958.33	3280.3	872.6
36	5760.00	3149.9	808.8	5860.00	3215.3	840.5	5960.00	3281.4	873.1
37	5761.67	3151.0	809.3	5861.67	3216.4	841.1	5961.67	3282.5	873.7
38	5763.33	3152.1	809.8	5863.33	3217.5	841.6	5963.33	3283.6	874.2
39	5765.00	3153.2	810.3	5865.00	3218.6	842.1	5965.00	3284.7	874.8
40	5766.67	3154.2	810.9	5866.67	3219.7	842.7	5966.67	3285.8	875.3
41	5768.33	3155.3	811.4	5868.33	3220.8	843.2	5968.33	3286.9	875.9
42	5770.00	3156.4	811.9	5870.00	3221.9	843.7	5970.00	3288.0	876.4
43	5771.67	3157.5	812.4	5871.67	3223.0	844.3	5971.67	3289.2	877.0
44	5773.33	3158.6	812.9	5873.33	3224.1	844.8	5973.33	3290.3	877.5
45	5775.00	3159.7	813.5	5875.00	3225.2	845.4	5975.00	3291.4	878.1
46	5776.67	3160.8	814.0	5876.67	3226.3	845.9	5976.67	3292.5	878.6
47	5778.33	3161.8	814.5	5878.33	3227.4	846.4	5978.33	3293.6	879.2
48	5780.00	3162.9	815.0	5880.00	3228.5	847.0	5980.00	3294.7	879.7
49	5781.67	3164.0	815.6	5881.67	3229.6	847.5	5981.67	3295.8	880.3
50	5783.33	3165.1	816.1	5883.33	3230.7	848.1	5983.33	3296.9	880.8
51	5785.00	3166.2	816.6	5885.00	3231.8	848.6	5985.00	3298.0	881.4
52	5786.67	3167.3	817.2	5886.67	3232.9	849.1	5986.67	3299.1	881.9
53	5788.33	3168.4	817.7	5888.33	3234.0	849.7	5988.33	3300.2	882.5
54	5790.00	3169.5	818.2	5890.00	3235.1	850.2	5990.00	3301.4	883.1
55	5791.67	3170.6	818.7	5891.67	3236.2	850.8	5991.67	3302.5	883.6
56	5793.33	3171.6	819.3	5893.33	3237.3	851.3	5993.33	3303.6	884.2
57	5795.00	3172.7	819.8	5895.00	3238.4	851.8	5995.00	3304.7	884.7
58	5796.67	3173.8	820.3	5896.67	3239.5	852.4	5996.67	3305.8	885.3
59	5798.33	3174.9	820.8	5898.33	3240.6	852.9	5998.33	3306.9	885.8

(All Definitions of Degree of Curve)

Min-utes	60°			61°			62°		
	Length L	Tan. T	Ext. E	Length L	Tan. T	Ext. E	Length L	Tan. T	Ext. E
0	6000.00	3308.0	886.4	6100.00	3375.0	920.1	6200.00	3442.7	954.8
1	6001.67	3309.1	886.9	6101.67	3376.1	920 7	6201.67	3443.9	955.3
2	6003.33	3310.2	887.5	6103.33	3377.3	921.3	6203.33	3445.0	955.9
3	6005.00	3311.3	888.1	6105.00	3378.4	921.9	6205.00	3446.1	956.5
4	6006.67	3312.5	888.6	6106.67	3379.5	922.4	6206.67	3447.3	957.1
5	6008.33	3313.6	889.2	6108.33	3380.6	923.0	6208.33	3448.4	957.7
6	6010.00	3314.7	889.7	6110.00	3381.8	923.6	6210.00	3449.5	958.3
7	6011.67	3315.8	890.3	6111.67	3382.9	924.1	6211.67	3450.7	958.8
8	6013.33	3316.9	890.8	6113.33	3384.0	924.7	6213.33	3451.8	959.4
9	6015.00	3318.0	891.4	6115.00	3385.1	925.3	6215.00	3452.9	960.0
10	6016.67	3319.1	891.9	6116.67	3386.3	925.8	6216.67	3454.1	960.6
11	6018.33	3320.2	892.5	6118.33	3387.4	926.4	6218.33	3455.2	961.2
12	6020.00	3321.4	893.1	6120.00	3388.5	927.0	6220.00	3456.5	961.8
13	6021.67	3322.5	893.6	6121.67	3389.6	927.6	6221.67	3457.5	962.4
14	6023.33	3323.6	894.2	6123.33	3390.8	928.1	6223.33	3458.6	963.0
15	6025.00	3324.7	894.7	6125.00	3391.9	928.7	6225.00	3459.8	963.5
16	6026.67	3325.8	895.3	6126.67	3393.0	929.3	6226.67	3460.9	964.1
17	6028.33	3326.9	895.9	6128.33	3394.1	929.9	6228.33	3462.0	964.7
18	6030.00	3328.0	896.4	6130.00	3395.3	930.4	6230.00	3463.2	965.3
19	6031.67	3329.2	897.0	6131.67	3396.4	931.0	6231.67	3464.3	965.9
20	6033.33	3330.3	897.5	6133.33	3397.5	931.6	6233.33	3465.4	966.5
21	6035.00	3331.4	898.1	6135.00	3398.6	932.2	6235.00	3466.6	967.1
22	6036.67	3332.5	898.7	6136.67	3399.8	932.7	6236.67	3467.7	967.7
23	6038.33	3333.6	899.2	6138.33	3400.9	933.3	6238.33	3468.9	968.2
24	6040.00	3334.7	899.8	6140.00	3402.0	933.9	6240.00	3470.0	968.8
25	6041.67	3335.9	900.3	6141.67	3403.1	934.5	6241.67	3471.1	969.4
26	6043.33	3337.0	900.9	6143.33	3404.3	935.0	6243.33	3472.3	970.0
27	6045.00	3338.1	901.5	6145.00	3405.4	935.6	6245.00	3473.4	970.6
28	6046.67	3339.2	902.0	6146.67	3406.5	936.2	6246.67	3474.6	971.2
29	6048.33	3340.3	902.6	6148.33	3407.7	936.8	6248.33	3475.7	971.8
30	6050.00	3341.4	903.2	6150.00	3408.8	937.3	6250.00	3476.8	972.4
31	6051.67	3342.6	903.7	6151.67	3409.9	937.9	6251.67	3478.0	973.0
32	6053.33	3343.7	904.3	6153.33	3411.0	938.5	6253.33	3479.1	973.6
33	6055.00	3344.8	904.8	6155.00	3412.2	939.1	6255.00	3480.3	974.2
34	6056.67	3345.9	905.4	6156.67	3413.3	939.7	6256.67	3481.4	974.8
35	6058.33	3347.0	906.0	6158.33	3414.4	940.2	6258.33	3482.5	975.3
36	6060.00	3348.1	906.5	6160.00	3415.6	940.8	6260.00	3483.7	975.9
37	6061.67	3349.3	907.1	6161.67	3416.7	941.4	6261.67	3484.8	976.5
38	6063.33	3350.4	907.7	6163.33	3417.8	942.0	6263.33	3486.0	977.1
39	6065.00	3351.5	908.2	6165.00	3418.9	942.5	6265.00	3487.1	977.7
40	6066.67	3352.6	908.8	6166.67	3420.1	943.1	6266.67	3488.3	978.3
41	6068.33	3353.7	909.4	6168.33	3421.2	943.7	6268.33	3489.4	978.9
42	6070.00	3354.8	909.9	6170.00	3422.3	944.3	6270.00	3490.5	979.5
43	6071.67	3356.0	910.5	6171.67	3423.5	944.9	6271.67	3491.7	980.1
44	6073.33	3357.1	911.1	6173.33	3424.6	945.4	6273.33	3492.8	980.7
45	6075.00	3358.2	911.6	6175.00	3425.7	946.0	6275.00	3494.0	981.3
46	6076.67	3359.3	912.2	6176.67	3426.9	946.6	6276.67	3495.1	981.9
47	6078.33	3360.4	912.8	6178.33	3428.0	947.2	6278.33	3496.2	982.5
48	6080.00	3361.6	913.3	6180.00	3429.1	947.8	6280.00	3497.4	983.1
49	6081.67	3362.7	913.9	6181.67	3430.3	948.3	6281.67	3498.5	983.7
50	6083.33	3363.8	914.5	6183.33	3431.4	948.9	6283.33	3499.7	984.3
51	6085.00	3364.9	915.0	6185.00	3432.5	949.5	6285.00	3500.8	984.9
52	6086.67	3366.0	915.6	6186.67	3433.7	950.1	6286.67	3502.0	985.5
53	6088.33	3367.2	916.2	6188.33	3434.8	950.7	6288.33	3503.1	986.1
54	6090.00	3368.3	916.7	6190.00	3435.9	951.3	6290.00	3504.3	986.7
55	6091.67	3369.4	917.3	6191.67	3437.1	951.8	6291.67	3505.4	987.3
56	6093.33	3370.5	917.9	6193.33	3438.2	952.4	6293.33	3506.6	987.9
57	6095.00	3371.7	918.4	6195.00	3439.3	953.0	6295.00	3507.7	988.4
58	6096.67	3372.8	918.0	6196.67	3440.5	953.6	6296.67	3508.8	989.0
59	6098.33	3373.9	919.6	6198.33	3441.6	954.2	6298.33	3510.0	989.6

(All Definitions of Degree of Curve)

Min-utes	63°			64°			65°		
	Length L	Tan. T	Ext. E	Length L	Tan. T	Ext. E	Length L	Tan. T	Ext. E
0	6300.00	3511.1	990.2	6400.00	3580.3	1026.6	6500.00	3650.2	1063.9
1	6301.67	3512.3	990.8	6401.67	3581.4	1027.2	6501.67	3651.4	1064.5
2	6303.33	3513.4	991.4	6403.33	3582.6	1027.8	6503.33	3652.5	1065.2
3	6305.00	3514.6	992.0	6405.00	3583.8	1028.5	6505.00	3653.7	1065.8
4	6306.67	3515.7	992.6	6406.67	3584.9	1029.1	6506.67	3654.9	1066.4
5	6308.33	3516.9	993.2	6408.33	3586.1	1029.7	6508.33	3656.1	1067.0
6	6310.00	3518.0	993.8	6410.00	3587.2	1030.3	6510.00	3657.2	1067.7
7	6311.67	3519.2	994.4	6411.67	3588.4	1030.9	6511.67	3658.4	1068.3
8	6313.33	3520.3	995.0	6413.33	3589.6	1031.6	6513.33	3659.6	1068.9
9	6315.00	3521.5	995.6	6415.00	3590.7	1032.2	6515.00	3660.7	1069.6
10	6316.67	3522.6	996.2	6416.67	3591.9	1032.8	6516.87	3661.9	1070.3
11	6318.33	3523.8	996.8	6418.33	3593.0	1033.4	6518.33	3663.1	1070.8
12	6320.00	3524.9	997.5	6420.00	3594.2	1034.0	6520.00	3664.3	1071.5
13	6321.67	3526.1	998.1	6421.67	3595.4	1034.7	6521.67	3665.4	1072.1
14	6323.33	3527.2	998.7	6423.33	3596.5	1035.3	6523.33	3666.6	1072.8
15	6325.00	3528.4	999.3	6425.00	3597.7	1035.9	6525.00	3667.8	1073.4
16	6326.67	3529.5	999.9	6426.67	3598.9	1036.5	6526.67	3669.0	1074.0
17	6328.33	3530.7	1000.5	6428.33	3600.0	1037.1	6528.33	3670.1	1074.7
18	6330.00	3531.8	1001.1	6430.00	3601.2	1037.8	6530.00	3671.3	1075.3
19	6331.67	3533.0	1001.7	6431.67	3602.3	1038.4	6531.67	3672.5	1076.0
20	6333.33	3534.1	1002.3	6433.33	3603.5	1039.0	6533.33	3673.7	1076.6
21	6335.00	3535.3	1002.9	6435.00	3604.7	1039.6	6535.00	3674.8	1077.2
22	6336.67	3536.4	1003.5	6436.67	3605.8	1040.2	6536.67	3676.0	1077.9
23	6338.33	3537.6	1004.1	6438.33	3607.0	1040.9	6538.33	3677.2	1078.5
24	6340.00	3538.7	1004.7	6440.00	3608.2	1041.5	6540.00	3678.4	1079.1
25	6341.67	3539.9	1005.3	6441.67	3609.3	1042.1	6541.67	3679.5	1079.7
26	6343.33	3541.0	1005.9	6443.33	3610.5	1042.7	6543.33	3680.7	1080.4
27	6345.00	3542.2	1006.5	6445.00	3611.6	1043.3	6545.00	3681.9	1081.0
28	6346.67	3543.3	1007.1	6446.67	3612.8	1044.0	6546.67	3683.1	1081.6
29	6348.33	3544.5	1007.7	6448.33	3614.0	1044.6	6548.33	3684.3	1082.3
39	6350.00	3545.6	1008.3	6450.00	3615.1	1045.2	6550.00	3685.4	1082.9
31	6351.67	3546.8	1008.9	6451.67	3616.3	1045.8	6551.67	3686.6	1083.5
32	6353.33	3547.9	1009.5	6453.33	3617.5	1046.4	6553.33	3687.8	1084.2
33	6355.00	3549.1	1010.1	6455.00	3618.6	1047.1	6555.00	3689.0	1084.8
34	6356.67	3550.2	1010.7	6456.67	3619.8	1047.7	6556.67	3690.1	1085.5
35	6358.33	3551.4	1011.3	6458.33	3621.0	1048.3	6558.33	3691.3	1086.1
36	6360.00	3552.5	1012.0	6460.00	3622.1	1048.9	6560.00	3692.5	1086.7
37	6361.67	3553.7	1012.6	6461.67	3623.3	1049.5	6561.67	3693.7	1087.4
38	6363.33	3554.8	1013.2	6463.33	3624.5	1050.2	6563.33	3694.9	1088.0
39	6365.00	3556.0	1013.8	6465.00	3625.6	1050.8	6565.00	3696.0	1088.7
40	6366.67	3557.2	1014.4	6466.67	3626.8	1051.4	6566.67	3697.2	1089.3
41	6368.33	3558.3	1015.0	6468.33	3628.0	1052.0	6568.33	3698.4	1089.9
42	6370.00	3559.5	1015.6	6470.00	3629.1	1052.7	6570.00	3699.6	1090.6
43	6371.67	3560.6	1016.2	6471.67	3630.3	1053.3	6571.67	3700.8	1091.2
44	6373.33	3561.8	1016.8	6473.33	3631.5	1053.9	6573.33	3702.0	1091.9
45	6375.00	3562.9	1017.4	6475.00	3632.6	1054.5	6575.00	3703.1	1092.5
46	6376.67	3564.1	1018.1	6476.67	3633.8	1055.2	6576.67	3704.3	1093.1
47	6378.33	3565.2	1018.7	6478.33	3635.0	1055.8	6578.33	3705.5	1093.8
48	6380.00	3566.4	1019.3	6480.00	3636.1	1056.4	6580.00	3706.7	1094.4
49	6381.67	3567.5	1019.9	6481.67	3637.3	1057.1	6581.67	3707.9	1095.1
50	6383.33	3568.7	1020.5	6483.33	3638.5	1057.7	6583.33	3709.0	1095.7
51	6385.00	3569.9	1021.1	6485.00	3639.7	1058.3	6585.00	3710.2	1096.3
52	6386.67	3571.0	1021.7	6486.67	3640.8	1058.9	6586.67	3711.4	1097.0
53	6388.33	3572.2	1022.3	6488.33	3642.0	1059.6	6588.33	3712.6	1097.6
54	6390.00	3573.3	1022.9	6490.00	3643.2	1060.2	6590.00	3713.8	1098.3
55	6391.67	3574.5	1023.5	6491.67	3644.3	1060.8	6591.67	3715.0	1098.9
56	6393.33	3575.7	1024.2	6493.33	3645.5	1061.4	6593.33	3716.1	1099.6
57	6395.00	3576.8	1024.8	6495.00	3646.7	1062.0	6595.00	3717.3	1100.2
58	6396.67	3578.0	1025.4	6496.67	3647.8	1062.7	6596.67	3718.5	1100.9
59	6398.33	3579.1	1026.0	6498.33	3649.0	1063.3	6598.33	3719.7	1101.5

(All Definitions of Degree of Curve)

Min-utes	66°			67°			68°		
	Length L	Tan. T	Ext. E	Length L	Tan. T	Ext. E	Length L	Tan. T	Ext. E
0	6600.00	3720.9	1102.2	6700.00	3792.4	1141.4	6800.00	3864.7	1181.6
1	6601.67	3722.1	1102.8	6701.67	3793.6	1142.1	6801.67	3865.9	1182.3
2	6603.33	3723.2	1103.5	6703.33	3794.8	1142.7	6803.33	3867.1	1183.0
3	6605.00	3724.4	1104.1	6705.00	3796.0	1143.4	6805.00	3868.3	1183.6
4	6606.67	3725.6	1104.8	6706.67	3797.2	1144.0	6806.67	3869.6	1184.3
5	6608.33	3726.8	1105.4	6708.33	3798.4	1144.7	6808.33	3870.8	1185.0
6	6610.00	3728.0	1106.0	6710.00	3799.6	1145.4	6810.00	3872.0	1185.7
7	6611.67	3729.2	1106.7	6711.67	3800.8	1146.0	6811.67	3873.2	1186.4
8	6613.33	3730.4	1107.3	6713.33	3802.0	1146.7	6813.33	3874.4	1187.0
9	6615.00	3731.6	1108.0	6715.00	3803.2	1147.3	6815.00	3875.6	1187.7
10	6616.67	3732.7	1108.6	6716.67	3804.4	1148.0	6816.67	3876.8	1188.4
11	6618.33	3733.9	1109.2	6718.33	3805.6	1148.7	6818.33	3878.1	1189.1
12	6620.00	3735.1	1109.9	6720.00	3806.8	1149.3	6820.00	3879.3	1189.8
13	6621.67	3736.3	1110.5	6721.67	3808.0	1150.0	6821.67	3880.5	1190.4
14	6623.33	3737.5	1111.2	6723.33	3809.2	1150.7	6823.33	3881.7	1191.1
15	6625.00	3738.7	1111.8	6725.00	3810.4	1151.3	6825.00	3882.9	1191.8
16	6626.67	3739.9	1112.5	6726.67	3811.6	1152.0	6826.67	3884.1	1192.5
17	6628.33	3741.1	1113.1	6728.33	3812.8	1152.7	6828.33	3885.3	1193.2
18	6630.00	3742.2	1113.8	6730.00	3814.0	1153.4	6830.00	3886.6	1193.8
19	6631.67	3743.4	1114.4	6731.67	3815.2	1154.0	6831.67	3887.8	1194.5
20	6633.33	3744.6	1115.1	6733.33	3816.4	1154.7	6833.33	3889.0	1195.2
21	6635.00	3745.8	1115.8	6735.00	3817.6	1155.4	6835.00	3890.2	1195.9
22	6636.67	3747.0	1116.4	6736.67	3818.8	1156.0	6836.67	3891.4	1196.6
23	6638.33	3748.2	1117.1	6738.33	3820.0	1156.7	6838.33	3892.6	1197.2
24	6640.00	3749.4	1117.7	6740.00	3821.2	1157.3	6840.00	3893.9	1197.9
25	6641.67	3750.6	1118.4	6741.67	3822.4	1158.0	6841.67	3895.1	1198.6
26	6643.33	3751.8	1119.1	6743.33	3823.6	1158.7	6843.33	3896.3	1199.3
27	6645.00	3752.9	1119.7	6745.00	3824.8	1159.3	6845.00	3897.5	1200.0
28	6646.67	3754.1	1120.4	6746.67	3826.0	1160.0	6846.67	3898.7	1200.6
29	6648.33	3755.3	1121.0	6748.33	3827.2	1160.6	6848.33	3900.0	1201.3
30	6650.00	3756.5	1121.7	6750.00	3828.4	1161.3	6850.00	3901.2	1202.0
31	6651.67	3757.7	1122.3	6751.67	3829.6	1162.0	6851.67	3902.4	1202.7
32	6653.33	3758.9	1123.0	6753.33	3830.8	1162.7	6853.33	3903.6	1203.4
33	6655.00	3760.1	1123.6	6755.00	3832.0	1163.3	6855.00	3904.8	1204.1
34	6656.67	3761.3	1124.3	6756.67	3833.3	1164.0	6856.67	3906.1	1204.8
35	6658.33	3762.5	1124.9	6758.33	3834.5	1164.7	6858.33	3907.3	1205.4
36	6660.00	3763.7	1125.6	6760.00	3835.7	1165.4	6860.00	3908.5	1206.1
37	6661.67	3764.9	1126.2	6761.67	3836.9	1166.1	6861.67	3909.7	1206.8
38	6663.33	3766.1	1126.9	6763.33	3838.1	1166.7	6863.33	3910.9	1207.5
39	6665.00	3767.3	1127.5	6765.00	3839.3	1167.4	6865.00	3912.2	1208.2
40	6666.67	3768.5	1128.2	6766.67	3840.5	1168.1	6866.67	3913.4	1208.9
41	6668.33	3769.6	1128.9	6768.33	3841.7	1168.8	6868.33	3914.6	1209.6
42	6670.00	3770.8	1129.5	6770.00	3842.9	1169.4	6870.00	3915.8	1210.3
43	6671.67	3772.0	1130.2	6771.67	3844.1	1170.1	6871.67	3917.1	1211.0
44	6673.33	3773.2	1130.8	6773.33	3845.3	1170.8	6873.33	3918.3	1211.7
45	6675.00	3774.4	1131.5	6775.00	3846.5	1171.4	6875.00	3919.5	1212.3
46	6676.67	3775.6	1132.2	6776.67	3847.7	1172.1	6876.67	3920.7	1213.0
47	6678.33	3776.8	1132.8	6778.33	3849.0	1172.8	6878.33	3921.9	1213.7
48	6680.00	3778.0	1133.5	6780.00	3850.2	1173.5	6880.00	3923.2	1214.4
49	6681.67	3779.2	1134.1	6781.67	3851.4	1174.1	6881.67	3924.4	1215.1
50	6683.33	3780.4	1134.8	6783.33	3852.6	1174.8	6883.33	3925.6	1215.8
51	6685.00	3781.6	1135.5	6785.00	3853.8	1175.5	6885.00	3926.8	1216.5
52	6686.67	3782.8	1136.1	6786.67	3855.0	1176.2	6886.67	3928.1	1217.2
53	6688.33	3784.0	1136.8	6788.33	3856.2	1176.8	6888.33	3929.3	1217.9
54	6690.00	3785.2	1137.4	6790.00	3857.4	1177.5	6890.00	3930.5	1218.6
55	6691.67	3786.4	1138.1	6791.67	3858.6	1178.2	6891.67	3931.7	1219.2
56	6693.33	3787.6	1138.8	6793.33	3859.8	1178.9	6893.33	3933.0	1219.9
57	6695.00	3788.8	1139.4	6795.00	3861.1	1179.6	6895.00	3934.2	1220.6
58	6696.67	3790.0	1140.1	6796.67	3862.3	1180.2	6896.67	3935.4	1221.3
59	6698.33	3791.2	1140.7	6798.33	3863.5	1180.9	6898.33	3936.7	1222.0

(All Definitions of Degree of Curve)

Min-utes	69° Length L	69° Tan. T	69° Ext. E	70° Length L	70° Tan. T	70° Ext. E	71° Length L	71° Tan. T	71° Ext. E
0	6900.00	3937.9	1222.7	7000.00	4011.9	1265.0	7100.00	4086.9	1308.2
1	6901.67	3939.1	1223.4	7001.67	4013.2	1265.7	7101.67	4088.2	1308.9
2	6903.33	3940.3	1224.1	7003.33	4014.4	1266.4	7103.33	4089.4	1309.7
3	6905.00	3941.6	1224.8	7005.00	4015.7	1267.1	7105.00	4090.7	1310.4
4	6906.67	3942.8	1225.5	7006.67	4016.9	1267.8	7106.67	4091.9	1311.2
5	6908.33	3944.0	1226.2	7008.33	4018.2	1268.5	7108.33	4093.2	1311.9
6	6910.00	3945.2	1226.9	7010.00	4019.4	1269.3	7110.00	4094.5	1312.6
7	6911.67	3946.5	1227.6	7011.67	4020.6	1270.0	7111.67	4095.7	1313.4
8	6913.33	3947.7	1228.3	7013.33	4021.9	1270.7	7113.33	4097.0	1314.1
9	6915.00	3948.9	1229.0	7015.00	4023.1	1271.4	7115.00	4098.2	1314.9
10	6916.67	3950.2	1229.7	7016.67	4024.4	1272.1	7116.67	4099.5	1315.5
11	6918.33	3951.4	1230.4	7018.33	4025.6	1272.8	7118.33	4100.8	1316.3
12	6920.00	3952.6	1231.1	7020.00	4026.9	1273.5	7120.00	4102.0	1317.1
13	6921.67	3953.9	1231.8	7021.67	4028.1	1274.3	7121.67	4103.3	1317.8
14	6923.33	3955.1	1232.5	7023.33	4029.4	1275.0	7123.33	4104.5	1318.5
15	6925.00	3956.3	1233.2	7025.00	4030.6	1275.7	7125.00	4105.8	1319.2
16	6926.67	3957.5	1233.9	7026.67	4031.8	1276.4	7126.67	4107.1	1320.0
17	6928.33	3958.8	1234.6	7028.33	4033.1	1277.1	7128.33	4108.3	1320.7
18	6930.00	3960.0	1235.3	7030.00	4034.3	1277.9	7130.00	4109.6	1321.4
19	6931.67	3961.2	1236.0	7031.67	4035.6	1278.6	7131.67	4110.9	1322.2
20	6933.33	3962.5	1236.7	7033.33	4036.8	1279.3	7133.33	4112.1	1322.9
21	6935.00	3963.7	1237.4	7035.00	4038.1	1280.0	7135.00	4113.4	1323.6
22	6936.67	3964.9	1238.1	7036.67	4039.3	1280.7	7136.67	4114.6	1324.4
23	6938.33	3966.2	1238.8	7038.33	4040.6	1281.5	7138.33	4115.9	1325.1
24	6940.00	3967.4	1239.5	7040.00	4041.8	1282.2	7140.00	4117.2	1325.9
25	6941.67	3968.6	1240.2	7041.67	4043.1	1282.9	7141.67	4118.4	1326.6
26	6943.33	3969.9	1240.9	7043.33	4044.3	1283.6	7143.33	4119.7	1327.3
27	6945.00	3971.1	1241.6	7045.00	4045.6	1284.3	7145.00	4121.0	1328.1
28	6946.67	3972.3	1242.3	7046.67	4046.8	1285.1	7146.67	4122.2	1328.8
29	6948.33	3973.6	1243.0	7048.33	4048.1	1285.8	7148.33	4123.5	1329.6
30	6950.00	3974.8	1243.7	7050.00	4049.3	1286.5	7150.00	4124.8	1330.3
31	6951.67	3976.0	1244.4	7051.67	4050.6	1287.2	7151.67	4126.0	1331.0
32	6953.33	3977.3	1245.1	7053.33	4051.8	1287.9	7153.33	4127.3	1331.8
33	6955.00	3978.5	1245.8	7055.00	4053.1	1288.6	7155.00	4128.6	1332.5
34	6956.67	3979.7	1246.5	7056.67	4054.3	1289.3	7156.67	4129.8	1333.3
35	6958.33	3981.0	1247.2	7058.33	4055.6	1290.0	7158.33	4131.1	1334.0
36	6960.00	3982.2	1248.0	7060.00	4056.8	1290.8	7160.00	4132.4	1334.7
37	6961.67	3983.4	1248.7	7061.67	4058.1	1291.5	7161.67	4133.6	1335.5
38	6963.33	3984.7	1249.4	7063.33	4059.3	1292.2	7163.33	4134.9	1336.2
39	6965.00	3985.9	1250.1	7065.00	4060.6	1292.9	7165.00	4136.2	1337.0
40	6966.67	3987.2	1250.8	7066.67	4061.8	1293.7	7166.67	4137.4	1337.7
41	6968.33	3988.4	1251.5	7068.33	4063.1	1294.3	7168.33	4138.7	1338.4
42	6970.00	3989.6	1252.2	7070.00	4064.3	1295.1	7170.00	4140.0	1339.2
43	6971.67	3990.9	1252.9	7071.67	4065.6	1295.8	7171.67	4141.2	1339.9
44	6973.33	3992.1	1253.6	7073.33	4066.8	1296.5	7173.33	4142.5	1340.7
45	6975.00	3993.3	1254.3	7075.00	4068.1	1297.2	7175.00	4143.8	1341.4
46	6976.67	3994.6	1255.1	7076.67	4069.3	1298.0	7176.67	4145.0	1342.1
47	6978.33	3995.8	1255.8	7078.33	4070.6	1298.7	7178.33	4146.3	1342.9
48	6980.00	3997.1	1256.5	7080.00	4071.9	1299.4	7180.00	4147.6	1343.6
49	6981.67	3998.3	1257.2	7081.67	4073.1	1300.2	7181.67	4148.8	1344.4
50	6983.33	3999.5	1257.9	7083.33	4074.4	1300.9	7183.33	4150.1	1345.1
51	6985.00	4000.8	1258.6	7085.00	4075.6	1301.6	7185.00	4151.4	1345.8
52	6986.67	4002.0	1259.3	7086.67	4076.9	1302.4	7186.67	4152.7	1346.6
53	6988.33	4003.3	1260.0	7088.33	4078.1	1393.1	7188.33	4153.9	1347.3
54	6990.00	4004.5	1260.7	7090.00	4079.4	1303.8	7190.00	4155.2	1348.1
55	6991.67	4005.7	1261.4	7091.67	4080.6	1304.5	7191.67	4156.5	1348.8
56	6993.33	4007.0	1262.2	7093.33	4081.9	1305.3	7193.33	4157.7	1349.6
57	6995.00	4008.2	1262.9	7095.00	4083.1	1306.0	7195.00	4159.0	1350.3
58	6996.67	4009.5	1263.6	7096.67	4084.4	1306.7	7196.67	4160.3	1351.1
59	6998.33	4010.7	1264.3	7098.33	4085.7	1307.5	7198.33	4161.6	1351.8

(All Definitions of Degree of Curve)

Min-utes	72°			73°			74°		
	Length L	Tan. T	Ext. E	Length L	Tan. T	Ext. E	Length L	Tan. T	Ext. E
0	7200.00	4162.8	1352.6	7300.00	4239.7	1398.0	7400.00	4317.6	1444.6
1	7201.67	4164.1	1353.3	7301.67	4241.0	1398.8	7401.67	4318.9	1445.4
2	7203.33	4165.4	1354.1	7303.33	4242.3	1399.5	7403.33	4320.2	1446.2
3	7205.00	4166.7	1354.8	7305.00	4243.6	1400.3	7405.00	4321.5	1447.0
4	7206.67	4167.9	1355.6	7306.67	4244.9	1401.1	7406.67	4322.8	1447.8
5	7208.33	4169.2	1356.3	7308.33	4246.2	1401.8	7408.33	4324.1	1448.5
6	7210.00	4170.5	1357.1	7310.00	4247.5	1402.6	7410.00	4325.4	1449.3
7	7211.67	4171.8	1357.8	7311.67	4248.8	1403.4	7411.67	4326.8	1450.1
8	7213.33	4173.0	1358.6	7313.33	4250.0	1404.2	7413.33	4328.1	1450.9
9	7215.00	4174.3	1359.3	7315.00	4251.3	1404.9	7415.00	4329.4	1451.7
10	7216.67	4175.6	1360.1	7316.67	4252.6	1405.7	7416.67	4330.7	1452.5
11	7218.33	4176.9	1360.8	7318.00	4253.9	1406.5	7418.33	4332.0	1453.3
12	7220.00	4178.1	1361.6	7320.00	4255.2	1407.3	7420.00	4333.3	1454.1
13	7221.67	4179.4	1362.3	7321.67	4256.5	1408.0	7421.67	4334.6	1454.9
14	7223.33	4180.7	1363.1	7323.33	4257.8	1408.8	7423.33	4335.9	1455.7
15	7225.00	4182.0	1363.8	7325.00	4259.1	1409.6	7425.00	4337.2	1456.4
16	7226.67	4183.2	1364.6	7326.67	4260.4	1410.4	7426.67	4338.5	1457.2
17	7228.33	4184.5	1365.3	7328.33	4261.7	1411.2	7428.33	4339.9	1458.0
18	7230.00	4185.8	1336.1	7330.00	4263.0	1411.9	7430.00	4341.2	1458.8
19	7231.67	4187.1	1366.8	7331.67	4264.3	1412.7	7431.67	4342.5	1459.6
20	7233.33	4188.4	1367.6	7333.33	4265.6	1413.5	7433.33	4343.8	1460.4
21	7235.00	4189.6	1338.4	7335.00	4266.9	1414.3	7435.00	4345.1	1461.2
22	7236.67	4190.9	1339.1	7336.67	4268.2	1415.0	7436.67	4346.4	1462.0
23	7238.33	4192.2	1339.9	7338.33	4269.5	1415.8	7438.33	4347.7	1462.8
24	7240.00	4193.5	1370.6	7340.00	4270.7	1416.6	7440.00	4349.0	1463.6
25	7241.67	4194.8	1371.4	7341.67	4272.0	1417.3	7441.67	4350.4	1464.4
26	7243.33	4196.0	1372.2	7343.33	4273.3	1418.1	7443.33	4351.7	1465.2
27	7245.00	4197.3	1372.9	7345.00	4274.6	1418.9	7445.00	4353.0	1466.0
28	7246.67	4198.6	1373.7	7346.67	4275.9	1419.7	7446.67	4354.3	1466.8
29	7248.33	4199.9	1374.4	7348.33	4277.2	1420.4	7448.33	4355.6	1467.6
30	7250.00	4201.2	1375.2	7350.00	4278.5	1421.2	7450.00	4356.9	1468.4
31	7251.67	4202.4	1376.0	7351.67	4279.8	1422.0	7451.67	4358.2	1469.2
32	7253.33	4203.7	1376.7	7353.33	4281.1	1422.8	7453.33	4359.6	1470.0
33	7255.00	4205.0	1377.5	7355.00	4282.4	1423.5	7455.00	4360.9	1470.8
34	7256.67	4206.3	1378.2	7356.67	4283.7	1424.3	7456.67	4362.2	1471.6
35	7258.33	4207.6	1379.0	7358.33	4285.0	1425.1	7458.33	4363.5	1472.4
36	7260.00	4208.8	1379.8	7360.00	4286.3	1425.9	7460.00	4364.8	1473.2
37	7261.67	4210.1	1380.5	7361.67	4287.6	1426.7	7461.67	4366.1	1474.0
38	7263.33	4211.4	1381.3	7363.33	4288.9	1427.4	7463.33	4367.5	1474.8
39	7265.00	4212.7	1382.0	7365.00	4290.2	1428.2	7465.00	4368.8	1475.6
40	7266.67	4214.0	1382.8	7366.67	4291.5	1429.0	7466.67	4370.1	1476.4
41	7268.33	4215.3	1383.6	7368.33	4292.8	1429.8	7468.33	4371.4	1477.2
42	7270.00	4216.5	1384.3	7370.00	4294.1	1430.6	7470.00	4372.7	1478.0
43	7271.67	4217.8	1385.1	7371.67	4295.4	1431.3	7471.67	4374.1	1478.8
44	7273.33	4219.1	1385.8	7373.33	4296.7	1432.1	7473.33	4375.4	1479.6
45	7275.00	4220.4	1386.6	7375.00	4298.0	1432.9	7475.00	4376.7	1480.4
46	7276.67	4221.7	1387.4	7376.67	4299.3	1433.7	7476.67	4378.0	1481.2
47	7278.33	4223.0	1388.1	7378.33	4300.6	1434.5	7478.33	4379.3	1482.0
48	7280.00	4224.3	1388.9	7380.00	4301.9	1435.2	7480.00	4380.6	1482.8
49	7281.67	4225.5	1389.6	7381.67	4303.2	1436.0	7481.67	4382.0	1483.6
50	7283.33	4226.8	1390.4	7383.33	4304.6	1436.8	7483.33	4383.3	1484.4
51	7285.00	4228.1	1391.2	7385.00	4305.9	1437.6	7485.00	4384.6	1485.2
52	7286.67	4229.4	1391.9	7386.67	4307.2	1438.4	7486.67	4385.9	1485.0
53	7288.33	4230.7	1392.7	7388.33	4308.5	1439.1	7488.33	4387.3	1486.8
54	7290.00	4232.0	1393.4	7390.00	4309.8	1439.9	7490.00	4388.6	1487.6
55	7291.67	4233.3	1394.2	7391.67	4311.1	1440.7	7491.67	4389.9	1488.4
56	7293.33	4234.6	1395.0	7393.33	4312.4	1441.5	7493.33	4391.2	1489.2
57	7295.00	4235.9	1395.7	7395.00	4313.7	1442.3	7495.00	4392.5	1490.0
58	7296.67	4237.1	1396.5	7396.67	4315.0	1443.0	7496.67	4393.9	1490.8
59	7298.33	4238.4	1397.2	7398.33	4316.3	1443.8	7498.33	4395.2	1491.6

(All Definitions of Degree of Curve)

Min-utes	75° Length L	75° Tan. T	75° Ext. E	76° Length L	76° Tan. T	76° Ext. E	77° Length L	77° Tan. T	77° Ext. E
0	7500.00	4396.5	1492.4	7600.00	4476.5	1541.4	7700.00	4557.6	1591.6
1	7501.67	4397.8	1493.2	7601.67	4477.8	1542.2	7701.67	4558.9	1592.4
2	7503.33	4399.2	1494.0	7603.33	4479.2	1543.1	7703.33	4560.3	1593.3
3	7505.00	4400.5	1494.8	7605.00	4480.5	1543.9	7705.00	4561.7	1594.1
4	7506.67	4401.8	1495.6	7606.67	4481.9	1544.7	7706.67	4563.0	1595.0
5	7508.33	4403.1	1496.4	7608.33	4483.2	1545.5	7708.33	4564.4	1595.8
6	7510.00	4404.5	1497.3	7610.00	4484.6	1546.4	7710.00	4565.7	1596.7
7	7511.67	4405.8	1498.1	7611.67	4485.9	1547.2	7711.67	4567.1	1597.5
8	7513.33	4407.1	1498.9	7613.33	4487.2	1548.0	7713.33	4568.5	1598.4
9	7515.00	4408.4	1499.7	7615.00	4488.6	1548.9	7715.00	4569.8	1599.2
10	7516.67	4409.8	1500.5	7616.67	4489.9	1549.7	7716.67	4571.2	1600.1
11	7518.33	4411.1	1501.3	7618.33	4491.3	1550.5	7718.33	4572.6	1600.9
12	7520.00	4412.4	1502.1	7620.00	4492.6	1551.4	7720.00	4573.9	1601.8
13	7521.67	4413.8	1502.9	7621.67	4494.0	1552.2	7721.67	4575.3	1602.6
14	7523.33	4415.1	1503.7	7623.33	4495.3	1553.0	7723.33	4576.6	1603.5
15	7525.00	4416.4	1504.5	7625.00	4496.7	1553.8	7725.00	4578.0	1604.3
16	7526.67	4417.7	1505.4	7626.67	4498.0	1554.7	7726.67	4579.4	1605.2
17	7528.33	4419.1	1506.2	7628.33	4499.4	1555.5	7728.33	4580.7	1606.0
18	7530.00	4420.4	1507.0	7630.00	4500.7	1556.3	7730.00	4582.1	1606.9
19	7531.67	4421.7	1507.8	7631.67	4502.0	1557.2	7731.67	4583.5	1607.7
20	7533.33	4423.1	1508.6	7633.33	4503.4	1558.0	7733.33	4584.8	1608.6
21	7535.00	4424.4	1509.4	7635.00	4504.7	1558.8	7735.00	4586.2	1609.4
22	7536.67	4425.7	1510.2	7636.67	4506.1	1559.7	7736.67	4587.6	1610.3
23	7538.33	4427.0	1511.0	7638.33	4507.4	1560.5	7738.33	4588.9	1611.1
24	7540.00	4428.4	1511.8	7640.00	4508.8	1561.3	7740.00	4590.3	1612.0
25	7541.67	4429.7	1512.6	7641.67	4510.1	1562.1	7741.67	4591.7	1612.8
26	7543.33	4431.0	1513.5	7643.33	4511.5	1563.0	7743.33	4593.1	1613.7
27	7545.00	4432.4	1514.3	7645.00	4512.8	1563.8	7745.00	4594.4	1614.5
28	7546.67	4433.7	1515.1	7646.67	4514.2	1564.6	7746.67	4595.8	1615.4
29	7548.33	4435.0	1515.9	7648.33	4515.5	1565.5	7748.33	4597.2	1616.2
30	7550.00	4436.4	1516.7	7650.00	4516.9	1566.3	7750.00	4598.5	1617.1
31	7551.67	4437.7	1517.5	7651.67	4518.2	1567.1	7751.67	4599.9	1618.0
32	7553.33	4439.0	1518.3	7653.33	4519.6	1568.0	7753.33	4601.3	1618.8
33	7555.00	4440.4	1519.2	7655.00	4520.9	1568.8	7755.00	4602.6	1619.7
34	7556.67	4441.7	1520.0	7656.67	4522.3	1569.7	7756.67	4604.0	1620.5
35	7558.33	4443.0	1520.8	7658.33	4523.7	1570.5	7758.33	4605.4	1621.4
36	7560.00	4444.4	1521.6	7660.00	4525.0	1571.3	7760.00	4606.8	1622.3
37	7561.67	4445.7	1522.4	7661.67	4526.4	1572.2	7761.67	4608.1	1623.1
38	7563.33	4447.0	1523.3	7663.33	4527.7	1573.0	7763.33	4609.5	1624.0
39	7565.00	4448.4	1524.1	7665.00	4529.1	1573.9	7765.00	4610.9	1624.8
40	7566.67	4449.7	1524.9	7666.67	4530.4	1574.7	7766.67	4612.2	1625.7
41	7568.33	4451.1	1525.7	7668.33	4531.8	1575.5	7768.33	4613.6	1626.6
42	7570.00	4452.4	1526.5	7670.00	4533.1	1576.4	7770.00	4615.0	1627.4
43	7571.67	4453.7	1527.4	7671.67	4534.5	1577.2	7771.67	4616.4	1628.3
44	7573.33	4455.1	1528.2	7673.33	4535.8	1578.1	7773.33	4617.7	1629.2
45	7575.00	4456.4	1529.0	7675.00	4537.2	1578.9	7775.00	4619.1	1630.0
46	7576.67	4457.7	1529.8	7676.67	4538.6	1579.7	7776.67	4620.5	1630.9
47	7578.33	4459.1	1530.6	7678.33	4539.9	1580.6	7778.33	4621.9	1631.8
48	7580.00	4460.4	1531.5	7680.00	4541.3	1581.4	7780.00	4623.2	1632.7
49	7581.67	4461.7	1532.3	7681.67	4542.6	1582.3	7781.67	4624.6	1633.5
50	7583.33	4463.1	1533.1	7683.33	4544.0	1583.1	7783.33	4626.0	1634.4
51	7585.00	4464.4	1533.9	7685.00	4545.3	1583.9	7785.00	4627.4	1635.3
52	7586.67	4465.8	1534.8	7686.67	4546.7	1584.8	7786.67	4628.8	1636.1
53	7588.33	4467.1	1535.6	7688.33	4548.1	1585.6	7788.33	4630.1	1637.0
54	7590.00	4468.4	1536.4	7690.00	4549.4	1586.5	7790.00	4631.5	1637.8
55	7591.67	4469.8	1537.2	7691.67	4550.8	1587.3	7791.67	4632.9	1638.7
56	7593.33	4471.1	1538.1	7693.33	4552.1	1588.2	7793.33	4634.3	1639.6
57	7595.00	4472.5	1538.9	7695.00	4553.5	1589.0	7795.00	4635.6	1640.4
58	7596.67	4473.8	1539.7	7696.67	4554.9	1589.9	7796.67	4637.0	1641.3
59	7598.33	4475.2	1540.6	7698.33	4556.2	1590.7	7798.33	4638.4	1642.1

(All Definitions of Degree of Curve)

Min-utes	78°			79°			80°		
	Length L	Tan. T	Ext. E	Length L	Tan. T	Ext. E	Length L	Tan. T	Ext. E
0	7800.00	4639.6	1643.0	7900.00	4723.2	1695.8	8000.00	4807.7	1749.9
1	7801.67	4341.2	1643.9	7901.67	4724.6	1696.7	8001.67	4809.2	1750.8
2	7803.33	4642.5	1344.7	7903.33	4726.0	1697.6	8003.33	4810.6	1751.7
3	7805.00	4343.9	1645.6	7905.00	4727.4	1698.5	8005.00	4812.0	1752.6
4	7806.67	4645.3	1646.5	7906.67	4728.8	1699.4	8006.67	4813.4	1753.5
5	7808.33	4646.7	1647.3	7908.33	4730.2	1700.2	8008.33	4814.9	1754.4
6	7810.00	4348.1	1648.2	7910.00	4731.6	1701.1	8010.00	4816.3	1755.4
7	7811.67	4649.4	1649.1	7911.67	4733.0	1702.0	8011.67	4817.7	1756.3
8	7813.33	4650.8	1650.0	7913.33	4734.4	1702.9	8013.33	4819.1	1757.2
9	7815.00	4652.2	1650.8	7915.00	4735.8	1703.8	8015.00	4820.5	1758.1
10	7816.67	4653.6	1651.7	7916.67	4737.2	1704.7	8016.67	4822.0	1759.0
11	7818.33	4355.0	1652.6	7918.33	4738.6	1705.6	8018.33	4823.4	1759.9
12	7820.00	4356.4	1653.5	7920.00	4740.0	1706.5	8020.00	4824.8	1760.8
13	7821.67	4357.7	1354.3	7921.67	4741.4	1707.4	8021.67	4826.2	1761.8
14	7823.33	4359.1	1655.2	7923.33	4742.8	1708.3	8023.33	4827.7	1762.7
15	7825.00	4660.5	1656.1	7925.00	4744.2	1709.2	8025.00	4829.1	1763.6
16	7826.67	4661.9	1657.0	7926.67	4745.6	1710.1	8026.67	4830.5	1764.5
17	7828.33	4663.3	1657.9	7928.33	4747.0	1711.0	8028.33	4831.9	1765.4
18	7830.00	4664.7	1658.7	7930.00	4748.4	1711.9	8030.00	4833.4	1766.4
19	7831.67	4666.1	1659.6	7931.67	4749.8	1712.8	8031.67	4834.8	1767.3
20	7833.33	4667.4	1660.5	7933.33	4751.2	1713.7	8033.33	4836.2	1768.2
21	7835.00	4668.8	1361.4	7935.00	4752.6	1714.6	8035.00	4837.6	1769.1
22	7836.67	4670.2	1662.2	7936.67	4754.0	1715.5	8036.67	4839.1	1770.0
23	7838.33	4671.6	1363.1	7938.33	4755.4	1716.4	8038.33	4840.5	1771.0
24	7840.00	4673.0	1664.0	7940.00	4756.8	1717.3	8040.00	4841.9	1771.9
25	7841.67	4674.4	1664.8	7941.67	4758.3	1718.2	8041.67	4843.4	1772.8
26	7843.33	4675.8	1665.7	7943.33	4759.7	1719.1	8043.33	4844.8	1773.7
27	7845.00	4677.2	1666.6	7945.00	4761.1	1720.0	8045.00	4846.2	1774.6
28	7846.67	4378.5	1667.5	7946.67	4762.5	1720.9	8046.67	4847.6	1775.6
29	7848.33	4679.9	1668.3	7948.33	4763.9	1721.8	8048.33	4849.1	1776.5
30	7850.00	4681.3	1669.2	7950.00	4765.3	1722.7	8050.00	4850.5	1777.4
31	7851.67	4082.7	1670.1	7951.67	4766.7	1723.6	8051.67	4851.9	1778.3
32	7853.33	4684.1	1671.0	7953.33	4768.1	1724.5	8053.33	4853.4	1779.3
33	7855.00	4385.5	1671.9	7955.00	4769.5	1725.4	8055.00	4854.8	1780.2
34	7856.67	4686.9	1672.8	7956.67	4770.9	1726.3	8056.67	4856.2	1781.1
35	7858.33	4688.3	1673.6	7958.33	4772.4	1727.2	8058.33	4857.7	1782.0
36	7860.00	4689.7	1674.5	7960.00	4773.8	1728.1	8060.00	4859.1	1783.0
37	7861.67	4691.1	1675.4	7961.67	4775.2	1729.0	8061.67	4860.5	1783.9
38	7863.33	4692.4	1676.3	7963.33	4776.6	1729.9	8063.33	4862.0	1784.8
39	7865.00	4693.8	1677.2	7965.00	4778.0	1730.8	8065.00	4863.4	1785.8
40	7866.67	4695.2	1678.1	7966.67	4779.4	1731.7	8066.67	4864.8	1786.7
41	7868.33	4696.6	1679.0	7968.33	4780.8	1732.6	8068.33	4866.3	1787.6
42	7870.00	4698.0	1679.9	7970.00	4782.2	1733.5	8070.00	4867.7	1788.6
43	7871.67	4699.4	1680.7	7971.67	4783.7	1734.4	8071.67	4869.1	1789.5
44	7873.33	4700.8	1681.6	7973.33	4785.1	1735.3	8073.33	4870.6	1790.4
45	7875.00	4702.2	1682.5	7975.00	4786.5	1736.2	8075.00	4872.0	1791.3
46	7876.67	4703.6	1683.4	7976.67	4787.9	1737.2	8076.67	4873.4	1792.3
47	7878.33	4705.0	1684.3	7978.33	4789.3	1738.1	8078.33	4874.9	1793.2
48	7880.00	4706.4	1685.1	7980.00	4790.7	1739.0	8080.00	4876.3	1794.1
49	7881.67	4707.8	1686.0	7981.67	4792.1	1739.9	8081.67	4877.8	1795.1
50	7883.33	4709.2	1686.9	7983.33	4793.6	1740.8	8083.33	4879.2	1796.0
51	7885.00	4710.6	1687.8	7985.00	4795.0	1741.7	8085.00	4880.6	1796.9
52	7886.67	4712.0	1688.7	7986.67	4796.4	1742.6	8086.67	4882.1	1797.9
53	7888.33	4713.4	1689.6	7988.33	4797.8	1743.5	8088.33	4883.5	1798.8
54	7890.00	4714.8	1690.5	7990.00	4799.2	1744.4	8090.00	4884.9	1799.7
55	7891.67	4716.2	1691.3	7991.67	4800.7	1745.3	8091.67	4886.4	1800.6
56	7892.33	4717.6	1692.2	7993.33	4802.1	1746.3	8093.33	4887.8	1801.6
57	7895.00	4719.0	1693.1	7995.00	4803.5	1747.2	8095.00	4889.3	1802.5
58	7896.67	4720.4	1694.0	7996.67	4804.9	1748.1	8096.67	4890.7	1803.4
59	7898.33	4721.8	1694.9	7998.33	4806.3	1749.0	8098.33	4892.1	1804.4

(All Definitions of Degree of Curve)

Min-utes	81°			82°			83°		
	Length L	Tan. T	Ext. E	Length L	Tan. T	Ext. E	Length L	Tan. T	Ext. E
0	8100.00	4893.6	1805.3	8200.00	4980.7	1862.2	8300.00	5069.2	1920.5
1	8101.67	4895.0	1806.2	8201.67	4982.2	1863.2	8301.67	5070.7	1921.5
2	8103.33	4896.5	1807.2	8203.33	4983.6	1864.1	8303.33	5072.1	1922.5
3	8105.00	4897.9	1808.1	8205.00	4985.1	1865.1	8305.00	5073.6	1923.5
4	8106.67	4899.4	1809.1	8206.67	4986.6	1866.0	8306.67	5075.1	1924.5
5	8108.33	4900.8	1810.0	8208.33	4988.0	1867.0	8308.33	5076.6	1925.4
6	8110.00	4902.2	1810.9	8210.00	4989.5	1868.0	8310.00	5078.1	1926.4
7	8111.67	4903.7	1811.9	8211.67	4991.0	1868.9	8311.67	5079.6	1927.4
8	8113.33	4905.1	1812.8	8213.33	4992.4	1869.9	8313.33	5081.1	1928.4
9	8115.00	4906.6	1813.8	8215.00	4993.9	1870.8	8315.00	5082.6	1929.4
10	8116.67	4908.0	1814.7	8216.67	4995.4	1871.8	8316.67	5084.0	1930.4
11	8118.33	4909.5	1815.6	8218.33	4996.8	1872.8	8318.33	5085.5	1931.4
12	8120.00	4910.9	1816.6	8220.00	4998.3	1873.7	8320.00	5087.0	1932.4
13	8121.67	4912.4	1817.5	8221.67	4999.8	1874.7	8321.67	5088.5	1933.4
14	8123.33	4913.8	1818.5	8223.33	5001.2	1875.7	8323.33	5090.0	1934.4
15	8125.00	4915.2	1819.4	8225.00	5002.7	1876.6	8325.00	5091.5	1935.3
16	8126.67	4916.7	1820.3	8226.67	5004.2	1877.6	8326.67	5093.0	1936.3
17	8128.33	4918.1	1821.3	8228.33	5005.6	1878.6	8328.33	5094.5	1937.3
18	8130.00	4919.6	1822.2	8230.00	5007.1	1879.6	8330.00	5096.0	1938.3
19	8131.67	4921.0	1823.2	8231.67	5008.6	1880.5	8331.67	5097.5	1939.3
20	8133.33	4922.5	1824.1	8233.33	5010.0	1881.5	8333.33	5099.0	1940.3
21	8135.00	4923.9	1825.0	8235.00	5011.5	1882.5	8335.00	5100.4	1941.3
22	8136.67	4925.4	1826.0	8236.67	5013.0	1883.4	8336.67	5101.9	1942.3
23	8138.33	4926.8	1826.9	8238.33	5014.5	1884.4	8338.33	5103.4	1943.3
24	8140.00	4928.3	1827.9	8240.00	5015.9	1885.4	8340.00	5104.9	1944.3
25	8141.67	4929.7	1828.8	8241.67	5017.4	1886.3	8341.67	5106.4	1945.3
26	8143.33	4931.2	1829.8	8243.33	5018.9	1887.3	8343.33	5107.9	1946.3
27	8145.00	4932.6	1830.7	8245.00	5020.3	1888.3	8345.00	5109.4	1947.3
28	8146.67	4934.1	1831.7	8246.67	5021.8	1889.3	8346.67	5110.9	1948.3
29	8148.33	4935.5	1832.6	8248.33	5023.3	1890.2	8348.33	5112.4	1949.3
30	8150.00	4937.0	1833.6	8250.00	5024.8	1891.2	8350.00	5113.9	1950.3
31	8151.67	4938.4	1834.5	8251.67	5026.2	1892.2	8351.67	5115.4	1951.3
32	8153.33	4939.9	1835.5	8253.33	5027.7	1893.1	8353.33	5116.9	1952.3
33	8155.00	4941.3	1836.4	8255.00	5029.2	1894.1	8355.00	5118.4	1953.3
34	8156.67	4942.8	1837.4	8256.67	5030.7	1895.1	8356.67	5119.9	1954.3
35	8158.33	4944.2	1838.3	8258.33	5032.1	1896.0	8358.33	5121.4	1955.2
36	8160.00	4945.7	1839.3	8260.00	5033.6	1897.0	8360.00	5122.9	1956.2
37	8161.67	4947.2	1840.2	8261.67	5035.1	1898.0	8361.67	5124.4	1957.2
38	8163.33	4948.6	1841.2	8263.33	5036.6	1899.0	8363.33	5125.9	1958.2
39	8165.00	4950.1	1842.1	8265.00	5038.1	1900.0	8365.00	5127.4	1959.2
40	8166.67	4951.5	1843.1	8266.67	5039.5	1900.9	8366.67	5128.9	1960.2
41	8168.33	4953.0	1844.0	8268.33	5041.0	1901.9	8368.33	5130.4	1961.2
42	8170.00	4954.4	1845.0	8270.00	5042.5	1902.9	8370.00	5131.9	1962.2
43	8171.67	4955.9	1845.9	8271.67	5044.0	1903.8	8371.67	5133.4	1963.2
44	8173.33	4957.3	1846.9	8273.33	5045.4	1904.8	8373.33	5134.9	1964.2
45	8175.00	4958.8	1847.8	8275.00	5046.9	1905.8	8375.00	5136.4	1965.2
46	8176.67	4960.3	1848.8	8276.67	5048.4	1906.8	8376.67	5137.9	1966.3
47	8178.33	4961.7	1849.7	8278.33	5049.9	1907.8	8378.33	5139.4	1967.3
48	8180.00	4963.2	1850.7	8280.00	5051.4	1908.7	8380.00	5140.9	1968.3
49	8181.67	4964.6	1851.6	8281.67	5052.8	1909.7	8381.67	5142.4	1969.3
50	8183.33	4966.1	1852.6	8283.33	5054.3	1910.7	8383.33	5143.9	1970.3
51	8185.00	4967.6	1853.6	8285.00	5055.8	1911.7	8385.00	5145.4	1971.3
52	8186.67	4969.0	1854.5	8286.67	5057.3	1912.7	8386.67	5146.9	1972.3
53	8188.33	4970.5	1855.5	8288.33	5058.8	1913.6	8388.33	5148.4	1973.3
54	8190.00	4971.9	1856.4	8290.00	5060.3	1914.6	8390.00	5150.0	1974.3
55	8191.67	4973.4	1857.4	8291.67	5061.7	1915.6	8391.67	5151.5	1975.3
56	8193.33	4974.9	1858.4	8293.33	5063.2	1916.6	8393.33	5153.0	1976.4
57	8195.00	4976.3	1859.3	8295.00	5064.7	1917.6	8395.00	5154.5	1977.4
58	8196.67	4977.8	1860.3	8296.67	5066.2	1918.5	8396.67	5156.0	1978.4
59	8198.33	4979.2	1861.2	8298.33	5067.7	1919.5	8398.33	5157.5	1979.4

(All Definitions of Degree of Curve)

Min-utes	84° Length L	84° Tan. T	84° Ext. E	85° Length L	85° Tan. T	85° Ext. E	86° Length L	86° Tan. T	86° Ext. E
0	8400.00	5159.0	1980.4	8500.00	5250.3	2041.6	8600.00	5343.0	2104.7
1	8401.67	5160.5	1981.4	8501.67	5251.8	2042.7	8601.67	5344.5	2105.8
2	8403.33	5162.0	1982.4	8503.33	5253.3	2043.8	8603.33	5346.1	2106.8
3	8405.00	5163.5	1983.4	8505.00	5254.9	2044.8	8605.00	5347.7	2107.9
4	8406.67	5165.0	1984.4	8506.67	5256.4	2045.9	8606.67	5349.2	2108.9
5	8408.33	5166.6	1985.4	8508.33	5257.9	2046.9	8608.33	5350.8	2110.0
6	8410.00	5168.1	1986.5	8510.00	5259.5	2047.9	8610.00	5352.3	2111.1
7	8411.67	5169.6	1987.5	8511.67	5261.0	2049.0	8611.67	5353.9	2112.1
8	8413.33	5171.1	1988.5	8513.33	5262.5	2050.0	8613.33	5355.5	2113.2
9	8415.00	5172.6	1989.5	8515.00	5264.1	2051.1	8615.00	5357.0	2114.2
10	8416.67	5174.1	1990.5	8516.67	5265.6	2052.1	8616.67	5358.6	2115.3
11	8418.33	5175.6	1991.5	8518.33	5267.1	2053.1	8618.33	5360.1	2116.4
12	8420.00	5177.1	1992.5	8520.00	5268.7	2054.2	8620.00	5361.7	2117.4
13	8421.67	5178.7	1993.5	8521.67	5270.2	2055.2	8621.67	5363.3	2118.5
14	8423.33	5180.2	1994.5	8523.33	5271.8	2056.3	8623.33	5364.8	2119.6
15	8425.00	5181.7	1995.5	8525.00	5273.3	2057.3	8625.00	5366.4	2120.6
16	8426.67	5183.2	1996.6	8526.67	5274.8	2058.3	8626.67	5368.0	2121.7
17	8428.33	5184.7	1997.6	8528.33	5276.4	2059.4	8628.33	5369.5	2122.8
18	8430.00	5186.2	1998.6	8530.00	5277.9	2060.4	8630.00	5371.1	2123.9
19	8431.67	5187.7	1999.6	8531.67	5279.5	2061.5	8631.67	5372.7	2124.9
20	8433.33	5189.3	2000.6	8533.33	5281.0	2062.5	8633.33	5374.2	2126.0
21	8435.00	5190.8	2001.6	8535.00	5282.5	2063.5	8635.00	5375.8	2127.1
22	8436.67	5192.3	2002.6	8536.67	5284.1	2064.6	8636.67	5377.4	2128.1
23	8438.33	5193.8	2003.7	8538.33	5285.6	2065.6	8638.33	5378.9	2129.2
24	8440.00	5195.3	2004.7	8540.00	5287.2	2066.7	8640.00	5380.5	2130.3
25	8441.67	5196.8	2005.7	8541.67	5288.7	2067.7	8641.67	5382.1	2131.3
26	8443.33	5198.4	2006.7	8543.33	5290.3	2068.8	8643.33	5383.6	2132.4
27	8445.00	5199.9	2007.7	8545.00	5291.8	2069.8	8645.00	5385.2	2133.5
28	8446.67	5201.4	2008.8	8546.67	5293.4	2070.9	8646.67	5386.8	2134.6
29	8448.33	5202.9	2009.8	8548.33	5294.9	2071.9	8648.33	5388.3	2135.6
30	8450.00	5204.5	2010.8	8550.00	5296.4	2073.0	8650.00	5389.9	2136.7
31	8451.67	5206.0	2011.8	8551.67	5298.0	2074.0	8651.67	5391.5	2137.8
32	8453.33	5207.5	2012.9	8553.33	5299.5	2075.1	8653.33	5393.1	2138.9
33	8455.00	5209.0	2013.9	8555.00	5301.1	2076.1	8655.00	5394.6	2139.9
34	8456.67	5210.5	2014.9	8556.67	5302.6	2077.2	8656.67	5396.2	2141.0
35	8458.33	5212.1	2015.9	8558.33	5304.2	2078.2	8658.33	5397.8	2142.1
36	8460.00	5213.6	2017.0	8560.00	5305.7	2079.3	8660.00	5399.3	2143.2
37	8461.67	5215.1	2018.0	8561.67	5307.3	2080.3	8661.67	5400.9	2144.3
38	8463.33	5216.6	2019.0	8563.33	5308.8	2081.4	8663.33	5402.5	2145.3
39	8465.00	5218.2	2020.1	8565.00	5310.4	2082.4	8665.00	5404.1	2146.4
40	8466.67	5219.7	2021.1	8566.67	5311.9	2083.5	8666.67	5405.6	2147.5
41	8468.33	5221.2	2022.1	8568.33	5313.5	2084.6	8668.33	5407.2	2148.6
42	8470.00	5222.7	2023.2	8570.00	5315.0	2085.6	8670.00	5408.8	2149.7
43	8471.67	5224.2	2024.2	8571.67	5316.6	2086.7	8671.67	5410.4	2150.8
44	8473.33	5225.8	2025.2	8573.33	5318.1	2087.7	8673.33	5412.0	2151.9
45	8475.00	5227.3	2026.2	8575.00	5319.7	2088.8	8675.00	5413.5	2152.9
46	8476.67	5228.8	2027.3	8576.67	5321.2	2089.9	8676.67	5415.1	2154.0
47	8478.33	5230.4	2028.3	8578.33	5322.8	2090.9	8678.33	5416.7	2155.1
48	8480.00	5231.9	2029.3	8580.00	5324.3	2092.0	8680.00	5418.3	2156.2
49	8481.67	5233.4	2030.4	8581.67	5325.9	2093.0	8681.67	5419.8	2157.3
50	8483.33	5234.9	2031.4	8583.33	5327.4	2094.1	8683.33	5421.4	2158.4
51	8485.00	5236.5	2032.4	8585.00	5329.0	2095.2	8685.00	5423.0	2159.5
52	8486.67	5238.0	2033.5	8586.67	5330.5	2096.2	8686.67	5424.6	2160.6
53	8488.33	5239.5	2034.5	8588.33	5332.1	2097.3	8688.33	5426.2	2161.6
54	8490.00	5241.1	2035.5	8590.00	5333.6	2098.3	8690.00	5427.7	2162.7
55	8491.67	5242.6	2036.5	8591.67	5335.2	2099.4	8691.67	5429.3	2163.8
56	8493.33	5244.1	2037.6	8593.33	5336.7	2100.5	8693.33	5430.9	2164.9
57	8495.00	5245.7	2038.6	8595.00	5338.3	2101.5	8695.00	5432.5	2166.0
58	8496.67	5247.2	2039.6	8596.67	5339.9	2102.6	8696.67	5434.1	2167.0
59	8498.33	5248.7	2040.7	8598.33	5341.4	2103.6	8698.33	5435.7	2168.1

(All Definitions of Degree of Curve)

Min-utes	87° Length L	87° Tan. T	87° Ext. E	88° Length L	88° Tan. T	88° Ext. E	89° Length L	89° Tan. T	89° Ext. E
0	8700.00	5437.2	2169.2	8800.00	5533.1	2235.5	8900.00	5630.5	2303.5
1	8701.67	5438.8	2170.3	8801.67	5534.7	2236.6	8901.67	5632.2	2304.6
2	8703.33	5440.4	2171.4	8803.33	5536.3	2237.7	8903.33	5633.8	2305.8
3	8705.00	5442.0	2172.5	8805.00	5537.9	2238.9	8905.00	5635.4	2306.9
4	8706.67	5443.6	2173.6	8806.67	5539.5	2240.0	8906.67	5637.1	2308.1
5	8708.33	5445.2	2174.7	8808.33	5541.1	2241.1	8908.33	5638.7	2309.2
6	8710.00	5446.7	2175.8	8810.00	5542.7	2242.2	8910.00	5640.3	2310.4
7	8711.67	5448.3	2176.9	8811.67	5544.3	2243.3	8911.67	5642.0	2311.5
8	8713.33	5449.9	2178.0	8813.33	5546.0	2244.5	8913.33	5643.6	2312.7
9	8715.00	5451.5	2179.1	8815.00	5547.6	2245.6	8915.00	5645.3	2313.8
10	8716.67	5453.1	2180.2	8816.67	5549.2	2246.7	8916.67	5646.9	2315.0
11	8718.33	5454.7	2181.3	8818.33	5550.8	2247.8	8918.33	5648.6	2316.2
12	8720.00	5456.3	2182.4	8820.00	5552.4	2249.0	8920.00	5650.2	2317.3
13	8721.67	5457.9	2183.5	8821.67	5554.0	2250.1	8921.67	5651.8	2318.5
14	8723.33	5459.5	2184.6	8823.33	5555.7	2251.2	8923.33	5653.5	2319.6
15	8725.00	5461.0	2185.6	8825.00	5557.3	2252.3	8925.00	5655.1	2320.8
16	8726.67	5462.6	2186.7	8826.67	5558.9	2253.5	8926.67	5656.8	2322.0
17	8728.33	5464.2	2187.8	8828.33	5560.5	2254.6	8928.33	5658.4	2323.1
18	8730.00	5465.8	2188.9	8830.00	5562.1	2255.7	8930.00	5660.1	2324.3
19	8731.67	5467.4	2190.0	8831.67	5563.7	2256.9	8931.67	5661.7	2325.4
20	8733.33	5469.0	2191.1	8833.33	5565.4	2258.0	8933.33	5663.4	2326.6
21	8735.00	5470.6	2192.2	8835.00	5567.0	2259.1	8935.00	5665.0	2327.8
22	8736.67	5472.2	2193.3	8836.67	5568.6	2260.3	8936.67	5666.7	2328.9
23	8738.33	5473.8	2194.4	8838.33	5570.2	2261.4	8938.33	5668.3	2330.1
24	8740.00	5475.4	2195.5	8840.00	5571.8	2262.5	8940.00	5670.0	2331.2
25	8741.67	5477.0	2196.6	8841.67	5573.5	2263.6	8941.67	5671.6	2332.4
26	8743.33	5478.6	2197.8	8843.33	5575.1	2264.8	8943.33	5673.3	2333.6
27	8745.00	5480.2	2198.9	8845.00	5576.7	2265.9	8945.00	5674.9	2334.7
28	8746.67	5481.8	2200.0	8846.67	5578.3	2267.0	8946.67	5676.6	2335.9
29	8748.33	5483.4	2201.1	8848.33	5580.0	2268.2	8948.33	5678.2	2337.0
30	8750.00	5484.9	2202.2	8850.00	5581.6	2269.3	8950.00	5679.9	2338.2
31	8751.67	5486.5	2203.3	8851.67	5583.2	2270.4	8951.67	5681.5	2339.4
32	8753.33	5488.1	2204.4	8853.33	5584.8	2271.6	8953.33	5683.2	2340.5
33	8755.00	5489.7	2205.5	8855.00	5586.5	2272.7	8955.00	5684.8	2341.7
34	8756.67	5491.3	2206.6	8856.67	5588.1	2273.8	8956.67	5686.5	2342.8
35	8758.33	5492.9	2207.7	8858.33	5589.7	2274.9	8958.33	5688.1	2344.0
36	8760.00	5494.5	2208.8	8860.00	5591.3	2276.1	8960.00	5689.8	2345.2
37	8761.67	5496.1	2209.9	8861.67	5593.0	2277.2	8961.67	5691.4	2346.3
38	8763.33	5497.7	2211.0	8863.33	5594.6	2278.3	8963.33	5693.1	2347.5
39	8765.00	5499.3	2212.1	8865.00	5596.2	2279.5	8965.00	5694.8	2348.6
40	8766.67	5500.9	2213.2	8866.67	5597.9	2280.6	8966.67	5696.4	2349.8
41	8768.33	5502.5	2214.3	8868.33	5599.5	2281.7	8968.33	5698.1	2351.0
42	8770.00	5504.1	2215.4	8870.00	5601.1	2282.9	8970.00	5699.7	2352.1
43	8771.67	5505.7	2216.5	8871.67	5602.7	2284.0	8971.67	5701.4	2353.3
44	8773.33	5507.3	2217.6	8873.33	5604.4	2285.2	8973.33	5703.0	2354.5
45	8775.00	5509.0	2218.7	8875.00	5606.0	2286.3	8975.00	5704.7	2355.6
46	8776.67	5510.6	2219.9	8876.67	5607.6	2287.4	8976.67	5706.4	2356.8
47	8778.33	5512.2	2221.0	8878.33	5609.3	2288.6	8978.33	5708.0	2358.0
48	8780.00	5513.8	2221.1	8880.00	5610.9	2289.7	8980.00	5709.7	2359.2
49	8781.67	5515.4	2223.2	8881.67	5612.5	2290.9	8981.67	5711.3	2360.3
50	8783.33	5517.0	2224.3	8883.33	5614.2	2292.0	8983.33	5713.0	2361.5
51	8785.00	5518.6	2225.4	8885.00	5615.8	2293.1	8985.00	5714.7	2362.7
52	8786.67	5520.2	2226.5	8886.67	5617.4	2294.3	8986.67	5716.3	2363.9
53	8788.33	5521.8	2227.7	8888.33	5619.1	2295.4	8988.33	5718.0	2365.0
54	8790.00	5523.4	2228.8	8890.00	5620.7	2296.6	8990.00	5719.7	2366.2
55	8791.67	5525.0	2229.9	8891.67	5622.3	2297.7	8991.67	5721.3	2367.4
56	8793.33	5526.6	2231.0	8893.33	5624.0	2298.9	8993.33	5723.0	2368.6
57	8795.00	5528.2	2232.1	8895.00	5625.6	2300.0	8995.00	5724.7	2369.8
58	8796.67	5529.8	2233.3	8896.67	5627.2	2301.2	8996.67	5726.3	2370.9
59	8798.33	5531.4	2234.4	8898.33	5628.9	2302.3	8998.33	5728.0	2372.1

(All Definitions of Degree of Curve)

Min-utes	90°			91°			92°		
	Length L	Tan. T	Ext. E	Length L	Tan. T	Ext. E	Length L	Tan. T	Ext. E
0	9000.00	5729.7	2373.3	9100.00	5830.5	2444.9	9200.00	5933.2	2518.5
1	9001.67	5731.3	2374.5	9101.67	5832.2	2446.1	9201.67	5935.0	2519.7
2	9003.33	5733.0	2375.7	9103.33	5833.9	2447.3	9203.33	5936.7	2521.0
3	9005.00	5734.7	2376.8	9105.00	5835.6	2448.6	9205.00	5938.4	2522.2
4	9006.67	5736.3	2378.0	9106.67	5837.3	2449.8	9206.67	5940.1	2523.5
5	9008.33	5738.0	2379.2	9108.33	5839.0	2451.0	9208.33	5941.9	2524.7
6	9010.00	5739.7	2380.4	9110.00	5840.7	2452.2	9210.00	5943.6	2526.0
7	9011.67	5741.3	2381.6	9111.67	5842.4	2453.4	9211.67	5945.3	2527.2
8	9013.33	5743.0	2382.7	9113.33	5844.1	2454.7	9213.33	5947.1	2528.5
9	9015.00	5744.7	2383.9	9115.00	5845.8	2455.9	9215.00	5948.8	2529.7
10	9016.67	5746.3	2385.1	9116.67	5847.5	2457.1	9216.67	5950.5	2531.0
11	9018.33	5748.0	2386.3	9118.33	5849.2	2458.3	9218.33	5952.3	2532.2
12	9020.00	5749.7	2387.5	9120.00	5850.9	2459.5	9220.00	5954.0	2533.5
13	9021.67	5751.4	2388.7	9121.67	5852.6	2460.8	9221.67	5955.7	2534.7
14	9023.33	5753.0	2389.9	9123.33	5854.3	2462.0	9223.33	5957.5	2536.0
15	9025.00	5754.7	2391.0	9125.00	5856.0	2463.2	9225.00	5959.2	2537.2
16	9026.67	5756.4	2392.2	9126.67	5857.7	2464.4	9226.67	5960.9	2538.5
17	9028.33	5758.1	2393.4	9128.33	5859.4	2465.6	9228.33	5962.7	2539.7
18	9030.00	5759.7	2394.6	9130.00	5861.1	2466.9	9230.00	5964.4	2541.0
19	9031.67	5761.4	2395.8	9131.67	5862.9	2468.1	9231.67	5966.1	2542.2
20	9033.33	5763.1	2397.0	9133.33	5864.6	2469.3	9233.33	5967.9	2543.5
21	9035.00	5764.8	2398.2	9135.00	5866.3	2470.5	9235.00	5969.6	2544.7
22	9036.67	5766.4	2399.4	9136.67	5868.0	2471.7	9236.67	5971.3	2546.0
23	9038.33	5768.1	2400.6	9138.33	5869.7	2473.0	9238.33	5973.1	2547.2
24	9040.00	5769.8	2401.8	9140.00	5871.4	2474.2	9240.00	5974.8	2548.5
25	9041.67	5771.5	2402.9	9141.67	5873.1	2475.4	9241.67	5976.6	2549.7
26	9043.33	5773.2	2404.1	9143.33	5874.8	2476.6	9243.33	5978.3	2551.0
27	9045.00	5774.8	2405.3	9145.00	5876.5	2477.8	9245.00	5980.0	2552.2
28	9046.67	5776.5	2406.5	9146.67	5878.2	2479.1	9246.67	5981.8	2553.5
29	9048.33	5778.2	2407.7	9148.33	5879.9	2480.3	9248.33	5983.5	2554.7
30	9050.00	5779.9	2408.9	9150.00	5881.7	2481.5	9250.00	5985.3	2556.0
31	9051.67	5781.6	2410.1	9151.67	5883.4	2482.7	9251.67	5987.0	2557.3
32	9053.33	5783.2	2411.3	9153.33	5885.1	2484.0	9253.33	5988.8	2558.5
33	9055.00	5784.9	2412.5	9155.00	5886.8	2485.2	9255.00	5990.5	2559.8
34	9056.67	5786.6	2413.7	9156.67	5888.5	2486.4	9256.67	5992.2	2561.0
35	9058.33	5788.3	2414.9	9158.33	5890.2	2487.6	9258.33	5994.0	2562.3
36	9060.00	5790.0	2416.1	9160.00	5891.9	2488.9	9260.00	5995.7	2563.6
37	9061.67	5791.7	2417.3	9161.67	5893.6	2490.1	9261.67	5997.5	2564.8
38	9063.33	5793.3	2418.5	9163.33	5895.4	2491.3	9263.33	5999.2	2566.1
39	9065.00	5795.0	2419.7	9165.00	5897.1	2492.6	9265.00	6001.0	2567.3
40	9066.67	5796.7	2420.9	9166.67	5898.8	2493.8	9266.67	6002.7	2568.6
41	9068.33	5798.4	2122.1	9168.33	5900.5	2495.0	9268.33	6004.5	2569.9
42	9070.00	5800.1	2423.3	9170.00	5902.2	2496.3	9270.00	6006.2	2571.1
43	9071.67	5801.8	2424.5	9171.67	5903.9	2497.5	9271.67	6008.0	2572.4
44	9073.33	5803.5	2425.7	9173.33	5905.7	2498.7	9273.33	6009.7	2573.7
45	9075.00	5805.1	2426.9	9175.00	5907.4	2499.9	9275.00	6011.5	2574.9
46	9076.67	5806.8	2428.1	9176.67	5909.1	2501.2	9276.67	6013.2	2576.2
47	9078.33	5808.5	2429.3	9178.33	5910.8	2502.4	9278.33	6015.0	2577.5
48	9080.00	5810.2	2430.5	9180.00	5912.5	2503.6	9280.00	6016.7	2578.8
49	9081.67	5811.9	2431.7	9181.67	5914.3	2504.9	9281.67	6018.5	2580.0
50	9083.33	5813.6	2432.9	9183.33	5916.0	2506.1	9283.33	6020.2	2581.3
51	9085.00	5815.3	2434.1	9185.00	5917.7	2507.3	9285.00	6022.0	2582.6
52	9086.67	5817.0	2435.3	9186.67	5919.4	2508.6	9286.67	6023.7	2583.8
53	9088.33	5818.7	2436.5	9188.33	5921.2	2509.8	9288.33	6025.5	2585.1
54	9090.00	5820.4	2437.7	9190.00	5922.9	2511.1	9290.00	6027.2	2586.4
55	9091.67	5822.1	2438.9	9191.67	5924.6	2512.3	9291.67	6029.0	2587.6
56	9093.33	5823.8	2440.1	9193.33	5926.3	2513.5	9293.33	6030.8	2588.9
57	9095.00	5825.4	2441.3	9195.00	5928.0	2514.8	9295.00	6032.5	2590.2
58	9096.67	5827.1	2442.5	9196.67	5929.8	2516.0	9296.67	6034.3	2591.5
59	9098.33	5828.8	2443.7	9198.33	5931.5	2517.3	9298.33	6036.0	2592.7

(All Definitions of Degree of Curve)

		Length L	Tan. T	Ext. E			Length L	Tan. T	Ext. E
93°	0	9300.00	6037.8	2594.0	**103°**	0	10300.00	7203.2	3474.4
	10	9316.67	6055.4	2606.8		10	10316.67	7224.7	3491.3
	20	9333.33	6073.1	2619.7		20	10333.33	7246.3	3508.2
	30	9350.00	6090.8	2632.6		30	10350.00	7268.0	3525.2
	40	9366.67	6108.6	2645.5		40	10366.67	7289.8	3542.4
	50	9383.33	6126.4	2658.5		50	10383.33	7311.7	3559.6
94°	0	9400.00	6144.3	2671.6	**104°**	0	10400.00	7333.6	3576.8
	10	9416.67	6162.2	2684.7		10	10416.67	7355.6	3594.2
	20	9433.33	6180.2	2697.9		20	10433.33	7377.8	3611.7
	30	9450.00	8198.3	2711.2		30	10450.00	7399.9	3629.2
	40	9466.67	6216.4	2724.5		40	10466.67	7422.2	3646.8
	50	9483.33	6234.6	2737.9		50	10483.33	7444.6	3664.5
95°	0	9500.00	6252.8	2751.3	**105°**	0	10500.00	7467.0	3682.3
	10	9516.67	6271.1	2764.8		10	10516.67	7489.6	3700.2
	20	9533.33	6289.4	2778.4		20	10533.33	7512.2	3718.2
	30	9550.00	6307.9	2792.0		30	10550.00	7534.9	3736.2
	40	9566.67	6326.3	2805.6		40	10566.67	7557.7	3754.4
	50	9583.33	6344.8	2819.4		50	10583.33	7580.5	3772.6
96°	0	9600.00	6363.4	2833.2	**106°**	0	10600.00	7603.5	3791.0
	10	9616.67	6382.1	2847.0		10	10616.67	7626.6	3809.4
	20	9633.33	6400.8	2861.0		20	10633.33	7649.7	3827.9
	30	9650.00	6419.5	2875.0		30	10350.00	7672.9	3846.5
	40	9666.67	6438.4	2889.0		40	10366.67	7696.3	3865.2
	50	9683.33	6457.2	2903.1		50	10683.33	7719.7	3884.0
97°	0	9700.00	6476.2	2917.3	**107°**	0	10700.00	7743.2	3902.9
	10	9716.67	6495.2	2931.6		10	10716.67	7766.8	3921.9
	20	9733.33	6514.3	2945.9		20	10733.33	7790.5	3940.9
	30	9750.00	6533.4	2960.2		30	10750.00	7814.3	3960.1
	40	9766.67	6552.6	2974.7		40	10766.67	7838.1	3979.4
	50	9783.33	6571.9	2989.2		50	10783.33	7862.1	3998.7
98°	0	9800.00	6591.2	3003.8	**108°**	0	10800.00	7886.2	4018.2
	10	9816.67	6610.6	3018.4		10	10816.67	7910.4	4037.8
	20	9833.33	6630.1	3033.1		20	10833.33	7934.6	4057.4
	30	9850.00	6649.6	3047.9		30	10850.00	7959.0	4077.2
	40	9866.67	6669.2	3062.8		40	10866.67	7983.5	4097.1
	50	9883.33	6688.8	3077.7		50	10883.33	8008.0	4117.0
99°	0	9900.00	6708.6	3092.7	**109°**	0	10900.00	8032.7	4137.1
	10	9916.67	6728.4	3107.7		10	10316.67	8057.4	4157.3
	20	9933.33	6748.2	3122.9		20	10933.33	8082.3	4177.5
	30	9950.00	6768.1	3138.1		30	10950.00	8107.3	4197.9
	40	9966.67	6788.1	3153.3		40	10966.67	8132.3	4218.4
	50	9983.33	6808.2	3168.7		50	10983.33	8157.5	4239.0
100°	0	10000.00	6828.3	3184.1	**110°**	0	11000.00	8182.8	4259.7
	10	10016.67	6848.5	3199.6		10	11016.67	8208.2	4280.5
	20	10033.33	6868.8	3215.1		20	11033.33	8233.7	4301.4
	30	10050.00	6889.2	3230.8		30	11050.00	8259.3	4322.4
	40	10066.67	6909.6	3246.5		40	11066.67	8285.0	4343.6
	50	10083.33	6930.1	3262.3		50	11083.33	8310.8	4364.8
101°	0	10100.00	6950.6	3278.1	**111°**	0	11100.00	8336.7	4386.1
	10	10116.67	6971.3	3294.1		10	11116.67	8362.7	4407.6
	20	10133.33	6992.0	3310.1		20	11133.33	8388.9	4429.2
	30	10150.00	7012.7	3326.1		30	11150.00	8415.1	4450.9
	40	10166.67	7033.6	3342.3		40	11166.67	8441.5	4472.7
	50	10183.33	7054.5	3358.5		50	11183.33	8468.0	4494.6
102°	0	10200.00	7075.5	3374.9	**112°**	0	11200.00	8494.6	4516.6
	10	10216.67	7096.6	3391.2		10	11216.67	8521.3	4538.8
	20	10233.33	7117.8	3407.7		20	11233.33	8548.1	4561.1
	30	10250.00	7139.0	3424.3		30	11250.00	8575.0	4583.4
	40	10266.67	7160.3	3440.9		40	11266.67	8602.1	4606.0
	50	10283.33	7181.7	3457.6		50	11283.33	8629.3	4628.6

(All Definitions of Degree of Curve)

	Length L	Tan. T	Ext. E		Length L	Tan. T	Ext. E
113° 0	11300.00	8656.6	4651.3	**117°** 0	11700.00	9349.9	5236.2
10	11316.67	8684.0	4674.2	10	11716.67	9380.5	5262.2
20	11333.33	8711.5	4697.2	20	11733.33	9411.3	5288.6
30	11350.00	8739.2	4720.3	30	11750.00	9442.2	5315.0
40	11366.67	8767.0	4743.6	40	11766.67	9473.2	5341.5
50	11383.33	8794.9	4766.9	50	11783.33	9504.4	5368.2
114° 0	11400.00	8822.9	4790.4	**118°** 0	11800.00	9535.7	5395.1
10	11416.67	8851.0	4814.1	10	11816.67	9567.2	5422.1
20	11433.33	8879.3	4837.8	20	11833.33	9598.9	5449.2
30	11450.00	8907.7	4861.7	30	11850.00	9630.7	5476.5
40	11466.67	8936.3	4885.7	40	11866.67	9662.6	5504.0
50	11483.33	8965.0	4909.9	50	11883.33	9694.7	5531.7
115° 0	11500.00	8993.8	4934.1	**119°** 0	11900.00	9727.0	5559.4
10	11516.67	9022.7	4958.6	10	11916.67	9759.4	5587.4
20	11533.33	9051.7	4983.1	20	11933.33	9792.0	5615.5
30	11550.00	9080.9	5007.8	30	11950.00	9824.8	5643.8
40	11566.67	9110.3	5032.6	40	11966.67	9857.7	5672.3
50	11583.33	9139.8	5057.6	50	11983.33	9890.8	5700.9
116° 0	11600.00	9169.4	5082.7	**120°** 0	12000.00	9924.0	5729.7
10	11616.67	9199.1	5107.9	10	12016.67	9957.5	5758.6
20	11633.33	9229.0	5133.3	20	12033.33	9991.0	5787.7
30	11650.00	9259.0	5158.8	30	12050.00	10024.8	5817.0
40	11666.67	9289.2	5184.5	40	12066.67	10058.7	5846.5
50	11683.33	9319.5	5210.3	50	12083.33	10092.8	5876.1

EXAMPLE.

Required the length of curve, tangent, and external distance for 20° 40′ (20.6667°) curve.   Intersection angle = 12° 34′.

For Arc Definition

	Length of Curve	Tangent	Ext. Dist.
Tabular entry	1256.67	630.9	34.6
Degree of curve	‾‾‾‾‾‾‾‾ =	‾‾‾‾‾‾‾ =	‾‾‾‾‾ =
Result	20.6667	20.6667	20.6667
	60.81 feet (exact)	30.53 feet (exact)	1.67 feet (exact)

Exact without corrections.

For Chord Definition

	Length of Curve	Tangent	Ext. Dist.
Tabular entry	1256.67	630.9	34.6
Degree of curve	‾‾‾‾‾‾‾ =	‾‾‾‾‾‾‾ =	‾‾‾‾‾ =
Result	20.6667	20.6667	20.6667
	60.81 (approx.)	30.53 (approx.)	1.67 (approx.

60.81 is slightly approximate due to the short chords at the ends. If the curve were one measured entirely in 100-foot chords, the value obtained would be exact.

Corrections from Table III for 20° 40′ and 12° 34′

(to be added)

	.17 feet	.01 feet
	‾‾‾‾ (exact)	‾‾‾‾ (exact)
	30.70	1.68

For 5730-Feet Definition

Increase tabular entries by 0.007%, usually negligible, and compute as for arc definition.

Table III. Tangent and External Corrections * [III]

or chord definition only, corrections are to be added after dividing tabular values from
ble II by the degree of curve. See example on preceding page. T = Tangent, E =
ternal.

Int. angle	Curve 5°	10°	15°	20°	25°	30°	35°	40°	45°	50°	55°	60°	65°
5°	T = .02	.03	.05	.06	.08	.10	.11	.13	.15	.16	.18	.20	.21
	E = .000	.000	.001	.001	.002	.002	.002	.003	.003	.004	.004	.004	.005
10°	T = .03	.06	.09	.13	.16	.19	.22	.25	.28	.31	.34	.38	.42
	E = .001	.003	.004	.006	.007	.008	.009	.011	.012	.014	.015	.017	.018
15°	T = .04	.10	.14	.19	.24	.29	.34	.39	.45	.51	.53	.58	.63
	E = .003	.007	.010	.014	.018	.023	.027	.029	.032	.035	.039	.043	.047
20°	T = .06	.13	.19	.26	.32	.39	.45	.51	.58	.65	.72	.79	.84
	E = .006	.011	.017	.022	.028	.034	.038	.045	.051	.057	.063	.070	.076
25°	T = .08	.16	.24	.33	.40	.49	.58	.67	.75	.83	.93	.99	1.06
	E = .009	.018	.027	.036	.046	.056	.065	.074	.083	.093	.106	.120	.127
30°	T = .10	.19	.29	.39	.49	.59	.69	.79	.89	.99	1.09	1.20	1.29
	E = .013	.025	.038	.051	.065	.078	.090	.103	.116	.129	.149	.170	.179
35°	T = .11	.22	.34	.47	.58	.69	.80	.93	1.05	1.17	1.29	1.42	1.54
	E = .018	.035	.054	.072	.086	.109	.131	.153	.175	.197	.213	.230	.247
40°	T = .13	.26	.40	.53	.67	.80	.93	1.06	1.20	1.34	1.49	1.64	1.79
	E = .023	.046	.070	.093	.117	.141	.172	.203	.234	.265	.277	.290	.315
45°	T = .15	.30	.44	.60	.76	.91	1.06	1.21	1.37	1.52	1.70	1.87	2.04
	E = .030	.060	.093	.119	.153	.184	.216	.254	.289	.325	.351	.378	.411
50°	T = .17	.34	.51	.68	.85	1.02	1.19	1.36	1.54	1.72	1.91	2.10	2.29
	E = .037	.075	.116	.151	.189	.227	.266	.305	.345	.384	.425	.467	.508
55°	T = .19	.38	.57	.76	.95	1.14	1.32	1.52	1.72	1.92	2.14	2.35	2.56
	E = .046	.093	.142	.188	.236	.283	.332	.381	.420	.479	.530	.582	.641
60°	T = .21	.42	.63	.84	1.05	1.27	1.49	1.71	1.94	2.17	2.38	2.60	2.83
	E = .056	.112	.168	.225	.283	.340	.398	.457	.516	.575	.636	.697	.774
65°	T = .23	.46	.69	.93	1.16	1.40	1.64	1.88	2.13	2.38	2.63	2.88	3.13
	E = .067	.135	.204	.273	.343	.412	.483	.554	.625	.697	.711	.845	.922
70°	T = .25	.51	.76	1.02	1.28	1.54	1.80	2.06	2.33	2.60	2.88	3.16	3.44
	E = .080	.159	.240	.321	.412	.485	.568	.652	.735	.819	.906	.994	1.08
75°	T = .27	.56	.83	1.12	1.40	1.69	1.98	2.27	2.57	2.87	3.16	3.47	3.78
	E = .095	.182	.286	.383	.480	.578	.678	.777	.877	.977	1.07	1.18	1.29
80°	T = .30	.61	.91	1.22	1.53	1.84	2.15	2.46	2.78	3.10	3.44	3.78	4.12
	E = .110	.220	.332	.445	.558	.671	.787	.903	1.02	1.13	1.25	1.38	1.50
85°	T = .33	.66	1.00	1.33	1.68	2.02	2.36	2.70	3.05	3.40	3.77	4.14	4.55
	E = .128	.259	.391	.524	.657	.790	.926	1.06	1.20	1.34	1.47	1.62	1.76
90°	T = .36	.72	1.09	1.45	1.83	2.20	2.57	2.94	3.32	3.70	4.10	4.50	4.91
	E = .149	.299	.450	.603	.756	.910	1.07	1.22	1.38	1.54	1.70	1.87	2.03
95°	T = .39	.79	1.19	1.55	2.00	2.40	2.80	3.20	3.61	4.02	4.49	4.98	5.38
	E = .174	.350	.522	.706	.985	1.06	1.25	1.43	1.62	1.80	1.99	2.18	2.38
100°	T = .43	.86	1.30	1.74	2.18	2.62	3.06	3.50	3.95	4.40	4.88	5.37	5.85
	E = .200	.401	.604	.809	1.01	1.22	1.43	1.64	1.85	2.06	2.28	2.50	2.73
105°	T = .47	.94	1.42	1.90	2.38	2.87	3.34	3.84	4.35	4.84	5.35	5.87	6.40
	E = .230	.470	.700	.938	1.17	1.42	1.65	1.90	2.14	2.39	2.64	2.90	3.16
110°	T = .50	1.03	1.55	2.08	2.60	3.14	3.66	4.21	4.76	5.31	5.86	6.43	7.01
	E = .260	.528	.808	1.08	1.36	1.63	1.91	2.19	2.49	2.61	3.05	3.35	3.65
115°	T = .54	1.13	1.70	2.29	2.86	3.45	4.03	4.63	5.23	5.83	6.44	7.07	7.70
	E = .307	.624	.939	1.26	1.57	1.89	2.21	2.54	2.87	3.20	3.53	3.88	4.23
120°	T = .58	1.25	1.89	2.52	3.16	3.81	4.44	5.11	5.78	6.44	7.11	7.80	8.51
	E = .339	.720	1.08	1.45	1.82	2.20	2.56	2.95	3.33	3.72	4.10	4.50	4.91

* From Keuffel and Esser Company Field Note Book.

For *arc definition* of degree of curve. Lengths are along arcs, offsets are at right angles to the tangent. Horizontal and vertical interpolation usually is sufficiently accurate. Except for the larger values, offsets are very closely correct for chord definition with lengths measured along chords.

Degree of Curve / Lengths in Feet	4°	8°	12°	16°	20°	24°	28°	32°	36°	40°
2	0.00	0.00	0.01	0.01	0.01	0.01	0.01	0.01	0.01	0.01
4	0.00	0.01	0.02	0.02	0.03	0.03	0.04	0.04	0.05	0.06
6	0.01	0.03	0.04	0.05	0.06	0.08	0.09	0.10	0.11	0.13
8	0.03	0.04	0.07	0.08	0.11	0.13	0.16	0.18	0.20	0.22
10	0.04	0.07	0.11	0.14	0.18	0.21	0.24	0.28	0.31	0.35
12	0.06	0.10	0.15	0.20	0.25	0.30	0.35	0.40	0.45	0.50
14	0.07	0.14	0.21	0.27	0.34	0.41	0.48	0.55	0.62	0.68
16	0.09	0.18	0.27	0.36	0.45	0.54	0.63	0.72	0.80	0.89
18	0.11	0.22	0.33	0.45	0.56	0.68	0.79	0.91	1.02	1.13
20	0.14	0.28	0.42	0.56	0.70	0.84	0.98	1.12	1.26	1.39
22	0.17	0.34	0.50	0.68	0.85	1.01	1.18	1.35	1.52	1.69
24	0.20	0.40	0.61	0.81	1.01	1.20	1.40	1.61	1.81	2.01
26	0.23	0.47	0.71	0.93	1.18	1.42	1.65	1.88	2.12	2.35
28	0.27	0.54	0.81	1.09	1.37	1.64	1.91	2.19	2.46	2.73
30	0.32	0.63	0.94	1.26	1.57	1.88	2.20	2.51	2.82	3.13
32	0.36	0.72	1.07	1.43	1.78	2.14	2.50	2.85	3.20	3.56
34	0.39	0.80	1.21	1.61	2.01	2.42	2.82	3.22	3.61	4.02
36	0.44	0.91	1.36	1.80	2.26	2.71	3.16	3.60	4.05	4.50
38	0.50	1.01	1.51	2.08	2.52	3.02	3.52	4.02	4.52	5.01
40	0.56	1.12	1.68	2.23	2.79	3.34	3.90	4.45	5.00	5.55
42	0.62	1.24	1.85	2.46	3.07	3.69	4.30	4.91	5.51	6.11
44	0.69	1.35	2.03	2.71	3.37	4.05	4.71	5.38	6.04	6.68
46	0.73	1.48	2.21	2.94	3.68	4.49	5.15	5.87	6.60	7.32
48	0.80	1.68	2.42	3.22	4.01	4.81	5.61	6.39	7.53	7.97
50	0.87	1.75	2.62	3.48	4.35	5.22	6.08	6.94	7.79	8.64
52	0.95	1.89	2.84	3.77	4.71	5.64	6.58	7.50	8.42	9.33
54	1.02	2.03	3.06	4.07	5.07	6.08	7.09	8.08	9.07	10.06
56	1.09	2.19	3.28	4.36	5.45	6.54	7.62	8.68	9.75	10.81
58	1.17	2.35	3.51	4.70	5.85	7.01	8.16	9.32	10.45	11.58
60	1.26	2.51	3.77	5.01	6.26	7.50	8.73	9.96	11.18	12.38
62	1.35	2.69	4.03	5.36	6.68	8.01	9.32	10.63	11.92	13.21
64	1.43	2.85	4.29	5.70	7.12	8.53	9.92	11.87	12.70	14.06
66	1.52	3.04	4.56	6.08	7.57	9.07	10.55	12.02	13.49	14.94
68	1.60	3.22	4.98	6.45	8.03	9.62	11.19	12.77	14.31	15.84
70	1.71	3.42	5.12	6.82	8.51	10.19	11.86	13.51	15.15	16.77
72	1.82	3.62	5.43	7.21	9.00	10.78	12.55	14.27	16.01	17.72
74	1.92	3.82	5.73	7.61	9.51	11.37	13.23	15.08	16.90	18.69
76	2.02	4.03	6.04	8.06	10.02	12.00	13.96	15.89	17.80	19.69
78	2.12	4.24	6.35	8.49	10.55	12.62	14.69	16.73	18.74	20.72
80	2.24	4.47	6.68	8.90	11.10	13.28	15.44	17.58	19.69	21.77
82	2.35	4.70	7.04	9.34	11.66	13.95	16.22	18.45	20.66	22.84
84	2.48	4.91	7.38	9.80	12.23	14.71	17.00	19.35	21.66	23.93
86	2.58	5.16	7.72	10.26	12.81	15.33	17.81	20.25	22.67	25.05
88	2.69	5.40	8.30	10.78	13.36	16.03	18.64	21.20	23.73	26.19
90	2.82	5.65	8.46	11.25	14.02	16.76	19.47	22.15	24.77	27.36
92	2.97	5.91	8.82	11.73	14.64	17.51	20.35	23.12	25.85	28.54
94	3.09	6.15	9.26	12.25	15.28	18.27	21.21	24.12	26.96	29.75
96	3.22	6.43	9.63	12.82	15.93	19.05	22.11	25.12	28.08	30.98
98	3.37	6.70	10.00	13.63	16.60	20.39	23.02	26.17	29.23	32.24
100	3.50	6.97	10 43	13.87	17.28	20.64	23.95	27.21	30.39	33.51
For 100-foot chord, and chord definition	3.49	6.98	10.45	13.92	17.38	20.79	24.19	27.56	30.90	34.20

* Modified from a table for logging engineers by Mr. Lester Calder, Weyerhaeuser Timber Company, Springfield, Oregon.

		Decimals of Stations						
		Chord Definition			Arc Definition			
D	Excess of Arc per Station	0.1	0.25	0.50	0.1	0.25	0.50	1.00
1°	0.00	10.000	25.000	50.000	10.000	25.000	50.000	99.999
2°	0.00	10.000	25.001	50.002	10.000	25.000	49.999	99.995
3°	0.01	10.001	25.003	50.004	10.000	25.000	49.999	99.987
4°	0.02	10.002	25.005	50.008	10.000	25.000	49.997	99.979
5°	0.03	10.003	25.007	50.012	10.000	25.000	49.996	99.970
6°	0.05	10.005	25.011	50.017	10.000	24.999	49.994	99.962
7°	0.06	10.006	25.015	50.023	10.000	24.999	49.992	99.940
8°	0.07	10.008	25.019	50.030	10.000	24.999	49.990	99.924
9°	0.10	10.010	25.024	50.039	10.000	24.998	49.987	99.898
10°	0.13	10.013	25.030	50.048	10.000	24.998	49.984	99.878
11°	0.15	10.015	25.036	50.058	10.000	24.998	49.981	99.851
12°	0.18	10.018	25.043	50.069	10.000	24.997	49.977	99.818
13°	0.21	10.021	25.050	50.081	10.000	24.997	49.974	99.784
14°	0.25	10.025	25.058	50.093	10.000	24.996	49.969	99.753
15°	0.29	10.028	25.067	50.107	10.000	24.995	49.964	99.717
16°	0.33	10.032	25.076	50.122	10.000	24.995	49.960	99.674
17°	0.37	10.036	25.086	50.138	10.000	24.994	49.954	99.633
18°	0.41	10.041	25.097	50.155	10.000	24.994	49.949	99.586
19°	0.46	10.045	25.108	50.172	10.000	24.993	49.943	99.545
20°	0.51	10.050	25.119	50.191	10.000	24.992	49.937	99.495
21°	0.56	10.056	25.132	50.211	10.000	24.992	49.931	99.445
22°	0.62	10.061	25.144	50.231	9.999	24.991	49.924	99.389
23°	0.67	10.067	25.158	50.253	9.999	24.989	49.916	99.330
24°	0.74	10.073	25.172	50.275	9.999	24.988	49.908	99.269
25°	0.80	10.079	25.187	50.299	9.999	24.988	49.900	99.207
26°	0.86	10.085	25.202	50.324	9.999	24.987	49.893	99.144
27°	0.93	10.092	25.218	50.349	9.999	24.986	49.885	99.081
28°	1.00	10.099	25.235	50.375	9.999	24.985	49.876	99.008
29°	1.08	10.106	25.252	50.403	9.999	24.983	49.866	98.935
30°	1.15	10.114	25.270	50.432	9.999	24.982	49.856	98.859
31°	1.23	10.122	25.288	50.461	9.999	24.981	49.846	98.783
32°	1.31	10.130	25.307	50.491	9.999	24.980	49.838	98.707
33°	1.40	10.138	25.327	50.523	9.998	24.978	49.826	98.623
34°	1.48	10.147	25.347	50.555	9.998	24.977	49.818	98.540
35°	1.57	10.156	25.368	50.589	9.998	24.975	49.805	98.452
36°	1.66	10.165	25.389	50.621	9.998	24.974	49.793	98.361
37°	1.76	10.174	25.413	50.659	9.998	24.973	49.782	98.268
38°	1.86	10.184	23.435	50.697	9.998	24.971	49.772	98.179
39°	1.96	10.194	25.459	50.734	9.998	24.969	49.758	98.080
40°	2.06	10.204	25.483	50.771	9.998	24.968	49.747	97.982
50°	3.25	10.321	25.760	51.214	9.997	24.951	49.604	96.856
60°	4.72	10.467	26.105	51.764	9.995	24.929	49.431	95.495
70°	6.50	10.643	26.212	52.426	9.994	24.903	49.226	93.895
80°	8.61	10.852	27.014	53.208	9.992	24.873	48.991	92.073
90°	11.07	11.097	27.588	54.119	9.990	24.840	48.699	90.029
100°	13.92	11.377	28.254	55.169	9.987	24.802	48.429	87.781

Use this table when points on the curve are to be set closer than 100 feet for precise construction. For example, for a 12° curve (chord definition) use 2 subchords each 50.069 feet long and deflection angles of 12°/4, or 3°.

Radius	Deflection = $\frac{1718.873}{R}$ Arc Length — Deflection for Arc Length			Chord = 2R Sin Def. — Chord for Arc Length			Degree of Curve. Arc Definition
	25'	50'	100'	25'	50'	100'	
150	4° 46.48'	9° 32.96'	19° 05.92'	24.97'	49.77'	98.16'	38° 12'
200	3° 34.86'	7° 09.72'	14° 19.44'	24.98'	49.87'	98.96'	28° 39'
225	3° 10.99'	6° 21.97'	12° 43.94'	24.99'	49.90'	99.18'	25° 28'
250	2° 51.89'	5° 43.78'	11° 27.55'	24.99'	49.92'	99.34'	22° 55'
275	2° 36.36'	5° 12.52'	10° 25.04'	24.99'	49.93'	99.45'	20° 50'
300	2° 23.24'	4° 46.48'	9° 32.96'	24.99'	49.94'	99.54'	19° 06'
325	2° 12.22'	4° 24.44'	8° 48.88'	24.99'	49.95'	99.61'	17° 38'
350	2° 02.78'	4° 05.55'	8° 11.11'	25.00'	49.96'	99.66'	16° 22'
375	1° 54.59'	3° 49.18'	7° 38.37'	25.00'	49.96'	99.70'	15° 17'
400	1° 47.43'	3° 34.86'	7° 09.72'	25.00'	49.97'	99.74'	14° 19'
450	1° 35.49'	3° 10.99'	6° 21.97'	25.00'	49.97'	99.79'	12° 44'
500	1° 25.94'	2° 51.89'	5° 43.77'	25.00'	49.98'	99.83'	11° 28'
550	1° 18.13'	2° 36.26'	5° 12.52'	25.00'	49.98'	99.86'	10° 25'
600	1° 11.62'	2° 23.24'	4° 46.48'	25.00'	49.99'	99.89'	9° 33'
650	1° 06.11'	2° 12.22'	4° 24.44'	25.00'	49.99'	99.90'	8° 49'
700	1° 01.39'	2° 02.78'	4° 05.55'	25.00'	49.99'	99.92'	8° 11'
750	0° 57.30'	1° 54.59'	3° 49.18'	25.00'	50.00'	99.93'	7° 38'
800	0° 53.71'	1° 47.43'	3° 34.86'	25.00'	50.00'	99.93'	7° 10'
850	0° 50.56'	1° 41.11'	3° 22.22'	25.00'	50.00'	99.94'	6° 44'
900	0° 47.75'	1° 35.49'	3° 10.99'	25.00'	50.00'	99.95'	6° 22'
950	0° 45.23'	1° 30.47'	3° 00.93'	25.00'	50.00'	99.95'	6° 02'
1000	0° 42.97'	1° 25.94'	2° 51.89'	25.00'	50.00'	99.96'	5° 44'
1050	0° 40.93'	1° 21.85'	2° 43.70'	25.00'	50.00'	99.96'	5° 27'
1100	0° 39.07'	1° 18.13'	2° 36.26'	25.00'	50.00'	99.96'	5° 13'
1150	0° 37.37'	1° 14.73'	2° 29.47'	25.00'	50.00'	99.97'	4° 59'
1200	0° 35.81'	1° 11.62'	2° 23.24'	25.00'	50.00'	99.97'	4° 46'
1300	0° 33.06'	1° 06.11'	2° 12.22'	25.00'	50.00'	99.97'	4° 24'
1400	0° 30.69'	1° 01.39'	2° 02.78'	25.00'	50.00'	99.98'	4° 06'
1500	0° 28.65'	0° 57.30'	1° 54.59'	25.00'	50.00'	99.98'	3° 49'
1600	0° 26.86'	0° 53.72'	1° 47.43'	25.00'	50.00'	99.98'	3° 35'
1700	0° 25.28'	0° 50.56'	1° 41.11'	25.00'	50.00'	99.99'	3° 22'
1800	0° 23.87'	0° 47.75'	1° 35.49'	25.00'	50.00'	99.99'	3° 11'
1900	0° 22.62'	0° 45.23'	1° 30.47'	25.00'	50.00'	100.00'	3° 01'
2000	0° 21.49'	0° 42.97'	1° 25.95'	25.00'	50.00'	100.00'	2° 52'
2100	0° 20.46'	0° 40.93'	1° 21.85'	25.00'	50.00'	100.00'	2° 44'
2200	0° 19.53'	0° 39.07'	1° 18.13'	25.00'	50.00'	100.00'	2° 36'
2300	0° 18.68'	0° 37.37'	1° 14.73'	25.00'	50.00'	100.00'	2° 29'
2400	0° 17.91'	0° 35.81'	1° 11.62'	25.00'	50.00'	100.00'	2° 23'
2500	0° 17.19'	0° 34.38'	1° 08.75'	25.00'	50.00'	100.00'	2° 18'
3000	0° 14.32'	0° 28.65'	0° 57.30'	25.00'	50.00'	100.00'	1° 55'
3500	0° 12.28'	0° 24.56'	0° 49.11'	25.00'	50.00'	100.00'	1° 38'
4000	0° 10.74'	0° 21.49'	0° 42.97'	25.00'	50.00'	100.00'	1° 26'
4500	0° 09.55'	0° 19.10'	0° 38.20'	25.00'	50.00'	100.00'	1° 16'
5000	0° 08.59'	0° 17.19'	0° 34.38'	25.00'	50.00'	100.00'	1° 09'
6000	0° 07.16'	0° 14.32'	0° 28.65'	25.00'	50.00'	100.00'	0° 57'
7000	0° 06.14'	0° 12.28'	0° 24.56'	25.00'	50.00'	100.00'	0° 49'
7500	0° 05.73'	0° 11.46'	0° 22.92'	25.00'	50.00'	100.00'	0° 46'
8000	0° 05.37'	0° 10.74'	0° 21.49'	25.00'	50.00'	100.00'	0° 43'
9000	0° 04.77'	0° 09.55'	0° 19.10'	25.00'	50.00'	100.00'	0° 38'
10000	0° 04.30'	0° 08.59'	0° 17.19'	25.00'	50.00'	100.00'	0° 34'

* Deflections for other lengths of radius should be computed from Table I, Column 3. Chord lengths may be obtained by interpolation.

† From California State Highway Manual of Instructions, Third edition, p. 112.

D	Excess of Arc over 100-foot Chord	Long Chords for Stations of							
		100-foot chords				100-foot arcs			
		2	3	4	5	2	3	4	5
0° 30'	0.00	199.99	299.99	399.98	499.96	200.00	299.99	399.98	499.96
1°	0.00	199.99	299.97	399.92	499.85	199.99	299.97	399.92	499.85
30'	0.00	199.98	299.93	399.83	499.66	199.98	299.92	399.85	499.62
2°	0.01	199.97	299.88	399.70	499.39	199.96	299.86	399.70	499.27
10'	0.01	199.96	299.83	399.59	499.17	199.95	299.81	399.56	499.16
20'	0.01	199.96	299.83	399.59	499.05	199.94	299.79	399.51	499.02
30'	0.01	199.95	299.81	399.53	498.92	199.94	299.76	399.42	498.86
40'	0.01	199.94	299.76	399.40	498.78	199.93	299.72	399.34	498.71
50'	0.01	199.93	299.73	399.32	498.63	199.92	299.69	399.28	498.59
3°	0.01	199.92	299.70	399.24	498.47	199.90	299.66	399.18	498.40
10'	0.01	199.91	299.66	399.15	498.31	199.89	299.63	399.09	498.23
20'	0.01	199.90	299.63	399.07	498.14	199.88	299.57	399.01	498.05
30'	0.02	199.90	299.59	398.98	497.96	199.87	299.55	398.90	497.88
40'	0.02	199.89	299.55	398.88	497.76	199.86	299.50	398.81	497.67
50'	0.02	199.88	299.51	398.78	497.57	199.85	299.46	398.69	497.47
4°	0.02	199.87	299.47	398.68	497.36	199.83	299.41	398.59	497.26
10'	0.02	199.86	299.43	398.57	497.15	199.81	299.35	398.49	497.02
20'	0.02	199.85	299.38	398.46	496.92	199.80	299.31	398.35	496.79
30'	0.03	199.83	299.34	398.34	496.69	199.78	299.26	398.24	496.56
40'	0.03	199.82	299.29	398.22	496.45	199.77	299.20	398.11	496.29
50'	0.03	199.81	299.24	398.10	496.20	199.76	299.15	397.98	496.05
5°	0.03	199.80	299.19	397.97	495.94	199.73	299.08	397.82	495.77
10'	0.03	199.78	299.13	397.84	495.68	199.71	299.02	397.68	495.51
20'	0.04	199.77	299.08	397.70	495.40	199.69	298.96	397.55	495.22
30'	0.04	199.76	299.02	397.56	495.12	199.67	298.90	397.40	494.91
40'	0.04	199.74	298.96	397.41	494.83	199.66	298.83	397.25	494.62
50'	0.04	199.73	298.90	397.26	494.53	199.64	298.76	397.08	494.31
6°	0.05	199.73	298.84	397.11	494.23	199.61	298.69	396.92	493.99
10'	0.05	199.71	298.78	396.95	493.92	199.59	298.61	396.75	493.66
20'	0.05	199.70	298.71	396.79	493.59	199.56	298.55	396.57	493.32
30'	0.06	199.68	298.65	396.62	493.26	199.54	298.48	396.41	492.97
40'	0.06	199.66	298.58	396.45	492.92	199.52	298.39	396.21	492.62
50'	0.06	199.63	298.51	396.28	492.57	199.50	298.33	396.03	492.27
7°	0.07	199.61	298.44	396.10	492.21	199.48	298.24	395.84	491.89
10'	0.07	199.59	298.36	395.92	491.85	199.45	298.16	395.66	491.51
20'	0.07	199.57	298.30	395.73	491.47	199.43	298.07	395.45	491.12
30'	0.07	199.55	298.21	395.54	491.09	199.40	297.99	395.24	490.73
40'	0.08	199.53	298.14	395.34	490.70	199.38	297.90	395.04	490.33
50'	0.08	199.51	298.05	395.14	490.31	199.35	297.81	394.83	489.91
8°	0.08	199.49	297.97	394.94	489.90	199.30	297.72	394.61	489.48
10'	0.09	199.47	297.89	394.73	489.49	199.29	297.63	394.38	489.05
20'	0.09	199.45	297.80	394.52	489.06	199.27	297.53	394.16	488.62
30'	0.09	199.43	297.72	394.30	488.63	199.25	297.43	393.93	488.18
40'	0.10	199.41	297.63	394.08	488.20	199.22	297.33	393.69	487.70
50'	0.10	199.38	297.54	393.86	487.75	199.17	297.24	393.46	487.24
9°	0.10	199.36	297.45	393.63	487.29	199.15	297.13	393.20	486.77
10'	0.11	199.34	297.35	393.40	486.83	199.12	297.02	392.96	486.29
20'	0.11	199.31	297.26	393.17	486.36	199.09	296.91	392.71	485.81
30'	0.12	199.29	297.16	392.92	485.82	199.06	296.81	392.45	485.31
40'	0.12	199.26	297.06	392.67	485.40	199.02	296.70	392.20	484.80
50'	0.12	199.26	297.06	392.67	485.40	199.02	296.70	392.20	484.80
10°	0.13	199.24	296.96	392.42	484.90	198.99	296.59	391.93	484.29
15°	0.29	198.29	293.18	383.06	466.38	197.72	292.35	381.97	465.06
20°	0.51	196.96	287.94	370.20	441.15	195.96	286.48	368.29	438.91
25°	0.79	195.26	281.26	353.93	409.82	193.72	279.03	351.13	406.58
30°	1.15	193.19	273.21	334.62	373.22	190.99	270.10	330.80	368.96
35°	*1.55 *	*190.75*	*263.84*	*312.50*	*332.16*	*188.45*	*259.75*	*307.66*	*327.02*
40°	*2.02 *	*187.94*	*253.21*	*287.94*	*287.94*	*184.15*	*248.10*	*282.13*	*282.13*

Arc definition. All entries above in this column are correct for both definitions.

EXPLANATION OF TABLE

C, X, Y, U, and V vary directly with the length of the spiral.   In other words, for a certain angle Δ, angular relations remain constant, a change in length merely increasing or decreasing the "scale" of the spiral.   To obtain C, X, Y, U, and V multiply tabular entries in columns 3, 4, 5, 6, and 7 by the length of the spiral.   Coefficients m and n are used to obtain o and Z.

EXAMPLE.   Obtain functions of a 300-foot spiral to connect to a 5° curve.   The spiral angle may be taken from Table VIII or obtained from formula 56b.

$$\Delta = 7.5°$$
$$C = 0.999248 \times 300 = 299.77 \text{ feet}$$
$$X = 0.998298 \times 300 = 299.49 \text{ feet}$$
$$Y = 0.043581 \times 300 = 13.07 \text{ feet}$$
$$U = 0.667271 \times 300 = 200.18 \text{ feet}$$
$$V = 0.333883 \times 300 = 100.16 \text{ feet}$$
$$o = (0.010902 \times 300) - (0.00062 \times 5) = 3.27 \text{ feet}$$
$$Z = (0.499724 \times 300) - (0.00953 \times 5) = 149.87 \text{ feet}$$

Interpolations may be made as necessary.   For functions of any intermediate point on spiral, proceed exactly as for the completed spiral.

This table is exact for the A.R.E.A. Ten-Chord Spiral.

If this table is to be used for the Barnett Spiral, see the minor corrections described on page 79 of tables.

Δ	A	$\dfrac{C}{L}$	$\dfrac{X}{L}$	$\dfrac{Y}{L}$
0.0°	0° 00′ 00″	1.000 000	1.000 000	.000 000
0.1°	0° 02′ 00″	1.000 000	1.000 000	.000 582
0.2°	0° 04′ 00″	.999 999	.999 999	.001 164
0.3°	0° 06′ 00″	.999 999	.999 997	.001 745
0.4°	0° 08′ 00″	.999 998	.999 995	.002 327
0.5°	0° 10′ 03″	.999 997	.999 992	.002 909
0.6°	0° 12′ 00″	.999 995	.999 989	.003 491
0.7°	0° 14′ 00″	.999 993	.999 985	.004 072
0.8°	0° 16′ 00″	.999 991	.999 981	.004 654
0.9°	0° 18′ 00″	.999 989	.999 975	.005 236
1.0°	0° 20′ 00″	.999 987	.999 970	.005 818
1.1°	0° 22′ 00″	.999 984	.999 963	.006 399
1.2°	0° 24′ 00″	.999 981	.999 956	.006 981
1.3°	0° 26′ 00″	.999 977	.999 949	.007 563
1.4°	0° 28′ 00″	.999 974	.999 941	.008 145
1.5°	0° 30′ 00″	.999 970	.999 932	.008 726
1.6°	0° 32′ 00″	.999 966	.999 922	.009 308
1.7°	4° 34′ 00″	.999 961	.999 912	.009 890
1.8°	0° 36′ 00″	.999 957	.999 902	.010 471
1.9°	0° 38′ 00″	.999 952	.999 891	.011 053
2.0°	0° 40′ 00″	.999 947	.999 879	.011 635
2.1°	0° 42′ 00″	.999 941	.999 866	.012 216
2.2°	0° 44′ 00″	.999 935	.999 853	.012 798
2.3°	0° 46′ 00″	.999 929	.999 840	.013 379
2.4°	0° 48′ 00″	.999 923	.999 826	.013 961
2.5°	0° 50′ 00″	.999 916	.999 811	.014 542
2.6°	0° 52′ 00″	.999 910	.999 795	.015 124
2.7°	0° 54′ 00″	.999 903	.999 779	.015 706
2.8°	0° 56′ 00″	.999 895	.999 763	.016 287
2.9°	0° 58′ 00″	.999 888	.999 745	.016 8C8
3.0°	1° 00′ 00″	.999 880	.999 727	.017 4C0
3.1°	1° 02′ 00″	.999 872	.999 709	.018 031
3.2°	1° 04′ 00″	.999 863	.999 690	.018 613
3.3°	1° 06′ 00″	.999 854	.999 670	.019 194
3.4°	1° 08′ 00″	.999 846	.999 650	.019 775
3.5°	1° 10′ 00″	.999 836	.999 629	.020 357
3.6°	1° 12′ 00″	.999 827	.999 608	.020 938
3.7°	1° 14′ 00″	.999 817	.999 585	.021 519
3.8°	1° 16′ 00″	.999 807	.999 563	.022 101
3.9°	1° 18′ 00″	.999 797	.999 539	.022 682
4.0°	1° 20′ 00″	.999 786	.999 515	.023 263
4.1°	1° 22′ 00″	.999 775	.999 491	.023 844
4.2°	1° 24′ 00″	.999 764	.999 466	.024 425
4.3°	1° 26′ 00″	.999 753	.999 440	.025 006
4.4°	1° 28′ 00″	.999 741	.999 414	.025 588
4.5°	1° 30′ 00″	.999 729	.999 387	.026 169
4.6°	1° 32′ 00″	.999 717	.999 359	.026 750
4.7°	1° 34′ 00″	.999 705	.999 331	.027 331
4.8°	1° 36′ 00″	.999 692	.999 302	.027 911
4.9°	1° 38′ 00″	.999 679	.999 273	.028 492
5.0°	1° 40′ 00″	.999 666	.999 243	.029 073

* From the Am. Ry. Eng. Assoc. Manual of 1929.

$\dfrac{U}{L}$	$\dfrac{V}{L}$	$0 = mL - nD$		$Z = mL - nD$		Δ
		m	n	m	n	
.666 667	.333 333	.000 000	.000 00	.500 000	.000 00	0.0°
.666 667	.333 333	.000 145	.000 00	.500 000	.000 13	0.1°
.666 667	.333 334	.000 291	.000 00	.500 000	.000 25	0.2°
.666 668	.333 334	.000 436	.000 00	.500 000	.000 38	0.3°
.666 668	.333 335	.000 582	.000 00	.499 999	.000 51	0.4°
.666 669	.333 336	.000 727	.000 00	.499 999	.000 64	0.5°
.666 671	.333 337	.000 873	.000 00	.499 998	.000 76	0.6°
.666 672	.333 338	.001 018	.000 01	.499 998	.000 89	0.7°
.666 674	.333 340	.001 164	.000 01	.499 997	.001 02	0.8°
.666 675	.333 341	.001 309	.000 01	.499 996	.001 15	0.9°
.666 677	.333 343	.001 454	.000 01	.499 995	.001 27	1.0°
.666 680	.333 345	.001 600	.000 01	.499 994	.001 40	1.1°
.666 682	.333 347	.001 745	.000 02	.499 993	.001 53	1.2°
.666 685	.333 350	.001 891	.000 02	.499 992	.001 66	1.3°
.666 688	.333 352	.002 036	.000 02	.499 990	.001 78	1.4°
.666 691	.333 355	.002 182	.000 03	.499 989	.001 91	1.5°
.666 694	.333 358	.002 327	.000 03	.499 987	.002 04	1.6°
.666 698	.333 362	.002 472	.000 03	.499 986	.002 17	1.7°
.666 701	.333 365	.002 618	.000 04	.499 984	.002 29	1.8°
.666 705	.333 369	.002 763	.000 04	.499 982	.002 42	1.9°
.666 710	.333 372	.002 909	.000 04	.499 980	.002 55	2.0°
.666 714	.333 376	.003 054	.000 05	.499 978	.002 68	2.1°
.666 719	.333 381	.003 200	.000 05	.499 976	.002 80	2.2°
.666 723	.333 385	.003 345	.000 06	.499 974	.002 93	2.3°
.666 728	.333 390	.003 490	.000 06	.499 972	.003 06	2.4°
.666 734	.333 394	.003 636	.000 07	.499 969	.003 18	2.5°
.666 739	.333 399	.003 781	.000 08	.499 967	.003 31	2.6°
.666 745	.333 405	.003 927	.000 08	.499 964	.003 44	2.7°
.666 751	.333 410	.004 072	.000 09	.499 962	.003 57	2.8°
.666 757	.333 415	.004 213	.000 09	.499 959	.003 69	2.9°
.666 763	.333 421	.004 363	.000 10	.499 956	.003 82	3.0°
.666 770	.333 427	.004 508	.000 11	.499 953	.003 95	3.1°
.666 776	.333 433	.004 654	.000 11	.499 950	.004 07	3.2°
.666 783	.333 440	.004 799	.000 12	.499 947	.004 20	3.3°
.666 791	.333 446	.004 945	.000 13	.499 943	.004 33	3.4°
.666 798	.333 453	.005 090	.000 14	.499 940	.004 46	3.5°
.666 806	.333 460	.005 235	.000 14	.499 936	.004 58	3.6°
.666 813	.333 467	.005 381	.000 15	.499 933	.004 71	3.7°
.666 822	.333 474	.005 526	.000 16	.499 929	.004 84	3.8°
.666 830	.333 482	.005 671	.000 17	.499 925	.004 97	3.9°
.666 838	.333 490	.005 817	.000 18	.499 922	.005 09	4.0°
.666 847	.333 498	.005 962	.000 19	.499 918	.005 22	4.1°
.666 856	.333 506	.006 108	.000 20	.499 914	.005 35	4.2°
.666 865	.333 514	.006 253	.000 21	.499 909	.005 47	4.3°
.666 874	.333 522	.006 398	.000 22	.499 905	.005 60	4.4°
.666 884	.333 531	.006 544	.000 23	.499 901	.005 73	4.5°
.666 894	.333 540	.006 689	.000 24	.499 896	.005 85	4.6°
.666 904	.333 549	.006 834	.000 25	.499 892	.005 98	4.7°
.666 914	.333 558	.006 980	.000 26	.499 887	.006 11	4.8°
.666 924	.333 568	.007 125	.000 27	.499 882	.006 24	4.9°
.666 935	.333 578	.007 270	.000 28	.499 877	.006 36	5.0°

Δ	A	$\dfrac{C}{L}$	$\dfrac{X}{L}$	$\dfrac{Y}{L}$
5.0°	1° 40′ 00″	.999 666	.999 243	.029 073
5.1°	1° 42′ 00″	.999 652	.999 212	.029 654
5.2°	1° 44′ 00″	.999 639	.999 181	.030 235
5.3°	1° 46′ 00″	.999 625	.999 150	.030 816
5.4°	1° 48′ 00″	.999 610	.999 117	.031 396
5.5°	1° 50′ 00″	.999 596	.999 084	.031 977
5.6°	1° 51′ 59″	.999 581	.999 051	.032 558
5.7°	1° 53′ 59″	.999 566	.999 016	.033 138
5.8°	1° 55′ 59″	.999 550	.998 982	.033 719
5.9°	1° 57′ 59″	.999 535	.998 946	.034 299
6.0°	1° 59′ 59″	.999 519	.998 910	.034 880
6.1°	2° 01′ 59″	.999 503	.998 874	.035 460
6.2°	2° 03′ 59″	.999 486	.998 836	.036 040
6.3°	2° 05′ 59″	.999 470	.998 799	.036 621
6.4°	2° 07′ 59″	.999 453	.998 760	.037 201
6.5°	2° 09′ 59″	.999 435	.998 721	.037 781
6.6°	2° 11′ 59″	.999 418	.998 681	.038 361
6.7°	2° 13′ 59″	.999 400	.998 641	.038 941
6.8°	2° 15′ 59″	.999 382	.998 600	.039 522
6.9°	2° 17′ 59″	.999 364	.998 559	.040 102
7.0°	2° 19′ 59″	.999 345	.998 517	.040 682
7.1°	2° 21′ 59″	.999 326	.998 474	.041 261
7.2°	2° 23′ 59″	.999 307	.998 431	.041 841
7.3°	2° 25′ 59″	.999 288	.998 387	.042 421
7.4°	2° 27′ 59″	.999 268	.998 343	.043 001
7.5°	2° 29′ 59″	.999 248	.998 298	.043 581
7.6°	2° 31′ 59″	.999 228	.998 252	.044 160
7.7°	2° 33′ 59″	.999 208	.998 206	.044 740
7.8°	2° 35′ 59″	.999 187	.998 159	.045 319
7.9°	2° 37′ 59″	.999 166	.998 111	.045 899
8.0°	2° 39′ 58″	.999 145	.998 063	.046 478
8.1°	2° 41′ 58″	.999 123	.998 015	.047 058
8.2°	2° 43′ 58″	.999 102	.997 965	.047 637
8.3°	2° 45′ 58″	.999 080	.997 915	.048 216
8.4°	2° 47′ 58″	.999 057	.997 865	.048 795
8.5°	2° 49′ 58″	.999 035	.997 814	.049 374
8.6°	2° 51′ 58″	.999 012	.997 762	.049 953
8.7°	2° 53′ 58″	.998 989	.997 710	.050 532
8.8°	2° 55′ 58″	.998 965	.997 657	.051 111
8.9°	2° 57′ 58″	.998 942	.997 603	.051 690
9.0°	2° 59′ 58″	.998 918	.997 549	.052 269
9.1°	3° 01′ 58″	.998 894	.997 495	.052 848
9.2°	3° 03′ 58″	.998 869	.997 439	.053 426
9.3°	3° 05′ 58″	.998 844	.997 383	.054 005
9.4°	3° 07′ 58″	.998 819	.997 327	.054 583
9.5°	3° 09′ 57″	.998 794	.997 270	.055 162
9.6°	3° 11′ 57″	.998 769	.997 212	.055 740
9.7°	3° 13′ 57″	.998 743	.997 154	.056 318
9.8°	3° 15′ 57″	.998 717	.997 095	.056 897
9.9°	3° 17′ 57″	.998 691	.997 035	.057 475
10.0°	3° 19′ 57″	.998 664	.996 975	.058 053

$\dfrac{U}{L}$	$\dfrac{V}{L}$	$0 = mL - nD$		$Z = mL - nD$		Δ
		m	**n**	**m**	**n**	
.666 935	.333 578	.007 270	.000 28	.499 877	.006 36	5.0°
.666 946	.333 587	.007 416	.000 29	.499 872	.006 49	5.1°
.666 957	.333 598	.007 561	.000 30	.499 867	.006 62	5.2°
.666 968	.333 608	.007 706	.000 31	.499 862	.006 74	5.3°
.666 979	.333 618	.007 852	.000 32	.499 857	.006 87	5.4°
.666 991	.333 629	.007 997	.000 34	.499 852	.007 00	5.5°
.667 003	.333 640	.008 142	.000 35	.499 846	.007 12	5.6°
.667 015	.333 651	.008 288	.000 36	.499 841	.007 25	5.7°
.667 028	.333 662	.008 433	.000 37	.499 835	.007 38	5.8°
.667 040	.333 674	.008 578	.000 39	.499 829	.007 50	5.9°
.667 053	.333 685	.008 724	.000 40	.499 824	.007 63	6.0°
.667 066	.333 697	.008 869	.000 41	.499 818	.007 76	6.1°
.667 079	.333 709	.009 014	.000 43	.499 812	.007 88	6.2°
.667 093	.333 721	.009 159	.000 44	.499 805	.008 01	6.3°
.667 106	.333 734	.009 305	.000 45	.499 799	.008 14	6.4°
.667 120	.333 746	.009 450	.000 47	.499 793	.008 26	6.5°
.667 134	.333 759	.009 595	.000 48	.499 786	.008 39	6.6°
.667 148	.333 772	.009 740	.000 50	.499 780	.008 52	6.7°
.667 163	.333 785	.009 886	.000 51	.499 773	.008 64	6.8°
.667 178	.333 799	.010 031	.000 53	.499 767	.008 77	6.9°
.667 193	.333 812	.010 176	.000 54	.499 760	.008 90	7.0°
.667 208	.333 826	.010 321	.000 56	.499 753	.009 02	7.1°
.667 223	.333 840	.010 467	.000 58	.499 746	.009 15	7.2°
.667 239	.333 854	.010 612	.000 59	.499 739	.009 28	7.3°
.667 255	.333 869	.010 757	.000 61	.499 732	.009 40	7.4°
.667 271	.333 883	.010 902	.000 62	.499 724	.009 53	7.5°
.667 287	.333 898	.011 048	.000 64	.499 717	.009 65	7.6°
.667 303	.333 913	.011 193	.000 66	.499 709	.009 78	7.7°
.667 320	.333 928	.011 338	.000 68	.499 702	.009 91	7.8°
.667 337	.333 944	.011 483	.000 69	.499 694	.010 03	7.9°
.667 354	.333 959	.011 628	.000 71	.499 686	.010 16	8.0°
.667 371	.333 975	.011 773	.000 73	.499 678	.010 29	8.1°
.667 389	.333 991	.011 919	.000 75	.499 670	.010 41	8.2°
.667 407	.334 007	.012 064	.000 76	.499 662	.010 54	8.3°
.667 424	.334 024	.012 209	.000 78	.499 654	.010 66	8.4°
.667 443	.334 040	.012 354	.000 80	.499 646	.010 79	8.5°
.667 461	.334 057	.012 499	.000 82	.499 637	.010 92	8.6°
.667 480	.334 074	.012 644	.000 84	.499 629	.011 04	8.7°
.667 499	.334 091	.012 789	.000 86	.499 620	.011 17	8.8°
.667 518	.334 109	.012 935	.000 88	.499 612	.011 29	8.9°
.667 537	.334 126	.013 080	.000 90	.499 603	.011 42	9.0°
.667 556	.334 144	.013 225	.000 92	.499 594	.011 55	9.1°
.667 576	.334 162	.013 370	.000 94	.499 585	.011 67	9.2°
.667 596	.334 180	.013 515	.000 96	.499 576	.011 80	9.3°
.667 616	.334 198	.013 660	.000 98	.499 567	.011 92	9.4°
.667 636	.334 217	.013 805	.001 00	.499 558	.012 05	9.5°
.667 657	.334 236	.013 950	.001 02	.499 548	.012 17	9.6°
.667 678	.334 255	.014 095	.001 04	.499 539	.012 30	9.7°
.667 699	.334 274	.014 240	.001 07	.499 529	.012 43	9.8°
.667 720	.334 293	.014 385	.001 09	.499 520	.012 55	9.9°
.667 742	.334 313	.014 530	.001 11	.499 510	.012 68	10.0°

Δ	A	$\dfrac{C}{L}$	$\dfrac{X}{L}$	$\dfrac{Y}{L}$
10.0°	3° 19′ 57″	.998 664	.996 975	.058 053
10.1°	3° 21′ 57″	.998 637	.996 915	.058 631
10.2°	3° 23′ 57″	.998 610	.996 853	.059 209
10.3°	3° 25′ 57″	.998 583	.996 791	.059 787
10.4°	3° 27′ 57″	.998 555	.996 729	.060 364
10.5°	3° 29′ 57″	.998 527	.996 666	.060 942
10.6°	3° 31′ 56″	.998 499	.996 602	.061 520
10.7°	3° 33′ 56″	.998 471	.996 538	.062 097
10.8°	3° 35′ 56″	.998 442	.996 473	.062 675
10.9°	3° 37′ 56″	.998 413	.996 407	.063 252
11.0°	3° 39′ 56″	.998 384	.996 341	.063 829
11.1°	3° 41′ 56″	.998 354	.996 274	.064 406
11.2°	3° 43′ 56″	.998 324	.996 207	.064 984
11.3°	3° 45′ 56″	.998 294	.996 139	.065 561
11.4°	3° 47′ 56″	.998 264	.996 071	.066 138
11.5°	3° 49′ 55″	.998 233	.996 002	.066 714
11.6°	3° 51′ 55″	.998 203	.995 932	.067 291
11.7°	3° 53′ 55″	.998 171	.995 862	.067 868
11.8°	3° 55′ 55″	.998 140	.995 791	.068 445
11.9°	3° 57′ 55″	.998 108	.995 719	.069 021
12.0°	3° 59′ 55″	.998 077	.995 647	.069 598
12.1°	4° 01′ 55″	.998 044	.995 574	.070 174
12.2°	4° 03′ 55″	.998 012	.995 501	.070 750
12.3°	4° 05′ 54″	.997 979	.995 427	.071 326
12.4°	4° 07′ 54″	.997 946	.995 353	.071 902
12.5°	4° 09′ 54″	.997 913	.995 278	.072 478
12.6°	4° 11′ 54″	.997 880	.995 202	.073 054
12.7°	4° 13′ 54″	.997 846	.995 126	.073 630
12.8°	4° 15′ 54″	.997 812	.995 049	.074 206
12.9°	4° 17′ 54″	.997 777	.994 971	.074 781
13.0°	4° 19′ 53″	.997 743	.994 893	.075 357
13.1°	4° 21′ 53″	.997 708	.994 814	.075 932
13.2°	4° 23′ 53″	.997 673	.994 735	.076 508
13.3°	4° 25′ 53″	.997 638	.994 655	.077 083
13.4°	4° 27′ 53″	.997 602	.994 575	.077 658
13.5°	4° 29′ 53″	.997 566	.994 494	.078 233
13.6°	4° 31′ 53″	.997 530	.994 412	.078 808
13.7°	4° 33′ 52″	.997 493	.994 330	.079 383
13.8°	4° 35′ 52″	.997 457	.994 247	.079 957
13.9°	4° 37′ 52″	.997 420	.994 163	.080 532
14.0°	4° 39′ 52″	.997 383	.994 079	.081 106
14.1°	4° 41′ 52″	.997 345	.993 995	.081 681
14.2°	4° 43′ 51″	.997 307	.993 909	.082 255
14.3°	4° 45′ 51″	.997 269	.993 824	.082 829
14.4°	4° 47′ 51″	.997 231	.993 737	.083 403
14.5°	4° 49′ 51″	.997 192	.993 650	.083 977
14.6°	4° 51′ 51″	.997 154	.993 563	.084 551
14.7°	4° 53′ 51″	.997 115	.993 474	.085 125
14.8°	4° 55′ 50″	.997 075	.993 385	.085 699
14.9°	4° 57′ 50″	.997 036	.993 296	.086 272
15.0°	4° 59′ 50″	.996 996	.993 206	.086 846

$\dfrac{U}{L}$	$\dfrac{V}{L}$	$0 = mL - nD$		$Z = mL - nD$		Δ
		m	n	m	n	
.667 742	.334 313	.014 530	.001 11	.499 510	.012 68	10.0°
.667 763	.334 332	.014 675	.001 13	.499 500	.012 80	10.1°
.667 785	.334 352	.014 820	.001 15	.499 490	.012 93	10.2°
.667 807	.334 373	.014 965	.001 18	.499 480	.013 05	10.3°
.667 830	.334 393	.015 110	.001 20	.499 470	.013 18	10.4°
.667 852	.334 413	.015 255	.001 22	.499 460	.013 30	10.5°
.667 875	.334 434	.015 400	.001 25	.499 449	.013 43	10.6°
.667 898	.334 455	.015 545	.001 27	.499 439	.013 55	10.7°
.667 921	.334 476	.015 690	.001 29	.499 428	.013 68	10.8°
.667 944	.334 498	.015 835	.001 32	.499 418	.013 80	10.9°
.667 968	.334 519	.015 980	.001 34	.499 407	.013 93	11.0°
.667 992	.334 541	.016 125	.001 37	.499 396	.014 05	11.1°
.668 016	.334 563	.016 270	.001 39	.499 385	.014 18	11.2°
.668 040	.334 585	.016 415	.001 42	.499 374	.014 30	11.3°
.668 065	.334 607	.016 560	.001 44	.499 363	.014 43	11.4°
.668 089	.334 630	.016 704	.001 47	.499 352	.014 55	11.5°
.668 114	.334 653	.016 849	.001 49	.499 341	.014 68	11.6°
.668 140	.334 676	.016 994	.001 52	.499 329	.014 80	11.7°
.668 165	.334 699	.017 139	.001 54	.499 318	.014 93	11.8°
.668 191	.334 722	.017 284	.001 57	.499 306	.015 05	11.9°
.668 216	.334 746	.017 429	.001 60	.499 294	.015 18	12.0°
.668 242	.334 769	.017 574	.001 62	.499 283	.015 30	12.1°
.668 269	.334 793	.017 718	.001 65	.499 271	.015 43	12.2°
.668 295	.334 817	.017 863	.001 68	.499 259	.015 55	12.3°
.668 322	.334 842	.018 008	.001 70	.499 247	.015 68	12.4°
.668 349	.334 866	.018 153	.001 73	.499 234	.015 80	12.5°
.668 376	.334 891	.018 298	.001 76	.499 222	.015 92	12.6°
.668 403	.334 916	.018 442	.001 79	.499 210	.016 05	12.7°
.668 431	.334 941	.018 587	.001 81	.499 197	.016 17	12.8°
.668 459	.334 967	.018 732	.001 84	.499 185	.016 30	12.9°
.668 487	.334 992	.018 877	.001 87	.499 172	.016 42	13.0°
.668 515	.335 018	.019 021	.001 90	.499 159	.016 55	13.1°
.668 543	.335 044	.019 166	.001 93	.499 146	.016 67	13.2°
.668 572	.335 070	.019 311	.001 96	.499 133	.016 79	13.3°
.668 601	.335 096	.019 455	.001 99	.499 120	.016 92	13.4°
.668 630	.335 123	.019 600	.002 02	.499 107	.017 04	13.5°
.668 660	.335 150	.019 745	.002 05	.499 094	.017 17	13.6°
.668 689	.335 177	.019 889	.002 08	.499 081	.017 29	13.7°
.668 719	.335 204	.020 034	.002 11	.499 067	.017 41	13.8°
.668 749	.335 231	.020 179	.002 14	.499 054	.017 54	13.9°
.668 779	.335 259	.020 323	.002 17	.499 040	.017 66	14.0°
.668 810	.335 287	.020 468	.002 20	.499 026	.017 78	14.1°
.668 840	.335 315	.020 612	.002 23	.499 012	.017 91	14.2°
.668 871	.335 343	.020 757	.002 26	.498 998	.018 03	14.3°
.668 902	.335 371	.020 902	.002 29	.498 984	.018 15	14.4°
.668 934	.335 400	.021 046	.002 33	.498 970	.018 28	14.5°
.668 965	.335 429	.021 191	.002 36	.498 956	.018 40	14.6°
.668 997	.335 458	.021 335	.002 39	.498 942	.018 52	14.7°
.669 029	.335 487	.021 480	.002 42	.498 927	.018 65	14.8°
.669 061	.335 516	.021 624	.002 45	.498 913	.018 77	14.9°
.669 094	.335 546	.021 769	.002 49	.498 898	.018 89	15.0°

Δ	A	$\dfrac{C}{L}$	$\dfrac{X}{L}$	$\dfrac{Y}{L}$
15.0°	4° 59′ 50″	.996 996	.993 206	.086 846
15.1°	5° 01′ 50″	.996 956	.993 115	.087 419
15.2°	5° 03′ 50″	.996 915	.993 024	.087 992
15.3°	5° 05′ 49″	.996 874	.992 932	.088 565
15.4°	5° 07′ 49″	.996 833	.992 840	.089 138
15.5°	5° 09′ 49″	.996 792	.992 747	.089 711
15.6°	5° 11′ 49″	.996 751	.992 654	.090 284
15.7°	5° 13′ 49″	.996 709	.992 559	.090 856
15.8°	5° 15′ 48″	.996 667	.992 465	.091 429
15.9°	5° 17′ 48″	.996 625	.992 369	.092 001
16.0°	5° 19′ 48″	.996 582	.992 273	.092 574
16.1°	5° 21′ 48″	.996 539	.992 177	.093 146
16.2°	5° 23′ 47″	.996 496	.992 080	.093 718
16.3°	5° 25′ 47″	.996 453	.991 982	.094 290
16.4°	5° 27′ 47″	.996 409	.991 884	.094 862
16.5°	5° 29′ 47″	.996 366	.991 785	.095 433
16.6°	5° 31′ 46″	.996 321	.991 685	.096 005
16.7°	5° 33′ 46″	.996 277	.991 585	.096 576
16.8°	5° 35′ 46″	.996 232	.991 484	.097 148
16.9°	5° 37′ 46″	.996 187	.991 383	.097 719
17.0°	5° 39′ 45″	.996 142	.991 281	.098 290
17.1°	5° 41′ 45″	.996 097	.991 179	.098 861
17.2°	5° 43′ 45″	.996 051	.991 076	.099 432
17.3°	5° 45′ 45″	.996 005	.990 972	.100 002
17.4°	5° 47′ 44″	.995 959	.990 868	.100 573
17.5°	5° 49′ 44″	.995 912	.990 763	.101 143
17.6°	5° 51′ 44″	.995 865	.990 658	.101 713
17.7°	5° 53′ 44″	.995 818	.990 552	.102 284
17.8°	5° 55′ 43″	.995 771	.990 445	.102 854
17.9°	5° 57′ 43″	.995 723	.990 338	.103 424
18.0°	5° 59′ 43″	.995 676	.990 230	.103 993
18.1°	6° 01′ 42″	.995 628	.990 122	.104 563
18.2°	6° 03′ 42″	.995 579	.990 013	.105 132
18.3°	6° 05′ 42″	.995 530	.989 903	.105 702
18.4°	6° 07′ 42″	.995 482	.989 793	.106 271
18.5°	6° 09′ 41″	.995 432	.989 682	.106 840
18.6°	6° 11′ 41″	.995 383	.989 571	.107 409
18.7°	6° 13′ 41″	.995 333	.989 459	.107 978
18.8°	6° 15′ 40″	.995 283	.989 347	.108 547
18.9°	6° 17′ 40″	.995 233	.989 233	.109 115
19.0°	6° 19′ 40″	.995 183	.989 120	.109 683
19.1°	6° 21′ 39″	.995 132	.989 005	.110 252
19.2°	6° 23′ 39″	.995 081	.988 891	.110 820
19.3°	6° 25′ 39″	.995 029	.988 775	.111 388
19.4°	6° 27′ 38″	.994 978	.988 659	.111 956
19.5°	6° 29′ 38″	.994 926	.988 543	.112 523
19.6°	6° 31′ 38″	.994 874	.988 425	.113 091
19.7°	6° 33′ 37″	.994 822	.988 308	.113 658
19.8°	6° 35′ 37″	.994 769	.988 189	.114 225
19.9°	6° 37′ 37″	.994 716	.988 070	.114 793
20.0°	6° 39′ 36″	.994 663	.987 951	.115 360

$\dfrac{U}{L}$	$\dfrac{V}{L}$	$0 = mL - nD$		$Z = mL - nD$		Δ
		m	n	m	n	
.669 094	.335 546	.021 769	.002 49	.498 898	.018 89	15.0°
.669 126	.335 576	.021 913	.002 52	.498 883	.019 02	15.1°
.669 159	.335 606	.022 058	.002 55	.498 869	.019 14	15.2°
.669 192	.335 636	.022 202	.002 59	.498 854	.019 26	15.3°
.669 226	.335 666	.022 347	.002 62	.498 839	.019 39	15.4°
.669 259	.335 697	.022 491	.002 65	.498 824	.019 51	15.5°
.669 293	.335 728	.022 635	.002 69	.498 808	.019 63	15.6°
.669 327	.335 759	.022 780	.002 72	.498 793	.019 75	15.7°
.669 361	.335 790	.022 924	.002 76	.498 778	.019 88	15.8°
.669 396	.335 821	.023 069	.002 79	.498 762	.020 00	15.9°
.669 431	.335 853	.023 213	.002 83	.498 747	.020 12	16.0°
.669 465	.335 885	.023 357	.002 86	.498 731	.020 24	16.1°
.669 501	.335 917	.023 502	.002 90	.498 715	.020 37	16.2°
.669 536	.335 949	.023 646	.002 93	.498 699	.020 49	16.3°
.669 572	.335 982	.023 790	.002 97	.498 683	.020 61	16.4°
.669 607	.336 014	.023 935	.003 01	.498 667	.020 73	16.5°
.669 643	.336 047	.024 079	.003 04	.498 651	.020 86	16.6°
.669 680	.336 080	.024 223	.003 08	.498 635	.020 98	16.7°
.669 716	.336 114	.024 367	.003 12	.498 618	.021 10	16.8°
.669 753	.336 147	.024 512	.003 15	.498 602	.021 22	16.9°
.669 790	.336 181	.024 656	.003 19	.498 585	.021 34	17.0°
.669 827	.336 215	.024 800	.003 23	.498 569	.021 46	17.1°
.669 864	.336 249	.024 944	.003 26	.498 552	.021 59	17.2°
.669 902	.336 283	.025 088	.003 30	.498 535	.021 71	17.3°
.669 940	.336 318	.025 233	.003 34	.498 518	.021 83	17.4°
.669 978	.336 353	.025 377	.003 38	.498 501	.021 95	17.5°
.670 016	.336 388	.025 521	.003 42	.498 484	.022 07	17.6°
.670 055	.336 423	.025 665	.003 46	.498 466	.022 19	17.7°
.670 093	.336 458	.025 809	.003 49	.498 449	.022 32	17.8°
.670 132	.336 494	.025 953	.003 53	.498 432	.022 44	17.9°
.670 172	.336 529	.026 097	.003 57	.498 414	.022 56	18.0°
.670 211	.336 565	.026 241	.003 61	.498 397	.022 68	18.1°
.670 251	.336 602	.026 385	.003 65	.498 379	.022 80	18.2°
.670 290	.336 638	.026 529	.003 69	.498 361	.022 92	18.3°
.670 331	.336 675	.026 673	.003 73	.498 343	.023 04	18.4°
.670 371	.336 711	.026 817	.003 77	.498 325	.023 16	18.5°
.670 411	.336 748	.026 961	.003 81	.498 307	.023 28	18.6°
.670 452	.336 786	.027 105	.003 85	.498 289	.023 40	18.7°
.670 493	.336 823	.027 249	.003 89	.489 270	.023 53	18.8°
.670 534	.336 861	.627 393	.003 94	.498 252	.023 65	18.9°
.670 576	.336.899	.027 537	.003 98	.498 233	.023 77	19.0°
.670 618	.336 937	.027 681	.004 02	.498 215	.023 89	19.1°
.670 660	.336 975	.027 825	.004 06	.498 196	.024 01	19.2°
.670 702	.337 013	.027 969	.004 10	.498 177	.024 13	19.3°
.670 744	.337 052	.028 113	.004 14	.498 158	.024 25	19.4°
.670 787	.337 091	.028 257	.004 19	.498 139	.024 37	19.5°
.670 829	.337 130	.028 400	.004 23	.498 120	.024 49	19.6°
.670 873	.337 169	.028 544	.004 27	.498 101	.024 61	19.7°
.670 916	.337 209	.028 688	.004 32	.498 082	.024 73	19.8°
.670 959	.337 249	.028 832	.004 36	.498 062	.024 85	19.9°
.671 003	.337 289	.028 976	.004 40	.498 043	.024 97	20.0°

Δ	A	$\frac{C}{L}$	$\frac{X}{L}$	$\frac{Y}{L}$
20.0°	6° 39′ 36″	.994 663	.987 951	.115 360
20.1°	6° 41′ 36″	.994 610	.987 831	.115 926
20.2°	6° 43′ 36″	.994 556	.987 710	.116 493
20.3°	6° 45′ 35″	.994 502	.987 589	.117 060
20.4°	6° 47′ 35″	.994 448	.987 467	.117 626
20.5°	6° 49′ 34″	.994 393	.987 344	.118 192
20.6°	6° 51′ 34″	.994 339	.987 221	.118 758
20.7°	6° 53′ 34″	.994 284	.987 098	.119 324
20.8°	6° 55′ 33″	.994 228	.986 973	.119 890
20.9°	6° 57′ 33″	.994 173	.986 849	.120 455
21.0°	6° 59′ 32″	.994 117	.986 723	.121 021
21.1°	7° 01′ 32″	.994 061	.986 597	.121 586
21.2°	7° 03′ 32″	.994 005	.986 471	.122 151
21.3°	7° 05′ 31″	.993 948	.986 343	.122 716
21.4°	7° 07′ 31″	.993 891	.986 216	.123 281
21.5°	7° 09′ 30″	.993 834	.986 087	.123 846
21.6°	7° 11′ 30″	.993 777	.985 959	.124 410
21.7°	7° 13′ 30″	.993 719	.985 829	.124 975
21.8°	7° 15′ 29″	.993 661	.985 699	.125 539
21.9°	7° 17′ 29″	.993 603	.985 568	.126 103
22.0°	7° 19′ 28″	.993 545	.985 437	.126 667
22.1°	7° 21′ 28″	.993 486	.985 305	.127 230
22.2°	7° 23′ 28″	.993 427	.985 173	.127 794
22.3°	7° 25′ 27″	.993 368	.985 040	.128 357
22.4°	7° 27′ 27″	.993 308	.984 906	.128 920
22.5°	7° 29′ 26″	.993 248	.984 772	.129 483
22.6°	7° 31′ 26″	.993 188	.984 638	.130 046
22.7°	7° 33′ 25″	.993 128	.984 502	.130 609
22.8°	7° 35′ 25″	.993 068	.984 366	.131 172
22.9°	7° 37′ 24″	.993 007	.984 230	.131 734
23.0°	7° 39′ 24″	.992 946	.984 093	.132 296
23.1°	7° 41′ 23″	.992 884	.983 955	.132 858
23.2°	7° 43′ 23″	.992 823	.983 817	.133 420
23.3°	7° 45′ 22″	.992 761	.983 678	.133 982
23.4°	7° 47′ 22″	.992 699	.983 539	.134 543
23.5°	7° 49′ 21″	.992 636	.983 399	.135 105
23.6°	7° 51′ 21″	.992 574	.983 259	.135 666
23.7°	7° 53′ 20″	.992 511	.983 118	.136 227
23.8°	7° 55′ 20″	.992 448	.982 976	.136 788
23.9°	7° 57′ 19″	.992 384	.982 834	.137 348
24.0°	7° 59′ 19″	.992 321	.982 691	.137 909
24.1°	8° 01′ 18″	.992 257	.982 547	.138 469
24.2°	8° 03′ 18″	.992 192	.982 403	.139 029
24.3°	8° 05′ 17″	.992 128	.982 259	.139 589
24.4°	8° 07′ 17″	.992 063	.982 114	.140 149
24.5°	8° 09′ 16″	.991 998	.981 968	.140 708
24.6°	8° 11′ 16″	.991 933	.981 822	.141 268
24.7°	8° 13′ 15″	.991 867	.981 675	.141 827
24.8°	8° 15′ 15″	.991 801	.981 528	.142 386
24.9°	8° 17′ 14″	.991 735	.981 380	.142 945
25.0°	8° 19′ 14″	.991 669	.981 231	.143 504

$\dfrac{U}{L}$	$\dfrac{V}{L}$	$0 = mL - nD$		$Z = mL - nD$		Δ
		m	n	m	n	
.671 003	.337 289	.028 976	.004 40	.498 043	.024 97	20.0°
.671 047	.337 329	.029 119	.004 45	.498 023	.025 09	20.1°
.671 091	.337 369	.029 263	.004 49	.498 004	.025 21	20.2°
.671 136	.337 410	.029 407	.004 53	.497 984	.025 33	20.3°
.671 180	.337 451	.029 550	.004 58	.497 964	.025 45	20.4°
.671 225	.337 492	.029 694	.004 62	.497 944	.025 57	20.5°
.671 270	.337 533	.029 838	.004 67	.497 924	.025 68	20.6°
.671 316	.337 574	.029 981	.004 71	.497 904	.025 80	20.7°
.671 361	.337 616	.030 125	.004 76	.497 884	.025 92	20.8°
.671 407	.337 658	.030 269	.004 80	.497 863	.026 04	20.9°
.671 453	.337 700	.030 412	.004 85	.497 843	.026 16	21.0°
.671 499	.337 742	.030 556	.004 89	.497 822	.026 28	21.1°
.671 546	.337 785	.030 699	.004 94	.497 802	.026 40	21.2°
.671 593	.337 827	.030 843	.004 99	.497 781	.026 52	21.3°
.671 640	.337 870	.030 986	.005 03	.497 760	.026 64	21.4°
.671 687	.337 913	.031 130	.005 08	.497 739	.026 75	21.5°
.671 734	.337 957	.031 273	.005 13	.497 718	.026 87	21.6°
.671 782	.338 000	.031 417	.005 17	.497 697	.026 99	21.7°
.671 830	.338 044	.031 560	.005 22	.497 676	.027 11	21.8°
.671 878	.338 088	.031 704	.005 27	.497 655	.027 23	21.9°
.671 926	.338 132	.031 847	.005 32	.497 633	.027 35	22.0°
.671 975	.338 177	.031 990	.005 36	.497 612	.027 46	22.1°
.672 024	.338 221	.032 134	.005 41	.497 590	.027 58	22.2°
.672 073	.338 266	.032 277	.005 46	.497 568	.027 70	22.3°
.672 122	.338 311	.032 421	.005 51	.497 547	.027 82	22.4°
.672 172	.338 356	.032 564	.005 56	.497 525	.027 94	22.5°
.672 221	.338 402	.032 707	.005 61	.497 503	.028 05	22.6°
.672 271	.338 448	.032 850	.005 65	.497 481	.028 17	22.7°
.672 322	.338 494	.032 994	.005 70	.497 458	.028 29	22.8°
.672 372	.338 540	.033 137	.005 75	.497 436	.028 41	22.9°
.672 423	.338 586	.033 280	.005 80	.497 414	.028 52	23.0°
.672 474	.338 633	.033 423	.005 85	.497 391	.028 64	23.1°
.672 525	.338 679	.033 567	.005 90	.497 369	.028 76	23.2°
.672 576	.338 726	.033 710	.005 95	.497 346	.028 87	23.3°
.672 628	.338 774	.033 853	.006 00	.497 323	.028 99	23.4°
.672 680	.338 821	.033 996	.006 05	.497 300	.029 11	23.5°
.672 732	.338 869	.034 139	.006 11	.497 277	.029 23	23.6°
.672 784	.338 917	.034 282	.006 16	.497 254	.029 34	23.7°
.672 837	.338 965	.034 425	.006 21	.497 231	.029 46	23.8°
.672 890	.339 013	.034 568	.006 26	.497 208	.029 58	23.9°
.672 943	.339 061	.034 711	.006 31	.497 185	.029 69	24.0°
.672 996	.339 110	.034 854	.006 36	.497 161	.029 81	24.1°
.673 050	.339 159	.034 997	.006 42	.497 138	.029 92	24.2°
.673 103	.339 208	.035 140	.006.47	.497 114	.030 04	24.3°
.673 157	.339 258	.035 283	.006 52	.497 090	.030 16	24.4°
.673 212	.339 307	.035 426	.006 57	.497 067	.030 27	24.5°
.673 266	.339 357	.035 569	.006 63	.497 043	.030 39	24.6°
.673 321	.339 407	.035 712	.006 68	.497 019	.030 50	34.7°
.673 376	.339 457	.035 855	.006 73	.496 995	.030 62	24.8°
.673 431	.339 508	.035 998	.006 79	.496 970	.030 74	24.9°
.673 486	.339 559	.036 140	.006 84	.496 946	.030 85	25.0°

Δ	A	$\dfrac{C}{L}$	$\dfrac{X}{L}$	$\dfrac{Y}{L}$
25.0°	8° 19′ 14″	.991 669	.981 231	.143 504
25.1°	8° 21′ 13″	.991 602	.981 082	.144 062
25.2°	8° 23′ 12″	.991 536	.980 932	.144 620
25.3°	8° 25′ 12″	.991 468	.980 782	.145 179
25.4°	8° 27′ 11″	.991 401	.980 631	.145 737
25.5°	8° 29′ 11″	.991 333	.980 479	.146 294
25.6°	8° 31′ 10″	.991 266	.980 327	.146 852
25.7°	8° 33′ 10″	.991 197	.980 175	.147 409
25.8°	8° 35′ 09″	.991 129	.980 022	.147 966
25.9°	8° 37′ 08″	.991 060	.979 868	.148 523
26.0°	8° 39′ 08″	.990 991	.979 714	.149 080
26.1°	8° 41′ 07″	.990 922	.979 559	.149 637
26.2°	8° 43′ 07″	.990 853	.979 403	.150 193
26.3°	8° 45′ 06″	.990 783	.979 247	.150 750
26.4°	8° 47′ 05″	.990 713	.979 091	.151 306
26.5°	8° 49′ 05″	.990 642	.978 933	.151 861
26.6°	8° 51′ 04″	.990 572	.978 776	.152 417
26.7°	8° 53′ 03″	.990 501	.978 617	.152 973
26.8°	8° 55′ 03″	.990 430	.978 458	.153 528
26.9°	8° 57′ 02″	.990 359	.978 299	.154 083
27.0°	8° 59′ 02″	.990 287	.978 139	.154 638
27.1°	9° 01′ 01″	.990 215	.977 978	.155 193
27.2°	9° 03′ 00″	.990 143	.977 817	.155 747
27.3°	9° 05′ 00″	.990 071	.977 655	.156 301
27.4°	9° 06′ 59″	.989 998	.977 493	.156 855
27.5°	9° 08′ 58″	.989 925	.977 330	.157 409
27.6°	9° 10′ 58″	.989 852	.977 167	.157 963
27.7°	9° 12′ 57″	.989 779	.977 003	.158 516
27.8°	9° 14′ 56″	.989 705	.976 838	.159 070
27.9°	9° 16′ 55″	.989 631	.976 673	.159 623
28.0°	9° 18′ 55″	.989 557	.976 507	.160 176
28.1°	9° 20′ 54″	.989 482	.976 341	.160 728
28.2°	9° 22′ 53″	.989 408	.976 174	.161 281
28.3°	9° 24′ 53″	.989 333	.976 007	.161 833
28.4°	9° 26′ 52″	.989 257	.975 839	.162 385
28.5°	9° 28′ 51″	.989 182	.975 670	.162 937
28.6°	9° 30′ 51″	.989 106	.975 501	.163 489
28.7°	9° 32′ 50″	.989 030	.975 331	.164 040
28.8°	9° 34′ 49″	.988 954	.975 161	.164 591
28.9°	9° 36′ 48″	.988 877	.974 990	.165 142
29.0°	9° 38′ 48″	.988 800	.974 819	.165 693
29.1°	9° 40′ 47″	.988 723	.974 647	.166 244
29.2°	9° 42′ 46″	.988 646	.974 475	.166 794
29.3°	9° 44′ 45″	.988 568	.974 302	.167 344
29.4°	9° 46′ 45″	.988 491	.974 128	.167 894
29.5°	9° 48′ 44″	.988 412	.973 954	.168 444
29.6°	9° 50′ 43″	.988 334	.973 779	.168 993
29.7°	9° 52′ 42″	.988 255	.973 604	.169 543
29.8°	9° 54′ 41″	.988 177	.973 428	.170 092
29.9°	9° 56′ 41″	.988 097	.973 251	.170 641
30.0°	9° 58′ 40″	.988 018	.973 074	.171 189

$\dfrac{U}{L}$	$\dfrac{V}{L}$	$0 = mL - nD$		$Z = mL - nD$		Δ
		m	**n**	**m**	**n**	
.673 486	.339 559	.036 140	.006 84	.496 946	.030 85	25.0°
.673 542	.339 610	.036 283	.006 89	.496 922	.030 97	25.1°
.673 598	.339 661	.036 426	.006 95	.496 897	.031 08	25.2°
.673 654	.339 712	.036 569	.007 00	.496 873	.031 20	25.3°
.673 710	.339 764	.036 711	.007 06	.496 848	.031 31	25.4°
.673 767	.339 815	.036 854	.007 11	.496 823	.031 43	25.5°
.673 824	.339 867	.036 997	.007 17	.496 798	.031 54	25.6°
.673 881	.339 920	.037 139	.007 22	.496 773	.031 66	25.7°
.673 938	.339 972	.037 282	.007 28	.496 748	.031 77	25.8°
.673 996	.340 025	.037 425	.007 33	.496 723	.031 89	25.9°
.674 054	.340 078	.037 567	.007 39	.496 698	.032 00	26.0°
.674 112	.340 131	.037 710	.007 44	.496 673	.032 12	26.1°
.674 170	.340 184	.037 852	.007 50	.496 647	.032 23	26.2°
.674 229	.340 238	.037 995	.007 56	.496 622	.032 34	26.3°
.674 287	.340 292	.038 138	.007 61	.496 596	.032 46	26 4°
.674 346	.340 346	.038 280	.007 67	.496 570	.032 57	26.5°
.674 406	.340 400	.038 422	.007 73	.496 544	.032 69	26.6°
.674 465	.340 454	.038 565	.007 78	.496 518	.032 80	26.7°
.674 525	.340 509	.038 707	.007 84	.496 492	.032 91	26.8°
.674 585	.340 564	.038 850	.007 90	.496 466	.033 03	26.9°
.674 645	.340 619	.038 992	.007 96	.496 440	.033 14	27.0°
.674 706	.340 674	.039 135	.008 01	.496 414	.033 25	27.1°
.674 766	.340 730	.039 277	.008 07	.496 387	.033 37	27.2°
.674 827	.340 786	.039 419	.008 13	.496 361	.033 48	27.3°
.674 888	.340 842	.039 561	.008 19	.496 334	.033 59	27.4°
.674 950	.340 808	.039 704	.008 25	.496 308	.033 71	27.5°
.675 012	.340 955	.039 846	.008 31	.496 281	.033 82	27.6°
.675 074	.341 011	.039 988	.008 37	.496 254	.033 93	27.7°
.675 136	.341 068	.040 130	.008 43	.496 227	.034 05	27.8°
.675 198	.341 125	.040 273	.008 49	.496 200	.034 16	27.9°
.675 261	.341 183	.040 415	.008 54	.496 173	.034 27	28.0°
.675 324	.341 240	.040 557	.008 60	.496 145	.034 38	28.1°
.675 387	.341 298	.040 699	.008 66	.496 118	.034 50	28.2°
.675 450	.341 356	.040 841	.008 73	.496 091	.034 61	28.3°
.675 514	.341 415	.040 983	.008 79	.496 063	.034 72	28.4°
.675 578	.341 473	.041 125	.008 85	.496 036	.034 83	28.5°
.675 642	.341 532	.041 267	.008 91	.496 008	.034 94	28.6°
.675 706	.341 591	.041 409	.008 97	.495 980	.035 06	28.7°
.675 771	.341 650	.041 551	.009 03	.495 952	.035 17	28.8°
.675 836	.341 710	.041 693	.009 09	.495 924	.035 28	28.9°
.675 901	.341 769	.041 835	.009 15	.495 896	.035 39	29.0°
.675 966	.341 829	.041 977	.009 21	.495 868	.035 50	29.1°
.676 032	.341 889	.042 119	.009 28	.495 839	.035 61	29.2°
.676 098	.341 950	.042 261	.009 34	.495 811	.035 72	29.3°
.676 164	.342 010	.042 402	.009 40	.495 782	.035 84	29.4°
.676 230	.342 071	.042 544	.009 46	.495 754	.035 95	29.5°
.676 297	.342 132	.042 686	.009 53	.495 725	.036 06	29.6°
.676 364	.342 193	.042 828	.009 59	.495 696	.036 17	29.7°
.676 431	.342 255	.042 970	.009 65	.495 668	.036 28	29.8°
.676 498	.342 316	.043 111	.009 72	.495 639	.036 39	29.9°
.676 566	.342 378	.043 253	.009 78	.495 610	.036 50	30.0°

Δ	A	$\dfrac{C}{L}$	$\dfrac{X}{L}$	$\dfrac{Y}{L}$
30.0°	9° 58′ 40″	.988 018	.973 074	.171 189
30.1°	10° 00′ 39″	.987 938	.972 897	.171 738
30.2°	10° 02′ 38″	.987 858	.972 719	.172 286
30.3°	10° 04′ 37″	.987 778	.972 540	.172 834
30.4°	10° 06′ 37″	.987 698	.972 361	.173 382
30.5°	10° 08′ 36″	.987 617	.972 181	.173 929
30.6°	10° 10′ 35″	.987 536	.972 000	.174 477
30.7°	10° 12′ 34″	.987 455	.971 820	.175 024
30.8°	10° 14′ 33″	.987 373	.971 638	.175 571
30.9°	10° 16′ 32″	.987 291	.971 456	.176 117
31.0°	10° 18′ 32″	.987 209	.971 273	.176 664
31.1°	10° 20′ 31″	.987 127	.971 090	.177 210
31.2°	10° 22′ 30″	.987 044	.970 907	.177 756
31.3°	10° 24′ 29″	.986 962	.970 722	.178 302
31.4°	10° 26′ 28″	.986 879	.970 737	.178 847
31.5°	10° 28′ 27″	.986 795	.970 352	.179 392
31.6°	10° 30′ 26″	.986 712	.970 166	.179 938
31.7°	10° 32′ 25″	.986 628	.969 980	.180 482
31.8°	10° 34′ 24″	.986 544	.969 792	.181 027
31.9°	10° 36′ 24″	.986 459	.969 605	.181 571
32.0°	10° 38′ 23″	.986 375	.969 417	.182 116
32.1°	10° 40′ 22″	.986 290	.969 228	.182 659
32.2°	10° 42′ 21″	.986 205	.969 039	.183 203
32.3°	10° 44′ 20″	.986 119	.968 849	.183 747
32.4°	10° 46′ 19″	.986 033	.968 658	.184 290
32.5°	10° 48′ 18″	.985 948	.968 467	.184 833
32.6°	10° 50′ 17″	.985 861	.968 276	.185 376
32.7°	10° 52′ 16″	.985 775	.968 084	.185 918
32.8°	10° 54′ 15″	.985 688	.967 891	.186 460
32.9°	10° 56′ 14″	.985 601	.967 698	.187 002
33.0°	10° 58′ 13″	.985 514	.967 504	.187 544
33.1°	11° 00′ 12″	.985 426	.967 310	.188 086
33.2°	11° 02′ 11″	.985 339	.967 115	.188 627
33.3°	11° 04′ 10″	.985 251	.966 920	.189 168
33.4°	11° 06′ 09″	.985 162	.966 724	.189 709
33.5°	11° 08′ 08″	.985 074	.966 528	.190 250
33.6°	11° 10′ 07″	.984 985	.966 331	.190 790
33.7°	11° 12′ 06″	.984 896	.966 133	.191 330
33.8°	11° 14′ 05″	.984 807	.965 935	.191 870
33.9°	11° 16′ 04″	.984 717	.965 736	.192 410
34.0°	11° 18′ 03″	.984 627	.965 537	.192 949
34.1°	11° 20′ 02″	.984 537	.965 337	.193 488
34.2°	11° 22′ 01″	.984 447	.965 137	.194 027
34.3°	11° 24′ 00″	.984 356	.964 936	.194 566
34.4°	11° 25′ 59″	.984 265	.964 735	.195 104
34.5°	11° 27′ 58″	.984 174	.964 533	.195 643
34.6°	11° 29′ 57″	.984 083	.964 330	.196 180
34.7°	11° 31′ 56″	.983 991	.964 127	.196 718
34.8°	11° 33′ 55″	.933 899	.963 923	.197 256
34.9°	11° 35′ 54″	.983 807	.963 719	.197 793
35.0°	11° 37′ 53″	.983 715	.963 515	.198 330

$\dfrac{U}{L}$	$\dfrac{V}{L}$	$0 = mL - nD$		$Z = mL - nD$		Δ
		m	n	m	n	
.676 566	.342 378	.043 253	.009 78	.495 610	.036 50	30.0°
.676 634	.342 441	.043 395	.009 84	.495 580	.036 61	30.1°
.676 702	.342 503	.043 536	.009 91	.495 551	.036 72	30.2°
.676 770	.342 566	.043 678	.009 97	.495 522	.036 83	30.3°
.676 839	.342 629	.043 819	.010 04	.495 492	.036 94	30.4°
.676 908	.342 692	.043 961	.010 10	.495 463	.037 05	30.5°
.676 977	.342 755	.044 102	.010 17	.495 433	.037 16	30.6°
.677 046	.342 819	.044 244	.010 23	.495 403	.037 27	30.7°
.677 116	.342 882	.044 385	.010 30	.495 374	.037 38	30.8°
.677 186	.342 947	.044 527	.010 36	.495 344	.037 49	30.9°
.677 256	.343 011	.044 668	.010 43	.495 314	.037 60	31.0°
.677 326	.343 075	.044 810	.010 49	.495 284	.037 71	31.1°
.677 397	.343 140	.044 951	.010 56	.495 253	.037 82	31.2°
.677 468	.343 205	.045 092	.010 62	.495 223	.037 92	31.3°
.677 539	.343 270	.045 234	.010 69	.495 193	.038 03	31.4°
.677 610	.343 336	.045 375	.010 76	.495 162	.038 14	31.5°
.677 682	.343 401	.045 516	.010 82	.495 132	.038 25	31.6°
.677 754	.343 467	.045 658	.010 89	.495 101	.038 36	31.7°
.677 826	.343 534	.045 799	.010 96	.495 070	.038 47	31.8°
.677 898	.343 600	.045 940	.011 03	.495 039	.038 58	31.9°
.677 971	.343 667	.046 081	.011 09	.495 008	.038 68	32.0°
.678 044	.343 733	.046 222	.011 16	.494 977	.038 79	32.1°
.678 117	.343 801	.046 363	.011 23	.494 946	.038 90	32.2°
.678 190	.343 868	.046 504	.011 30	.494 915	.039 01	32.3°
.678 264	.343 936	.046 646	.011 36	.494 884	.039 12	32.4°
.678 338	.344 003	.046 787	.011 43	.494 852	.039 22	33.5°
.678 412	.344 071	.046 928	.011 50	.494 821	.039 33	32.6°
.678 487	.344 140	.047 069	.011 57	.494 789	.039 44	32.7°
.678 561	.344 208	.047 210	.011 64	.494 757	.039 54	32.8°
.678 636	.344 277	.047 350	.011 71	.494 725	.039 65	32.9°
.678 712	.344 346	.047 491	.011 78	.494 694	.039 76	33.0°
.678 787	.344 415	.047 632	.011 85	.494 662	.039 87	33.1°
.678 863	.344 485	.047 773	.011 92	.494 629	.039 97	33.2°
.678 939	.344 555	.047 914	.011 99	.494 597	.040 08	33.3°
.679 015	.344 625	.048 055	.012 06	.494 565	.040 19	33.4°
.679 092	.344 695	.048 195	.012 13	.494 533	.040 29	33.5°
.679 168	.344 765	.048 336	.012 20	.494 500	.040 40	33.6°
.679 245	.344 836	.048 477	.012 27	.494 468	.040 50	33.7°
.679 323	.344 907	.048 618	.012 34	.494 435	.040 61	33.8°
.679 400	.344 978	.048 758	.012 41	.494 402	.040 72	33.9°
.679 478	.345 049	.048 899	.012 48	.494 369	.040 82	34.0°
.679 556	.345 121	.049 039	.012 55	.494 336	.040 93	34.1°
.679 634	.345 193	.049 180	.012 62	.494 303	.041 03	34.2°
.679 713	.345 265	.049 321	.012 69	.494 270	.041 14	34.3°
.679 792	.345 338	.049 461	.012 77	.494 237	.041 24	34.4°
.679 871	.345 410	.049 602	.012 84	.494 204	.041 35	34.5°
.679 950	.345 483	.049 742	.012 91	.494 170	.041 45	34.6°
.680 030	.345 556	.049 882	.012 98	.494 137	.041 56	34.7°
.680 110	.345 630	.050 023	.013 06	.494 103	.041 66	34.8°
.680 190	.345 703	.050 163	.013 13	.494 070	.041 77	34.9°
.680 270	.345 777	.050 304	.013 20	.494 036	.041 87	35.0°

Δ	A	$\frac{C}{L}$	$\frac{X}{L}$	$\frac{Y}{L}$
35.0°	11° 37′ 53″	.983 715	.963 515	.198 330
35.1°	11° 39′ 52″	.983 622	.963 309	.198 866
35.2°	11° 41′ 50″	.983 529	.963 103	.199 403
35.3°	11° 43′ 49″	.983 436	.962 897	.199 939
35.4°	11° 45′ 48″	.983 343	.962 690	.200 475
35.5°	11° 47′ 47″	.983 249	.962 483	.201 010
35.6°	11° 49′ 46″	.983 155	.962 275	.201 546
35.7°	11° 51′ 45″	.983 061	.962 066	.202 081
35.8°	11° 53′ 44″	.982 966	.961 857	.202 616
35.9°	11° 55′ 43″	.982 872	.961 648	.203 151
36.0°	11° 57′ 41″	.982 777	.961 438	.203 685
36.1°	11° 59′ 40″	.982 681	.961 227	.204 219
36.2°	12° 01′ 39″	.982 586	.961 016	.204 753
36.3°	12° 03′ 38″	.982 490	.960 804	.205 286
36.4°	12° 05′ 37″	.982 394	.960 592	.205 820
36.5°	12° 07′ 36″	.982 298	.960 379	.206 353
36.6°	12° 09′ 34″	.982 201	.960 165	.206 886
36.7°	12° 11′ 33″	.982 104	.959 951	.207 418
36.8°	12° 13′ 32″	.982 007	.959 737	.207 951
36.9°	12° 15′ 31″	.981 910	.959 522	.208 483
37.0°	12° 17′ 30″	.981 812	.959 306	.209 014
37.1°	12° 19′ 28″	.981 715	.959 090	.209 546
37.2°	12° 21′ 27″	.981 617	.958 874	.210 077
37.3°	12° 23′ 26″	.981 518	.958 657	.210 608
37.4°	12° 25′ 25″	.981 420	.958 439	.211 139
37.5°	12° 27′ 23″	.981 321	.958 221	.211 669
37.6°	12° 29′ 22″	.981 222	.958 002	.212 199
37.7°	12° 31′ 21″	.981 122	.957 783	.212 729
37.8°	12° 33′ 20″	.981 023	.957 563	.213 259
37.9°	12° 35′ 18″	.980 923	.957 342	.213 788
38.0°	12° 37′ 17″	.980 823	.957 121	.214 317
38.1°	12° 39′ 16″	.980 722	.956 900	.214 846
38.2°	12° 41′ 14″	.980 622	.956 678	.215 375
38.3°	12° 43′ 13″	.980 521	.956 455	.215 903
38.4°	12° 45′ 12″	.980 420	.956 232	.216 431
38.5°	12° 47′ 11″	.980 318	.956 009	.216 959
38.6°	12° 49′ 09″	.980 217	.955 785	.217 486
38.7°	12° 51′ 08″	.980 115	.955 560	.218 013
38.8°	12° 53′ 07″	.980 012	.955 335	.218 540
38.9°	12° 55′ 05″	.979 910	.955 109	.219 067
39.0°	12° 57′ 04″	.979 807	.954 883	.219 593
39.1°	12° 59′ 02″	.979 704	.954 656	.220 119
39.2°	13° 01′ 01″	.979 601	.954 429	.220 645
39.3°	13° 03′ 00″	.979 498	.954 201	.221 171
39.4°	13° 04′ 58″	.979 394	.953 973	.221 696
39.5°	13° 06′ 57″	.979 290	.953 744	.222 221
39.6°	13° 08′ 56″	.979 186	.953 514	.222 745
39.7°	13° 10′ 54″	.979 081	.953 284	.223 270
39.8°	13° 12′ 53″	.978 977	.953 054	.223 794
39.9°	13° 14′ 51″	.978 872	.952 823	.224 318
40.0°	13° 16′ 50″	.978 766	.952 591	.224 841

$\dfrac{U}{L}$	$\dfrac{V}{L}$	$0 = mL - nD$		$Z = mL - nD$		Δ
		m	n	m	n	
.680 270	.345 777	.050 304	.013 20	.494 036	.041 87	35.0°
.680 351	.345 851	.050 444	.013 28	.494 002	.041 98	35.1°
.680 432	.345 926	.050 584	.013 35	.493 968	.042 08	35.2°
.680 513	.346 000	.050 724	.013 42	.493 934	.042 18	35.3°
.680 595	.346 075	.050 865	.013 50	.493 900	.042 29	35.4°
.680 677	.346 150	.051 005	.013 57	.493 866	.042 39	35.5°
.680 759	.346 226	.051 145	.013 64	.493 831	.042 49	35.6°
.680 841	.346 301	.051 285	.013 72	.493 797	.042 60	35.7°
.680 923	.346 377	.051 425	.013 79	.493 762	.042 70	35.8°
.681 006	.346 453	.051 565	.013 87	.493 728	.042 81	35.9°
.681 089	.346 529	.051 705	.013 94	.493 693	.042 91	36.0°
.681 173	.346 606	.051 845	.014 02	.493 658	.043 01	36.1°
.681 256	.346 683	.051 985	.014 09	.493 623	.043 11	36.2°
.681 340	.346 760	.052 125	.014 17	.493 588	.043 22	36.3°
.681 424	.346 837	.052 265	.014 24	.493 553	.043 32	36.4°
.681 509	.346 915	.052 405	.014 32	.493 518	.043 42	36.5°
.681 594	.346 993	.052 545	.014 39	.493 483	.043 52	36.6°
.681 679	.347 071	.052 685	.014 47	.493 447	.043 63	36.7°
.681 764	.347 149	.052 825	.014 55	.493 412	.043 73	36.8°
.681 849	.347 228	.052 965	.014 62	.493 376	.043 83	36.9°
.681 935	.347 307	.053 104	.014 70	.493 341	.043 93	37.0°
.682 021	.347 386	.053 244	.014 78	.493 305	.044 03	37.1°
.682 107	.347 465	.053 384	.014 85	.493 269	.044 14	37.2°
.682 194	.347 545	.053 523	.014 93	.493 233	.044 24	37.3°
.682 281	.347 625	.053 663	.015 01	.493 197	.044 34	37.4°
.682 368	.347 705	.053 803	.015 09	.493 161	.044 44	37.5°
.682 455	.347 785	.053 942	.015 16	.493 125	.044 54	37.6°
.682 543	.347 866	.054 082	.015 24	.493 089	.044 64	37.7°
.682 631	.347 947	.054 221	.015 32	.493 052	.044 74	37.8°
.682 719	.348 028	.054 361	.015 40	.493 016	.044 84	37.9°
.682 808	.348 109	.054 500	.015 48	.492 979	.044 94	38.0°
.682 896	.348 191	.054 640	.015 55	.492 943	.045 04	38.1°
.682 986	.348 273	.054 779	.015 63	.492 906	.045 14	38.2°
.683 075	.348 355	.054 919	.015 71	.492 869	.045 24	38.3°
.683 164	.348 437	.055 058	.015 79	.492 832	.045 34	38.4°
.683 254	.348 520	.055 197	.015 87	.492 795	.045 44	38.5°
.683 344	.348 603	.055 336	.015 95	.492 758	.045 54	38.6°
.683 435	.348 686	.055 476	.016 03	.492 721	.045 64	38.7°
.683 526	.348 769	.055 615	.016 11	.492 683	.045 74	38.8°
.683 617	.348 853	.055 754	.016 19	.492 646	.045 84	38.9°
.683 708	.348 937	.055 893	.016 27	.492 608	.045 94	39.0°
.683 799	.349 021	.056 032	.016 35	.492 571	.046 04	39.1°
.683 891	.349 106	.056 171	.016 43	.492 533	.046 14	39.2°
.683 983	.349 190	.056 310	.016 51	.492 495	.046 24	39.3°
.684 076	.349 275	.056 450	.016 59	.492 458	.046 34	39.4°
.684 168	.349 361	.056 589	.016 67	.492 420	.046 43	39.5°
.684 261	.349 446	.056 727	.016 75	.492 382	.046 53	39.6°
.684 354	.349 532	.056 866	.016 83	.492 343	.046 63	39.7°
.684 448	.349 618	.057 005	.016 92	.492 305	.046 73	39.8°
.684 542	.349 704	.057 144	.017 00	.492 267	.046 83	39.9°
.684 636	.349 791	.057 283	.017 08	.492 229	.046 92	40.0°

Δ	A	$\frac{C}{L}$	$\frac{X}{L}$	$\frac{Y}{L}$
40.0°	13° 16′ 50″	.978 766	.952 591	.224 841
40.1°	13° 18′ 48″	.978 661	.952 359	.225 365
40.2°	13° 20′ 47″	.978 555	.952 127	.225 888
40.3°	13° 22′ 46″	.978 449	.951 893	.226 410
40.4°	13° 24′ 44″	.978 343	.951 660	.226 933
40.5°	13° 26′ 43″	.978 236	.951 426	.227 455
40.6°	13° 28′ 41″	.978 130	.951 191	.227 977
40.7°	13° 30′ 40″	.978 023	.950 956	.228 498
40.8°	13° 32′ 38″	.977 915	.950 720	.229 019
40.9°	13° 34′ 37″	.977 808	.950 484	.229 540
41.0°	13° 36′ 25″	.977 700	.950 247	.230 061
41.1°	13° 38′ 34″	.977 592	.950 010	.230 581
41.2°	13° 40′ 32″	.977 484	.949 772	.231 102
41.3°	13° 42′ 31″	.977 375	.949 533	.231 621
41.4°	13° 44′ 29″	.977 266	.949 294	.232 141
41.5°	13° 46′ 28″	.977 157	.949 055	.232 660
41.6°	13° 48′ 26″	.977 048	.948 815	.233 179
41.7°	13° 50′ 25″	.976 938	.948 575	.233 698
41.8°	13° 52′ 23″	.976 828	.948 334	.234 216
41.9°	13° 54′ 22″	.976 718	.948 092	.234 734
42.0°	13° 56′ 20″	.976 608	.947 850	.235 252
42.1°	13° 58′ 18″	.976 497	.947 608	.235 769
42.2°	14° 00′ 17″	.976 387	.947 365	.236 286
42.3°	14° 02′ 15″	.976 276	.947 121	.236 803
42.4°	14° 04′ 14″	.976 164	.946 877	.237 320
42.5°	14° 06′ 12″	.976 053	.946 632	.237 836
42.6°	14° 08′ 10″	.975 941	.946 387	.238 352
42.7°	14° 10′ 09″	.975 829	.946 142	.238 868
42.8°	14° 12′ 07″	.975 716	.945 895	.239 383
42.9°	14° 14′ 06″	.975 604	.945 649	.239 898
43.0°	14° 16′ 04″	.975 491	.945 401	.240 413
43.1°	14° 18′ 02″	975 378	.945 154	.240 927
43.2°	14° 20′ 01″	.975 264	.944 906	.241 442
43.3°	14° 21′ 59″	.975 151	.944 657	.241 956
43.4°	14° 23′ 57″	.975 037	.944 408	.242 469
43.5°	14° 25′ 56″	.974 923	.944 158	.242 982
43.6°	14° 27′ 54″	.974 808	.943 908	.243 495
43.7°	14° 29′ 52″	974 694	.943 657	.244 008
43.8°	14° 31′ 50″	.974 579	.943 405	.244 520
43.9°	14° 33′ 49″	.974 464	.943 154	.245 032
44.0°	14° 35′ 47″	.974 348	.942 901	.245 544
44.1°	14° 37′ 45″	.974 233	.942 648	.246 055
44.2°	14° 39′ 44″	.974 117	.942 395	.246 566
44.3°	14° 41′ 42″	.974 001	.942 141	.247 077
44.4°	14° 43′ 40″	.973 884	.941 887	.247 588
44.5°	14° 45′ 38″	.973 768	.941 632	.248 098
44.6°	14° 47′ 37″	.973 651	.941 377	.248 608
44.7°	14° 49′ 35″	.973 534	.941 121	.249 117
44.8°	14° 51′ 33″	.973 416	.940 864	.249 627
44.9°	14° 53′ 31″	.973 299	.940 607	.250 135
45.0°	14° 55′ 29″	.973 181	.940 350	.250 644

$\frac{U}{L}$	$\frac{V}{L}$	$0 = mL - nD$		$Z = mL - nD$		Δ
		m	n	m	n	
.684 636	.349 791	.057 283	.017 08	.492 229	.046 92	40.0°
.684 730	.349 878	.057 422	.017 16	.492 190	.047 02	40.1°
.684 825	.349 965	.057 561	.017 24	.492 151	.047 12	40.2°
.684 920	.350 052	.057 699	.017 33	.492 113	.047 22	40.3°
.685 015	.350 140	.057 838	.017 41	.492 074	.047 31	40.4°
.685 110	.350 228	.057 977	.017 49	.492 035	.047 41	40.5°
.685 206	.350 316	.058 115	.017 57	.491 996	.047 51	40.6°
.685 302	.350 404	.058 254	.017 66	.491 957	.047 60	40.7°
.685 398	.350 493	.058 393	.017 74	.491 918	.047 70	40.8°
.685 495	.350 582	.058 531	.017 82	.491 879	.047 80	40.9°
.685 592	.350 671	.058 670	.017 91	.491 839	.047 89	41.0°
.685 689	.350 761	.058 808	.017 99	.491 800	.047 99	41.1°
.685 786	.350 851	.058 946	.018 07	.491 760	.048 08	41.2°
.685 884	.350 941	.059 085	.018 16	.491 721	.048 18	41.3°
.685 982	.351 031	.059 223	.018 24	.491 681	.048 28	41.4°
.386 081	.351 121	.059 362	.018 33	.491 641	.048 37	41.5°
.686 179	.351 212	.059 500	.018 41	.491 602	.048 47	41.6°
.686 278	.351 303	.059 638	.018 50	.491 562	.048 56	41.7°
.686 377	.351 395	.059 776	.018 58	.491 521	.048 66	41.8°
.686 477	.351 486	.059 915	.018 67	.491 481	.048 75	41.9°
.686 576	.351 578	.060 053	.018 75	.491 441	.048 85	42.0°
.685 677	.351 671	.060 191	.018 84	.491 401	.048 94	42.1°
.686 777	.351 763	.030 329	.018 92	.491 360	.049 04	42.2°
.686 878	.351 856	.060 467	.019 01	.491 320	.049 13	42.3°
.686 978	.351 949	.060 605	.019 09	.491 279	.049 22	42.4°
.687 080	.352 042	.030 743	.019 18	.491 239	.049 32	42.5°
.687 181	.352 136	.060 881	.019 26	.491 198	.049 41	42.6°
.687 283	.352 229	.031 019	.019 35	.491 157	.049 51	42.7°
.687 385	.352 324	.031 157	.019 44	.491 116	.049 60	42.8°
.687 487	.352 418	.061 295	.019 52	.491 075	.049 69	42.9°
.687 590	.352 513	.061 433	.019 61	.491 034	.049 79	43.0°
.687 693	.352 608	.061 571	.019 70	.490 992	.049 88	43.1°
.687 796	.352 703	.061 708	.019 79	.490 951	.049 97	43.2°
.687 900	.352 798	.061 846	.019 87	.490 910	.050 06	43.3°
.688 004	.352 894	.061 984	.019 96	.490 868	.050 16	43.4°
.688 108	.352 990	.032 122	.020 05	.490 827	.050 25	43.5°
.688 212	.353 086	.062 259	.020 14	.490 785	.050 34	43.6°
.688 317	.353 183	.062 397	.020 22	.490 743	.050 43	43.7°
.688 422	.353 280	.062 534	.020 31	.490 701	.050 53	43.8°
.688 527	.353 377	.062 672	.020 40	.490 659	.050 62	43.9°
.688 633	.353 474	.062 809	.020 49	.490 617	.050 71	44.0°
.688 739	.353 572	.062 947	.020 58	.490 575	.050 80	44.1°
.688 845	.353 670	.063 084	.020 67	.490 533	.050 89	44.2°
.688 952	.353 768	.063 222	.020 75	.490 491	.050 98	44.3°
.689 059	.353 867	.063 359	.020 84	.490 448	.051 08	44.4°
.689 166	.353 966	.033 496	.020 93	.490 406	.051 17	44.5°
.689 273	.354 065	.033 634	.021 02	.490 363	.051 26	44.6°
.689 381	.354 164	.063 771	.021 11	.490 320	.051 35	44.7°
.689 489	.354 264	.033 908	.021 20	.490 278	.051 44	44.8°
.689 597	.354 364	.064 045	.021 29	.490 235	.051 53	44.9°
.689 706	.354 464	.064 182	.021 38	.490 192	.051 62	45.0°

EXPLANATION TO ACCOMPANY TABLES VII AND VIII

The length of the spiral usually is determined from the degree of curve of the circular curve and the speed. Since $\dfrac{D}{S} = k$, it is possible

L	D	Δ	A	Z	O	C	X	Y	U	V
	° ′	° ′	° ′	′						
10	0 0.6	0 0.1	0 0.0	5.00	0.00	10.00	10.00	0.00	6.67	3.33
20	1.2	.1	.1	10.00	.00	20.00	20.00	.00	13.33	6.67
30	1.8	.3	.1	15.00	.00	30.00	30.00	.00	20.00	10.00
40	2.4	.5	.2	20.00	.00	40.00	40.00	.00	26.67	13.33
50	3.0	.8	.2	25.00	.00	50.00	50.00	.00	33.33	16.67
60	3.6	1.1	.4	30.00	.00	60.00	60.00	.01	40.00	20.00
70	4.2	1.5	.5	35.00	.00	70.00	70.00	.01	46.67	23.33
80	4.8	1.9	.7	40.00	.00	80.00	80.00	.01	53.33	26.67
90	5.4	2.5	.8	45.00	.01	90.00	90.00	.02	60.00	30.00
100	6.0	3.0	1.0	50.00	.01	100.00	100.00	.03	66.67	33.33
110	6.6	3.7	1.2	55.00	.01	110.00	110.00	.04	73.33	36.67
120	7.2	4.3	1.4	60.00	.01	120.00	120.00	.05	80.00	40.00
130	7.8	5.1	1.7	65.00	.02	130.00	130.00	.06	86.67	43.33
140	8.4	5.9	1.9	70.00	.02	140.00	140.00	.08	93.33	46.67
150	9.0	6.8	2.2	75.00	.03	150.00	150.00	.10	100.00	50.00
160	9.6	7.7	2.5	80.00	.03	160.00	160.00	.12	106.67	53.33
170	10.2	8.7	2.9	85.00	.04	170.00	170.00	.14	113.33	56.67
180	10.8	9.7	3.2	90.00	.04	180.00	180.00	.17	120.00	60.00
190	11.4	10.9	3.6	95.00	.05	190.00	190.00	.20	126.67	63.33
200	12.0	12.0	4.0	100.00	.06	200.00	200.00	.23	133.33	66.67
210	12.6	13.2	4.4	105.00	.07	210.00	210.00	.27	140.00	70.00
220	13.2	14.5	4.9	110.00	.08	220.00	220.00	.31	146.67	73.33
230	13.8	15.9	5.3	115.00	.09	230.00	230.00	.35	153.33	76.67
240	14.4	17.3	5.8	120.00	.10	240.00	240.00	.40	160.00	80.00
250	15.0	18.8	6.2	125.00	.12	250.00	250.00	.46	166.67	83.33
260	15.6	20.3	6.8	130.00	.13	260.00	260.00	.51	173.33	86.67
270	16.2	21.9	7.3	135.00	.14	270.00	270.00	.57	180.00	90.00
280	16.8	23.5	7.9	140.00	.16	280.00	280.00	.64	186.67	93.33
290	17.4	25.3	8.4	145.00	.18	290.00	290.00	.71	193.33	96.67
300	18.0	27.0	9.0	150.00	.20	300.00	300.00	.79	200.00	100.00
310	18.6	28.9	9.6	155.00	.22	310.00	310.00	.87	206.67	103.34
320	19.2	30.7	10.3	160.00	.24	320.00	320.00	.95	213.33	106.67
330	19.8	32.7	10.9	165.00	.26	330.00	330.00	1.05	220.00	110.00
340	20.4	34.7	11.6	170.00	.29	340.00	340.00	1.15	226.67	113.34
350	21.0	36.9	12.3	175.00	.31	350.00	350.00	1.25	233.33	116.67
360	21.6	38.9	13.0	180.00	.34	360.00	360.00	1.36	240.00	120.00
370	22.2	41.1	13.7	185.00	.37	370.00	370.00	1.47	246.67	123.34
380	22.8	43.3	14.4	190.00	.40	380.00	380.00	1.60	253.33	126.67
390	23.4	45.7	15.2	195.00	.43	390.00	390.00	1.73	260.00	130.00
400	24.0	48.0	16.0	200.00	.46	400.00	399.99	1.86	266.67	133.34
410	24.6	50.5	16.9	205.00	.50	410.00	409.99	2.00	273.34	136.67
420	25.2	52.9	17.6	210.00	.54	420.00	419.99	2.15	280.01	140.00
430	25.8	55.5	18.5	215.00	.58	430.00	429.99	2.32	286.67	143.34
440	26.4	58.1	19.3	220.00	.62	440.00	439.99	2.48	293.34	146.67
450	27.0	1 00.8	20.2	225.00	.66	450.00	449.99	2.66	300.01	150.00
460	27.6	03.5	21.1	230.00	.70	459.99	459.98	2.83	306.67	153.34
470	28.2	06.3	22.1	235.00	.76	469.99	469.98	3.03	313.34	156.67
480	28.8	09.1	23.0	240.00	.81	479.99	479.98	3.22	320.01	160.01
490	29.4	12.1	24.0	245.00	.86	489.99	489.98	3.43	326.67	163.34
500	30.0	15.0	25.0	250.00	.91	499.99	499.97	3.64	333.34	166.67

* Am. Ry. Eng. Assoc. Ten-Chord Spiral.

to turn in this table directly to the page giving the nearest value of k, and to use these values of k, L, and D or some slight modification of them. Interpolation within a table or between adjacent tables is usually sufficiently precise.

Note that not only are the values for the final point of the spiral, the S.C., given on a horizontal line, but the successive deflection

L	D	Δ	A	Z	O	C	X	Y	U	V
	° ′	° ′	° ′	′						
510	0 30.6	1 18.1	0 26.0	254.99	0.96	509.99	509.97	3.86	340.01	170.01
520	31.2	21.1	27.0	259.99	1.02	519.98	519.97	4.09	346.68	173.34
530	31.8	24.3	28.1	264.99	1.08	529.98	529.97	4.34	353.35	176.68
540	32.4	27.5	29.2	269.99	1.14	539.98	539.96	4.58	360.01	180.01
550	33.0	30.8	30.2	274.99	1.21	549.98	549.96	4.85	366.68	183.35
560	33.6	34.1	31.3	279.99	1.28	559.98	559.96	5.11	373.35	186.68
570	34.2	37.5	32.5	284.99	1.35	569.93	569.95	5.38	380.01	190.02
580	34.8	40.9	33.6	289.99	1.42	579.98	579.95	5.68	386.68	193.35
590	35.4	44.5	34.8	294.99	1.49	589.98	589.95	5.98	393.35	196.68
600	36.0	48.0	36.0	299.99	1.57	599.98	599.95	6.28	400.02	200.02
610	36.6	51.7	37.2	304.99	1.65	609.97	609.93	6.60	406.69	203.36
620	37.2	55.3	38.4	309.99	1.73	619.97	619.93	6.93	413.36	206.69
630	37.8	59.1	39.7	314.99	1.81	629.97	629.92	7.27	420.03	210.02
640	38.4	2 02.9	40.9	319.99	1.91	639.97	639.92	7.62	426.69	213.36
650	39.0	06.8	42.2	324.99	2.00	649 96	649.92	7.99	433.36	216.70
660	39.6	10.7	43.6	329.99	2.09	659.96	659.90	8.36	440.03	220.03
670	40.2	14.7	45.0	334.99	2.19	669.96	669.90	8.75	446.70	223.36
680	40.8	18.7	46.3	339.98	2.29	679.95	679.89	9.15	453.37	226.70
690	41.4	22.9	47.6	344.98	2.39	689.94	689.88	9.56	460.04	230.04
700	42.0	27.0	49.0	349.98	2.49	699.94	699.87	9.98	466.71	233.37
710	42.6	31.3	50.4	354.98	2.60	709.94	709.87	10.42	473.38	236.71
720	43.2	35.5	51.8	359.98	2.71	719.94	719.86	10.85	480.05	240.05
730	43.8	39.9	53.3	364.97	2.83	729.93	729.84	11.31	486.72	243.38
740	44.4	44.3	54.7	369.97	2.95	739.93	739.84	11.79	493.30	246.72
750	45.0	48.8	56.2	374.97	3.07	749.93	749.82	12.28	500.06	250.06
760	45.6	53.2	57.7	379.97	3.19	759.92	759.81	12.78	506.74	253.40
770	46.2	57.9	59.3	384.97	3.32	769.92	769.80	13.28	513.41	256.73
780	46.8	3 02.5	1 00.8	389.97	3.45	779.91	779.78	13.80	520.08	260.07
790	47.4	07.3	02.4	394.96	3.59	789.90	789.77	14.34	526.75	263.41
800	48.0	12.0	04.0	399.96	3.72	799.89	799.75	14.89	533.42	266.74
810	48.6	16.9	05.6	404.96	3.86	809.88	809.73	15.45	540.09	270.09
820	49.2	21.7	07.3	409.95	4.01	819.88	819.72	16.03	546.77	273.43
830	49.8	26.7	08.9	414.95	4.16	829.88	829.70	16.62	553.44	276.76
840	50.4	31.7	10.6	419.95	4.31	839.87	839.68	17.23	560.11	280.10
850	51.0	36.8	12.2	424.95	4.47	849.86	849.67	17.87	566.79	283.44
860	51.6	41.9	14.0	429.94	4.63	859.84	859.65	18.50	573.46	286.78
870	52.2	47.1	15.7	434.94	4.79	869.83	869.62	19.16	580.13	290.12
880	52.8	52.3	17.5	439.94	4.96	879.82	879.60	19.82	586.81	293.46
890	53.4	57.6	19.2	444.93	5.13	889.81	889.58	20.50	593.48	296.81
900	54.0	4 03.0	21.0	449.93	5.30	899.80	899.55	21.20	600.16	300.14
910	54.6	07.5	22.9	454.93	5.48	909.79	909.53	21.91	606.83	303.49
920	55.2	13.9	24.7	459.92	5.67	919.78	919.50	22.65	613.51	306.83
930	55.8	19.5	26.5	464.91	5.86	929.77	929.47	23.40	620.18	310.16
940	56.4	25.1	28.4	469.91	6.04	939.76	939.45	24.15	626.86	313.51
950	57.0	30.8	30.2	474.90	6.23	949.74	949.42	24.94	633.54	316.85
960	57.6	36.5	32.2	479.89	6.43	959.72	959.39	25.73	640.21	320.20
970	58.2	42.3	34.1	484.88	6.63	969.70	969.35	26.54	646.89	323.54
980	58.8	48.1	36.1	489.88	6.84	979.70	979.31	27.36	653.57	326.89
990	59.4	54.1	38.0	494.87	7.06	989.68	989.28	28.20	660.25	330.23
1000	1 00.0	5 00.0	40.0	499.87	7.27	999.67	999.24	29.07	666.93	333.58

angles and the x and y coordinates for intermediate points on the same spiral are given in the respective vertical columns under A, X, and Y.

For the A.R.E.A. Spiral (Chord Definition)

Tabular entries in Tables VII and VIII are precisely correct.

L	D	Δ	A	Z	O	C	X	Y	U	V
	° ′	° ′	° ′	′						
10	0 1.2	0 0.1	0 0.0	5.00	0.00	10.00	10.00	0.00	6.67	3.33
20	2.4	.2	.1	10.00	.00	20.00	20.00	.00	13.33	6.67
30	3.6	.5	.2	15.00	.00	30.00	30.00	.00	20.00	10.00
40	4.8	1.0	.3	20.00	.00	40.00	40.00	.00	26.67	13.33
50	6.0	1.5	.5	25.00	.00	50.00	50.00	.01	33.33	16.67
60	7.2	2.2	.7	30.00	.00	60.00	60.00	.01	40.00	20.00
70	8.4	2.9	1.0	35.00	.00	70.00	70.00	.02	46.67	23.33
80	9.6	3.8	1.3	40.00	.01	80.00	80.00	.03	53.33	26.67
90	10.8	4.9	1.6	45.00	.01	90.00	90.00	.04	60.00	30.00
100	12.0	6.0	2.0	50.00	.01	100.00	100.00	.06	66.67	33.33
110	13.2	7.3	2.4	55.00	.02	110.00	110.00	.08	73.33	36.67
120	14.4	8.6	2.9	60.00	.03	120.00	120.00	.10	80.00	40.00
130	15.6	10.1	3.4	65.00	.03	130.00	130.00	.13	86.67	43.33
140	16.8	11.8	3.9	70.00	.04	140.00	140.00	.16	93.33	46.67
150	18.0	13.5	4.5	75.00	.05	150.00	150.00	.20	100.00	50.00
160	19.2	15.4	5.1	80.00	.06	160.00	160.00	.24	106.67	53.33
170	20.4	17.3	5.8	85.00	.07	170.00	170.00	.28	113.33	56.67
180	21.6	19.4	6.5	90.00	.08	180.00	180.00	.34	120.00	60.00
190	22.8	21.7	7.2	95.00	.10	190.00	190.00	.40	126.67	63.33
200	24.0	24.0	8.0	100.00	.12	200.00	200.00	.47	133.33	66.67
210	25.2	26.5	8.8	105.00	.13	210.00	210.00	.54	140.00	70.00
220	26.4	29.0	9.7	110.00	.15	220.00	220.00	.62	146.67	73.33
230	27.6	31.7	10.6	115.00	.18	230.00	230.00	.71	153.33	76.67
240	28.8	34.6	11.5	120.00	.20	240.00	240.00	.80	160.00	80.00
250	30.0	37.5	12.5	125.00	.23	250.00	250.00	.91	166.67	83.33
260	31.2	40.6	13.5	130.00	.26	260.00	260.00	1.02	173.33	86.67
270	32.4	43.7	14.6	135.00	.29	270.00	270.00	1.14	180.00	90.00
280	33.6	47.0	15.7	140.00	.32	280.00	279.99	1.28	186.67	93.34
290	34.8	50.5	16.8	145.00	.35	290.00	289.99	1.42	193.33	96.67
300	36.0	54.0	18.0	150.00	.39	300.00	299.99	1.57	200.00	100.00
310	37.2	57.7	19.2	155.00	.43	310.00	309.99	1.73	206.67	103.34
320	38.4	1 1.4	20.5	160.00	.48	320.00	319.99	1.91	213.33	106.67
330	39.6	5.3	21.8	165.00	.52	329.99	329.99	2.00	220.00	110.00
340	40.8	9.4	23.1	170.00	.57	339.99	339.99	2.29	226.67	113.34
350	42.0	13.5	24.5	175.00	.62	349.99	349.98	2.49	233.34	116.67
360	43.2	17.8	25.9	180.00	.68	359.99	359.98	2.71	240.01	120.01
370	44.4	22.1	27.4	185.00	.74	369.99	369.98	2.95	246.67	123.34
380	45.6	26.6	28.9	189.99	.80	379.99	379.98	3.19	253.34	126.67
390	46.8	31.3	30.4	194.99	.86	389.99	389.98	3.45	260.01	130.01
400	48.0	36.0	32.0	199.99	.93	399.99	399.99	3.72	266.68	133.34
410	49.2	40.9	33.6	204.99	1.00	409.98	409.96	4.01	273.35	136.68
420	50.4	45.8	35.3	209.99	1.08	419.98	419.96	4.31	280.02	140.01
430	51.6	50.9	37.1	214.99	1.16	429.98	429.96	4.63	286.68	143.35
440	52.8	56.2	38.7	219.99	1.24	439.98	439.95	4.96	293.35	146.68
450	54.0	2 1.5	40.5	224.99	1.33	449.98	449.94	5.30	300.02	150.02
460	55.2	7.0	42.3	229.99	1.42	459.97	459.94	5.66	306.69	153.35
470	56.4	12.5	44.2	234.99	1.51	469.97	469.93	6.04	313.36	156.69
480	57.6	18.2	46.1	239.98	1.61	479.97	479.92	6.43	320.03	160.02
490	58.8	24.1	48.0	244.98	1.71	489.96	489.91	6.84	326.70	163.36
500	1 0.0	30.0	50.0	249.98	1.82	499.96	499.91	7.27	333.37	166.70

For the Barnett Spiral (Arc Definition)

Values of O and Z from Tables VII and VIII must be increased by the corrections of the following table, usually negligible, to secure Barnett values.

Other tabular values are precise for both A.R.E.A. and Barnett spirals except for values of k over 7.5°.

Add the Corrections Below to O and Z Values from Tables VII or VIII to Get Corresponding Values for Barnett Spiral.

Side and Heading in Degrees, O and Z in Feet.

D° Δ° →	5		10		15		20		25		30		35	
↓	O	Z	O	Z	O	Z	O	Z	O	Z	O	Z	O	Z
5	.00	.03	.01	.06	.01	.09	.02	.12	.03	.15	.04	.18	.06	.21
10	.00	.06	.01	.13	.02	.19	.04	.25	.07	.31	.10	.37	.13	.42
15	.00	.10	.02	.19	.04	.28	.07	.37	.10	.46	.15	.55	.20	.63
20	.00	.13	.02	.25	.05	.38	.09	.50	.14	.62	.20	.75	.26	.84
25	.00	.16	.05	.32	.06	.47	.11	.63	.17	.77	.25	.92	.33	1.05

L	D	Δ	A	Z	O	C	X	Y	U	V
	° ′	° ′	° ′							
510	1 01.2	2 33.1	0 52.0	254.98	1.93	509.95	509.90	7.74	340.04	170.03
520	02.4	42.2	54.1	259.93	2.04	519.95	519.89	8.19	346.70	173.37
530	03.6	48.5	56.2	264.98	2.16	529.95	529.88	8.66	353.38	176.71
540	04.8	55.0	58.3	269.98	2.29	539.94	539.87	9.10	360.05	180.05
550	06.0	3 01.5	1 00.5	274.98	2.42	549.93	549.85	9.68	366.72	183.38
560	07.2	08.2	02.7	279.97	2.56	559.93	559.84	10.21	373.39	186.72
570	08.4	15.0	05.0	234.97	2.70	569.92	569.82	10.76	380.06	190.06
580	09.6	21.9	07.3	289.97	2.84	579.91	579.80	11.34	386.74	193.40
590	10.8	28.9	09.6	294.96	2.99	589.91	589.79	11.93	393.41	196.74
600	12.0	36.0	12.0	299.96	3.14	599.90	599.77	12.55	400.09	200.08
610	13.2	43.3	14.5	304.95	3.30	609.89	609.75	13.20	406.76	203.42
620	14.4	50.6	17.0	309.95	3.47	619.88	619.72	13.86	413.43	206.76
630	15.6	58.1	19.4	314.95	3.64	629.87	629.70	14.54	420.11	210.10
640	16.8	4 05.8	21.9	319.94	3.82	639.86	639.67	15.24	426.78	213.44
650	18.0	13.5	24.5	324.93	4.00	649.84	649.64	15.97	433.46	216.78
660	19.2	21.4	27.1	329.93	4.18	659.83	659.61	16.72	440.13	220.12
670	20.4	29.3	29.8	334.92	4.37	669.82	669.59	17.49	446.81	223.47
680	21.6	37.4	32.5	339.92	4.57	679.81	679.56	18.29	453.49	226.81
690	22.8	45.7	35.2	344.91	4.77	689.79	689.52	19.10	460.17	230.16
700	24.0	54.0	38.0	349.91	4.98	699.78	699.49	19.94	466.84	233.50
710	25.2	5 02.5	40.9	354.90	5.20	709.76	709.45	20.81	473.52	236.84
720	26.4	11.0	43.7	359.99	5.43	719.74	719.41	21.70	480.21	240.19
730	27.6	19.7	46.6	354.89	5.66	729.72	729.37	22.62	486.89	243.54
740	28.8	28.6	49.5	369.88	5.90	739.70	739.33	23.56	493.57	246.89
750	30.0	37.5	52.5	374.88	6.14	749.68	749.28	24.53	500.25	250.23
760	31.2	46.6	55.5	379.87	6.38	759.66	759.23	25.52	506.94	253.58
770	32.4	55.7	58.6	384.85	6.63	769.64	769.18	26.54	513.62	256.93
780	33.6	6 05.0	2 01.7	389.85	6.90	779.61	779.13	27.60	520.31	260.28
790	34.8	14.5	04.9	394.84	7.17	789.59	789.07	28.66	526.99	263.63
800	36.0	24.0	08.0	399.83	7.44	799.56	799.01	29.76	533.69	266.98

L	D	Δ	A	Z	O	C	X	Y	U	V
	° ′	° ′	° ′	′						
10	0 1.8	0 0.1	0 0.1	5.00	0.00	10.00	10.00	0.00	6.67	3.33
20	3.6	0.4	0.1	10.00	.00	20.00	20.00	.00	13.33	6.67
30	5.4	0.8	0.3	15.00	.00	30.00	30.00	.00	20.00	10.00
40	7.2	1.4	0.4	20.00	.00	40.00	40.00	.00	26.67	13.33
50	9.0	2.2	0.8	25.00	.00	50.00	50.00	.01	33.33	16.67
60	10.8	3.2	1.1	30.00	.00	60.00	60.00	.02	40.00	20.00
70	12.6	4.4	1.5	35.00	.01	70.00	70.00	.03	46.67	23.33
80	14.4	5.8	1.9	40.00	.01	80.00	80.00	.04	53.33	26.67
90	16.2	7.3	2.5	45.00	.02	90.00	90.00	.06	60.00	30.00
100	18.0	9.0	3.0	50.00	.02	100.00	100.00	.09	66.67	33.33
110	19.8	10.9	3.7	55.00	.03	110.00	110.00	.12	73.33	36.67
120	21.6	13.0	4.3	60.00	.04	120.00	120.00	.15	80.00	40.00
130	23.4	15.2	5.1	65.00	.05	130.00	130.00	.19	86.67	43.33
140	25.2	17.6	5.9	70.00	.06	140.00	140.00	.24	93.33	46.67
150	27.0	20.2	6.8	75.00	.07	150.00	150.00	.29	100.00	50.00
160	28.8	23.0	7.7	80.00	.09	160.00	160.00	.36	106.67	53.33
170	30.6	26.0	8.7	85.00	.11	170.00	170.00	.43	113.33	56.67
180	32.4	29.2	9.7	90.00	.13	180.00	180.00	.51	120.00	60.00
190	34.2	32.5	10.8	95.00	.15	190.00	190.00	.60	126.67	63.33
200	36.0	36.0	12.0	100.00	.17	200.00	200.00	.70	133.33	66.67
210	37.8	39.7	13.3	105.00	.20	210.00	210.00	.81	140.00	70.00
220	39.6	43.6	14.5	110.00	.23	220.00	220.00	.93	146.67	73.33
230	41.4	47.6	15.9	115.00	.27	230.00	230.00	1.06	153.33	76.67
240	43.2	51.8	17.3	120.00	.30	240.00	240.00	1.21	160.00	80.00
250	45.0	56.2	18.8	125.00	.34	250.00	250.00	1.36	166.67	83.34
260	46.8	1 0.8	20.3	130.00	.38	260.00	259.99	1.53	173.34	86.67
270	48.6	5.6	21.9	135.00	.43	269.99	269.99	1.72	180.00	90.00
280	50.4	10.6	23.5	140.00	.48	279.99	279.99	1.92	186.67	93.34
290	52.2	15.7	25.3	145.00	.53	289.99	289.99	2.13	193.34	96.67
300	54.0	21.0	27.0	150.00	.59	299.99	299.98	2.36	200.01	100.01
310	55.8	26.5	28.9	155.00	.65	309.99	309.98	2.60	206.67	103.34
320	57.6	32.2	30.7	160.00	.71	319.99	319.98	2.86	213.34	106.67
330	58.4	38.0	32.7	165.00	.79	329.99	329.97	3.14	220.01	110.01
340	1 1.2	44.0	34.7	170.00	.86	339.99	339.96	3.43	226.68	113.34
350	3.0	50.2	36.8	175.00	.93	349.99	349.96	3.74	233.35	116.68
360	4.8	56.6	38.9	180.00	1.02	359.98	359.96	4.07	240.02	120.01
370	6.6	2 3.2	41.1	184.99	1.11	369.98	369.95	4.42	246.68	123.35
380	8.4	10.0	43.3	189.99	1.20	379.98	379.94	4.79	253.35	126.68
390	10.2	16.9	45.7	194.98	1.29	389.97	389.94	5.18	260.02	130.02
400	12.0	24.0	48.0	199.98	1.40	399.97	399.93	5.58	266.69	133.36
410	13.8	31.3	50.5	204.98	1.50	409.96	409.92	6.01	273.36	136.69
420	15.6	38.8	53.0	209.98	1.62	419.96	419.91	6.46	280.03	140.03
430	17.4	46.4	55.5	214.98	1.74	429.96	429.90	6.94	286.70	143.37
440	19.2	54.2	58.1	219.98	1.86	439.95	439.89	7.43	293.37	146.70
450	21.0	3 2.2	1 0.8	224.98	1.98	449.95	449.87	7.95	300.04	150.04
460	22.8	10.4	3.5	229.97	2.13	459.94	459.86	8.49	306.72	153.38
470	24.6	18.8	6.3	234.97	2.27	469.93	469.84	9.06	313.39	156.72
480	26.4	27.4	9.1	239.96	2.41	479.92	479.83	9.65	320.06	160.06
490	28.2	36.1	12.1	244.96	2.57	489.92	489.81	10.27	326.74	163.40
500	30.0	45.0	15.0	249.96	2.72	499.90	499.79	10.91	333.41	166.74

L	D	Δ	A	Z	O	C	X	Y	U	V
	° ′	° ′	° ′	′						
510	1 31.8	3 54.1	1 18.1	254.95	2.89	509.90	509.77	11.57	340.08	170.07
520	33.6	4 03.4	21.1	259.95	3.07	519.89	519.74	12.27	346.76	173.41
530	35.4	12.8	24.3	264.94	3.25	529.87	529.72	12.99	353.44	176.76
540	37.2	22.4	27.5	269.94	3.43	539.86	539.69	13.74	360.11	180.10
550	39.0	32.3	30.8	274.94	3.63	549.85	549.66	14.51	366.78	183.44
560	40.8	42.2	34.1	279.93	3.83	559.83	559.62	15.32	373.46	186.79
570	42.6	52.4	37.5	284.92	4.04	569.82	569.59	16.15	380.14	190.13
580	44.4	5 02.8	40.9	289.92	4.26	579.81	579.55	17.01	386.83	193.48
590	46.2	13.3	44.4	294.91	4.48	589.79	589.51	17.91	393.51	196.82
600	48.0	24.0	48.0	299.91	4.71	599.76	599.47	18.84	400.19	200.17
610	49.8	34.9	51.6	304.90	4.95	609.74	609.43	19.80	406.87	203.52
620	51.6	46.0	55.3	309.89	5.20	619.72	619.38	20.78	413.56	206.87
630	53.4	57.2	59.1	314.88	5.46	629.70	629.33	21.80	420.24	210.22
640	55.2	6 08.6	2 02.9	319.87	5.72	639.68	639.27	22.86	426.92	213.57
650	57.0	20.3	03.8	324.86	5.99	649.65	649.21	23.95	433.61	216.92
660	58.8	32.0	10.7	329.84	6.27	659.62	659.15	25.07	440.30	220.28
670	2 00.6	44.0	14.6	334.83	6.56	669.59	669.08	26.22	446.99	223.63
680	02.4	56.2	18.7	339.82	6.85	679.56	679.01	27.41	453.68	226.98
690	04.2	7 08.5	22.9	344.81	7.16	689.53	688.93	28.64	460.37	230.34
700	06.0	21.0	27.0	349.79	7.48	699.50	698.84	29.90	467.07	233.70

L	D	Δ	A	Z	O	C	X	Y	U	V
	° ′	° ′	° ′	′						
10	0 2.4	0 0.1	0 0.1	5.00	0.00	10.00	10.00	0.00	6.67	3.33
20	4.8	0.5	0.2	10.00	.00	20.00	20.00	.00	13.33	6.67
30	7.2	1.1	0.4	15.00	.00	30.00	30.00	.00	20.00	10.00
40	9.6	1.9	0.7	20.00	.00	40.00	40.00	.01	26.67	13.33
50	12.0	3.0	1.0	25.00	.00	50.00	50.00	.02	33.33	16.67
60	14.4	4.3	1.4	30.00	.01	60.00	60.00	.03	40.00	20.00
70	16.8	5.9	2.0	35.00	.01	70.00	70.00	.04	46.67	23.33
80	19.2	7.7	2.6	40.00	.01	80.00	80.00	.06	53.33	26.67
90	21.6	9.7	3.2	45.00	.02	90.00	90.00	.08	60.00	30.00
100	24.0	12.0	4.0	50.00	.03	100.00	100.00	.12	66.67	33.33
110	26.4	14.5	4.9	55.00	.04	110.00	110.00	.16	73.33	36.67
120	28.8	17.3	5.8	60.00	.05	120.00	120.00	.20	80.00	40.00
130	31.2	20.3	6.8	65.00	.06	130.00	130.00	.26	86.67	43.33
140	33.6	23.5	7.9	70.00	.08	140.00	140.00	.32	93.33	46.67
150	36.0	27.0	9.0	75.00	.10	150.00	150.00	.39	100.00	50.00
160	38.4	30.7	10.3	80.00	.12	160.00	160.00	.48	106.67	53.33
170	40.8	34.7	11.6	85.00	.14	170.00	170.00	.57	113.33	56.67
180	43.2	38.9	13.0	90.00	.17	180.00	180.00	.68	120.00	60.00
190	45.6	43.3	14.5	95.00	.20	190.00	190.00	.80	126.67	63.33
200	48.0	48.0	16.0	100.00	.23	200.00	200.00	.93	133.33	66.67
210	50.4	52.9	17.6	105.00	.27	210.00	210.00	1.08	140.00	70.00
220	52.8	58.1	19.4	110.00	.31	220.00	219.99	1.24	146.67	73.33
230	55.2	1 3.5	21.2	115.00	.35	230.00	229.99	1.41	153.34	76.67
240	57.6	9.1	23.0	120.00	.40	240.00	239.98	1.61	160.00	80.00
250	1 0.0	15.0	25.0	125.00	.46	250.00	249.98	1.82	166.67	83.34
260	2.4	21.1	27.1	130.00	.51	259.99	259.98	2.04	173.34	86.67
270	4.8	27.5	29.2	135.00	.57	269.99	269.98	2.29	180.01	90.01
280	7.2	34.1	31.4	140.00	.64	279.99	279.98	2.55	186.67	93.34
290	9.6	40.9	33.7	144.99	.71	289.99	289.97	2.84	193.34	96.67
300	12.0	48.0	36.0	149.99	.79	299.99	299.97	3.14	200.01	100.01
310	14.4	55.3	38.5	154.99	.86	309.98	309.97	3.47	206.68	103.34
320	16.8	2 2.9	41.0	159.99	.95	319.98	319.96	3.81	213.35	106.68
330	19.2	10.7	43.6	164.99	1.05	329.98	329.95	4.18	220.02	110.02
340	21.6	18.7	46.3	169.99	1.14	339.98	339.95	4.57	226.68	113.35
350	24.0	27.0	49.0	174.98	1.25	349.97	349.94	4.99	233.36	116.69
360	26.4	35.5	51.8	179.98	1.36	359.97	359.93	5.43	240.03	120.02
370	28.8	44.3	54.8	184.98	1.48	369.96	369.91	5.89	246.69	123.36
380	31.2	53.3	57.8	189.98	1.60	379.96	379.90	6.38	253.37	126.70
390	33.6	3 2.5	1 0.8	194.98	1.72	389.95	389.89	6.90	260.04	130.03
400	36.0	12.0	4.0	199.97	1.86	399.94	399.88	7.44	266.71	133.37
410	38.4	21.7	7.3	204.97	2.00	409.94	409.86	8.02	273.38	136.71
420	40.8	31.7	10.6	209.97	2.15	419.93	419.84	8.61	280.06	140.05
430	43.2	41.9	14.0	214.96	2.31	429.92	429.82	9.25	286.73	143.39
440	45.6	52.3	17.5	219.96	2.48	439.91	439.80	9.90	293.41	146.73
450	48.0	4 3.0	21.0	224.95	2.65	449.90	449.78	10.60	300.08	150.07
460	50.4	13.9	24.6	229.95	2.83	459.89	459.75	11.32	306.76	153.41
470	52.8	25.1	28.4	234.95	3.02	469.88	469.72	12.07	313.43	156.75
480	55.2	36.5	32.0	239.94	3.22	479.87	479.69	12.86	320.11	160.10
490	57.6	48.1	36.1	244.93	3.42	489.85	489.66	13.68	326.79	163.44
500	2 0.0	5 0.0	40.0	249.93	3.63	499.84	499.62	14.53	333.47	166.79
510	02.4	12.1	44.0	254.92	3.86	509.83	509.58	15.42	340.15	170.13
520	04.8	24.5	48.2	259.91	4.09	519.80	519.54	16.35	346.83	173.48
530	07.2	37.1	52.4	264.90	4.33	529.78	529.49	17.31	353.51	176.83
540	09.6	49.9	56.6	269.89	4.58	539.75	539.44	18.31	360.20	180.18
550	12.0	6 03.0	2 01.0	274.88	4.83	549.73	549.39	19.34	366.88	183.54
560	14.4	16.3	05.5	279.87	5.10	559.71	559.33	20.42	373.57	186.88
570	16.8	29.9	10.0	284.86	5.39	569.68	569.27	21.53	380.26	190.24
580	19.2	43.7	14.6	289.85	5.67	579.65	579.21	22.68	386.95	193.59
590	21.6	57.7	19.3	294.84	5.97	589.62	589.14	23.88	393.64	196.95
600	24.0	7 12.0	24.0	299.83	6.28	599.59	599.06	25.10	400.33	200.30

L	D	Δ	A	Z	O	C	X	Y	U	V
	° ′	° ′	° ′	′						
10	0 3.0	0 0.1	0 0.1	5.00	0.00	10.00	10.00	0.00	6.67	3.33
20	6.0	0.6	0.2	10.00	.00	20.00	20.00	.00	13.33	6.67
30	9.0	1.5	0.5	15.00	.00	30.00	30.00	.00	20.00	10.00
40	12.0	2.4	0.8	20.00	.00	40.00	40.00	.01	26.67	13.33
50	15.0	3.7	1.3	25.00	.00	50.00	50.00	.02	33.33	16.67
60	18.0	5.4	1.8	30.00	.01	60.00	60.00	.03	40.00	20.00
70	21.0	7.3	2.5	35.00	.01	70.00	70.00	.05	46.67	23.33
80	24.0	9.6	3.2	40.00	.02	80.00	80.00	.07	53.33	26.67
90	27.0	12.1	4.0	45.00	.03	90.00	90.00	.11	60.00	30.00
100	30.0	15.0	5.0	50.00	.04	100.00	100.00	.15	66.67	33.33
110	33.0	18.1	6.1	55.00	.05	110.00	110.00	.19	73.33	36.67
120	36.0	21.6	7.2	60.00	.06	120.00	120.00	.25	80.00	40.00
130	39.0	25.3	8.5	65.00	.08	130.00	130.00	.32	86.67	43.33
140	42.0	29.4	9.8	70.00	.10	140.00	140.00	.40	93.33	46.67
150	45.0	33.7	11.2	75.00	.12	150.00	150.00	.59	100.00	50.00
160	48.0	38.4	12.8	80.00	.15	160.00	160.00	.60	106.67	53.33
170	51.0	43.3	14.5	85.00	.18	170.00	170.00	.71	113.33	56.67
180	54.0	48.6	16.2	90.00	.21	180.00	180.00	.85	120.00	60.00
190	57.0	54.0	18.1	95.00	.25	190.00	189.99	1.00	126.67	63.33
200	1 0.0	1 0.0	20.0	100.00	.29	200.00	199.99	1.16	133.34	66.67
210	3.0	6.1	22.0	105.00	.34	210.00	209.99	1.35	140.00	70.00
220	6.0	12.6	24.2	110.00	.39	220.00	219.99	1.55	146.67	73.34
230	9.0	19.3	26.5	115.00	.44	230.00	229.99	1.77	153.34	76.67
240	12.0	26.4	28.8	120.00	.50	239.99	239.99	2.01	160.01	80.00
250	15.0	33.7	31.3	125.00	.57	249.99	249.98	2.27	166.67	83.34
260	18.0	41.4	33.8	129.99	.64	259.99	259.98	2.56	173.34	86.67
270	21.0	49.3	36.4	134.99	.72	269.99	269.97	2.86	180.01	90.01
280	24.0	57.6	39.2	139.99	.80	279.99	279.97	3.19	186.68	93.34
290	27.0	2 6.1	42.1	144.99	.88	289.98	289.96	3.55	193.35	96.68
300	30.0	15.0	45.0	149.99	.98	299.98	299.96	3.93	200.01	100.01
310	33.0	24.1	48.1	154.99	1.08	309.98	309.95	4.33	206.69	103.35
320	36.0	33.6	51.2	159.98	1.19	319.97	319.94	4.76	213.36	106.69
330	39.0	43.3	54.4	164.98	1.31	329.97	329.93	5.23	220.02	110.02
340	42.0	53.4	57.8	169.98	1.43	339.96	339.92	5.72	226.70	113.36
350	45.0	3 3.7	1 1.3	174.98	1.56	349.96	349.90	6.23	233.37	116.70
360	48.0	14.4	4.8	179.97	1.70	359.95	359.88	6.78	240.04	120.03
370	51.0	25.3	8.5	184.97	1.84	369.94	369.87	7.37	246.71	123.38
380	54.0	36.6	12.2	189.97	2.00	379.94	379.85	7.98	253.39	126.71
390	57.0	48.1	16.0	194.96	2.16	389.93	389.83	8.63	260.06	130.05
400	2 0.0	4 0.0	20.0	199.96	2.33	399.92	399.81	9.30	266.74	133.40
410	03.0	12.2	24.1	204.95	2.51	409.90	409.78	10.02	273.41	136.74
420	06.0	24.6	28.2	209.95	2.70	419.89	419.75	10.77	280.09	140.08
430	09.0	37.4	32.5	214.95	2.89	429.88	429.72	11.56	286.76	143.42
440	12.0	50.4	36.9	219.94	3.10	439.86	439.69	12.38	293.44	146.77
450	15.0	5 03.8	41.3	224.93	3.31	449.85	449.65	13.23	300.12	150.11
460	18.0	17.4	45.8	229.92	3.54	459.83	459.61	14.15	306.81	153.46
470	21.0	31.4	50.5	234.91	3.77	469.81	469.56	15.09	313.49	156.71
480	24.0	45.6	55.3	239.90	4.02	479.79	479.52	16.08	320.17	160.16
490	27.0	6 00.2	2 00.1	244.89	4.27	489.76	489.47	17.10	326.85	163.51
500	30.0	15.0	05.0	249.88	4.54	499.74	499.41	18.17	333.55	166.86

84 Table VIII. Selected Spirals. K = 0.75° [VIII

L	D	Δ	A	Z	O	C	X	Y	U	V
	° '	° '	° '	'						
10	0 4.5	0 0.2	0 0.1	5.00	0.00	10.00	10.00	0.00	6.67	3.33
20	9.0	0.9	0.3	10.00	.00	20.00	20.00	.00	13.33	6.67
30	13.5	2.0	0.7	15.00	.00	30.00	30.00	.01	20.00	10.00
40	18.0	3.6	1.2	20.00	.00	40.00	40.00	.01	26.67	13.33
50	22.5	5.6	1.9	25.00	.01	50.00	50.00	.03	33.33	16.67
60	27.0	8.1	2.7	30.00	.01	60.00	60.00	.05	40.00	20.00
70	31.5	11.0	3.7	35.00	.02	70.00	70.00	.07	46.67	23.33
80	36.0	14.4	4.8	40.00	.03	80.00	80.00	.11	53.33	26.67
90	40.5	18.2	6.1	45.00	.04	90.00	90.00	.16	60.00	30.00
100	45.0	22.5	7.5	50.00	.06	100.00	100.00	.22	66.67	33.33
110	49.5	27.2	9.1	55.00	.07	110.00	110.00	.29	73.33	36.67
120	54.0	32.4	10.8	60.00	.09	120.00	120.00	.38	80.00	40.00
130	58.5	38.0	12.7	65.00	.12	130.00	130.00	.48	86.67	43.33
140	1 3.0	44.1	14.7	70.00	.15	140.00	140.00	.60	93.33	46.67
150	7.5	50.6	16.9	75.00	.18	150.00	150.00	.74	100.00	50.00
160	12.0	57.6	19.2	80.00	.22	160.00	160.00	.89	106.67	53.33
170	16.5	1 5.0	21.7	85.00	.27	170.00	169.99	1.07	113.33	56.67
180	21.0	12.9	24.3	90.00	.32	180.00	179.99	1.27	120.00	60.00
190	25.5	21.2	27.1	95.00	.37	189.99	189.99	1.50	126.67	63.34
200	30.0	30.0	30.0	100.00	.44	199.99	199.99	1.75	133.34	66.67
210	34.5	39.2	33.1	104.99	.51	209.99	209.98	2.02	140.01	70.01
220	39.0	48.9	36.3	109.99	.58	219.99	219.98	2.32	146.67	73.34
230	43.5	59.0	39.7	114.99	.66	229.99	229.97	2.65	153.34	76.68
240	48.0	2 9.6	43.2	119.99	.73	239.99	239.97	3.02	160.01	80.01
250	52.5	20.6	46.9	124.99	.85	249.98	249.96	3.41	166.68	83.34
260	57.0	32.1	50.7	129.99	.96	259.98	259.95	3.84	173.35	86.68
270	2 1.5	44.0	54.7	134.98	1.07	269.97	269.94	4.30	180.02	90.02
280	6.0	56.4	58.8	139.98	1.20	279.97	279.93	4.79	186.69	93.36
290	10.5	3 9.2	1 3.1	144.98	1.33	289.96	289.91	5.32	193.37	96.69
300	15.0	22.5	7.5	149.97	1.47	299.96	299.90	5.86	200.04	100.03
310	19.5	36.2	12.1	154.97	1.63	309.95	309.88	6.50	206.71	103.37
320	24.0	50.4	16.8	159.97	1.79	319.94	319.86	7.15	213.38	106.71
330	28.5	4 5.0	21.7	164.96	1.96	329.93	329.83	7.84	220.06	110.04
340	33.0	20.1	26.7	169.96	2.14	339.92	339.81	8.57	226.73	113.29
350	37.5	35.6	31.9	174.95	2.34	349.90	349.78	9.35	233.41	116.74
360	42.0	51.6	37.2	179.94	2.54	359.88	359.74	10.17	240.09	120.09
370	46.5	5 8.0	42.7	184.93	2.76	369.87	369.70	11.04	246.77	123.43
380	51.0	24.9	48.3	189.93	2.99	379.85	379.67	11.97	253.45	126.78
390	55.5	42.2	54.1	194.92	3.24	389.83	389.62	12.93	260.14	130.12
400	3 0.0	6 0.0	2 0.0	199.91	3.49	399.81	399.56	13.95	266.82	133.34
410	04.5	18.2	06.1	204.90	3.76	409.78	409.51	15.02	273.51	136.83
420	09.0	36.9	12.3	209.88	4.04	419.75	419.44	16.15	280.19	140.18
430	13.5	56.0	18.7	214.87	4.33	429.72	429.38	17.33	286.89	143.53
440	18.0	7 15.6	25.2	219.86	4.65	439.69	439.30	18.56	293.58	146.89
450	22.5	35.6	31.9	224.84	4.97	449.65	449.21	19.86	300.28	150.25
460	27.0	56.1	38.7	229.83	5.30	459.61	459.12	21.21	306.98	153.61
470	31.5	8 17.0	45.7	234.80	5.66	469.57	469.03	22.62	313.68	156.98
480	36.0	38.4	52.7	239.79	6.03	479.52	478.92	24.09	320.39	160.34
490	40.5	9 00.2	3 00.0	244.76	6.41	489.47	488.80	25.62	327.09	163.72
500	45.0	22.5	07.4	249.74	6.81	499.41	498.67	27.22	333.81	167.10

L	D	Δ	A	Z	O	C	X	Y	U	V
	° ′	° ′	° ′	′						
10	0 6.0	0 0.3	0 0.1	5.00	0.00	10.00	10.00	.00	6.67	3.33
20	12.0	1.2	0.4	10.00	.00	20.00	20.00	.00	13.33	6.66
30	18.0	2.7	0.9	15.00	.00	30.00	30.00	.01	20.00	10.00
40	24.0	4.8	1.6	20.00	.00	40.00	40.00	.02	26.67	13.33
50	30.0	7.5	2.5	25.00	.01	50.00	50.00	.04	33.33	16.67
60	36.0	10.8	3.6	30.00	.02	60.00	60.00	.06	40.00	20.00
70	42.0	14.7	4.9	35.00	.03	70.00	70.00	.10	46.67	23.33
80	48.0	19.2	6.4	40.00	.03	80.00	80.00	.15	53.33	26.67
90	54.0	24.3	8.1	45.00	.05	90.00	90.00	.21	60.00	30.00
100	1 0.0	30.0	10.0	50.00	.07	100.00	100.00	.29	66.67	33.33
110	6.0	36.3	12.1	55.00	.10	110.00	110.00	.39	73.33	36.67
120	12.0	43.2	14.4	60.00	.13	120.00	120.00	.50	80.00	40.00
130	18.0	50.7	16.9	65.00	.16	130.00	130.00	.64	86.67	43.33
140	24.0	58.8	19.6	70.00	.20	140.00	140.00	.80	93.34	46.67
150	30.0	1 7.5	22.5	75.00	.25	150.00	149.99	.98	100.00	50.00
160	36.0	16.8	25.6	80.00	.30	160.00	159.99	1.19	106.67	53.34
170	42.0	26.7	28.9	85.00	.36	169.99	169.99	1.43	113.34	56.67
180	48.0	37.2	32.4	90.00	.42	179.99	179.99	1.70	120.00	60.00
190	54.0	48.3	36.1	94.99	.50	189.99	189.98	1.99	126.67	63.64
200	2 0.0	2 0.0	40.0	99.99	.58	199.99	199.98	2.33	133.34	66.67
210	6.0	12.3	44.1	104.99	.67	209.99	209.97	2.69	140.01	70.01
220	12.0	25.2	48.4	109.99	.77	219.98	219.96	3.10	146.68	73.35
230	18.0	38.7	52.9	114.99	.89	229.98	229.95	3.54	153.35	76.68
240	24.0	52.8	57.6	119.98	1.01	239.97	239.94	4.02	160.02	80.02
250	30.0	3 7.5	1 2.5	124.98	1.14	249.97	249.93	4.54	166.69	83.36
260	36.0	22.8	7.6	129.97	1.28	259.96	259.91	5.11	173.37	86.70
270	42.0	38.7	12.9	134.97	1.43	269.95	269.89	5.72	180.04	90.03
280	48.0	55.2	18.4	139.97	1.60	279.94	279.87	6.38	186.71	93.27
290	54.0	4 12.3	24.1	144.96	1.77	289.93	289.85	7.09	193.39	96.72
300	3 0.0	30.0	30.0	149.95	1.96	299.92	299.82	7.85	200.06	100.06
310	6.0	48.3	36.1	154.95	2.16	309.90	309.78	8.66	206.74	103.40
320	12.0	5 7.2	42.4	159.94	2.38	319.89	319.75	9.53	213.42	106.75
330	18.0	26.7	48.9	164.93	2.61	329.87	329.70	10.44	220.10	110.09
340	24.0	46.8	55.6	169.92	2.86	339.85	339.66	11.42	226.79	113.44
350	30.0	6 7.5	2 2.5	174.91	3.12	349.82	349.60	12.46	233.47	116.80
360	36.0	28.8	9.6	179.89	3.39	359.80	359.54	13.56	240.16	120.15
370	42.0	50.7	16.9	184.88	3.68	369.77	369.47	14.71	246.85	123.50
380	48.0	7 13.2	24.4	189.87	3.99	379.73	379.40	15.94	253.54	126.86
390	54.0	36.3	32.1	194.85	4.31	389.70	389.32	17.23	260.24	130.22
400	4 0.0	8 0.0	40.0	199.84	4.65	399.66	399.22	18.59	266.94	133.58
410	6.0	24.3	48.1	204.82	5.01	409.61	409.12	20.02	273.64	136.95
420	12.0	49.2	56.4	209.79	5.38	419.56	419.01	21.52	280.35	140.32
430	18.0	9 14.7	3 04.9	214.77	5.77	429.51	428.89	23.09	287.06	143.69
440	24.0	40.8	13.6	219.75	6.18	439.45	438.75	24.73	293.78	147.07
450	30.0	10 07.5	22.5	224.72	6.61	449.38	448.61	26.45	300.49	150.45
460	36.0	34.8	31.6	229.69	7.06	459.32	458.44	28.24	307.22	153.84
470	42.0	11 12.7	40.9	234.65	7.65	469.24	468.26	30.12	313.95	157.23
480	48.0	31.2	50.4	239.62	8.02	479.73	478.08	32.07	320.68	160.63
490	54.0	12 0.3	4 0.1	244.58	8.54	489.06	487.87	34.10	327.43	164.03
500	5 0.0	30.0	09.9	249.54	9.07	498.96	497.64	36.24	334.18	167.44

L	D	Δ	A	Z	O	C	X	Y	U	V
	° ′	° ′	° ′	′						
10	0 8.0	0 0.4	0 0.1	5.00	0.00	10.00	10.00	0.00	6.67	3.33
20	16.0	1.6	0.5	10.00	.00	20.00	20.00	.00	13.33	6.67
30	24.0	3.6	1.2	15.00	.00	30.00	30.00	.01	20.00	10.00
40	32.0	6.4	2.2	20.00	.01	40.00	40.00	.02	26.67	13.33
50	40.0	10.0	3.4	25.00	.01	50.00	50.00	.05	33.33	16.67
60	48.0	14.4	4.8	30.00	.02	60.00	60.00	.08	40.00	20.00
70	56.0	19.6	6.5	35.00	.03	70.00	70.00	.13	46.67	23.33
80	1 4.0	25.6	8.5	40.00	.05	80.00	80.00	.20	53.33	26.67
90	12.0	32.4	10.8	45.00	.07	90.00	90.00	.28	60.00	30.00
100	20.0	40.0	13.3	50.00	.10	100.00	100.00	.39	66.67	33.33
110	28.0	48.4	16.1	55.00	.13	110.00	110.00	.52	73.33	36.67
120	36.0	57.6	19.2	60.00	.17	120.00	120.00	.67	80.00	40.00
130	44.0	1 7.6	22.6	65.00	.21	130.00	129.99	.85	86.67	43.34
140	52.0	18.4	26.2	70.00	.27	140.00	139.99	1.06	93.34	46.67
150	2 0.0	30.0	30.0	74.99	.33	150.00	149.99	1.31	100.00	50.00
160	8.0	42.4	34.1	79.99	.40	159.99	159.99	1.59	106.67	53.34
170	16.0	55.6	38.5	84.99	.48	169.99	169.98	1.91	113.34	56.67
180	24.0	2 9.6	43.2	89.99	.57	179.99	179.97	2.26	120.01	60.01
190	32.0	24.4	48.1	94.99	.66	189.98	189.97	2.66	126.68	63.34
200	40.0	40.0	53.3	99.98	.78	199.98	199.96	3.10	133.35	66.68
210	48.0	56.4	58.8	104.98	.90	209.97	209.94	3.59	140.02	70.02
220	56.0	3 13.6	1 4.6	109.98	1.03	219.97	219.93	4.12	146.69	73.35
230	3 4.0	31.6	10.6	114.97	1.18	229.95	229.91	4.71	153.36	76.69
240	12.0	50.4	16.8	119.97	1.34	239.95	239.89	5.35	160.04	80.03
250	20.0	4 10.0	23.3	124.96	1.51	249.94	249.87	6.05	166.72	83.38
260	28.0	30.4	30.1	129.95	1.70	259.93	259.84	6.81	173.39	86.72
270	36.0	51.6	37.2	134.95	1.91	269.91	269.81	7.62	180.07	90.06
280	44.0	5 13.6	44.5	139.94	2.13	279.90	279.77	8.50	186.75	93.41
290	52.0	56.4	52.1	144.94	2.36	289.88	289.72	9.43	193.43	96.76
300	4 0.0	6 0.0	2 0.0	149.92	2.61	299.86	299.67	10.46	200.12	100.11
310	8.0	24.4	8.1	154.91	2.89	309.83	309.62	11.54	206.80	103.46
320	16.0	49.6	16.6	159.89	3.17	319.80	319.55	12.70	213.49	106.81
330	24.0	7 15.6	25.2	164.87	3.48	329.77	329.48	13.92	220.19	110.17
340	32.0	42.4	34.1	169.85	3.81	339.73	339.39	15.22	226.88	113.53
350	40.0	8 10.0	43.3	174.83	4.15	349.69	349.29	16.61	233.59	116.90
360	48.0	38.4	52.7	179.81	4.52	359.64	359.19	18.06	240.29	120.26
370	56.0	9 7.6	3 2.4	184.79	4.90	369.59	369.07	19.61	247.00	123.63
380	5 4.0	37.6	12.5	189.77	5.31	379.53	378.93	21.24	253.71	127.01
390	12.0	10 8.4	22.7	194.74	5.74	389.47	388.78	22.96	260.43	130.39
400	20.0	40.0	33.2	199.71	6.19	399.39	398.62	24.76	267.16	133.78

L	D	Δ	A	Z	O	C	X	Y	U	V
	° ′	° ′	° ′	′						
10	0 9.0	0 0.5	0 0.1	5.00	0.00	10.00	10.00	0.00	6.67	3.33
20	18.0	1.8	0.6	10.00	.00	20.00	20.00	.00	13.33	6.67
30	27.0	4.1	1.3	15.00	.00	30.00	30.00	.01	20.00	10.00
40	36.0	7.2	2.4	20.00	.01	40.00	40.00	.03	26.67	13.33
50	45.0	11.3	3.7	25.00	.01	50.00	50.00	.05	33.33	16.67
60	54.0	16.2	5.4	30.00	.02	60.00	60.00	.09	40.00	20.00
70	1 3.0	22.1	7.3	35.00	.04	70.00	70.00	.15	46.67	23.33
80	12.0	28.8	9.6	40.00	.06	80.00	80.00	.22	53.33	26.67
90	21.0	36.5	12.1	45.00	.08	90.00	90.00	.32	60.00	30.00
100	30.0	45.0	15.0	50.00	.11	100.00	100.00	.44	66.67	33.33
110	39.0	54.4	18.1	55.00	.15	110.00	110.00	.58	73.33	36.67
120	48.0	1 4.8	21.6	60.00	.19	120.00	120.00	.75	80.00	40.00
130	57.0	16.1	25.3	65.00	.24	130.00	129.99	.96	86.67	43.34
140	2 6.0	28.2	29.4	69.99	.30	140.00	139.99	1.20	93.34	46.67
150	15.0	41.3	33.7	74.99	.37	149.99	149.99	1.47	100.00	50.00
160	24.0	55.2	38.4	79.99	.45	159.99	159.98	1.79	106.67	53.34
170	33.0	2 10.1	43.3	84.99	.54	169.99	169.97	2.14	113.34	56.67
180	42.0	25.8	48.6	89.99	.64	179.99	179.97	2.54	120.01	60.01
190	51.0	42.5	54.1	94.98	.75	189.98	189.96	2.99	126.68	63.35
200	3 0.0	3 0.0	1 0.0	99.98	.87	199.98	199.95	3.49	133.35	66.68
210	9.0	18.5	6.1	104.98	1.01	209.97	209.93	4.04	140.02	70.02
220	18.0	37.8	12.6	109.97	1.16	219.96	219.91	4.64	146.70	73.36
230	27.0	58.1	19.3	114.96	1.33	229.95	229.89	5.30	153.37	76.70
240	36.0	4 19.2	26.4	119.96	1.51	239.94	239.87	6.03	160.05	80.04
250	45.0	41.3	33.7	124.95	1.70	249.93	249.83	6.81	166.73	83.39
260	54.0	5 4.2	41.4	129.94	1.92	259.91	259.80	7.66	173.41	86.73
270	4 3.0	28.1	49.3	134.93	2.15	269.89	269.76	8.58	180.09	90.08
280	12.0	52.8	57.6	139.92	2.39	279.87	279.71	9.55	186.77	93.43
290	21.0	6 18.5	2 6.1	144.91	2.66	289.85	289.65	10.61	193.46	96.78
300	30.0	45.0	15.0	149.90	2.94	299.82	299.59	11.77	200.15	100.13

Table VIII.   Selected Spirals.   K = 1⅔° [VIII

L	D	Δ	A	Z	O	C	X	Y	U	V
	° ′	° ′	° ′	′						
10	0 10.0	0 0.5	0 0.2	5.00	0.00	10.00	10.00	0.00	6.67	3.33
20	20.0	2.0	0.7	10.00	.00	20.00	20.00	.00	13.33	6.67
30	30.0	4.5	1.5	15.00	.00	30.00	30.00	.01	20.00	10.00
40	40.0	8.0	2.6	20.00	.01	40.00	40.00	.03	26.67	13.33
50	50.0	12.5	4.1	25.00	.02	50.00	50.00	.06	33.33	16.67
60	1 0.0	17.0	6.0	30.00	.03	60.00	60.00	.11	40.00	20.00
70	10.0	24.5	8.2	35.00	.04	70.00	70.00	.17	46.67	23.33
80	20.0	32.0	10.7	40.00	.06	80.00	80.00	.25	53.33	26.67
90	30.0	40.5	13.5	45.00	.09	90.00	90.00	.35	60.00	30.00
100	40.0	50.0	16.7	50.00	.12	100.00	100.00	.48	66.67	33.33
110	50.0	1 0.5	20.2	55.00	.16	110.00	110.00	.65	73.33	36.67
120	2 0.0	12.0	24.0	60.00	.21	120.00	120.00	.84	80.00	40.00
130	10.0	24.5	28.2	65.00	.27	130.00	129.99	1.06	86.67	43.34
140	20.0	38.0	32.7	69.99	.33	140.00	139.99	1.33	93.34	46.67
150	30.0	52.5	37.5	74.99	.41	149.99	149.98	1.64	100.01	50.01
160	40.0	2 8.0	42.7	79.99	.50	159.99	159.98	1.99	106.67	53.34
170	50.0	24.5	48.2	84.99	.60	169.99	169.97	2.38	113.34	56.68
180	3 0.0	42.0	54.0	89.98	.71	179.98	179.96	2.83	120.01	60.01
190	10.0	3 0.5	1 0.2	94.98	.83	189.98	189.95	3.33	126.68	63.35
200	20.0	20.0	6.7	99.98	.97	199.97	199.93	3.88	133.36	66.69
210	30.0	40.5	13.5	104.97	1.12	209.96	209.91	4.49	140.03	70.03
220	40.0	4 2.0	20.6	109.96	1.29	219.95	219.89	5.16	146.70	73.37
230	50.0	24.1	28.1	114.95	1.47	229.94	229.86	5.90	153.38	76.71
240	4 0.0	48.0	36.0	119.95	1.68	239.93	239.83	6.70	160.06	80.05
250	10.0	5 12.5	44.2	124.94	1.89	249.91	249.81	7.57	166.74	83.40
260	20.0	38.0	52.7	129.93	2.13	259.89	259.76	8.52	173.42	86.75
270	30.0	6 4.5	2 1.5	134.92	2.38	269.87	269.70	9.54	180.11	90.10
280	40.0	32.0	10.7	139.91	2.66	279.84	279.64	10.63	186.79	93.45
290	50.0	7 0.5	20.2	144.89	2.96	289.81	289.57	11.81	193.49	96.80
300	5 0.0	30.0	30.0	149.87	3.27	299.78	299.49	13.07	200.18	100.16
310	10.0	8 0.5	40.1	154.85	3.61	309.73	309.40	14.42	206.87	103.53
320	20.0	32.0	50.6	159.83	3.97	319.69	319.29	15.86	213.58	106.90
330	30.0	9 4.5	3 1.4	164.80	4.35	329.64	329.18	17.39	220.29	110.27
340	40.0	38.0	12.6	169.77	4.76	339.58	339.04	19.02	227.01	113.64
350	50.0	10 12.5	24.1	174.74	5.19	349.51	348.90	20.74	233.73	117.02
360	6 0.0	48.0	35.9	179.71	5.65	359.44	358.73	22.55	240.45	120.41
370	10.0	11 24.5	48.1	184.67	6.13	369.36	368.54	24.49	247.18	123.81
380	20.0	12 2.0	4 0.6	189.63	6.64	379.27	378.34	26.52	253.93	127.21
390	30.0	40.5	13.4	194.59	7.18	389.17	388.11	28.66	260.68	130.61
400	40.0	13 20.0	26.5	199.54	7.74	399.05	397.86	30.90	267.43	134.03

L	D	Δ	A	Z	O	C	X	Y	U	V
	° ′	° ′	° ′	′						
10	0 12.0	0 0.6	0 0.2	5.00	0.00	10.00	10.00	0.00	6.97	3.33
20	24.0	2.4	0.8	10.00	.00	20.00	20.00	.00	13.33	6.67
30	33.0	5.4	1.8	15.00	.00	30.00	30.00	.02	20.00	10.00
40	48.0	9.6	3.2	20.00	.01	40.00	40.00	.04	26.67	13.33
50	1 0.0	15.0	5.0	25.00	.02	50.00	50.00	.07	33.33	16.67
60	12.0	21.6	7.2	30.00	.03	60.00	60.00	.13	40.00	20.00
70	24.0	29.4	9.8	35.00	.05	70.00	70.00	.20	46.67	23.33
80	36.0	38.4	12.8	49.00	.07	80.00	80.00	.30	53.33	26.67
90	48.0	48.6	16.2	45.00	.11	90.90	90.00	.42	60.00	30.00
100	2 0.0	1 0.0	20.0	50.00	.14	100.00	100.00	.58	66.67	33.33
110	12.0	12.6	24.2	55.00	.19	110.00	109.99	.77	73.33	36.67
120	24.0	26.4	28.8	59.99	.25	120.00	119.99	1.00	80.00	40.00
130	36.0	41.4	33.8	64.99	.34	129.99	129.99	1.28	86.67	43.34
140	48.0	57.6	39.2	69.99	.40	139.99	139.98	1.60	93.34	46.67
150	3 0.0	2 15.0	45.0	74.99	.49	149.99	149.98	1.96	100.01	50.01
160	12.0	33.6	51.2	79.98	.60	159.99	159.97	2.38	106.68	53.34
170	24.0	33.4	57.8	84.98	.71	169.98	169.96	2.86	113.35	56.68
180	36.0	3 14.4	1 4.8	89.98	.85	179.97	179.94	3.39	120.02	60.02
190	48.0	36.6	12.2	94.97	1.00	189.97	189.93	3.99	126.69	63.36
200	4 0.0	4 0.0	20.0	99.96	1.16	199.96	199.90	4.65	133.37	66.70
210	12.0	24.6	28.2	104.96	1.35	209.95	209.88	5.38	140.04	70.04
220	24.0	50.4	36.8	109.95	1.55	219.93	219.84	6.19	146.72	73.38
230	36.0	5 17.4	45.8	114.94	1.77	229.91	229.80	7.07	153.40	76.73
240	48.0	45.6	55.2	119.93	2.01	239.89	239.76	8.03	160.09	80.08
250	5 0.0	6 15.0	2 5.0	124.91	2.27	249.87	249.70	9.08	166.77	83.43
260	12.0	45.6	15.2	129.90	2.55	259.84	259.64	10.21	173.46	86.78
270	24.0	7 17.4	25.8	134.88	2.86	269.81	269.57	11.44	180.15	90.14
280	36.0	50.4	33.8	139.86	3.19	279.77	279.48	12.75	186.85	93.50
290	48.0	8 24.6	48.1	144.84	3.54	289.73	289.38	14.17	193.55	96.87
300	6 0.0	9 0.0	59.9	149.81	3.92	299.68	299.26	15.68	200.26	100.24

L	D	Δ	A	Z	O	C	X	Y	U	V
	° ′	° ′	° ′	′						
10	0 15.0	0 0.7	0 0.2	5.00	0.00	10.00	10.00	0.00	6.67	3.33
20	30.0	3.0	1.0	10.00	.00	20.00	20.00	.01	13.33	6.67
30	45.0	6.7	2.2	15.00	.00	30.00	30.00	.02	20.00	10.00
40	1 0.0	12.0	4.0	20.00	.01	40.00	40.00	.05	26.67	13.33
50	15.0	18.7	6.2	25.00	.02	50.00	50.00	.09	33.33	16.67
60	30.0	27.0	9.0	30.00	.04	60.00	60.00	.16	40.00	20.00
70	45.0	36.7	12.2	35.00	.06	70.00	70.00	.21	46.67	23.33
80	2 0.0	48.0	16.0	40.00	.09	80.00	80.00	.37	53.33	26.67
90	15.0	1 0.7	20.2	45.00	.13	90.00	90.00	.53	60.00	30.00
100	30.0	15.0	25.0	50.00	.18	100.00	100.00	.73	66.67	33.34
110	45.0	30.7	30.2	54.99	.24	110.00	109.99	.97	73.34	36.67
120	3 0.0	48.0	36.0	59.99	.31	120.00	119.99	1.26	80.00	40.00
130	15.0	2 6.7	42.2	64.99	.40	129.99	129.98	1.60	86.67	43.34
140	30.0	27.0	49.0	69.98	.50	139.99	139.97	2.00	93.34	46.67
150	45.0	48.7	56.2	74.98	.61	149.98	149.96	2.45	100.01	50.01
160	4 0.0	3 12.0	1 4.0	79.98	.74	159.98	159.95	2.98	106.68	53.35
170	15.0	36.7	12.2	84.97	.89	169.97	169.93	3.57	113.36	56.69
180	30.0	4 3.0	21.0	89.96	1.06	179.96	179.91	4.24	120.03	60.03
190	45.0	30.7	30.2	94.95	1.25	189.95	189.88	4.99	126.71	63.37
200	5 0.0	5 0.0	40.0	99.94	1.45	199.93	199.85	5.81	133.39	66.72
210	15.0	30.7	50.2	104.93	1.68	209.91	209.81	6.73	140.07	70.06
220	30.0	6 3.0	2 1.0	109.92	1.93	219.89	219.76	7.74	146.76	73.41
230	45.0	36.7	12.2	114.90	2.21	229.87	229.70	8.84	153.44	76.76
240	6 0.0	7 12.0	24.0	119.89	2.51	239.83	239.62	10.04	160.13	80.12
250	15.0	48.7	36.2	124.86	2.84	249.80	249.54	11.35	166.83	83.48
260	30.0	8 27.0	49.0	129.84	3.19	259.75	259.44	12.76	173.53	86.85
270	45.0	9 6.7	3 2.2	134.81	3.57	269.70	269.32	14.29	180.24	90.22
280	7 0.0	48.0	16.0	139.78	3.98	279.64	279.19	15.93	186.96	93.60
290	15.0	10 30.7	30.2	144.75	4.42	289.57	289.03	17.69	193.68	96.98
300	30.0	11 15.0	44.9	149.71	4.89	299.49	298.85	19.58	200.41	100.37

K = 3.0°

L	D	Δ	A	Z	O	C	X	Y	U	V
	° ′	° ′	° ′	′						
10	0 18.0	0 0.9	0 0.3	5.00	0.00	10.00	10.00	0.00	6.67	3.33
20	33.0	3.6	1.2	10.00	.00	20.00	20.00	.01	13.33	6.67
30	54.0	8.1	2.7	15.00	.01	30.00	30.00	.02	20.00	10.00
40	1 12.0	14.4	4.8	20.00	.01	40.00	40.00	.06	26.67	13.33
50	30.0	22.5	7.5	25.00	.03	50.00	50.00	.11	33.33	16.67
60	48.0	32.4	10.8	30.00	.05	60.00	60.00	.19	40.00	20.00
70	2 6.0	44.1	14.7	35.00	.07	70.00	70.00	.30	46.67	23.33
80	24.0	57.6	19.2	40.00	.11	80.00	80.00	.45	53.34	26.67
90	42.0	1 12.9	24.3	45.00	.16	90.00	90.00	.64	60.00	30.00
100	3 0.0	30.0	30.0	49.99	.22	100.00	99.99	.87	66.67	33.34
110	18.0	48.9	36.3	54.99	.29	109.99	109.99	1.16	73.34	36.67
120	36.0	2 9.6	43.2	59.99	.36	119.99	119.98	1.51	80.01	40.01
130	54.0	32.1	50.7	64.98	.48	129.99	129.98	1.92	86.67	43.34
140	4 12.0	56.4	58.8	69.98	.60	139.98	139.96	2.39	93.35	46.68
150	30.0	3 22.5	1 7.5	74.97	.74	149.98	149.95	2.94	100.02	50.02
160	48.0	50.4	16.8	79.97	.89	159.97	159.93	3.57	106.69	53.36
170	5 6.0	4 20.1	26.7	84.96	1.07	169.96	169.90	4.28	113.37	56.70
180	24.0	51.6	37.2	89.95	1.27	179.94	179.87	5.08	120.05	60.04
190	42.0	5 24.9	48.3	94.93	1.49	189.92	189.83	5.98	126.73	63.39
200	6 0.0	6 0.0	2 0.0	99.92	1.74	199.90	199.78	6.98	133.41	66.74
210	18.0	36.9	12.3	104.90	2.02	209.88	209.72	8.06	140.10	70.09
220	36.0	7 15.6	25.2	109.88	2.32	219.85	219.65	9.26	146.79	73.45
230	54.0	56.1	38.7	114.86	2.65	229.81	229.56	10.59	153.49	76.81
240	7 12.0	8 38.4	52.7	119.83	3.01	239.76	239.46	12.04	160.19	80.17
250	30.0	9 22.5	3 7.4	124.80	3.40	249.71	249.34	13.60	166.90	83.55

L	D	Δ	A	Z	O	C	X	Y	U	V
	° ′	° ′	° ′	′						
10	0 24.0	0 1.2	0 0.4	5.00	0.00	10.00	10.00	0.00	6.67	3.33
20	48.0	4.8	1.6	10.00	.00	20.00	20.00	.01	13.33	6.67
30	1 12.0	10.8	3.6	15.00	.01	30.00	30.00	.03	20.00	10.00
40	36.0	19.2	6.4	20.00	.02	40.00	40.00	.07	26.67	13.33
50	2 0.0	30.0	10.0	25.00	.04	50.00	50.00	.15	33.33	16.67
60	24.0	43.2	14.4	30.00	.06	60.00	60.00	.25	40.00	20.00
70	48.0	58.8	19.6	35.00	.10	70.00	70.00	.40	46.67	23.33
80	3 12.0	1 16.8	25.6	39.99	.15	80.00	80.00	.60	53.33	26.67
90	36.0	37.2	32.4	44.99	.21	90.00	89.99	.85	60.00	30.00
100	4 0.0	2 0.0	40.0	49.99	.29	99.99	99.99	1.16	66.67	33.34
110	24.0	25.2	48.4	54.98	.39	109.99	109.98	1.55	73.33	36.67
120	48.0	52.8	57.6	59.98	.50	119.99	119.97	1.84	80.01	40.01
130	5 12.0	3 22.8	1 7.6	64.97	.64	129.98	129.95	2.56	86.68	43.35
140	36.0	55.2	18.4	69.96	.80	139.97	139.93	3.19	93.36	46.69
150	6 0.0	4 30.0	30.0	74.95	.98	149.96	149.91	3.93	100.03	50.03
160	24.0	5 7.2	42.4	79.94	1.19	159.94	159.87	4.76	106.71	53.47
170	48.0	46.8	55.6	84.92	1.43	169.92	169.83	5.71	113.40	56.72
180	7 12.0	6 28.8	2 9.6	89.90	1.77	179.90	179.77	6.78	120.08	60.08
190	36.0	7 13.2	24.4	94.88	1.99	189.87	189.70	7.97	126.77	63.43
200	8 0.0	8 0.0	40.0	99.86	2.32	199.83	199.63	9.30	133.47	66.79
210	24.0	49.2	56.3	104.83	2.68	209.78	209.51	10.76	140.18	70.16
220	48.0	9 40.8	3 13.3	109.79	3.09	219.72	219.38	12.38	146.89	73.54
230	9 12.0	10 34.8	31.6	114.75	3.52	229.66	229.22	14.11	153.61	76.92
240	36.0	11 31.2	50.3	119.70	4.00	239.57	239.03	16.03	160.34	80.31
250	10 0.0	12 30.0	4 9.9	124.65	4.52	249.48	248.82	18.12	167.09	83.72

K = 5.0°

L	D	Δ	A	Z	O	C	X	Y	U	V
	° ′	° ′	° ′	′						
10	0 30.0	0 1.5	0 0.5	5.00	0.00	10.00	10.00	0.00	6.67	3.33
20	1 0.0	6.0	2.0	10.00	.00	20.00	20.00	.01	13.33	6.67
30	30.0	13.5	4.5	15.00	.01	30.00	30.00	.04	20.00	10.00
40	2 0.0	24.0	8.0	20.00	.02	40.00	40.00	.09	26.67	13.33
50	30.0	37.5	12.5	25.00	.05	50.00	50.00	.18	33.33	16.67
60	3 0.0	54.0	18.0	30.00	.08	60.00	60.00	.31	40.00	20.00
70	30.0	1 13.5	24.5	34.99	.13	70.00	70.00	.50	46.67	23.33
80	4 0.0	36.0	32.0	39.99	.19	80.00	79.99	.74	53.34	26.67
90	30.0	2 1.5	40.5	44.99	.27	90.00	89.99	1.06	60.00	30.00
100	5 0.0	30.0	50.0	49.98	.36	99.99	99.98	1.45	66.67	33.34
110	30.0	3 1.5	1 0.5	54.97	.48	109.99	109.97	1.93	73.34	36.67
120	6 0.0	36.0	12.0	59.97	.63	119.98	119.95	2.51	80.02	40.02
130	30.0	4 13.5	24.5	64.95	.80	129.97	129.93	3.19	86.69	43.36
140	7 0.0	54.0	38.0	69.94	1.00	139.96	139.90	3.99	93.37	46.70
150	30.0	5 37.5	52.5	74.92	1.20	149.94	149.86	4.90	100.05	50.05
160	8 0.0	6 24.0	2 8.0	79.90	1.48	159.91	159.80	5.94	106.74	53.40
170	30.0	7 13.5	24.5	84.88	1.78	169.88	169.73	7.13	113.43	56.75
180	9 0.0	8 6.0	41.9	89.85	2.11	179.84	179.64	8.46	120.13	60.12
190	30.0	9 1.5	3 0.5	94.82	2.48	189.79	189.53	9.95	126.83	63.48
200	10 0.0	10 0.0	19.9	99.78	2.90	199.73	199.40	11.61	133.55	66.86
210	30.0	11 1.5	40.4	104.73	3.35	209.66	209.23	13.41	140.27	70.25
220	11 0.0	12 6.0	4 1.9	109.67	3.82	219.57	219.04	15.42	147.01	73.65
230	30.0	13 13.5	24.4	114.61	4.40	229.46	228.79	17.62	153.76	77.06
240	12 0.0	14 24.0	47.8	119.54	5.99	239.34	238.50	20.02	160.54	80.49
250	30.0	15 37.5	5 12.3	124.46	5.64	249.18	248.16	22.62	167.32	83.94

L	D	Δ	A	Z	O	C	X	Y	U	V
	° ′	° ′	° ′	′						
10	0 45.0	0 2.3	0 0.7	5.00	0.00	10.00	10.00	0.00	6.67	3.33
20	1 30.0	9.0	3.0	10.00	.00	20.00	20.00	.02	13.33	6.67
30	2 15.0	20.3	6.8	15.00	.01	30.00	30.00	.06	20.00	10.00
40	3 0.0	36.0	12.0	20.00	.03	40.00	40.00	.14	26.67	13.33
50	45.0	56.3	18.8	25.00	.07	50.00	50.00	.27	33.33	16.67
60	4 30.0	1 21.0	27.0	29.99	.12	60.00	60.00	.47	40.00	20.00
70	5 15.0	50.3	36.8	34.99	.19	70.00	69.99	.75	46.67	23.34
80	6 0.0	2 24.0	48.0	39.98	.28	79.99	79.99	1.12	53.34	26.67
90	45.0	3 2.3	1 0.8	44.97	.40	89.99	89.97	1.59	60.01	30.01
100	7 30.0	45.0	15.0	49.96	.54	99.98	99.96	2.18	66.68	33.35
110	8 15.0	4 32.3	30.8	54.94	.71	109.97	109.93	2.90	73.36	36.69
120	9 0.0	5 24.0	48.0	59.92	.94	119.95	119.89	3.77	80.04	40.03
130	45.0	6 20.3	2 6.8	64.90	1.19	129.93	129.84	4.78	86.72	43.38
140	10 30.0	7 21.0	27.0	69.86	1.49	139.90	139.77	5.98	93.41	46.74
150	11 15.0	8 26.3	48.7	74.83	1.83	149.86	149.68	7.35	100.11	50.10
160	12 0.0	9 36.0	3 11.9	79.78	2.22	159.80	159.55	8.92	106.83	53.48
170	45.0	10 50.3	36.7	84.73	2.66	169.73	169.40	10.67	113.55	56.86
180	13 30.0	12 9.0	4 2.9	89.66	3.15	179.64	179.20	12.66	120.29	60.26
190	14 15.0	13 32.3	30.7	94.59	3.51	189.54	188.95	14.89	127.04	63.68
200	15 0.0	15 0.0	59.8	99.50	4.32	199.40	198.64	17.37	133.82	67.11
210	45.0	16 32.3	5 30.5	104.40	4.99	209.23	208.27	20.09	140.62	70.57
220	16 30.0	18 9.0	6 2.7	109.27	5.73	219.03	217.82	23.07	147.45	74.05
230	17 15.0	19 50.3	36.4	114.13	6.54	228.79	227.28	26.40	154.31	77.56
240	18 0.0	21 36.0	7 11.5	118.97	7.41	238.51	236.63	29.86	161.22	81.11

K = 10°

L	D	Δ	A	Z	O	C	X	Y	U	V
	° ′	° ′	° ′	′						
10	0 1 0.0	0 3.0	0 1.0	5.00	0.00	10.00	10.00	0.00	6.67	3.33
20	2 0.0	12.0	4.0	10.00	.01	20.00	20.00	.02	13.33	6.67
30	3 0.0	27.0	9.0	15.00	.02	30.00	30.00	.08	20.00	10.00
40	4 0.0	48.0	16.0	20.00	.05	40.00	40.00	.19	26.67	13.33
50	5 0.0	1 15.0	25.0	24.99	.09	50.00	50.00	.36	33.33	16.67
60	6 0.0	48.0	36.0	29.98	.16	60.00	59.99	.63	40.00	20.00
70	7 0.0	2 27.0	49.0	34.98	.25	70.00	69.99	.98	46.67	23.34
80	8 0.0	3 12.0	1 4.0	39.96	.37	79.99	79.97	1.49	53.34	26.67
90	9 0.0	4 3.0	21.0	44.95	.53	89.98	89.96	2.12	60.02	30.01
100	10 0.0	5 0.0	40.0	49.92	.72	99.97	99.92	2.91	66.69	33.36
110	11 0.0	6 3.0	2 1.0	54.89	.98	109.95	109.88	3.87	73.38	36.71
120	12 0.0	7 12.0	24.0	59.86	1.25	119.92	119.81	5.02	80.07	40.06
130	13 0.0	8 27.0	49.0	64.81	1.59	129.88	129.72	6.38	86.77	43.42
140	14 0.0	9 48.0	3 16.0	69.76	1.98	139.82	139.59	7.97	93.48	46.80
150	15 0.0	11 15.0	44.9	74.69	2.43	149.74	149.43	9.78	100.20	50.19
160	16 0.0	12 48.0	4 15.9	79.61	2.95	159.65	159.21	11.87	106.95	53.59
170	17 0.0	14 27.0	48.8	84.52	3.53	169.53	168.93	14.21	113.72	57.01
180	18 0.0	16 12.0	5 23.8	89.40	4.18	179.37	178.57	16.87	120.45	60.47
190	19 0.0	18 3.0	6 0.7	94.26	4.91	189.18	188.13	19.78	127.34	63.94
200	20 0.0	20 0.0	39.6	99.11	5.71	198.93	197.59	23.07	134.20	67.46
210	21 0.0	22 3.0	7 20.5	103.92	6.69	208.64	206.93	26.66	141.11	71.01
220	22 0.0	24 12.0	8 3.3	108.71	7.56	218.28	216.13	30.59	148.07	74.62
230	23 0.0	26 27.0	48.1	113.46	8.51	227.86	225.17	34.86	155.09	78.27
240	24 0.0	28 48.0	9 34.8	118.18	9.76	237.35	234.04	39.50	162.18	82.00
250	25 0.0	31 15.0	10 23.5	122.86	10.99	246.75	242.70	44.51	169.36	85.79

Table IX. Spiral Deflections
(For All Spirals)

Δ	1	2	3	4	5	6	7	8	9	10
°	° '	° '	° '	° '	° '	° '	° '	° '	° '	° '
0.0	0 00.00	0 00.0	0 00.0	0 00.0	0 00.0	0 00.0	0 00.0	0 00.0	0 00.0	0 00.0
.1	.02	.1	.2	.3	.5	.7	1.0	1.3	1.6	2.0
.2	.04	.2	.4	.6	1.0	1.4	2.0	2.6	3.2	4.0
.3	.06	.2	.5	1.0	1.5	2.2	2.9	3.8	4.9	6.0
.4	.08	.3	.7	1.3	2.0	2.9	3.9	5.1	6.5	8.0
.5	.10	.4	.9	1.6	2.5	3.6	4.9	6.4	8.1	10.0
.6	.12	.5	1.1	1.9	3.0	4.3	5.9	7.7	9.7	12.0
.7	.14	.6	1.3	2.2	3.5	5.0	6.9	9.0	11.3	14.0
.8	.16	.6	1.4	2.6	4.0	5.8	7.8	10.2	13.0	16.0
.9	.18	.7	1.6	2.9	4.5	6.5	8.8	11.5	14.6	18.0
1.0	0 .20	0 .8	0 1.8	0 3.2	0 5.0	0 7.2	0 9.8	0 12.8	0 16.2	0 20.0
.1	.22	.9	2.0	3.5	5.5	7.9	10.8	14.1	17.8	22.0
.2	.24	1.0	2.2	3.8	6.0	8.6	11.8	15.4	19.4	24.0
.3	.26	1.0	2.3	4.2	6.5	9.4	12.7	16.6	21.1	26.0
.4	.28	1.1	2.5	4.5	7.0	10.1	13.7	17.9	22.7	28.0
.5	.30	1.2	2.7	4.8	7.5	10.8	14.7	19.2	24.3	30.0
.6	.32	1.3	2.9	5.1	8.0	11.5	15.7	20.5	25.9	32.0
.7	.34	1.4	3.1	5.4	8.5	12.2	16.7	21.8	27.5	34.0
.8	.36	1.4	3.2	5.8	9.0	13.0	17.6	23.0	29.2	36.0
.9	.38	1.5	3.4	6.1	9.5	13.7	18.6	24.3	30.8	38.0
2.0	0 .40	0 1.6	0 3.6	0 6.4	0 10.0	0 14.4	0 19.6	0 25.6	0 32.4	0 40.0
.1	.42	1.7	3.8	6.7	10.5	15.1	20.6	26.9	34.0	42.0
.2	.44	1.8	4.0	7.0	11.0	15.8	21.6	28.2	35.6	44.0
.3	.46	1.8	4.1	7.4	11.5	16.6	22.5	29.4	37.3	46.0
.4	.48	1.9	4.3	7.7	12.0	17.3	23.5	30.7	38.9	48.0
.5	.50	2.0	4.5	8.0	12.5	18.0	24.5	32.0	40.5	50.0
.6	.52	2.1	4.7	8.3	13.0	18.7	25.5	33.3	42.1	52.0
.7	.54	2.2	4.9	8.6	13.5	19.4	26.5	34.6	43.7	54.0
.8	.56	2.2	5.0	9.0	14.0	20.2	27.4	35.8	45.4	56.0
.9	.58	2.3	5.2	9.3	14.5	20.9	28.4	37.1	47.0	58.0
3.0	0 .60	0 2.4	0 5.4	0 9.6	0 15.0	0 21.6	0 29.4	0 38.4	0 48.6	1 00.0
.1	.62	2.5	5.6	9.9	15.5	22.3	30.4	39.7	50.2	2.0
.2	.64	2.6	5.8	10.2	16.0	23.0	31.4	41.0	51.8	4.0
.3	.66	2.6	5.9	10.6	16.5	23.8	32.3	42.2	53.5	6.0
.4	.68	2.7	6.1	10.9	17.0	24.5	33.3	43.5	55.1	8.0
.5	.70	2.8	6.3	11.2	17.5	25.2	34.3	44.8	56.7	10.0
.6	.72	2.9	6.5	11.5	18.0	25.9	35.3	46.1	58.3	12.0
.7	.74	3.0	6.7	11.8	18.5	26.6	36.3	47.4	59.9	14.0
.8	.76	3.0	6.8	12.2	19.0	27.3	37.2	48.6	1 01.6	16.0
.9	.78	3.1	7.0	12.5	19.5	28.1	38.2	49.9	03.2	18.0
4.0	0 .80	0 3.2	0 7.2	0 12.8	0 20.0	0 28.8	0 39.2	0 51.2	1 04.8	1 20.0
.1	.82	3.3	7.4	13.1	20.5	29.5	40.2	52.5	06.4	22.0
.2	.84	3.4	7.6	13.4	21.0	30.2	41.2	53.8	08.0	24.0
.3	.86	3.4	7.7	13.8	21.5	31.0	42.1	55.0	09.7	26.0
.4	.88	3.5	7.9	14.1	22.0	31.7	43.1	56.3	11.3	28.0
.5	.90	3.6	8.1	14.4	22.5	32.4	44.1	57.6	12.9	30.0
.6	.92	3.7	8.3	14.7	23.0	33.1	45.1	58.9	14.5	32.0
.7	.94	3.8	8.5	15.0	23.5	33.8	46.1	1 00.2	16.1	34.0
.8	.96	3.8	8.6	15.4	24.0	34.6	47.0	01.4	17.8	36.0
.9	.98	3.9	8.8	15.7	24.5	35.3	48.0	02.7	19.4	38.0
5.0	0 1.00	0 4.0	0 9.0	0 16.0	0 25.0	0 36.0	0 49.0	1 04.0	1 21.0	1 40.0
.1	1.02	4.1	9.2	16.3	25.5	36.7	50.0	05.3	22.6	42.0
.2	1.04	4.2	9.4	16.6	26.0	37.4	51.0	06.6	24.2	44.0
.3	1.06	4.2	9.5	17.0	26.5	38.1	51.9	07.8	25.9	46.0
.4	1.08	4.3	9.7	17.3	27.0	38.9	52.9	09.1	27.5	48.0
.5	1.10	4.4	9.9	17.6	27.5	39.6	53.9	10.4	29.1	50.0
.6	1.12	4.5	10.1	17.9	28.0	40.3	54.9	11.7	30.7	52.0
.7	1.14	4.6	10.3	18.2	28.5	41.0	55.9	13.0	32.3	54.0
.8	1.16	4.6	10.4	18.6	29.0	41.8	56.8	14.2	34.0	56.0
.9	1.18	4.7	10.6	18.9	29.5	42.5	57.8	15.5	35.6	58.0

(For All Spirals)

Δ	1	2	3	4	5	6	7	8	9	10
6.0	0 01.20	0 04.8	0 10.8	0 19.2	0 30.0	0 43.2	0 58.8	1 16.8	1 37.2	2 00.0
.1	1.22	4.9	11.0	19.5	30.5	43.9	59.8	18.1	38.8	2.0
.2	1.24	5.0	11.2	19.8	31.0	44.6	1 00.8	19.4	40.4	4.0
.3	1.26	5.0	11.3	20.2	31.5	45.4	1.7	20.6	42.1	6.0
.4	1.28	5.1	11.5	20.5	32.0	46.1	2.7	21.9	43.7	8.0
.5	1.30	5.2	11.7	20.8	32.5	46.8	3.7	23.2	45.3	10.0
.6	1.32	5.3	11.9	21.1	33.0	47.5	4.7	24.5	46.9	12.0
.7	1.34	5.4	12.1	21.4	33.5	48.2	5.7	25.8	48.5	14.0
.8	1.36	5.4	12.2	21.8	34.0	49.0	6.6	27.0	50.2	16.0
.9	1.38	5.5	12.4	22.1	34.5	49.7	7.6	28.3	51.8	18.0
7.0	0 1.40	0 5.6	0 12.6	0 22.4	0 35.0	0 50.4	1 8.6	1 29.6	1 53.4	2 20.0
.1	1.42	5.7	12.8	22.7	35.5	51.1	9.6	30.9	55.0	22.0
.2	1.44	5.8	13.0	23.0	36.0	51.8	10.6	32.2	56.6	24.0
.3	1.46	5.8	13.1	23.4	36.5	52.6	11.5	33.4	58.3	26.0
.4	1.48	5.9	13.3	23.7	37.0	53.3	12.5	34.7	59.9	28.0
.5	1.50	6.0	13.5	24.0	37.5	54.0	13.5	36.0	2 1.5	30.0
.6	1.52	6.1	13.7	24.3	38.0	54.7	14.5	37.3	3.1	32.0
.7	1.54	6.2	13.9	24.6	38.5	55.4	15.5	38.6	4.7	34.0
.8	1.56	6.2	14.0	25.0	39.0	56.2	16.4	39.8	6.4	36.0
.9	1.58	6.3	14.2	25.3	39.5	56.9	17.4	41.1	8.0	38.0
8.0	0 1.60	0 6.4	0 14.4	0 25.6	0 40.0	0 57.6	1 18.4	1 42.4	2 9.6	2 40.0
9.0	1.80	7.2	16.2	28.8	45.0	1 04.8	28.2	55.2	25.8	3 0.0
10.0	2.00	8.0	18.0	32.0	50.0	12.0	38.0	2 8.0	42.0	20.0
11.0	2.20	8.8	19.8	35.2	55.0	19.2	47.8	20.8	58.2	40.0
12.0	2.40	9.6	21.6	38.4	1 00.0	26.4	57.6	33.6	3 14.4	59.9
13.0	2.60	10.4	23.4	41.6	05.0	33.6	2 7.4	46.4	30.5	4 19.9
14.0	2.80	11.2	25.2	44.8	10.0	40.8	17.2	59.2	46.7	39.9
15.0	3.00	12.0	27.0	48.0	15.0	48.0	27.0	3 12.0	4 2.9	59.9
16.0	3.20	12.8	28.8	51.2	20.0	55.2	36.8	24.8	19.1	5 19.8
17.0	3.40	13.6	30.6	54.4	25.0	2 02.4	46.6	37.5	35.3	39.8
18.0	3.60	14.4	32.4	57.6	30.0	9.6	56.4	50.3	51.5	59.7
19.0	3.80	15.2	34.2	1 0.8	35.0	16.8	3 6.2	4 3.1	5 7.6	6 19.7
20.0	0 4.00	0 16.0	0 36.0	1 4.0	1 40.0	2 24.0	3 16.0	4 15.9	5 23.8	6 39.6
21.0	4.20	16.8	37.8	7.2	45.0	31.2	25.8	28.7	40.0	59.5
22.0	4.40	17.6	39.6	10.4	50.0	38.4	35.6	41.5	56.1	7 19.5
23.0	4.60	18.4	41.4	13.6	55.0	45.6	45.3	54.2	6 12.3	39.4
24.0	4.80	19.2	43.2	16.8	2 0.0	52.8	55.1	5 7.0	28.4	59.3
25.0	5.00	20.0	45.0	20.0	5.0	3 0.0	4 4.9	19.8	44.6	8 19.2
26.0	5.20	20.8	46.8	23.2	10.0	7.2	14.7	32.6	7 0.7	39.1
27.0	5.40	21.6	48.6	26.4	15.0	14.4	24.5	45.3	16.9	59.0
28.0	5.60	22.4	50.4	29.6	20.0	21.6	34.3	58.1	33.0	9 18.9
29.0	5.80	23.2	52.2	32.8	25.0	28.8	44.1	6 10.9	49.2	38.8
30.0	0 6.00	0 24.0	0 54.0	1 36.0	2 30.0	3 35.9	4 53.8	6 23.7	8 5.3	9 58.7
31.0	6.20	24.8	55.8	39.2	35.0	43.1	5 3.6	36.4	21.4	10 18.5
32.0	6.40	25.6	57.6	42.4	40.0	50.3	13.4	49.2	37.5	38.4
33.0	6.60	26.4	59.4	45.6	45.0	57.5	23.2	7 1.9	53.7	58.2
34.0	6.80	27.2	1 1.2	48.8	50.0	4 4.7	33.0	14.7	9 9.8	11 18.1
35.0	7.00	28.0	3.0	52.0	55.0	11.9	42.7	27.5	25.9	37.9
36.0	7.20	28.8	4.8	55.2	3 0.0	19.1	52.5	40.2	42.0	57.7
37.0	7.40	29.6	6.6	58.4	5.0	26.3	6 2.3	53.0	58.1	12 17.5
38.0	7.60	30.4	8.4	2 1.6	10.0	33.5	12.1	8 5.7	10 14.2	37.3
39.0	7.80	31.2	10.2	4.8	15.0	40.6	21.8	18.4	30.3	57.1
40.0	0 8.00	0 32.0	1 12.0	2 8.0	3 20.0	4 47.8	6 31.6	8 31.2	10 46.3	13 16.8
41.0	8.20	32.8	13.8	11.2	24.9	55.0	41.4	43.9	11 2.4	36.6
42.0	8.40	33.6	15.6	14.4	29.9	5 2.2	51.1	56.6	18.5	56.3
43.0	8.60	34.4	17.4	17.6	34.9	9.4	7 0.9	9 9.3	34.5	14 16.1
44.0	8.80	35.2	19.2	20.8	39.9	16 6	10.6	22.0	50.6	35.8
45.0	9.00	36.0	21.0	24.0	44.9	23.7	20.4	34.7	12 6.6	55.5

Deflection Angle to Chord Point Number	Transit at Chord Point Number										
	0 T.S.	1	2	3	4	5	6	7	8	9	10 S.C.
0 T.S.	0	2	8	18	32	50	72	98	128	162	200
1	1	0	5	14	27	44	65	90	119	152	189
2	4	4	0	8	20	36	56	80	108	140	176
3	9	10	7	0	11	26	45	68	95	126	161
4	16	18	16	10	0	14	32	54	80	110	144
5	25	28	27	22	13	0	17	38	63	92	125
6	36	40	40	36	28	16	0	20	44	72	104
7	49	54	55	52	45	34	19	0	23	50	81
8	64	70	72	70	64	54	40	22	0	26	56
9	81	88	91	90	85	76	63	46	25	0	29
S.C.	100	108	112	112	108	100	88	72	52	28	0

This Table is used to obtain deflection angles from the tangent at an intermediate point on the spiral to any other point.

EXAMPLE.   Given spiral angle $\Delta = 3.6°$, obtain forward deflection to point 6 and back deflection to point 2 from point 4.

From Table IX

$$a_1 = 00.72'   \text{(for } \Delta = 3.6°)$$

From Table X, obtain coefficients 28 and 20

Forward deflection to point 6 $= 00.72' \times 28 = 20'$
Back deflection to point 2 $= 00.72' \times 20 = 14'$

The values obtained are slightly approximate and, according to the American Railway Engineering Association, should not be used "when the central angle from the transit point to the point of sight exceeds the central angle from the TS to the transit point by more than 15°".

* From the Am. Ry. Eng. Assoc. Manual.   Can be used for A.R.E.A. Ten-Chord Spiral and for other spirals.

Table XI.
Correction to Spiral Deflection Angles

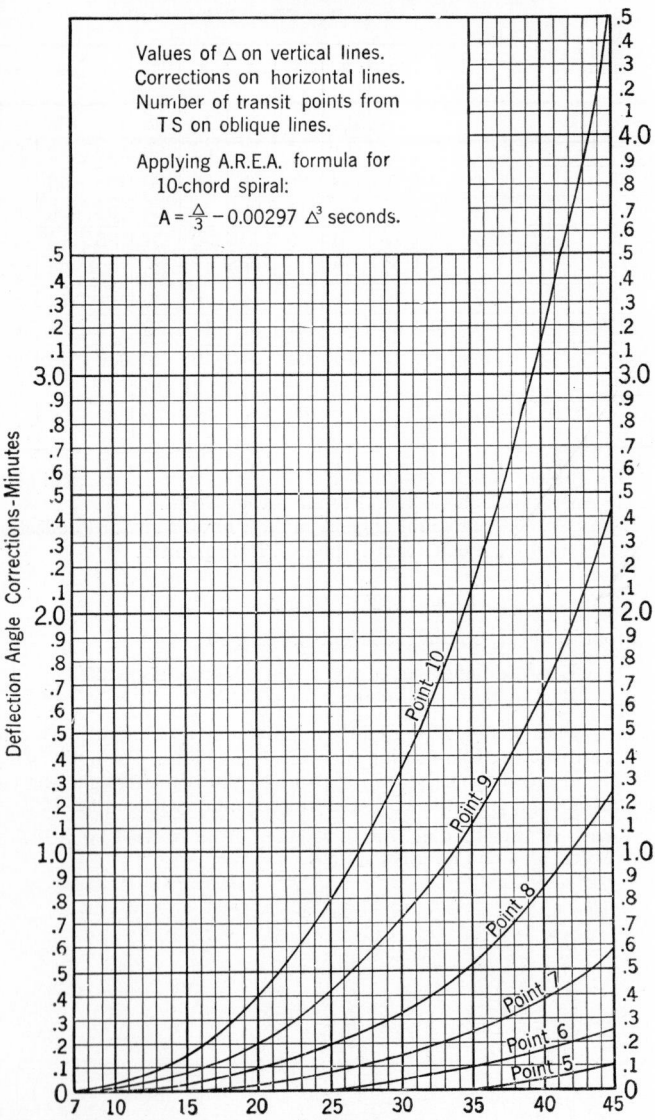

Values of △ on vertical lines.
Corrections on horizontal lines.
Number of transit points from
TS on oblique lines.

Applying A.R.E.A. formula for
10-chord spiral:

$$A = \frac{\triangle}{3} - 0.00297 \,\triangle^3 \text{ seconds.}$$

Deflection Angle Corrections-Minutes

Point 10
Point 9
Point 8
Point 7
Point 6
Point 5

△-Degrees

Table XII.
Theoretical (or Balanced) Superelevation
(Feet Per Foot of Width)

$$e = \frac{v^2}{15R} \text{ (closely)}$$

Degree of curve (Arc definition)	Velocity (miles per hour)									Radius (feet)
	20	30	40	50	60	70	80	90	100	
0° 34'	....	.006	.011	.017	.024	.033	.043	.054	.067	10000
0° 38'	....	.007	.012	.018	.027	.036	.047	.060	.074	9000
0° 43'	....	.008	.013	.021	.030	.041	.053	.067	.083	8000
0° 49'	....	.009	.015	.024	.034	.047	.061	.077	.095	7000
0° 57'	....	.010	.018	.028	.040	.054	.071	.090	.111	6000
1° 00'	.005	.010	.019	.029	.042	.057	.074	.094	.116	5730
1° 09'	.005	.012	.021	.033	.048	.065	.085	.108	.133	5000
1° 26'	.007	.015	.027	.042	.060	.082	.107	.135	.167	4000
1° 55'	.009	.020	.036	.056	.080	.109	.142	.180	.222	3000
2° 00'	.009	.021	.037	.058	.084	.114	.149	.188	.233	2865
2° 18'	.011	.024	.043	.067	.096	.131	.171	.216	.267	2500
2° 52'	.013	.030	.053	.083	.120	.163	.213	.270	.333	2000
3° 00'	.014	.031	.056	.087	.126	.171	.223	.283	.349	1910
3° 49'	.018	.040	.071	.111	.160	.218	.284	.360	.444	1500
4° 00'	.019	.042	.074	.116	.168	.228	.298	.377	.465	1432
5° 00'	.023	.052	.093	.145	.209	.285	.372	.471	.581	1146
5° 44'	.027	.060	.107	.167	.240	.327	.427	.540	.667	1000
6° 00'	.028	.063	.112	.175	.251	.342	.447	.565	.698	955
6° 22'	.030	.067	.118	.185	.267	.363	.474	.600	.741	900
7° 00'	.033	.073	.130	.204	.293	.399	.521	.660	.814	819
7° 10'	.033	.075	.133	.208	.300	.408	.533	.675	.833	800
8° 00'	.037	.084	.149	.233	.335	.456	.596	.754	.931	716
8° 11'	.038	.086	.152	.238	.343	.467	.609	.771		700
9° 00'	.042	.094	.168	.262	.377	.513	.670	.848		637
9° 33'	.044	.100	.178	.278	.400	.544	.711	.900		600
10° 00'	.046	.105	.186	.291	.419	.570				573
11° 00'	.051	.115	.205	.320	.461	.627				521
11° 28'	.053	.120	.213	.333	.480	.653				500
12° 00'	.056	.126	.223	.349	.503	.684				477
13° 00'	.060	.136	.242	.378	.545					441
14° 00'	.065	.147	.261	.407	.586					409
14° 19'	.067	.150	.267	.417	.600					400
15° 00'	.070	.157	.279	.436	.628					382
16° 00'	.074	.168	.298	.465	.670					358
17° 00'	.079	.178	.316	.494						337
18° 00'	.084	.188	.335	.524						313
19° 06'	.089	.200	.356	.556						300
20° 00'	.093	.209	.372	.582						286
21° 00'	.098	.220	.391	.611						273
22° 00'	.102	.230	.410	.640						260
23° 00'	.107	.241	.428	.669						249
24° 00'	.112	.251	.447	.698						239
25° 00'	.116	.262	.465	.727						229
28° 39'	.133	.300	.533	.833						200

To obtain total superelevation of highway, multiply by width, in feet.
To obtain total superelevation for standard gage railway, multiply by 4.9 feet.
In railway and highway practice, superelevations seldom exceed (and are frequently less than) those values above the heavy line. See text pages 128 to 135.

Table XIII.
1 — Logarithms of Numbers — 100

N	Log	N	Log	N	Log	N	Log	N	Log
0	———	20	1.30 103	40	1.60 206	60	1.77 815	80	1.90 309
1	0.00 000	21	1.32 222	41	1.61 278	61	1.78 533	81	1.90 849
2	0.30 103	22	1.34 242	42	1.62 325	62	1.79 239	82	1.91 381
3	0.47 712	23	1.36 173	43	1.63 347	63	1.79 934	83	1.91 908
4	0.60 206	24	1.38 021	44	1.64 345	64	1.80 618	84	1.92 428
5	0.69 897	25	1.39 794	45	1.65 321	65	1.81 291	85	1.92 942
6	0.77 815	26	1.41 497	46	1.66 276	66	1.81 954	86	1.93 450
7	0.84 510	27	1.43 136	47	1.67 210	67	1.82 607	87	1.93 952
8	0.90 309	28	1.44 716	48	1.68 124	68	1.83 251	88	1.94 448
9	0.95 424	29	1.46 240	49	1.69 020	69	1.83 885	89	1.94 939
10	1.00 000	30	1.47 712	50	1.69 897	70	1.84 510	90	1.95 424
11	1.04 139	31	1.49 136	51	1.70 757	71	1.85 126	91	1.95 904
12	1.07 918	32	1.50 515	52	1.71 600	72	1.85 733	92	1.96 379
13	1.11 394	33	1.51 851	53	1.72 428	73	1.86 332	93	1.96 848
14	1.14 613	34	1.53 148	54	1.73 239	74	1.86 923	94	1.97 313
15	1.17 609	35	1.54 407	55	1.74 036	75	1.87 506	95	1.97 772
16	1.20 412	36	1.55 630	56	1.74 819	76	1.88 081	96	1.98 227
17	1.23 045	37	1.56 820	57	1.75 587	77	1.88 649	97	1.98 677
18	1.25 527	38	1.57 978	58	1.76 343	78	1.89 209	98	1.99 123
19	1.27 875	39	1.59 106	59	1.77 085	79	1.89 763	99	1.99 564
N	Log	N	Log	N	Log	N	Log	N	Log

100 — Logarithms of Numbers — 150

N.	0	1	2	3	4	5	6	7	8	9	Prop. Pts.
100	00 000	043	087	130	173	217	260	303	346	389	
101	432	475	518	561	604	647	689	732	775	817	**44 43 42**
102	860	903	945	988	*030	*072	*115	*157	*199	*242	1 4.4 4.3 4.2
103	01 284	326	368	410	452	494	536	578	620	662	2 8.8 8.6 8.4
104	703	745	787	828	870	912	953	995	*036	*078	3 13.2 12.9 12.6
105	02 119	160	202	243	284	325	366	407	449	490	4 17.6 17.2 16.8
106	531	572	612	653	694	735	776	816	857	898	5 22.0 21.5 21.0
107	938	979	*019	*060	*100	*141	*181	*222	*262	*302	6 26.4 25.8 25.2
108	03 342	383	423	463	503	543	583	623	663	703	7 30.8 30.1 29.4
109	743	782	822	862	902	941	981	*021	*060	*100	8 35.2 34.4 33.6
											9 39.6 38.7 37.8
110	04 139	179	218	258	297	336	376	415	454	493	
111	532	571	610	650	689	727	766	805	844	883	**41 40 39**
112	922	961	999	*038	*077	*115	*154	*192	*231	*269	1 4.1 4.0 3.9
113	05 308	346	385	423	461	500	538	576	614	652	2 8.2 8.0 7.8
114	690	729	767	805	843	881	918	956	994	*032	3 12.3 12.0 11.7
115	06 070	108	145	183	221	258	296	333	371	408	4 16.4 16.0 15.6
116	446	483	521	558	595	633	670	707	744	781	5 20.5 20.0 19.5
117	819	856	893	930	967	*004	*041	*078	*115	*151	6 24.6 24.0 23.4
118	07 188	225	262	298	335	372	408	445	482	518	7 28.7 28.0 27.3
119	555	591	628	664	700	737	773	809	846	882	8 32.8 32.0 31.2
											9 36.9 36.0 35.1
120	918	954	990	*027	*063	*099	*135	*171	*207	*243	
121	08 279	314	350	386	422	458	493	529	565	600	**38 37 36**
122	636	672	707	743	778	814	849	884	920	955	1 3.8 3.7 3.6
123	991	*026	*061	*096	*132	*167	*202	*237	*272	*307	2 7.6 7.4 7.2
124	09 342	377	412	447	482	517	552	587	621	656	3 11.4 11.1 10.8
125	691	726	760	795	830	864	899	934	968	*003	4 15.2 14.8 14.4
126	10 037	072	106	140	175	209	243	278	312	346	5 19.0 18.5 18.0
127	380	415	449	483	517	551	585	619	653	687	6 22.8 22.2 21.6
128	721	755	789	823	857	890	924	958	992	*025	7 26.6 25.9 25.2
129	11 059	093	126	160	193	227	261	294	327	361	8 30.4 29.6 28.8
											9 34.2 33.3 32.4
130	394	428	461	494	528	561	594	628	661	694	
131	727	760	793	826	860	893	926	959	992	*024	**35 34 33**
132	12 057	090	123	156	189	222	254	287	320	352	1 3.5 3.4 3.3
133	385	418	450	483	516	548	581	613	646	678	2 7.0 6.8 6.6
134	710	743	775	808	840	872	905	937	969	*001	3 10.5 10.2 9.9
135	13 033	066	098	130	162	194	226	258	290	322	4 14.0 13.6 13.2
136	354	386	418	450	481	513	545	577	609	640	5 17.5 17.0 16.5
137	672	704	735	767	799	830	862	893	925	956	6 21.0 20.4 19.8
138	988	*019	*051	*082	*114	*145	*176	*208	*239	*270	7 24.5 23.8 23.1
139	14 301	333	364	395	426	457	489	520	551	582	8 28.0 27.2 26.4
											9 31.5 30.6 29.7
140	613	644	675	706	737	768	799	829	860	891	
141	922	953	983	*014	*045	*076	*106	*137	*168	*198	**32 31 30**
142	15 229	259	290	320	351	381	412	442	473	503	1 3.2 3.1 3.0
143	534	564	594	625	655	685	715	746	776	806	2 6.4 6.2 6.0
144	836	866	897	927	957	987	*017	*047	*077	*107	3 9.6 9.3 9.0
145	16 137	167	197	227	256	286	316	346	376	406	4 12.8 12.4 12.0
146	435	465	495	524	554	584	613	643	673	702	5 16.0 15.5 15.0
147	732	761	791	820	850	879	909	938	967	997	6 19.2 18.6 18.0
148	17 026	056	085	114	143	173	202	231	260	289	7 22.4 21.7 21.0
149	319	348	377	406	435	464	493	522	551	580	8 25.6 24.8 24.0
											9 28.8 27.9 27.0
150	609	638	667	696	725	754	782	811	840	869	
N.	0	1	2	3	4	5	6	7	8	9	Prop. Pts.

N.	0	1	2	3	4	5	6	7	8	9
150	17 609	638	667	696	725	754	782	811	840	869
151	898	926	955	984	*013	*041	*070	*099	*127	*156
152	18 184	213	241	270	298	327	355	384	412	441
153	469	498	526	554	583	611	639	667	696	724
154	752	780	808	837	865	893	921	949	977	*005
155	19 033	061	089	117	145	173	201	229	257	285
156	312	340	368	396	424	451	479	507	535	562
157	590	618	645	673	700	728	756	783	811	838
158	866	893	921	948	976	*003	*030	*058	*085	*112
159	20 140	167	194	222	249	276	303	330	358	385
160	412	439	466	493	520	548	575	602	629	656
161	683	710	737	763	790	817	844	871	898	925
162	952	978	*005	*032	*059	*085	*112	*139	*165	*192
163	21 219	245	272	299	325	352	378	405	431	458
164	484	511	537	564	590	617	643	669	696	722
165	748	775	801	827	854	880	906	932	958	985
166	22 011	037	063	089	115	141	167	194	220	246
167	272	298	324	350	376	401	427	453	479	505
168	531	557	583	608	634	660	686	712	737	763
169	789	814	840	866	891	917	943	968	994	*019
170	23 045	070	096	121	147	172	198	223	249	274
171	300	325	350	376	401	426	452	477	502	528
172	553	578	603	629	654	679	704	729	754	779
173	805	830	855	880	905	930	955	980	*005	*030
174	24 055	080	105	130	155	180	204	229	254	279
175	304	329	353	378	403	428	452	477	502	527
176	551	576	601	625	650	674	699	724	748	773
177	797	822	846	871	895	920	944	969	993	*018
178	25 042	066	091	115	139	164	188	212	237	261
179	285	310	334	358	382	406	431	455	479	503
180	527	551	575	600	624	648	672	696	720	744
181	768	792	816	840	864	888	912	935	959	983
182	26 007	031	055	079	102	126	150	174	198	221
183	245	269	293	316	340	364	387	411	435	458
184	482	505	529	553	576	600	623	647	670	694
185	717	741	764	788	811	834	858	881	905	928
186	951	975	998	*021	*045	*068	*091	*114	*138	*161
187	27 184	207	231	254	277	300	323	346	370	393
188	416	439	462	485	508	531	554	577	600	623
189	646	669	692	715	738	761	784	807	830	852
190	875	898	921	944	967	989	*012	*035	*058	*081
191	28 103	126	149	171	194	217	240	262	285	307
192	330	353	375	398	421	443	466	488	511	533
193	556	578	601	623	646	668	691	713	735	758
194	780	803	825	847	870	892	914	937	959	981
195	29 003	026	048	070	092	115	137	159	181	203
196	226	248	270	292	314	336	358	380	403	425
197	447	469	491	513	535	557	579	601	623	645
198	667	688	710	732	754	776	798	820	842	863
199	885	907	929	951	973	994	*016	*038	*060	*081
200	30 103	125	146	168	190	211	233	255	276	298
N.	0	1	2	3	4	5	6	7	8	9

Prop. Pts.

	29	28		27	26		25	24		23	22		21
1	2.9	2.8	1	2.7	2.6	1	2.5	2.4	1	2.3	2.2	1	2.1
2	5.8	5.6	2	5.4	5.2	2	5.0	4.8	2	4.6	4.4	2	4.2
3	8.7	8.4	3	8.1	7.8	3	7.5	7.2	3	6.9	6.6	3	6.3
4	11.6	11.2	4	10.8	10.4	4	10.0	9.6	4	9.2	8.8	4	8.4
5	14.5	14.0	5	13.5	13.0	5	12.5	12.0	5	11.5	11.0	5	10.5
6	17.4	16.8	6	16.2	15.6	6	15.0	14.4	6	13.8	13.2	6	12.6
7	20.3	19.6	7	18.9	18.2	7	17.5	16.8	7	16.1	15.4	7	14.7
8	23.2	22.4	8	21.6	20.8	8	20.0	19.2	8	18.4	17.6	8	16.8
9	26.1	25.2	9	24.3	23.4	9	22.5	21.6	9	20.7	19.8	9	18.9

200 — Logarithms of Numbers — 250

N.	0	1	2	3	4	5	6	7	8	9	Prop. Pts.	
200	30 103	125	146	168	190	211	233	255	276	298		
201	320	341	363	384	406	428	449	471	492	514		
202	535	557	578	600	621	643	664	685	707	728	log 2	
203	750	771	792	814	835	856	878	899	920	942	=.30102 99957	
204	963	984	*006	*027	*048	*069	*091	*112	*133	*154		
205	31 175	197	218	239	260	281	302	323	345	366		
206	387	408	429	450	471	492	513	534	555	576		

		22	**21**
	1	2.2	2.1
	2	4.4	4.2
	3	6.6	6.3
	4	8.8	8.4
	5	11.0	10.5
	6	13.2	12.6
	7	15.4	14.7
	8	17.6	16.8
	9	19.8	18.9

N.	0	1	2	3	4	5	6	7	8	9
207	597	618	639	660	681	702	723	744	765	785
208	806	827	848	869	890	911	931	952	973	994
209	32 015	035	056	077	098	118	139	160	181	201
210	222	243	263	284	305	325	346	366	387	408
211	428	449	469	490	510	531	552	572	593	613
212	634	654	675	695	715	736	756	777	797	818
213	838	858	879	899	919	940	960	980	*001	*021
214	33 041	062	082	102	122	143	163	183	203	224
215	244	264	284	304	325	345	365	385	405	425
216	445	465	486	506	526	546	566	586	606	626
217	646	666	686	706	726	746	766	786	806	826
218	846	866	885	905	925	945	965	985	*005	*025
219	34 044	064	084	104	124	143	163	183	203	223
220	242	262	282	301	321	341	361	380	400	420

		20	**19**
	1	2.0	1.9
	2	4.0	3.8
	3	6.0	5.7
	4	8.0	7.6
	5	10.0	9.5
	6	12.0	11.4
	7	14.0	13.3
	8	16.0	15.2
	9	18.0	17.1

N.	0	1	2	3	4	5	6	7	8	9
221	439	459	479	498	518	537	557	577	596	616
222	635	655	674	694	713	733	753	772	792	811
223	830	850	869	889	908	928	947	967	986	*005
224	35 025	044	064	083	102	122	141	160	180	199
225	218	238	257	276	295	315	334	353	372	392
226	411	430	449	468	488	507	526	545	564	583
227	603	622	641	660	679	698	717	736	755	774
228	793	813	832	851	870	889	908	927	946	965
229	984	*003	*021	*040	*059	*078	*097	*116	*135	*154
230	36 173	192	211	229	248	267	286	305	324	342
231	361	380	399	418	436	455	474	493	511	530
232	549	568	586	605	624	642	661	680	698	717
233	736	754	773	791	810	829	847	866	884	903
234	922	940	959	977	996	*014	*033	*051	*070	*088
235	37 107	125	144	162	181	199	218	236	254	273
236	291	310	328	346	365	383	401	420	438	457

		18	**17**
	1	1.8	1.7
	2	3.6	3.4
	3	5.4	5.1
	4	7.2	6.8
	5	9.0	8.5
	6	10.8	10.2
	7	12.6	11.9
	8	14.4	13.6
	9	16.2	15.3

N.	0	1	2	3	4	5	6	7	8	9
237	475	493	511	530	548	566	585	603	621	639
238	658	676	694	712	731	749	767	785	803	822
239	840	858	876	894	912	931	949	967	985	*003
240	38 021	039	057	075	093	112	130	148	166	184
241	202	220	238	256	274	292	310	328	346	364
242	382	399	417	435	453	471	489	507	525	543
243	561	578	596	614	632	650	668	686	703	721
244	739	757	775	792	810	828	846	863	881	899
245	917	934	952	970	987	*005	*023	*041	*058	*076
246	39 094	111	129	146	164	182	199	217	235	252
247	270	287	305	322	340	358	375	393	410	428
248	445	463	480	498	515	533	550	568	585	602
249	620	637	655	672	690	707	724	742	759	777
250	794	811	829	846	863	881	898	915	933	950

N.	0	1	2	3	4	5	6	7	8	9	Prop. Pts.

250 — Logarithms of Numbers — 300

N.	0	1	2	3	4	5	6	7	8	9
250	39 794	811	829	846	863	881	898	915	933	950
251	967	985	*002	*019	*037	*054	*071	*088	*106	*123
252	40 140	157	175	192	209	226	243	261	278	295
253	312	329	346	364	381	398	415	432	449	466
254	483	500	518	535	552	569	586	603	620	637
255	654	671	688	705	722	739	756	773	790	807
256	824	841	858	875	892	909	926	943	960	976
257	993	*010	*027	*044	*061	*078	*095	*111	*128	*145
258	41 162	179	196	212	229	246	263	280	296	313
259	330	347	363	380	397	414	430	447	464	481
260	497	514	531	547	564	581	597	614	631	647
261	664	681	697	714	731	747	764	780	797	814
262	830	847	863	880	896	913	929	946	963	979
263	996	*012	*029	*045	*062	*078	*095	*111	*127	*144
264	42 160	177	193	210	226	243	259	275	292	308
265	325	341	357	374	390	406	423	439	455	472
266	488	504	521	537	553	570	586	602	619	635
267	651	667	684	700	716	732	749	765	781	797
268	813	830	846	862	878	894	911	927	943	959
269	975	991	*008	*024	*040	*056	*072	*088	*104	*120
270	43 136	152	169	185	201	217	233	249	265	281
271	297	313	329	345	361	377	393	409	425	441
272	457	473	489	505	521	537	553	569	584	600
273	616	632	648	664	680	696	712	727	743	759
274	775	791	807	823	838	854	870	886	902	917
275	933	949	965	981	996	*012	*028	*044	*059	*075
276	44 091	107	122	138	154	170	185	201	217	232
277	248	264	279	295	311	326	342	358	373	389
278	404	420	436	451	467	483	498	514	529	545
279	560	576	592	607	623	638	654	669	685	700
280	716	731	747	762	778	793	809	824	840	855
281	871	886	902	917	932	948	963	979	994	*010
282	45 025	040	056	071	086	102	117	133	148	163
283	179	194	209	225	240	255	271	286	301	317
284	332	347	362	378	393	408	423	439	454	469
285	484	500	515	530	545	561	576	591	606	621
286	637	652	667	682	697	712	728	743	758	773
287	788	803	818	834	849	864	879	894	909	924
288	939	954	969	984	*000	*015	*030	*045	*060	*075
289	46 090	105	120	135	150	165	180	195	210	225
290	240	255	270	285	300	315	330	345	359	374
291	389	404	419	434	449	464	479	494	509	523
292	538	553	568	583	598	613	627	642	657	672
293	687	702	716	731	746	761	776	790	805	820
294	835	850	864	879	894	909	923	938	953	967
295	982	997	*012	*026	*041	*056	*070	*085	*100	*114
296	47 129	144	159	173	188	202	217	232	246	261
297	276	290	305	319	334	349	363	378	392	407
298	422	436	451	465	480	494	509	524	538	553
299	567	582	596	611	625	640	654	669	683	698
300	712	727	741	756	770	784	799	813	828	842
N.	0	1	2	3	4	5	6	7	8	9

Prop. Pts.

	18	17
1	1.8	1.7
2	3.6	3.4
3	5.4	5.1
4	7.2	6.8
5	9.0	8.5
6	10.8	10.2
7	12.6	11.9
8	14.4	13.6
9	16.2	15.3

M
$=\log_{10} e$
$=\log_{10} 2.718\cdots$
$=.43429\ 44819$

	16	15
1	1.6	1.5
2	3.2	3.0
3	4.8	4.5
4	6.4	6.0
5	8.0	7.5
6	9.6	9.0
7	11.2	10.5
8	12.8	12.0
9	14.4	13.5

	14
1	1.4
2	2.8
3	4.2
4	5.6
5	7.0
6	8.4
7	9.8
8	11.2
9	12.6

N.	0	1	2	3	4	5	6	7	8	9
300	47 712	727	741	756	770	784	799	813	828	842
301	857	871	885	900	914	929	943	958	972	986
302	48 001	015	029	044	058	073	087	101	116	130
303	144	159	173	187	202	216	230	244	259	273
304	287	302	316	330	344	359	373	387	401	416
305	430	444	458	473	487	501	515	530	544	558
306	572	586	601	615	629	643	657	671	686	700
307	714	728	742	756	770	785	799	813	827	841
308	855	869	883	897	911	926	940	954	968	982
309	996	*010	*024	*038	*052	*066	*080	*094	*108	*122
310	49 136	150	164	178	192	206	220	234	248	262
311	276	290	304	318	332	346	360	374	388	402
312	415	429	443	457	471	485	499	513	527	541
313	554	568	582	596	610	624	638	651	665	679
314	693	707	721	734	748	762	776	790	803	817
315	831	845	859	872	886	900	914	927	941	955
316	969	982	996	*010	*024	*037	*051	*065	*079	*092
317	50 106	120	133	147	161	174	188	202	215	229
318	243	256	270	284	297	311	325	338	352	365
319	379	393	406	420	433	447	461	474	488	501
320	515	529	542	556	569	583	596	610	623	637
321	651	664	678	691	705	718	732	745	759	772
322	786	799	813	826	840	853	866	880	893	907
323	920	934	947	961	974	987	*001	*014	*028	*041
324	51 055	068	081	095	108	121	135	148	162	175
325	188	202	215	228	242	255	268	282	295	308
326	322	335	348	362	375	388	402	415	428	441
327	455	468	481	495	508	521	534	548	561	574
328	587	601	614	627	640	654	667	680	693	706
329	720	733	746	759	772	786	799	812	825	838
330	851	865	878	891	904	917	930	943	957	970
331	983	996	*009	*022	*035	*048	*061	*075	*088	*101
332	52 114	127	140	153	166	179	192	205	218	231
333	244	257	270	284	297	310	323	336	349	362
334	375	388	401	414	427	440	453	466	479	492
335	504	517	530	543	556	569	582	595	608	621
336	634	647	660	673	686	699	711	724	737	750
337	763	776	789	802	815	827	840	853	866	879
338	892	905	917	930	943	956	969	982	994	*007
339	53 020	033	046	058	071	084	097	110	122	135
340	148	161	173	186	199	212	224	237	250	263
341	275	288	301	314	326	339	352	364	377	390
342	403	415	428	441	453	466	479	491	504	517
343	529	542	555	567	580	593	605	618	631	643
344	656	668	681	694	706	719	732	744	757	769
345	782	794	807	820	832	845	857	870	882	895
346	908	920	933	945	958	970	983	995	*008	*020
347	54 033	045	058	070	083	095	108	120	133	145
348	158	170	183	195	208	220	233	245	258	270
349	283	295	307	320	332	345	357	370	382	394
350	407	419	432	444	456	469	481	494	506	518
N.	0	1	2	3	4	5	6	7	8	9

Prop. Pts.

log 3 = .47712 12547

log π = .49714 98727

	15	14
1	1.5	1.4
2	3.0	2.8
3	4.5	4.2
4	6.0	5.6
5	7.5	7.0
6	9.0	8.4
7	10.5	9.8
8	12.0	11.2
9	13.5	12.6

	13	12
1	1.3	1.2
2	2.6	2.4
3	3.9	3.6
4	5.2	4.8
5	6.5	6.0
6	7.8	7.2
7	9.1	8.4
8	10.4	9.6
9	11.7	10.8

N.	0	1	2	3	4	5	6	7	8	9
350	54 407	419	432	444	456	469	481	494	506	518
351	531	543	555	568	580	593	605	617	630	642
352	654	667	679	691	704	716	728	741	753	765
353	777	790	802	814	827	839	851	864	876	888
354	900	913	925	937	949	962	974	986	998	*011
355	55 023	035	047	060	072	084	096	108	121	133
356	145	157	169	182	194	206	218	230	242	255
357	267	279	291	303	315	328	340	352	364	376
358	388	400	413	425	437	449	461	473	485	497
359	509	522	534	546	558	570	582	594	606	618
360	630	642	654	666	678	691	703	715	727	739
361	751	763	775	787	799	811	823	835	847	859
362	871	883	895	907	919	931	943	955	967	979
363	991	*003	*015	*027	*038	*050	*062	*074	*086	*098
364	56 110	122	134	146	158	170	182	194	205	217
365	229	241	253	265	277	289	301	312	324	336
366	348	360	372	384	396	407	419	431	443	455
367	467	478	490	502	514	526	538	549	561	573
368	585	597	608	620	632	644	656	667	679	691
369	703	714	726	738	750	761	773	785	797	808
370	820	832	844	855	867	879	891	902	914	926
371	937	949	961	972	984	996	*008	*019	*031	*043
372	57 054	066	078	089	101	113	124	136	148	159
373	171	183	194	206	217	229	241	252	264	276
374	287	299	310	322	334	345	357	368	380	392
375	403	415	426	438	449	461	473	484	496	507
376	519	530	542	553	565	576	588	600	611	623
377	634	646	657	669	680	692	703	715	726	738
378	749	761	772	784	795	807	818	830	841	852
379	864	875	887	898	910	921	933	944	955	967
380	978	990	*001	*013	*024	*035	*047	*058	*070	*081
381	58 092	104	115	127	138	149	161	172	184	195
382	206	218	229	240	252	.263	274	286	297	309
383	320	331	343	354	365	377	388	399	410	422
384	433	444	456	467	478	490	501	512	524	535
385	546	557	569	580	591	602	614	625	636	647
386	659	670	681	692	704	715	726	737	749	760
387	771	782	794	805	816	827	838	850	861	872
388	883	894	906	917	928	939	950	961	973	984
389	995	*006	*017	*028	*040	*051	*062	*073	*084	*095
390	59 106	118	129	140	151	162	173	184	195	207
391	218	229	240	251	262	273	284	295	306	318
392	329	340	351	362	373	384	395	406	417	428
393	439	450	461	472	483	494	506	517	528	539
394	550	561	572	583	594	605	616	627	638	649
395	660	671	682	693	704	715	726	737	748	759
396	770	780	791	802	813	824	835	846	857	868
397	879	890	901	912	923	934	945	956	966	977
398	988	999	*010	*021	*032	*043	*054	*065	*076	*086
399	60 097	108	119	130	141	152	163	173	184	195
400	206	217	228	239	249	260	271	282	293	304
N.	0	1	2	3	4	5	6	7	8	9

Prop. Pts.

	13	12
1	1.3	1.2
2	2.6	2.4
3	3.9	3.6
4	5.2	4.8
5	6.5	6.0
6	7.8	7.2
7	9.1	8.4
8	10.4	9.6
9	11.7	10.8

	11	10
1	1.1	1.0
2	2.2	2.0
3	3.3	3.0
4	4.4	4.0
5	5.5	5.0
6	6.6	6.0
7	7.7	7.0
8	8.8	8.0
9	9.9	9.0

400 — Logarithms of Numbers — 450

N.	0	1	2	3	4	5	6	7	8	9	Prop. Pts.
400	60 206	217	228	239	249	260	271	282	293	304	
401	314	325	336	347	358	369	379	390	401	412	
402	423	433	444	455	466	477	487	498	509	520	
403	531	541	552	563	574	584	595	606	617	627	
404	638	649	660	670	681	692	703	713	724	735	
405	746	756	767	778	788	799	810	821	831	842	
406	853	863	874	885	895	906	917	927	938	949	
407	959	970	981	991	*002	*013	*023	*034	*045	*055	
408	61 066	077	087	098	109	119	130	140	151	162	
409	172	183	194	204	215	225	236	247	257	268	
410	278	289	300	310	321	331	342	352	363	374	
411	384	395	405	416	426	437	448	458	469	479	
412	490	500	511	521	532	542	553	563	574	584	
413	595	606	616	627	637	648	658	669	679	690	
414	700	711	721	731	742	752	763	773	784	794	
415	805	815	826	836	847	857	868	878	888	899	
416	909	920	930	941	951	962	972	982	993	*003	
417	62 014	024	034	045	055	066	076	086	097	107	
418	118	128	138	149	159	170	180	190	201	211	
419	221	232	242	252	263	273	284	294	304	315	
420	325	335	346	356	366	377	387	397	408	418	
421	428	439	449	459	469	480	490	500	511	521	
422	531	542	552	562	572	583	593	603	613	624	
423	634	644	655	665	675	685	696	706	716	726	
424	737	747	757	767	778	788	798	808	818	829	
425	839	849	859	870	880	890	900	910	921	931	
426	941	951	961	972	982	992	*002	*012	*022	*033	
427	63 043	053	063	073	083	094	104	114	124	134	
428	144	155	165	175	185	195	205	215	225	236	
429	246	256	266	276	286	296	306	317	327	337	
430	347	357	367	377	387	397	407	417	428	438	
431	448	458	468	478	488	498	508	518	528	538	
432	548	558	568	579	589	599	609	619	629	639	
433	649	659	669	679	689	699	709	719	729	739	
434	749	759	769	779	789	799	809	819	829	839	
435	849	859	869	879	889	899	909	919	929	939	
436	949	959	969	979	988	998	*008	*018	*028	*038	
437	64 048	058	068	078	088	098	108	118	128	137	
438	147	157	167	177	187	197	207	217	227	237	
439	246	256	266	276	286	296	306	316	326	335	
440	345	355	365	375	385	395	404	414	424	434	
441	444	454	464	473	483	493	503	513	523	532	
442	542	552	562	572	582	591	601	611	621	631	
443	640	650	660	670	680	689	699	709	719	729	
444	738	748	758	768	777	787	797	807	816	826	
445	836	846	856	865	875	885	895	904	914	924	
446	933	943	953	963	972	982	992	*002	*011	*021	
447	65 031	040	050	060	070	079	089	099	108	118	
448	128	137	147	157	167	176	186	196	205	215	
449	225	234	244	254	263	273	283	292	302	312	
450	321	331	341	350	360	369	379	389	398	408	
N.	0	1	2	3	4	5	6	7	8	9	Prop. Pts.

Prop. Pts.

	11	10
1	1.1	1.0
2	2.2	2.0
3	3.3	3.0
4	4.4	4.0
5	5.5	5.0
6	6.6	6.0
7	7.7	7.0
8	8.8	8.0
9	9.9	9.0

$$\log M = \log [\log e] = 9.63778\,431 - 10$$

	9
1	0.9
2	1.8
3	2.7
4	3.6
5	4.5
6	5.4
7	6.3
8	7.2
9	8.1

N.	0	1	2	3	4	5	6	7	8	9	Prop. Pts.
450	65 321	331	341	350	360	369	379	389	398	408	
451	418	427	437	447	456	466	475	485	495	504	
452	514	523	533	543	552	562	571	581	591	600	
453	610	619	629	639	648	658	667	677	686	696	
454	706	715	725	734	744	753	763	772	782	792	
455	801	811	820	830	839	849	858	868	877	887	
456	896	906	916	925	935	944	954	963	973	982	
457	992	*001	*011	*020	*030	*039	*049	*058	*068	*077	
458	66 087	096	106	115	124	134	143	153	162	172	
459	181	191	200	210	219	229	238	247	257	266	
460	276	285	295	304	314	323	332	342	351	361	
461	370	380	389	398	408	417	427	436	445	455	**10**　**9**
462	464	474	483	492	502	511	521	530	539	549	1	1.0	0.9
463	558	567	577	586	596	605	614	624	633	642	2	2.0	1.8
464	652	661	671	680	689	699	708	717	727	736	3	3.0	2.7
465	745	755	764	773	783	792	801	811	820	829	4	4.0	3.6
466	839	848	857	867	876	885	894	904	913	922	5	5.0	4.5
467	932	941	950	960	969	978	987	997	*006	*015	6	6.0	5.4
468	67 025	034	043	052	062	071	080	089	099	108	7	7.0	6.3
469	117	127	136	145	154	164	173	182	191	201	8	8.0	7.2
470	210	219	228	237	247	256	265	274	284	293	9	9.0	8.1
471	302	311	321	330	339	348	357	367	376	385	
472	394	403	413	422	431	440	449	459	468	477	
473	486	495	504	514	523	532	541	550	560	569	
474	578	587	596	605	614	624	633	642	651	660	
475	669	679	688	697	706	715	724	733	742	752	
476	761	770	779	788	797	806	815	825	834	843	
477	852	861	870	879	888	897	906	916	925	934	
478	943	952	961	970	979	988	997	*006	*015	*024	
479	68 034	043	052	061	070	079	088	097	106	115	
480	124	133	142	151	160	169	178	187	196	205	
481	215	224	233	242	251	260	269	278	287	296	**8**
482	305	314	323	332	341	350	359	368	377	386	1	0.8
483	395	404	413	422	431	440	449	458	467	476	2	1.6
484	485	494	502	511	520	529	538	547	556	565	3	2.4
485	574	583	592	601	610	619	628	637	646	655	4	3.2
486	664	673	681	690	699	708	717	726	735	744	5	4.0
487	753	762	771	780	789	797	806	815	824	833	6	4.8
488	842	851	860	869	878	886	895	904	913	922	7	5.6
489	931	940	949	958	966	975	984	993	*002	*011	8	6.4
490	69 020	028	037	046	055	064	073	082	090	099	9	7.2
491	108	117	126	135	144	152	161	170	179	188	
492	197	205	214	223	232	241	249	258	267	276	
493	285	294	302	311	320	329	338	346	355	364	
494	373	381	390	399	408	417	425	434	443	452	
495	461	469	478	487	496	504	513	522	531	539	
496	548	557	566	574	583	592	601	609	618	627	
497	636	644	653	662	671	679	688	697	705	714	
498	723	732	740	749	758	767	775	784	793	801	
499	810	819	827	836	845	854	862	871	880	888	
500	897	906	914	923	932	940	949	958	966	975	
N.	0	1	2	3	4	5	6	7	8	9	Prop. Pts.

N.	0	1	2	3	4	5	6	7	8	9
500	69 897	906	914	923	932	940	949	958	966	975
501	984	992	*001	*010	*018	*027	*036	*044	*053	*062
502	70 070	079	088	096	105	114	122	131	140	148
503	157	165	174	183	191	200	209	217	226	234
504	243	252	260	269	278	286	295	303	312	321
505	329	338	346	355	364	372	381	389	398	406
506	415	424	432	441	449	458	467	475	484	492
507	501	509	518	526	535	544	552	561	569	578
508	586	595	603	612	621	629	638	646	655	663
509	672	680	689	697	706	714	723	731	740	749
510	757	766	774	783	791	800	808	817	825	834
511	842	851	859	868	876	885	893	902	910	919
512	927	935	944	952	961	969	978	986	995	*003
513	71 012	020	029	037	046	054	063	071	079	088
514	096	105	113	122	130	139	147	155	164	172
515	181	189	198	206	214	223	231	240	248	257
516	265	273	282	290	299	307	315	324	332	341
517	349	357	366	374	383	391	399	408	416	425
518	433	441	450	458	466	475	483	492	500	508
519	517	525	533	542	550	559	567	575	584	592
520	600	609	617	625	634	642	650	659	667	675
521	684	692	700	709	717	725	734	742	750	759
522	767	775	784	792	800	809	817	825	834	842
523	850	858	867	875	883	892	900	908	917	925
524	933	941	950	958	966	975	983	991	999	*008
525	72 016	024	032	041	049	057	066	074	082	090
526	099	107	115	123	132	140	148	156	165	173
527	181	189	198	206	214	222	230	239	247	255
528	263	272	280	288	296	304	313	321	329	337
529	346	354	362	370	378	387	395	403	411	419
530	428	436	444	452	460	469	477	485	493	501
531	509	518	526	534	542	550	558	567	575	583
532	591	599	607	616	624	632	640	648	656	665
533	673	681	689	697	705	713	722	730	738	746
534	754	762	770	779	787	795	803	811	819	827
535	835	843	852	860	868	876	884	892	900	908
536	916	925	933	941	949	957	965	973	981	989
537	997	*006	*014	*022	*030	*038	*046	*054	*062	*070
538	73 078	086	094	102	111	119	127	135	143	151
539	159	167	175	183	191	199	207	215	223	231
540	239	247	255	263	272	280	288	296	304	312
541	320	328	336	344	352	360	368	376	384	392
542	400	408	416	424	432	440	448	456	464	472
543	480	488	496	504	512	520	528	536	544	552
544	560	568	576	584	592	600	608	616	624	632
545	640	648	656	664	672	679	687	695	703	711
546	719	727	735	743	751	759	767	775	783	791
547	799	807	815	823	830	838	846	854	862	870
548	878	886	894	902	910	918	926	933	941	949
549	957	965	973	981	989	997	*005	*013	*020	*028
550	74 036	044	052	060	068	076	084	092	099	107
N.	0	1	2	3	4	5	6	7	8	9

Prop. Pts.

log 5
=.69897 00043

	9	8
1	0.9	0.8
2	1.8	1.6
3	2.7	2.4
4	3.6	3.2
5	4.5	4.0
6	5.4	4.8
7	6.3	5.6
8	7.2	6.4
9	8.1	7.2

	7
1	0.7
2	1.4
3	2.1
4	2.8
5	3.5
6	4.2
7	4.9
8	5.6
9	6.3

550 — Logarithms of Numbers — 600

N.	0	1	2	3	4	5	6	7	8	9
550	74 036	044	052	060	068	076	084	092	099	107
551	115	123	131	139	147	155	162	170	178	186
552	194	202	210	218	225	233	241	249	257	265
553	273	280	288	296	304	312	320	327	335	343
554	351	359	367	374	382	390	398	406	414	421
555	429	437	445	453	461	468	476	484	492	500
556	507	515	523	531	539	547	554	562	570	578
557	586	593	601	609	617	624	632	640	648	656
558	663	671	679	687	695	702	710	718	726	733
559	741	749	757	764	772	780	788	796	803	811
560	819	827	834	842	850	858	865	873	881	889
561	896	904	912	920	927	935	943	950	958	966
562	974	981	989	997	*005	*012	*020	*028	*035	*043
563	75 051	059	066	074	082	089	097	105	113	120
564	128	136	143	151	159	166	174	182	189	197
565	205	213	220	228	236	243	251	259	266	274
566	282	289	297	305	312	320	328	335	343	351
567	358	366	374	381	389	397	404	412	420	427
568	435	442	450	458	465	473	481	488	496	504
569	511	519	526	534	542	549	557	565	572	580
570	587	595	603	610	618	626	633	641	648	656
571	664	671	679	686	694	702	709	717	724	732
572	740	747	755	762	770	778	785	793	800	808
573	815	823	831	838	846	853	861	868	876	884
574	891	899	906	914	921	929	937	944	952	959
575	967	974	982	989	997	*005	*012	*020	*027	*035
576	76 042	050	057	065	072	080	087	095	103	110
577	118	125	133	140	148	155	163	170	178	185
578	193	200	208	215	223	230	238	245	253	260
579	268	275	283	290	298	305	313	320	328	335
580	343	350	358	365	373	380	388	395	403	410
581	418	425	433	440	448	455	462	470	477	485
582	492	500	507	515	522	530	537	545	552	559
583	567	574	582	589	597	604	612	619	626	634
584	641	649	656	664	671	678	686	693	701	708
585	716	723	730	738	745	753	760	768	775	782
586	790	797	805	812	819	827	834	842	849	856
587	864	871	879	886	893	901	908	916	923	930
588	938	945	953	960	967	975	982	989	997	*004
589	77 012	019	026	034	041	048	056	063	070	078
590	085	093	100	107	115	122	129	137	144	151
591	159	166	173	181	188	195	203	210	217	225
592	232	240	247	254	262	269	276	283	291	298
593	305	313	320	327	335	342	349	357	364	371
594	379	386	393	401	408	415	422	430	437	444
595	452	459	466	474	481	488	495	503	510	517
596	525	532	539	546	554	561	568	576	583	590
597	597	605	612	619	627	634	641	648	656	663
598	670	677	685	692	699	706	714	721	728	735
599	743	750	757	764	772	779	786	793	801	808
600	815	822	830	837	844	851	859	866	873	880
N.	0	1	2	3	4	5	6	7	8	9

Prop. Pts.

	8	7
1	0.8	0.7
2	1.6	1.4
3	2.4	2.1
4	3.2	2.8
5	4.0	3.5
6	4.8	4.2
7	5.6	4.9
8	6.4	5.6
9	7.2	6.3

600 — Logarithms of Numbers — 650

N.	0	1	2	3	4	5	6	7	8	9	Prop. Pts.
600	77 815	822	830	837	844	851	859	866	873	880	
601	887	895	902	909	916	924	931	938	945	952	
602	960	967	974	981	988	996	*003	*010	*017	*025	
603	78 032	039	046	053	061	068	075	082	089	097	
604	104	111	118	125	132	140	147	154	161	168	
605	176	183	190	197	204	211	219	226	233	240	
606	247	254	262	269	276	283	290	297	305	312	
607	319	326	333	340	347	355	362	369	376	383	
608	390	398	405	412	419	426	433	440	447	455	
609	462	469	476	483	490	497	504	512	519	526	
610	533	540	547	554	561	569	576	583	590	597	
611	604	611	618	625	633	640	647	654	661	668	
612	675	682	689	696	704	711	718	725	732	739	
613	746	753	760	767	774	781	789	796	803	810	
614	817	824	831	838	845	852	859	866	873	880	
615	888	895	902	909	916	923	930	937	944	951	
616	958	965	972	979	986	993	*000	*007	*014	*021	
617	79 029	036	043	050	057	064	071	078	085	092	
618	099	106	113	120	127	134	141	148	155	162	
619	169	176	183	190	197	204	211	218	225	232	
620	239	246	253	260	267	274	281	288	295	302	
621	309	316	323	330	337	344	351	358	365	372	
622	379	386	393	400	407	414	421	428	435	442	
623	449	456	463	470	477	484	491	498	505	511	
624	518	525	532	539	546	553	560	567	574	581	
625	588	595	602	609	616	623	630	637	644	650	
626	657	664	671	678	685	692	699	706	713	720	
627	727	734	741	748	754	761	768	775	782	789	
628	796	803	810	817	824	831	837	844	851	858	
629	865	872	879	886	893	900	906	913	920	927	
630	934	941	948	955	962	969	975	982	989	996	
631	80 003	010	017	024	030	037	044	051	058	065	
632	072	079	085	092	099	106	113	120	127	134	
633	140	147	154	161	168	175	182	188	195	202	
634	209	216	223	229	236	243	250	257	264	271	
635	277	284	291	298	305	312	318	325	332	339	
636	346	353	359	366	373	380	387	393	400	407	
637	414	421	428	434	441	448	455	462	468	475	
638	482	489	496	502	509	516	523	530	536	543	
639	550	557	564	570	577	584	591	598	604	611	
640	618	625	632	638	645	652	659	665	672	679	
641	686	693	699	706	713	720	726	733	740	747	
642	754	760	767	774	781	787	794	801	808	814	
643	821	828	835	841	848	855	862	868	875	882	
644	889	895	902	909	916	922	929	936	943	949	
645	956	963	969	976	983	990	996	*003	*010	*017	
646	81 023	030	037	043	050	057	064	070	077	084	
647	090	097	104	111	117	124	131	137	144	151	
648	158	164	171	178	184	191	198	204	211	218	
649	224	231	238	245	251	258	265	271	278	285	
650	291	298	305	311	318	325	331	338	345	351	
N.	0	1	2	3	4	5	6	7	8	9	Prop. Pts.

Prop. Pts.

	8	7
1	0.8	0.7
2	1.6	1.4
3	2.4	2.1
4	3.2	2.8
5	4.0	3.5
6	4.8	4.2
7	5.6	4.9
8	6.4	5.6
9	7.2	6.3

	6
1	0.6
2	1.2
3	1.8
4	2.4
5	3.0
6	3.6
7	4.2
8	4.8
9	5.4

650 — Logarithms of Numbers — 700

N.	0	1	2	3	4	5	6	7	8	9	Prop. Pts.
650	81 291	298	305	311	318	325	331	338	345	351	
651	358	365	371	378	385	391	398	405	411	418	
652	425	431	438	445	451	458	465	471	478	485	
653	491	498	505	511	518	525	531	538	544	551	
654	558	564	571	578	584	591	598	604	611	617	
655	624	631	637	644	651	657	664	671	677	684	
656	690	697	704	710	717	723	730	737	743	750	
657	757	763	770	776	783	790	796	803	809	816	
658	823	829	836	842	849	856	862	869	875	882	
659	889	895	902	908	915	921	928	935	941	948	
660	954	961	968	974	981	987	994	*000	*007	*014	
661	82 020	027	033	040	046	053	060	066	073	079	
662	086	092	099	105	112	119	125	132	138	145	
663	151	158	164	171	178	184	191	197	204	210	
664	217	223	230	236	243	249	256	263	269	276	
665	282	289	295	302	308	315	321	328	334	341	
666	347	354	360	367	373	380	387	393	400	406	
667	413	419	426	432	439	445	452	458	465	471	
668	478	484	491	497	504	510	517	523	530	536	
669	543	549	556	562	569	575	582	588	595	601	
670	607	614	620	627	633	640	646	653	659	666	
671	672	679	685	692	698	705	711	718	724	730	
672	737	743	750	756	763	769	776	782	789	795	
673	802	808	814	821	827	834	840	847	853	860	
674	866	872	879	885	892	898	905	911	918	924	
675	930	937	943	950	956	963	969	975	982	988	
676	995	*001	*008	*014	*020	*027	*033	*040	*046	*052	
677	83 059	065	072	078	085	091	097	104	110	117	
678	123	129	136	142	149	155	161	168	174	181	
679	187	193	200	206	213	219	225	232	238	245	
680	251	257	264	270	276	283	289	296	302	308	
681	315	321	327	334	340	347	353	359	366	372	
682	378	385	391	398	404	410	417	423	429	436	
683	442	448	455	461	467	474	480	487	493	499	
684	506	512	518	525	531	537	544	550	556	563	
685	569	575	582	588	594	601	607	613	620	626	
686	632	639	645	651	658	664	670	677	683	689	
687	696	702	708	715	721	727	734	740	746	753	
688	759	765	771	778	784	790	797	803	809	816	
689	822	828	835	841	847	853	860	866	872	879	
690	885	891	897	904	910	916	923	929	935	942	
691	948	954	960	967	973	979	985	992	998	*004	
692	84 011	017	023	029	036	042	048	055	061	067	
693	073	080	086	092	098	105	111	117	123	130	
694	136	142	148	155	161	167	173	180	186	192	
695	198	205	211	217	223	230	236	242	248	255	
696	261	267	273	280	286	292	298	305	311	317	
697	323	330	336	342	348	354	361	367	373	379	
698	386	392	398	404	410	417	423	429	435	442	
699	448	454	460	466	473	479	485	491	497	504	
700	510	516	522	528	535	541	547	553	559	566	
N.	0	1	2	3	4	5	6	7	8	9	Prop. Pts.

Prop. Pts.

	7	6
1	0.7	0.6
2	1.4	1.2
3	2.1	1.8
4	2.8	2.4
5	3.5	3.0
6	4.2	3.6
7	4.9	4.2
8	5.6	4.8
9	6.3	5.4

N.	0	1	2	3	4	5	6	7	8	9
700	84 510	516	522	528	535	541	547	553	559	566
701	572	578	584	590	597	603	609	615	621	628
702	634	640	646	652	658	665	671	677	683	689
703	696	702	708	714	720	726	733	739	745	751
704	757	763	770	776	782	788	794	800	807	813
705	819	825	831	837	844	850	856	862	868	874
706	880	887	893	899	905	911	917	924	930	936
707	942	948	954	960	967	973	979	985	991	997
708	85 003	009	016	022	028	034	040	046	052	058
709	065	071	077	083	089	095	101	107	114	120
710	126	132	138	144	150	156	163	169	175	181
711	187	193	199	205	211	217	224	230	236	242
712	248	254	260	266	272	278	285	291	297	303
713	309	315	321	327	333	339	345	352	358	364
714	370	376	382	388	394	400	406	412	418	425
715	431	437	443	449	455	461	467	473	479	485
716	491	497	503	509	516	522	528	534	540	546
717	552	558	564	570	576	582	588	594	600	606
718	612	618	625	631	637	643	649	655	661	667
719	673	679	685	691	697	703	709	715	721	727
720	733	739	745	751	757	763	769	775	781	788
721	794	800	806	812	818	824	830	836	842	848
722	854	860	866	872	878	884	890	896	902	908
723	914	920	926	932	938	944	950	956	962	968
724	974	980	986	992	998	*004	*010	*016	*022	*028
725	86 034	040	046	052	058	064	070	076	082	088
726	094	100	106	112	118	124	130	136	141	147
727	153	159	165	171	177	183	189	195	201	207
728	213	219	225	231	237	243	249	255	261	267
729	273	279	285	291	297	303	308	314	320	326
730	332	338	344	350	356	362	368	374	380	386
731	392	398	404	410	415	421	427	433	439	445
732	451	457	463	469	475	481	487	493	499	504
733	510	516	522	528	534	540	546	552	558	564
734	570	576	581	587	593	599	605	611	617	623
735	629	635	641	646	652	658	664	670	676	682
736	688	694	700	705	711	717	723	729	735	741
737	747	753	759	764	770	776	782	788	794	800
738	806	812	817	823	829	835	841	847	853	859
739	864	870	876	882	888	894	900	906	911	917
740	923	929	935	941	947	953	958	964	970	976
741	982	988	994	999	*005	*011	*017	*023	*029	*035
742	87 040	046	052	058	064	070	075	081	087	093
743	099	105	111	116	122	128	134	140	146	151
744	157	163	169	175	181	186	192	198	204	210
745	216	221	227	233	239	245	251	256	262	268
746	274	280	286	291	297	303	309	315	320	326
747	332	338	344	349	355	361	367	373	379	384
748	390	396	402	408	413	419	425	431	437	442
749	448	454	460	466	471	477	483	489	495	500
750	506	512	518	523	529	535	541	547	552	558
N.	0	1	2	3	4	5	6	7	8	9

Prop. Pts.

log 7 = .84509 80400

	7	6
1	0.7	0.6
2	1.4	1.2
3	2.1	1.8
4	2.8	2.4
5	3.5	3.0
6	4.2	3.6
7	4.9	4.2
8	5.6	4.8
9	6.3	5.4

	5
1	0.5
2	1.0
3	1.5
4	2.0
5	2.5
6	3.0
7	3.5
8	4.0
9	4.5

N.	0	1	2	3	4	5	6	7	8	9	Prop. Pts.	
750	87 506	512	518	523	529	535	541	547	552	558		
751	564	570	576	581	587	593	599	604	610	616		
752	622	628	633	639	645	651	656	662	668	674		
753	679	685	691	697	703	708	714	720	726	731		
754	737	743	749	754	760	766	772	777	783	789		
755	795	800	806	812	818	823	829	835	841	846		
756	852	858	864	869	875	881	887	892	898	904		
757	910	915	921	927	933	938	944	950	955	961		
758	967	973	978	984	990	996	*001	*007	*013	*018		
759	88 024	030	036	041	047	053	058	064	070	076		
760	081	087	093	098	104	110	116	121	127	133		
761	138	144	150	156	161	167	173	178	184	190		
762	195	201	207	213	218	224	230	235	241	247		
763	252	258	264	270	275	281	287	292	298	304		
764	309	315	321	326	332	338	343	349	355	360		
765	366	372	377	383	389	395	400	406	412	417		
766	423	429	434	440	446	451	457	463	468	474		
767	480	485	491	497	502	508	513	519	525	530		
768	536	542	547	553	559	564	570	576	581	587		
769	593	598	604	610	615	621	627	632	638	643		
770	649	655	660	666	672	677	683	689	694	700		
771	705	711	717	722	728	734	739	745	750	756		**6** **5**
772	762	767	773	779	784	790	795	801	807	812	1	0.6 0.5
773	818	824	829	835	840	846	852	857	863	868	2	1.2 1.0
774	874	880	885	891	897	902	908	913	919	925	3	1.8 1.5
775	930	936	941	947	953	958	964	969	975	981	4	2.4 2.0
776	986	992	997	*003	*009	*014	*020	*025	*031	*037	5	3.0 2.5
777	89 042	048	053	059	064	070	076	081	087	092	6 7	3.6 3.0 4.2 3.5
778	098	104	109	115	120	126	131	137	143	148	8	4.8 4.0
779	154	159	165	170	176	182	187	193	198	204	9	5.4 4.5
780	209	215	221	226	232	237	243	248	254	260		
781	265	271	276	282	287	293	298	304	310	315		
782	321	326	332	337	343	348	354	360	365	371		
783	376	382	387	393	398	404	409	415	421	426		
784	432	437	443	448	454	459	465	470	476	481		
785	487	492	498	504	509	515	520	526	531	537		
786	542	548	553	559	564	570	575	581	586	592		
787	597	603	609	614	620	625	631	636	642	647		
788	653	658	664	669	675	680	686	691	697	702		
789	708	713	719	724	730	735	741	746	752	757		
790	763	768	774	779	785	790	796	801	807	812		
791	818	823	829	834	840	845	851	856	862	867		
792	873	878	883	889	894	900	905	911	916	922		
793	927	933	938	944	949	955	960	966	971	977		
794	982	988	993	998	*004	*009	*015	*020	*026	*031		
795	90 037	042	048	053	059	064	069	075	080	086		
796	091	097	102	108	113	119	124	129	135	140		
797	146	151	157	162	168	173	179	184	189	195		
798	200	206	211	217	222	227	233	238	244	249		
799	255	260	266	271	276	282	287	293	298	304		
800	309	314	320	325	331	336	342	347	352	358		
N.	0	1	2	3	4	5	6	7	8	9	Prop. Pts.	

N.	0	1	2	3	4	5	6	7	8	9	Prop. Pts.
800	90 309	314	320	325	331	336	342	347	352	358	
801	363	369	374	380	385	390	396	401	407	412	
802	417	423	428	434	439	445	450	455	461	466	
803	472	477	482	488	493	499	504	509	515	520	
804	526	531	536	542	547	553	558	563	569	574	
805	580	585	590	596	601	607	612	617	623	628	
806	634	639	644	650	655	660	666	671	677	682	
807	687	693	698	703	709	714	720	725	730	736	
808	741	747	752	757	763	768	773	779	784	789	
809	795	800	806	811	816	822	827	832	838	843	
810	849	854	859	865	870	875	881	886	891	897	
811	902	907	913	918	924	929	934	940	945	950	
812	956	961	966	972	977	982	988	993	998	*004	
813	91 009	014	020	025	030	036	041	046	052	057	
814	062	068	073	078	084	089	094	100	105	110	
815	116	121	126	132	137	142	148	153	158	164	
816	169	174	180	185	190	196	201	206	212	217	
817	222	228	233	238	243	249	254	259	265	270	
818	275	281	286	291	297	302	307	312	318	323	
819	328	334	339	344	350	355	360	365	371	376	
820	381	387	392	397	403	408	413	418	424	429	
821	434	440	445	450	455	461	466	471	477	482	
822	487	492	498	503	508	514	519	524	529	535	
823	540	545	551	556	561	566	572	577	582	587	
824	593	598	603	609	614	619	624	630	635	640	
825	645	651	656	661	666	672	677	682	687	693	
826	698	703	709	714	719	724	730	735	740	745	
827	751	756	761	766	772	777	782	787	793	798	
828	803	808	814	819	824	829	834	840	845	850	
829	855	861	866	871	876	882	887	892	897	903	
830	908	913	918	924	929	934	939	944	950	955	
831	960	965	971	976	981	986	991	997	*002	*007	
832	92 012	018	023	028	033	038	044	049	054	059	
833	065	070	075	080	085	091	096	101	106	111	
834	117	122	127	132	137	143	148	153	158	163	
835	169	174	179	184	189	195	200	205	210	215	
836	221	226	231	236	241	247	252	257	262	267	
837	273	278	283	288	293	298	304	309	314	319	
838	324	330	335	340	345	350	355	361	366	371	
839	376	381	387	392	397	402	407	412	418	423	
840	428	433	438	443	449	454	459	464	469	474	
841	480	485	490	495	500	505	511	516	521	526	
842	531	536	542	547	552	557	562	567	572	578	
843	583	588	593	598	603	609	614	619	624	629	
844	634	639	645	650	655	660	665	670	675	681	
845	686	691	696	701	706	711	716	722	727	732	
846	737	742	747	752	758	763	768	773	778	783	
847	788	793	799	804	809	814	819	824	829	834	
848	840	845	850	855	860	865	870	875	881	886	
849	891	896	901	906	911	916	921	927	932	937	
850	942	947	952	957	962	967	973	978	983	988	
N.	0	1	2	3	4	5	6	7	8	9	Prop. Pts.

Prop. Pts.

	6	5
1	0.6	0.5
2	1.2	1.0
3	1.8	1.5
4	2.4	2.0
5	3.0	2.5
6	3.6	3.0
7	4.2	3.5
8	4.8	4.0
9	5.4	4.5

850 — Logarithms of Numbers — 900

N.	0	1	2	3	4	5	6	7	8	9	Prop. Pts.
850	92 942	947	952	957	962	967	973	978	983	988	
851	993	998	*003	*008	*013	*018	*024	*029	*034	*039	
852	93 044	049	054	059	064	069	075	080	085	090	
853	095	100	105	110	115	120	125	131	136	141	
854	146	151	156	161	166	171	176	181	186	192	
855	197	202	207	212	217	222	227	232	237	242	
856	247	252	258	263	268	273	278	283	288	293	
857	298	303	308	313	318	323	328	334	339	344	
858	349	354	359	364	369	374	379	384	389	394	
859	399	404	409	414	420	425	430	435	440	445	
860	450	455	460	465	470	475	480	485	490	495	
861	500	505	510	515	520	526	531	536	541	546	
862	551	556	561	566	571	576	581	586	591	596	
863	601	606	611	616	621	626	631	636	641	646	
864	651	6.6	661	666	671	676	682	687	692	697	
855	702	707	712	717	722	727	732	737	742	747	
866	752	757	762	767	772	777	782	787	792	797	
867	802	807	812	817	822	827	832	837	842	847	
868	852	857	862	867	872	877	882	887	892	897	
869	902	907	912	917	922	927	932	937	942	947	
870	952	957	962	967	972	977	982	987	992	997	
871	94 002	007	012	017	022	027	032	037	042	047	
872	052	057	062	067	072	077	082	086	091	096	
873	101	106	111	116	121	126	131	136	141	146	
874	151	156	161	166	171	176	181	186	191	196	
875	201	206	211	216	221	226	231	236	240	245	
876	250	255	260	265	270	275	280	285	290	295	
877	300	305	310	315	320	325	330	335	340	345	
878	349	354	359	364	369	374	379	384	389	394	
879	399	404	409	414	419	424	429	433	438	443	
880	448	453	458	463	468	473	478	483	488	493	
881	498	503	507	512	517	522	527	532	537	542	
882	547	552	557	562	567	571	576	581	586	591	
883	596	601	606	611	616	621	626	630	635	640	
884	645	650	655	660	665	670	675	680	685	689	
885	694	699	704	709	714	719	724	729	734	738	
886	743	748	753	758	763	768	773	778	783	787	
887	792	797	802	807	812	817	822	827	832	836	
888	841	846	851	856	861	866	871	876	880	885	
889	890	895	900	905	910	915	919	924	929	934	
890	939	944	949	954	959	963	968	973	978	983	
891	988	993	998	*002	*007	*012	*017	*022	*027	*032	
892	95 036	041	046	051	056	061	066	071	075	080	
893	085	090	095	100	105	109	114	119	124	129	
894	134	139	143	148	153	158	163	168	173	177	
895	182	187	192	197	202	207	211	216	221	226	
896	231	236	240	245	250	255	260	265	270	274	
897	279	284	289	294	299	303	308	313	318	323	
898	328	332	337	342	347	352	357	361	366	371	
899	376	381	386	390	395	400	405	410	415	419	
900	424	429	434	439	444	448	453	458	463	468	
N.	0	1	2	3	4	5	6	7	8	9	Prop. Pts.

Prop. Pts.

	6	5
1	0.6	0.5
2	1.2	1.0
3	1.8	1.5
4	2.4	2.0
5	3.0	2.5
6	3.6	3.0
7	4.2	3.5
8	4.8	4.0
9	5.4	4.5

	4
1	0.4
2	0.8
3	1.2
4	1.6
5	2.0
6	2.4
7	2.8
8	3.2
9	3.6

900 — Logarithms of Numbers — 950

N.	0	1	2	3	4	5	6	7	8	9	Prop. Pts.
900	95 424	429	434	439	444	448	453	458	463	468	
901	472	477	482	487	492	497	501	506	511	516	
902	521	525	530	535	540	545	550	554	559	564	
903	569	574	578	583	588	593	598	602	607	612	
904	617	622	626	631	636	641	646	650	655	660	
905	665	670	674	679	684	689	694	698	703	708	
906	713	718	722	727	732	737	742	746	751	756	
907	761	766	770	775	780	785	789	794	799	804	
908	809	813	818	823	828	832	837	842	847	852	
909	856	861	866	871	875	880	885	890	895	899	
910	904	909	914	918	923	928	933	938	942	947	
911	952	957	961	966	971	976	980	985	990	995	
912	999	*004	*009	*014	*019	*023	*028	*033	*038	*042	
913	96 047	052	057	061	066	071	076	080	085	090	
914	095	099	104	109	114	118	123	128	133	137	
915	142	147	152	156	161	166	171	175	180	185	
916	190	194	199	204	209	213	218	223	227	232	
917	237	242	246	251	256	261	265	270	275	280	
918	284	289	294	298	303	308	313	317	322	327	
919	332	336	341	346	350	355	360	365	369	374	
920	379	384	388	393	398	402	407	412	417	421	
921	426	431	435	440	445	450	454	459	464	468	
922	473	478	483	487	492	497	501	506	511	515	
923	520	525	530	534	539	544	548	553	558	562	
924	567	572	577	581	586	591	595	600	605	609	
925	614	619	624	628	633	638	642	647	652	656	
926	661	666	670	675	680	685	689	694	699	703	
927	708	713	717	722	727	731	736	741	745	750	
928	755	759	764	769	774	778	783	788	792	797	
929	802	806	811	816	820	825	830	834	839	844	
930	848	853	858	862	867	872	876	881	886	890	
931	895	900	904	909	914	918	923	928	932	937	
932	942	946	951	956	960	965	970	974	979	984	
933	988	993	997	*002	*007	*011	*016	*021	*025	*030	
934	97 035	039	044	049	053	058	063	067	072	077	
935	081	086	090	095	100	104	109	114	118	123	
936	128	132	137	142	146	151	155	160	165	169	
937	174	179	183	188	192	197	202	206	211	216	
938	220	225	230	234	239	243	248	253	257	262	
939	267	271	276	280	285	290	294	299	304	308	
940	313	317	322	327	331	336	340	345	350	354	
941	359	364	368	373	377	382	387	391	396	400	
942	405	410	414	419	424	428	433	437	442	447	
943	451	456	460	465	470	474	479	483	488	493	
944	497	502	506	511	516	520	525	529	534	539	
945	543	548	552	557	562	566	571	575	580	585	
946	589	594	598	603	607	612	617	621	626	630	
947	635	640	644	649	653	658	663	667	672	676	
948	681	685	690	695	699	704	708	713	717	722	
949	727	731	736	740	745	749	754	759	763	768	
950	772	777	782	786	791	795	800	804	809	813	
N.	0	1	2	3	4	5	6	7	8	9	Prop. Pts.

Prop. Pts.

	5	4
1	0.5	0.4
2	1.0	0.8
3	1.5	1.2
4	2.0	1.6
5	2.5	2.0
6	3.0	2.4
7	3.5	2.8
8	4.0	3.2
9	4.5	3.6

Table XIII.
950 — Logarithms of Numbers — 1000

N.	0	1	2	3	4	5	6	7	8	9	Prop. Pts.
950	97 772	777	782	786	791	795	800	804	809	813	
951	818	823	827	832	836	841	845	850	855	859	
952	864	868	873	877	882	886	891	896	900	905	
953	909	914	918	923	928	932	937	941	946	950	
954	955	959	964	968	973	978	982	987	991	996	
955	98 000	005	009	014	019	023	028	032	037	041	
956	046	050	055	059	064	068	073	078	082	087	
957	091	096	100	105	109	114	118	123	127	132	
958	137	141	146	150	155	159	164	168	173	177	
959	182	186	191	195	200	204	209	214	218	223	
960	227	232	236	241	245	250	254	259	263	268	
961	272	277	281	286	290	295	299	304	308	313	
962	318	322	327	331	336	340	345	349	354	358	
963	363	367	372	376	381	385	390	394	399	403	
964	408	412	417	421	426	430	435	439	444	448	
965	453	457	462	466	471	475	480	484	489	493	
966	498	502	507	511	516	520	525	529	534	538	
967	543	547	552	556	561	565	570	574	579	583	
968	588	592	597	601	605	610	614	619	623	628	
969	632	637	641	646	650	655	659	664	668	673	
970	677	682	686	691	695	700	704	709	713	717	
971	722	726	731	735	740	744	749	753	758	762	
972	767	771	776	780	784	789	793	798	802	807	
973	811	816	820	825	829	834	838	843	847	851	
974	856	860	865	869	874	878	883	887	892	896	
975	900	905	909	914	918	923	927	932	936	941	
976	945	949	954	958	963	967	972	976	981	985	
977	989	994	998	*003	*007	*012	*016	*021	*025	*029	
978	99 034	038	043	047	052	056	061	065	069	074	
979	078	083	087	092	096	100	105	109	114	118	
980	123	127	131	136	140	145	149	154	158	162	
981	167	171	176	180	185	189	193	198	202	207	
982	211	216	220	224	229	233	238	242	247	251	
983	255	260	264	269	273	277	282	286	291	295	
984	300	304	308	313	317	322	326	330	335	339	
985	344	348	352	357	361	366	370	374	379	383	
986	388	392	396	401	405	410	414	419	423	427	
987	432	436	441	445	449	454	458	463	467	471	
988	476	480	484	489	493	498	502	506	511	515	
989	520	524	528	533	537	542	546	550	555	559	
990	564	568	572	577	581	585	590	594	599	603	
991	607	612	616	621	625	629	634	638	642	647	
992	651	656	660	664	669	673	677	682	686	691	
993	695	699	704	708	712	717	721	726	730	734	
994	739	743	747	752	756	760	765	769	774	778	
995	782	787	791	795	800	804	808	813	817	822	
996	826	830	835	839	843	848	852	856	861	865	
997	870	874	878	883	887	891	896	900	904	909	
998	913	917	922	926	930	935	939	944	948	952	
999	957	961	965	970	974	978	983	987	991	996	
1000	00 000	004	009	013	017	022	026	030	035	039	
N.	0	1	2	3	4	5	6	7	8	9	Prop. Pts.

Prop. Pts.

	5	4
1	0.5	0.4
2	1.0	0.8
3	1.5	1.2
4	2.0	1.6
5	2.5	2.0
6	3.0	2.4
7	3.5	2.8
8	4.0	3.2
9	4.5	3.6

Table XIVa.
Auxiliary Table of S and T for A in Minutes

$$S = \log \sin A - \log A' \quad \text{and} \quad T = \log \tan A - \log A'$$

A'	$S+10$	A'	$T+10$	A'	$T+10$
0′ — 13′	6.46373	0′ — 26′	6.46373	131′ — 133′	6.46394
14′ — 42′	72	27′ — 39′	74	134′ — 136′	95
43′ — 58′	71	40′ — 48′	75	137′ — 139′	96
59′ — 71′	6.46370	49′ — 56′	6.46376	140′ — 142′	6.46397
72′ — 81′	69	57′ — 63′	77	143′ — 145′	98
82′ — 91′	68	64′ — 69′	78	146′ — 148′	99
92′ — 99′	6.46367	70′ — 74′	6.46379	149′ — 150′	6.46400
100′ — 107′	66	75′ — 80′	80	151′ — 153′	01
108′ — 115′	65	81′ — 85′	81	154′ — 156′	02
116′ — 121′	6.46364	86′ — 89′	6.46382	157′ — 158′	6.46403
122′ — 128′	63	90′ — 94′	83	159′ — 161′	04
129′ — 134′	62	95′ — 98′	84	162′ — 163′	05
135′ — 140′	6.46361	99′ — 102′	6.46385	164′ — 166′	6.46406
141′ — 146′	60	103′ — 106′	86	167′ — 168′	07
147′ — 151′	59	107′ — 110′	87	169′ — 171′	08
152′ — 157′	6.46358	111′ — 113′	6.46388	172′ — 173′	6.46409
158′ — 162′	57	114′ — 117′	89	174′ — 175′	10
163′ — 167′	56	118′ — 120′	90	176′ — 178′	11
168′ — 171′	6.46355	121′ — 124′	6.46391	179′ — 180′	6.46412
172′ — 176′	54	125′ — 127′	92	181′ — 182′	13
177′ — 181′	53	128′ — 130′	93	183′ — 184′	14

For small angles: $\log \sin A = \log A' + S$ and $\log \tan A = \log A' + T$.
For angles near 90°: $\log \cos A = \log (90° - A)' + S$, $\log \operatorname{ctn} A = \log (90° - A)' + T$ where A' = number of minutes in A, and $(90° - A)'$ = number of minutes in $90° - A$

Table XIV.
0° — Logarithms of Trigonometric Functions

′	L Sin	d	L Tan	c d	L Ctn	L Cos	
0	——		——		10.00 000	10.00 000	60
1	6.46 373		6.46 373		13.53 627	10.00 000	59
2	6.76 476	30103	6.76 476	30103	13.23 524	10.00 000	58
3	6.94 085	17609	6.94 085	17609	13.05 915	10.00 000	57
4	7.06 579	12494	7.06 579	12494	12.93 421	10.00 000	56
5	7.16 270	9691	7.16 270	9691	12.83 730	10.00 000	55
6	7.24 188	7918	7.24 188	7918	12.75 812	10.00 000	54
7	7.30 882	6694	7.30 882	6694	12.69 118	10.00 000	53
8	7.36 682	5800	7.36 682	5800	12.63 318	10.00 000	52
9	7.41 797	5115	7.41 797	5115	12.58 203	10.00 000	51
10	7.46 373	4576	7.46 373	4576	12.53 627	10.00 000	50
11	7.50 512	4139	7.50 512	4139	12.49 488	10.00 000	49
12	7.54 291	3779	7.54 291	3779	12.45 709	10.00 000	48
13	7.57 767	3476	7.57 767	3476	12.42 233	10.00 000	47
14	7.60 985	3218	7.60 986	3219	12.39 014	10.00 000	46
15	7.63 982	2997	7.63 982	2996	12.36 018	10.00 000	45
16	7.66 784	2802	7.66 785	2803	12.33 215	10.00 000	44
17	7.69 417	2633	7.69 418	2633	12.30 582	9.99 999	43
18	7.71 900	2483	7.71 900	2482	12.28 100	9.99 999	42
19	7.74 248	2348	7.74 248	2348	12.25 752	9.99 999	41
20	7.76 475	2227	7.76 476	2228	12.23 524	9.99 999	40
21	7.78 594	2119	7.78 595	2119	12.21 405	9.99 999	39
22	7.80 615	2021	7.80 615	2020	12.19 385	9.99 999	38
23	7.82 545	1930	7.82 546	1931	12.17 454	9.99 999	37
24	7.84 393	1848	7.84 394	1848	12.15 606	9.99 999	36
25	7.86 166	1773	7.86 167	1773	12.13 833	9.99 999	35
26	7.87 870	1704	7.87 871	1704	12.12 129	9.99 999	34
27	7.89 509	1639	7.89 510	1639	12.10 490	9.99 999	33
28	7.91 088	1579	7.91 089	1579	12.08 911	9.99 999	32
29	7.92 612	1524	7.92 613	1524	12.07 387	9.99 998	31
30	7.94 084	1472	7.94 086	1473	12.05 914	9.99 998	30
31	7.95 508	1424	7.95 510	1424	12.04 490	9.99 998	29
32	7.96 887	1379	7.96 889	1379	12.03 111	9.99 998	28
33	7.98 223	1336	7.98 225	1336	12.01 775	9.99 998	27
34	7.99 520	1297	7.99 522	1297	12.00 478	9.99 998	26
35	8.00 779	1259	8.00 781	1259	11.99 219	9.99 998	25
36	8.02 002	1223	8.02 004	1223	11.97 996	9.99 997	24
37	8.03 192	1190	8.03 194	1190	11.96 806	9.99 997	23
38	8.04 350	1158	8.04 353	1159	11.95 647	9.99 997	22
39	8.05 478	1128	8.05 481	1128	11.94 519	9.99 997	21
40	8.06 578	1100	8.06 581	1100	11.93 419	9.99 997	20
41	8.07 650	1072	8.07 653	1072	11.92 347	9.99 997	19
42	8.08 696	1046	8.08 700	1047	11.91 300	9.99 997	18
43	8.09 718	1022	8.09 722	1022	11.90 278	9.99 997	17
44	8.10 717	999	8.10 720	998	11.89 280	9.99 996	16
45	8.11 693	976	8.11 696	976	11.88 304	9.99 996	15
46	8.12 647	954	8.12 651	955	11.87 349	9.99 996	14
47	8.13 581	934	8.13 585	934	11.86 415	9.99 996	13
48	8.14 495	914	8.14 500	915	11.85 500	9.99 996	12
49	8.15 391	896	8.15 395	895	11.84 605	9.99 996	11
50	8.16 268	877	8.16 273	878	11.83 727	9.99 995	10
51	8.17 128	860	8.17 133	860	11.82 867	9.99 995	9
52	8.17 971	843	8.17 976	843	11.82 024	9.99 995	8
53	8.18 798	827	8.18 804	828	11.81 196	9.99 995	7
54	8.19 610	812	8.19 616	812	11.80 384	9.99 995	6
55	8.20 407	797	8.20 413	797	11.79 587	9.99 994	5
56	8.21 189	782	8.21 195	782	11.78 805	9.99 994	4
57	8.21 958	769	8.21 964	769	11.78 036	9.99 994	3
58	8.22 713	755	8.22 720	756	11.77 280	9.99 994	2
59	8.23 456	743	8.23 462	742	11.76 538	9.99 994	1
60	8.24 186	730	8.24 192	730	11.75 808	9.99 993	0
	L Cos	d	L Ctn	c d	L Tan	L Sin	′

For logarithms of sines or tangents of angles less than 3° (or logarithms of cosines or cotangents of angles greater than 87°), see Table XIVa, p. 117. When the tabular differences are large, that method is usually better. The proportional parts stated for 1° and 2° in this table are sufficient when great accuracy is not required, even if the ordinary method of interpolation is used.

89° — Logarithms of Trigonometric Functions

1° — Logarithms of Trigonometric Functions

′	L Sin	d	L Tan	c d	L Ctn	L Cos		′
0	8.24 186	717	8.24 192	718	11.75 808	9.99 993		60
1	8.24 903	706	8.24 910	706	11.75 090	9.99 993		59
2	8.25 609	695	8.25 616	696	11.74 384	9.99 993		58
3	8.26 304	684	8.26 312	684	11.73 688	9.99 993		57
4	8.26 988	673	8.26 996	673	11.73 004	9.99 992		56
5	8.27 661	663	8.27 669	663	11.72 331	9.99 992		55
6	8.28 324	653	8.28 332	654	11.71 668	9.99 992		54
7	8.28 977	644	8.28 986	643	11.71 014	9.99 992		53
8	8.29 621	634	8.29 629	634	11.70 371	9.99 992		52
9	8.30 255	624	8.30 263	625	11.69 737	9.99 991		51
10	8.30 879	616	8.30 888	617	11.69 112	9.99 991		50
11	8.31 495	607	8.31 505	607	11.68 495	9.99 990		49
12	8.32 103	599	8.32 112	599	11.67 888	9.99 990		48
13	8.32 702	590	8.32 711	591	11.67 289	9.99 990		47
14	8.33 292	583	8.33 302	584	11.66 698	9.99 990		46
15	8.33 875	575	8.33 886	575	11.66 114	9.99 989		45
16	8.34 450	568	8.34 461	568	11.65 539	9.99 989		44
17	8.35 018	560	8.35 029	561	11.64 971	9.99 989		43
18	8.35 578	553	8.35 590	553	11.64 410	9.99 989		42
19	8.36 131	547	8.36 143	546	11.63 857	9.99 989		41
20	8.36 678	539	8.36 689	533	11.63 311	9.99 988		40
21	8.37 217	533	8.37 229	533	11.62 771	9.99 988		39
22	8.37 750	526	8.37 762	527	11.62 238	9.99 988		38
23	8.38 276	520	8.38 289	520	11.61 711	9.99 987		37
24	8.38 796	514	8.38 809	514	11.61 191	9.99 987		36
25	8.39 310	508	8.39 323	508	11.60 677	9.99 987		35
26	8.39 818	502	8.39 832	502	11.60 168	9.99 986		34
27	8.40 320	496	8.40 334	496	11.59 666	9.99 986		33
28	8.40 816	491	8.40 830	491	11.59 170	9.99 986		32
29	8.41 307	485	8.41 321	486	11.58 679	9.99 985		31
30	8.41 792	480	8.41 807	480	11.58 193	9.99 985		30
31	8.42 272	474	8.42 287	475	11.57 713	9.99 985		29
32	8.42 746	470	8.42 762	470	11.57 238	9.99 984		28
33	8.43 216	464	8.43 232	464	11.56 768	9.99 984		27
34	8.43 680	459	8.43 696	459	11.56 304	9.99 984		26
35	8.44 139	455	8.44 156	455	11.55 844	9.99 983		25
36	8.44 594	450	8.44 611	450	11.55 389	9.99 983		24
37	8.45 044	445	8.45 061	446	11.54 939	9.99 983		23
38	8.45 489	441	8.45 507	441	11.54 493	9.99 982		22
39	8.45 930	436	8.45 948	437	11.54 052	9.99 982		21
40	8.46 366	433	8.46 385	432	11.53 615	9.99 982		20
41	8.46 799	427	8.46 817	428	11.53 183	9.99 981		19
42	8.47 226	424	8.47 245	424	11.52 755	9.99 981		18
43	8.47 650	419	8.47 669	420	11.52 331	9.99 981		17
44	8.48 069	416	8.48 089	416	11.51 911	9.99 980		16
45	8.48 485	411	8.48 505	412	11.51 495	9.99 980		15
46	8.48 896	408	8.48 917	408	11.51 083	9.99 979		14
47	8.49 304	404	8.49 325	404	11.50 675	9.99 979		13
48	8.49 708	400	8.49 729	401	11.50 271	9.99 979		12
49	8.50 108	396	8.50 130	397	11.49 870	9.99 978		11
50	8.50 504	393	8.50 527	393	11.49 473	9.99 978		10
51	8.50 897	390	8.50 920	390	11.49 080	9.99 977		9
52	8.51 287	386	8.51 310	386	11.48 690	9.99 977		8
53	8.51 673	382	8.51 696	383	11.48 304	9.99 977		7
54	8.52 055	379	8.52 079	380	11.47 921	9.99 976		6
55	8.52 434	376	8.52 459	376	11.47 541	9.99 976		5
56	8.52 810	373	8.52 835	373	11.47 165	9.99 975		4
57	8.53 183	369	8.53 208	370	11.46 792	9.99 975		3
58	8.53 552	367	8.53 578	367	11.46 422	9.99 974		2
59	8.53 919	363	8.53 945	363	11.46 055	9.99 974		1
60	8.54 282		8.54 308		11.45 692	9.99 974		0
	L Cos	d	L Ctn	c d	L Tan	L Sin		′

Prop. Pts.

	710	690	670	650
2	142	138	134	130
3	213	207	201	195
4	284	276	268	260
5	355	345	335	325
6	426	414	402	390
7	497	483	469	455
8	568	552	536	520
9	639	621	603	585

	630	620	610	600
2	126	124	122	120
3	189	186	183	180
4	252	248	244	240
5	315	310	305	300
6	378	372	366	360
7	441	434	427	420
8	504	496	488	480
9	567	558	549	540

	590	580	570	560
2	118	116	114	112
3	177	174	171	168
4	236	232	228	224
5	295	290	285	280
6	354	348	342	336
7	413	406	399	392
8	472	464	456	448
9	531	522	513	504

	550	540	530	520
2	110	108'	106	104
3	165	162	159	156
4	220	216	212	208
5	275	270	265	260
6	330	324	318	312
7	385	378	371	364
8	440	432	424	416
9	495	486	477	468

	510	500	490	480
2	102	100	98	96
3	153	150	147	144
4	204	200	196	192
5	255	250	245	240
6	306	300	294	288
7	357	350	343	336
8	408	400	392	384
9	459	450	441	432

	470	460	450	440
2	94	92	90	88
3	141	138	135	132
4	188	184	180	176
5	235	230	225	220
6	282	276	270	264
7	329	322	315	308
8	376	368	360	352
9	423	414	405	396

	430	420	410	400
2	86	84	82	80
3	129	126	123	120
4	172	168	164	160
5	215	210	205	200
6	258	252	246	240
7	301	294	287	280
8	344	336	328	320
9	387	378	369	360

	390	380	370	360
2	78	76	74	72
3	117	114	111	108
4	156	152	148	144
5	195	190	185	180
6	234	228	222	216
7	273	266	259	252
8	312	304	296	288
9	351	342	333	324

88° — Logarithms of Trigonometric Functions

2° — Logarithms of Trigonometric Functions

′	L Sin	d	L Tan	c d	L Ctn	L Cos	
0	8.54 282	360	8.54 308	361	11.45 692	9.99 974	60
1	8.54 642	357	8.54 669	358	11.45 331	9.99 973	59
2	8.54 999	355	8.55 027	355	11.44 973	9.99 973	58
3	8.55 354	351	8.55 382	352	11.44 618	9.99 972	57
4	8.55 705		8.55 734	349	11.44 266	9.99 972	56
5	8.56 054		8.56 083		11.43 917	9.99 971	55
6	8.56 400	346	8.56 429	346	11.43 571	9.99 971	54
7	8.56 743	343	8.56 773	344	11.43 227	9.99 970	53
8	8.57 084	341	8.57 114	341	11.42 886	9.99 970	52
9	8.57 421	337	8.57 452	338	11.42 548	9.99 969	51
10	8.57 757	336	8.57 788	336	11.42 212	9.99 969	50
11	8.58 089	332	8.58 121	333	11.41 879	9.99 968	49
12	8.58 419	330	8.58 451	330	11.41 549	9.99 968	48
13	8.58 747	328	8.58 779	328	11.41 221	9.99 967	47
14	8.59 072		8.59 105	323	11.40 895	9.99 967	46
15	8.59 395		8.59 428		11.40 572	9.99 967	45
16	8.59 715	320	8.59 749	321	11.40 251	9.99 966	44
17	8.60 033	318	8.60 068	319	11.39 932	9.99 966	43
18	8.60 349	316	8.60 384	316	11.39 616	9.99 965	42
19	8.60 662	313	8.60 698	313	11.39 302	9.99 964	41
20	8.60 973	311	8.61 009	311	11.38 991	9.99 964	40
21	8.61 282	309	8.61 319	310	11.38 681	9.99 963	39
22	8.61 589	307	8.61 626	307	11.38 374	9.99 963	38
23	8.61 894	305	8.61 931	305	11.38 069	9.99 962	37
24	8.62 196	302	8.62 234	303	11.37 766	9.99 962	36
25	8.62 497	301	8.62 535	301	11.37 465	9.99 961	35
26	8.62 795	298	8.62 834	299	11.37 166	9.99 961	34
27	8.63 091	296	8.63 131	297	11.36 869	9.99 960	33
28	8.63 385	294	8.63 426	295	11.36 574	9.99 960	32
29	8.63 678	293	8.63 718	292	11.36 282	9.99 959	31
30	8.63 968	290	8.64 009	291	11.35 991	9.99 959	30
31	8.64 256	288	8.64 298	289	11.35 702	9.99 958	29
32	8.64 543	287	8.64 585	287	11.35 415	9.99 958	28
33	8.64 827	284	8.64 870	285	11.35 130	9.99 957	27
34	8.65 110	283	8.65 154	284	11.34 846	9.99 956	26
35	8.65 391	281	8.65 435	281	11.34 565	9.99 956	25
36	8.65 670	279	8.65 715	280	11.34 285	9.99 955	24
37	8.65 947	277	8.65 993	278	11.34 007	9.99 955	23
38	8.66 223	276	8.66 269	274	11.33 731	9.99 954	22
39	8.66 497	274	8.66 543	273	11.33 457	9.99 954	21
40	8.66 769	272	8.66 816	271	11.33 184	9.99 953	20
41	8.67 039	270	8.67 087	269	11.32 913	9.99 952	19
42	8.67 308	269	8.67 356	269	11.32 644	9.99 952	18
43	8.67 575	267	8.67 624	266	11.32 376	9.99 951	17
44	8.67 841	266	8.67 890	264	11.32 110	9.99 951	16
45	8.68 104	263	8.68 154	263	11.31 846	9.99 950	15
46	8.68 367	263	8.68 417	261	11.31 583	9.99 949	14
47	8.68 627	260	8.68 678	260	11.31 322	9.99 949	13
48	8.68 886	259	8.68 938	258	11.31 062	9.99 948	12
49	8.69 144	258	8.69 196	257	11.30 804	9.99 948	11
50	8.69 400	256	8.69 453	255	11.30 547	9.99 947	10
51	8.69 654	254	8.69 708	254	11.30 292	9.99 946	9
52	8.69 907	252	8.69 962	252	11.30 038	9.99 946	8
53	8.70 159	250	8.70 214	251	11.29 786	9.99 945	7
54	8.70 409	249	8.70 465	249	11.29 535	9.99 944	6
55	8.70 658	247	8.70 714	248	11.29 286	9.99 944	5
56	8.70 905	246	8.70 962	246	11.29 038	9.99 943	4
57	8.71 151	244	8.71 208	245	11.28 792	9.99 942	3
58	8.71 395	243	8.71 453	244	11.28 547	9.99 942	2
59	8.71 638	242	8.71 697	243	11.28 303	9.99 941	1
60	8.71 880		8.71 940		11.28 060	9.99 940	0
	L Cos	d	L Ctn	c d	L Tan	L Sin	′

Prop. Pts.

	360	355	350
2	72	71.0	70
3	108	106.5	105
4	144	142.0	140
5	180	177.5	175
6	216	213.0	210
7	252	248.5	245
8	288	284.0	280
9	324	319.5	315

	345	340	335
2	69.0	68	67.0
3	103.5	102	100.5
4	138.0	136	134.0
5	172.5	170	167.5
6	207.0	204	201.0
7	241.5	238	234.5
8	276.0	272	268.0
9	310.5	306	301.5

	330	325	320
2	66	65.0	64
3	99	97.5	96
4	132	130.0	128
5	165	162.5	160
6	198	195.0	192
7	231	227.5	224
8	264	260.0	256
9	297	292.5	288

	315	310	305
2	63.0	62	61.0
3	94.5	93	91.5
4	126.0	124	122.0
5	157.5	155	152.5
6	189.0	186	183.0
7	220.5	217	213.5
8	252.0	248	244.0
9	283.5	279	274.5

	300	295	290
2	60	59.0	58
3	90	88.5	87
4	120	118.0	116
5	150	147.5	145
6	180	177.0	174
7	210	206.5	203
8	240	236.0	232
9	270	265.5	261

	285	280	275
2	57.0	56	55.0
3	85.5	84	82.5
4	114.0	112	110.0
5	142.5	140	137.5
6	171.0	168	165.0
7	199.5	196	192.5
8	228.0	224	220.0
9	256.5	252	247.5

	270	265	260
2	54	53.0	52
3	81	79.5	78
4	108	106.0	104
5	135	132.5	130
6	162	159.0	156
7	189	185.5	182
8	216	212.0	208
9	243	238.5	234

	255	250	245
2	51.0	50	49.0
3	76.5	75	73.5
4	102.0	100	98.0
5	127.5	125	122.5
6	153.0	150	147.0
7	178.5	175	171.5
8	204.0	200	196.0
9	229.5	225	220.5

Prop. Pts.

3° — Logarithms of Trigonometric Functions

′	L Sin	d	L Tan	c d	L Ctn	L Cos		Prop. Pts.		
0	8.71 880		8.71 940		11.28 060	9.99 940	60			
1	8.72 120	240	8.72 181	241	11.27 819	9.99 940	59		240	235	230
2	8.72 359	239	8.72 420	239	11.27 580	9.99 939	58	2	48	47.0	46
3	8.72 597	238	8.72 659	239	11.27 341	9.99 938	57	3	72	70.5	69
4	8.72 834	237	8.72 896	237	11.27 104	9.99 938	56	4	96	94.0	92
		235		236				5	120	117.5	115
5	8.73 069		8.73 132		11.26 868	9.99 937	55	6	144	141.0	138
6	8.73 303	234	8.73 366	234	11.26 634	9.99 936	54	7	168	164.5	161
7	8.73 535	232	8.73 600	234	11.26 400	9.99 936	53	8	192	188.0	184
8	8.73 767	232	8.73 832	232	11.26 168	9.99 935	52	9	216	211.5	207
9	8.73 997	230	8.74 063	231	11.25 937	9.99 934	51				
		229		229					225	220	215
10	8.74 226		8.74 292		11.25 708	9.99 934	50	2	45.0	44.0	43.0
11	8.74 454	228	8.74 521	229	11.25 479	9.99 933	49	3	67.5	66.0	64.5
12	8.74 680	226	8.74 748	227	11.25 252	9.99 932	48	4	90.0	88.0	86.0
13	8.74 906	226	8.74 974	226	11.25 026	9.99 932	47	5	112.5	110.0	107.5
14	8.75 130	224	8.75 199	225	11.24 801	9.99 931	46	6	135.0	132.0	129.0
		223		224				7	157.5	154.0	150.5
15	8.75 353		8.75 423		11.24 577	9.99 930	45	8	180.0	176.0	172.0
16	8.75 575	222	8.75 645	222	11.24 355	9.99 929	44	9	202.5	198.0	193.5
17	8.75 795	220	8.75 867	222	11.24 133	9.99 929	43				
18	8.76 015	220	8.76 087	220	11.23 913	9.99 928	42		213	211	208
19	8.76 234	219	8.76 306	219	11.23 694	9.99 927	41	2	42.6	42.2	41.6
20	8.76 451	217	8.76 525	219	11.23 475	9.99 926	40	3	63.9	63.3	62.4
21	8.76 667	216	8.76 742	217	11.23 258	9.99 926	39	4	85.2	84.4	83.2
22	8.76 883	216	8.76 958	216	11.23 042	9.99 925	38	5	106.5	105.5	104.0
23	8.77 097	213	8.77 173	215	11.22 827	9.99 924	37	6	127.8	126.6	124.8
24	8.77 310	212	8.77 387	214	11.22 613	9.99 923	36	7	149.1	147.7	145.6
				213				8	170.4	168.8	166.4
25	8.77 522	211	8.77 600		11.22 400	9.99 923	35	9	191.7	189.9	187.2
26	8.77 733	210	8.77 811	211	11.22 189	9.99 922	34				
27	8.77 943	209	8.78 022	211	11.21 978	9.99 921	33		206	203	201
28	8.78 152	208	8.78 232	210	11.21 768	9.99 920	32	2	41.2	40.6	40.2
29	8.78 360	208	8.78 441	209	11.21 559	9.99 920	31	3	61.8	60.9	60.3
		208		208				4	82.4	81.2	80.4
30	8.78 568		8.78 649		11.21 351	9.99 919	30	5	103.0	101.5	100.5
31	8.78 774	206	8.78 855	206	11.21 145	9.99 918	29	6	123.6	121.8	120.6
32	8.78 979	205	8.79 061	206	11.20 939	9.99 917	28	7	144.2	142.1	140.7
33	8.79 183	204	8.79 266	205	11.20 734	9.99 917	27	8	164.8	162.4	160.8
34	8.79 386	203	8.79 470	204	11.20 530	9.99 916	26	9	185.4	182.7	180.9
		202		203							
35	8.79 588		8.79 673		11.20 327	9.99 915	25		199	197	195
36	8.79 789	201	8.79 875	202	11.20 125	9.99 914	24	2	39.8	39.4	39.0
37	8.79 990	201	8.80 076	201	11.19 924	9.99 913	23	3	59.7	59.1	58.5
38	8.80 189	199	8.80 277	201	11.19 723	9.99 913	22	4	79.6	78.8	78.0
39	8.80 388	199	8.80 476	199	11.19 524	9.99 912	21	5	99.5	98.5	97.5
		197		198				6	119.4	118.2	117.0
40	8.80 585		8.80 674		11.19 326	9.99 911	20	7	139.3	137.9	136.5
41	8.80 782	197	8.80 872	198	11.19 128	9.99 910	19	8	159.2	157.6	156.0
42	8.80 978	196	8.81 068	196	11.18 932	9.99 909	18	9	179.1	177.3	175.5
43	8.81 173	195	8.81 264	196	11.18 736	9.99 909	17				
44	8.81 367	194	8.81 459	195	11.18 541	9.99 908	16		193	192	190
		193		194				2	38.6	38.4	38.0
45	8.81 560		8.81 653		11.18 347	9.99 907	15	3	57.9	57.6	57.0
46	8.81 752	192	8.81 846	193	11.18 154	9.99 906	14	4	77.2	76.8	76.0
47	8.81 944	192	8.82 038	192	11.17 962	9.99 905	13	5	96.5	96.0	95.0
48	8.82 134	190	8.82 230	192	11.17 770	9.99 904	12	6	115.8	115.2	114.0
49	8.82 324	190	8.82 420	190	11.17 580	9.99 904	11	7	135.1	134.4	133.0
		189		190				8	154.4	153.6	152.0
50	8.82 513		8.82 610		11.17 390	9.99 903	10	9	173.7	172.8	171.0
51	8.82 701	188	8.82 799	189	11.17 201	9.99 902	9				
52	8.82 888	187	8.82 987	188	11.17 013	9.99 901	8		188	186	184
53	8.83 075	187	8.83 175	188	11.16 825	9.99 900	7	2	37.6	37.2	36.8
54	8.83 261	186	8.83 361	186	11.16 639	9.99 899	6	3	56.4	55.8	55.2
		185		186				4	75.2	74.4	73.6
55	8.83 446		8.83 547		11.16 453	9.99 898	5	5	94.0	93.0	92.0
56	8.83 630	184	8.83 732	185	11.16 268	9.99 898	4	6	112.8	111.6	110.4
57	8.83 813	183	8.83 916	184	11.16 084	9.99 897	3	7	131.6	130.2	128.8
58	8.83 996	183	8.84 100	184	11.15 900	9.99 896	2	8	150.4	148.8	147.2
59	8.84 177	181	8.84 282	182	11.15 718	9.99 895	1	9	169.2	167.4	165.6
		181		182							
60	8.84 358		8.84 464		11.15 536	9.99 894	0		183	182	181
								2	36.6	36.4	36.2
								3	54.9	54.6	54.3
								4	73.2	72.8	72.4
								5	91.5	91.0	90.5
								6	109.8	109.2	108.6
								7	128.1	127.4	126.7
								8	146.4	145.6	144.8
								9	164.7	163.8	162.9

	L Cos	d	L Ctn	c d	L Tan	L Sin	′		Prop. Pts.		

86° — Logarithms of Trigonometric Functions

Table XIV.
4° — Logarithms of Trigonometric Functions

′	L Sin	d	L Tan	c d	L Ctn	L Cos		Prop. Pts.		
0	8.84 358		8.84 464		11.15 536	9.99 894	60			
1	8.84 539	181	8.84 646	182	11.15 354	9.99 893	59	**181**	**180**	**179**
2	8.84 718	179	8.84 826	180	11.15 174	9.99 892	58	2 36.2	36.0	35.8
3	8.84 897	179	8.85 006	180	11.14 994	9.99 891	57	3 54.3	54.0	53.7
4	8.85 075	178	8.85 185	179	11.14 815	9.99 891	56	4 72.4	72.0	71.6
		177		178				5 90.5	90.0	89.5
5	8.85 252		8.85 363		11.14 637	9.99 890	55	6 108.6	108.0	107.4
6	8.85 429	177	8.85 540	177	11.14 460	9.99 889	54	7 126.7	126.0	125.3
7	8.85 605	176	8.85 717	177	11.14 283	9.99 888	53	8 144.8	144.0	143.2
8	8.85 780	175	8.85 893	176	11.14 107	9.99 887	52	9 162.9	162.0	161.1
9	8.85 955	175	8.86 069	176	11.13 931	9.99 886	51			
		173		174					**177**	**175**	**173**
10	8.86 128		8.86 243		11.13 757	9.99 885	50	2 35.4	35.0	34.6
11	8.86 301	173	8.86 417	174	11.13 583	9.99 884	49	3 53.1	52.5	51.9
12	8.86 474	173	8.86 591	174	11.13 409	9.99 883	48	4 70.8	70.0	69.2
13	8.86 645	171	8.86 763	172	11.13 237	9.99 882	47	5 88.5	87.5	86.5
14	8.86 816	171	8.86 935	172	11.13 065	9.99 881	46	6 106.2	105.0	103.8
		171		171				7 123.9	122.5	121.1
15	8.86 987		8.87 106		11.12 894	9.99 880	45	8 141.6	140.0	138.4
16	8.87 156	169	8.87 277	171	11.12 723	9.99 879	44	9 159.3	157.5	155.7
17	8.87 325	169	8.87 447	170	11.12 553	9.99 879	43			
18	8.87 494	169	8.87 616	169	11.12 384	9.99 878	42		**171**	**170**	**169**
19	8.87 661	167	8.87 785	169	11.12 215	9.99 877	41	2 34.2	34.0	33.8
		168		168				3 51.3	51.0	50.7
20	8.87 829		8.87 953		11.12 047	9.99 876	40	4 68.4	68.0	67.6
21	8.87 995	166	8.88 120	167	11.11 880	9.99 875	39	5 85.5	85.0	84.5
22	8.88 161	166	8.88 287	167	11.11 713	9.99 874	38	6 102.6	102.0	101.4
23	8.88 326	165	8.88 453	166	11.11 547	9.99 873	37	7 119.7	119.0	118.3
24	8.88 490	164	8.88 618	165	11.11 382	9.99 872	36	8 136.8	136.0	135.2
		164		165				9 153.9	153.0	152.1
25	8.88 654		8.88 783		11.11 217	9.99 871	35			
26	8.88 817	163	8.88 948	165	11.11 052	9.99 870	34		**167**	**165**	**163**
27	8.88 980	163	8.89 111	163	11.10 889	9.99 869	33	2 33.4	33.0	32.6
28	8.89 142	162	8.89 274	163	11.10 726	9.99 868	32	3 50.1	49.5	48.9
29	8.89 304	162	8.89 437	163	11.10 563	9.99 867	31	4 66.8	66.0	65.2
		160		161				5 83.5	82.5	81.5
30	8.89 464		8.89 598		11.10 402	9.99 866	30	6 100.2	99.0	97.8
31	8.89 625	161	8.89 760	162	11.10 240	9.99 865	29	7 116.9	115.5	114.1
32	8.89 784	159	8.89 920	160	11.10 080	9.99 864	28	8 133.6	132.0	130.4
33	8.89 943	159	8.90 080	160	11.09 920	9.99 863	27	9 150.3	148.5	146.7
34	8.90 102	159	8.90 240	160	11.09 760	9.99 862	26			
		158		159					**161**	**160**	**159**
35	8.90 260		8.90 399		11.09 601	9.99 861	25	2 32.2	32.0	31.8
36	8.90 417	157	8.90 557	158	11.09 443	9.99 860	24	3 48.3	48.0	47.7
37	8.90 574	157	8.90 715	158	11.09 285	9.99 859	23	4 64.4	64.0	63.6
38	8.90 730	156	8.90 872	157	11.09 128	9.99 858	22	5 80.5	80.0	79.5
39	8.90 885	155	8.91 029	157	11.08 971	9.99 857	21	6 96.6	96.0	95.4
		155		156				7 112.7	112.0	111.3
40	8.91 040		8.91 185		11.08 815	9.99 856	20	8 128.8	128.0	127.2
41	8.91 195	155	8.91 340	155	11.08 660	9.99 855	19	9 144.9	144.0	143.1
42	8.91 349	154	8.91 495	155	11.08 505	9.99 854	18			
43	8.91 502	153	8.91 650	155	11.08 350	9.99 853	17		**157**	**155**	**153**
44	8.91 655	153	8.91 803	153	11.08 197	9.99 852	16	2 31.4	31.0	30.6
		152		154				3 47.1	46.5	45.9
45	8.91 807		8.91 957		11.08 043	9.99 851	15	4 62.8	62.0	61.2
46	8.91 959	152	8.92 110	153	11.07 890	9.99 850	14	5 78.5	77.5	76.5
47	8.92 110	151	8.92 262	152	11.07 738	9.99 848	13	6 94.2	93.0	91.8
48	8.92 261	151	8.92 414	152	11.07 586	9.99 847	12	7 109.9	108.5	107.1
49	8.92 411	150	8.92 565	151	11.07 435	9.99 846	11	8 125.6	124.0	122.4
		150		151				9 141.3	139.5	137.7
50	8.92 561		8.92 716		11.07 284	9.99 845	10			
51	8.92 710	149	8.92 866	150	11.07 134	9.99 844	9		**151**	**150**	**149**
52	8.92 859	149	8.93 016	150	11.06 984	9.99 843	8	2 30.2	30.0	29.8
53	8.93 007	148	8.93 165	149	11.06 835	9.99 842	7	3 45.3	45.0	44.7
54	8.93 154	147	8.93 313	148	11.06 687	9.99 841	6	4 60.4	60.0	59.6
		147		149				5 75.5	75.0	74.5
55	8.93 301		8.93 462		11.06 538	9.99 840	5	6 90.6	90.0	89.4
56	8.93 448	147	8.93 609	147	11.06 391	9.99 839	4	7 105.7	105.0	104.3
57	8.93 594	146	8.93 756	147	11.06 244	9.99 838	3	8 120.8	120.0	119.2
58	8.93 740	146	8.93 903	147	11.06 097	9.99 837	2	9 135.9	135.0	134.1
59	8.93 885	145	8.94 049	146	11.05 951	9.99 836	1			
		145		146					**147**	**145**	**144**
60	8.94 030		8.94 195		11.05 805	9.99 834	0	2 29.4	29.0	28.8
								3 44.1	43.5	43.2
								4 58.8	58.0	57.6
								5 73.5	72.5	72.0
								6 88.2	87.0	86.4
								7 102.9	101.5	100.8
								8 117.6	116.0	115.2
								9 132.3	130.5	129.6
	L Cos	d	L Ctn	c d	L Tan	L Sin	′	Prop. Pts.		

85° — Logarithms of Trigonometric Functions

5° — Logarithms of Trigonometric Functions

′	L Sin	d	L Tan	c d	L Ctn	L Cos		Prop. Pts.
0	8.94 030	144	8.94 195	145	11.05 805	9.99 834	60	
1	8.94 174	143	8.94 340	145	11.05 660	9.99 833	59	. 143 142 141
2	8.94 317	144	8.94 485	145	11.05 515	9.99 832	58	2 28.6 28.4 28.2
3	8.94 461	142	8.94 630	143	11.05 370	9.99 831	57	3 42.9 42.6 42.3
4	8.94 603	143	8.94 773	144	11.05 227	9.99 830	56	4 57.2 56.8 56.4
5	8.94 746	141	8.94 917	143	11.05 083	9.99 829	55	5 71.5 71.0 70.5
6	8.94 887	142	8.95 060	142	11.04 940	9.99 828	54	6 85.8 85.2 84.6
7	8.95 029	141	8.95 202	142	11.04 798	9.99 827	53	7 100.1 99.4 98.7
8	8.95 170	140	8.95 344	142	11.04 656	9.99 825	52	8 114.4 113.6 112.8
9	8.95 310	140	8.95 486	141	11.04 514	9.99 824	51	9 128.7 127.8 126.9
10	8.95 450	139	8.95 627	140	11.04 373	9.99 823	50	140 139 138
11	8.95 589	139	8.95 767	141	11.04 233	9.99 822	49	2 28.0 27.8 27.6
12	8.95 728	139	8.95 908	139	11.04 092	9.99 821	48	3 42.0 41.7 41.4
13	8.95 867	138	8.96 047	140	11.03 953	9.99 820	47	4 56.0 55.6 55.2
14	8.96 005	138	8.96 187	138	11.03 813	9.99 819	46	5 70.0 69.5 69.0
15	8.96 143	137	8.96 325	139	11.03 675	9.99 817	45	6 84.0 83.4 82.8
16	8.96 280	137	8.96 464	138	11.03 536	9.99 816	44	7 98.0 97.3 96.6
17	8.96 417	136	8.96 602	137	11.03 398	9.99 815	43	8 112.0 111.2 110.4
18	8.96 553	136	8.96 739	138	11.03 261	9.99 814	42	9 126.0 125.1 124.2
19	8.96 689	136	8.96 877	136	11.03 123	9.99 813	41	137 136 135
20	8.96 825	135	8.97 013	137	11.02 987	9.99 812	40	2 27.4 27.2 27.0
21	8.96 960	135	8.97 150	135	11.02 850	9.99 810	39	3 41.1 40.8 40.5
22	8.97 095	134	8.97 285	136	11.02 715	9.99 809	38	4 54.8 54.4 54.0
23	8.97 229	134	8.97 421	135	11.02 579	9.99 808	37	5 68.5 68.0 67.5
24	8.97 363	133	8.97 556	135	11.02 444	9.99 807	36	6 82.2 81.6 81.0
25	8.97 496	133	8.97 691	134	11.02 309	9.99 806	35	7 95.9 95.2 94.5
26	8.97 629	133	8.97 825	134	11.02 175	9.99 804	34	8 109.6 108.8 108.0
27	8.97 762	132	8.97 959	133	11.02 041	9.99 803	33	9 123.3 122.4 121.5
28	8.97 894	132	8.98 092	133	11.01 908	9.99 802	32	134 133 132
29	8.98 026	131	8.98 225	133	11.01 775	9.99 801	31	2 26.8 26.6 26.4
30	8.98 157	131	8.98 358	132	11.01 642	9.99 800	30	3 40.2 39.9 39.6
31	8.98 288	131	8.98 490	132	11.01 510	9.99 798	29	4 53.6 53.2 52.8
32	8.98 419	130	8.98 622	131	11.01 378	9.99 797	28	5 67.0 66.5 66.0
33	8.98 549	130	8.98 753	131	11.01 247	9.99 796	27	6 80.4 79.8 79.2
34	8.98 679	129	8.98 884	131	11.01 116	9.99 795	26	7 93.8 93.1 92.4
35	8.98 808	129	8.99 015	130	11.00 985	9.99 793	25	8 107.2 106.4 105.6
36	8.98 937	129	8.99 145	130	11.00 855	9.99 792	24	9 120.6 119.7 118.8
37	8.99 066	128	8.99 275	130	11.00 725	9.99 791	23	131 130 129
38	8.99 194	128	8.99 405	129	11.00 595	9.99 790	22	2 26.2 26.0 25.8
39	8.99 322	128	8.99 534	128	11.00 466	9.99 788	21	3 39.3 39.0 38.7
40	8.99 450	127	8.99 662	129	11.00 338	9.99 787	20	4 52.4 52.0 51.6
41	8.99 577	127	8.99 791	128	11.00 209	9.99 786	19	5 65.5 65.0 64.5
42	8.99 704	126	8.99 919	127	11.00 081	9.99 785	18	6 78.6 78.0 77.4
43	8.99 830	126	9.00 046	128	10.99 954	9.99 783	17	7 91.7 91.0 90.3
44	8.99 956	126	9.00 174	127	10.99 826	9.99 782	16	8 104.8 104.0 103.2
45	9.00 082	125	9.00 301	126	10.99 699	9.99 781	15	9 117.9 117.0 116.1
46	9.00 207	125	9.00 427	126	10.99 573	9.99 780	14	128 127 126
47	9.00 332	124	9.00 553	126	10.99 447	9.99 778	13	2 25.6 25.4 25.2
48	9.00 456	125	9.00 679	126	10.99 321	9.99 777	12	3 38.4 38.1 37.8
49	9.00 581	123	9.00 805	125	10.99 195	9.99 776	11	4 51.2 50.8 50.4
50	9.00 704	124	9.00 930	125	10.99 070	9.99 775	10	5 64.0 63.5 63.0
51	9.00 828	123	9.01 055	124	10.98 945	9.99 773	9	6 76.8 76.2 75.6
52	9.00 951	123	9.01 179	124	10.98 821	9.99 772	8	7 89.6 88.9 88.2
53	9.01 074	122	9.01 303	124	10.98 697	9.99 771	7	8 102.4 101.6 100.8
54	9.01 196	122	9.01 427	123	10.98 573	9.99 769	6	9 115.2 114.3 113.4
55	9.01 318	122	9.01 550	123	10.98 450	9.99 768	5	125 124 123
56	9.01 440	121	9.01 673	123	10.98 327	9.99 767	4	2 25.0 24.8 24.6
57	9.01 561	121	9.01 796	122	10.98 204	9.99 765	3	3 37.5 37.2 36.9
58	9.01 682	121	9.01 918	122	10.98 082	9.99 764	2	4 50.0 49.6 49.2
59	9.01 803	120	9.02 040	122	10.97 960	9.99 763	1	5 62.5 62.0 61.5
60	9.01 923		9.02 162		10.97 838	9.99 761	0	6 75.0 74.4 73.8
								7 87.5 86.8 86.1
								8 100.0 99.2 98.4
								9 112.5 111.6 110.7
								122 121 120
								2 24.4 24.2 24.0
								3 36.6 36.3 36.0
								4 48.8 48.4 48.0
								5 61.0 60.5 60.0
								6 73.2 72.6 72.0
								7 85.4 84.7 84.0
								8 97.6 96.8 96.0
								9 109.8 108.9 108.0
	L Cos	d	L Ctn	c d	L Tan	L Sin	′	Prop. Pts.

84° — Logarithms of Trigonometric Functions

Table XIV. [XIV

6° — Logarithms of Trigonometric Functions

′	L Sin	d	L Tan	c d	L Ctn	L Cos		Prop. Pts.
0	9.01 923		9.02 162		10.97 838	9.99 761	60	
1	9.02 043	120	9.02 283	121	10.97 717	9.99 760	59	**121 120 119**
2	9.02 163	120	9.02 404	121	10.97 596	9.99 759	58	2 | 24.2 24.0 23.8
3	9.02 283	120	9.02 525	121	10.97 475	9.99 757	57	3 | 36.3 36.0 35.7
4	9.02 402	119	9.02 645	120	10.97 355	9.99 756	56	4 | 48.4 48.0 47.6
		118		121				5 | 60.5 60.0 59.5
5	9.02 520		9.02 766		10.97 234	9.99 755	55	6 | 72.6 72.0 71.4
6	9.02 639	119	9.02 885	119	10.97 115	9.99 753	54	7 | 84.7 84.0 83.3
7	9.02 757	118	9.03 005	120	10.96 995	9.99 752	53	8 | 96.8 96.0 95.2
8	9.02 874	117	9.03 124	119	10.96 876	9.99 751	52	9 | 108.9 108.0 107.1
9	9.02 992	118	9.03 242	118	10.96 758	9.99 749	51	
		117		119				**118 117 116**
10	9.03 109		9.03 361		10.96 639	9.99 748	50	2 | 23.6 23.4 23.2
11	9.03 226	117	9.03 479	118	10.96 521	9.99 747	49	3 | 35.4 35.1 34.8
12	9.03 342	116	9.03 597	118	10.96 403	9.99 745	48	4 | 47.2 46.8 46.4
13	9.03 458	116	9.03 714	117	10.96 286	9.99 744	47	5 | 59.0 58.5 58.0
14	9.03 574	116	9.03 832	118	10.96 168	9.99 742	46	6 | 70.8 70.2 69.6
		116		116				7 | 82.6 81.9 81.2
15	9.03 690		9.03 948		10.96 052	9.99 741	45	8 | 94.4 93.6 92.8
16	9.03 805	115	9.04 065	117	10.95 935	9.99 740	44	9 | 106.2 105.3 104.4
17	9.03 920	115	9.04 181	116	10.95 819	9.99 738	43	
18	9.04 034	114	9.04 297	116	10.95 703	9.99 737	42	**115 114 113**
19	9.04 149	115	9.04 413	116	10.95 587	9.99 735	41	2 | 23.0 22.8 22.6
		113		115				3 | 34.5 34.2 33.9
20	9.04 262		9.04 528		10.95 472	9.99 734	40	4 | 46.0 45.6 45.2
21	9.04 376	114	9.04 643	115	10.95 357	9.99 733	39	5 | 57.5 57.0 56.5
22	9.04 490	114	9.04 758	115	10.95 242	9.99 731	38	6 | 69.0 68.4 67.8
23	9.04 603	113	9.04 873	115	10.95 127	9.99 730	37	7 | 80.5 79.8 79.1
24	9.04 715	112	9.04 987	114	10.95 013	9.99 728	36	8 | 92.0 91.2 90.4
		113		114				9 | 103.5 102.6 101.7
25	9.04 828		9.05 101		10.94 899	9.99 727	35	
26	9.04 940	112	9.05 214	113	10.94 786	9.99 726	34	**112 111 110**
27	9.05 052	112	9.05 328	114	10.94 672	9.99 724	33	2 | 22.4 22.2 22.0
28	9.05 164	112	9.05 441	113	10.94 559	9.99 723	32	3 | 33.6 33.3 33.0
29	9.05 275	111	9.05 553	112	10.94 447	9.99 721	31	4 | 44.8 44.4 44.0
		111		113				5 | 56.0 55.5 55.0
30	9.05 386		9.05 666		10.94 334	9.99 720	30	6 | 67.2 66.6 66.0
31	9.05 497	111	9.05 778	112	10.94 222	9.99 718	29	7 | 78.4 77.7 77.0
32	9.05 607	110	9.05 890	112	10.94 110	9.99 717	28	8 | 89.6 88.8 88.0
33	9.05 717	110	9.06 002	112	10.93 998	9.99 715	27	9 | 100.8 99.9 99.0
34	9.05 827	110	9.06 113	111	10.93 887	9.99 714	26	
		110		111				**109 108 107**
35	9.05 937		9.06 224		10.93 776	9.99 713	25	2 | 21.8 21.6 21.4
36	9.06 046	109	9.06 335	111	10.93 665	9.99 711	24	3 | 32.7 32.4 32.1
37	9.06 155	109	9.06 445	110	10.93 555	9.99 710	23	4 | 43.6 43.2 42.8
38	9.06 264	109	9.06 556	111	10.93 444	9.99 708	22	5 | 54.5 54.0 53.5
39	9.06 372	108	9.06 666	110	10.93 334	9.99 707	21	6 | 65.4 64.8 64.2
		109		109				7 | 76.3 75.6 74.9
40	9.06 481		9.06 775		10.93 225	9.99 705	20	8 | 87.2 86.4 85.6
41	9.06 589	108	9.06 885	110	10.93 115	9.99 704	19	9 | 98.1 97.2 96.3
42	9.06 696	107	9.06 994	109	10.93 006	9.99 702	18	
43	9.06 804	108	9.07 103	109	10.92 897	9.99 701	17	**106 105 104**
44	9.06 911	107	9.07 211	108	10.92 789	9.99 699	16	2 | 21.2 21.0 20.8
		107		109				3 | 31.8 31.5 31.2
45	9.07 018		9.07 320		10.92 680	9.99 698	15	4 | 42.4 42.0 41.6
46	9.07 124	106	9.07 428	108	10.92 572	9.99 696	14	5 | 53.0 52.5 52.0
47	9.07 231	107	9.07 536	108	10.92 464	9.99 695	13	6 | 63.6 63.0 62.4
48	9.07 337	106	9.07 643	107	10.92 357	9.99 693	12	7 | 74.2 73.5 72.8
49	9.07 442	105	9.07 751	108	10.92 249	9.99 692	11	8 | 84.8 84.0 83.2
		106		107				9 | 95.4 94.5 93.6
50	9.07 548		9.07 858		10.92 142	9.99 690	10	
51	9.07 653	105	9.07 964	106	10.92 036	9.99 689	9	*From the top:*
52	9.07 758	105	9.08 071	107	10.91 929	9.99 687	8	For 6°+ or 186°+,
53	9.07 863	105	9.08 177	106	10.91 823	9.99 686	7	read as printed; for
54	9.07 968	105	9.08 283	106	10.91 717	9.99 684	6	96°+ or 276°+, read
		104		106				co-function.
55	9.08 072		9.08 389		10.91 611	9.99 683	5	
56	9.08 176	104	9.08 495	106	10.91 505	9.99 681	4	*From the bottom:*
57	9.08 280	104	9.08 600	105	10.91 400	9.99 680	3	For 83°+ or 263°+,
58	9.08 383	103	9.08 705	105	10.91 295	9.99 678	2	read as printed; for
59	9.08 486	103	9.08 810	105	10.91 190	9.99 677	1	173°+ or 353°+, read
60	9.08 589	103	9.08 914	104	10.91 086	9.99 675	0	co-function.
	L Cos	d	L Ctn	c d	L Tan	L Sin	′	Prop. Pts.

83° — Logarithms of Trigonometric Functions

7° — Logarithms of Trigonometric Functions

'	L Sin	d	L Tan	c d	L Ctn	L Cos	'
0	9.08 589		9.08 914		10.91 086	9.99 675	60
1	9.08 692	103	9.09 019	105	10.90 981	9.99 674	59
2	9.08 795	103	9.09 123	104	10.90 877	9.99 672	58
3	9.08 897	102	9.09 227	104	10.90 773	9.99 670	57
4	9.08 999	102	9.09 330	103	10.90 670	9.99 669	56
5	9.09 101	102	9.09 434	104	10.90 566	9.99 667	55
6	9.09 202	101	9.09 537	103	10.90 463	9.99 666	54
7	9.09 304	102	9.09 640	103	10.90 360	9.99 664	53
8	9.09 405	101	9.09 742	102	10.90 258	9.99 663	52
9	9.09 506	101	9.09 845	103	10.90 155	9.99 661	51
10	9.09 606	100	9.09 947	102	10.90 053	9.99 659	50
11	9.09 707	100	9.10 049	102	10.89 951	9.99 658	49
12	9.09 807	100	9.10 150	101	10.89 850	9.99 656	48
13	9.09 907	100	9.10 252	102	10.89 748	9.99 655	47
14	9.10 006	99	9.10 353	101	10.89 647	9.99 653	46
15	9.10 106	100	9.10 454	101	10.89 546	9.99 651	45
16	9.10 205	99	9.10 555	101	10.89 445	9.99 650	44
17	9.10 304	99	9.10 656	101	10.89 344	9.99 648	43
18	9.10 402	99	9.10 756	100	10.89 244	9.99 647	42
19	9.10 501	99	9.10 856	100	10.89 144	9.99 645	41
20	9.10 599	98	9.10 956	100	10.89 044	9.99 643	40
21	9.10 697	98	9.11 056	100	10.88 944	9.99 642	39
22	9.10 795	98	9.11 155	99	10.88 845	9.99 640	38
23	9.10 893	98	9.11 254	99	10.88 746	9.99 638	37
24	9.10 990	97	9.11 353	99	10.88 647	9.99 637	36
25	9.11 087	97	9.11 452	99	10.88 548	9.99 635	35
26	9.11 184	97	9.11 551	99	10.88 449	9.99 633	34
27	9.11 281	97	9.11 649	98	10.88 351	9.99 632	33
28	9.11 377	97	9.11 747	98	10.88 253	9.99 630	32
29	9.11 474	96	9.11 845	98	10.88 155	9.99 629	31
30	9.11 570	96	9.11 943	97	10.88 057	9.99 627	30
31	9.11 666	95	9.12 040	98	10.87 960	9.99 625	29
32	9.11 761	96	9.12 138	97	10.87 862	9.99 624	28
33	9.11 857	95	9.12 235	97	10.87 765	9.99 622	27
34	9.11 952	95	9.12 332	96	10.87 668	9.99 620	26
35	9.12 047	95	9.12 428	97	10.87 572	9.99 618	25
36	9.12 142	95	9.12 525	96	10.87 475	9.99 617	24
37	9.12 236	94	9.12 621	96	10.87 379	9.99 615	23
38	9.12 331	95	9.12 717	96	10.87 283	9.99 613	22
39	9.12 425	94	9.12 813	96	10.87 187	9.99 612	21
40	9.12 519	94	9.12 909	95	10.87 091	9.99 610	20
41	9.12 612	93	9.13 004	95	10.86 996	9.99 608	19
42	9.12 706	94	9.13 099	95	10.86 901	9.99 607	18
43	9.12 799	93	9.13 194	95	10.86 806	9.99 605	17
44	9.12 892	93	9.13 289	95	10.86 711	9.99 603	16
45	9.12 985	93	9.13 384	94	10.86 616	9.99 601	15
46	9.13 078	93	9.13 478	95	10.86 522	9.99 600	14
47	9.13 171	92	9.13 573	94	10.86 427	9.99 598	13
48	9.13 263	92	9.13 667	94	10.86 333	9.99 596	12
49	9.13 355	92	9.13 761	93	10.86 239	9.99 595	11
50	9.13 447	92	9.13 854	94	10.86 146	9.99 593	10
51	9.13 539	91	9.13 948	93	10.86 052	9.99 591	9
52	9.13 630	92	9.14 041	93	10.85 959	9.99 589	8
53	9.13 722	91	9.14 134	93	10.85 866	9.99 588	7
54	9.13 813	91	9.14 227	93	10.85 773	9.99 586	6
55	9.13 904	90	9.14 320	92	10.85 680	9.99 584	5
56	9.13 994	91	9.14 412	92	10.85 588	9.99 582	4
57	9.14 085	90	9.14 504	93	10.85 496	9.99 581	3
58	9.14 175	91	9.14 597	91	10.85 403	9.99 579	2
59	9.14 266	90	9.14 688	92	10.85 312	9.99 577	1
60	9.14 356		9.14 780		10.85 220	9.99 575	0
	L Cos	d	L Ctn	c d	L Tan	L Sin	'

Prop. Pts.

	105	104	103
2	21.0	20.8	20.6
3	31.5	31.2	30.9
4	42.0	41.6	41.2
5	52.5	52.0	51.5
6	63.0	62.4	61.8
7	73.5	72.8	72.1
8	84.0	83.2	82.4
9	94.5	93.6	92.7

	102	101	99
2	20.4	20.2	19.8
3	30.6	30.3	29.7
4	40.8	40.4	39.6
5	51.0	50.5	49.5
6	61.2	60.6	59.4
7	71.4	70.7	69.3
8	81.6	80.8	79.2
9	91.8	90.9	89.1

	98	97	96
2	19.6	19.4	19.2
3	29.4	29.1	28.8
4	39.2	38.8	38.4
5	49.0	48.5	48.0
6	58.8	58.2	57.6
7	68.6	67.9	67.2
8	78.4	77.6	76.8
9	88.2	87.3	86.4

	95	94	93
2	19.0	18.8	18.6
3	28.5	28.2	27.9
4	38.0	37.6	37.2
5	47.5	47.0	46.5
6	57.0	56.4	55.8
7	66.5	65.8	65.1
8	76.0	75.2	74.4
9	85.5	84.6	83.7

	92	91	90
2	18.4	18.2	18.0
3	27.6	27.3	27.0
4	36.8	36.4	36.0
5	46.0	45.5	45.0
6	55.2	54.6	54.0
7	64.4	63.7	63.0
8	73.6	72.8	72.0
9	82.8	81.9	81.0

From the top:
For 7°+ or 187°+, read as printed; for 97°+ or 277°+, read co-function.

From the bottom:
For 82°+ or 262°+, read as printed; for 172°+ or 352°+, read co-function.

8° — Logarithms of Trigonometric Functions

′	L Sin	d	L Tan	c d	L Ctn	L Cos		Prop. Pts.
0	9.14 356		9.14 780		10.85 220	9.99 575	60	
1	9.14 445	89	9.14 872	92	10.85 128	9.99 574	59	
2	9.14 535	90	9.14 963	91	10.85 037	9.99 572	58	
3	9.14 624	89	9.15 054	91	10.84 946	9.99 570	57	**92 | 91 | 90**
4	9.14 714	90	9.15 145	91	10.84 855	9.99 568	56	2 18.4 | 18.2 | 18.0
5	9.14 803	89	9.15 236	91	10.84 764	9.99 566	55	3 27.6 | 27.3 | 27.0
6	9.14 891	88	9.15 327	91	10.84 673	9.99 565	54	4 36.8 | 36.4 | 36.0
7	9.14 980	89	9.15 417	90	10.84 583	9.99 563	53	5 46.0 | 45.5 | 45.0
8	9.15 069	89	9.15 508	91	10.84 492	9.99 561	52	6 55.2 | 54.6 | 54.0
9	9.15 157	88	9.15 598	90	10.84 402	9.99 559	51	7 64.4 | 63.7 | 63.0
10	9.15 245	88	9.15 688	90	10.84 312	9.99 557	50	8 73.6 | 72.8 | 72.0
11	9.15 333	88	9.15 777	89	10.84 223	9.99 556	49	9 82.8 | 81.9 | 81.0
12	9.15 421	88	9.15 867	90	10.84 133	9.99 554	48	
13	9.15 508	87	9.15 956	89	10.84 044	9.99 552	47	**89 | 88 | 87**
14	9.15 596	88	9.16 046	90	10.83 954	9.99 550	46	2 17.8 | 17.6 | 17.4
15	9.15 683	87	9.16 135	89	10.83 865	9.99 548	45	3 26.7 | 26.4 | 26.1
16	9.15 770	87	9.16 224	89	10.83 776	9.99 546	44	4 35.6 | 35.2 | 34.8
17	9.15 857	87	9.16 312	88	10.83 688	9.99 545	43	5 44.5 | 44.0 | 43.5
18	9.15 944	86	9.16 401	89	10.83 599	9.99 543	42	6 53.4 | 52.8 | 52.2
19	9.16 030	86	9.16 489	88	10.83 511	9.99 541	41	7 62.3 | 61.6 | 60.9
20	9.16 116	87	9.16 577	88	10.83 423	9.99 539	40	8 71.2 | 70.4 | 69.6
21	9.16 203	86	9.16 665	88	10.83 335	9.99 537	39	9 80.1 | 79.2 | 78.3
22	9.16 289	85	9.16 753	88	10.83 247	9.99 535	38	
23	9.16 374	86	9.16 841	87	10.83 159	9.99 533	37	**86 | 85 | 84**
24	9.16 460	85	9.16 928	88	10.83 072	9.99 532	36	2 17.2 | 17.0 | 16.8
25	9.16 545	86	9.17 016	87	10.82 984	9.99 530	35	3 25.8 | 25.5 | 25.2
26	9.16 631	85	9.17 103	87	10.82 897	9.99 528	34	4 34.4 | 34.0 | 33.6
27	9.16 716	85	9.17 190	87	10.82 810	9.99 526	33	5 43.0 | 42.5 | 42.0
28	9.16 801	85	9.17 277	86	10.82 723	9.99 524	32	6 51.6 | 51.0 | 50.4
29	9.16 886	84	9.17 363	87	10.82 637	9.99 522	31	7 60.2 | 59.5 | 58.8
30	9.16 970	85	9.17 450	86	10.82 550	9.99 520	30	8 68.8 | 68.0 | 67.2
31	9.17 055	84	9.17 536	86	10.82 464	9.99 518	29	9 77.4 | 76.5 | 75.6
32	9.17 139	84	9.17 622	86	10.82 378	9.99 517	28	
33	9.17 223	84	9.17 708	86	10.82 292	9.99 515	27	
34	9.17 307	84	9.17 794	86	10.82 206	9.99 513	26	**83 | 82 | 81**
35	9.17 391	83	9.17 880	85	10.82 120	9.99 511	25	2 16.6 | 16.4 | 16.2
36	9.17 474	84	9.17 965	86	10.82 035	9.99 509	24	3 24.9 | 24.6 | 24.3
37	9.17 558	83	9.18 051	85	10.81 949	9.99 507	23	4 33.2 | 32.8 | 32.4
38	9.17 641	83	9.18 136	85	10.81 864	9.99 505	22	5 41.5 | 41.0 | 40.5
39	9.17 724	83	9.18 221	85	10.81 779	9.99 503	21	6 49.8 | 49.2 | 48.6
40	9.17 807	83	9.18 306	85	10.81 694	9.99 501	20	7 58.1 | 57.4 | 56.7
41	9.17 890	83	9.18 391	84	10.81 609	9.99 499	19	8 66.4 | 65.6 | 64.8
42	9.17 973	82	9.18 475	85	10.81 525	9.99 497	18	9 74.7 | 73.8 | 72.9
43	9.18 055	82	9.18 560	84	10.81 440	9.99 495	17	
44	9.18 137	83	9.18 644	84	10.81 356	9.99 494	16	
45	9.18 220	82	9.18 728	84	10.81 272	9.99 492	15	*From the top:*
46	9.18 302	81	9.18 812	84	10.81 188	9.99 490	14	For 8°⁺ or 188°⁺,
47	9.18 383	82	9.18 896	83	10.81 104	9.99 488	13	read as printed; for
48	9.18 465	82	9.18 979	84	10.81 021	9.99 486	12	98°⁺ or 278°⁺, read
49	9.18 547	81	9.19 063	83	10.80 937	9.99 484	11	co-function.
50	9.18 628	81	9.19 146	83	10.80 854	9.99 482	10	
51	9.18 709	81	9.19 229	83	10.80 771	9.99 480	9	
52	9.18 790	81	9.19 312	83	10.80 688	9.99 478	8	
53	9.18 871	81	9.19 395	83	10.80 605	9.99 476	7	*From the bottom:*
54	9.18 952	81	9.19 478	83	10.80 522	9.99 474	6	For 81°⁺ or 261°⁺,
55	9.19 033	80	9.19 561	82	10.80 439	9.99 472	5	read as printed; for
56	9.19 113	80	9.19 643	82	10.80 357	9.99 470	4	171°⁺ or 351°⁺, read
57	9.19 193	80	9.19 725	82	10.80 275	9.99 468	3	co-function.
58	9.19 273	80	9.19 807	82	10.80 193	9.99 466	2	
59	9.19 353	80	9.19 889	82	10.80 111	9.99 464	1	
60	9.19 433		9.19 971		10.80 029	9.99 462	0	
	L Cos	d	L Ctn	c d	L Tan	L Sin	′	Prop. Pts.

81° — Logarithms of Trigonometric Functions

9° — Logarithms of Trigonometric Functions

′	L Sin	d	L Tan	c d	L Ctn	L Cos	′
0	9.19 433	80	9.19 971	82	10.80 029	9.99 462	60
1	9.19 513	79	9.20 053	81	10.79 947	9.99 460	59
2	9.19 592	80	9.20 134	82	10.79 866	9.99 458	58
3	9.19 672	79	9.20 216	81	10.79 784	9.99 456	57
4	9.19 751	79	9.20 297	81	10.79 703	9.99 454	56
5	9.19 830	79	9.20 378	81	10.79 622	9.99 452	55
6	9.19 909	79	9.20 459	81	10.79 541	9.99 450	54
7	9.19 988	79	9.20 540	81	10.79 460	9.99 448	53
8	9.20 067	78	9.20 621	80	10.79 379	9.99 446	52
9	9.20 145	78	9.20 701	81	10.79 299	9.99 444	51
10	9.20 223	78	9.20 782	80	10.79 218	9.99 442	50
11	9.20 302	78	9.20 862	80	10.79 138	9.99 440	49
12	9.20 380	78	9.20 942	80	10.79 058	9.99 438	48
13	9.20 458	77	9.21 022	80	10.78 978	9.99 436	47
14	9.20 535	78	9.21 102	80	10.78 898	9.99 434	46
15	9.20 613		9.21 182		10.78 818	9.99 432	45
16	9.20 691	78	9.21 261	79	10.78 739	9.99 429	44
17	9.20 768	77	9.21 341	80	10.78 659	9.99 427	43
18	9.20 845	77	9.21 420	79	10.78 580	9.99 425	42
19	9.20 922	77	9.21 499	79	10.78 501	9.99 423	41
20	9.20 999	77	9.21 578	79	10.78 422	9.99 421	40
21	9.21 076	77	9.21 657	79	10.78 343	9.99 419	39
22	9.21 153	76	9.21 736	78	10.78 264	9.99 417	38
23	9.21 229	77	9.21 814	79	10.78 186	9.99 415	37
24	9.21 306	76	9.21 893	78	10.78 107	9.99 413	36
25	9.21 382	76	9.21 971	78	10.78 029	9.99 411	35
26	9.21 458	76	9.22 049	78	10.77 951	9.99 409	34
27	9.21 534	76	9.22 127	78	10.77 873	9.99 407	33
28	9.21 610	75	9.22 205	78	10.77 795	9.99 404	32
29	9.21 685	76	9.22 283	78	10.77 717	9.99 402	31
30	9.21 761	75	9.22 361	77	10.77 639	9.99 400	30
31	9.21 836	76	9.22 438	78	10.77 562	9.99 398	29
32	9.21 912	75	9.22 516	77	10.77 484	9.99 396	28
33	9.21 987	75	9.22 593	77	10.77 407	9.99 394	27
34	9.22 062	75	9.22 670	77	10.77 330	9.99 392	26
35	9.22 137	74	9.22 747	77	10.77 253	9.99 390	25
36	9.22 211	75	9.22 824	77	10.77 176	9.99 388	24
37	9.22 286	75	9.22 901	76	10.77 099	9.99 385	23
38	9.22 361	74	9.22 977	77	10.77 023	9.99 383	22
39	9.22 435	74	9.23 054	76	10.76 946	9.99 381	21
40	9.22 509	74	9.23 130	76	10.76 870	9.99 379	20
41	9.22 583	74	9.23 206	77	10.76 794	9.99 377	19
42	9.22 657	74	9.23 283	76	10.76 717	9.99 375	18
43	9.22 731	74	9.23 359	76	10.76 641	9.99 372	17
44	9.22 805	73	9.23 435	75	10.76 565	9.99 370	16
45	9.22 878	74	9.23 510	76	10.76 490	9.99 368	15
46	9.22 952	73	9.23 586	75	10.76 414	9.99 366	14
47	9.23 025	73	9.23 661	76	10.76 339	9.99 364	13
48	9.23 098	73	9.23 737	75	10.76 263	9.99 362	12
49	9.23 171	73	9.23 812	75	10.76 188	9.99 359	11
50	9.23 244	73	9.23 887	75	10.76 113	9.99 357	10
51	9.23 317	73	9.23 962	75	10.76 038	9.99 355	9
52	9.23 390	72	9.24 037	75	10.75 963	9.99 353	8
53	9.23 462	73	9.24 112	74	10.75 888	9.99 351	7
54	9.23 535	72	9.24 186	75	10.75 814	9.99 348	6
55	9.23 607	72	9.24 261	74	10.75 739	9.99 346	5
56	9.23 679	73	9.24 335	75	10.75 665	9.99 344	4
57	9.23 752	71	9.24 410	74	10.75 590	9.99 342	3
58	9.23 823	72	9.24 484	74	10.75 516	9.99 340	2
59	9.23 895	72	9.24 558	74	10.75 442	9.99 337	1
60	9.23 967		9.24 632		10.75 368	9.99 335	0
	L Cos	d	L Ctn	c d	L Tan	L Sin	′

Prop. Pts.

	82	81	80
2	16.4	16.2	16.0
3	24.6	24.3	24.0
4	32.8	32.4	32.0
5	41.0	40.5	40.0
6	49.2	48.6	48.0
7	57.4	56.7	56.0
8	65.6	64.8	64.0
9	73.8	72.9	72.0

	79	78	77
2	15.8	15.6	15.4
3	23.7	23.4	23.1
4	31.6	31.2	30.8
5	39.5	39.0	38.5
6	47.4	46.8	46.2
7	55.3	54.6	53.9
8	63.2	62.4	61.6
9	71.1	70.2	69.3

	76	75	74
2	15.2	15.0	14.8
3	22.8	22.5	22.2
4	30.4	30.0	29.6
5	38.0	37.5	37.0
6	45.6	45.0	44.4
7	53.2	52.5	51.8
8	60.8	60.0	59.2
9	68.4	67.5	66.6

	73	72	71
2	14.6	14.4	14.2
3	21.9	21.6	21.3
4	29.2	28.8	28.4
5	36.5	36.0	35.5
6	43.8	43.2	42.6
7	51.1	50.4	49.7
8	58.4	57.6	56.8
9	65.7	64.8	63.9

From the top:

For **9°+**, or **189°+**, read as printed; for **99°+** or **279°+**, read co-function.

From the bottom:

For **80°+** or **260°+**, read as printed; for **170°+** or **350°+**, read co-function.

80° — Logarithms of Trigonometric Functions

10° — Logarithms of Trigonometric Functions

′	L Sin	d	L Tan	cd	L Ctn	L Cos	d	′	Prop. Pts.
0	9.23 967	72	9.24 632	74	10.75 368	9.99 335	2	60	
1	9.24 039	71	9.24 706	73	10.75 294	9.99 333	2	59	
2	9.24 110	71	9.24 779	74	10.75 221	9.99 331	2	58	**74** **73** **72**
3	9.24 181	72	9.24 853	73	10.75 147	9.99 328	3	57	2 14.8 14.6 14.4
4	9.24 253	71	9.24 926	74	10.75 074	9.99 326	2	56	3 22.2 21.9 21.6
5	9.24 324	71	9.25 000	73	10.75 000	9.99 324	2	55	4 29.6 29.2 28.8
6	9.24 395	71	9.25 073	73	10.74 927	9.99 322	3	54	5 37.0 36.5 36.0
7	9.24 466	70	9.25 146	73	10.74 854	9.99 319	2	53	6 44.4 43.8 43.2
8	9.24 536	71	9.25 219	73	10.74 781	9.99 317	2	52	7 51.8 51.1 50.4
9	9.24 607	70	9.25 292	73	10.74 708	9.99 315	2	51	8 59.2 58.4 57.6
10	9.24 677	71	9.25 365	72	10.74 635	9.99 313	3	50	9 66.6 65.7 64.8
11	9.24 748	70	9.25 437	73	10.74 563	9.99 310	2	49	
12	9.24 818	70	9.25 510	72	10.74 490	9.99 308	2	48	**71** **70** **69**
13	9.24 888	70	9.25 582	73	10.74 418	9.99 306	2	47	2 14.2 14.0 13.8
14	9.24 958	70	9.25 655	72	10.74 345	9.99 304	3	46	3 21.3 21.0 20.7
15	9.25 028	70	9.25 727	72	10.74 273	9.99 301	2	45	4 28.4 28.0 27.6
16	9.25 098	70	9.25 799	72	10.74 201	9.99 299	2	44	5 35.5 35.0 34.5
17	9.25 168	69	9.25 871	72	10.74 129	9.99 297	3	43	6 42.6 42.0 41.4
18	9.25 237	70	9.25 943	72	10.74 057	9.99 294	2	42	7 49.7 49.0 48.3
19	9.25 307	69	9.26 015	71	10.73 985	9.99 292	2	41	8 56.8 56.0 55.2
20	9.25 376	69	9.26 086	72	10.73 914	9.99 290	2	40	9 63.9 63.0 62.1
21	9.25 445	69	9.26 158	71	10.73 842	9.99 288	3	39	
22	9.25 514	69	9.26 229	72	10.73 771	9.99 285	2	38	
23	9.25 583	69	9.26 301	71	10.73 699	9.99 283	2	37	**68** **67** **66**
24	9.25 652	69	9.26 372	71	10.73 628	9.99 281	3	36	2 13.6 13.4 13.2
25	9.25 721	69	9.26 443	71	10.73 557	9.99 278	2	35	3 20.4 20.1 19.8
26	9.25 790	68	9.26 514	71	10.73 486	9.99 276	2	34	4 27.2 26.8 26.4
27	9.25 858	69	9.26 585	70	10.73 415	9.99 274	3	33	5 34.0 33.5 33.0
28	9.25 927	68	9.26 655	71	10.73 345	9.99 271	2	32	6 40.8 40.2 39.6
29	9.25 995	68	9.26 726	71	10.73 274	9.99 269	2	31	7 47.6 46.9 46.2
30	9.26 063	68	9.26 797	70	10.73 203	9.99 267	3	30	8 54.4 53.6 52.8
31	9.26 131	68	9.26 867	70	10.73 133	9.99 264	2	29	9 61.2 60.3 59.4
32	9.26 199	68	9.26 937	71	10.73 063	9.99 262	2	28	
33	9.26 267	68	9.27 008	70	10.72 992	9.99 260	3	27	
34	9.26 335	68	9.27 078	70	10.72 922	9.99 257	2	26	**65** **3** **2**
35	9.26 403	67	9.27 148	70	10.72 852	9.99 255	3	25	2 13.0 0.6 0.4
36	9.26 470	68	9.27 218	70	10.72 782	9.99 252	2	24	3 19.5 0.9 0.6
37	9.26 538	67	9.27 288	69	10.72 712	9.99 250	2	23	4 26.0 1.2 0.8
38	9.26 605	67	9.27 357	70	10.72 643	9.99 248	3	22	5 32.5 1.5 1.0
39	9.26 672	67	9.27 427	69	10.72 573	9.99 245	2	21	6 39.0 1.8 1.2
40	9.26 739	67	9.27 496	70	10.72 504	9.99 243	2	20	7 45.5 2.1 1.4
41	9.26 806	67	9.27 566	69	10.72 434	9.99 241	3	19	8 52.0 2.4 1.6
42	9.26 873	67	9.27 635	69	10.72 365	9.99 238	2	18	9 58.5 2.7 1.8
43	9.26 940	67	9.27 704	69	10.72 296	9.99 236	3	17	
44	9.27 007	66	9.27 773	69	10.72 227	9.99 233	2	16	
45	9.27 073	67	9.27 842	69	10.72 158	9.99 231	2	15	*From the top:*
46	9.27 140	66	9.27 911	69	10.72 089	9.99 229	3	14	For 10°+ or 190°+,
47	9.27 206	67	9.27 980	69	10.72 020	9.99 226	2	13	read as printed; for
48	9.27 273	66	9.28 049	69	10.71 951	9.99 224	2	12	100°+ or 280°+, read
49	9.27 339	66	9.28 117	69	10.71 883	9.99 221	2	11	co-function.
50	9.27 405	66	9.28 186	68	10.71 814	9.99 219	2	10	
51	9.27 471	66	9.28 254	69	10.71 746	9.99 217	3	9	
52	9.27 537	65	9.28 323	68	10.71 677	9.99 214	2	8	
53	9.27 602	66	9.28 391	68	10.71 609	9.99 212	3	7	
54	9.27 668	66	9.28 459	68	10.71 541	9.99 209	2	6	
55	9.27 734	65	9.28 527	68	10.71 473	9.99 207	3	5	*From the bottom:*
56	9.27 799	65	9.28 595	67	10.71 405	9.99 204	2	4	For 79°+ or 259°+,
57	9.27 864	66	9.28 662	68	10.71 338	9.99 202	2	3	read as printed; for
58	9.27 930	65	9.28 730	68	10.71 270	9.99 200	3	2	169°+ or 349°+, read
59	9.27 995	65	9.28 798	67	10.71 202	9.99 197	2	1	co-function.
60	9.28 060		9.28 865		10.71 135	9.99 195		0	
′	L Cos	d	L Ctn	cd	L Tan	L Sin	d	′	Prop. Pts.

11° — Logarithms of Trigonometric Functions

′	L Sin	d	L Tan	c d	L Ctn	L Cos	d		′	Prop. Pts.
0	9.28 060	65	9.28 865	68	10.71 135	9.99 195	3		60	
1	9.28 125	65	9.28 933	67	10.71 067	9.99 192	3		59	
2	9.28 190	64	9.29 000	67	10.71 000	9.99 190	2		58	**68** **67** **66**
3	9.28 254	65	9.29 067	67	10.70 933	9.99 187	3		57	2 13.6 13.4 13.2
4	9.28 319	65	9.29 134	67	10.70 866	9.99 185	2		56	3 20.4 20.1 19.8
5	9.28 384	64	9.29 201	67	10.70 799	9.99 182	3		55	4 27.2 26.8 26.4
6	9.28 448	64	9.29 268	67	10.70 732	9.99 180	2		54	5 34.0 33.5 33.0
7	9.28 512	65	9.29 335	67	10.70 665	9.99 177	3		53	6 40.8 40.2 39.6
8	9.28 577	64	9.29 402	66	10.70 598	9.99 175	2		52	7 47.6 46.9 46.2
9	9.28 641	64	9.29 468	67	10.70 532	9.99 172	2		51	8 54.4 53.6 52.8
10	9.28 705	64	9.29 535	66	10.70 465	9.99 170	3		50	9 61.2 60.3 59.4
11	9.28 769	64	9.29 601	67	10.70 399	9.99 167	2		49	
12	9.28 833	63	9.29 668	66	10.70 332	9.99 165	3		48	
13	9.28 896	64	9.29 734	66	10.70 266	9.99 162	2		47	**65** **64** **63**
14	9.28 960	64	9.29 800	66	10.70 200	9.99 160	3		46	2 13.0 12.8 12.6
15	9.29 024	63	9.29 866	66	10.70 134	9.99 157	2		45	3 19.5 19.2 18.9
16	9.29 087	63	9.29 932	66	10.70 068	9.99 155	3		44	4 26.0 25.6 25.2
17	9.29 150	64	9.29 998	66	10.70 002	9.99 152	2		43	5 32.5 32.0 31.5
18	9.29 214	63	9.30 064	66	10.69 936	9.99 150	3		42	6 39.0 38.4 37.8
19	9.29 277	63	9.30 130	65	10.69 870	9.99 147	2		41	7 45.5 44.8 44.1
20	9.29 340	63	9.30 195	66	10.69 805	9.99 145	3		40	8 52.0 51.2 50.4
21	9.29 403	63	9.30 261	65	10.69 739	9.99 142	2		39	9 58.5 57.6 56.7
22	9.29 466	63	9.30 326	65	10.69 674	9.99 140	3		38	
23	9.29 529	62	9.30 391	66	10.69 609	9.99 137	2		37	
24	9.29 591	63	9.30 457	65	10.69 543	9.99 135	3		36	**62** **61** **60**
25	9.29 654	62	9.30 522	65	10.69 478	9.99 132	2		35	2 12.4 12.2 12.0
26	9.29 716	63	9.30 587	65	10.69 413	9.99 130	3		34	3 18.6 18.3 18.0
27	9.29 779	62	9.30 652	65	10.69 348	9.99 127	3		33	4 24.8 24.4 24.0
28	9.29 841	62	9.30 717	65	10.69 283	9.99 124	2		32	5 31.0 30.5 30.0
29	9.29 903	63	9.30 782	64	10.69 218	9.99 122	3		31	6 37.2 36.6 36.0
30	9.29 966	62	9.30 846	65	10.69 154	9.99 119	2		30	7 43.4 42.7 42.0
31	9.30 028	62	9.30 911	64	10.69 089	9.99 117	3		29	8 49.6 48.8 48.0
32	9.30 090	61	9.30 975	65	10.69 025	9.99 114	2		28	9 55.8 54.9 54.0
33	9.30 151	62	9.31 040	64	10.68 960	9.99 112	3		27	
34	9.30 213	62	9.31 104	64	10.68 896	9.99 109	2		26	**59** **3** **2**
35	9.30 275	61	9.31 168	65	10.68 832	9.99 106	3		25	2 11.8 0.6 0.4
36	9.30 336	62	9.31 233	64	10.68 767	9.99 104	2		24	3 17.7 0.9 0.6
37	9.30 398	61	9.31 297	64	10.68 703	9.99 101	3		23	4 23.6 1.2 0.8
38	9.30 459	62	9.31 361	64	10.68 639	9.99 099	2		22	5 29.5 1.5 1.0
39	9.30 521	61	9.31 425	64	10.68 575	9.99 096	3		21	7 41.3 2.1 1.4
40	9.30 582	61	9.31 489	63	10.68 511	9.99 093	2		20	8 47.2 2.4 1.6
41	9.30 643	61	9.31 552	64	10.68 448	9.99 091	3		19	9 53.1 2.7 1.8
42	9.30 704	61	9.31 616	63	10.68 384	9.99 088	2		18	
43	9.30 765	61	9.31 679	64	10.68 321	9.99 086	3		17	
44	9.30 826	61	9.31 743	63	10.68 257	9.99 083	3		16	
45	9.30 887	60	9.31 806	64	10.68 194	9.99 080	2		15	*From the top:*
46	9.30 947	61	9.31 870	63	10.68 130	9.99 078	3		14	For 11°⁺ or 191°⁺,
47	9.31 008	60	9.31 933	63	10.68 067	9.99 075	3		13	read as printed; for
48	9.31 068	61	9.31 996	63	10.68 004	9.99 072	2		12	101°⁺ or 281°⁺, read
49	9.31 129	60	9.32 059	63	10.67 941	9.99 070	3		11	co-function.
50	9.31 189	61	9.32 122	63	10.67 878	9.99 067	3		10	
51	9.31 250	60	9.32 185	63	10.67 815	9.99 064	2		9	
52	9.31 310	60	9.32 248	63	10.67 752	9.99 062	3		8	*From the bottom:*
53	9.31 370	60	9.32 311	62	10.67 689	9.99 059	3		7	For 78°⁺ or 258°⁺,
54	9.31 430	60	9.32 373	63	10.67 627	9.99 056	2		6	read as printed; for
55	9.31 490	59	9.32 436	62	10.67 564	9.99 054	3		5	168°⁺ or 348°⁺, read
56	9.31 549	60	9.32 498	63	10.67 502	9.99 051	3		4	co-function.
57	9.31 609	60	9.32 561	62	10.67 439	9.99 048	2		3	
58	9.31 669	59	9.32 623	62	10.67 377	9.99 046	3		2	
59	9.31 728	60	9.32 685	62	10.67 315	9.99 043	3		1	
60	9.31 788		9.32 747		10.67 253	9.99 040			0	
	L Cos	d	L Ctn	c d	L Tan	L Sin	d		′	Prop. Pts.

78° — Logarithms of Trigonometric Functions

12° — Logarithms of Trigonometric Functions

'	L Sin	d	L Tan	c d	L Ctn	L Cos	d		Prop. Pts.		
0	9.31 788		9.32 747		10.67 253	9.99 040		60			
1	9.31 847	59	9.32 810	63	10.67 190	9.99 038	2	59			
2	9.31 907	60	9.32 872	62	10.67 128	9.99 035	3	58		63	62	61
3	9.31 966	59	9.32 933	61	10.67 067	9.99 032	3	57	2	12.6	12.4	12.2
4	9.32 025	59	9.32 995	62	10.67 005	9.99 030	2	56	3	18.9	18.6	18.3
5	9.32 084	59	9.33 057	62	10.66 943	9.99 027	3	55	4	25.2	24.8	24.4
6	9.32 143	59	9.33 119	62	10.66 881	9.99 024	3	54	5	31.5	31.0	30.5
7	9.32 202	59	9.33 180	61	10.66 820	9.99 022	2	53	6	37.8	37.2	36.6
8	9.32 261	59	9.33 242	62	10.66 758	9.99 019	3	52	7	44.1	43.4	42.7
9	9.32 319	58	9.33 303	61	10.66 697	9.99 016	3	51	8	50.4	49.6	48.8
10	9.32 378	59	9.33 365	62	10.66 635	9.99 013	3	50	9	56.7	55.8	54.9
11	9.32 437	59	9.33 426	61	10.66 574	9.99 011	2	49				
12	9.32 495	58	9.33 487	61	10.66 513	9.99 008	3	48				
13	9.32 553	58	9.33 548	61	10.66 452	9.99 005	3	47		60	59	58
14	9.32 612	59	9.33 609	61	10.66 391	9.99 002	3	46	2	12.0	11.8	11.6
15	9.32 670	58	9.33 670	61	10.66 330	9.99 000	2	45	3	18.0	17.7	17.4
16	9.32 728	58	9.33 731	61	10.66 269	9.98 997	3	44	4	24.0	23.6	23.2
17	9.32 786	58	9.33 792	61	10.66 208	9.98 994	3	43	5	30.0	29.5	29.0
18	9.32 844	58	9.33 853	60	10.66 147	9.98 991	2	42	6	36.0	35.4	34.8
19	9.32 902	58	9.33 913	61	10.66 087	9.98 989	3	41	7	42.0	41.3	40.6
20	9.32 960	58	9.33 974	60	10.66 026	9.98 986	3	40	8	48.0	47.2	46.4
21	9.33 018	57	9.34 034	61	10.65 966	9.98 983	3	39	9	54.0	53.1	52.2
22	9.33 075	58	9.34 095	60	10.65 905	9.98 980	2	38				
23	9.33 133	57	9.34 155	60	10.65 845	9.98 978	3	37				
24	9.33 190	58	9.34 215	61	10.65 785	9.98 975	3	36		57	56	
25	9.33 248	57	9.34 276	60	10.65 724	9.98 972	3	35	2	11.4	11.2	
26	9.33 305	57	9.34 336	60	10.65 664	9.98 969	2	34	3	17.1	16.8	
27	9.33 362	58	9.34 396	60	10.65 604	9.98 967	3	33	4	22.8	22.4	
28	9.33 420	57	9.34 456	60	10.65 544	9.98 964	3	32	5	28.5	28.0	
29	9.33 477	57	9.34 516	60	10.65 484	9.98 961	3	31	6	34.2	33.6	
30	9.33 534	57	9.34 576	59	10.65 424	9.98 958	3	30	7	39.9	39.2	
31	9.33 591	56	9.34 635	60	10.65 365	9.98 955	3	29	8	45.6	44.8	
32	9.33 647	57	9.34 695	60	10.65 305	9.98 953	2	28	9	51.3	50.4	
33	9.33 704	57	9.34 755	59	10.65 245	9.98 950	3	27				
34	9.33 761	57	9.34 814	60	10.65 186	9.98 947	3	26				
35	9.33 818	56	9.34 874	59	10.65 126	9.98 944	3	25		55	3	2
36	9.33 874	57	9.34 933	59	10.65 067	9.98 941	3	24	2	11.0	0.6	0.4
37	9.33 931	56	9.34 992	59	10.65 008	9.98 938	2	23	3	16.5	0.9	0.6
38	9.33 987	56	9.35 051	59	10.64 949	9.98 936	3	22	4	22.0	1.2	0.8
39	9.34 043	57	9.35 111	60	10.64 889	9.98 933	3	21	5	27.5	1.5	1.0
40	9.34 100	56	9.35 170	59	10.64 830	9.98 930	3	20	6	33.0	1.8	1.2
41	9.34 156	56	9.35 229	59	10.64 771	9.98 927	3	19	7	38.5	2.1	1.4
42	9.34 212	56	9.35 288	59	10.64 712	9.98 924	3	18	8	44.0	2.4	1.6
43	9.34 268	56	9.35 347	58	10.64 653	9.98 921	2	17	9	49.5	2.7	1.8
44	9.34 324	56	9.35 405	59	10.64 595	9.98 919	3	16				
45	9.34 380	56	9.35 464	59	10.64 536	9.98 916	3	15	*From the top:*			
46	9.34 436	55	9.35 523	58	10.64 477	9.98 913	3	14	For 12°+ or 192°+,			
47	9.34 491	56	9.35 581	59	10.64 419	9.98 910	3	13	read as printed; for			
48	9.34 547	55	9.35 640	58	10.64 360	9.98 907	3	12	102°+ or 282°+, read			
49	9.34 602	56	9.35 698	59	10.64 302	9.98 904	3	11	co-function.			
50	9.34 658	55	9.35 757	58	10.64 243	9.98 901	3	10				
51	9.34 713	56	9.35 815	58	10.64 185	9.98 898	2	9				
52	9.34 769	55	9.35 873	58	10.64 127	9.98 896	3	8				
53	9.34 824	55	9.35 931	58	10.64 069	9.98 893	3	7	*From the bottom:*			
54	9.34 879	55	9.35 989	58	10.64 011	9.98 890	3	6	For 77°+ or 257°+,			
55	9.34 934	55	9.36 047	58	10.63 953	9.98 887	3	5	read as printed; for			
56	9.34 989	55	9.36 105	58	10.63 895	9.98 884	3	4	167°+ or 347°+, read			
57	9.35 044	55	9.36 163	58	10.63 837	9.98 881	3	3	co-function.			
58	9.35 099	55	9.36 221	58	10.63 779	9.98 878	3	2				
59	9.35 154	55	9.36 279	57	10.63 721	9.98 875	3	1				
60	9.35 209		9.36 336		10.63 664	9.98 872		0				
	L Cos	d	L Ctn	c d	L Tan	L Sin	d	'	Prop. Pts.		

13° — Logarithms of Trigonometric Functions

′	L Sin	d	L Tan	c d	L Ctn	L Cos	d		Prop. Pts.
0	9.35 209	54	9.36 336	58	10.63 664	9.98 872	3	60	
1	9.35 263	55	9.36 394	58	10.63 606	9.98 869	2	59	
2	9.35 318	55	9.36 452	57	10.63 548	9.98 867	3	58	**58 57 56**
3	9.35 373	54	9.36 509	57	10.63 491	9.98 864	3	57	2 11.6 11.4 11.2
4	9.35 427	54	9.36 566	58	10.63 434	9.98 861	3	56	3 17.4 17.1 16.8
5	9.35 481	55	9.36 624	57	10.63 376	9.98 858	3	55	4 23.2 22.8 22.4
6	9.35 536	54	9.36 681	57	10.63 319	9.98 855	3	54	5 29.0 28.5 28.0
7	9.35 590	54	9.36 738	57	10.63 262	9.98 852	3	53	6 34.8 34.2 33.6
8	9.35 644	54	9.36 795	57	10.63 205	9.98 849	3	52	7 40.6 39.9 39.2
9	9.35 698	54	9.36 852	57	10.63 148	9.98 846	3	51	8 46.4 45.6 44.8
10	9.35 752	54	9.36 909	57	10.63 091	9.98 843	3	50	9 52.2 51.3 50.4
11	9.35 806	54	9.36 966	57	10.63 034	9.98 840	3	49	
12	9.35 860	54	9.37 023	57	10.62 977	9.98 837	3	48	
13	9.35 914	54	9.37 080	57	10.62 920	9.98 834	3	47	**55 54 53**
14	9.35 968	54	9.37 137	56	10.62 863	9.98 831	3	46	2 11.0 10.8 10.6
15	9.36 022	53	9.37 193	57	10.62 807	9.98 828	3	45	3 16.5 16.2 15.9
16	9.36 075	54	9.37 250	56	10.62 750	9.98 825	3	44	4 22.0 21.6 21.2
17	9.36 129	53	9.37 306	57	10.62 694	9.98 822	3	43	5 27.5 27.0 26.5
18	9.36 182	54	9.37 363	56	10.62 637	9.98 819	3	42	6 33.0 32.4 31.8
19	9.36 236	53	9.37 419	57	10.62 581	9.98 816	3	41	7 38.5 37.8 37.1
20	9.36 289	53	9.37 476	56	10.62 524	9.98 813	3	40	8 44.0 43.2 42.4
21	9.36 342	53	9.37 532	56	10.62 468	9.98 810	3	39	9 49.5 48.6 47.7
22	9.36 395	54	9.37 588	56	10.62 412	9.98 807	3	38	
23	9.36 449	53	9.37 644	56	10.62 356	9.98 804	3	37	
24	9.36 502	53	9.37 700	56	10.62 300	9.98 801	3	36	**52 51**
25	9.36 555	53	9.37 756	56	10.62 244	9.98 798	3	35	2 10.4 10.2
26	9.36 608	52	9.37 812	56	10.62 188	9.98 795	3	34	3 15.6 15.3
27	9.36 660	53	9.37 868	56	10.62 132	9.98 792	3	33	4 20.8 20.4
28	9.36 713	53	9.37 924	56	10.62 076	9.98 789	3	32	5 26.0 25.5
29	9.36 766	53	9.37 980	55	10.62 020	9.98 786	3	31	6 31.2 30.6
30	9.36 819	52	9.38 035	56	10.61 965	9.98 783	3	30	7 36.4 35.7
31	9.36 871	53	9.38 091	56	10.61 909	9.98 780	3	29	8 41.6 40.8
32	9.36 924	52	9.38 147	55	10.61 853	9.98 777	3	28	9 46.8 45.9
33	9.36 976	52	9.38 202	55	10.61 798	9.98 774	3	27	
34	9.37 028	53	9.38 257	56	10.61 743	9.98 771	3	26	**4 3 2**
35	9.37 081	52	9.38 313	55	10.61 687	9.98 768	3	25	2 0.8 0.6 0.4
36	9.37 133	52	9.38 368	55	10.61 632	9.98 765	3	24	3 1.2 0.9 0.6
37	9.37 185	52	9.38 423	56	10.61 577	9.98 762	3	23	4 1.6 1.2 0.8
38	9.37 237	52	9.38 479	55	10.61 521	9.98 759	3	22	5 2.0 1.5 1.0
39	9.37 289	52	9.38 534	55	10.61 466	9.98 756	3	21	6 2.4 1.8 1.2
40	9.37 341	52	9.38 589	55	10.61 411	9.98 753	3	20	7 2.8 2.1 1.4
41	9.37 393	52	9.38 644	55	10.61 356	9.98 750	3	19	8 3.2 2.4 1.6
42	9.37 445	52	9.38 699	55	10.61 301	9.98 746	4	18	9 3.6 2.7 1.8
43	9.37 497	52	9.38 754	54	10.61 246	9.98 743	3	17	
44	9.37 549	52	9.38 808	55	10.61 192	9.98 740	3	16	
45	9.37 600	52	9.38 863	55	10.61 137	9.98 737	3	15	*From the top:*
46	9.37 652	51	9.38 918	54	10.61 082	9.98 734	3	14	For 13°+ or 193°+,
47	9.37 703	52	9.38 972	55	10.61 028	9.98 731	3	13	read as printed; for
48	9.37 755	51	9.39 027	55	10.60 973	9.98 728	3	12	103°+ or 283°+, read
49	9.37 806	52	9.39 082	54	10.60 918	9.98 725	3	11	co-function.
50	9.37 858	51	9.39 136	54	10.60 864	9.98 722	3	10	
51	9.37 909	51	9.39 190	55	10.60 810	9.98 719	4	9	
52	9.37 960	51	9.39 245	54	10.60 755	9.98 715	3	8	*From the bottom:*
53	9.38 011	51	9.39 299	54	10.60 701	9.98 712	3	7	For 76°+ or 256°+,
54	9.38 062	51	9.39 353	54	10.60 647	9.98 709	3	6	read as printed; for
55	9.38 113	51	9.39 407	54	10.60 593	9.98 706	3	5	166°+ or 346°+, read
56	9.38 164	51	9.39 461	54	10.60 539	9.98 703	3	4	co-function.
57	9.38 215	51	9.39 515	54	10.60 485	9.98 700	3	3	
58	9.38 266	51	9.39 569	54	10.60 431	9.98 697	3	2	
59	9.38 317	51	9.39 623	54	10.60 377	9.98 694	4	1	
60	9.38 368		9.39 677		10.60 323	9.98 690		0	
	L Cos	d	L Ctn	c d	L Tan	L Sin	d	′	Prop. Pts.

76° — Logarithms of Trigonometric Functions

14° — Logarithms of Trigonometric Functions

′	L Sin	d	L Tan	c d	L Ctn	L Cos	d		Prop. Pts.		
0	9.38 368		9.39 677		10.60 323	9.98 690	3	60			
1	9.38 418	50	9.39 731	54	10.60 269	9.98 687	3	59			
2	9.38 469	51	9.39 785	54	10.60 215	9.98 684	3	58		**54**	**53**	**52**
3	9.38 519	50	9.39 838	53	10.60 162	9.98 681	3	57	2	10.8	10.6	10.4
4	9.38 570	51	9.39 892	54	10.60 108	9.98 678	3	56	3	16.2	15.9	15.6
5	9.38 620	50	9.39 945	53	10.60 055	9.98 675	4	55	4	21.6	21.2	20.8
6	9.38 670	50	9.39 999	54	10.60 001	9.98 671	3	54	5	27.0	26.5	26.0
7	9.38 721	51	9.40 052	53	10.59 948	9.98 668	3	53	6	32.4	31.8	31.2
8	9.38 771	50	9.40 106	54	10.59 894	9.98 665	3	52	7	37.8	37.1	36.4
9	9.38 821	50	9.40 159	53	10.59 841	9.98 662	3	51	8	43.2	42.4	41.6
10	9.38 871	50	9.40 212	54	10.59 788	9.98 659	3	50	9	48.6	47.7	46.8
11	9.38 921	50	9.40 266	53	10.59 724	9.98 656	4	49			
12	9.38 971	50	9.40 319	53	10.59 681	9.98 652	3	48		**51**	**50**	**49**
13	9.39 021	50	9.40 372	53	10.59 628	9.98 649	3	47	2	10.2	10.0	9.8
14	9.39 071	50	9.40 425	53	10.59 575	9.98 646	3	46	3	15.3	15.0	14.7
15	9.39 121	49	9.40 478	53	10.59 522	9.98 643	3	45	4	20.4	20.0	19.6
16	9.39 170	50	9.40 531	53	10.59 469	9.98 640	4	44	5	25.5	25.0	24.5
17	9.39 220	50	9.40 584	52	10.59 416	9.98 636	3	43	6	30.6	30.0	29.4
18	9.39 270	49	9.40 636	53	10.59 364	9.98 633	3	42	7	35.7	35.0	34.3
19	9.39 319	50	9.40 689	53	10.59 311	9.98 630	3	41	8	40.8	40.0	39.2
20	9.39 369	49	9.40 742	53	10.59 258	9.98 627	4	40	9	45.9	45.0	44.1
21	9.39 467	49	9.40 795	52	10.59 205	9.98 623	3	39			
22	9.39 467	50	9.40 847	53	10.59 153	9.98 620	3	38			
23	9.39 517	49	9.40 900	52	10.59 100	9.98 617	3	37		**48**	**47**
24	9.39 566	49	9.40 952	53	10.59 048	9.98 614	4	36	2	9.6	9.4
25	9.39 615	49	9.41 005	52	10.58 995	9.98 610	3	35	3	14.4	14.1
26	9.39 664	49	9.41 057	52	10.58 943	9.98 607	3	34	4	19.2	18.8
27	9.39 713	49	9.41 109	52	10.58 891	9.98 604	3	33	5	24.0	23.5
28	9.39 762	49	9.41 161	53	10.58 839	9.98 601	4	32	6	28.8	28.2
29	9.39 811	49	9.41 214	52	10.58 786	9.98 597	3	31	7	33.6	32.9
30	9.39 860	49	9.41 266	52	10.58 734	9.98 594	3	30	8	38.4	37.6
31	9.39 909	49	9.41 318	52	10.58 682	9.98 591	3	29	9	43.2	42.3
32	9.39 958	48	9.41 370	52	10.58 630	9.98 588	4	28			
33	9.40 006	49	9.41 422	52	10.58 578	9.98 584	3	27			
34	9.40 055	48	9.41 474	52	10.58 526	9.98 581	3	26		**4**	**3**
35	9.40 103	49	9.41 526	52	10.58 474	9.98 578	3	25	2	0.8	0.6
36	9.40 152	48	9.41 578	51	10.58 422	9.98 574	4	24	3	1.2	0.9
37	9.40 200	49	9.41 629	52	10.58 371	9.98 571	3	23	4	1.6	1.2
38	9.40 249	48	9.41 681	52	10.58 319	9.98 568	3	22	5	2.0	1.5
39	9.40 297	49	9.41 733	51	10.58 267	9.98 565	4	21	6	2.4	1.8
40	9.40 346	48	9.41 784	52	10.58 216	9.98 561	3	20	7	2.8	2.1
41	9.40 394	48	9.41 836	51	10.58 164	9.98 558	3	19	8	3.2	2.4
42	9.40 442	48	9.41 887	52	10.58 113	9.98 555	4	18	9	3.6	2.7
43	9.40 490	48	9.41 939	51	10.58 061	9.98 551	3	17			
44	9.40 538	48	9.41 990	51	10.58 010	9.98 548	3	16			
45	9.40 586	48	9.42 041	52	10.57 959	9.98 545	4	15	*From the top:*		
46	9.40 634	48	9.42 093	51	10.57 907	9.98 541	3	14	For 14°+ or 194°+,		
47	9.40 682	48	9.42 144	51	10.57 856	9.98 538	3	13	read as printed; for		
48	9.40 730	48	9.42 195	51	10.57 805	9.98 535	4	12	104°+ or 284°+, read		
49	9.40 778	47	9.42 246	51	10.57 754	9.98 531	3	11	co-function.		
50	9.40 825	48	9.42 297	51	10.57 703	9.98 528	3	10			
51	9.40 873	48	9.42 348	51	10.57 652	9.98 525	4	9			
52	9.40 921	47	9.42 399	51	10.57 601	9.98 521	3	8	*From the bottom:*		
53	9.40 968	48	9.42 450	51	10.57 550	9.98 518	3	7	For 75°+ or 255°+,		
54	9.41 016	47	9.42 501	51	10.57 499	9.98 515	4	6	read as printed; for		
55	9.41 063	48	9.42 552	51	10.57 448	9.98 511	3	5	165°+ or 345°+,		
56	9.41 111	47	9.42 603	50	10.57 397	9.98 508	3	4	read co-function.		
57	9.41 158	47	9.42 653	51	10.57 347	9.98 505	4	3			
58	9.41 205	47	9.42 704	51	10.57 296	9.98 501	3	2			
59	9.41 252	48	9.42 755	50	10.57 245	9.98 498	4	1			
60	9.41 300		9.42 805		10.57 195	9.98 494		0			
′	L Cos	d	L Ctn	c d	L Tan	L Sin	d	′	Prop. Pts.		

15° — Logarithms of Trigonometric Functions

′	L Sin	d	L Tan	cd	L Ctn	L Cos	d	′
0	9.41 300		9.42 805		10.57 195	9.98 494		60
1	9.41 347	47	9.42 856	51	10.57 144	9.98 491	3	59
2	9.41 394	47	9.42 906	50	10.57 094	9.98 488	3	58
3	9.41 441	47	9.42 957	51	10.57 043	9.98 484	4	57
4	9.41 488	47	9.43 007	50	10.56 993	9.98 481	3	56
5	9.41 535	47	9.43 057	50	10.56 943	9.98 477	4	55
6	9.41 582		9.43 108	51	10.56 892	9.98 474	3	54
7	9.41 628	47	9.43 158	50	10.56 842	9.98 471	3	53
8	9.41 675	46	9.43 208	50	10.56 792	9.98 467	4	52
9	9.41 722	47	9.43 258	50	10.56 742	9.98 464	3	51
10	9.41 768	47	9.43 308	50	10.56 692	9.98 460	4	50
11	9.41 815	46	9.43 358	50	10.56 642	9.98 457	3	49
12	9.41 861	47	9.43 408	50	10.56 592	9.98 453	4	48
13	9.41 908	46	9.43 458	50	10.56 542	9.98 450	3	47
14	9.41 954	47	9.43 508	50	10.56 492	9.98 447	4	46
15	9.42 001	47	9.43 558	50	10.56 442	9.98 443	3	45
16	9.42 047	46	9.43 607	49	10.56 393	9.98 440	3	44
17	9.42 093	46	9.43 657	50	10.56 343	9.98 436	4	43
18	9.42 140	47	9.43 707	50	10.56 293	9.98 433	3	42
19	9.42 186	46	9.43 756	49	10.56 244	9.98 429	4	41
20	9.42 232	46	9.43 806	50	10.56 194	9.98 426	3	40
21	9.42 278	46	9.43 855	49	10.56 145	9.98 422	4	39
22	9.42 324	46	9.43 905	50	10.56 095	9.98 419	3	38
23	9.42 370	46	9.43 954	49	10.56 046	9.98 415	4	37
24	9.42 416	46	9.44 004	50	10.55 996	9.98 412	4	36
25	9.42 461	45	9.44 053	49	10.55 947	9.98 409	3	35
26	9.42 507	46	9.44 102	49	10.55 898	9.98 405	4	34
27	9.42 553	46	9.44 151	49	10.55 849	9.98 402	3	33
28	9.42 599	45	9.44 201	50	10.55 799	9.98 398	4	32
29	9.42 644	46	9.44 250	49	10.55 750	9.98 395	3	31
30	9.42 690	45	9.44 299	49	10.55 701	9.98 391	4	30
31	9.42 735	46	9.44 348	49	10.55 652	9.98 388	3	29
32	9.42 781	45	9.44 397	49	10.55 603	9.98 384	4	28
33	9.42 826	46	9.44 446	49	10.55 554	9.98 381	3	27
34	9.42 872	45	9.44 495	49	10.55 505	9.98 377	4	26
35	9.42 917	45	9.44 544	48	10.55 456	9.98 373	4	25
36	9.42 962	46	9.44 592	49	10.55 408	9.98 370	3	24
37	9.43 008	45	9.44 641	49	10.55 359	9.98 366	4	23
38	9.43 053	45	9.44 690	48	10.55 310	9.98 363	3	22
39	9.43 098	45	9.44 738	49	10.55 262	9.98 359	4	21
40	9.43 143	45	9.44 787	49	10.55 213	9.98 356	3	20
41	9.43 188	45	9.44 836	48	10.55 164	9.98 352	4	19
42	9.43 233	45	9.44 884	49	10.55 116	9.98 349	4	18
43	9.43 278	45	9.44 933	48	10.55 067	9.98 345	3	17
44	9.43 323	44	9.44 981	48	10.55 019	9.98 342	4	16
45	9.43 367	45	9.45 029	49	10.54 971	9.98 338	4	15
46	9.43 412	45	9.45 078	48	10.54 922	9.98 334	3	14
47	9.43 457	45	9.45 126	48	10.54 874	9.98 331	4	13
48	9.43 502	44	9.45 174	48	10.54 826	9.98 327	4	12
49	9.43 546	45	9.45 222	49	10.54 778	9.98 324	3	11
50	9.43 591	44	9.45 271	48	10.54 729	9.98 320	4	10
51	9.43 635	45	9.45 319	48	10.54 681	9.98 317	4	9
52	9.43 680	44	9.45 367	48	10.54 633	9.98 313	4	8
53	9.43 724	45	9.45 415	48	10.54 585	9.98 309	3	7
54	9.43 769	44	9.45 463	48	10.54 537	9.98 306	4	6
55	9.43 813	44	9.45 511	48	10.54 489	9.98 302	4	5
56	9.43 857	44	9.45 559	47	10.54 441	9.98 299	3	4
57	9.43 901	45	9.45 606	48	10.54 394	9.98 295	4	3
58	9.43 946	44	9.45 654	48	10.54 346	9.98 291	4	2
59	9.43 990	44	9.45 702	48	10.54 298	9.98 288	3	1
60	9.44 034		9.45 750		10.54 250	9.98 284	4	0
	L Cos	d	L Ctn	cd	L Tan	L Sin	d	′

Prop. Pts.

	51	50	49
2	10.2	10.0	9.8
3	15.3	15.0	14.7
4	20.4	20.0	19.6
5	25.5	25.0	24.5
6	30.6	30.0	29.4
7	35.7	35.0	34.3
8	40.8	40.0	39.2
9	45.9	45.0	44.1

	48	47	46
3	14.4	14.1	13.8
4	19.2	18.8	18.4
5	24.0	23.5	23.0
6	28.8	28.2	27.6
7	33.6	32.9	32.2
8	38.4	37.6	36.8
9	43.2	42.3	41.4

	45	44
2	9.0	8.8
3	13.5	13.2
4	18.0	17.6
5	22.5	22.0
6	27.0	26.4
7	31.5	30.8
8	36.0	35.2
9	40.5	39.6

	4	3
2	0.8	0.6
3	1.2	0.9
4	1.6	1.2
5	2.0	1.5
6	2.4	1.8
7	2.8	2.1
8	3.2	2.4
9	3.6	2.7

From the top:
For 15°+ or 195°+, read as printed; for 105°+ or 285°+, read co-function.

From the bottom:
For 74°+ or 254°+, read as printed; for 164°+ or 344°+, read co-function.

74° — Logarithms of Trigonometric Functions

′	L Sin	d	L Tan	c d	L Ctn	L Cos	d		Prop. Pts.		
0	9.44 034	44	9.45 750	47	10.54 250	9.98 284	3	60			
1	9.44 078	44	9.45 797	47	10.54 203	9.98 281	4	59			
2	9.44 122	44	9.45 845	48	10.54 155	9.98 277	4	58		48	47	46
3	9.44 166	44	9.45 892	47	10.54 108	9.98 273	3	57	2	9.6	9.4	9.2
4	9.44 210	43	9.45 940	48	10.54 060	9.98 270	4	56	3	14.4	14.1	13.8
5	9.44 253	44	9.45 987	47	10.54 013	9.98 266	4	55	4	19.2	18.8	18.4
6	9.44 297	44	9.46 035	48	10.53 965	9.98 262	3	54	5	24.0	23.5	23.0
7	9.44 341	44	9.46 082	47	10.53 918	9.98 259	4	53	6	28.8	28.2	27.6
8	9.44 385	43	9.46 130	47	10.53 870	9.98 255	4	52	7	33.6	32.9	32.2
9	9.44 428	44	9.46 177	47	10.53 823	9.98 251	3	51	8	38.4	37.6	36.8
10	9.44 472	44	9.46 224	47	10.53 776	9.98 248	4	50	9	43.2	42.3	41.4
11	9.44 516	43	9.46 271	48	10.53 729	9.98 244	4	49			
12	9.44 559	43	9.46 319	47	10.53 681	9.98 240	3	48			
13	9.44 602	44	9.46 366	47	10.53 634	9.98 237	4	47		45	44	43
14	9.44 646	43	9.46 413	47	10.53 587	9.98 233	4	46	2	9.0	8.8	8.6
15	9.44 689	44	9.46 460	47	10.53 540	9.98 229	3	45	3	13.5	13.2	12.9
16	9.44 733	43	9.46 507	47	10.53 493	9.98 226	4	44	4	18.0	17.6	17.2
17	9.44 776	43	9.46 554	47	10.53 446	9.98 222	4	43	5	22.5	22.0	21.5
18	9.44 819	43	9.46 601	47	10.53 399	9.98 218	3	42	6	27.0	26.4	25.8
19	9.44 862	43	9.46 648	46	10.53 352	9.98 215	4	41	7	31.5	30.8	30.1
20	9.44 905	43	9.46 694	47	10.53 306	9.98 211	4	40	8	36.0	35.2	34.4
21	9.44 948	44	9.46 741	47	10.53 259	9.98 207	3	39	9	40.5	39.6	38.7
22	9.44 992	43	9.46 788	47	10.53 212	9.98 204	4	38			
23	9.45 035	42	9.46 835	46	10.53 165	9.98 200	4	37		42	41
24	9.45 077	43	9.46 881	47	10.53 119	9.98 196	4	36	2	8.4	8.2
25	9.45 120	43	9.46 928	47	10.53 072	9.98 192	3	35	4	12.6	12.3
26	9.45 163	43	9.46 975	46	10.53 025	9.98 189	4	34	4	16.8	16.4
27	9.45 206	43	9.47 021	47	10.52 979	9.98 185	4	33	5	21.0	20.5
28	9.45 249	43	9.47 068	46	10.52 932	9.98 181	4	32	6	25.2	24.6
29	9.45 292	42	9.47 114	46	10.52 886	9.98 177	3	31	7	29.4	28.7
30	9.45 334	43	9.47 160	47	10.52 840	9.98 174	4	30	8	33.6	32.8
31	9.45 377	42	9.47 207	46	10.52 793	9.98 170	4	29	9	37.8	36.9
32	9.45 419	43	9.47 253	46	10.52 747	9.98 166	4	28			
33	9.45 462	42	9.47 299	47	10.52 701	9.98 162	3	27			
34	9.45 504	43	9.47 346	46	10.52 654	9.98 159	4	26		4	3
35	9.45 547	42	9.47 392	46	10.52 608	9.98 155	4	25	2	0.8	0.6
36	9.45 589	43	9.47 438	46	10.52 562	9.98 151	4	24	3	1.2	0.9
37	9.45 632	42	9.47 484	46	10.52 516	9.98 147	3	23	4	1.6	1.2
38	9.45 674	42	9.47 530	46	10.52 470	9.98 144	4	22	5	2.0	1.5
39	9.45 716	42	9.47 576	46	10.52 424	9.98 140	4	21	6	2.4	1.8
40	9.45 758	43	9.47 622	46	10.52 378	9.98 136	4	20	7	2.8	2.1
41	9.45 801	42	9.47 668	46	10.52 332	9.98 132	3	19	8	3.2	2.4
42	9.45 843	42	9.47 714	46	10.52 286	9.98 129	4	18	9	3.6	2.7
43	9.45 885	42	9.47 760	46	10.52 240	9.98 125	4	17			
44	9.45 927	42	9.47 806	46	10.52 194	9.98 121	4	16			
45	9.45 969	42	9.47 852	45	10.52 148	9.98 117	4	15	*From the top:*		
46	9.46 011	42	9.47 897	46	10.52 103	9.98 113	3	14	For 16°+ or 196°+,		
47	9.46 053	42	9.47 943	46	10.52 057	9.98 110	4	13	read as printed; for		
48	9.46 095	41	9.47 989	46	10.52 011	9.98 106	4	12	106°+ or 286°+, read		
49	9.46 136	42	9.48 035	45	10.51 965	9.98 102	4	11	co-function.		
50	9.46 178	42	9.48 080	46	10.51 920	9.98 098	4	10			
51	9.46 220	42	9.48 126	45	10.51 874	9.98 094	4	9			
52	9.46 262	41	9.48 171	46	10.51 829	9.98 090	3	8	*From the bottom:*		
53	9.46 303	42	9.48 217	45	10.51 783	9.98 087	4	7	For 73°+ or 253°+,		
54	9.46 345	41	9.48 262	45	10.51 738	9.98 083	4	6	read as printed; for		
55	9.46 386	42	9.48 307	46	10.51 693	9.98 079	4	5	163°+ or 343°+, read		
56	9.46 428	41	9.48 353	45	10.51 647	9.98 075	4	4	co-function.		
57	9.46 469	42	9.48 398	45	10.51 602	9.98 071	4	3			
58	9.46 511	41	9.48 443	46	10.51 557	9.98 067	4	2			
59	9.46 552	42	9.48 489	45	10.51 511	9.98 063	3	1			
60	9.46 594		9.48 534		10.51 466	9.98 060		0			
	L Cos	d	L Ctn	c d	L Tan	L Sin	d	′	Prop. Pts.		

Table XIV.
17° — Logarithms of Trigonometric Functions

′	L Sin	d	L Tan	c d	L Ctn	L Cos	d		Prop. Pts.
0	9.46 594	41	9.48 534	45	10.51 466	9.98 060	4	60	
1	9.46 635	41	9.48 579	45	10.51 421	9.98 056	4	59	
2	9.46 676	41	9.48 624	45	10.51 376	9.98 052	4	58	**45 44 43**
3	9.46 717	41	9.48 669	45	10.51 331	9.98 048	4	57	2 9.0 8.8 8.6
4	9.46 758	42	9.48 714	45	10.51 286	9.98 044	4	56	3 13.5 13.2 12.9
5	9.46 800	41	9.48 759	45	10.51 241	9.98 040	4	55	4 18.0 17.6 17.2
6	9.46 841	41	9.48 804	45	10.51 196	9.98 036	4	54	5 22.5 22.0 21.5
7	9.46 882	41	9.48 849	45	10.51 151	9.98 032	3	53	6 27.0 26.4 25.8
8	9.46 923	41	9.48 894	45	10.51 106	9.98 029	4	52	7 31.5 30.8 30.1
9	9.46 964	41	9.48 939	45	10.51 061	9.98 025	4	51	8 36.0 35.2 34.4
10	9.47 005	40	9.48 984	45	10.51 016	9.98 021	4	50	9 40.5 39.6 38.7
11	9.47 045	41	9.49 029	44	10.50 971	9.98 017	4	49	
12	9.47 086	41	9.49 073	45	10.50 927	9.98 013	4	48	
13	9.47 127	41	9.49 118	45	10.50 882	9.98 009	4	47	**42 41 40**
14	9.47 168	41	9.49 163	44	10.50 837	9.98 005	4	46	2 8.4 8.2 8.0
15	9.47 209	40	9.49 207	45	10.50 793	9.98 001	4	45	3 12.6 12.3 12.0
16	9.47 249	41	9.49 252	44	10.50 748	9.97 997	4	44	4 16.8 16.4 16.0
17	9.47 290	40	9.49 296	45	10.50 704	9.97 993	4	43	5 21.0 20.5 20.0
18	9.47 330	41	9.49 341	44	10.50 659	9.97 989	3	42	6 25.2 24.6 24.0
19	9.47 371	40	9.49 385	45	10.50 615	9.97 986	4	41	7 29.4 28.7 28.0
20	9.47 411	41	9.49 430	44	10.50 570	9.97 982	4	40	8 33.6 32.8 32.0
21	9.47 452	40	9.49 474	45	10.50 526	9.97 978	4	39	9 37.8 36.9 36.0
22	9.47 492	41	9.49 519	44	10.50 481	9.97 974	4	38	
23	9.47 533	40	9.49 563	44	10.50 437	9.97 970	4	37	
24	9.47 573	40	9.49 607	45	10.50 393	9.97 966	4	36	**39 5**
25	9.47 613	41	9.49 652	44	10.50 348	9.97 962	4	35	2 7.8 1.0
26	9.47 654	40	9.49 696	44	10.50 304	9.97 958	4	34	3 11.7 1.5
27	9.47 694	40	9.49 740	44	10.50 260	9.97 954	4	33	4 15.6 2.0
28	9.47 734	40	9.49 784	44	10.50 216	9.97 950	4	32	5 19.5 2.5
29	9.47 774	40	9.49 828	44	10.50 172	9.97 946	4	31	6 23.4 3.0
30	9.47 814	40	9.49 872	44	10.50 128	9.97 942	4	30	7 27.3 3.5
31	9.47 854	40	9.49 916	44	10.50 084	9.97 938	4	29	8 31.2 4.0
32	9.47 894	40	9.49 960	44	10.50 040	9.97 934	4	28	9 35.1 4.5
33	9.47 934	40	9.50 004	44	10.49 996	9.97 930	4	27	
34	9.47 974	40	9.50 048	44	10.49 952	9.97 926	4	26	
35	9.48 014	40	9.50 092	44	10.49 908	9.97 922	4	25	**4 3**
36	9.48 054	40	9.50 136	44	10.49 864	9.97 918	4	24	2 0.8 0.6
37	9.48 094	39	9.50 180	43	10.49 820	9.97 914	4	23	3 1.2 0.9
38	9.48 133	40	9.50 223	44	10.49 777	9.97 910	4	22	4 1.6 1.2
39	9.48 173	40	9.50 267	44	10.49 733	9.97 906	4	21	5 2.0 1.5
40	9.48 213	39	9.50 311	44	10.49 689	9.97 902	4	20	6 2.4 1.8
41	9.48 252	40	9.50 355	43	10.49 645	9.97 898	4	19	7 2.8 2.1
42	9.48 292	40	9.50 398	44	10.49 602	9.97 894	4	18	8 3.2 2.4
43	9.48 332	39	9.50 442	43	10.49 558	9.97 890	4	17	9 3.6 2.7
44	9.48 371	40	9.50 485	44	10.49 515	9.97 886	4	16	
45	9.48 411	39	9.50 529	43	10.49 471	9.97 882	4	15	*From the top:*
46	9.48 450	40	9.50 572	44	10.49 428	9.97 878	4	14	For 17°+ or 197°+,
47	9.48 490	39	9.50 616	43	10.49 384	9.97 874	4	13	read as printed; for
48	9.48 529	39	9.50 659	44	10.49 341	9.97 870	4	12	107°+ or 287°+, read
49	9.48 568	39	9.50 703	43	10.49 297	9.97 866	5	11	co-function.
50	9.48 607	40	9.50 746	43	10.49 254	9.97 861	4	10	
51	9.48 647	39	9.50 789	44	10.49 211	9.97 857	4	9	
52	9.48 686	39	9.50 833	43	10.49 167	9.97 853	4	8	*From the bottom:*
53	9.48 725	39	9.50 876	43	10.49 124	9.97 849	4	7	For 72°+ or 252°+,
54	9.48 764	39	9.50 919	43	10.49 081	9.97 845	4	6	read as printed; for
55	9.48 803	39	9.50 962	43	10.49 038	9.97 841	4	5	162°+ or 342°+, read
56	9.48 842	39	9.51 005	43	10.48 995	9.97 837	4	4	co-function.
57	9.48 881	39	9.51 048	44	10.48 952	9.97 833	4	3	
58	9.48 920	39	9.51 092	43	10.48 908	9.97 829	4	2	
59	9.48 959	39	9.51 135	43	10.48 865	9.97 825	4	1	
60	9.48 998		9.51 178		10.48 822	9.97 821		0	
	L Cos	d	L Ctn	c d	L Tan	L Sin	d	′	Prop. Pts.

72° — Logarithms of Trigonometric Functions

Table XIV.
18° — Logarithms of Trigonometric Functions

'	L Sin	d	L Tan	cd	L Ctn	L Cos	d	'
0	9.48 998	39	9.51 178	43	10.48 822	9.97 821	4	60
1	9.49 037	39	9.51 221	43	10.48 779	9.97 817	5	59
2	9.49 076	39	9.51 264	42	10.48 736	9.97 812	4	58
3	9.49 115	38	9.51 306	43	10.48 694	9.97 808	4	57
4	9.49 153	39	9.51 349	43	10.48 651	9.97 804	4	56
5	9.49 192	39	9.51 392	43	10.48 608	9.97 800	4	55
6	9.49 231	38	9.51 435	43	10.48 565	9.97 796	4	54
7	9.49 269	39	9.51 478	42	10.48 522	9.97 792	4	53
8	9.49 308	39	9.51 520	43	10.48 480	9.97 788	4	52
9	9.49 347	38	9.51 563	43	10.48 437	9.97 784	5	51
10	9.49 385	39	9.51 606	42	10.48 394	9.97 779	4	50
11	9.49 424	38	9.51 648	43	10.48 352	9.97 775	4	49
12	9.49 462	38	9.51 691	43	10.48 309	9.97 771	4	48
13	9.49 500	39	9.51 734	42	10.48 266	9.97 767	4	47
14	9.49 539	38	9.51 776	43	10.48 224	9.97 763	4	46
15	9.49 577	38	9.51 819	42	10.48 181	9.97 759	5	45
16	9.49 615	39	9.51 861	42	10.48 139	9.97 754	4	44
17	9.49 654	38	9.51 903	43	10.48 097	9.97 750	4	43
18	9.49 692	38	9.51 946	42	10.48 054	9.97 746	4	42
19	9.49 730	38	9.51 988	43	10.48 012	9.97 742	4	41
20	9.49 768	38	9.52 031	42	10.47 969	9.97 738	4	40
21	9.49 806	38	9.52 073	42	10.47 927	9.97 734	5	39
22	9.49 844	38	9.52 115	42	10.47 885	9.97 729	4	38
23	9.49 882	38	9.52 157	43	10.47 843	9.97 725	4	37
24	9.49 920	38	9.52 200	42	10.47 800	9.97 721	4	36
25	9.49 958	38	9.52 242	42	10.47 758	9.97 717	4	35
26	9.49 996	38	9.52 284	42	10.47 716	9.97 713	5	34
27	9.50 034	38	9.52 326	42	10.47 674	9.97 708	4	33
28	9.50 072	38	9.52 368	42	10.47 632	9.97 704	4	32
29	9.50 110	38	9.52 410	42	10.47 590	9.97 700	4	31
30	9.50 148	37	9.52 452	42	10.47 548	9.97 696	5	30
31	9.50 185	38	9.52 494	42	10.47 506	9.97 691	4	29
32	9.50 223	38	9.52 536	42	10.47 464	9.97 687	4	28
33	9.50 261	37	9.52 578	42	10.47 422	9.97 683	4	27
34	9.50 298	38	9.52 620	41	10.47 380	9.97 679	5	26
35	9.50 336	38	9.52 661	42	10.47 339	9.97 674	4	25
36	9.50 374	37	9.52 703	42	10.47 297	9.97 670	4	24
37	9.50 411	38	9.52 745	42	10.47 255	9.97 666	4	23
38	9.50 449	37	9.52 787	42	10.47 213	9.97 662	5	22
39	9.50 486	37	9.52 829	41	10.47 171	9.97 657	4	21
40	9.50 523	38	9.52 870	42	10.47 130	9.97 653	4	20
41	9.50 561	37	9.52 912	41	10.47 088	9.97 649	4	19
42	9.50 598	37	9.52 953	42	10.47 047	9.97 645	5	18
43	9.50 635	38	9.52 995	42	10.47 005	9.97 640	4	17
44	9.50 673	37	9.53 037	41	10.46 963	9.97 636	4	16
45	9.50 710	37	9.53 078	42	10.46 922	9.97 632	4	15
46	9.50 747	37	9.53 120	41	10.46 880	9.97 628	5	14
47	9.50 784	37	9.53 161	41	10.46 839	9.97 623	4	13
48	9.50 821	37	9.53 202	42	10.46 798	9.97 619	4	12
49	9.50 858	38	9.53 244	41	10.46 756	9.97 615	5	11
50	9.50 896	37	9.53 285	42	10.46 715	9.97 610	4	10
51	9.50 933	37	9.53 327	41	10.46 673	9.97 606	4	9
52	9.50 970	37	9.53 368	41	10.46 632	9.97 602	5	8
53	9.51 007	36	9.53 409	41	10.46 591	9.97 597	4	7
54	9.51 043	37	9.53 450	42	10.46 550	9.97 593	4	6
55	9.51 080	37	9.53 492	41	10.46 508	9.97 589	5	5
56	9.51 117	37	9.53 533	41	10.46 467	9.97 584	4	4
57	9.51 154	37	9.53 574	41	10.46 426	9.97 580	4	3
58	9.51 191	36	9.53 615	41	10.46 385	9.97 576	5	2
59	9.51 227	37	9.53 656	41	10.46 344	9.97 571	4	1
60	9.51 264		9.53 697		10.46 303	9.97 567		0
	L Cos	d	L Ctn	cd	L Tan	L Sin	d	'

Prop. Pts.

	43	42	41
2	8.6	8.4	8.2
3	12.9	12.6	12.3
4	17.2	16.8	16.4
5	21.5	21.0	20.5
6	25.8	25.2	24.6
7	30.1	29.4	28.7
8	34.4	33.6	32.8
9	38.7	37.8	36.9

	39	38	37
2	7.8	7.6	7.4
3	11.7	11.4	11.1
4	15.6	15.2	14.8
5	19.5	19.0	18.5
6	23.4	22.8	22.2
7	27.3	26.6	25.9
8	31.2	30.4	29.6
9	35.1	34.2	33.3

	36	5	4
2	7.2	1.0	0.8
3	10.8	1.5	1.2
4	14.4	2.0	1.6
5	18.0	2.5	2.0
6	21.6	3.0	2.4
7	25.2	3.5	2.8
8	28.8	4.0	3.2
9	32.4	4.5	3.6

From the top:
For 18°+ or 198°+, read as printed; for 108°+ or 288°+, read co-function.

From the bottom:
For 71°+ or 251°+, read as printed; for 161°+ or 341°+, read co-function.

71° — Logarithms of Trigonometric Functions

19° — Logarithms of Trigonometric Functions

′	L Sin	d	L Tan	cd	L Ctn	L Cos	d		Prop. Pts.		
0	9.51 264	37	9.53 697	41	10.46 303	9.97 567		60			
1	9.51 301	37	9.53 738	41	10.46 262	9.97 563	4	59			
2	9.51 338	36	9.53 779	41	10.46 221	9.97 558	5	58			
3	9.51 374	37	9.53 820	41	10.46 180	9.97 554	4	57			
4	9.51 411	36	9.53 861	41	10.46 139	9.97 550	4	56			
5	9.51 447	37	9.53 902	41	10.46 098	9.97 545	5	55	**41**	**40**	**39**
6	9.51 484	36	9.53 943	41	10.46 057	9.97 541	4	54			
7	9.51 520	37	9.53 984	41	10.46 016	9.97 536	5	53	2 8.2	8.0	7.8
8	9.51 557	36	9.54 025	40	10.45 975	9.97 532	4	52	3 12.3	12.0	11.7
9	9.51 593	36	9.54 065	41	10.45 935	9.97 528	4	51	4 16.4	16.0	15.6
10	9.51 629	37	9.54 106	41	10.45 894	9.97 523	5	50	5 20.5	20.0	19.5
11	9.51 666	36	9.54 147	40	10.45 853	9.97 519	4	49	6 24.6	24.0	23.4
12	9.51 702	36	9.54 187	41	10.45 813	9.97 515	5	48	7 28.7	28.0	27.3
13	9.51 738	36	9.54 228	41	10.45 772	9.97 510	4	47	8 32.8	32.0	31.2
14	9.51 774	37	9.54 269	40	10.45 731	9.97 506	5	46	9 36.9	36.0	35.1
15	9.51 811	36	9.54 309	41	10.45 691	9.97 501	4	45			
16	9.51 847	36	9.54 350	40	10.45 650	9.97 497	5	44	**37**	**36**	**35**
17	9.51 883	36	9.54 390	41	10.45 610	9.97 492	4	43			
18	9.51 919	36	9.54 431	40	10.45 569	9.97 488	5	42	2 7.4	7.2	7.0
19	9.51 955	36	9.54 471	41	10.45 529	9.97 484	5	41	3 11.1	10.8	10.5
20	9.51 991	36	9.54 512	40	10.45 488	9.97 479	4	40	4 14.8	14.4	14.0
21	9.52 027	36	9.54 552	41	10.45 448	9.97 475	5	39	5 18.5	18.0	17.5
22	9.52 063	36	9.54 593	40	10.45 407	9.97 470	4	38	6 22.2	21.6	21.0
23	9.52 099	36	9.54 633	40	10.45 367	9.97 466	5	37	7 25.9	25.2	24.5
24	9.52 135	36	9.54 673	41	10.45 327	9.97 461	4	36	8 29.6	28.8	28.0
25	9.52 171	36	9.54 714	40	10.45 286	9.97 457	4	35	9 33.3	32.4	31.5
26	9.52 207	35	9.54 754	40	10.45 246	9.97 453	5	34			
27	9.52 242	36	9.54 794	41	10.45 206	9.97 448	4	33			
28	9.52 278	36	9.54 835	40	10.45 165	9.97 444	5	32	**34**	**5**	**4**
29	9.52 314	36	9.54 875	40	10.45 125	9.97 439	4	31	2 6.8	1.0	0.8
30	9.52 350	35	9.54 915	40	10.45 085	9.97 435	5	30	3 10.2	1.5	1.2
31	9.52 385	36	9.54 955	40	10.45 045	9.97 430	4	29	4 13.6	2.0	1.6
32	9.52 421	35	9.54 995	40	10.45 005	9.97 426	5	28	5 17.0	2.5	2.0
33	9.52 456	36	9.55 035	40	10.44 965	9.97 421	4	27	6 20.4	3.0	2.4
34	9.52 492	35	9.55 075	40	10.44 925	9.97 417	5	26	7 23.8	3.5	2.8
35	9.52 527	36	9.55 115	40	10.44 885	9.97 412	4	25	8 27.2	4.0	3.2
36	9.52 563	35	9.55 155	40	10.44 845	9.97 408	5	24	9 30.6	4.5	3.6
37	9.52 598	36	9.55 195	40	10.44 805	9.97 403	4	23			
38	9.52 634	35	9.55 235	40	10.44 765	9.97 399	5	22			
39	9.52 669	36	9.55 275	40	10.44 725	9.97 394	4	21			
40	9.52 705	35	9.55 315	40	10.44 685	9.97 390	5	20			
41	9.52 740	35	9.55 355	40	10.44 645	9.97 385	4	19			
42	9.52 775	36	9.55 395	39	10.44 605	9.97 381	5	18	*From the top:*		
43	9.52 811	35	9.55 434	40	10.44 566	9.97 376	4	17	For 19°+ or 199°+,		
44	9.52 846	35	9.55 474	40	10.44 526	9.97 372	5	16	read as printed; for		
45	9.52 881	35	9.55 514	40	10.44 486	9.97 367	4	15	**109°+ or 289°+**, read		
46	9.52 916	35	9.55 554	39	10.44 446	9.97 363	5	14	co-function.		
47	9.52 951	35	9.55 593	40	10.44 407	9.97 358	5	13			
48	9.52 986	35	9.55 633	40	10.44 367	9.97 353	4	12			
49	9.53 021	35	9.55 673	39	10.44 327	9.97 349	5	11	*From the bottom:*		
50	9.53 056	36	9.55 712	40	10.44 288	9.97 344	4	10	For 70°+ or 250°+,		
51	9.53 092	34	9.55 752	39	10.44 248	9.97 340	5	9	read as printed; for		
52	9.53 126	35	9.55 791	40	10.44 209	9.97 335	4	8	**160°+ or 340°+**, read		
53	9.53 161	35	9.55 831	39	10.44 169	9.97 331	5	7	co-function.		
54	9.53 196	35	9.55 870	40	10.44 130	9.97 326	4	6			
55	9.53 231	35	9.55 910	39	10.44 090	9.97 322	5	5			
56	9.53 266	35	9.55 949	40	10.44 051	9.97 317	5	4			
57	9.53 301	35	9.55 989	39	10.44 011	9.97 312	4	3			
58	9.53 336	34	9.56 028	39	10.43 972	9.97 308	5	2			
59	9.53 370	35	9.56 067	40	10.43 933	9.97 303	4	1			
60	9.53 405		9.56 107		10.43 893	9.97 299		0			

| | L Cos | d | L Ctn | cd | L Tan | L Sin | d | ′ | Prop. Pts. | | |

70° — Logarithms of Trigonometric Functions

20° — Logarithms of Trigonometric Functions

'	L Sin	d	L Tan	c d	L Ctn	L Cos	d		
0	9.53 405	35	9.56 107	39	10.43 893	9.97 299	5	60	
1	9.53 440	35	9.56 146	39	10.43 854	9.97 294	5	59	
2	9.53 475	35	9.56 185	39	10.43 815	9.97 289	4	58	
3	9.53 509	35	9.56 224	40	10.43 776	9.97 285	4	57	
4	9.53 544	34	9.56 264	39	10.43 736	9.97 280	4	56	
5	9.53 578	35	9.56 303	39	10.43 697	9.97 276	5	55	
6	9.53 613	34	9.56 342	39	10.43 658	9.97 271	5	54	
7	9.53 647	35	9.56 381	39	10.43 619	9.97 266	4	53	
8	9.53 682	34	9.56 420	39	10.43 580	9.97 262	5	52	
9	9.53 716	35	9.56 459	39	10.43 541	9.97 257	5	51	
10	9.53 751	34	9.56 498	39	10.43 502	9.97 252	4	50	
11	9.53 785	34	9.56 537	39	10.43 463	9.97 248	5	49	
12	9.53 819	34	9.56 576	39	10.43 424	9.97 243	5	48	
13	9.53 853	35	9.56 615	39	10.43 385	9.97 238	4	47	
14	9.53 888	34	9.56 654	39	10.43 346	9.97 234	5	46	
15	9.53 922	35	9.56 693	39	10.43 307	9.97 229	5	45	
16	9.53 957	34	9.56 732	39	10.43 268	9.97 224	4	44	
17	9.53 991	34	9.56 771	39	10.43 229	9.97 220	5	43	
18	9.54 025	34	9.56 810	39	10.43 190	9.97 215	5	42	
19	9.54 059	34	9.56 849	38	10.43 151	9.97 210	4	41	
20	9.54 093	34	9.56 887	39	10.43 113	9.97 206	5	40	
21	9.54 127	34	9.56 926	39	10.43 074	9.97 201	5	39	
22	9.54 161	34	9.56 965	39	10.43 035	9.97 196	4	38	
23	9.54 195	34	9.57 004	38	10.42 996	9.97 192	5	37	
24	9.54 229	34	9.57 042	39	10.42 958	9.97 187	5	36	
25	9.54 263	34	9.57 081	39	10.42 919	9.97 182	4	35	
26	9.54 297	34	9.57 120	38	10.42 880	9.97 178	5	34	
27	9.54 331	34	9.57 158	39	10.42 842	9.97 173	5	33	
28	9.54 365	34	9.57 197	38	10.42 803	9.97 168	5	32	
29	9.54 399	34	9.57 235	39	10.42 765	9.97 163	4	31	
30	9.54 433	33	9.57 274	38	10.42 726	9.97 159	5	30	
31	9.54 466	34	9.57 312	39	10.42 688	9.97 154	5	29	
32	9.54 500	34	9.57 351	38	10.42 649	9.97 149	4	28	
33	9.54 534	33	9.57 389	39	10.42 611	9.97 145	5	27	
34	9.54 567	34	9.57 428	38	10.42 572	9.97 140	5	26	
35	9.54 601	34	9.57 466	38	10.42 534	9.97 135	5	25	
36	9.54 635	33	9.57 504	39	10.42 496	9.97 130	4	24	
37	9.54 668	34	9.57 543	38	10.42 457	9.97 126	5	23	
38	9.54 702	33	9.57 581	38	10.42 419	9.97 121	5	22	
39	9.54 735	34	9.57 619	39	10.42 381	9.97 116	5	21	
40	9.54 769	33	9.57 658	38	10.42 342	9.97 111	4	20	
41	9.54 802	34	9.57 696	38	10.42 304	9.97 107	5	19	
42	9.54 836	33	9.57 734	38	10.42 266	9.97 102	5	18	
43	9.54 869	34	9.57 772	38	10.42 228	9.97 097	5	17	
44	9.54 903	33	9.57 810	39	10.42 190	9.97 092	5	16	
45	9.54 936	33	9.57 849	38	10.42 151	9.97 087	4	15	
46	9.54 969	34	9.57 887	38	10.42 113	9.97 083	5	14	
47	9.55 003	33	9.57 925	38	10.42 075	9.97 078	5	13	
48	9.55 036	33	9.57 963	38	10.42 037	9.97 073	5	12	
49	9.55 069	33	9.58 001	38	10.41 999	9.97 068	5	11	
50	9.55 102	34	9.58 039	38	10.41 961	9.97 063	4	10	
51	9.55 136	33	9.58 077	38	10.41 923	9.97 059	5	9	
52	9.55 169	33	9.58 115	38	10.41 885	9.97 054	5	8	
53	9.55 202	33	9.58 153	38	10.41 847	9.97 049	5	7	
54	9.55 235	33	9.58 191	38	10.41 809	9.97 044	5	6	
55	9.55 268	33	9.58 229	38	10.41 771	9.97 039	4	5	
56	9.55 301	33	9.58 267	37	10.41 733	9.97 035	5	4	
57	9.55 334	33	9.58 304	38	10.41 696	9.97 030	5	3	
58	9.55 367	33	9.58 342	38	10.41 658	9.97 025	5	2	
59	9.55 400	33	9.58 380	38	10.41 620	9.97 020	5	1	
60	9.55 433		9.58 418		10.41 582	9.97 015		0	
	L Cos	d	L Ctn	c d	L Tan	L Sin	d	'	

Prop. Pts.

	40	39	38
2	8.0	7.8	7.6
3	12.0	11.7	11.4
4	16.0	15.6	15.2
5	20.0	19.5	19.0
6	24.0	23.4	22.8
7	28.0	27.3	26.6
8	32.0	31.2	30.4
9	36.0	35.1	34.2

	37	35	34
2	7.4	7.0	6.8
3	11.1	10.5	10.2
4	14.8	14.0	13.6
5	18.5	17.5	17.0
6	22.2	21.0	20.4
7	25.9	24.5	23.8
8	29.6	28.0	27.2
9	33.3	31.5	30.6

	33	5	4
2	6.6	1.0	0.8
3	9.9	1.5	1.2
4	13.2	2.0	1.6
5	16.5	2.5	2.0
6	19.8	3.0	2.4
7	23.1	3.5	2.8
8	26.4	4.0	3.2
9	29.7	4.5	3.6

From the top:
For 20°+ or 200°+, read as printed; for 110°+ or 290°+, read co-function.

From the bottom:
For 69°+ or 249°+, read as printed; for 159°+ or 339°+, read co-function.

69° — Logarithms of Trigonometric Functions

21° — Logarithms of Trigonometric Functions

′	L Sin	d	L Tan	c d	L Ctn	L Cos	d		Prop. Pts.
0	9.55 433	33	9.58 418	37	10.41 582	9.97 015	5	60	
1	9.55 466	33	9.58 455	38	10.41 545	9.97 010	5	59	
2	9.55 499	33	9.58 493	38	10.41 507	9.97 005	4	58	
3	9.55 532	32	9.58 531	38	10.41 469	9.97 001	5	57	
4	9.55 564	33	9.58 569	37	10.41 431	9.96 996	5	56	
5	9.55 597	33	9.58 606	38	10.41 394	9.96 991	5	55	**38 37 36**
6	9.55 630	33	9.58 644	37	10.41 356	9.96 986	5	54	2 7.6 7.4 7.2
7	9.55 663	32	9.58 681	38	10.41 319	9.96 981	5	53	3 11.4 11.1 10.8
8	9.55 695	33	9.58 719	38	10.41 281	9.96 976	5	52	4 15.2 14.8 14.4
9	9.55 728	33	9.58 757	37	10.41 243	9.96 971	5	51	5 19.0 18.5 18.0
10	9.55 761	32	9.58 794	38	10.41 206	9.96 966	4	50	6 22.8 22.2 21.6
11	9.55 793	33	9.58 832	37	10.41 168	9.96 962	5	49	7 26.6 25.9 25.2
12	9.55 826	32	9.58 869	38	10.41 131	9.96 957	5	48	8 30.4 29.6 28.8
13	9.55 858	33	9.58 907	37	10.41 093	9.96 952	5	47	9 34.2 33.3 32.4
14	9.55 891	32	9.58 944	37	10.41 056	9.96 947	5	46	
15	9.55 923	33	9.58 981	38	10.41 019	9.96 942	5	45	
16	9.55 956	32	9.59 019	37	10.40 981	9.96 937	5	44	**33 32 31**
17	9.55 988	33	9.59 056	38	10.40 944	9.96 932	5	43	
18	9.56 021	32	9.59 094	37	10.40 906	9.96 927	5	42	2 6.6 6.4 6.2
19	9.56 053	32	9.59 131	37	10.40 869	9.96 922	5	41	3 9.9 9.6 9.3
20	9.56 085	33	9.59 168	37	10.40 832	9.96 917	5	40	4 13.2 12.8 12.4
21	9.56 118	32	9.59 205	38	10.40 795	9.96 912	5	39	5 16.5 16.0 15.5
22	9.56 150	32	9.59 243	37	10.40 757	9.96 907	4	38	6 19.8 19.2 18.6
23	9.56 182	33	9.59 280	37	10.40 720	9.96 903	5	37	7 23.1 22.4 21.7
24	9.56 215	32	9.59 317	37	10.40 683	9.96 898	5	36	8 26.4 25.6 24.8
25	9.56 247	32	9.59 354	37	10.40 646	9.96 893	5	35	9 29.7 28.8 27.9
26	9.56 279	32	9.59 391	38	10.40 609	9.96 888	5	34	
27	9.56 311	32	9.59 429	37	10.40 571	9.96 883	5	33	
28	9.56 343	32	9.59 466	37	10.40 534	9.96 878	5	32	**6 5 4**
29	9.56 375	32	9.59 503	37	10.40 497	9.96 873	5	31	2 1.2 1.0 0.8
30	9.56 408	32	9.59 540	37	10.40 460	9.96 868	5	30	3 1.8 1.5 1.2
31	9.56 440	32	9.59 577	37	10.40 423	9.96 863	5	29	4 2.4 2.0 1.6
32	9.56 472	32	9.59 614	37	10.40 386	9.96 858	5	28	5 3.0 2.5 2.0
33	9.56 504	32	9.59 651	37	10.40 349	9.96 853	5	27	6 3.6 3.0 2.4
34	9.56 536	32	9.59 688	37	10.40 312	9.96 848	5	26	7 4.2 3.5 2.8
35	9.56 568	31	9.59 725	37	10.40 275	9.96 843	5	25	8 4.8 4.0 3.2
36	9.56 599	32	9.59 762	37	10.40 238	9.96 838	5	24	9 5.4 4.5 3.6
37	9.56 631	32	9.59 799	37	10.40 201	9.96 833	5	23	
38	9.56 663	32	9.59 835	36	10.40 165	9.96 828	5	22	
39	9.56 695	32	9.59 872	37	10.40 128	9.96 823	5	21	
40	9.56 727	32	9.59 909	37	10.40 091	9.96 818	5	20	
41	9.56 759	31	9.59 946	37	10.40 054	9.96 813	5	19	
42	9.56 790	32	9.59 983	37	10.40 017	9.96 808	5	18	*From the top:*
43	9.56 822	32	9.60 019	36	10.39 981	9.96 803	5	17	For **21°+** or **201°+**,
44	9.56 854	32	9.60 056	37	10.39 944	9.96 798	5	16	read as printed; for
45	9.56 886	31	9.60 093	37	10.39 907	9.96 793	5	15	**111°+** or **291°+**, read
46	9.56 917	32	9.60 130	36	10.39 870	9.96 788	5	14	co-function.
47	9.56 949	31	9.60 166	37	10.39 834	9.96 783	5	13	
48	9.56 980	32	9.60 203	37	10.39 797	9.96 778	6	12	
49	9.57 012	32	9.60 240	36	10.39 760	9.96 772	5	11	*From the bottom:*
50	9.57 044	31	9.60 276	37	10.39 724	9.96 767	5	10	For **68°+** or **248°+**,
51	9.57 075	32	9.60 313	36	10.39 687	9.96 762	5	9	read as printed; for
52	9.57 107	31	9.60 349	37	10.39 651	9.96 757	5	8	**158°+** or **338°+**, read
53	9.57 138	31	9.60 386	36	10.39 614	9.96 752	5	7	co-function.
54	9.57 169	32	9.60 422	37	10.39 578	9.96 747	5	6	
55	9.57 201	31	9.60 459	36	10.39 541	9.96 742	5	5	
56	9.57 232	32	9.60 495	37	10.39 505	9.96 737	5	4	
57	9.57 264	31	9.60 532	36	10.39 468	9.96 732	5	3	
58	9.57 295	31	9.60 568	37	10.39 432	9.96 727	5	2	
59	9.57 326	32	9.60 605	36	10.39 395	9.96 722	5	1	
60	9.57 358		9.60 641		10.39 359	9.96 717		0	
	L Cos	d	L Ctn	c d	L Tan	L Sin	d	′	Prop. Pts.

68° — Logarithms of Trigonometric Functions

22° — Logarithms of Trigonometric Functions

′	L Sin	d	L Tan	cd	L Ctn	L Cos	d	
0	9.57 358		9.60 641		10.39 359	9.96 717		60
1	9.57 389	31	9.60 677	36	10.39 323	9.96 711	6	59
2	9.57 420	31	9.60 714	37	10.39 286	9.96 706	5	58
3	9.57 451	31	9.60 750	36	10.39 250	9.96 701	5	57
4	9.57 482	31	9.60 786	36	10.39 214	9.96 696	5	56
5	9.57 514	32	9.60 823	37	10.39 177	9.96 691	5	55
6	9.57 545	31	9.60 859	36	10.39 141	9.96 686	5	54
7	9.57 576	31	9.60 895	36	10.39 105	9.96 681	5	53
8	9.57 607	31	9.60 931	36	10.39 069	9.96 676	5	52
9	9.57 638	31	9.60 967	36	10.39 033	9.96 670	6	51
10	9.57 669	31	9.61 004	37	10.38 996	9.96 665	5	50
11	9.57 700	31	9.61 040	36	10.38 960	9.96 660	5	49
12	9.57 731	31	9.61 076	36	10.38 924	9.96 655	5	48
13	9.57 762	31	9.61 112	36	10.38 888	9.96 650	5	47
14	9.57 793	31	9.61 148	36	10.38 852	9.96 645	5	46
15	9.57 824	31	9.61 184	36	10.38 816	9.96 640	6	45
16	9.57 855	31	9.61 220	36	10.38 780	9.96 634	5	44
17	9.57 885	30	9.61 256	36	10.38 744	9.96 629	5	43
18	9.57 916	31	9.61 292	36	10.38 708	9.96 624	5	42
19	9.57 947	31	9.61 328	36	10.38 672	9.96 619	5	41
20	9.57 978	31	9.61 364	36	10.38 636	9.96 614	6	40
21	9.58 008	30	9.61 400	36	10.38 600	9.96 608	5	39
22	9.58 039	31	9.61 436	36	10.38 564	9.96 603	5	38
23	9.58 070	31	9.61 472	36	10.38 528	9.96 598	5	37
24	9.58 101	31	9.61 508	36	10.38 492	9.96 593	5	36
25	9.58 131	30	9.61 544	36	10.38 456	9.96 588	6	35
26	9.58 162	31	9.61 579	35	10.38 421	9.96 582	5	34
27	9.58 192	30	9.61 615	36	10.38 385	9.96 577	5	33
28	9.58 223	31	9.61 651	36	10.38 349	9.96 572	5	32
29	9.58 253	30	9.61 687	36	10.38 313	9.96 567	5	31
30	9.58 284	31	9.61 722	35	10.38 278	9.96 562	6	30
31	9.58 314	30	9.61 758	36	10.38 242	9.96 556	5	29
32	9.58 345	31	9.61 794	36	10.38 206	9.96 551	5	28
33	9.58 375	30	9.61 830	36	10.38 170	9.96 546	5	27
34	9.58 406	31	9.61 865	35	10.38 135	9.96 541	6	26
35	9.58 436	30	9.61 901	36	10.38 099	9.96 535	5	25
36	9.58 467	31	9.61 936	35	10.38 064	9.96 530	5	24
37	9.58 497	30	9.61 972	36	10.38 028	9.96 525	5	23
38	9.58 527	30	9.62 008	36	10.37 992	9.96 520	6	22
39	9.58 557	30	9.62 043	35	10.37 957	9.96 514	5	21
40	9.58 588	31	9.62 079	36	10.37 921	9.96 509	5	20
41	9.58 618	30	9.62 114	35	10.37 886	9.96 504	6	19
42	9.58 648	30	9.62 150	36	10.37 850	9.96 498	5	18
43	9.58 678	30	9.62 185	35	10.37 815	9.96 493	5	17
44	9.58 709	31	9.62 221	36	10.37 779	9.96 488	5	16
45	9.58 739	30	9.62 256	35	10.37 744	9.96 483	6	15
46	9.58 769	30	9.62 292	36	10.37 708	9.96 477	5	14
47	9.58 799	30	9.62 327	35	10.37 673	9.96 472	5	13
48	9.58 829	30	9.62 362	35	10.37 638	9.96 467	6	12
49	9.58 859	30	9.62 398	36	10.37 602	9.96 461	5	11
50	9.58 889	30	9.62 433	35	10.37 567	9.96 456	5	10
51	9.58 919	30	9.62 468	35	10.37 532	9.96 451	6	9
52	9.58 949	30	9.62 504	36	10.37 496	9.96 445	5	8
53	9.58 979	30	9.62 539	35	10.37 461	9.96 440	5	7
54	9.59 009	30	9.62 574	35	10.37 426	9.96 435	6	6
55	9.59 039	30	9.62 609	35	10.37 391	9.96 429	5	5
56	9.59 069	30	9.62 645	36	10.37 355	9.96 424	5	4
57	9.59 098	29	9.62 680	35	10.37 320	9.96 419	6	3
58	9.59 128	30	9.62 715	35	10.37 285	9.96 413	5	2
59	9.59 158	30	9.62 750	35	10.37 250	9.96 408	5	1
60	9.59 188	30	9.62 785	35	10.37 215	9.96 403	5	0
	L Cos	d	L Ctn	cd	L Tan	L Sin	d	′

Prop. Pts.

	37	36	35
2	7.4	7.2	7.0
3	11.1	10.8	10.5
4	14.8	14.4	14.0
5	18.5	18.0	17.5
6	22.2	21.6	21.0
7	25.9	25.2	24.5
8	29.6	28.8	28.0
9	33.3	32.4	31.5

	32	31	30
2	6.4	6.2	6.0
3	9.6	9.3	9.0
4	12.8	12.4	12.0
5	16.0	15.5	15.0
6	19.2	18.6	18.0
7	22.4	21.7	21.0
8	25.6	24.8	24.0
9	28.8	27.9	27.0

	29	6	5
2	5.8	1.2	1.0
3	8.7	1.8	1.5
4	11.6	2.4	2.0
5	14.5	3.0	2.5
6	17.4	3.6	3.0
7	20.3	4.2	3.5
8	23.2	4.8	4.0
9	26.1	5.4	4.5

From the top:
For 22°+ or 202°+, read as printed; for 112°+ or 292°+, read co-function.

From the bottom:
For 67°+ or 247°+, read as printed; for 157°+ or 337°+, read co-function.

23° — Logarithms of Trigonometric Functions

′	L Sin	d	L Tan	c d	L Ctn	L Cos	d		Prop. Pts.	
0	9.59 188	30	9.62 785	35	10.37 215	9.96 403	6	60		
1	9.59 218	29	9.62 820	35	10.37 180	9.96 397	5	59		
2	9.59 247	30	9.62 855	35	10.37 145	9.96 392	5	58	**36**	**35**
3	9.59 277	30	9.62 890	36	10.37 110	9.96 387	6	57	2 7.2	7.0
4	9.59 307	29	9.62 926	35	10.37 074	9.96 381	5	56	3 10.8	10.5
5	9.59 336	30	9.62 961	35	10.37 039	9.96 376	6	55	4 14.4	14.0
6	9.59 366	30	9.62 996	35	10.37 004	9.96 370	5	54	5 18.0	17.5
7	9.59 396	29	9.63 031	35	10.36 969	9.96 365	5	53	6 21.6	21.0
8	9.59 425	30	9.63 066	35	10.36 934	9.96 360	6	52	7 25.2	24.5
9	9.59 455	29	9.63 101	34	10.36 899	9.96 354	5	51	8 28.8	28.0
10	9.59 484	30	9.63 135	35	10.36 865	9.96 349	6	50	9 32.4	31.5
11	9.59 514	29	9.63 170	35	10.36 830	9.96 343	5	49		
12	9.59 543	30	9.63 205	35	10.36 795	9.96 338	5	48		
13	9.59 573	29	9.63 240	35	10.36 760	9.96 333	6	47	**34**	**30**
14	9.59 602	30	9.63 275	35	10.36 725	9.96 327	5	46	2 6.8	6.0
15	9.59 632	29	9.63 310	35	10.36 690	9.96 322	6	45	3 10.2	9.0
16	9.59 661	29	9.63 345	34	10.36 655	9.96 316	5	44	4 13.6	12.0
17	9.59 690	30	9.63 379	35	10.36 621	9.96 311	6	43	5 17.0	15.0
18	9.59 720	29	9.63 414	35	10.36 586	9.96 305	5	42	6 20.4	18.0
19	9.59 749	29	9.63 449	35	10.36 551	9.96 300	6	41	7 23.8	21.0
20	9.59 778	30	9.63 484	35	10.36 516	9.96 294	5	40	8 27.2	24.0
21	9.59 808	29	9.63 519	34	10.36 481	9.96 289	5	39	9 30.6	27.0
22	9.59 837	29	9.63 553	35	10.36 447	9.96 284	6	38		
23	9.59 866	29	9.63 588	35	10.36 412	9.96 278	5	37	**29**	**28**
24	9.59 895	29	9.63 623	34	10.36 377	9.96 273	6	36	2 5.8	5.6
25	9.59 924	30	9.63 657	35	10.36 343	9.96 267	5	35	3 8.7	8.4
26	9.59 954	29	9.63 692	34	10.36 308	9.96 262	6	34	4 11.6	11.2
27	9.59 983	29	9.63 726	35	10.36 274	9.96 256	5	33	5 14.5	14.0
28	9.60 012	29	9.63 761	35	10.36 239	9.96 251	6	32	6 17.4	16.8
29	9.60 041	29	9.63 796	34	10.36 204	9.96 245	5	31	7 20.3	19.6
30	9.60 070	29	9.63 830	35	10.36 170	9.96 240	6	30	8 23.2	22.4
31	9.60 099	29	9.63 865	34	10.36 135	9.96 234	5	29	9 26.1	25.2
32	9.60 128	29	9.63 899	35	10.36 101	9.96 229	6	28		
33	9.60 157	29	9.63 934	34	10.36 066	9.96 223	5	27		
34	9.60 186	29	9.63 968	35	10.36 032	9.96 218	6	26	**6**	**5**
35	9.60 215	29	9.64 003	34	10.35 997	9.96 212	5	25	2 1.2	1.0
36	9.60 244	29	9.64 037	35	10.35 963	9.96 207	6	24	3 1.8	1.5
37	9.60 273	29	9.64 072	34	10.35 928	9.96 201	5	23	4 2.4	2.0
38	9.60 302	29	9.64 106	34	10.35 894	9.96 196	6	22	5 3.0	2.5
39	9.60 331	28	9.64 140	35	10.35 860	9.96 190	5	21	6 3.6	3.0
40	9.60 359	29	9.64 175	34	10.35 825	9.96 185	6	20	7 4.2	3.5
41	9.60 388	29	9.64 209	34	10.35 791	9.96 179	5	19	8 4.8	4.0
42	9.60 417	29	9.64 243	35	10.35 757	9.96 174	6	18	9 5.4	4.5
43	9.60 446	28	9.64 278	34	10.35 722	9.96 168	6	17		
44	9.60 474	29	9.64 312	34	10.35 688	9.96 162	5	16		
45	9.60 503	29	9.64 346	35	10.35 654	9.96 157	6	15	*From the top:*	
46	9.60 532	29	9.64 381	34	10.35 619	9.96 151	5	14	For 23°+ or 203°+,	
47	9.60 561	28	9.64 415	34	10.35 585	9.96 146	6	13	read as printed; for	
48	9.60 589	29	9.64 449	34	10.35 551	9.96 140	5	12	113°+ or 293°+, read	
49	9.60 618	28	9.64 483	34	10.35 517	9.96 135	6	11	co-function.	
50	9.60 646	29	9.64 517	35	10.35 483	9.96 129	6	10		
51	9.60 675	29	9.64 552	34	10.35 448	9.96 123	5	9		
52	9.60 704	29	9.64 586	34	10.35 414	9.96 118	6	8	*From the bottom:*	
53	9.60 732	29	9.64 620	34	10.35 380	9.96 112	5	7	For 66°+ or 246°+,	
54	9.60 761	28	9.64 654	34	10.35 346	9.96 107	6	6	read as printed; for	
55	9.60 789	29	9.64 688	34	10.35 312	9.96 101	6	5	156°+ or 336°+, read	
56	9.60 818	28	9.64 722	34	10.35 278	9.96 095	5	4	co-function.	
57	9.60 846	29	9.64 756	34	10.35 244	9.96 090	6	3		
58	9.60 875	28	9.64 790	34	10.35 210	9.96 084	5	2		
59	9.60 903	28	9.64 824	34	10.35 176	9.96 079	6	1		
60	9.60 931		9.64 858		10.35 142	9.96 073		0		
′	L Cos	d	L Ctn	c d	L Tan	L Sin	d	′	Prop. Pts.	

66° — Logarithms of Trigonometric Functions

24° — Logarithms of Trigonometric Functions

′	L Sin	d	L Tan	c d	L Ctn	L Cos	d	′
0	9.60 931		9.64 858		10.35 142	9.96 073		60
1	9.60 960	29	9.64 892	34	10.35 108	9.96 067	6	59
2	9.60 988	28	9.64 926	34	10.35 074	9.96 062	5	58
3	9.61 016	28	9.64 960	34	10.35 040	9.96 056	6	57
4	9.61 045	28	9.64 994	34	10.35 006	9.96 050	6	56
5	9.61 073	28	9.65 028	34	10.34 972	9.96 045	5	55
6	9.61 101	28	9.65 062	34	10.34 938	9.96 039	6	54
7	9.61 129	28	9.65 096	34	10.34 904	9.96 034	5	53
8	9.61 158	29	9.65 130	34	10.34 870	9.96 028	6	52
9	9.61 186	28	9.65 164	34	10.34 836	9.96 022	6	51
10	9.61 214	28	9.65 197	33	10.34 803	9.96 017	5	50
11	9.61 242	28	9.65 231	34	10.34 769	9.96 011	6	49
12	9.61 270	28	9.65 265	34	10.34 735	9.96 005	6	48
13	9.61 298	28	9.65 299	34	10.34 701	9.96 000	5	47
14	9.61 326	28	9.65 333	34	10.34 667	9.95 994	6	46
15	9.61 354	28	9.65 366	33	10.34 634	9.95 988	6	45
16	9.61 382	28	9.65 400	34	10.34 600	9.95 982	6	44
17	9.61 411	29	9.65 434	34	10.34 566	9.95 977	5	43
18	9.61 438	27	9.65 467	33	10.34 533	9.95 971	6	42
19	9.61 466	28	9.65 501	34	10.34 499	9.95 965	6	41
20	9.61 494	28	9.65 535	34	10.34 465	9.95 960	5	40
21	9.61 522	28	9.65 568	33	10.34 432	9.95 954	6	39
22	9.61 550	28	9.65 602	34	10.34 398	9.95 948	6	38
23	9.61 578	28	9.65 636	34	10.34 364	9.95 942	6	37
24	9.61 606	28	9.65 669	33	10.34 331	9.95 937	5	36
25	9.61 634	28	9.65 703	34	10.34 297	9.95 931	6	35
26	9.61 662	28	9.65 736	33	10.34 264	9.95 925	6	34
27	9.61 689	27	9.65 770	34	10.34 230	9.95 920	5	33
28	9.61 717	28	9.65 803	33	10.34 197	9.95 914	6	32
29	9.61 745	28	9.65 837	34	10.34 163	9.95 908	6	31
30	9.61 773	28	9.65 870	34	10.34 130	9.95 902	6	30
31	9.61 800	28	9.65 904	33	10.34 096	9.95 897	5	29
32	9.61 828	28	9.65 937	34	10.34 063	9.95 891	6	28
33	9.61 856	27	9.65 971	33	10.34 029	9.95 885	6	27
34	9.61 883	28	9.66 004	34	10.33 996	9.95 879	6	26
35	9.61 911	28	9.66 038	33	10.33 962	9.95 873	6	25
36	9.61 939	27	9.66 071	33	10.33 929	9.95 868	5	24
37	9.61 966	28	9.66 104	34	10.33 896	9.95 862	6	23
38	9.61 994	27	9.66 138	33	10.33 862	9.95 856	6	22
39	9.62 021	28	9.66 171	33	10.33 829	9.95 850	6	21
40	9.62 049	27	9.66 204	34	10.33 796	9.95 844	6	20
41	9.62 076	28	9.66 238	33	10.33 762	9.95 839	5	19
42	9.62 104	27	9.66 271	33	10.33 729	9.95 833	6	18
43	9.62 131	28	9.66 304	33	10.33 696	9.95 827	6	17
44	9.62 159	27	9.66 337	34	10.33 663	9.95 821	6	16
45	9.62 186	28	9.66 371	33	10.33 629	9.95 815	5	15
46	9.62 214	27	9.66 404	33	10.33 596	9.95 810	6	14
47	9.62 241	27	9.66 437	33	10.33 563	9.95 804	6	13
48	9.62 268	28	9.66 470	33	10.33 530	9.95 798	6	12
49	9.62 296	27	9.66 503	34	10.33 497	9.95 792	6	11
50	9.62 323	27	9.66 537	33	10.33 463	9.95 786	5	10
51	9.62 350	27	9.66 570	33	10.33 430	9.95 780	6	9
52	9.62 377	28	9.66 603	33	10.33 397	9.95 775	5	8
53	9.62 405	27	9.66 636	33	10.33 364	9.95 769	6	7
54	9.62 432	27	9.66 669	33	10.33 331	9.95 763	6	6
55	9.62 459	27	9.66 702	33	10.33 298	9.95 757	6	5
56	9.62 486	27	9.66 735	33	10.33 265	9.95 751	6	4
57	9.62 513	28	9.66 768	33	10.33 232	9.95 745	6	3
58	9.62 541	27	9.66 801	33	10.33 199	9.95 739	6	2
59	9.62 568	27	9.66 834	33	10.33 166	9.95 733	5	1
60	9.62 595		9.66 867		10.33 133	9.95 728		0
	L Cos	d	L Ctn	c d	L Tan	L Sin	d	′

Prop. Pts.

	34	33
2	6.8	6.6
3	10.2	9.9
4	13.6	13.2
5	17.0	16.5
6	20.4	19.8
7	23.8	23.1
8	27.2	26.4
9	30.6	29.7

	29	28
2	5.8	5.6
3	8.7	8.4
4	11.6	11.2
5	14.5	14.0
6	17.4	16.8
7	20.3	19.6
8	23.2	22.4
9	26.1	25.2

	27	6
2	5.4	1.2
3	8.1	1.8
4	10.8	2.4
5	13.5	3.0
6	16.2	3.6
7	18.9	4.2
8	21.6	4.8
9	24.3	5.4

	5
2	1.0
3	1.5
4	2.0
5	2.5
6	3.0
7	3.5
8	4.0
9	4.5

From the top:
For 24°+ or 204°+, read as printed; for 114°+ or 294°+, read co-function.

From the bottom:
For 65°+ or 245°+, read as printed; for 155°+ or 335°+, read co-function.

65° — Logarithms of Trigonometric Functions

25° — Logarithms of Trigonometric Functions

′	L Sin	d	L Tan	c d	L Ctn	L Cos	d		Prop. Pts.
0	9.62 595	27	9.66 857	33	10.33 133	9.95 728	6	60	
1	9.62 622	27	9.66 900	33	10.33 100	9.95 722	6	59	
2	9.62 649	27	9.66 933	33	10.33 067	9.95 716	6	58	**33** **32**
3	9.62 676	27	9.66 966	33	10.33 034	9.95 710	6	57	2 6.6 6.4
4	9.62 703	27	9.66 999	33	10.33 001	9.95 704	6	56	3 9.9 9.6
5	9.62 730	27	9.67 032	33	10.32 968	9.95 698	6	55	4 13.2 12.8
6	9.62 757	27	9.67 065	33	10.32 935	9.95 692	6	54	5 16.5 16.0
7	9.62 784	27	9.67 098	33	10.32 902	9.95 686	6	53	6 19.8 19.2
8	9.62 811	27	9.67 131	32	10.32 869	9.95 680	6	52	7 23.1 22.4
9	9.62 838	27	9.67 163	33	10.32 837	9.95 674	6	51	8 26.4 25.6
10	9.62 865	27	9.67 196	33	10.32 804	9.95 668	5	50	9 29.7 28.8
11	9.62 892	26	9.67 229	33	10.32 771	9.95 663	6	49	
12	9.62 918	27	9.67 262	33	10.32 738	9.95 657	6	48	
13	9.62 945	27	9.67 295	32	10.32 705	9.95 651	6	47	**27** **26**
14	9.62 972	27	9.67 327	33	10.32 673	9.95 645	6	46	2 5.4 5.2
15	9.62 999	27	9.67 360	33	10.32 640	9.95 639	6	45	3 8.1 7.8
16	9.63 026	26	9.67 393	33	10.32 607	9.95 633	6	44	4 10.8 10.4
17	9.63 052	27	9.67 426	32	10.32 574	9.95 627	6	43	5 13.5 13.0
18	9.63 079	27	9.67 458	33	10.32 542	9.95 621	6	42	6 16.2 15.6
19	9.63 106	27	9.67 491	33	10.32 509	9.95 615	6	41	7 18.9 18.2
20	9.63 133	26	9.67 524	32	10.32 476	9.95 609	6	40	8 21.6 20.8
21	9.63 159	27	9.67 556	33	10.32 444	9.95 603	6	39	9 24.3 23.4
22	9.63 186	27	9.67 589	33	10.32 411	9.95 597	6	38	
23	9.63 213	26	9.67 622	32	10.32 378	9.95 591	6	37	
24	9.63 239	27	9.67 654	33	10.32 346	9.95 585	6	36	**7** **6**
25	9.63 266	26	9.67 687	32	10.32 313	9.95 579	6	35	2 1.4 1.2
26	9.63 292	27	9.67 719	33	10.32 281	9.95 573	6	34	3 2.1 1.8
27	9.63 319	26	9.67 752	33	10.32 248	9.95 567	6	33	4 2.8 2.4
28	9.63 345	27	9.67 785	32	10.32 215	9.95 561	6	32	5 3.5 3.0
29	9.63 372	26	9.67 817	33	10.32 183	9.95 555	6	31	6 4.2 3.6
30	9.63 398	27	9.67 850	32	10.32 150	9.95 549	6	30	7 4.9 4.2
31	9.63 425	26	9.67 882	33	10.32 118	9.95 543	6	29	8 5.6 4.8
32	9.63 451	27	9.67 915	32	10.32 085	9.95 537	6	28	9 6.3 5.4
33	9.63 478	26	9.67 947	33	10.32 053	9.95 531	6	27	
34	9.63 504	27	9.67 980	32	10.32 020	9.95 525	6	26	
35	9.63 531	26	9.68 012	32	10.31 988	9.95 519	6	25	**5**
36	9.63 557	26	9.68 044	33	10.31 956	9.95 513	6	24	2 1.0
37	9.63 583	27	9.68 077	32	10.31 923	9.95 507	7	23	3 1.5
38	9.63 610	26	9.68 109	33	10.31 891	9.95 500	6	22	4 2.0
39	9.63 636	26	9.68 142	32	10.31 858	9.95 494	6	21	5 2.5
40	9.63 662	27	9.68 174	32	10.31 826	9.95 488	6	20	6 3.0
41	9.63 689	26	9.68 206	33	10.31 794	9.95 482	6	19	7 3.5
42	9.63 715	26	9.68 239	32	10.31 761	9.95 476	6	18	8 4.0
43	9.63 741	26	9.68 271	32	10.31 729	9.95 470	6	17	9 4.5
44	9.63 767	27	9.68 303	33	10.31 697	9.95 464	6	16	
45	9.63 794	26	9.68 336	32	10.31 664	9.95 458	6	15	*From the top:*
46	9.63 820	26	9.68 368	32	10.31 632	9.95 452	6	14	For 25°+ or 205°+,
47	9.63 846	26	9.68 400	32	10.31 600	9.95 446	6	13	read as printed; for
48	9.63 872	26	9.68 432	33	10.31 568	9.95 440	6	12	115°+ or 295°+, read
49	9.63 898	26	9.68 465	32	10.31 535	9.95 434	7	11	co-function.
50	9.63 924	26	9.68 497	32	10.31 503	9.95 427	6	10	
51	9.63 950	26	9.68 529	32	10.31 471	9.95 421	6	9	
52	9.63 976	26	9.68 561	32	10.31 439	9.95 415	6	8	
53	9.64 002	26	9.68 593	33	10.31 407	9.95 409	6	7	*From the bottom:*
54	9.64 028	26	9.68 626	32	10.31 374	9.95 403	6	6	For 64°+ or 244°+,
55	9.64 054	26	9.68 658	32	10.31 342	9.95 397	6	5	read as printed; for
56	9.64 080	26	9.68 690	32	10.31 310	9.95 391	7	4	154°+ or 334°+, read
57	9.64 106	26	9.68 722	32	10.31 278	9.95 384	6	3	co-function.
58	9.64 132	26	9.68 754	32	10.31 246	9.95 378	6	2	
59	9.64 158	26	9.68 786	32	10.31 214	9.95 372	6	1	
60	9.64 184		9.68 818		10.31 182	9.95 366		0	
	L Cos	d	L Ctn	c d	L Tan	L Sin	d	′	Prop. Pts.

64° — Logarithms of Trigonometric Functions

Table XIV. [XIV

26° — Logarithms of Trigonometric Functions

′	L Sin	d	L Tan	c d	L Ctn	L Cos	d		Prop. Pts.
0	9.64 184	26	9.68 818	32	10.31 182	9.95 366	6	60	
1	9.64 210	26	9.68 850	32	10.31 150	9.95 360	6	59	
2	9.64 236	26	9.68 882	32	10.31 118	9.95 354	6	58	**32** **31**
3	9.64 262	26	9.68 914	32	10.31 086	9.95 348	7	57	2 6.4 6.2
4	9.64 288	25	9.68 946	32	10.31 054	9.95 341	6	56	3 9.6 9.3
5	9.64 313	26	9.68 978	32	10.31 022	9.95 335	6	55	4 12.8 12.4
6	9.64 339	26	9.69 010	32	10.30 990	9.95 329	6	54	5 16.0 15.5
7	9.64 365	26	9.69 042	32	10.30 958	9.95 323	6	53	6 19.2 18.6
8	9.64 391	26	9.69 074	32	10.30 926	9.95 317	7	52	7 22.4 21.7
9	9.64 417	26	9.69 106	32	10.30 894	9.95 310	6	51	8 25.6 24.8
10	9.64 442	26	9.69 138	32	10.30 862	9.95 304	6	50	9 28.8 27.9
11	9.64 468	26	9.69 170	32	10.30 830	9.95 298	6	49	
12	9.64 494	25	9.69 202	32	10.30 798	9.95 292	6	48	
13	9.64 519	26	9.69 234	32	10.30 766	9.95 286	7	47	**26** **25**
14	9.64 545	26	9.69 266	32	10.30 734	9.95 279	6	46	2 5.2 5.0
15	9.64 571	25	9.69 298	31	10.30 702	9.95 273	6	45	3 7.8 7.5
16	9.64 596	26	9.69 329	32	10.30 671	9.95 267	6	44	4 10.4 10.0
17	9.64 622	25	9.69 361	32	10.30 639	9.95 261	7	43	5 13.0 12.5
18	9.64 647	25	9.69 393	32	10.30 607	9.95 254	6	42	6 15.6 15.0
19	9.64 673	25	9.69 425	32	10.30 575	9.95 248	6	41	7 18.2 17.5
20	9.64 698	26	9.69 457	31	10.30 543	9.95 242	6	40	8 20.8 20.0
21	9.64 724	25	9.69 488	32	10.30 512	9.95 236	7	39	9 23.4 22.5
22	9.64 749	26	9.69 520	32	10.30 480	9.95 229	6	38	
23	9.64 775	25	9.69 552	32	10.30 448	9.95 223	6	37	**24** **7**
24	9.64 800	26	9.69 584	31	10.30 416	9.95 217	6	36	2 4.8 1.4
25	9.64 826	25	9.69 615	32	10.30 385	9.95 211	7	35	3 7.2 2.1
26	9.64 851	26	9.69 647	32	10.30 353	9.95 204	6	34	4 9.6 2.8
27	9.64 877	25	9.69 679	31	10.30 321	9.95 198	6	33	5 12.0 3.5
28	9.64 902	25	9.69 710	32	10.30 290	9.95 192	7	32	6 14.4 4.2
29	9.64 927	26	9.69 742	32	10.30 258	9.95 185	6	31	7 16.8 4.9
30	9.64 953	25	9.69 774	31	10.30 226	9.95 179	6	30	8 19.2 5.6
31	9.64 978	25	9.69 805	32	10.30 195	9.95 173	6	29	9 21.6 6.3
32	9.65 003	26	9.69 837	31	10.30 163	9.95 167	7	28	
33	9.65 029	25	9.69 868	32	10.30 132	9.95 160	6	27	
34	9.65 054	25	9.69 900	32	10.30 100	9.95 154	6	26	**6**
35	9.65 079	25	9.69 932	31	10.30 068	9.95 148	7	25	2 1.2
36	9.65 104	26	9.69 963	32	10.30 037	9.95 141	6	24	3 1.8
37	9.65 130	25	9.69 995	31	10.30 005	9.95 135	6	23	4 2.4
38	9.65 155	25	9.70 026	32	10.29 974	9.95 129	7	22	5 3.0
39	9.65 180	25	9.70 058	31	10.29 942	9.95 122	6	21	6 3.6
40	9.65 205	25	9.70 089	32	10.29 911	9.95 116	6	20	7 4.2
41	9.65 230	25	9.70 121	31	10.29 879	9.95 110	7	19	8 4.8
42	9.65 255	26	9.70 152	32	10.29 848	9.95 103	6	18	9 5.4
43	9.65 281	25	9.70 184	31	10.29 816	9.95 097	7	17	
44	9.65 306	25	9.70 215	32	10.29 785	9.95 090	6	16	
45	9.65 331	25	9.70 247	31	10.29 753	9.95 084	6	15	*From the top:*
46	9.65 356	25	9.70 278	31	10.29 722	9.95 078	7	14	For 26°+ or 206°+,
47	9.65 381	25	9.70 309	32	10.29 691	9.95 071	6	13	read as printed; for
48	9.65 406	25	9.70 341	31	10.29 659	9.95 065	6	12	116°+ or 296°+, read
49	9.65 431	25	9.70 372	32	10.29 628	9.95 059	7	11	co-function.
50	9.65 456	25	9.70 404	31	10.29 596	9.95 052	6	10	
51	9.65 481	25	9.70 435	31	10.29 565	9.95 046	7	9	
52	9.65 506	25	9.70 466	32	10.29 534	9.95 039	6	8	*From the bottom:*
53	9.65 531	25	9.70 498	31	10.29 502	9.95 033	6	7	For 63°+ or 243°+,
54	9.65 556	24	9.70 529	31	10.29 471	9.95 027	7	6	read as printed; for
55	9.65 580	25	9.70 560	32	10.29 440	9.95 020	6	5	153°+ or 333°+, read
56	9.65 605	25	9.70 592	31	10.29 408	9.95 014	7	4	co-function.
57	9.65 630	25	9.70 623	31	10.29 377	9.95 007	7	3	
58	9.65 655	25	9.70 654	31	10.29 346	9.95 001	6	2	
59	9.65 680	25	9.70 685	32	10.29 315	9.94 995	7	1	
60	9.65 705		9.70 717		10.29 283	9.94 988		0	
	L Cos	d	L Ctn	c d	L Tan	L Sin	d	′	Prop. Pts.

63° — Logarithms of Trigonometric Functions

27° — Logarithms of Trigonometric Functions

′	L Sin	d	L Tan	c d	L Ctn	L Cos	d		Prop. Pts.
0	9.65 705		9.70 717		10.29 283	9.94 988		60	
1	9.65 729	24	9.70 748	31	10.29 252	9.94 982	6	59	
2	9.65 754	25	9.70 779	31	10.29 221	9.94 975	7	58	**32** | **31**
3	9.65 779	25	9.70 810	31	10.29 190	9.94 969	6	57	2 | 6.4 | 6.2
4	9.65 804	25	9.70 841	31	10.29 159	9.94 962	7	56	3 | 9.6 | 9.3
5	9.65 828	24	9.70 873	32	10.29 127	9.94 956	6	55	4 | 12.8 | 12.4
6	9.65 853	25	9.70 904	31	10.29 096	9.94 949	7	54	5 | 16.0 | 15.5
7	9.65 878	25	9.70 935	31	10.29 065	9.94 943	6	53	6 | 19.2 | 18.6
8	9.65 902	24	9.70 966	31	10.29 034	9.94 936	7	52	7 | 22.4 | 21.7
9	9.65 927	25	9.70 997	31	10.29 003	9.94 930	6	51	8 | 25.6 | 24.8
10	9.65 952	25	9.71 028	31	10.28 972	9.94 923	7	50	9 | 28.8 | 27.9
11	9.65 976	24	9.71 059	31	10.28 941	9.94 917	6	49	
12	9.66 001	25	9.71 090	31	10.28 910	9.94 911	6	48	
13	9.66 025	24	9.71 121	31	10.28 879	9.94 904	7	47	**30** | **25**
14	9.66 050	25	9.71 153	32	10.28 847	9.94 898	6	46	2 | 6.0 | 5.0
15	9.66 075	25	9.71 184	31	10.28 816	9.94 891	7	45	3 | 9.0 | 7.5
16	9.66 099	24	9.71 215	31	10.28 785	9.94 885	6	44	4 | 12.0 | 10.0
17	9.66 124	25	9.71 246	31	10.28 754	9.94 878	7	43	5 | 15.0 | 12.5
18	9.66 148	24	9.71 277	31	10.28 723	9.94 871	7	42	6 | 18.0 | 15.0
19	9.66 173	25	9.71 308	31	10.28 692	9.94 865	6	41	7 | 21.0 | 17.5
20	9.66 197	24	9.71 339	31	10.28 661	9.94 858	7	40	8 | 24.0 | 20.0
21	9.66 221	24	9.71 370	31	10.28 630	9.94 852	6	39	9 | 27.0 | 22.5
22	9.66 246	25	9.71 401	31	10.28 599	9.94 845	7	38	
23	9.66 270	24	9.71 431	30	10.28 569	9.94 839	6	37	
24	9.66 295	25	9.71 462	31	10.28 538	9.94 832	7	36	**24** | **23**
25	9.66 319	24	9.71 493	31	10.28 507	9.94 826	6	35	2 | 4.8 | 4.6
26	9.66 343	24	9.71 524	31	10.28 476	9.94 819	7	34	3 | 7.2 | 6.9
27	9.66 368	25	9.71 555	31	10.28 445	9.94 813	6	33	4 | 9.6 | 9.2
28	9.66 392	24	9.71 586	31	10.28 414	9.94 806	7	32	5 | 12.0 | 11.5
29	9.66 416	24	9.71 617	31	10.28 383	9.94 799	7	31	6 | 14.4 | 13.8
30	9.66 441	25	9.71 648	31	10.28 352	9.94 793	6	30	7 | 16.8 | 16.1
31	9.66 465	24	9.71 679	31	10.28 321	9.94 786	7	29	8 | 19.2 | 18.4
32	9.66 489	24	9.71 709	30	10.28 291	9.94 780	6	28	9 | 21.6 | 20.7
33	9.66 513	24	9.71 740	31	10.28 260	9.94 773	7	27	
34	9.66 537	24	9.71 771	31	10.28 229	9.94 767	6	26	
35	9.66 562	25	9.71 802	31	10.28 198	9.94 760	7	25	**7** | **6**
36	9.66 586	24	9.71 833	31	10.28 167	9.94 753	7	24	2 | 1.4 | 1.2
37	9.66 610	24	9.71 863	30	10.28 137	9.94 747	6	23	3 | 2.1 | 1.8
38	9.66 634	24	9.71 894	31	10.28 106	9.94 740	7	22	4 | 2.8 | 2.4
39	9.66 658	24	9.71 925	31	10.28 075	9.94 734	6	21	5 | 3.5 | 3.0
40	9.66 682	24	9.71 955	30	10.28 045	9.94 727	7	20	6 | 4.2 | 3.6
41	9.66 706	24	9.71 986	31	10.28 014	9.94 720	7	19	7 | 4.9 | 4.2
42	9.66 731	25	9.72 017	31	10.27 983	9.94 714	6	18	8 | 5.6 | 4.8
43	9.66 755	24	9.72 048	31	10.27 952	9.94 707	7	17	9 | 6.3 | 5.4
44	9.66 779	24	9.72 078	30	10.27 922	9.94 700	7	16	
45	9.66 803	24	9.72 109	31	10.27 891	9.94 694	6	15	*From the top:*
46	9.66 827	24	9.72 140	31	10.27 860	9.94 687	7	14	For 27°+ or 207°+,
47	9.66 851	24	9.72 170	30	10.27 830	9.94 680	7	13	read as printed; for
48	9.66 875	24	9.72 201	31	10.27 799	9.94 674	6	12	117°+ or 297°+, read
49	9.66 899	23	9.72 231	31	10.27 769	9.94 667	7	11	co-function.
50	9.66 922	24	9.72 262	31	10.27 738	9.94 660	7	10	
51	9.66 946	24	9.72 293	30	10.27 707	9.94 654	6	9	
52	9.66 970	24	9.72 323	31	10.27 677	9.94 647	7	8	*From the bottom:*
53	9.66 994	24	9.72 354	30	10.27 646	9.94 640	7	7	For 62°+ or 242°+,
54	9.67 018	24	9.72 384	31	10.27 616	9.94 634	7	6	read as printed; for
55	9.67 042	24	9.72 415	30	10.27 585	9.94 627	7	5	152°+ or 332°+, read
56	9.67 066	24	9.72 445	31	10.27 555	9.94 620	6	4	co-function.
57	9.67 090	23	9.72 476	30	10.27 524	9.94 614	7	3	
58	9.67 113	24	9.72 506	31	10.27 494	9.94 607	7	2	
59	9.67 137	24	9.72 537	30	10.27 463	9.94 600	7	1	
60	9.67 161		9.72 567		10.27 433	9.94 593		0	
	L Cos	d	L Ctn	c d	L Tan	L Sin	d	′	Prop. Pts.

62° — Logarithms of Trigonometric Functions

28° — Logarithms of Trigonometric Functions

′	L Sin	d	L Tan	c d	L Ctn	L Cos	d		Prop. Pts.
0	9.67 161		9.72 567		10.27 433	9.94 593		60	
1	9.67 185	24	9.72 598	31	10.27 402	9.94 587	6	59	
2	9.67 208	23	9.72 628	30	10.27 372	9.94 580	7	58	**31** | **30**
3	9.67 232	24	9.72 659	31	10.27 341	9.94 573	7	57	2 | 6.2 | 6.0
4	9.67 256	24	9.72 689	30	10.27 311	9.94 567	6	56	3 | 9.3 | 9.0
5	9.67 280	24	9.72 720	31	10.27 280	9.94 560	7	55	4 | 12.4 | 12.0
6	9.67 303	23	9.72 750	30	10.27 250	9.94 553	7	54	5 | 15.5 | 15.0
7	9.67 327	24	9.72 780	30	10.27 220	9.94 546	7	53	6 | 18.6 | 18.0
8	9.67 350	23	9.72 811	31	10.27 189	9.94 540	6	52	7 | 21.7 | 21.0
9	9.67 374	24	9.72 841	30	10.27 159	9.94 533	7	51	8 | 24.8 | 24.0
10	9.67 398	24	9.72 872	31	10.27 128	9.94 526	7	50	9 | 27.9 | 27.0
11	9.67 421	23	9.72 902	30	10.27 098	9.94 519	7	49	
12	9.67 445	24	9.72 932	30	10.27 068	9.94 513	6	48	
13	9.67 468	23	9.72 963	31	10.27 037	9.94 506	7	47	**29** | **24**
14	9.67 492	24	9.72 993	30	10.27 007	9.94 499	7	46	2 | 5.8 | 4.8
15	9.67 515	23	9.73 023	30	10.26 977	9.94 492	7	45	3 | 8.7 | 7.2
16	9.67 539	24	9.73 054	31	10.26 946	9.94 485	7	44	4 | 11.6 | 9.6
17	9.67 562	23	9.73 084	30	10.26 916	9.94 479	6	43	5 | 14.5 | 12.0
18	9.67 586	24	9.73 114	30	10.26 886	9.94 472	7	42	6 | 17.4 | 14.4
19	9.67 609	23	9.73 144	30	10.26 856	9.94 465	7	41	7 | 20.3 | 16.8
20	9.67 633	24	9.73 175	31	10.26 825	9.94 458	7	40	8 | 23.2 | 19.2
21	9.67 656	23	9.73 205	30	10.26 795	9.94 451	7	39	9 | 26.1 | 21.6
22	9.67 680	24	9.73 235	30	10.26 765	9.94 445	6	38	
23	9.67 703	23	9.73 265	30	10.26 735	9.94 438	7	37	
24	9.67 726	24	9.73 295	31	10.26 705	9.94 431	7	36	**23** | **22**
25	9.67 750	23	9.73 326	30	10.26 674	9.94 424	7	35	2 | 4.6 | 4.4
26	9.67 773	23	9.73 356	30	10.26 644	9.94 417	7	34	3 | 6.9 | 6.6
27	9.67 796	24	9.73 386	30	10.26 614	9.94 410	7	33	4 | 9.2 | 8.8
28	9.37 820	23	9.73 416	30	10.26 584	9.94 404	6	32	5 | 11.5 | 11.0
29	9.67 843	23	9.73 446	30	10.26 554	9.94 397	7	31	6 | 13.8 | 13.2
30	9.67 866	24	9.73 476	31	10.26 524	9.94 390	7	30	7 | 16.1 | 15.4
31	9.67 890	23	9.73 507	30	10.26 493	9.94 383	7	29	8 | 18.4 | 17.6
32	9.67 913	23	9.73 537	30	10.26 463	9.94 376	7	28	9 | 20.7 | 19.8
33	9.67 936	23	9.73 567	30	10.26 433	9.94 369	7	27	
34	9.67 959	23	9.73 597	30	10.26 403	9.94 362	7	26	
35	9.67 982	24	9.73 627	30	10.26 373	9.94 355	6	25	**7** | **6**
36	9.68 006	23	9.73 657	30	10.26 343	9.94 349	7	24	2 | 1.4 | 1.2
37	9.68 029	23	9.73 687	30	10.26 313	9.94 342	7	23	3 | 2.1 | 1.8
38	9.68 052	23	9.73 717	30	10.26 283	9.94 335	7	22	4 | 2.8 | 2.4
39	9.68 075	23	9.73 747	30	10.26 253	9.94 328	7	21	5 | 3.5 | 3.0
40	9.68 098	23	9.73 777	30	10.26 223	9.94 321	7	20	6 | 4.2 | 3.6
41	9.68 121	23	9.73 807	30	10.26 193	9.94 314	7	19	7 | 4.9 | 4.2
42	9.68 144	23	9.73 837	30	10.26 163	9.94 307	7	18	8 | 5.6 | 4.8
43	9.68 167	23	9.73 867	30	10.26 133	9.94 300	7	17	9 | 6.3 | 5.4
44	9.68 190	23	9.73 897	30	10.26 103	9.94 293	7	16	
45	9.68 213	24	9.73 927	30	10.26 073	9.94 286	7	15	*From the top:*
46	9.68 237	23	9.73 957	30	10.26 043	9.94 279	7	14	For 28°+ or 208°+,
47	9.68 260	23	9.73 987	30	10.26 013	9.94 273	7	13	read as printed; for
48	9.68 283	22	9.74 017	30	10.25 983	9.94 266	7	12	118°+ or 298°+, read
49	9.68 305	23	9.74 047	30	10.25 953	9.94 259	7	11	co-function.
50	9.68 328	23	9.74 077	30	10.25 923	9.94 252	7	10	
51	9.68 351	23	9.74 107	30	10.25 893	9.94 245	7	9	
52	9.68 374	23	9.74 137	29	10.25 863	9.94 238	7	8	*From the bottom:*
53	9.68 397	23	9.74 166	30	10.25 834	9.94 231	7	7	For 61°+ or 241°+,
54	9.68 420	23	9.74 196	30	10.25 804	9.94 224	7	6	read as printed; for
55	9.68 443	23	9.74 226	30	10.25 774	9.94 217	7	5	151°+ or 331°+, read
56	9.68 466	23	9.74 256	30	10.25 744	9.94 210	7	4	co-function.
57	9.68 489	23	9.74 286	30	10.25 714	9.94 203	7	3	
58	9.68 512	22	9.74 316	30	10.25 684	9.94 196	7	2	
59	9.68 534	23	9.74 345	29	10.25 655	9.94 189	7	1	
60	9.68 557		9.74 375	30	10.25 625	9.94 182		0	
	L Cos	d	L Ctn	c d	L Tan	L Sin	d	′	Prop. Pts.

61° — Logarithms of Trigonometric Functions

29° — Logarithms of Trigonometric Functions

'	L Sin	d	L Tan	cd	L Ctn	L Cos	d	'
0	9.68 557	23	9.74 375	30	10.25 625	9.94 182	7	60
1	9.68 580	23	9.74 405	30	10.25 595	9.94 175	7	59
2	9.68 603	22	9.74 435	30	10.25 565	9.94 168	7	58
3	9.68 625	22	9.74 465	29	10.25 535	9.94 161	7	57
4	9.68 648	23	9.74 494	30	10.25 506	9.94 154	7	56
5	9.68 671	23	9.74 524	30	10.25 476	9.94 147	7	55
6	9.68 694	23	9.74 554	29	10.25 446	9.94 140	7	54
7	9.68 716	22	9.74 583	30	10.25 417	9.94 133	7	53
8	9.68 739	23	9.74 613	30	10.25 387	9.94 126	7	52
9	9.68 762	22	9.74 643	30	10.25 357	9.94 119	7	51
10	9.68 784	23	9.74 673	29	10.25 327	9.94 112	7	50
11	9.68 807	22	9.74 702	30	10.25 298	9.94 105	7	49
12	9.68 829	23	9.74 732	30	10.25 268	9.94 098	7	48
13	9.68 852	23	9.74 762	29	10.25 238	9.94 090	8	47
14	9.68 875	22	9.74 791	30	10.25 209	9.94 083	7	46
15	9.68 897	23	9.74 821	30	10.25 179	9.94 076	7	45
16	9.68 920	22	9.74 851	29	10.25 149	9.94 069	7	44
17	9.68 942	23	9.74 880	30	10.25 120	9.94 062	7	43
18	9.68 965	23	9.74 910	29	10.25 090	9.94 055	7	42
19	9.68 987	23	9.74 939	30	10.25 061	9.94 048	7	41
20	9.69 010	22	9.74 969	29	10.25 031	9.94 041	7	40
21	9.69 032	23	9.74 998	30	10.25 002	9.94 034	7	39
22	9.69 055	22	9.75 028	30	10.24 972	9.94 027	7	38
23	9.69 077	23	9.75 058	29	10.24 942	9.94 020	8	37
24	9.69 100	22	9.75 087	30	10.24 913	9.94 012	7	36
25	9.69 122	22	9.75 117	29	10.24 883	9.94 005	7	35
26	9.69 144	23	9.75 146	30	10.24 854	9.93 998	7	34
27	9.69 167	22	9.75 176	29	10.24 824	9.93 991	7	33
28	9.69 189	23	9.75 205	30	10.24 795	9.93 984	7	32
29	9.69 212	22	9.75 235	29	10.24 765	9.93 977	7	31
30	9.69 234	22	9.75 264	30	10.24 736	9.93 970	7	30
31	9.69 256	23	9.75 294	29	10.24 706	9.93 963	8	29
32	9.69 279	22	9.75 323	30	10.24 677	9.93 955	7	28
33	9.69 301	22	9.75 353	29	10.24 647	9.93 948	7	27
34	9.69 323	22	9.75 382	29	10.24 618	9.93 941	7	26
35	9.69 345	23	9.75 411	30	10.24 589	9.93 934	7	25
36	9.69 368	22	9.75 441	29	10.24 559	9.93 927	7	24
37	9.69 390	22	9.75 470	30	10.24 530	9.93 920	8	23
38	9.69 412	22	9.75 500	29	10.24 500	9.93 912	7	22
39	9.69 434	22	9.75 529	29	10.24 471	9.93 905	7	21
40	9.69 456	23	9.75 558	30	10.24 442	9.93 898	7	20
41	9.69 479	22	9.75 588	29	10.24 412	9.93 891	7	19
42	9.69 501	22	9.75 617	30	10.24 383	9.93 884	8	18
43	9.69 523	22	9.75 647	29	10.24 353	9.93 876	7	17
44	9.69 545	22	9.75 676	29	10.24 324	9.93 869	7	16
45	9.69 567	22	9.75 705	30	10.24 295	9.93 862	7	15
46	9.69 589	22	9.75 735	29	10.24 265	9.93 855	8	14
47	9.69 611	22	9.75 764	29	10.24 236	9.93 847	7	13
48	9.69 633	22	9.75 793	29	10.24 207	9.93 840	7	12
49	9.69 655	22	9.75 822	30	10.24 178	9.93 833	7	11
50	9.69 677	22	9.75 852	29	10.24 148	9.93 826	7	10
51	9.69 699	22	9.75 881	29	10.24 119	9.93 819	8	9
52	9.69 721	22	9.75 910	29	10.24 090	9.93 811	7	8
53	9.69 743	22	9.75 939	30	10.24 061	9.93 804	7	7
54	9.69 765	22	9.75 969	29	10.24 031	9.93 797	8	6
55	9.69 787	22	9.75 998	29	10.24 002	9.93 789	7	5
56	9.69 809	22	9.76 027	29	10.23 973	9.93 782	7	4
57	9.69 831	22	9.76 056	30	10.23 944	9.93 775	7	3
58	9.69 853	22	9.76 086	29	10.23 914	9.93 768	8	2
59	9.69 875	22	9.76 115	29	10.23 885	9.93 760	7	1
60	9.69 897		9.76 144		10.23 856	9.93 753		0
	L Cos	d	L Ctn	cd	L Tan	L Sin	d	'

Prop. Pts.

	30	29
2	6.0	5.8
3	9.0	8.7
4	12.0	11.6
5	15.0	14.5
6	18.0	17.4
7	21.0	20.3
8	24.0	23.2
9	27.0	26.1

	23	22
2	4.6	4.4
3	6.9	6.6
4	9.2	8.8
5	11.5	11.0
6	13.8	13.2
7	16.1	15.4
8	18.4	17.6
9	20.7	19.8

	8	7
2	1.6	1.4
3	2.4	2.1
4	3.2	2.8
5	4.0	3.5
6	4.8	4.2
7	5.6	4.9
8	6.4	5.6
9	7.2	6.3

From the top:
For 29°+ or 209°+, read as printed; for 119°+ or 299°+, read co-function.

From the bottom:
For 60°+ or 240°+, read as printed; for 150°+ or 330°+, read co-function.

60° — Logarithms of Trigonometric Functions

Table XIV. [XIV
30° — Logarithms of Trigonometric Functions

′	L Sin	d	L Tan	c d	L Ctn	L Cos	d		′
0	9.69 897		9.76 144		10.23 856	9.93 753			60
1	9.69 919	22	9.76 173	29	10.23 827	9.93 746	7		59
2	9.69 941	22	9.76 202	29	10.23 798	9.93 738	8		58
3	9.69 963	22	9.76 231	29	10.23 769	9.93 731	7		57
4	9.69 984	21	9.76 261	30	10.23 739	9.93 724	7		56
5	9.70 006	22	9.76 290	29	10.23 710	9.93 717	8		55
6	9.70 028	22	9.76 319	29	10.23 681	9.93 709	7		54
7	9.70 050	22	9.76 348	29	10.23 652	9.93 702	7		53
8	9.70 072	21	9.76 377	29	10.23 623	9.93 695	8		52
9	9.70 093	22	9.76 406	29	10.23 594	9.93 687	7		51
10	9.70 115	22	9.76 435	29	10.23 565	9.93 680	7		50
11	9.70 137	22	9.76 464	29	10.23 536	9.93 673	8		49
12	9.70 159	21	9.76 493	29	10.23 507	9.93 665	7		48
13	9.70 180	22	9.76 522	29	10.23 478	9.93 658	8		47
14	9.70 202	22	9.76 551	29	10.23 449	9.93 650	7		46
15	9.70 224	21	9.76 580	29	10.23 420	9.93 643	7		45
16	9.70 245	22	9.76 609	30	10.23 391	9.93 636	8		44
17	9.70 267	21	9.76 639	29	10.23 361	9.93 628	7		43
18	9.70 288	22	9.76 668	29	10.23 332	9.93 621	7		42
19	9.70 310	22	9.76 697	28	10.23 303	9.93 614	8		41
20	9.70 332	21	9.76 725	29	10.23 275	9.93 606	7		40
21	9.70 353	22	9.76 754	29	10.23 246	9.93 599	8		39
22	9.70 375	21	9.76 783	29	10.23 217	9.93 591	7		38
23	9.70 396	22	9.76 812	29	10.23 188	9.93 584	7		37
24	9.70 418	21	9.76 841	29	10.23 159	9.93 577	8		36
25	9.70 439	22	9.76 870	29	10.23 130	9.93 569	7		35
26	9.70 461	21	9.76 899	29	10.23 101	9.93 562	8		34
27	9.70 482	22	9.76 928	29	10.23 072	9.93 554	7		33
28	9.70 504	21	9.76 957	29	10.23 043	9.93 547	8		32
29	9.70 525	22	9.76 986	29	10.23 014	9.93 539	7		31
30	9.70 547	21	9.77 015	29	10.22 985	9.93 532	7		30
31	9.70 568	22	9.77 044	29	10.22 956	9.93 525	8		29
32	9.70 590	22	9.77 073	28	10.22 927	9.93 517	7		28
33	9.70 611	21	9.77 101	29	10.22 899	9.93 510	8		27
34	9.70 633	22	9.77 130	29	10.22 870	9.93 502	7		26
35	9.70 654	21	9.77 159	29	10.22 841	9.93 495	8		25
36	9.70 675	22	9.77 188	29	10.22 812	9.93 487	7		24
37	9.70 697	21	9.77 217	29	10.22 783	9.93 480	8		23
38	9.70 718	21	9.77 246	28	10.22 754	9.93 472	7		22
39	9.70 739	22	9.77 274	29	10.22 726	9.93 465	8		21
40	9.70 761	21	9.77 303	29	10.22 697	9.93 457	7		20
41	9.70 782	21	9.77 332	29	10.22 668	9.93 450	8		19
42	9.70 803	21	9.77 361	29	10.22 639	9.93 442	7		18
43	9.70 824	22	9.77 390	28	10.22 610	9.93 435	8		17
44	9.70 846	21	9.77 418	29	10.22 582	9.93 427	7		16
45	9.70 867	21	9.77 447	29	10.22 553	9.93 420	8		15
46	9.70 888	22	9.77 476	29	10.22 524	9.93 412	7		14
47	9.70 909	22	9.77 505	28	10.22 495	9.93 405	8		13
48	9.70 931	21	9.77 533	29	10.22 467	9.93 397	7		12
49	9.70 952	21	9.77 562	29	10.22 438	9.93 390	8		11
50	9.70 973	21	9.77 591	28	10.22 409	9.93 382	7		10
51	9.70 994	21	9.77 619	29	10.22 381	9.93 375	8		9
52	9.71 015	21	9.77 648	29	10.22 352	9.93 367	7		8
53	9.71 036	22	9.77 677	29	10.22 323	9.93 360	8		7
54	9.71 058	21	9.77 706	28	10.22 294	9.93 352	8		6
55	9.71 079	21	9.77 734	29	10.22 266	9.93 344	7		5
56	9.71 100	21	9.77 763	28	10.22 237	9.93 337	8		4
57	9.71 121	21	9.77 791	29	10.22 209	9.93 329	7		3
58	9.71 142	21	9.77 820	29	10.22 180	9.93 322	8		2
59	9.71 163	21	9.77 849	28	10.22 151	9.93 314	7		1
60	9.71 184		9.77 877		10.22 123	9.93 307			0
	L Cos	d	L Ctn	c d	L Tan	L Sin	d	′	Prop. Pts.

Prop. Pts.

	30	29
2	6.0	5.8
3	9.0	8.7
4	12.0	11.6
5	15.0	14.5
6	18.0	17.4
7	21.0	20.3
8	24.0	23.2
9	27.0	26.1

	28	22
2	5.6	4.4
3	8.4	6.6
4	11.2	8.8
5	14.0	11.0
6	16.8	13.2
7	19.6	15.4
8	22.4	17.6
9	25.2	19.8

	21	8
2	4.2	1.6
3	6.3	2.4
4	8.4	3.2
5	10.5	4.0
6	12.6	4.8
7	14.7	5.6
8	16.8	6.4
9	18.9	7.2

	7
2	1.4
3	2.1
4	2.8
5	3.5
6	4.2
7	4.9
8	5.6
9	6.3

From the top:
For 30°+ or 210°+, read as printed; for 120°+ or 300°+, read co-function.

From the bottom:
For 59°+ or 239°+, read as printed; for 149°+ or 329°+, read co-function.

59° — Logarithms of Trigonometric Functions

′	L Sin	d	L Tan	c d	L Ctn	L Cos	d		Prop. Pts.
0	9.71 184	21	9.77 877	29	10.22 123	9.93 307	8	60	
1	9.71 205	21	9.77 906	29	10.22 094	9.93 299	8	59	
2	9.71 226	21	9.77 935	29	10.22 065	9.93 291	7	58	
3	9.71 247	21	9.77 963	28	10.22 037	9.93 284	8	57	
4	9.71 268	21	9.77 992	29	10.22 008	9.93 276	7	56	
5	9.71 289	21	9.78 020	28	10.21 980	9.93 269	8	55	29 28
6	9.71 310	21	9.78 049	29	10.21 951	9.93 261	8	54	2 5.8 5.6
7	9.71 331	21	9.78 077	29	10.21 923	9.93 253	7	53	3 8.7 8.4
8	9.71 352	21	9.78 106	29	10.21 894	9.93 246	8	52	4 11.6 11.2
9	9.71 373	20	9.78 135	28	10.21 865	9.93 238	8	51	5 14.5 14.0
10	9.71 393	21	9.78 163	29	10.21 837	9.93 220	7	50	6 17.4 16.8
11	9.71 414	21	9.78 192	28	10.21 808	9.93 223	8	49	7 20.3 19.6
12	9.71 435	21	9.78 220	29	10.21 780	9.93 215	8	48	8 23.2 22.4
13	9.71 456	21	9.78 249	28	10.21 751	9.93 207	7	47	9 26.1 25.2
14	9.71 477	21	9.78 277	29	10.21 723	9.93 200	8	46	
15	9.71 498	21	9.78 306	28	10.21 694	9.93 192	8	45	
16	9.71 519	20	9.78 334	29	10.21 666	9.93 184	7	44	21 20
17	9.71 539	21	9.78 363	28	10.21 637	9.93 177	8	43	
18	9.71 560	21	9.78 391	28	10.21 609	9.93 169	8	42	2 4.2 4.0
19	9.71 581	21	9.78 419	29	10.21 581	9.93 161	7	41	3 6.3 6.0
20	9.71 602	20	9.78 448	28	10.21 552	9.93 154	8	40	4 8.4 8.0
21	9.71 622	21	9.78 476	29	10.21 524	9.93 146	8	39	5 10.5 10.0
22	9.71 643	21	9.78 505	28	10.21 495	9.93 138	7	38	6 12.6 12.0
23	9.71 664	21	9.78 533	29	10.21 467	9.93 131	8	37	7 14.7 14.0
24	9.71 685	20	9.78 562	28	10.21 438	9.93 123	8	36	8 16.8 16.0
25	9.71 705	21	9.78 590	28	10.21 410	9.93 115	7	35	9 18.9 18.0
26	9.71 726	21	9.78 618	29	10.21 382	9.93 108	8	34	
27	9.71 747	20	9.78 647	28	10.21 353	9.93 100	8	33	
28	9.71 767	21	9.78 675	29	10.21 325	9.93 092	8	32	8 7
29	9.71 788	21	9.78 704	28	10.21 296	9.93 084	7	31	2 1.6 1.4
30	9.71 809	20	9.78 732	28	10.21 268	9.93 077	8	30	3 2.4 2.1
31	9.71 829	21	9.78 760	29	10.21 240	9.93 069	8	29	4 3.2 2.8
32	9.71 850	20	9.78 789	28	10.21 211	9.93 061	8	28	5 4.0 3.5
33	9.71 870	21	9.78 817	28	10.21 183	9.93 053	7	27	6 4.8 4.2
34	9.71 891	20	9.78 845	29	10.21 155	9.93 046	8	26	7 5.6 4.9
35	9.71 911	21	9.78 874	28	10.21 126	9.93 038	8	25	8 6.4 5.6
36	9.71 932	20	9.78 902	28	10.21 098	9.93 030	8	24	9 7.2 6.3
37	9.71 952	20	9.78 930	29	10.21 070	9.93 022	8	23	
38	9.71 973	21	9.78 959	28	10.21 041	9.93 014	7	22	
39	9.71 994	20	9.78 987	28	10.21 013	9.93 007	8	21	
40	9.72 014	20	9.79 015	28	10.20 985	9.92 999	8	20	
41	9.72 034	21	9.79 043	29	10.20 957	9.92 991	8	19	
42	9.72 055	20	9.79 072	28	10.20 928	9.92 983	7	18	*From the top:*
43	9.72 075	21	9.79 100	28	10.20 900	9.92 976	8	17	For 31°+ or 211°+,
44	9.72 096	20	9.79 128	28	10.20 872	9.92 968	8	16	read as printed; for
45	9.72 116	21	9.79 156	29	10.20 844	9.92 960	8	15	121°+ or 301°+, read
46	9.72 137	20	9.79 185	28	10.20 815	9.92 952	8	14	co-function.
47	9.72 157	20	9.79 213	28	10.20 787	9.92 944	8	13	
48	9.72 177	21	9.79 241	28	10.20 759	9.92 936	7	12	
49	9.72 198	20	9.79 269	28	10.20 731	9.92 929	8	11	*From the bottom:*
50	9.72 218	20	9.79 297	29	10.20 703	9.92 921	8	10	For 58°+ or 238°+,
51	9.72 238	21	9.79 326	28	10.20 674	9.92 913	8	9	read as printed; for
52	9.72 259	20	9.79 354	28	10.20 646	9.92 905	8	8	148°+ or 328°+, read
53	9.72 279	20	9.79 382	28	10.20 618	9.92 897	8	7	co-function.
54	9.72 299	21	9.79 410	28	10.20 590	9.92 889	8	6	
55	9.72 320	20	9.79 438	28	10.20 562	9.92 881	7	5	
56	9.72 340	20	9.79 466	29	10.20 534	9.92 874	8	4	
57	9.72 360	21	9.79 495	28	10.20 505	9.92 866	8	3	
58	9.72 381	20	9.79 523	28	10.20 477	9.92 858	8	2	
59	9.72 401	20	9.79 551	28	10.20 449	9.92 850	8	1	
60	9.72 421		9.79 579		10.20 421	9.92 842		0	
	L Cos	d	L Ctn	c d	L Tan	L Sin	d	′	Prop. Pts.

32° — Logarithms of Trigonometric Functions

′	L Sin	d	L Tan	c d	L Ctn	L Cos	d		Prop. Pts.
0	9.72 421	20	9.79 579	28	10.20 421	9.92 842	8	60	
1	9.72 441	20	9.79 607	28	10.20 393	9.92 834	8	59	
2	9.72 461	21	9.79 635	28	10.20 365	9.92 826	8	58	**29** **28**
3	9.72 482	20	9.79 663	28	10.20 337	9.92 818	8	57	2 5.8 5.6
4	9.72 502	20	9.79 691	28	10.20 309	9.92 810	7	56	3 8.7 8.4
5	9.72 522	20	9.79 719	28	10.20 281	9.92 803	8	55	4 11.6 11.2
6	9.72 542	20	9.79 747	29	10.20 253	9.92 795	8	54	5 14.5 14.0
7	9.72 562	20	9.79 776	28	10.20 224	9.92 787	8	53	6 17.4 16.8
8	9.72 582	20	9.79 804	28	10.20 196	9.92 779	8	52	7 20.3 19.6
9	9.72 602	20	9.79 832	28	10.20 168	9.92 771	8	51	8 23.2 22.4
10	9.72 622	21	9.79 860	28	10.20 140	9.92 763	8	50	9 26.1 25.2
11	9.72 643	20	9.79 888	28	10.20 112	9.92 755	8	49	
12	9.72 663	20	9.79 916	28	10.20 084	9.92 747	8	48	
13	9.72 683	20	9.79 944	28	10.20 056	9.92 739	8	47	**27** **21**
14	9.72 703	20	9.79 972	28	10.20 028	9.92 731	8	46	2 5.4 4.2
15	9.72 723	20	9.80 000	28	10.20 000	9.92 723	8	45	3 8.1 6.3
16	9.72 743	20	9.80 028	28	10.19 972	9.92 715	8	44	4 10.8 8.4
17	9.72 763	20	9.80 056	28	10.19 944	9.92 707	8	43	5 13.5 10.5
18	9.72 783	20	9.80 084	28	10.19 916	9.92 699	8	42	6 16.2 12.6
19	9.72 803	20	9.80 112	28	10.19 888	9.92 691	8	41	7 18.9 14.7
20	9.72 823	20	9.80 140	28	10.19 860	9.92 683	8	40	8 21.6 16.8
21	9.72 843	20	9.80 168	27	10.19 832	9.92 675	8	39	9 24.3 18.9
22	9.72 863	20	9.80 195	28	10.19 805	9.92 667	8	38	
23	9.72 883	19	9.80 223	28	10.19 777	9.92 659	8	37	
24	9.72 902	20	9.80 251	28	10.19 749	9.92 651	8	36	**20** **19**
25	9.72 922	20	9.80 279	28	10.19 721	9.92 643	8	35	2 4.0 3.8
26	9.72 942	20	9.80 307	28	10.19 693	9.92 635	8	34	3 6.0 5.7
27	9.72 962	20	9.80 335	28	10.19 665	9.92 627	8	33	4 8.0 7.6
28	9.72 982	20	9.80 363	28	10.19 637	9.92 619	8	32	5 10.0 9.5
29	9.73 002	20	9.80 391	28	10.19 609	9.92 611	8	31	6 12.0 11.4
30	9.73 022	19	9.80 419	28	10.19 581	9.92 603	8	30	7 14.0 13.3
31	9.73 041	20	9.80 447	27	10.19 553	9.92 595	8	29	8 16.0 15.2
32	9.73 061	20	9.80 474	28	10.19 526	9.92 587	8	28	9 18.0 17.1
33	9.73 081	20	9.80 502	28	10.19 498	9.92 579	8	27	
34	9.73 101	20	9.80 530	28	10.19 470	9.92 571	8	26	
35	9.73 121	19	9.80 558	28	10.19 442	9.92 563	8	25	**9** **8** **7**
36	9.73 140	20	9.80 586	28	10.19 414	9.92 555	9	24	2 1.8 1.6 1.4
37	9.73 160	20	9.80 614	28	10.19 386	9.92 546	8	23	3 2.7 2.4 2.1
38	9.73 180	20	9.80 642	27	10.19 358	9.92 538	8	22	4 3.6 3.2 2.8
39	9.73 200	19	9.80 669	28	10.19 331	9.92 530	8	21	5 4.5 4.0 3.5
40	9.73 219	20	9.80 697	28	10.19 303	9.92 522	8	20	6 5.4 4.8 4.2
41	9.73 239	20	9.80 725	28	10.19 275	9.92 514	8	19	7 6.3 5.6 4.9
42	9.73 259	19	9.80 753	28	10.19 247	9.92 506	8	18	8 7.2 6.4 5.6
43	9.73 278	20	9.80 781	27	10.19 219	9.92 498	8	17	9 8.1 7.2 6.3
44	9.73 298	20	9.80 808	28	10.19 192	9.92 490	8	16	
45	9.73 318	19	9.80 836	28	10.19 164	9.92 482	9	15	*From the top:*
46	9.73 337	20	9.80 864	28	10.19 136	9.92 473	8	14	For 32°+ or 212°+,
47	9.73 357	20	9.80 892	27	10.19 108	9.92 465	8	13	read as printed; for
48	9.73 377	19	9.80 919	28	10.19 081	9.92 457	8	12	122°+ or 302°+, read
49	9.73 396	20	9.80 947	28	10.19 053	9.92 449	8	11	co-function.
50	9.73 416	19	9.80 975	28	10.19 025	9.92 441	8	10	
51	9.73 435	20	9.81 003	27	10.18 997	9.92 433	8	9	
52	9.73 455	19	9.81 030	28	10.18 970	9.92 425	9	8	*From the bottom:*
53	9.73 474	20	9.81 058	28	10.18 942	9.92 416	8	7	For 57°+ or 237°+,
54	9.73 494	19	9.81 086	27	10.18 914	9.92 408	8	6	read as printed; for
55	9.73 513	20	9.81 113	28	10.18 887	9.92 400	8	5	147°+ or 327°+, read
56	9.73 533	19	9.81 141	28	10.18 859	9.92 392	8	4	co-function.
57	9.73 552	20	9.81 169	27	10.18 831	9.92 384	8	3	
58	9.73 572	19	9.81 196	28	10.18 804	9.92 376	9	2	
59	9.73 591	20	9.81 224	28	10.18 776	9.92 367	8	1	
60	9.73 611		9.81 252		10.18 748	9.92 359		0	
	L Cos	d	L Ctn	c d	L Tan	L Sin	d	′	Prop. Pts.

57° — Logarithms of Trigonometric Functions

33° — Logarithms of Trigonometric Functions

′	L Sin	d	L Tan	c d	L Ctn	L Cos	d	′
0	9.73 611	19	9.81 252	27	10.18 748	9.92 359	8	60
1	9.73 630	19	9.81 279	28	10.18 721	9.92 351	8	59
2	9.73 650	20	9.81 307	28	10.18 693	9.92 343	8	58
3	9.73 669	19	9.81 335	28	10.18 665	9.92 335	8	57
4	9.73 689	20	9.81 362	28	10.18 638	9.92 326	8	56
5	9.73 708	19	9.81 390	28	10.18 610	9.92 318	8	55
6	9.73 727	19	9.81 418	27	10.18 582	9.92 310	8	54
7	9.73 747	20	9.81 445	28	10.18 555	9.92 302	9	53
8	9.73 766	19	9.81 473	27	10.18 527	9.92 293	8	52
9	9.73 785	19	9.81 500	28	10.18 500	9.92 285	8	51
10	9.73 805	19	9.81 528	28	10.18 472	9.92 277	8	50
11	9.73 824	19	9.81 556	27	10.18 444	9.92 269	9	49
12	9.73 843	20	9.81 583	28	10.18 417	9.92 260	8	48
13	9.73 863	19	9.81 611	27	10.18 389	9.92 252	8	47
14	9.73 882	19	9.81 638	28	10.18 362	9.92 244	9	46
15	9.73 901	20	9.81 666	27	10.18 334	9.92 235	8	45
16	9.73 921	19	9.81 693	28	10.18 307	9.92 227	8	44
17	9.73 940	19	9.81 721	27	10.18 279	9.92 219	8	43
18	9.73 959	19	9.81 748	28	10.18 252	9.92 211	9	42
19	9.73 978	19	9.81 776	27	10.18 224	9.92 202	8	41
20	9.73 997	20	9.81 803	28	10.18 197	9.92 194	8	40
21	9.74 017	19	9.81 831	27	10.18 169	9.92 186	9	39
22	9.74 036	19	9.81 858	28	10.18 142	9.92 177	9	38
23	9.74 055	19	9.81 886	27	10.18 114	9.92 169	8	37
24	9.74 074	19	9.81 913	28	10.18 087	9.92 161	9	36
25	9.74 093	20	9.81 941	27	10.18 059	9.92 152	8	35
26	9.74 113	19	9.81 968	28	10.18 032	9.92 144	8	34
27	9.74 132	19	9.81 996	27	10.18 004	9.92 136	9	33
28	9.74 151	19	9.82 023	28	10.17 977	9.92 127	8	32
29	9.74 170	19	9.82 051	27	10.17 949	9.92 119	9	31
30	9.74 189	19	9.82 078	28	10.17 922	9.92 111	9	30
31	9.74 208	19	9.82 106	27	10.17 894	9.92 102	8	29
32	9.74 227	19	9.82 133	28	10.17 867	9.92 094	8	28
33	9.74 246	19	9.82 161	27	10.17 839	9.92 086	9	27
34	9.74 265	19	9.82 188	27	10.17 812	9.92 077	8	26
35	9.74 284	19	9.82 215	28	10.17 785	9.92 069	9	25
36	9.74 303	19	9.82 243	27	10.17 757	9.92 060	8	24
37	9.74 322	19	9.82 270	28	10.17 730	9.92 052	8	23
38	9.74 341	19	9.82 298	27	10.17 702	9.92 044	9	22
39	9.74 360	19	9.82 325	27	10.17 675	9.92 035	8	21
40	9.74 379	19	9.82 352	28	10.17 648	9.92 027	9	20
41	9.74 398	19	9.82 380	27	10.17 620	9.92 018	8	19
42	9.74 417	19	9.82 407	28	10.17 593	9.92 010	9	18
43	9.74 436	19	9.82 435	27	10.17 565	9.92 002	8	17
44	9.74 455	19	9.82 462	27	10.17 538	9.91 993	8	16
45	9.74 474	19	9.82 489	28	10.17 511	9.91 985	9	15
46	9.74 493	19	9.82 517	27	10.17 483	9.91 976	8	14
47	9.74 512	19	9.82 544	27	10.17 456	9.91 968	9	13
48	9.74 531	18	9.82 571	28	10.17 429	9.91 959	8	12
49	9.74 549	19	9.82 599	27	10.17 401	9.91 951	9	11
50	9.74 568	19	9.82 626	27	10.17 374	9.91 942	8	10
51	9.74 587	19	9.82 653	28	10.17 347	9.91 934	9	9
52	9.74 606	19	9.82 681	27	10.17 319	9.91 925	8	8
53	9.74 625	19	9.82 708	27	10.17 292	9.91 917	9	7
54	9.74 644	18	9.82 735	27	10.17 265	9.91 908	8	6
55	9.74 662	19	9.82 762	28	10.17 238	9.91 900	9	5
56	9.74 681	19	9.82 790	27	10.17 210	9.91 891	8	4
57	9.74 700	19	9.82 817	27	10.17 183	9.91 883	9	3
58	9.74 719	18	9.82 844	27	10.17 156	9.91 874	8	2
59	9.74 737	19	9.82 871	28	10.17 129	9.91 866	9	1
60	9.74 756		9.82 899		10.17 101	9.91 857		0
	L Cos	d	L Ctn	c d	L Tan	L Sin	d	′

Prop. Pts.

	28	27
2	5.6	5.4
3	8.4	8.1
4	11.2	10.8
5	14.0	13.5
6	16.8	16.2
7	19.6	18.9
8	22.4	21.6
9	25.2	24.3

	20	19
2	4.0	3.8
3	6.0	5.7
4	8.0	7.6
5	10.0	9.5
6	12.0	11.4
7	14.0	13.3
8	16.0	15.2
9	18.0	17.1

	18	9
2	3.6	1.8
3	5.4	2.7
4	7.2	3.6
5	9.0	4.5
6	10.8	5.4
7	12.6	6.3
8	14.4	7.2
9	16.2	8.1

	8
2	1.6
3	2.4
4	3.2
5	4.0
6	4.8
7	5.6
8	6.4
9	7.2

From the top:
For **33°+ or 213°+**, read as printed; for **123°+ or 303°+**, read co-function.

From the bottom:
For **56°+ or 236°+**, read as printed; for **146°+ or 326°+**, read co-function.

Prop. Pts.

56° — Logarithms of Trigonometric Functions

Table XIV. [XIV
34° — Logarithms of Trigonometric Functions

′	L Sin	d	L Tan	c d	L Ctn	L Cos	d		Prop. Pts.
0	9.74 756	19	9.82 899	27	10.17 101	9.91 857	8	60	
1	9.74 775	19	9.82 926	27	10.17 074	9.91 849	9	59	
2	9.74 794	18	9.82 953	27	10.17 047	9.91 840	8	58	28 | 27
3	9.74 812	19	9.82 980	28	10.17 020	9.91 832	9	57	2 | 5.6 | 5.4
4	9.74 831	19	9.83 008	27	10.16 992	9.91 823	8	56	3 | 8.4 | 8.1
5	9.74 850	18	9.83 035	27	10.16 965	9.91 815	9	55	4 | 11.2 | 10.8
6	9.74 868	19	9.83 062	27	10.16 938	9.91 806	8	54	5 | 14.0 | 13.5
7	9.74 887	19	9.83 089	28	10.16 911	9.91 798	9	53	6 | 16.8 | 16.2
8	9.74 906	18	9.83 117	27	10.16 883	9.91 789	8	52	7 | 19.6 | 18.9
9	9.74 924	19	9.83 144	27	10.16 856	9.91 781	9	51	8 | 22.4 | 21.6
10	9.74 943	18	9.83 171	27	10.16 829	9.91 772	9	50	9 | 25.2 | 24.3
11	9.74 961	19	9.83 198	27	10.16 802	9.91 763	8	49	
12	9.74 980	19	9.83 225	27	10.16 775	9.91 755	9	48	
13	9.74 999	18	9.83 252	28	10.16 748	9.91 746	8	47	26 | 19
14	9.75 017	19	9.83 280	27	10.16 720	9.91 738	9	46	2 | 5.2 | 3.8
15	9.75 036	18	9.83 307	27	10.16 693	9.91 729	9	45	3 | 7.8 | 5.7
16	9.75 054	19	9.83 334	27	10.16 666	9.91 720	8	44	4 | 10.4 | 7.6
17	9.75 073	18	9.83 361	27	10.16 639	9.91 712	9	43	5 | 13.0 | 9.5
18	9.75 091	19	9.83 388	27	10.16 612	9.91 703	8	42	6 | 15.6 | 11.4
19	9.75 110	18	9.83 415	27	10.16 585	9.91 695	9	41	7 | 18.2 | 13.3
20	9.75 128	19	9.83 442	28	10.16 558	9.91 686	9	40	8 | 20.8 | 15.2
21	9.75 147	18	9.83 470	27	10.16 530	9.91 677	8	39	9 | 23.4 | 17.1
22	9.75 165	19	9.83 497	27	10.16 503	9.91 669	9	38	
23	9.75 184	18	9.83 524	27	10.16 476	9.91 660	9	37	
24	9.75 202	19	9.83 551	27	10.16 449	9.91 651	8	36	18 | 9
25	9.75 221	18	9.83 578	27	10.16 422	9.91 643	9	35	2 | 3.6 | 1.8
26	9.75 239	19	9.83 605	27	10.16 395	9.91 634	9	34	3 | 5.4 | 2.7
27	9.75 258	18	9.83 632	27	10.16 368	9.91 625	8	33	4 | 7.2 | 3.6
28	9.75 276	18	9.83 659	27	10.16 341	9.91 617	9	32	5 | 9.0 | 4.5
29	9.75 294	19	9.83 686	27	10.16 314	9.91 608	9	31	6 | 10.8 | 5.4
30	9.75 313	18	9.83 713	27	10.16 287	9.91 599	8	30	7 | 12.6 | 6.3
31	9.75 331	19	9.83 740	28	10.16 260	9.91 591	9	29	8 | 14.4 | 7.2
32	9.75 350	18	9.83 768	27	10.16 232	9.91 582	9	28	9 | 16.2 | 8.1
33	9.75 368	18	9.83 795	27	10.16 205	9.91 573	8	27	
34	9.75 386	19	9.83 822	27	10.16 178	9.91 565	9	26	8
35	9.75 405	18	9.83 849	27	10.16 151	9.91 556	9	25	2 | 1.6
36	9.75 423	18	9.83 876	27	10.16 124	9.91 547	9	24	3 | 2.4
37	9.75 441	18	9.83 903	27	10.16 097	9.91 538	8	23	4 | 3.2
38	9.75 459	19	9.83 930	27	10.16 070	9.91 530	9	22	5 | 4.0
39	9.75 478	18	9.83 957	27	10.16 043	9.91 521	9	21	6 | 4.8
40	9.75 496	18	9.83 984	27	10.16 016	9.91 512	8	20	7 | 5.6
41	9.75 514	19	9.84 011	27	10.15 989	9.91 504	9	19	8 | 6.4
42	9.75 533	18	9.84 038	27	10.15 962	9.91 495	9	18	9 | 7.2
43	9.75 551	18	9.84 065	27	10.15 935	9.91 486	9	17	
44	9.75 569	18	9.84 092	27	10.15 908	9.91 477	8	16	
45	9.75 587	18	9.84 119	27	10.15 881	9.91 469	9	15	*From the top:*
46	9.75 605	19	9.84 146	27	10.15 854	9.91 460	9	14	For 34°+ or 214°+,
47	9.75 624	18	9.84 173	27	10.15 827	9.91 451	9	13	read as printed; for
48	9.75 642	18	9.84 200	27	10.15 800	9.91 442	9	12	124°+ or 304°+, read
49	9.75 660	18	9.84 227	27	10.15 773	9.91 433	8	11	co-function.
50	9.75 678	18	9.84 254	26	10.15 746	9.91 425	9	10	
51	9.75 696	18	9.84 280	27	10.15 720	9.91 416	9	9	
52	9.75 714	19	9.84 307	27	10.15 693	9.91 407	9	8	*From the bottom:*
53	9.75 733	18	9.84 334	27	10.15 666	9.91 398	9	7	For 55°+ or 235°+,
54	9.75 751	18	9.84 361	27	10.15 639	9.91 389	8	6	read as printed; for
55	9.75 769	18	9.84 388	27	10.15 612	9.91 381	9	5	145°+ or 325°+, read
56	9.75 787	18	9.84 415	27	10.15 585	9.91 372	9	4	co-function.
57	9.75 805	18	9.84 442	27	10.15 558	9.91 363	9	3	
58	9.75 823	18	9.84 469	27	10.15 531	9.91 354	9	2	
59	9.75 841	18	9.84 496	27	10.15 504	9.91 345	9	1	
60	9.75 859		9.84 523		10.15 477	9.91 336		0	
′	L Cos	d	L Ctn	c d	L Tan	L Sin	d	′	Prop. Pts.

55° — Logarithms of Trigonometric Functions

35° — Logarithms of Trigonometric Functions

′	L Sin	d	L Tan	cd	L Ctn	L Cos	d		Prop. Pts.
0	9.75 859	18	9.84 523	27	10.15 477	9.91 336	8	60	
1	9.75 877	18	9.84 550	27	10.15 450	9.91 328	9	59	
2	9.75 895	18	9.84 576	26	10.15 424	9.91 319	9	58	
3	9.75 913	18	9.84 603	27	10.15 397	9.91 310	9	57	
4	9.75 931	18	9.84 630	27	10.15 370	9.91 301	9	56	
5	9.75 949	18	9.84 657	27	10.15 343	9.91 292	9	55	
6	9.75 967	18	9.84 684	27	10.15 316	9.91 283	9	54	
7	9.75 985	18	9.84 711	27	10.15 289	9.91 274	8	53	
8	9.76 003	18	9.84 738	26	10.15 262	9.91 266	9	52	
9	9.76 021	18	9.84 764	27	10.15 236	9.91 257	9	51	
10	9.76 039	18	9.84 791	27	10.15 209	9.91 248	9	50	
11	9.76 057	18	9.84 818	27	10.15 182	9.91 239	9	49	
12	9.76 075	18	9.84 845	27	10.15 155	9.91 230	9	48	
13	9.76 093	18	9.84 872	27	10.15 128	9.91 221	9	47	
14	9.76 111	18	9.84 899	26	10.15 101	9.91 212	9	46	
15	9.76 129	17	9.84 925	27	10.15 075	9.91 203	9	45	
16	9.76 146	18	9.84 952	27	10.15 048	9.91 194	9	44	
17	9.76 164	18	9.84 979	27	10.15 021	9.91 185	9	43	
18	9.76 182	18	9.85 006	27	10.14 994	9.91 176	9	42	
19	9.76 200	18	9.85 033	26	10.14 967	9.91 167	9	41	
20	9.76 218	18	9.85 059	27	10.14 941	9.91 158	9	40	
21	9.76 236	17	9.85 086	27	10.14 914	9.91 149	8	39	
22	9.76 253	18	9.85 113	27	10.14 887	9.91 141	9	38	
23	9.76 271	18	9.85 140	26	10.14 860	9.91 132	9	37	
24	9.76 289	18	9.85 166	27	10.14 834	9.91 123	9	36	
25	9.76 307	17	9.85 193	27	10.14 807	9.91 114	9	35	
26	9.76 324	18	9.85 220	27	10.14 780	9.91 105	9	34	
27	9.76 342	18	9.85 247	26	10.14 753	9.91 096	9	33	
28	9.76 360	18	9.85 273	27	10.14 727	9.91 087	9	32	
29	9.76 378	17	9.85 300	27	10.14 700	9.91 078	9	31	
30	9.76 395	18	9.85 327	27	10.14 673	9.91 069	9	30	
31	9.76 413	18	9.85 354	27	10.14 646	9.91 060	9	29	
32	9.76 431	17	9.85 380	26	10.14 620	9.91 051	9	28	
33	9.76 448	18	9.85 407	27	10.14 593	9.91 042	9	27	
34	9.76 466	18	9.85 434	26	10.14 566	9.91 033	10	26	
35	9.76 484	17	9.85 460	27	10.14 540	9.91 023	9	25	
36	9.76 501	18	9.85 487	27	10.14 513	9.91 014	9	24	
37	9.76 519	18	9.85 514	26	10.14 486	9.91 005	9	23	
38	9.76 537	18	9.85 540	27	10.14 460	9.90 996	9	22	
39	9.76 554	18	9.85 567	27	10.14 433	9.90 987	9	21	
40	9.76 572	18	9.85 594	26	10.14 406	9.90 978	9	20	
41	9.76 590	17	9.85 620	27	10.14 380	9.90 969	9	19	
42	9.76 607	18	9.85 647	27	10.14 353	9.90 960	9	18	
43	9.76 625	18	9.85 674	26	10.14 326	9.90 951	9	17	
44	9.76 642	18	9.85 700	27	10.14 300	9.90 942	9	16	
45	9.76 660	17	9.85 727	27	10.14 273	9.90 933	9	15	
46	9.76 677	18	9.85 754	26	10.14 246	9.90 924	9	14	
47	9.76 695	18	9.85 780	27	10.14 220	9.90 915	9	13	
48	9.76 712	18	9.85 807	27	10.14 193	9.90 906	10	12	
49	9.76 730	17	9.85 834	26	10.14 166	9.90 896	9	11	
50	9.76 747	18	9.85 860	27	10.14 140	9.90 887	9	10	
51	9.76 765	17	9.85 887	26	10.14 113	9.90 878	9	9	
52	9.76 782	18	9.85 913	27	10.14 087	9.90 869	9	8	
53	9.76 800	17	9.85 940	27	10.14 060	9.90 860	9	7	
54	9.76 817	18	9.85 967	26	10.14 033	9.90 851	9	6	
55	9.76 835	17	9.85 993	27	10.14 007	9.90 842	10	5	
56	9.76 852	18	9.86 020	26	10.13 980	9.90 832	9	4	
57	9.76 870	18	9.86 046	27	10.13 954	9.90 823	9	3	
58	9.76 887	17	9.86 073	27	10.13 927	9.90 814	9	2	
59	9.76 904	18	9.86 100	26	10.13 900	9.90 805	9	1	
60	9.76 922		9.86 126		10.13 874	9.90 796		0	
	L Cos	d	L Ctn	cd	L Tan	L Sin	d	′	Prop. Pts.

Prop. Pts.

	27	26
2	5.4	5.2
3	8.1	7.8
4	10.8	10.4
5	13.5	13.0
6	16.2	15.6
7	18.9	18.2
8	21.6	20.8
9	24.3	23.4

	18	17
2	3.6	3.4
3	5.4	5.1
4	7.2	6.8
5	9.0	8.5
6	10.8	10.2
7	12.6	11.9
8	14.4	13.6
9	16.2	15.3

	10	9
2	2.0	1.8
3	3.0	2.7
4	4.0	3.6
5	5.0	4.5
6	6.0	5.4
7	7.0	6.3
8	8.0	7.2
9	9.0	8.1

	8
2	1.6
3	2.4
4	3.2
5	4.0
6	4.8
7	5.6
8	6.4
9	7.2

From the top:
For 35°+ or 215°+, read as printed; for 125°+ or 305°+, read co-function.

From the bottom:
For 54°+ or 234°+, read as printed; for 144°+ or 324°+, read co-function.

54° — Logarithms of Trigonometric Functions

36° — Logarithms of Trigonometric Functions

′	L Sin	d	L Tan	cd	L Ctn	L Cos	d	
0	9.76 922		9.86 126		10.13 874	9.90 796		60
1	9.76 939	17	9.86 153	27	10.13 847	9.90 787	9	59
2	9.76 957	18	9.86 179	26	10.13 821	9.90 777	10	58
3	9.76 974	17	9.86 206	27	10.13 794	9.90 768	9	57
4	9.76 991	17	9.86 232	26	10.13 768	9.90 759	9	56
5	9.77 009	18	9.86 259	27	10.13 741	9.90 750	9	55
6	9.77 026	17	9.86 285	26	10.13 715	9.90 741	9	54
7	9.77 043	17	9.86 312	27	10.13 688	9.90 731	10	53
8	9.77 061	18	9.86 338	26	10.13 662	9.90 722	9	52
9	9.77 078	17	9.86 365	27	10.13 635	9.90 713	9	51
10	9.77 095	17	9.86 392	26	10.13 608	9.90 704	9	50
11	9.77 112	17	9.86 418	26	10.13 582	9.90 694	10	49
12	9.77 130	17	9.86 445	27	10.13 555	9.90 685	9	48
13	9.77 147	17	9.86 471	26	10.13 529	9.90 676	9	47
14	9.77 164	17	9.86 498	27	10.13 502	9.90 667	9	46
15	9.77 181	17	9.86 524	26	10.13 476	9.90 657	10	45
16	9.77 199	18	9.86 551	27	10.13 449	9.90 648	9	44
17	9.77 216	17	9.86 577	26	10.13 423	9.90 639	9	43
18	9.77 233	17	9.86 603	27	10.13 397	9.90 630	9	42
19	9.77 250	17	9.86 630	26	10.13 370	9.90 620	10	41
20	9.77 268	18	9.86 656	27	10.13 344	9.90 611	9	40
21	9.77 285	17	9.86 683	26	10.13 317	9.90 602	9	39
22	9.77 302	17	9.86 709	27	10.13 291	9.90 592	10	38
23	9.77 319	17	9.86 736	26	10.13 264	9.90 583	9	37
24	9.77 336	17	9.86 762	27	10.13 238	9.90 574	9	36
25	9.77 353	17	9.86 789	26	10.13 211	9.90 565	9	35
26	9.77 370	17	9.86 815	27	10.13 185	9.90 555	10	34
27	9.77 387	18	9.86 842	26	10.13 158	9.90 546	9	33
28	9.77 405	17	9.86 868	26	10.13 132	9.90 537	9	32
29	9.77 422	17	9.86 894	27	10.13 106	9.90 527	10	31
30	9.77 439	17	9.86 921	26	10.13 079	9.90 518	9	30
31	9.77 456	17	9.86 947	27	10.13 053	9.90 509	9	29
32	9.77 473	17	9.86 974	26	10.13 026	9.90 499	10	28
33	9.77 490	17	9.87 000	27	10.13 000	9.90 490	10	27
34	9.77 507	17	9.87 027	26	10.12 973	9.90 480	10	26
35	9.77 524	17	9.87 053	26	10.12 947	9.90 471	9	25
36	9.77 541	17	9.87 079	27	10.12 921	9.90 462	10	24
37	9.77 558	17	9.87 106	26	10.12 894	9.90 452	9	23
38	9.77 575	17	9.87 132	26	10.12 868	9.90 443	9	22
39	9.77 592	17	9.87 158	27	10.12 842	9.90 434	10	21
40	9.77 609	17	9.87 185	26	10.12 815	9.90 424	9	20
41	9.77 626	17	9.87 211	27	10.12 789	9.90 415	9	19
42	9.77 643	17	9.87 238	26	10.12 762	9.90 405	10	18
43	9.77 660	17	9.87 264	26	10.12 736	9.90 396	9	17
44	9.77 677	17	9.87 290	27	10.12 710	9.90 386	10	16
45	9.77 694	17	9.87 317	26	10.12 683	9.90 377	9	15
46	9.77 711	17	9.87 343	26	10.12 657	9.90 368	10	14
47	9.77 728	16	9.87 369	27	10.12 631	9.90 358	9	13
48	9.77 744	17	9.87 396	26	10.12 604	9.90 349	10	12
49	9.77 761	17	9.87 422	26	10.12 578	9.90 339	9	11
50	9.77 778	17	9.87 448	27	10.12 552	9.90 330	10	10
51	9.77 795	17	9.87 475	26	10.12 525	9.90 320	10	9
52	9.77 812	17	9.87 501	26	10.12 499	9.90 311	10	8
53	9.77 829	17	9.87 527	27	10.12 473	9.90 301	9	7
54	9.77 846	16	9.87 554	26	10.12 446	9.90 292	10	6
55	9.77 862	17	9.87 580	26	10.12 420	9.90 282	9	5
56	9.77 879	17	9.87 606	27	10.12 394	9.90 273	10	4
57	9.77 896	17	9.87 633	26	10.12 367	9.90 263	9	3
58	9.77 913	17	9.87 659	26	10.12 341	9.90 254	10	2
59	9.77 930	16	9.87 685	26	10.12 315	9.90 244	9	1
60	9.77 946		9.87 711	26	10.12 289	9.90 235		0
	L Cos	d	L Ctn	cd	L Tan	L Sin	d	′

Prop. Pts.

	27	26
2	5.4	5.2
3	8.1	7.8
4	10.8	10.4
5	13.5	13.0
6	16.2	15.6
7	18.9	18.2
8	21.6	20.8
9	24.3	23.4

	18	17
2	3.6	3.4
3	5.4	5.1
4	7.2	6.8
5	9.0	8.5
6	10.8	10.2
7	12.6	11.9
8	14.4	13.6
9	16.2	15.3

	16	10
2	3.2	2.0
3	4.8	3.0
4	6.4	4.0
5	8.0	5.0
6	9.6	6.0
7	11.2	7.0
8	12.8	8.0
9	14.4	9.0

	9
2	1.8
3	2.7
4	3.6
5	4.5
6	5.4
7	6.3
8	7.2
9	8.1

From the top:
For **36°+ or 216°+**, read as printed; for **126°+ or 306°+**, read co-function.

From the bottom:
For **53°+ or 233°+**, read as printed; for **143°+ or 323°+**, read co-function.

53° — Logarithms of Trigonometric Functions

37° — Logarithms of Trigonometric Functions

′	L Sin	d	L Tan	cd	L Ctn	L Cos	d		Prop. Pts.
0	9.77946	17	9.87711	27	10.12289	9.90235	10	60	
1	9.77963	17	9.87738	26	10.12262	9.90225	9	59	
2	9.77980	17	9.87764	26	10.12236	9.90216	10	58	
3	9.77997	16	9.87790	27	10.12210	9.90206	9	57	
4	9.78013	17	9.87817	26	10.12183	9.90197	10	56	
5	9.78030	17	9.87843	26	10.12157	9.90187	9	55	**27** **26**
6	9.78047	16	9.87869	26	10.12131	9.90178	10	54	2 5.4 5.2
7	9.78063	17	9.87895	27	10.12105	9.90168	9	53	3 8.1 7.8
8	9.78080	17	9.87922	26	10.12078	9.90159	10	52	4 10.8 10.4
9	9.78097	16	9.87948	26	10.12052	9.90149	10	51	5 13.5 13.0
10	9.78113	17	9.87974	26	10.12026	9.90139	9	50	6 16.2 15.6
11	9.78130	17	9.88000	27	10.12000	9.90130	10	49	7 18.9 18.2
12	9.78147	16	9.88027	26	10.11973	9.90120	9	48	8 21.6 20.8
13	9.78163	17	9.88053	26	10.11947	9.90111	10	47	9 24.3 23.4
14	9.78180	17	9.88079	26	10.11921	9.90101	10	46	
15	9.78197	16	9.88105	26	10.11895	9.90091	9	45	
16	9.78213	17	9.88131	27	10.11869	9.90082	10	44	**17** **16**
17	9.78230	16	9.88158	26	10.11842	9.90072	9	43	
18	9.78246	17	9.88184	26	10.11816	9.90063	10	42	2 3.4 3.2
19	9.78263	17	9.88210	26	10.11790	9.90053	10	41	3 5.1 4.8
20	9.78280	16	9.88236	26	10.11764	9.90043	9	40	4 6.8 6.4
21	9.78296	17	9.88262	27	10.11738	9.90034	10	39	5 8.5 8.0
22	9.78313	16	9.88289	26	10.11711	9.90024	10	38	6 10.2 9.6
23	9.78329	17	9.88315	26	10.11685	9.90014	9	37	7 11.9 11.2
24	9.78346	16	9.88341	26	10.11659	9.90005	10	36	8 13.6 12.8
25	9.78362	17	9.88367	26	10.11633	9.89995	10	35	9 15.3 14.4
26	9.78379	16	9.88393	27	10.11607	9.89985	9	34	
27	9.78395	17	9.88420	26	10.11580	9.89976	10	33	
28	9.78412	16	9.88446	26	10.11554	9.89966	10	32	**10** **9**
29	9.78428	17	9.88472	26	10.11528	9.89956	9	31	2 2.0 1.8
30	9.78445	16	9.88498	26	10.11502	9.89947	10	30	3 3.0 2.7
31	9.78461	17	9.88524	26	10.11476	9.89937	10	29	4 4.0 3.6
32	9.78478	16	9.88550	27	10.11450	9.89927	10	28	5 5.0 4.5
33	9.78494	16	9.88577	26	10.11423	9.89918	10	27	6 6.0 5.4
34	9.78510	17	9.88603	26	10.11397	9.89908	10	26	7 7.0 6.3
35	9.78527	16	9.88629	26	10.11371	9.89898	10	25	8 8.0 7.2
36	9.78543	17	9.88655	26	10.11345	9.89888	9	24	9 9.0 8.1
37	9.78560	16	9.88681	26	10.11319	9.89879	10	23	
38	9.78576	16	9.88707	26	10.11293	9.89869	10	22	
39	9.78592	17	9.88733	26	10.11267	9.89859	10	21	
40	9.78609	16	9.88759	27	10.11241	9.89849	9	20	
41	9.78625	17	9.88786	26	10.11214	9.89840	10	19	
42	9.78642	16	9.88812	26	10.11188	9.89830	10	18	*From the top:*
43	9.78658	16	9.88838	26	10.11162	9.89820	10	17	For **37°+** or **217°+**,
44	9.78674	17	9.88864	26	10.11136	9.89810	9	16	read as printed; for
45	9.78691	16	9.88890	26	10.11110	9.89801	10	15	**127°+** or **307°+**, read
46	9.78707	16	9.88916	26	10.11084	9.89791	10	14	co-function.
47	9.78723	16	9.88942	26	10.11058	9.89781	10	13	
48	9.78739	17	9.88968	26	10.11032	9.89771	10	12	
49	9.78756	16	9.88994	26	10.11006	9.89761	9	11	*From the bottom:*
50	9.78772	16	9.89020	26	10.10980	9.89752	10	10	For **52°+** or **232°+**,
51	9.78788	17	9.89046	27	10.10954	9.89742	10	9	read as printed; for
52	9.78805	16	9.89073	26	10.10927	9.89732	10	8	**142°+** or **322°+**, read
53	9.78821	16	9.89099	26	10.10901	9.89722	10	7	co-function.
54	9.78837	16	9.89125	26	10.10875	9.89712	10	6	
55	9.78853	16	9.89151	26	10.10849	9.89702	9	5	
56	9.78869	17	9.89177	26	10.10823	9.89693	10	4	
57	9.78886	16	9.89203	26	10.10797	9.89683	10	3	
58	9.78902	16	9.89229	26	10.10771	9.89673	10	2	
59	9.78918	16	9.89255	26	10.10745	9.89663	10	1	
60	9.78934		9.89281		10.10719	9.89653		0	
	L Cos	d	L Ctn	cd	L Tan	L Sin	d	′	Prop. Pts.

52° — Logarithms of Trigonometric Functions

38° — Logarithms of Trigonometric Functions

'	L Sin	d	L Tan	cd	L Ctn	L Cos	d	'
0	9.78934	16	9.89281	26	10.10719	9.89653	10	60
1	9.78950	17	9.89307	26	10.10693	9.89643	10	59
2	9.78967	16	9.89333	26	10.10667	9.89633	10	58
3	9.78983	16	9.89359	26	10.10641	9.89624	9	57
4	9.78999	16	9.89385	26	10.10615	9.89614	10	56
5	9.79015	16	9.89411	26	10.10589	9.89604	10	55
6	9.79031	16	9.89437	26	10.10563	9.89594	10	54
7	9.79047	16	9.89463	26	10.10537	9.89584	10	53
8	9.79063	16	9.89489	26	10.10511	9.89574	10	52
9	9.79079	16	9.89515	26	10.10485	9.89564	10	51
10	9.79095	16	9.89541	26	10.10459	9.89554	10	50
11	9.79111	17	9.89567	26	10.10433	9.89544	10	49
12	9.79128	16	9.89593	26	10.10407	9.89534	10	48
13	9.79144	16	9.89619	26	10.10381	9.89524	10	47
14	9.79160	16	9.89645	26	10.10355	9.89514	10	46
15	9.79176	16	9.89671	26	10.10329	9.89504	9	45
16	9.79192	16	9.89697	26	10.10303	9.89495	10	44
17	9.79208	16	9.89723	26	10.10277	9.89485	10	43
18	9.79224	16	9.89749	26	10.10251	9.89475	10	42
19	9.79240	16	9.89775	26	10.10225	9.89465	10	41
20	9.79256	16	9.89801	26	10.10199	9.89455	10	40
21	9.79272	16	9.89827	26	10.10173	9.89445	10	39
22	9.79288	16	9.89853	26	10.10147	9.89435	10	38
23	9.79304	15	9.89879	26	10.10121	9.89425	10	37
24	9.79319	16	9.89905	26	10.10095	9.89415	10	36
25	9.79335	16	9.89931	26	10.10069	9.89405	10	35
26	9.79351	16	9.89957	26	10.10043	9.89395	10	34
27	9.79367	16	9.89983	26	10.10017	9.89385	10	33
28	9.79383	16	9.90009	26	10.09991	9.89375	11	32
29	9.79399	16	9.90035	26	10.09965	9.89364	10	31
30	9.79415	16	9.90061	26	10.09939	9.89354	10	30
31	9.79431	16	9.90086	25	10.09914	9.89344	10	29
32	9.79447	16	9.90112	26	10.09888	9.89334	10	28
33	9.79463	15	9.90138	26	10.09862	9.89324	10	27
34	9.79478	16	9.90164	26	10.09836	9.89314	10	26
35	9.79494	16	9.90190	26	10.09810	9.89304	10	25
36	9.79510	16	9.90216	26	10.09784	9.89294	10	24
37	9.79526	16	9.90242	26	10.09758	9.89284	10	23
38	9.79542	16	9.90268	26	10.09732	9.89274	10	22
39	9.79558	15	9.90294	26	10.09706	9.89264	10	21
40	9.79573	16	9.90320	26	10.09680	9.89254	10	20
41	9.79589	16	9.90346	25	10.09654	9.89244	11	19
42	9.79605	16	9.90371	26	10.09629	9.89233	10	18
43	9.79621	15	9.90397	26	10.09603	9.89223	10	17
44	9.79636	16	9.90423	26	10.09577	9.89213	10	16
45	9.79652	16	9.90449	26	10.09551	9.89203	10	15
46	9.79668	16	9.90475	26	10.09525	9.89193	10	14
47	9.79684	15	9.90501	26	10.09499	9.89183	10	13
48	9.79699	16	9.90527	26	10.09473	9.89173	11	12
49	9.79715	16	9.90553	25	10.09447	9.89162	10	11
50	9.79731	15	9.90578	26	10.09422	9.89152	10	10
51	9.79746	16	9.90604	26	10.09396	9.89142	10	9
52	9.79762	16	9.90630	26	10.09370	9.89132	10	8
53	9.79778	15	9.90656	26	10.09344	9.89122	11	7
54	9.79793	16	9.90682	26	10.09318	9.89111	10	6
55	9.79809	16	9.90708	26	10.09292	9.89101	10	5
56	9.79825	15	9.90734	25	10.09266	9.89091	10	4
57	9.79840	16	9.90759	26	10.09241	9.89081	10	3
58	9.79856	16	9.90785	26	10.09215	9.89071	11	2
59	9.79872	15	9.90811	26	10.09189	9.89060	10	1
60	9.79887		9.90837		10.09163	9.89050		0
	L Cos	d	L Ctn	cd	L Tan	L Sin	d	'

Prop. Pts.

	26	25
2	5.2	5.0
3	7.8	7.5
4	10.4	10.0
5	13.0	12.5
6	15.6	15.0
7	18.2	17.5
8	20.8	20.0
9	23.4	22.5

	17	16
2	3.4	3.2
3	5.1	4.8
4	6.8	6.4
5	8.5	8.0
6	10.2	9.6
7	11.9	11.2
8	13.6	12.8
9	15.3	14.4

	15	11
2	3.0	2.2
3	4.5	3.3
4	6.0	4.4
5	7.5	5.5
6	9.0	6.6
7	10.5	7.7
8	12.0	8.8
9	13.5	9.9

	10	9
2	2.0	1.8
3	3.0	2.7
4	4.0	3.6
5	5.0	4.5
6	6.0	5.4
7	7.0	6.3
8	8.0	7.2
9	9.0	8.1

From the top:

For **38°+ or 218°+**, read as printed; for **128°+ or 308°+**, read co-function.

From the bottom:

For **51°+ or 231°+**, read as printed; for **141°+ or 321°+**, read co-function.

51° — Logarithms of Trigonometric Functions

39° — Logarithms of Trigonometric Functions

′	L Sin	d	L Tan	cd	L Ctn	L Cos	d		Prop. Pts.
0	9.79887		9.90837		10.09163	9.89050		60	
1	9.79903	16	9.90863	26	10.09137	9.89040	10	59	
2	9.79918	15	9.90889	26	10.09111	9.89030	10	58	
3	9.79934	16	9.90914	25	10.09086	9.89020	10	57	
4	9.79950	16	9.90940	26	10.09060	9.89009	11	56	
5	9.79965	15	9.90966	26	10.09034	9.88999	10	55	
6	9.79981	16	9.90992	26	10.09008	9.88989	10	54	
7	9.79996	15	9.91018	26	10.08982	9.88978	11	53	
8	9.80012	16	9.91043	25	10.08957	9.88968	10	52	
9	9.80027	15	9.91069	26	10.08931	9.88958	10	51	
10	9.80043	16	9.91095	26	10.08905	9.88948	10	50	
11	9.80058	15	9.91121	26	10.08879	9.88937	11	49	
12	9.80074	16	9.91147	26	10.08853	9.88927	10	48	
13	9.80089	15	9.91172	25	10.08828	9.88917	10	47	
14	9.80105	16	9.91198	26	10.08802	9.88906	11	46	
15	9.80120	15	9.91224	26	10.08776	9.88896	10	45	
16	9.80136	16	9.91250	26	10.08750	9.88886	10	44	
17	9.80151	15	9.91276	26	10.08724	9.88875	11	43	
18	9.80166	15	9.91301	25	10.08699	9.88865	10	42	
19	9.80182	16	9.91327	26	10.08673	9.88855	10	41	
20	9.80197	15	9.91353	26	10.08647	9.88844	11	40	
21	9.80213	16	9.91379	26	10.08621	9.88834	10	39	
22	9.80228	15	9.91404	25	10.08596	9.88824	10	38	
23	9.80244	16	9.91430	26	10.08570	9.88813	11	37	
24	9.80259	15	9.91456	26	10.08544	9.88803	10	36	
25	9.80274	15	9.91482	26	10.08518	9.88793	10	35	
26	9.80290	16	9.91507	25	10.08493	9.88782	11	34	
27	9.80305	15	9.91533	26	10.08467	9.88772	10	33	
28	9.80320	15	9.91559	26	10.08441	9.88761	11	32	
29	9.80336	16	9.91585	26	10.08415	9.88751	10	31	
30	9.80351	15	9.91610	25	10.08390	9.88741	10	30	
31	9.80366	15	9.91636	26	10.08364	9.88730	11	29	
32	9.80382	16	9.91662	26	10.08338	9.88720	10	28	
33	9.80397	15	9.91688	26	10.08312	9.88709	11	27	
34	9.80412	15	9.91713	25	10.08287	9.88699	10	26	
35	9.80428	16	9.91739	26	10.08261	9.88688	11	25	
36	9.80443	15	9.91765	26	10.08235	9.88678	10	24	
37	9.80458	15	9.91791	26	10.08209	9.88668	10	23	
38	9.80473	15	9.91816	25	10.08184	9.88657	11	22	
39	9.80489	16	9.91842	26	10.08158	9.88647	10	21	
40	9.80504	15	9.91868	26	10.08132	9.88636	11	20	
41	9.80519	15	9.91893	25	10.08107	9.88626	10	19	
42	9.80534	15	9.91919	26	10.08081	9.88615	11	18	
43	9.80550	16	9.91945	26	10.08055	9.88605	10	17	
44	9.80565	15	9.91971	26	10.08029	9.88594	11	16	
45	9.80580	15	9.91996	25	10.08004	9.88584	10	15	
46	9.80595	15	9.92022	26	10.07978	9.88573	11	14	
47	9.80610	15	9.92048	26	10.07952	9.88563	10	13	
48	9.80625	15	9.92073	25	10.07927	9.88552	11	12	
49	9.80641	16	9.92099	26	10.07901	9.88542	10	11	
50	9.80656	15	9.92125	26	10.07875	9.88531	11	10	
51	9.80671	15	9.92150	25	10.07850	9.88521	10	9	
52	9.80686	15	9.92176	26	10.07824	9.88510	11	8	
53	9.80701	15	9.92202	26	10.07798	9.88499	11	7	
54	9.80716	15	9.92227	25	10.07773	9.88489	10	6	
55	9.80731	15	9.92253	26	10.07747	9.88478	11	5	
56	9.80746	15	9.92279	26	10.07721	9.88468	10	4	
57	9.80762	16	9.92304	25	10.07696	9.88457	11	3	
58	9.80777	15	9.92330	26	10.07670	9.88447	10	2	
59	9.80792	15	9.92356	26	10.07644	9.88436	11	1	
60	9.80807	15	9.92381	25	10.07619	9.88425	11	0	
	L Cos	d	L Ctn	cd	L Tan	L Sin	d	′	Prop. Pts.

Prop. Pts.

	26	25
2	5.2	5.0
3	7.8	7.5
4	10.4	10.0
5	13.0	12.5
6	15.6	15.0
7	18.2	17.5
8	20.8	20.0
9	23.4	22.5

	16	15
2	3.2	3.0
3	4.8	4.5
4	6.4	6.0
5	8.0	7.5
6	9.6	9.0
7	11.2	10.5
8	12.8	12.0
9	14.4	13.5

	11	10
2	2.2	2.0
3	3.3	3.0
4	4.4	4.0
5	5.5	5.0
6	6.6	6.0
7	7.7	7.0
8	8.8	8.0
9	9.9	9.0

From the top:
For 39°+ or 219°+,
read as printed; for
129°+ or 309°+,
co-function.

From the bottom:
For 50°+ or 230°+,
read as printed; for
140°+ or 320°+, read
co-function.

50° — Logarithms of Trigonometric Functions

Table XIV.
40° — Logarithms of Trigonometric Functions

′	L Sin	d	L Tan	cd	L Ctn	L Cos	d		
0	9.80 807	15	9.92 381	26	10.07 619	9.88 425	10	60	
1	9.80 822	15	9.92 407	26	10.07 593	9.88 415	11	59	
2	9.80 837	15	9.92 433	25	10.07 567	9.88 404	10	58	
3	9.80 852	15	9.92 458	26	10.07 542	9.88 394	11	57	
4	9.80 867	15	9.92 484	26	10.07 516	9.88 383	11	56	
5	9.80 882	15	9.92 510	25	10.07 490	9.88 372	10	55	
6	9.80 897	15	9.92 535	26	10.07 465	9.88 362	11	54	
7	9.80 912	15	9.92 561	26	10.07 439	9.88 351	11	53	
8	9.80 927	15	9.92 587	25	10.07 413	9.88 340	10	52	
9	9.80 942	15	9.92 612	26	10.07 388	9.88 330	11	51	
10	9.80 957	15	9.92 638	25	10.07 362	9.88 319	11	50	
11	9.80 972	15	9.92 663	26	10.07 337	9.88 308	10	49	
12	9.80 987	15	9.92 689	26	10.07 311	9.88 298	11	48	
13	9.81 002	15	9.92 715	25	10.07 285	9.88 287	11	47	
14	9.81 017	15	9.92 740	26	10.07 260	9.88 276	10	46	
15	9.81 032	15	9.92 766	26	10.07 234	9.88 266	11	45	
16	9.81 047	14	9.92 792	25	10.07 208	9.88 255	11	44	
17	9.81 061	15	9.92 817	26	10.07 183	9.88 244	10	43	
18	9.81 076	15	9.92 843	25	10.07 157	9.88 234	11	42	
19	9.81 091	15	9.92 868	26	10.07 132	9.88 223	11	41	
20	9.81 106	15	9.92 894	26	10.07 106	9.88 212	11	40	
21	9.81 121	15	9.92 920	25	10.07 080	9.88 201	10	39	
22	9.81 136	15	9.92 945	26	10.07 055	9.88 191	11	38	
23	9.81 151	15	9.92 971	25	10.07 029	9.88 180	11	37	
24	9.81 166	14	9.92 996	26	10.07 004	9.88 169	11	36	
25	9.81 180	15	9.93 022	26	10.06 978	9.88 158	10	35	
26	9.81 195	15	9.93 048	25	10.06 952	9.88 148	11	34	
27	9.81 210	15	9.93 073	26	10.06 927	9.88 137	11	33	
28	9.81 225	15	9.93 099	25	10.06 901	9.88 126	11	32	
29	9.81 240	14	9.93 124	26	10.06 876	9.88 115	10	31	
30	9.81 254	15	9.93 150	25	10.06 850	9.88 105	11	30	
31	9.81 269	15	9.93 175	26	10.06 825	9.88 094	11	29	
32	9.81 284	15	9.93 201	26	10.06 799	9.88 083	11	28	
33	9.81 299	15	9.93 227	25	10.06 773	9.88 072	11	27	
34	9.81 314	14	9.93 252	26	10.06 748	9.88 061	10	26	
35	9.81 328	15	9.93 278	25	10.06 722	9.88 051	11	25	
36	9.81 343	15	9.93 303	26	10.06 697	9.88 040	11	24	
37	9.81 358	14	9.93 329	25	10.06 671	9.88 029	11	23	
38	9.81 372	15	9.93 354	26	10.06 646	9.88 018	11	22	
39	9.81 387	15	9.93 380	26	10.06 620	9.88 007	11	21	
40	9.81 402	15	9.93 406	25	10.06 594	9.87 996	11	20	
41	9.81 417	14	9.93 431	26	10.06 569	9.87 985	10	19	
42	9.81 431	15	9.93 457	25	10.06 543	9.87 975	11	18	
43	9.81 446	15	9.93 482	26	10.06 518	9.87 964	11	17	
44	9.81 461	14	9.93 508	25	10.06 492	9.87 953	11	16	
45	9.81 475	15	9.93 533	26	10.06 467	9.87 942	11	15	
46	9.81 490	15	9.93 559	25	10.06 416	9.87 931	11	14	
47	9.81 505	14	9.93 584	26	10.06 416	9.87 920	11	13	
48	9.81 519	15	9.93 610	26	10.06 390	9.87 909	11	12	
49	9.81 534	15	9.93 636	25	10.06 364	9.87 898	11	11	
50	9.81 549	14	9.93 661	26	10.06 339	9.87 887	10	10	
51	9.81 563	15	9.93 687	25	10.06 313	9.87 877	11	9	
52	9.81 578	14	9.93 712	26	10.06 288	9.87 866	11	8	
53	9.81 592	15	9.93 738	25	10.06 262	9.87 855	11	7	
54	9.81 607	15	9.93 763	26	10.06 237	9.87 844	11	6	
55	9.81 622	14	9.93 789	25	10.06 211	9.87 833	11	5	
56	9.81 636	15	9.93 814	26	10.06 186	9.87 822	11	4	
57	9.81 651	14	9.93 840	25	10.06 160	9.87 811	11	3	
58	9.81 665	15	9.93 865	26	10.06 135	9.87 800	11	2	
59	9.81 680	14	9.93 891	25	10.06 109	9.87 789	11	1	
60	9.81 694		9.93 916		10.06 084	9.87 778		0	
	L Cos	d	L Ctn	cd	L Tan	L Sin	d	′	Prop. Pts.

Prop. Pts.

	26	25
2	5.2	5.0
3	7.8	7.5
4	10.4	10.0
5	13.0	12.5
6	15.6	15.0
7	18.2	17.5
8	20.8	20.0
9	23.4	22.5

	15	14
2	3.0	2.8
3	4.5	4.2
4	6.0	5.6
5	7.5	7.0
6	9.0	8.4
7	10.5	9.8
8	12.0	11.2
9	13.5	12.6

	11	10
2	2.2	2.0
3	3.3	3.0
4	4.4	4.0
5	5.5	5.0
6	6.6	6.0
7	7.7	7.0
8	8.8	8.0
9	9.9	9.0

From the top:
For 40°+ or 220°+,
read as printed; for
130°+ or 310°+, read
co-function.

From the bottom:
For 49°+ or 229°+,
read as printed; for
139°+ or 319°+, read
co-function.

49° — Logarithms of Trigonometric Functions

Table XIV.
41° — Logarithms of Trigonometric Functions

′	L Sin	d	L Tan	cd	L Ctn	L Cos	d		Prop. Pts.
0	9.81694	15	9.93916	26	10.06084	9.87778	11	60	
1	9.81709	14	9.93942	25	10.06058	9.87767	11	59	
2	9.81723	15	9.93967	26	10.06033	9.87756	11	58	
3	9.81738	14	9.93993	25	10.06007	9.87745	11	57	
4	9.81752	15	9.94018	26	10.05982	9.87734	11	56	
5	9.81767	14	9.94044	25	10.05956	9.87723	11	55	**26** **25**
6	9.81781	15	9.94069	26	10.05931	9.87712	11	54	2 5.2 5.0
7	9.81796	14	9.94095	25	10.05905	9.87701	11	53	3 7.8 7.5
8	9.81810	15	9.94120	26	10.05880	9.87690	11	52	4 10.4 10.0
9	9.81825	14	9.94146	25	10.05854	9.87679	11	51	5 13.0 12.5
10	9.81839	15	9.94171	26	10.05829	9.87668	11	50	6 15.6 15.0
11	9.81854	14	9.94197	25	10.05803	9.87657	11	49	7 18.2 17.5
12	9.81868	14	9.94222	26	10.05778	9.87646	11	48	8 20.8 20.0
13	9.81882	15	9.94248	25	10.05752	9.87635	11	47	9 23.4 22.5
14	9.81897	14	9.94273	26	10.05727	9.87624	11	46	
15	9.81911	15	9.94299	25	10.05701	9.87613	11	45	
16	9.81926	14	9.94324	26	10.05676	9.87601	12	44	**15** **14**
17	9.81940	15	9.94350	25	10.05650	9.87590	11	43	
18	9.81955	14	9.94375	26	10.05625	9.87579	11	42	2 3.0 2.8
19	9.81969	14	9.94401	25	10.05599	9.87568	11	41	3 4.5 4.2
20	9.81983	15	9.94426	26	10.05574	9.87557	11	40	4 6.0 5.6
21	9.81998	14	9.94452	25	10.05548	9.87546	11	39	5 7.5 7.0
22	9.82012	14	9.94477	26	10.05523	9.87535	11	38	6 9.0 8.4
23	9.82026	15	9.94503	25	10.05497	9.87524	11	37	7 10.5 9.8
24	9.82041	14	9.94528	26	10.05472	9.87513	12	36	8 12.0 11.2
25	9.82055	14	9.94554	25	10.05446	9.87501	11	35	9 13.5 12.6
26	9.82069	15	9.94579	25	10.05421	9.87490	11	34	
27	9.82084	14	9.94604	26	10.05396	9.87479	11	33	
28	9.82098	14	9.94630	25	10.05370	9.87468	11	32	**12** **11**
29	9.82112	14	9.94655	26	10.05345	9.87457	11	31	2 2.4 2.2
30	9.82126	15	9.94681	25	10.05319	9.87446	11	30	3 3.6 3.3
31	9.82141	14	9.94706	26	10.05294	9.87434	12	29	4 4.8 4.4
32	9.82155	14	9.94732	25	10.05268	9.87423	11	28	5 6.0 5.5
33	9.82169	15	9.94757	26	10.05243	9.87412	11	27	6 7.2 6.6
34	9.82184	14	9.94783	25	10.05217	9.87401	11	26	7 8.4 7.7
35	9.82198	14	9.94808	26	10.05192	9.87390	12	25	8 9.6 8.8
36	9.82212	14	9.94834	25	10.05166	9.87378	11	24	9 10.8 9.9
37	9.82226	14	9.94859	25	10.05141	9.87367	11	23	
38	9.82240	15	9.94884	26	10.05116	9.87356	11	22	
39	9.82255	14	9.94910	25	10.05090	9.87345	11	21	
40	9.82269	14	9.94935	26	10.05065	9.87334	12	20	
41	9.82283	14	9.94961	25	10.05039	9.87322	11	19	
42	9.82297	14	9.94986	26	10.05014	9.87311	11	18	*From the top:*
43	9.82311	15	9.95012	25	10.04988	9.87300	12	17	For **41°+** or **221°+**,
44	9.82326	14	9.95037	25	10.04963	9.87288	11	16	read as printed; for
45	9.82340	14	9.95062	26	10.04938	9.87277	11	15	**131°+** or **311°+**, read
46	9.82354	14	9.95088	25	10.04912	9.87266	11	14	co-function.
47	9.82368	14	9.95113	26	10.04887	9.87255	12	13	
48	9.82382	14	9.95139	25	10.04861	9.87243	11	12	
49	9.82396	14	9.95164	26	10.04836	9.87232	11	11	
50	9.82410	14	9.95190	25	10.04810	9.87221	12	10	*From the bottom:*
51	9.82424	15	9.95215	25	10.04785	9.87209	11	9	For **48°+** or **228°+**,
52	9.82439	14	9.95240	26	10.04760	9.87198	11	8	read as printed; for
53	9.82453	14	9.95266	25	10.04734	9.87187	12	7	**138°+** or **318°+**, read
54	9.82467	14	9.95291	26	10.04709	9.87175	11	6	co-function.
55	9.82481	14	9.95317	25	10.04683	9.87164	11	5	
56	9.82495	14	9.95342	26	10.04658	9.87153	12	4	
57	9.82509	14	9.95368	25	10.04632	9.87141	11	3	
58	9.82523	14	9.95393	25	10.04607	9.87130	11	2	
59	9.82537	14	9.95418	26	10.04582	9.87119	12	1	
60	9.82551		9.95444		10.04556	9.87107		0	
	L Cos	d	L Ctn	cd	L Tan	L Sin	d	′	Prop. Pts.

48° — Logarithms of Trigonometric Functions

Table XIV.
42° — Logarithms of Trigonometric Functions [XIV

′	L Sin	d	L Tan	cd	L Ctn	L Cos	d		Prop. Pts.
0	9.82 551	14	9.95 444	25	10.04 556	9.87 107	11	60	
1	9.82 565	14	9.95 469	26	10.04 531	9.87 096	11	59	
2	9.82 579	14	9.95 495	25	10.04 505	9.87 085	11	58	
3	9.82 593	14	9.95 520	25	10.04 480	9.87 073	12	57	
4	9.82 607	14	9.95 545	26	10.04 455	9.87 062	11	56	
5	9.82 621	14	9.95 571	25	10.04 429	9.87 050	12	55	
6	9.82 635	14	9.95 596	26	10.04 404	9.87 039	11	54	2 5.2 5.0
7	9.82 649	14	9.95 622	25	10.04 378	9.87 028	11	53	3 7.8 7.5
8	9.82 663	14	9.95 647	25	10.04 353	9.87 016	12	52	4 10.4 10.0
9	9.82 677	14	9.95 672	26	10.04 328	9.87 005	11	51	5 13.0 12.5
10	9.82 691	14	9.95 698	25	10.04 302	9.86 993	12	50	6 15.6 15.0
11	9.82 705	14	9.95 723	25	10.04 277	9.86 982	12	49	7 18.2 17.5
12	9.82 719	14	9.95 748	26	10.04 252	9.86 970	11	48	8 20.8 20.0
13	9.82 733	14	9.95 774	25	10.04 226	9.86 959	12	47	9 23.4 22.5
14	9.82 747	14	9.95 799	26	10.04 201	9.86 947	11	46	
15	9.82 761	14	9.95 825	25	10.04 175	9.86 936	12	45	
16	9.82 775	13	9.95 850	25	10.04 150	9.86 924	11	44	14 13
17	9.82 788	14	9.95 875	26	10.04 125	9.86 913	11	43	2 2.8 2.6
18	9.82 802	14	9.95 901	25	10.04 099	9.86 902	12	42	3 4.2 3.9
19	9.82 816	14	9.95 926	26	10.04 074	9.86 890	11	41	4 5.6 5.2
20	9.82 830	14	9.95 952	25	10.04 048	9.86 879	12	40	5 7.0 6.5
21	9.82 844	14	9.95 977	25	10.04 023	9.86 867	12	39	6 8.4 7.8
22	9.82 858	14	9.96 002	26	10.03 998	9.86 855	11	38	7 9.8 9.1
23	9.82 872	13	9.96 028	25	10.03 972	9.86 844	12	37	8 11.2 10.4
24	9.82 885	14	9.96 053	25	10.03 947	9.86 832	11	36	9 12.6 11.7
25	9.82 899	14	9.96 078	26	10.03 922	9.86 821	12	35	
26	9.82 913	14	9.96 104	25	10.03 896	9.86 809	11	34	
27	9.82 927	14	9.96 129	26	10.03 871	9.86 798	12	33	12 11
28	9.82 941	14	9.96 155	25	10.03 845	9.86 786	11	32	2 2.4 2.2
29	9.82 955	13	9.96 180	25	10.03 820	9.86 775	12	31	3 3.6 3.3
30	9.82 968	14	9.96 205	26	10.03 795	9.86 763	11	30	4 4.8 4.4
31	9.82 982	14	9.96 231	25	10.03 769	9.86 752	12	29	5 6.0 5.5
32	9.82 996	14	9.96 256	25	10.03 744	9.86 740	12	28	6 7.2 6.6
33	9.83 010	13	9.96 281	26	10.03 719	9.86 728	11	27	7 8.4 7.7
34	9.83 023	14	9.96 307	25	10.03 693	9.86 717	12	26	8 9.6 8.8
35	9.83 037	14	9.96 332	25	10.03 668	9.86 705	11	25	9 10.8 9.9
36	9.83 051	14	9.96 357	26	10.03 643	9.86 694	12	24	
37	9.83 065	13	9.96 383	25	10.03 617	9.86 682	12	23	
38	9.83 078	14	9.96 408	25	10.03 592	9.86 670	11	22	
39	9.83 092	14	9.96 433	26	10.03 567	9.86 659	12	21	
40	9.83 106	14	9.96 459	25	10.03 541	9.86 647	12	20	
41	9.83 120	13	9.96 484	26	10.03 516	9.86 635	11	19	
42	9.83 133	14	9.96 510	25	10.03 490	9.86 624	12	18	*From the top:*
43	9.83 147	14	9.96 535	25	10.03 465	9.86 612	12	17	For 42°+ or 222°+,
44	9.83 161	13	9.96 560	26	10.03 440	9.86 600	11	16	read as printed; for
45	9.83 174	14	9.96 586	25	10.03 414	9.86 589	12	15	132°+ or 312°+, read
46	9.83 188	14	9.96 611	25	10.03 389	9.86 577	12	14	co-function.
47	9.83 202	13	9.96 636	26	10.03 364	9.86 565	11	13	
48	9.83 215	14	9.96 662	25	10.03 338	9.86 554	12	12	
49	9.83 229	13	9.96 687	25	10.03 313	9.86 542	12	11	*From the bottom:*
50	9.83 242	14	9.96 712	26	10.03 288	9.86 530	12	10	For 47°+ or 227°+,
51	9.83 256	14	9.96 738	25	10.03 262	9.86 518	11	9	read as printed; for
52	9.83 270	13	9.96 763	25	10.03 237	9.86 507	12	8	137°+ or 317°+, read
53	9.83 283	14	9.96 788	26	10.03 212	9.86 495	12	7	co-function.
54	9.83 297	13	9.96 814	25	10.03 186	9.86 483	11	6	
55	9.83 310	14	9.96 839	25	10.03 161	9.86 472	12	5	
56	9.83 324	14	9.96 864	26	10.03 136	9.86 460	12	4	
57	9.83 338	13	9.96 890	25	10.03 110	9.86 448	12	3	
58	9.83 351	14	9.96 915	25	10.03 085	9.86 436	11	2	
59	9.83 365	13	9.96 940	26	10.03 060	9.86 425	12	1	
60	9.83 378		9.96 966		10.03 034	9.86 413		0	
	L Cos	d	L Ctn	cd	L Tan	L Sin	d	′	Prop. Pts.

47° — Logarithms of Trigonometric Functions

43° — Logarithms of Trigonometric Functions

′	L Sin	d	L Tan	cd	L Ctn	L Cos	d		Prop. Pts.
0	9.83 378	14	9.96 966	25	10.03 034	9.86 413	12	60	
1	9.83 392	13	9.96 991	25	10.03 009	9.86 401	12	59	
2	9.83 405	14	9.97 016	26	10.02 984	9.86 389	12	58	
3	9.83 419	13	9.97 042	25	10.02 958	9.86 377	11	57	
4	9.83 432	14	9.97 067	25	10.02 933	9.86 366	12	56	
5	9.83 446	13	9.97 092	26	10.02 908	9.86 354	12	55	**26** **25**
6	9.83 459	14	9.97 118	25	10.02 882	9.86 342	12	54	2 5.2 5.0
7	9.83 473	13	9.97 143	25	10.02 857	9.86 330	12	53	3 7.8 7.5
8	9.83 486	14	9.97 168	25	10.02 832	9.86 318	12	52	4 10.4 10.0
9	9.83 500	13	9.97 193	26	10.02 807	9.86 306	11	51	5 13.0 12.5
10	9.83 513	14	9.97 219	25	10.02 781	9.86 295	12	50	6 15.6 15.0
11	9.83 527	13	9.97 244	25	10.02 756	9.86 283	12	49	7 18.2 17.5
12	9.83 540	14	9.97 269	26	10.02 731	9.86 271	12	48	8 20.8 20.0
13	9.83 554	13	9.97 295	25	10.02 705	9.86 259	12	47	9 23.4 22.5
14	9.83 567	14	9.97 320	25	10.02 680	9.86 247	12	46	
15	9.83 581	13	9.97 345	26	10.02 655	9.86 235	12	45	
16	9.83 594	14	9.97 371	25	10.02 629	9.86 223	12	44	**14** **13**
17	9.83 608	13	9.97 396	25	10.02 604	9.86 211	11	43	2 2.8 2.6
18	9.83 621	13	9.97 421	26	10.02 579	9.86 200	12	42	3 4.2 3.9
19	9.83 634	14	9.97 447	25	10.02 553	9.86 188	12	41	4 5.6 5.2
20	9.83 648	13	9.97 472	25	10.02 528	9.86 176	12	40	5 7.0 6.5
21	9.83 661	13	9.97 497	26	10.02 503	9.86 164	12	39	6 8.4 7.8
22	9.83 674	14	9.97 523	25	10.02 477	9.86 152	12	38	7 9.8 9.1
23	9.83 688	13	9.97 548	25	10.02 452	9.86 140	12	37	8 11.2 10.4
24	9.83 701	14	9.97 573	25	10.02 427	9.86 128	12	36	9 12.6 11.7
25	9.83 715	13	9.97 598	26	10.02 402	9.86 116	12	35	
26	9.83 728	13	9.97 624	25	10.02 376	9.86 104	12	34	
27	9.83 741	14	9.97 649	25	10.02 351	9.86 092	12	33	**12** **11**
28	9.83 755	13	9.97 674	26	10.02 326	9.86 080	12	32	2 2.4 2.2
29	9.83 768	13	9.97 700	25	10.02 300	9.86 068	12	31	3 3.6 3.3
30	9.83 781	14	9.97 725	25	10.02 275	9.86 056	12	30	4 4.8 4.4
31	9.83 795	13	9.97 750	26	10.02 250	9.86 044	12	29	5 6.0 5.5
32	9.83 808	13	9.97 776	25	10.02 224	9.86 032	12	28	6 7.2 6.6
33	9.83 821	13	9.97 801	25	10.02 199	9.86 020	12	27	7 8.4 7.7
34	9.83 834	14	9.97 826	25	10.02 174	9.86 008	12	26	8 9.6 8.8
35	9.83 848	13	9.97 851	26	10.02 149	9.85 996	12	25	9 10.8 9.9
36	9.83 861	13	9.97 877	25	10.02 123	9.85 984	12	24	
37	9.83 874	13	9.97 902	25	10.02 098	9.85 972	12	23	
38	9.83 887	14	9.97 927	26	10.02 073	9.85 960	12	22	
39	9.83 901	13	9.97 953	25	10.02 047	9.85 948	12	21	
40	9.83 914	13	9.97 978	25	10.02 022	9.85 936	12	20	
41	9.83 927	13	9.98 003	26	10.01 997	9.85 924	12	19	
42	9.83 940	14	9.98 029	25	10.01 971	9.85 912	12	18	*From the top:*
43	9.83 954	13	9.98 054	25	10.01 946	9.85 900	12	17	For 43°+ or 223°+,
44	9.83 967	13	9.98 079	25	10.01 921	9.85 888	12	16	read as printed; for
45	9.83 980	13	9.98 104	26	10.01 896	9.85 876	12	15	**133°+ or 313°+,** read
46	9.83 993	13	9.98 130	25	10.01 870	9.85 864	12	14	co-function.
47	9.84 006	14	9.98 155	25	10.01 845	9.85 851	12	13	
48	9.84 020	13	9.98 180	26	10.01 820	9.85 839	12	12	
49	9.84 033	13	9.98 206	25	10.01 794	9.85 827	12	11	*From the bottom:*
50	9.84 046	13	9.98 231	25	10.01 769	9.85 815	12	10	For 46°+ or 226°+,
51	9.84 059	13	9.98 256	25	10.01 744	9.85 803	12	9	read as printed; for
52	9.84 072	13	9.98 281	26	10.01 719	9.85 791	12	8	**136°+ or 316°+,** read
53	9.84 085	13	9.98 307	25	10.01 693	9.85 779	13	7	co-function.
54	9.84 098	14	9.98 332	25	10.01 668	9.85 766	12	6	
55	9.84 112	13	9.98 357	26	10.01 643	9.85 754	12	5	
56	9.84 125	13	9.98 383	25	10.01 617	9.85 742	12	4	
57	9.84 138	13	9.98 408	25	10.01 592	9.85 730	12	3	
58	9.84 151	13	9.98 433	25	10.01 567	9.85 718	12	2	
59	9.84 164	13	9.98 458	26	10.01 542	9.85 706	13	1	
60	9.84 177		9.98 484		10.01 516	9.85 693		0	
	L Cos	d	L Ctn	cd	L Tan	L Sin	d	′	Prop. Pts.

46° — Logarithms of Trigonometric Functions

44° — Logarithms of Trigonometric Functions

	L Sin	d	L Tan	cd	L Ctn	L Cos	d		Prop. Pts.
0	9.84 177		9.98 484		10.01 516	9.85 693		60	
1	9.84 190	13	9.98 509	25	10.01 491	9.85 681	12	59	
2	9.84 203	13	9.98 534	25	10.01 466	9.85 669	12	58	
3	9.84 216	13	9.98 560	26	10.01 440	9.85 657	12	57	
4	9.84 229	13	9.98 585	25	10.01 415	9.85 645	12	56	
5	9.84 242	13	9.98 610	25	10.01 390	9.85 632	13	55	
6	9.84 255	13	9.98 635	25	10.01 365	9.85 620	12	54	26 25
7	9.84 269	14	9.98 661	26	10.01 339	9.85 608	12	53	2 5.2 5.0
8	9.84 282	13	9.98 686	25	10.01 314	9.85 596	12	52	3 7.8 7.5
9	9.84 295	13	9.98 711	25	10.01 289	9.85 583	13	51	4 10.4 10.0
10	9.84 308	13	9.98 737	26	10.01 263	9.85 571	12	50	5 13.0 12.5
11	9.84 321	13	9.98 762	25	10.01 238	9.85 559	12	49	6 15.6 15.0
12	9.84 334	13	9.98 787	25	10.01 213	9.85 547	13	48	7 18.2 17.5
13	9.84 347	13	9.98 812	25	10.01 188	9.85 534	12	47	8 20.8 20.0
14	9.84 360	13	9.98 838	26	10.01 162	9.85 522	12	46	9 23.4 22.5
15	9.84 373	13	9.98 863	25	10.01 137	9.85 510	13	45	
16	9.84 385	12	9.98 888	25	10.01 112	9.85 497	12	44	
17	9.84 398	13	9.98 913	25	10.01 087	9.85 485	12	43	14 13
18	9.84 411	13	9.98 939	26	10.01 061	9.85 473	13	42	2 2.8 2.6
19	9.84 424	13	9.98 964	25	10.01 036	9.85 460	12	41	3 4.2 3.9
20	9.84 437	13	9.98 989	25	10.01 011	9.85 448	12	40	4 5.6 5.2
21	9.84 450	13	9.99 015	26	10.00 985	9.85 436	13	39	5 7.0 6.5
22	9.84 463	13	9.99 040	25	10.00 960	9.85 423	12	38	6 8.4 7.8
23	9.84 476	13	9.99 065	25	10.00 935	9.85 411	12	37	7 9.8 9.1
24	9.84 489	13	9.99 090	26	10.00 910	9.85 399	13	36	8 11.2 10.4
25	9.84 502	13	9.99 116	25	10.00 884	9.85 386	12	35	9 12.6 11.7
26	9.84 515	13	9.99 141	25	10.00 859	9.85 374	12	34	
27	9.84 528	12	9.99 166	25	10.00 834	9.85 361	12	33	
28	9.84 540	13	9.99 191	26	10.00 809	9.85 349	13	32	12
29	9.84 553	13	9.99 217	25	10.00 783	9.85 337	12	31	2 2.4
30	9.84 566	13	9.99 242	25	10.00 758	9.85 324	12	30	3 3.6
31	9.84 579	13	9.99 267	26	10.00 733	9.85 312	13	29	4 4.8
32	9.84 592	13	9.99 293	25	10.00 707	9.85 299	12	28	5 6.0
33	9.84 605	13	9.99 318	25	10.00 682	9.85 287	12	27	6 7.2
34	9.84 618	12	9.99 343	25	10.00 657	9.85 274	12	26	7 8.4
35	9.84 630	13	9.99 368	26	10.00 632	9.85 262	12	25	8 9.6
36	9.84 643	13	9.99 394	25	10.00 606	9.85 250	13	24	9 10.8
37	9.84 656	13	9.99 419	25	10.00 581	9.85 237	12	23	
38	9.84 669	13	9.99 444	25	10.00 556	9.85 225	12	22	
39	9.84 682	12	9.99 469	26	10.00 531	9.85 212	12	21	
40	9.84 694	13	9.99 495	25	10.00 505	9.85 200	13	20	
41	9.84 707	13	9.99 520	25	10.00 480	9.85 187	12	19	*From the top:*
42	9.84 720	13	9.99 545	25	10.00 455	9.85 175	13	18	For 44°+ or 224°+,
43	9.84 733	12	9.99 570	26	10.00 430	9.85 162	12	17	read as printed; for
44	9.84 745	13	9.99 596	25	10.00 404	9.85 150	13	16	134°+ or 314°+, read
45	9.84 758	13	9.99 621	25	10.00 379	9.85 137	12	15	co-function.
46	9.84 771	13	9.99 646	26	10.00 354	9.85 125	13	14	
47	9.84 784	12	9.99 672	25	10.00 328	9.85 112	12	13	
48	9.84 796	13	9.99 697	25	10.00 303	9.85 100	13	12	*From the bottom:*
49	9.84 809	13	9.99 722	25	10.00 278	9.85 087	13	11	For 45°+ or 225°+,
50	9.84 822	13	9.99 747	26	10.00 253	9.85 074	12	10	read as printed; for
51	9.84 835	12	9.99 773	25	10.00 227	9.85 062	13	9	135°+ or 315°+, read
52	9.84 847	13	9.99 798	25	10.00 202	9.85 049	12	8	co-function.
53	9.84 860	13	9.99 823	25	10.00 177	9.85 037	13	7	
54	9.84 873	12	9.99 848	26	10.00 152	9.85 024	12	6	
55	9.84 885	13	9.99 874	25	10.00 126	9.85 012	13	5	
56	9.84 898	13	9.99 899	25	10.00 101	9.84 999	13	4	
57	9.84 911	12	9.99 924	25	10.00 076	9.84 986	12	3	
58	9.84 923	13	9.99 949	26	10.00 051	9.84 974	13	2	
59	9.84 936	13	9.99 975	25	10.00 025	9.84 961	12	1	
60	9.84 949		10.0000		10.00 000	9.84 949		0	
	L Cos	d	L Ctn	cd	L Tan	L Sin	d	′	Prop. Pts.

45° — Logarithms of Trigonometric Functions

0° — Values of Trigonometric Functions — 1°

′	Sin	Tan	Ctn	Cos		′	Sin	Tan	Ctn	Cos	
0	.00000	.00000	——	1.0000	60	0	.01745	.01746	57.290	.99985	60
1	029	029	3437.7	000	59	1	774	775	56.351	984	59
2	058	058	1718.9	000	58	2	803	804	55.442	984	58
3	087	087	1145.9	000	57	3	832	833	54.561	983	57
4	116	116	859.44	000	56	4	862	862	53.709	983	56
5	.00145	.00145	687.55	1.0000	55	5	.01891	.01891	52.882	.99982	55
6	175	175	572.96	000	54	6	920	920	52.081	982	54
7	204	204	491.11	000	53	7	949	949	51.303	981	53
8	233	233	429.72	000	52	8	.01978	.01978	50.549	980	52
9	262	262	381.97	000	51	9	.02007	.02007	49.816	980	51
10	.00291	.00291	343.77	1.0000	50	10	.02036	.02036	49.104	.99979	50
11	320	320	312.52	.99999	49	11	065	066	48.412	979	49
12	349	349	286.48	999	48	12	094	095	47.740	978	48
13	378	378	264.44	999	47	13	123	124	47.085	977	47
14	407	407	245.55	999	46	14	152	153	46.449	977	46
15	.00436	.00436	229.18	.99999	45	15	.02181	.02182	45.829	.99976	45
16	465	465	214.86	999	44	16	211	211	45.226	976	44
17	495	495	202.22	999	43	17	240	240	44.639	975	43
18	524	524	190.98	999	42	18	269	269	44.066	974	42
19	553	553	180.93	998	41	19	298	298	43.508	974	41
20	.00582	.00582	171.89	.99998	40	20	.02327	.02328	42.964	.99973	40
21	611	611	163.70	998	39	21	356	357	42.433	972	39
22	640	640	156.26	998	38	22	385	386	41.916	972	38
23	669	669	149.47	998	37	23	414	415	41.411	971	37
24	698	698	143.24	998	36	24	443	444	40.917	970	36
25	.00727	.00727	137.51	.99997	35	25	.02472	.02473	40.436	.99969	35
26	756	756	132.22	997	34	26	501	502	39.965	969	34
27	785	785	127.32	997	33	27	530	531	39.506	968	33
28	814	815	122.77	997	32	28	560	560	39.057	967	32
29	844	844	118.54	996	31	29	589	589	38.618	966	31
30	.00873	.00873	114.59	.99996	30	30	.02618	.02619	38.188	.99966	30
31	902	902	110.89	996	29	31	647	648	37.769	965	29
32	931	931	107.43	996	28	32	676	677	37.358	964	28
33	960	960	104.17	995	27	33	705	706	36.956	963	27
34	.00989	.00989	101.11	995	26	34	734	735	36.563	963	26
35	.01018	.01018	98.218	.99995	25	35	.02763	.02764	36.178	.99962	25
36	047	047	95.489	995	24	36	792	793	35.801	961	24
37	076	076	92.908	994	23	37	821	822	35.431	960	23
38	105	105	90.463	994	22	38	850	851	35.070	959	22
39	134	135	88.144	994	21	39	879	881	34.715	959	21
40	.01164	.01164	85.940	.99993	20	40	.02908	.02910	34.368	.99958	20
41	193	193	83.844	993	19	41	938	939	34.027	957	19
42	222	222	81.847	993	18	42	967	968	33.694	956	18
43	251	251	79.943	992	17	43	.02996	.02997	33.366	955	17
44	280	280	78.126	992	16	44	.03025	.03026	33.045	954	16
45	.01309	.01309	76.390	.99991	15	45	.03054	.03055	32.730	.99953	15
46	338	338	74.729	991	14	46	083	084	32.421	952	14
47	367	367	73.139	991	13	47	112	114	32.118	952	13
48	396	396	71.615	990	12	48	141	143	31.821	951	12
49	425	425	70.153	990	11	49	170	172	31.528	950	11
50	.01454	.01455	68.750	.99989	10	50	.03199	.03201	31.242	.99949	10
51	483	484	67.402	989	9	51	228	230	30.960	948	9
52	513	513	66.105	989	8	52	257	259	30.683	947	8
53	542	542	64.858	988	7	53	286	288	30.412	946	7
54	571	571	63.657	988	6	54	316	317	30.145	945	6
55	.01600	.01600	62.499	.99987	5	55	.03345	.03346	29.882	.99944	5
56	629	629	61.383	987	4	56	374	376	29.624	943	4
57	658	658	60.306	986	3	57	403	405	29.371	942	3
58	687	687	59.266	986	2	58	432	434	29.122	941	2
59	716	716	58.261	985	1	59	461	463	28.877	940	1
60	.01745	.01746	57.290	.99985	0	60	.03490	.03492	28.636	.99939	0
	Cos	Ctn	Tan	Sin	′		Cos	Ctn	Tan	Sin	′

         89°   **88°**

2° — Values of Trigonometric Functions — 3°

′	Sin	Tan	Ctn	Cos		′	Sin	Tan	Ctn	Cos	
0	.03490	.03492	28.636	.99939	60	0	.05234	.05241	19.081	.99863	60
1	519	521	.399	938	59	1	263	270	18.976	861	59
2	548	550	28.166	937	58	2	292	299	.871	860	58
3	577	579	27.937	936	57	3	321	328	.768	858	57
4	606	609	.712	935	56	4	350	357	.666	857	56
5	.03635	.03638	27.490	.99934	55	5	.05379	.05387	18.564	.99855	55
6	664	667	.271	933	54	6	408	416	18.464	854	54
7	693	696	27.057	932	53	7	437	445	.366	852	53
8	723	725	26.845	931	52	8	466	474	.268	851	52
9	752	754	.637	930	51	9	495	503	.171	849	51
10	.03781	.03783	26.432	.99929	50	10	.05524	.05533	18.075	.99847	50
11	810	812	.230	927	49	11	553	562	17.980	846	49
12	839	842	26.031	926	48	12	582	591	.886	844	48
13	868	871	25.835	925	47	13	611	620	.793	842	47
14	897	900	.642	924	46	14	640	649	.702	841	46
15	.03926	.03929	25.452	.99923	45	15	.05669	.05678	17.611	.99839	45
16	955	958	.264	922	44	16	698	708	.521	838	44
17	.03984	.03987	25.080	921	43	17	727	737	.431	836	43
18	.04013	.04016	24.898	919	42	18	756	766	.343	834	42
19	042	046	.719	918	41	19	785	795	.256	833	41
20	.04071	.04075	24.542	.99917	40	20	.05814	.05824	17.169	.99831	40
21	100	104	.368	916	39	21	844	854	17.084	829	39
22	129	133	.196	915	38	22	873	883	16.999	827	38
23	159	162	24.026	913	37	23	902	912	.915	826	37
24	188	191	23.859	912	36	24	931	941	.832	824	36
25	.04217	.04220	23.695	.99911	35	25	.05960	.05970	16.750	.99822	35
26	246	250	.532	910	34	26	.05989	.05999	.668	821	34
27	275	279	.372	909	33	27	.06018	.06029	.587	819	33
28	304	308	.214	'907	32	28	047	058	.507	817	32
29	333	337	23.058	906	31	29	076	087	.428	815	31
30	.04362	.04366	22.904	.99905	30	30	.06105	.06116	16.350	.99813	30
31	391	395	.752	904	29	31	134	145	.272	812	29
32	420	424	.602	902	28	32	163	175	.195	810	28
33	449	454	.454	901	27	33	192	204	.119	808	27
34	478	483	.308	900	26	34	221	233	16.043	806	26
35	.04507	.04512	22.164	.99898	25	35	.06250	.06262	15.969	.99804	25
36	536	541	22.022	897	24	36	279	291	.895	803	24
37	565	570	21.881	896	23	37	308	321	.821	801	23
38	594	599	.743	894	22	38	337	350	.748	799	22
39	623	628	.606	893	21	39	366	379	.676	797	21
40	.04653	.04658	21.470	.99892	20	40	.06395	.06408	15.605	.99795	20
41	682	687	.337	890	19	41	424	438	.534	793	19
42	711	716	.205	889	18	42	453	467	.464	792	18
43	740	745	21.075	888	17	43	482	496	.394	790	17
44	769	774	20.946	886	16	44	511	525	.325	788	16
45	.04798	.04803	20.819	.99885	15	45	.06540	.06554	15.257	.99786	15
46	827	833	.693	883	14	46	569	584	.189	784	14
47	856	862	.569	882	13	47	598	613	.122	782	13
48	885	891	.446	881	12	48	627	642	15.056	780	12
49	914	920	.325	879	11	49	656	671	14.990	778	11
50	.04943	.04949	20.206	.99878	10	50	.06685	.06700	14.924	.99776	10
51	.04972	.04978	20.087	876	9	51	714	730	.860	774	9
52	.05001	.05007	19.970	875	8	52	743	759	.795	772	8
53	030	037	.855	873	7	53	773	788	.732	770	7
54	059	066	.740	872	6	54	802	817	.669	768	6
55	.05088	.05095	19.627	.99870	5	55	.06831	.06847	14.606	.99766	5
56	117	124	.516	869	4	56	860	876	.544	764	4
57	146	153	.405	867	3	57	889	905	.482	762	3
58	175	182	.296	866	2	58	918	934	.421	760	2
59	205	212	.188	864	1	59	947	963	.361	758	1
60	.05234	.05241	19.081	.99863	0	60	.06976	.06993	14.301	.99756	0
	Cos	Ctn	Tan	Sin	′		Cos	Ctn	Tan	Sin	′

4° — Values of Trigonometric Functions — 5°

'	Sin	Tan	Ctn	Cos		'	Sin	Tan	Ctn	Cos	
0	.06976	.06993	14.301	.99756	60	0	.08716	.08749	11.430	.99619	60
1	.07005	.07022	.241	754	59	1	745	778	.392	617	59
2	034	051	.182	752	58	2	774	807	.354	614	58
3	063	080	.124	750	57	3	803	837	.316	612	57
4	092	110	.065	748	56	4	831	866	.279	609	56
5	.07121	.07139	14.008	.99746	55	5	.08860	.08895	11.242	.99607	55
6	150	168	13.951	744	54	6	889	925	.205	604	54
7	179	197	.894	742	53	7	918	954	.168	602	53
8	208	227	.838	740	52	8	947	.08983	132	599	52
9	237	256	.782	738	51	9	.08976	.09013	.095	596	51
10	.07266	.07285	13.727	.99736	50	10	.09005	.09042	11.059	.99594	50
11	295	314	.672	734	49	11	034	071	11.024	591	49
12	324	344	.617	731	48	12	063	101	10.988	588	48
13	353	373	.563	729	47	13	092	130	.953	586	47
14	382	402	.510	727	46	14	121	159	918	583	46
15	.07411	.07431	13.457	.99725	45	15	.09150	.09189	10.883	.99580	45
16	440	461	.404	723	44	16	179	218	.848	578	44
17	469	490	.352	721	43	17	208	247	.814	575	43
18	498	519	.300	719	42	18	237	277	.780	572	42
19	527	548	.248	716	41	19	266	306	.746	570	41
20	.07556	.07578	13.197	.99714	40	20	.09295	.09335	10.712	.99567	40
21	585	607	.146	712	39	21	324	365	.678	564	39
22	614	636	.096	710	38	22	353	394	.645	562	38
23	643	665	13.046	708	37	23	382	423	.612	559	37
24	672	695	12.996	705	36	24	411	453	.579	556	36
25	.07701	.07724	12.947	.99703	35	25	.09440	.09482	10.546	.99553	35
26	730	753	.898	701	34	26	469	511	.514	551	34
27	759	782	.850	699	33	27	498	541	.481	548	33
28	788	812	.801	696	32	28	527	570	.449	545	32
29	817	841	.754	694	31	29	556	600	.417	542	31
30	.07846	.07870	12.706	.99692	30	30	.09585	.09629	10.385	.99540	30
31	875	899	.659	689	29	31	614	658	.354	537	29
32	904	929	.612	687	28	32	642	688	.322	534	28
33	933	958	.566	685	27	33	671	717	.291	531	27
34	962	.07987	.520	683	26	34	700	746	.260	528	26
35	.07991	.08017	12.474	.99680	25	35	.09729	.09776	10.229	.99526	25
36	.08020	046	.429	678	24	36	758	805	.199	523	24
37	049	075	.384	676	23	37	787	834	.168	520	23
38	078	104	.339	673	22	38	816	864	.138	517	22
39	107	134	.295	671	21	39	845	893	.108	514	21
40	.08136	.08163	12.251	.99668	20	40	.09874	.09923	10.078	.99511	20
41	165	192	.207	666	19	41	903	952	.048	508	19
42	194	221	.163	664	18	42	932	.09981	10.019	506	18
43	223	251	.120	661	17	43	961	.10011	9.9893	503	17
44	252	280	.077	659	16	44	.09990	040	.9601	500	16
45	.08281	.08309	12.035	.99657	15	45	.10019	.10069	9.9310	.99497	15
46	310	339	11.992	654	14	46	048	099	.9021	494	14
47	339	368	.950	652	13	47	077	128	.8734	491	13
48	368	397	.909	649	12	48	106	158	.8448	488	12
49	397	427	.867	647	11	49	135	187	.8164	485	11
50	.08426	.08456	11.826	.99644	10	50	.10164	.10216	9.7882	.99482	10
51	455	485	.785	642	9	51	192	246	.7601	479	9
52	484	514	.745	639	8	52	221	275	.7322	476	8
53	513	544	.705	637	7	53	250	305	.7044	473	7
54	542	573	.664	635	6	54	279	334	.6768	470	6
55	.08571	.08602	11.625	.99632	5	55	.10308	.10363	9.6493	.99467	5
56	600	632	.585	630	4	56	337	393	.6220	464	4
57	629	661	.546	627	3	57	366	422	.5949	461	3
58	658	690	.507	625	2	58	395	452	.5679	458	2
59	687	720	.468	622	1	59	424	481	.5411	455	1
60	.08716	.08749	11.430	.99619	0	60	.10453	.10510	9.5144	.99452	0
	Cos	Ctn	Tan	Sin	'		Cos	Ctn	Tan	Sin	'

85°   **84°**

′	Sin	Tan	Ctn	Cos			Sin	Tan	Ctn	Cos	
0	.10453	.10510	9.5144	.99452	60	0	.12187	.12278	8.1443	.99255	60
1	482	540	.4878	449	59	1	216	308	.1248	251	59
2	511	569	.4614	446	58	2	245	338	.1054	248	58
3	540	599	.4352	443	57	3	274	367	.0860	244	57
4	569	628	.4090	440	56	4	302	397	.0667	240	56
5	.10597	.10657	9.3831	.99437	55	5	.12331	.12426	8.0476	.99237	55
6	626	687	.3572	434	54	6	360	456	.0285	233	54
7	655	716	.3315	431	53	7	389	485	8.0095	230	53
8	684	746	.3060	428	52	8	418	515	7.9906	226	52
9	713	775	.2806	424	51	9	447	544	.9718	222	51
10	.10742	.10805	9.2553	.99421	50	10	.12476	.12574	7.9530	.99219	50
11	771	834	.2302	418	49	11	504	603	.9344	215	49
12	800	863	.2052	415	48	12	533	633	.9158	211	48
13	829	893	.1803	412	47	13	562	662	.8973	208	47
14	858	922	.1555	409	46	14	591	692	.8789	204	46
15	.10887	.10952	9.1309	.99406	45	15	.12620	.12722	7.8606	.99200	45
16	916	.10981	.1065	402	44	16	649	751	.8424	197	44
17	945	.11011	.0821	399	43	17	678	781	.8243	193	43
18	.10973	040	.0579	396	42	18	706	810	.8062	189	42
19	.11002	070	.0338	393	41	19	735	840	.7882	186	41
20	.11031	.11099	9.0098	.99390	40	20	.12764	.12869	7.7704	.99182	40
21	060	128	8.9860	386	39	21	793	899	.7525	178	39
22	089	158	.9623	383	38	22	822	929	.7348	175	38
23	118	187	.9387	380	37	23	851	958	.7171	171	37
24	147	217	.9152	377	36	24	880	.12988	.6996	167	36
25	.11176	.11246	8.8919	.99374	35	25	.12908	.13017	7.6821	.99163	35
26	205	276	.8686	370	34	26	937	047	.6647	160	34
27	234	305	.8455	367	33	27	966	076	.6473	156	33
28	263	335	.8225	364	32	28	.12995	106	.6301	152	32
29	291	364	.7996	360	31	29	.13024	136	.6129	148	31
30	.11320	.11394	8.7769	.99357	30	30	.13053	.13165	7.5958	.99144	30
31	349	423	.7542	354	29	31	081	195	.5787	141	29
32	378	452	.7317	351	28	32	110	224	.5618	137	28
33	407	482	.7093	347	27	33	139	254	.5449	133	27
34	436	511	.6870	344	26	34	168	284	.5281	129	26
35	.11465	.11541	8.6648	.99341	25	35	.13197	.13313	7.5113	.99125	25
36	494	570	.6427	337	24	36	226	343	.4947	122	24
37	523	600	.6208	334	23	37	254	372	.4781	118	23
38	552	629	.5989	331	22	38	283	402	.4615	114	22
39	580	659	.5772	327	21	39	312	432	.4451	110	21
40	.11609	.11688	8.5555	.99324	20	40	.13341	.13461	7.4287	.99106	20
41	638	718	.5340	320	19	41	370	491	.4124	102	19
42	667	747	.5126	317	18	42	399	521	.3962	098	18
43	696	777	.4913	314	17	43	427	550	.3800	094	17
44	725	806	.4701	310	16	44	456	580	.3639	091	16
45	.11754	.11836	8.4490	.99307	15	45	.13485	.13609	7.3479	.99087	15
46	783	865	.4280	303	14	46	514	639	.3319	083	14
47	812	895	.4071	300	13	47	543	669	.3160	079	13
48	840	924	.3863	297	12	48	572	698	.3002	075	12
49	869	954	.3656	293	11	49	600	728	.2844	071	11
50	.11898	.11983	8.3450	.99290	10	50	.13629	.13758	7.2687	.99067	10
51	927	.12013	.3245	286	9	51	658	787	.2531	063	9
52	956	042	.3041	283	8	52	687	817	.2375	059	8
53	.11985	072	.2838	279	7	53	716	846	.2220	055	7
54	.12014	101	.2636	276	6	54	744	876	.2066	051	6
55	.12043	.12131	8.2434	.99272	5	55	.13773	.13906	7.1912	.99047	5
56	071	160	.2234	269	4	56	802	935	.1759	043	4
57	100	190	.2035	265	3	57	831	965	.1607	039	3
58	129	219	.1837	262	2	58	860	.13995	.1455	035	2
59	158	249	.1640	258	1	59	889	.14024	.1304	031	1
60	.12187	.12278	8.1443	.99255	0	60	.13917	.14054	7.1154	.99027	0
′	Cos	Ctn	Tan	Sin	′		Cos	Ctn	Tan	Sin	′

83°   82°

8° — Values of Trigonometric Functions — 9°

′	Sin	Tan	Ctn	Cos	′
0	.13917	14054	7.1154	.99027	60
1	946	084	.1004	023	59
2	.13975	113	.0855	019	58
3	.14004	143	.0706	015	57
4	033	173	.0558	011	56
5	.14061	.14202	7.0410	.99006	55
6	090	232	.0264	.99002	54
7	119	262	7.0117	.98998	53
8	148	291	6.9972	994	52
9	177	321	.9827	990	51
10	.14205	.14351	6.9682	.98986	50
11	234	381	.9538	982	49
12	263	410	.9395	978	48
13	292	440	.9252	973	47
14	320	470	.9110	969	46
15	.14349	.14499	6.8969	.98965	45
16	378	529	.8828	961	44
17	407	559	.8687	957	43
18	436	588	.8548	953	42
19	464	618	.8408	948	41
20	.14493	.14648	6.8269	.98944	40
21	522	678	.8131	940	39
22	551	707	.7994	936	38
23	580	737	.7856	931	37
24	608	767	.7720	927	36
25	.14637	.14796	6.7584	.98923	35
26	666	826	.7448	919	34
27	695	856	.7313	914	33
28	723	886	.7179	910	32
29	752	915	.7045	906	31
30	.14781	.14945	6.6912	.98902	30
31	810	.14975	.6779	897	29
32	838	.15005	.6646	893	28
33	867	034	.6514	889	27
34	896	064	.6383	884	26
35	.14925	.15094	6.6252	.98880	25
36	954	124	.6122	876	24
37	.14982	153	.5992	871	23
38	.15011	183	.5863	867	22
39	040	213	.5734	863	21
40	.15069	.15243	6.5606	.98858	20
41	097	272	.5478	854	19
42	126	302	.5350	849	18
43	155	332	.5223	845	17
44	184	362	.5097	841	16
45	.15212	.15391	6.4971	.98836	15
46	241	421	.4846	832	14
47	270	451	.4721	827	13
48	299	481	.4596	823	12
49	327	511	.4472	818	11
50	.15356	.15540	6.4348	.98814	10
51	385	570	.4225	809	9
52	414	600	.4103	805	8
53	442	630	.3980	800	7
54	471	660	.3859	796	6
55	.15500	.15689	6.3737	.98791	5
56	529	719	.3617	787	4
57	557	749	.3496	782	3
58	586	779	.3376	778	2
59	615	809	.3257	773	1
60	.15643	.15838	6.3138	.98769	0
	Cos	Ctn	Tan	Sin	′

81°

′	Sin	Tan	Ctn	Cos	′
0	.15643	.15838	6.3138	.98769	60
1	672	868	.3019	764	59
2	701	898	.2901	760	58
3	730	928	.2783	755	57
4	758	958	.2666	751	56
5	.15787	.15988	6.2549	.98746	55
6	816	.16017	.2432	741	54
7	845	047	.2316	737	53
8	873	077	.2200	732	52
9	902	107	.2085	728	51
10	.15931	.16137	6.1970	.98723	50
11	959	167	.1856	718	49
12	.15988	196	.1742	714	48
13	.16017	226	.1628	709	47
14	046	256	.1515	704	46
15	.16074	.16286	6.1402	.98700	45
16	103	316	.1290	695	44
17	132	346	.1178	690	43
18	160	376	.1066	686	42
19	189	405	.0955	681	41
20	.16218	.16435	6.0844	.98676	40
21	246	465	.0734	671	39
22	275	495	.0624	667	38
23	304	525	.0514	662	37
24	333	555	.0405	657	36
25	.16361	.16585	6.0296	.98652	35
26	390	615	.0188	648	34
27	419	645	6.0080	643	33
28	447	674	5.9972	638	32
29	476	704	.9865	633	31
30	.16505	.16734	5.9758	.98629	30
31	533	764	.9651	624	29
32	562	794	.9545	619	28
33	591	824	.9439	614	27
34	620	854	.9333	609	26
35	.16648	.16884	5.9228	.98604	25
36	677	914	.9124	600	24
37	706	944	.9019	595	23
38	734	.16974	.8915	590	22
39	763	.17004	.8811	585	21
40	.16792	.17033	5.8708	.98580	20
41	820	063	.8605	575	19
42	849	093	.8502	570	18
43	878	123	.8400	565	17
44	906	153	.8298	561	16
45	.16935	.17183	5.8197	.98556	15
46	964	213	.8095	551	14
47	.16992	243	.7994	546	13
48	.17021	273	.7894	541	12
49	050	303	.7794	536	11
50	.17078	.17333	5.7694	.98531	10
51	107	363	.7594	526	9
52	136	393	.7495	521	8
53	164	423	.7396	516	7
54	193	453	.7297	511	6
55	.17222	.17483	5.7199	.98506	5
56	250	513	.7101	501	4
57	279	543	.7004	496	3
58	308	573	.6906	491	2
59	336	603	.6809	486	1
60	.17365	.17633	5.6713	.98481	0
	Cos	Ctn	Tan	Sin	′

80°

′	Sin	Tan	Ctn	Cos	
0	.17365	.17633	5.6713	.98481	60
1	393	663	.6617	476	59
2	422	693	.6521	471	58
3	451	723	.6425	466	57
4	479	753	.6329	461	56
5	.17508	.17783	5.6234	.98455	55
6	537	813	.6140	450	54
7	565	843	.6045	445	53
8	594	873	.5951	440	52
9	623	903	.5857	435	51
10	.17651	.17933	5.5764	.98430	50
11	680	963	.5671	425	49
12	708	.17993	.5578	420	48
13	737	.18023	.5485	414	47
14	766	053	.5393	409	46
15	.17794	.18083	5.5301	.98404	45
16	823	113	.5209	399	44
17	852	143	.5118	394	43
18	880	173	.5026	389	42
19	909	203	.4936	383	41
20	.17937	.18233	5.4845	.98378	40
21	966	263	.4755	373	39
22	.17995	293	.4665	368	38
23	.18023	323	.4575	362	37
24	052	353	.4486	?57	36
25	.18081	.18384	5.4397	.98352	35
26	109	414	.4308	347	34
27	138	444	.4219	341	33
28	166	474	.4131	336	32
29	195	504	.4043	331	31
30	.18224	.18534	5.3955	.98325	30
31	252	564	.3868	320	29
32	281	594	.3781	315	28
33	309	624	.3694	310	27
34	338	654	.3607	304	26
35	.18367	.18684	5.3521	.98299	25
36	395	714	.3435	294	24
37	424	745	.3349	288	23
38	452	775	.3263	283	22
39	481	805	.3178	277	21
40	.18509	.18835	5.3093	.98272	20
41	538	865	.3008	267	19
42	567	895	.2924	261	18
43	595	925	.2839	256	17
44	624	955	.2755	250	16
45	.18652	.18986	5.2672	.98245	15
46	681	.19016	.2588	240	14
47	710	046	.2505	234	13
48	738	076	.2422	229	12
49	767	106	.2339	223	11
50	.18795	.19136	5.2257	.98218	10
51	824	166	.2174	212	9
52	852	197	.2092	207	8
53	881	227	.2011	201	7
54	910	257	.1929	196	6
55	.18938	.19287	5.1848	.98190	5
56	967	317	.1767	185	4
57	.18995	347	.1686	179	3
58	.19024	378	.1606	174	2
59	052	408	.1526	168	1
60	.19081	.19438	5.1446	.98163	0
	Cos	Ctn	Tan	Sin	′

′	Sin	Tan	Ctn	Cos	
0	.19081	.19438	5.1446	.98163	60
1	109	468	.1366	157	59
2	138	498	.1286	152	58
3	167	529	.1207	146	57
4	195	559	.1128	140	56
5	.19224	.19589	5.1049	.98135	55
6	252	619	.0970	129	54
7	281	649	.0892	124	53
8	309	680	.0814	118	52
9	338	710	.0736	112	51
10	.19366	.19740	5.0658	.98107	50
11	395	770	.0581	101	49
12	423	801	.0504	096	48
13	452	831	.0427	090	47
14	481	861	.0350	084	46
15	.19509	.19891	5.0273	.98079	45
16	538	921	.0197	073	44
17	566	952	.0121	067	43
18	595	.19982	5.0045	061	42
19	623	.20012	4.9969	056	41
20	.19652	.20042	4.9894	.98050	40
21	680	073	.9819	044	39
22	709	103	.9744	039	38
23	737	133	.9669	033	37
24	766	164	.9594	027	36
25	.19794	.20194	4.9520	.98021	35
26	823	224	.9446	016	34
27	851	254	.9372	010	33
28	880	285	.9298	.98004	32
29	908	315	.9225	.97998	31
30	.19937	.20345	4.9152	.97992	30
31	965	376	.9078	987	29
32	.19994	406	.9006	981	28
33	.20022	436	.8933	975	27
34	051	466	.8860	969	26
35	.20079	.20497	4.8788	.97963	25
36	108	527	.8716	958	24
37	136	557	.8644	952	23
38	165	588	.8573	946	22
39	193	618	.8501	940	21
40	.20222	.20648	4.8430	.97934	20
41	250	679	.8359	928	19
42	279	709	.8288	922	18
43	307	739	.8218	916	17
44	336	770	.8147	910	16
45	.20364	.20800	4.8077	.97905	15
46	393	830	.8007	899	14
47	421	861	.7937	893	13
48	450	891	.7867	887	12
49	478	921	.7798	881	11
50	.20507	.20952	4.7729	.97875	10
51	535	.20982	.7659	869	9
52	563	.21013	.7591	863	8
53	592	043	.7522	857	7
54	620	073	.7453	851	6
55	.20649	.21104	4.7385	.97845	5
56	677	134	.7317	839	4
57	706	164	.7249	833	3
58	734	195	.7181	827	2
59	763	225	.7114	821	1
60	.20791	.21256	4.7046	.97815	0
	Cos	Ctn	Tan	Sin	′

12° — Values of Trigonometric Functions — 13°

′	Sin	Tan	Ctn	Cos		′	Sin	Tan	Ctn	Cos	
0	.20791	.21256	4.7046	.97815	60	0	.22495	.23087	4.3315	.97437	60
1	820	286	.6979	809	59	1	523	117	.3257	430	59
2	848	316	.6912	803	58	2	552	148	.3200	424	58
3	877	347	.6845	797	57	3	580	179	.3143	417	57
4	905	377	.6779	791	56	4	608	209	.3086	411	56
5	.20933	.21408	4.6712	.97785	55	5	.22637	.23240	4.3029	.97404	55
6	962	438	.6646	778	54	6	665	271	.2972	398	54
7	.20990	469	.6580	772	53	7	693	301	.2916	391	53
8	.21019	499	.6514	766	52	8	722	332	.2859	384	52
9	047	529	.6448	760	51	9	750	363	.2803	378	51
10	.21076	.21560	4.6382	.97754	50	10	.22778	.23393	4.2747	.97371	50
11	104	590	.6317	748	49	11	807	424	.2691	365	49
12	132	621	.6252	742	48	12	835	455	.2635	358	48
13	161	651	.6187	735	47	13	863	485	.2580	351	47
14	189	682	.6122	729	46	14	892	516	.2524	345	46
15	.21218	.21712	4.6057	.97723	45	15	.22920	.23547	4.2468	.97338	45
16	246	743	.5993	717	44	16	948	578	.2413	331	44
17	275	773	.5928	711	43	17	.22977	608	.2358	325	43
18	303	804	.5864	705	42	18	.23005	639	.2303	318	42
19	331	834	.5800	698	41	19	033	670	.2248	311	41
20	.21360	.21864	4.5736	.97692	40	20	.23062	.23700	4.2193	.97304	40
21	388	895	.5673	686	39	21	090	731	.2139	298	39
22	417	925	.5609	680	38	22	118	762	.2084	291	38
23	445	956	.5546	673	37	23	146	793	.2030	284	37
24	474	.21986	.5483	667	36	24	175	823	.1976	278	36
25	.21502	.22017	4.5420	.97661	35	25	.23203	.23854	4.1922	.97271	35
26	530	047	.5357	655	34	26	231	885	.1868	264	34
27	559	078	.5294	648	33	27	260	916	.1814	257	33
28	587	108	.5232	642	32	28	288	946	.1760	251	32
29	616	139	.5169	636	31	29	316	.23977	.1706	244	31
30	.21644	.22169	4.5107	.97630	30	30	.23345	.24008	4.1653	.97237	30
31	672	200	.5045	623	29	31	373	039	.1600	230	29
32	701	231	.4983	617	28	32	401	069	.1547	223	28
33	729	261	.4922	611	27	33	429	100	.1493	217	27
34	758	292	.4860	604	26	34	458	131	.1441	210	26
35	.21786	.22322	4.4799	.97598	25	35	.23486	.24162	4.1388	.97203	25
36	814	353	.4737	592	24	36	514	193	.1335	196	24
37	843	383	.4676	585	23	37	542	223	.1282	189	23
38	871	414	.4615	579	22	38	571	254	.1230	182	22
39	899	444	.4555	573	21	39	599	285	.1178	176	21
40	.21928	.22475	4.4494	.97566	20	40	.23627	.24316	4.1126	.97169	20
41	956	505	.4434	560	19	41	656	347	.1074	162	19
42	.21985	536	.4373	553	18	42	684	377	.1022	155	18
43	.22013	567	.4313	547	17	43	712	408	.0970	148	17
44	041	597	.4253	541	16	44	740	439	.0918	141	16
45	.22070	.22628	4.4194	.97534	15	45	.23769	.24470	4.0867	.97134	15
46	098	658	.4134	528	14	46	797	501	.0815	127	14
47	126	689	.4075	521	13	47	825	532	.0764	120	13
48	155	719	.4015	515	12	48	853	562	.0713	113	12
49	183	750	.3956	508	11	49	882	593	.0662	106	11
50	.22212	.22781	4.3897	.97502	10	50	.23910	.24624	4.0611	.97100	10
51	240	811	.3838	496	9	51	938	655	.0560	093	9
52	268	842	.3779	489	8	52	966	686	.0509	086	8
53	297	872	.3721	483	7	53	.23995	717	.0459	079	7
54	325	903	.3662	476	6	54	.24023	747	.0408	072	6
55	.22353	.22934	4.3604	.97470	5	55	.24051	.24778	4.0358	.97065	5
56	382	964	.3546	463	4	56	079	809	.0308	058	4
57	410	.22995	.3488	457	3	57	108	840	.0257	051	3
58	438	.23026	.3430	450	2	58	136	871	.0207	044	2
59	467	056	.3372	444	1	59	164	902	.0158	037	1
60	.22495	.23087	4.3315	.97437	0	60	.24192	.24933	4.0108	.97030	0
	Cos	Ctn	Tan	Sin	′		Cos	Ctn	Tan	Sin	′

14° — Values of Trigonometric Functions — 15°

′	Sin	Tan	Ctn	Cos		′	Sin	Tan	Ctn	Cos	
0	.24192	.24933	4.0108	.97030	60	0	.25882	.26795	3.7321	.96593	60
1	220	964	.0058	023	59	1	910	826	.7277	585	59
2	249	.24995	4.0009	015	58	2	938	857	.7234	578	58
3	277	.25026	3.9959	008	57	3	966	888	.7191	570	57
4	305	056	.9910	.97001	56	4	.25994	920	.7148	562	56
5	.24333	.25087	3.9861	.96994	55	5	.26022	.26951	3.7105	.96555	55
6	362	118	.9812	987	54	6	050	.26982	.7062	547	54
7	390	149	.9763	980	53	7	079	.27013	.7019	540	53
8	418	180	.9714	973	52	8	107	044	.6976	532	52
9	446	211	.9665	966	51	9	135	076	.6933	524	51
10	.24474	.25242	3.9617	.96959	50	10	.26163	.27107	3.6891	.96517	50
11	503	273	.9568	952	49	11	191	138	.6848	509	49
12	531	304	.9520	945	48	12	219	169	.6806	502	48
13	559	335	.9471	937	47	13	247	201	.6764	494	47
14	587	366	.9423	930	46	14	275	232	.6722	486	46
15	.24615	.25397	3.9375	.96923	45	15	.26303	.27263	3.6680	.96479	45
16	644	428	.9327	916	44	16	331	294	.6638	471	44
17	672	459	.9279	909	43	17	359	326	.6596	463	43
18	700	490	.9232	902	42	18	387	357	.6554	456	42
19	728	521	.9184	894	41	19	415	388	.6512	448	41
20	.24756	.25552	3.9136	.96887	40	20	.26443	.27419	3.6470	.96440	40
21	784	583	.9089	880	39	21	471	451	.6429	433	39
22	813	614	.9042	873	38	22	500	482	.6387	425	38
23	841	645	.8995	866	37	23	528	513	.6346	417	37
24	869	676	.8947	858	36	24	556	545	.6305	410	36
25	.24897	.25707	3.8900	.96851	35	25	.26584	.27576	3.6264	.96402	35
26	925	738	.8854	844	34	26	612	607	.6222	394	34
27	954	769	.8807	837	33	27	640	638	.6181	386	33
28	.24982	800	.8760	829	32	28	668	670	.6140	379	32
29	.25010	831	.8714	822	31	29	696	701	.6100	371	31
30	.25038	.25862	3.8667	.96815	30	30	.26724	.27732	3.6059	.96363	30
31	066	893	.8621	807	29	31	752	764	.6018	355	29
32	094	924	.8575	800	28	32	780	795	.5978	347	28
33	122	955	.8528	793	27	33	808	826	.5937	340	27
34	151	.25986	.8482	786	26	34	836	858	.5897	332	26
35	.25179	.26017	3.8436	.96778	25	35	.26864	.27889	3.5856	.96324	25
36	207	048	.8391	771	24	36	892	921	.5816	316	24
37	235	079	.8345	764	23	37	920	952	.5776	308	23
38	263	110	.8299	756	22	38	948	.27983	.5736	301	22
39	291	141	.8254	749	21	39	.26976	.28015	.5696	293	21
40	.25320	.26172	3.8208	.96742	20	40	.27004	.28046	3.5656	.96285	20
41	348	203	.8163	734	19	41	032	077	.5616	277	19
42	376	235	.8118	727	18	42	060	109	.5576	269	18
43	404	266	.8073	719	17	43	088	140	.5536	261	17
44	432	297	.8028	712	16	44	116	172	.5497	253	16
45	.25460	.26328	3.7983	.96705	15	45	.27144	.28203	3.5457	.96246	15
46	488	359	.7938	697	14	46	172	234	.5418	238	14
47	516	390	.7893	690	13	47	200	266	.5379	230	13
48	545	421	.7848	682	12	48	228	297	.5339	222	12
49	573	452	.7804	675	11	49	256	329	.5300	214	11
50	.25601	.26483	3.7760	.96667	10	50	.27284	.28360	3.5261	.96206	10
51	629	515	.7715	660	9	51	312	391	.5222	198	9
52	657	546	.7671	653	8	52	340	423	.5183	190	8
53	685	577	.7627	645	7	53	368	454	.5144	182	7
54	713	608	.7583	638	6	54	396	486	.5105	174	6
55	.25741	.26639	3.7539	.96630	5	55	.27424	.28517	3.5067	.96166	5
56	769	670	.7495	623	4	56	452	549	.5028	158	4
57	798	701	.7451	615	3	57	480	580	.4989	150	3
58	826	733	.7408	608	2	58	508	612	.4951	142	2
59	854	764	.7364	600	1	59	536	643	.4912	134	1
60	.25882	.26795	3.7321	.96593	0	60	.27564	.28675	3.4874	.96126	0
	Cos	Ctn	Tan	Sin	′		Cos	Ctn	Tan	Sin	′

75°   **74°**

Table XV.
16° — Values of Trigonometric Functions — 17°

′	Sin	Tan	Ctn	Cos		′	Sin	Tan	Ctn	Cos	
0	.27564	.28675	3.4874	.96126	60	0	.29237	.30573	3.2709	.95630	60
1	592	706	.4836	118	59	1	265	605	.2675	622	59
2	620	738	.4798	110	58	2	293	637	.2641	613	58
3	648	769	.4760	102	57	3	321	669	.2607	605	57
4	676	801	.4722	094	56	4	348	700	.2573	596	56
5	.27704	.28832	3.4684	.96086	55	5	.29376	.30732	3.2539	.95588	55
6	731	864	.4646	078	54	6	404	764	.2506	579	54
7	759	895	.4608	070	53	7	432	796	.2472	571	53
8	787	927	.4570	062	52	8	460	828	.2438	562	52
9	815	958	.4533	054	51	9	487	860	.2405	554	51
10	.27843	.28990	3.4495	.96046	50	10	.29515	.30891	3.2371	.95545	50
11	871	.29021	.4458	037	49	11	543	923	.2338	536	49
12	899	053	.4420	029	48	12	571	955	.2305	528	48
13	927	084	.4383	021	47	13	599	.30987	.2272	519	47
14	955	116	.4346	013	46	14	626	.31019	.2238	511	46
15	.27983	.29147	3.4308	.96005	45	15	.29654	.31051	3.2205	.95502	45
16	.28011	179	.4271	.95997	44	16	682	083	.2172	493	44
17	039	210	.4234	989	43	17	710	115	.2139	485	43
18	067	242	.4197	981	42	18	737	147	.2106	476	42
19	095	274	.4160	972	41	19	765	178	.2073	467	41
20	.28123	.29305	3.4124	.95964	40	20	.29793	.31210	3.2041	.95459	40
21	150	337	.4087	956	39	21	821	242	.2008	450	39
22	178	368	.4050	948	38	22	849	274	.1975	441	38
23	206	400	.4014	940	37	23	876	306	.1943	433	37
24	234	432	.3977	931	36	24	904	338	.1910	424	36
25	.28262	.29463	3.3941	.95923	35	25	.29932	.31370	3.1878	.95415	35
26	290	495	.3904	915	34	26	960	402	.1845	407	34
27	318	526	.3868	907	33	27	.29987	434	.1813	398	33
28	346	558	.3832	898	32	28	.30015	466	.1780	389	32
29	374	590	.3796	890	31	29	043	498	.1748	380	31
30	28402	.29621	3.3759	.95882	30	30	.30071	.31530	3.1716	.95372	30
31	429	653	.3723	874	29	31	098	562	.1684	363	29
32	457	685	.3687	865	28	32	126	594	.1652	354	28
33	485	716	.3652	857	27	33	154	626	.1620	345	27
34	513	748	.3616	849	26	34	182	658	.1588	337	26
35	.28541	.29780	3.3580	.95841	25	35	.30209	.31690	3.1556	.95328	25
36	569	811	.3544	832	24	36	237	722	.1524	319	24
37	597	843	.3509	824	23	37	265	754	.1492	310	23
38	625	875	.3473	816	22	38	292	786	.1460	301	22
39	652	906	.3438	807	21	39	320	818	.1429	293	21
40	.28680	.29938	3.3402	.95799	20	40	.30348	.31850	3.1397	.95284	20
41	708	.29970	.3367	791	19	41	376	882	.1366	275	19
42	736	.30001	.3332	782	18	42	403	914	.1334	266	18
43	764	033	.3297	774	17	43	431	946	.1303	257	17
44	792	065	.3261	766	16	44	459	.31978	.1271	248	16
45	.28820	.30097	3.3226	.95757	15	45	.30486	.32010	3.1240	.95240	15
46	847	128	.3191	749	14	46	514	042	.1209	231	14
47	875	160	.3156	740	13	47	542	074	.1178	222	13
48	903	192	.3122	732	12	48	570	106	.1146	213	12
49	931	224	.3087	724	11	49	597	139	.1115	204	11
50	.28959	.30255	3.3052	.95715	10	50	.30625	.32171	3.1084	.95195	10
51	.28987	287	.3017	707	9	51	653	203	.1053	186	9
52	.29015	319	.2983	698	8	52	680	235	.1022	177	8
53	042	351	.2948	690	7	53	708	267	.0991	168	7
54	070	382	.2914	681	6	54	736	299	.0961	159	6
55	.29098	.30414	3.2879	.95673	5	55	.30763	.32331	3.0930	.95150	5
56	126	446	.2845	664	4	56	791	363	.0899	142	4
57	154	478	.2811	656	3	57	819	396	.0868	133	3
58	182	509	.2777	647	2	58	846	428	.0838	124	2
59	209	541	.2743	639	1	59	874	460	.0807	115	1
60	.29237	.30573	3.2709	.95630	0	60	.30902	.32492	3.0777	.95106	0
	Cos	Ctn	Tan	Sin	′		Cos	Ctn	Tan	Sin	′

73°   72°

18° — Values of Trigonometric Functions — 19°

′	Sin	Tan	Ctn	Cos	
0	.30902	.32492	3.0777	.95106	60
1	929	524	.0746	097	59
2	957	556	.0716	088	58
3	.30985	588	.0686	079	57
4	.31012	621	.0655	070	56
5	.31040	.32653	3.0625	.95061	55
6	068	685	.0595	052	54
7	095	717	.0565	043	53
8	123	749	.0535	033	52
9	151	782	.0505	024	51
10	.31178	.32814	3.0475	.95015	50
11	206	846	.0445	95006	49
12	233	878	.0415	.94997	48
13	261	911	.0385	988	47
14	289	943	.0356	979	46
15	.31316	.32975	3.0326	.94970	45
16	344	.33007	.0296	961	44
17	372	040	.0267	952	43
18	399	072	.0237	943	42
19	427	104	.0208	933	41
20	.31454	.33136	3.0178	.94924	40
21	482	169	.0149	915	39
22	510	201	.0120	906	38
23	537	233	.0090	897	37
24	565	266	.0061	888	36
25	.31593	.33298	3.0032	.94878	35
26	620	330	3.0003	869	34
27	648	363	2.9974	860	33
28	675	395	.9945	851	32
29	703	427	.9916	842	31
30	.31730	.33460	2.9887	.94832	30
31	758	492	.9858	823	29
32	786	524	.9829	814	28
33	813	557	.9800	805	27
34	841	589	.9772	795	26
35	.31868	.33621	2.9743	.94786	25
36	896	654	.9714	777	24
37	923	686	.9686	768	23
38	951	718	.9657	758	22
39	.31979	751	.9629	749	21
40	.32006	.33783	2.9600	.94740	20
41	034	816	.9572	730	19
42	061	848	.9544	721	18
43	089	881	.9515	712	17
44	116	913	.9487	702	16
45	.32144	.33945	2.9459	.94693	15
46	171	.33978	.9431	684	14
47	199	.34010	.9403	674	13
48	227	043	.9375	665	12
49	254	075	.9347	656	11
50	.32282	.34108	2.9319	.94646	10
51	309	140	.9291	637	9
52	337	173	.9263	627	8
53	364	205	.9235	618	7
54	392	238	.9208	609	6
55	.32419	.34270	2.9180	.94599	5
56	447	303	.9152	590	4
57	474	335	.9125	580	3
58	502	368	.9097	571	2
59	529	400	.9070	561	1
60	.32557	.34433	2.9042	.94552	0
	Cos	Ctn	Tan	Sin	′

71°

′	Sin	Tan	Ctn	Cos	
0	.32557	.34433	2.9042	.94552	60
1	584	465	.9015	542	59
2	612	498	.8987	533	58
3	639	530	.8960	523	57
4	667	563	.8933	514	56
5	.32694	.34596	2.8905	.94504	55
6	722	628	.8878	495	54
7	749	661	.8851	485	53
8	777	693	.8824	476	52
9	804	726	.8797	466	51
10	.32832	.34758	2.8770	.94457	50
11	859	791	.8743	447	49
12	887	824	.8716	438	48
13	914	856	.8689	428	47
14	942	889	.8662	418	46
15	.32969	.34922	2.8636	.94409	45
16	.32997	954	.8609	399	44
17	.33024	.34987	.8582	390	43
18	051	.35020	.8556	380	42
19	079	052	.8529	370	41
20	.33106	.35085	2.8502	.94361	40
21	134	118	.8476	351	39
22	161	150	.8449	342	38
23	189	183	.8423	332	37
24	216	216	.8397	322	36
25	.33244	.35248	2.8370	.94313	35
26	271	281	.8344	303	34
27	298	314	.8318	293	33
28	326	346	.8291	284	32
29	353	379	.8265	274	31
30	.33381	.35412	2.8239	.94264	30
31	408	445	.8213	254	29
32	436	477	.8187	245	28
33	463	510	.8161	235	27
34	490	543	.8135	225	26
35	.33518	.35576	2.8109	.94215	25
36	545	608	.8083	206	24
37	573	641	.8057	196	23
38	600	674	.8032	186	22
39	627	707	.8006	176	21
40	.33655	.35740	2.7980	.94167	20
41	682	772	.7955	157	19
42	710	805	.7929	147	18
43	737	838	.7903	137	17
44	764	871	.7878	127	16
45	.33792	.35904	2.7852	.94118	15
46	819	937	.7827	108	14
47	846	.35969	.7801	098	13
48	874	.36002	.7776	088	12
49	901	035	.7751	078	11
50	.33929	.36068	2.7725	.94068	10
51	956	101	.7700	058	9
52	.33983	134	.7675	049	8
53	.34011	167	.7650	039	7
54	038	199	.7625	029	6
55	.34065	.36232	2.7600	.94019	5
56	093	265	.7575	94009	4
57	120	298	.7550	.93999	3
58	147	331	.7525	989	2
59	175	364	.7500	979	1
60	.34202	.36397	2.7475	.93969	0
	Cos	Ctn	Tan	Sin	′

70°

20° — Values of Trigonometric Functions — 21°

′	Sin	Tan	Ctn	Cos		′	Sin	Tan	Ctn	Cos	
0	.34202	.36397	2.7475	.93969	60	0	.35837	.38386	2.6051	.93358	60
1	229	430	.7450	959	59	1	864	420	.6028	348	59
2	257	463	.7425	949	58	2	891	453	.6006	337	58
3	284	496	.7400	939	57	3	918	487	.5983	327	57
4	311	529	.7376	929	56	4	945	520	.5961	316	56
5	.34339	.36562	2.7351	.93919	55	5	.35973	.38553	2.5938	.93306	55
6	366	595	.7326	909	54	6	.36000	587	.5916	295	54
7	393	628	.7302	899	53	7	027	620	.5893	285	53
8	421	661	.7277	889	52	8	054	654	.5871	274	52
9	448	694	.7253	879	51	9	081	687	.5848	264	51
10	.34475	.36727	2.7228	.93869	50	10	.36108	.38721	2.5826	.93253	50
11	503	760	.7204	859	49	11	135	754	.5804	243	49
12	530	793	.7179	849	48	12	162	787	.5782	232	48
13	557	826	.7155	839	47	13	190	821	.5759	222	47
14	584	859	.7130	829	46	14	217	854	.5737	211	46
15	.34612	.36892	2.7106	.93819	45	15	.36244	.38888	2.5715	.93201	45
16	639	925	.7082	809	44	16	271	921	.5693	190	44
17	666	958	.7058	799	43	17	298	955	.5671	180	43
18	694	.36991	.7034	789	42	18	325	.38988	.5649	169	42
19	721	.37024	.7009	779	41	19	352	.39022	.5627	159	41
20	.34748	.37057	2.6985	.93769	40	20	.36379	.39055	2.5605	.93148	40
21	775	090	.6961	759	39	21	406	089	.5583	137	39
22	803	123	.6937	748	38	22	434	122	.5561	127	38
23	830	157	.6913	738	37	23	461	156	.5539	116	37
24	857	190	.6889	728	36	24	488	190	.5517	106	36
25	.34884	.37223	2.6865	.93718	35	25	.36515	.39223	2.5495	.93095	35
26	912	256	.6841	708	34	26	542	257	.5473	084	34
27	939	289	.6818	698	33	27	569	290	.5452	074	33
28	966	322	.6794	688	32	28	596	324	.5430	063	32
29	.34993	355	.6770	677	31	29	623	357	.5408	052	31
30	.35021	.37388	2.6746	.93667	30	30	.36650	.39391	2.5386	.93042	30
31	048	422	.6723	657	29	31	677	425	.5365	031	29
32	075	455	.6699	647	28	32	704	458	.5343	020	28
33	102	488	.6675	637	27	33	731	492	.5322	.93010	27
34	130	521	.6652	626	26	34	758	526	.5300	.92999	26
35	.35157	.37554	2.6628	.93616	25	35	.36785	.39559	2.5279	.92988	25
36	184	588	.6605	606	24	36	812	593	.5257	978	24
37	211	621	.6581	596	23	37	839	626	.5236	967	23
38	239	654	.6558	585	22	38	867	660	.5214	956	22
39	266	687	.6534	575	21	39	894	694	.5193	945	21
40	.35293	.37720	2.6511	.93565	20	40	.36921	.39727	2.5172	.92935	20
41	320	754	.6488	555	19	41	948	761	.5150	924	19
42	347	787	.6464	544	18	42	.36975	795	.5129	913	18
43	375	820	.6441	534	17	43	.37002	829	.5108	902	17
44	402	853	.6418	524	16	44	029	862	.5086	892	16
45	.35429	.37887	2.6395	.93514	15	45	.37056	.39896	2.5065	.92881	15
46	456	920	.6371	503	14	46	083	930	.5044	870	14
47	484	953	.6348	493	13	47	110	963	.5023	859	13
48	511	.37986	.6325	483	12	48	137	.39997	.5002	849	12
49	538	.38020	.6302	472	11	49	164	.40031	.4981	838	11
50	.35565	.38053	2.6279	.93462	10	50	.37191	.40065	2.4960	.92827	10
51	592	086	.6256	452	9	51	218	098	.4939	816	9
52	619	120	.6233	441	8	52	245	132	.4918	805	8
53	647	153	.6210	431	7	53	272	166	.4897	794	7
54	674	186	.6187	420	6	54	299	200	.4876	784	6
55	.35701	.38220	2.6165	.93410	5	55	.37326	.40234	2.4855	.92773	5
56	728	253	.6142	400	4	56	353	267	.4834	762	4
57	755	286	.6119	389	3	57	380	301	.4813	751	3
58	782	320	.6096	379	2	58	407	335	.4792	740	2
59	810	353	.6074	368	1	59	434	369	.4772	729	1
60	.35837	.38386	2.6051	.93358	0	60	.37461	.40403	2.4751	.92718	0
	Cos	Ctn	Tan	Sin	′		Cos	Ctn	Tan	Sin	′

69°   **68°**

Table XX. [XV

22° — Values of Trigonometric Functions — 23°

′	Sin	Tan	Ctn	Cos	
0	.37461	.40403	2.4751	.92718	60
1	488	436	.4730	707	59
2	515	470	.4709	697	58
3	542	504	.4689	686	57
4	569	538	.4668	675	56
5	.37595	.40572	2.4648	.92664	55
6	622	606	.4627	653	54
7	649	640	.4606	642	53
8	676	674	.4586	631	52
9	703	707	.4566	620	51
10	.37730	.40741	2.4545	.92609	50
11	757	775	.4525	598	49
12	784	809	.4504	587	48
13	811	843	.4484	576	47
14	838	877	.4464	565	46
15	.37865	.40911	2.4443	.92554	45
16	892	945	.4423	543	44
17	919	.40979	.4403	532	43
18	946	.41013	.4383	521	42
19	973	047	.4362	510	41
20	.37999	.41081	2.4342	.92499	40
21	.38026	115	.4322	488	39
22	053	149	.4302	477	38
23	080	183	.4282	466	37
24	107	217	.4262	455	36
25	.38134	.41251	2.4242	.92444	35
26	161	285	.4222	432	34
27	188	319	.4202	421	33
28	215	353	.4182	410	32
29	241	387	.4162	399	31
30	.38268	.41421	2.4142	.92388	30
31	295	455	.4122	377	29
32	322	490	.4102	366	28
33	349	524	.4083	355	27
34	376	558	.4063	343	26
35	.38403	.41592	2.4043	.92332	25
36	430	626	.4023	321	24
37	456	660	.4004	310	23
38	483	694	.3984	299	22
39	510	728	.3964	287	21
40	.38537	.41763	2.3945	.92276	20
41	564	797	.3925	265	19
42	591	831	.3906	254	18
43	617	865	.3886	243	17
44	644	899	.3867	231	16
45	.38671	.41933	2.3847	.92220	15
46	698	.41968	.3828	209	14
47	725	.42002	.3808	198	13
48	752	036	.3789	186	12
49	778	070	.3770	175	11
50	.38805	.42105	2.3750	.92164	10
51	832	139	.3731	152	9
52	859	173	.3712	141	8
53	886	207	.3693	130	7
54	912	242	.3673	119	6
55	.38939	.42276	2.3654	.92107	5
56	966	310	.3635	096	4
57	.38993	345	.3616	085	3
58	.39020	379	.3597	073	2
59	046	413	.3578	062	1
60	.39073	.42447	2.3559	.92050	0
	Cos	Ctn	Tan	Sin	′

′	Sin	Tan	Ctn	Cos	
0	.39073	.42447	2.3559	.92050	60
1	100	482	.3539	039	59
2	127	516	.3520	028	58
3	153	551	.3501	016	57
4	180	585	.3483	.92005	56
5	.39207	.42619	2.3464	.91994	55
6	234	654	.3445	982	54
7	260	688	.3426	971	53
8	287	722	.3407	959	52
9	314	757	.3388	948	51
10	.39341	.42791	2.3369	.91936	50
11	367	826	.3351	925	49
12	394	860	.3332	914	48
13	421	894	.3313	902	47
14	448	929	.3294	891	46
15	.39474	.42963	2.3276	.91879	45
16	501	.42998	.3257	868	44
17	528	.43032	.3238	856	43
18	555	067	.3220	845	42
19	581	101	.3201	833	41
20	.39608	.43136	2.3183	.91822	40
21	635	170	.3164	810	39
22	661	205	.3146	799	38
23	688	239	.3127	787	37
24	715	274	.3109	775	36
25	.39741	.43308	2.3090	.91764	35
26	768	343	.3072	752	34
27	795	378	.3053	741	33
28	822	412	.3035	729	32
29	848	447	.3017	718	31
30	.39875	.43481	2.2998	.91706	30
31	902	516	.2980	694	29
32	928	550	.2962	683	28
33	955	585	.2944	671	27
34	.39982	620	.2925	660	26
35	.40008	.43654	2.2907	.91648	25
36	035	689	.2889	636	24
37	062	724	.2871	625	23
38	088	758	.2853	613	22
39	115	793	.2835	601	21
40	.40141	.43828	2.2817	.91590	20
41	168	862	.2799	578	19
42	195	897	.2781	566	18
43	221	932	.2763	555	17
44	248	.43966	.2745	543	16
45	.40275	.44001	2.2727	.91531	15
46	301	036	.2709	519	14
47	328	071	.2691	508	13
48	355	105	.2673	496	12
49	381	140	.2655	484	11
50	.40408	.44175	2.2637	.91472	10
51	434	210	.2620	461	9
52	461	244	.2602	449	8
53	488	279	.2584	437	7
54	514	314	.2566	425	6
55	.40541	.44349	2.2549	.91414	5
56	567	384	.2531	402	4
57	594	418	.2513	390	3
58	621	453	.2496	378	2
59	647	488	.2478	366	1
60	.40674	.44523	2.2460	.91355	0
	Cos	Ctn	Tan	Sin	′

67°　　　　**66°**

Table XV.
24° — Values of Trigonometric Functions — 25°

′	Sin	Tan	Ctn	Cos	
0	.40674	.44523	2.2460	.91355	60
1	700	558	.2443	343	59
2	727	593	.2425	331	58
3	753	627	.2408	319	57
4	780	662	.2390	307	56
5	.40806	.44697	2.2373	.91295	55
6	833	732	.2355	283	54
7	860	767	.2338	272	53
8	886	802	.2320	260	52
9	913	837	.2303	248	51
10	.40939	.44872	2.2286	.91236	50
11	966	907	.2268	224	49
12	992	942	.2251	212	48
13	.41019	.44977	.2234	200	47
14	045	.45012	.2216	188	46
15	.41072	.45047	2.2199	.91176	45
16	098	082	.2182	164	44
17	125	117	.2165	152	43
18	151	152	.2148	140	42
19	178	187	.2130	128	41
20	.41204	.45222	2.2113	.91116	40
21	231	257	.2096	104	39
22	257	292	.2079	092	38
23	284	327	.2062	080	37
24	310	362	.2045	068	36
25	.41337	.45397	2.2028	.91056	35
26	363	432	.2011	044	34
27	390	467	.1994	032	33
28	416	502	.1977	020	32
29	443	538	.1960	.91008	31
30	.41469	.45573	2.1943	.90996	30
31	496	608	.1926	984	29
32	522	643	.1909	972	28
33	549	678	.1892	960	27
34	575	713	.1876	948	26
35	.41602	.45748	2.1859	.90936	25
36	628	784	.1842	924	24
37	655	819	.1825	911	23
38	681	854	.1808	899	22
39	707	889	.1792	887	21
40	.41734	.45924	2.1775	.90875	20
41	760	960	.1758	863	19
42	787	.45995	.1742	851	18
43	813	.46030	.1725	839	17
44	840	065	.1708	826	16
45	.41866	.46101	2.1692	.90814	15
46	892	136	.1675	802	14
47	919	171	.1659	790	13
48	945	206	.1642	778	12
49	972	242	.1625	766	11
50	.41998	.46277	2.1609	.90753	10
51	.42024	312	.1592	741	9
52	051	348	.1576	729	8
53	077	383	.1560	717	7
54	104	418	.1543	704	6
55	.42130	.46454	2.1527	.90692	5
56	156	489	.1510	680	4
57	183	525	.1494	668	3
58	209	560	.1478	655	2
59	235	595	.1461	643	1
60	.42262	.46631	2.1445	.90631	0
	Cos	Ctn	Tan	Sin	′

′	Sin	Tan	Ctn	Cos	
0	.42262	.46631	2.1445	.90631	60
1	288	666	.1429	618	59
2	315	702	.1413	606	58
3	341	737	.1396	594	57
4	367	772	.1380	582	56
5	.42394	.46808	2.1364	.90569	55
6	420	843	.1348	557	54
7	446	879	.1332	545	53
8	473	914	.1315	532	52
9	499	950	.1299	520	51
10	.42525	.46985	2.1283	.90507	50
11	552	.47021	.1267	495	49
12	578	056	.1251	483	48
13	604	092	.1235	470	47
14	631	128	.1219	458	46
15	.42657	.47163	2.1203	.90446	45
16	683	199	.1187	433	44
17	709	234	.1171	421	43
18	736	270	.1155	408	42
19	762	305	.1139	396	41
20	.42788	.47341	2.1123	.90383	40
21	815	377	.1107	371	39
22	841	412	.1092	358	38
23	867	448	.1076	346	37
24	894	483	.1060	334	36
25	.42920	.47519	2.1044	.90321	35
26	946	555	.1028	309	34
27	972	590	.1013	296	33
28	.42999	626	.0997	284	32
29	.43025	662	.0981	271	31
30	.43051	.47698	2.0965	.90259	30
31	077	733	.0950	246	29
32	104	769	.0934	233	28
33	130	805	.0918	221	27
34	156	840	.0903	208	26
35	.43182	.47876	2.0887	.90196	25
36	209	912	.0872	183	24
37	235	948	.0856	171	23
38	261	.47984	.0840	158	22
39	287	.48019	.0825	146	21
40	.43313	.48055	2.0809	.90133	20
41	340	091	.0794	120	19
42	366	127	.0778	108	18
43	392	163	.0763	095	17
44	418	198	.0748	082	16
45	.43445	.48234	2.0732	.90070	15
46	471	270	.0717	057	14
47	497	306	.0701	045	13
48	523	342	.0686	032	12
49	549	378	.0671	019	11
50	.43575	.48414	2.0655	.90007	10
51	602	450	.0640	.89994	9
52	628	486	.0625	981	8
53	654	521	.0609	968	7
54	680	557	.0594	956	6
55	.43706	.48593	2.0579	.89943	5
56	733	629	.0564	930	4
57	759	665	.0549	918	3
58	785	701	.0533	905	2
59	811	737	.0518	892	1
60	.43837	.48773	2.0503	.89879	0
	Cos	Ctn	Tan	Sin	′

26° — Values of Trigonometric Functions — 27°

′	Sin	Tan	Ctn	Cos	
0	.43837	.48773	2.0503	.89879	60
1	863	809	.0488	867	59
2	889	845	.0473	854	58
3	916	881	.0458	841	57
4	942	917	.0443	828	56
5	.43968	.48953	2.0428	.89816	55
6	.43994	.48989	.0413	803	54
7	.44020	.49026	.0398	790	53
8	046	062	.0383	777	52
9	072	098	.0368	764	51
10	.44098	.49134	2.0353	.89752	50
11	124	170	.0338	739	49
12	151	206	.0323	726	48
13	177	242	.0308	713	47
14	203	278	.0293	700	46
15	.44229	.49315	2.0278	.89687	45
16	255	351	.0263	674	44
17	281	387	.0248	662	43
18	307	423	.0233	649	42
19	333	459	.0219	636	41
20	.44359	.49495	2.0204	.89623	40
21	385	532	.0189	610	39
22	411	568	.0174	597	38
23	437	604	.0160	584	37
24	464	640	.0145	571	36
25	.44490	.49677	2.0130	.89558	35
26	516	713	.0115	545	34
27	542	749	.0101	532	33
28	568	786	.0086	519	32
29	594	822	.0072	506	31
30	.44620	.49858	2.0057	.89493	30
31	646	894	.0042	480	29
32	672	931	.0028	467	28
33	698	.49967	2.0013	454	27
34	724	.50004	1.9999	441	26
35	.44750	.50040	1.9984	.89428	25
36	776	076	.9970	415	24
37	802	113	.9955	402	23
38	828	149	.9941	389	22
39	854	185	.9926	376	21
40	.44880	.50222	1.9912	.89363	20
41	906	258	.9897	350	19
42	932	295	.9883	337	18
43	958	331	.9868	324	17
44	984	368	.9854	311	16
45	.45010	.50404	1.9840	.89298	15
46	036	441	.9825	285	14
47	062	477	.9811	272	13
48	088	514	.9797	259	12
49	114	550	.9782	245	11
50	.45140	.50587	1.9768	.89232	10
51	166	623	.9754	219	9
52	192	660	.9740	206	8
53	218	696	.9725	193	7
54	243	733	.9711	180	6
55	.45269	.50769	1.9697	.89167	5
56	295	806	.9683	153	4
57	321	843	.9669	140	3
58	347	879	.9654	127	2
59	373	916	.9640	114	1
60	.45399	.50953	1.9626	.89101	0
	Cos	Ctn	Tan	Sin	′

63°

′	Sin	Tan	Ctn	Cos	
0	45399	.50953	1.9626	.89101	60
1	425	.50989	.9612	087	59
2	451	.51026	.9598	074	58
3	477	063	.9584	061	57
4	503	099	.9570	048	56
5	.45529	.51136	1.9556	.89035	55
6	554	173	.9542	021	54
7	580	209	.9528	.89008	53
8	606	246	.9514	.88995	52
9	632	283	.9500	981	51
10	.45658	.51319	1.9486	.88968	50
11	684	356	.9472	955	49
12	710	393	.9458	942	48
13	736	430	.9444	928	47
14	762	467	.9430	915	46
15	.45787	.51503	1.9416	.88902	45
16	813	540	.9402	888	44
17	839	577	.9388	875	43
18	865	614	.9375	862	42
19	891	651	.9361	848	41
20	.45917	.51688	1.9347	.88835	40
21	942	724	.9333	822	39
22	968	761	.9319	808	38
23	.45994	798	.9306	795	37
24	.46020	835	.9292	782	36
25	.46046	.51872	1.9278	.88768	35
26	072	909	.9265	755	34
27	097	946	.9251	741	33
28	123	.51983	.9237	728	32
29	149	.52020	.9223	715	31
30	.46175	.52057	1.9210	.88701	30
31	201	094	.9196	688	29
32	226	131	.9183	674	28
33	252	168	.9169	661	27
34	278	205	.9155	647	26
35	.46304	.52242	1.9142	.88634	25
36	330	279	.9128	620	24
37	355	316	.9115	607	23
38	381	353	.9101	593	22
39	407	390	.9088	580	21
40	.46433	.52427	1.9074	.88566	20
41	458	464	.9061	553	19
42	484	501	.9047	539	18
43	510	538	.9034	526	17
44	536	575	.9020	512	16
45	.46561	.52613	1.9007	.88499	15
46	587	650	.8993	485	14
47	613	687	.8980	472	13
48	639	724	.8967	458	12
49	664	761	.8953	445	11
50	.46690	.52798	1.8940	.88431	10
51	716	836	.8927	417	9
52	742	873	.8913	404	8
53	767	910	.8900	390	7
54	793	947	.8887	377	6
55	.46819	.52985	1.8873	.88363	5
56	844	.53022	.8860	349	4
57	870	059	.8847	336	3
58	896	096	.8834	322	2
59	921	134	.8820	308	1
60	.46947	.53171	1.8807	.88295	0
	Cos	Ctn	Tan	Sin	′

62°

′	Sin	Tan	Ctn	Cos		′	Sin	Tan	Ctn	Cos	
0	.46947	.53171	1.8807	.88295	60	0	.48481	.55431	1.8040	.87462	60
1	973	208	.8794	281	59	1	506	469	.8028	448	59
2	.46999	246	.8781	267	58	2	532	507	.8016	434	58
3	.47024	283	.8768	254	57	3	557	545	.8003	420	57
4	050	320	.8755	240	56	4	583	583	.7991	406	56
5	.47076	.53358	1.8741	.88226	55	5	.48608	.55621	1.7979	.87391	55
6	101	395	.8728	213	54	6	634	659	.7966	377	54
7	127	432	.8715	199	53	7	659	697	.7954	363	53
8	153	470	.8702	185	52	8	684	736	.7942	349	52
9	178	507	.8689	172	51	9	710	774	.7930	335	51
10	.47204	.53545	1.8676	.88158	50	10	.48735	.55812	1.7917	.87321	50
11	229	582	.8663	144	49	11	761	850	.7905	306	49
12	255	620	.8650	130	48	12	786	888	.7893	292	48
13	281	657	.8637	117	47	13	811	926	.7881	278	47
14	306	694	.8624	103	46	14	837	.55964	.7868	264	46
15	.47332	.53732	1.8611	.88089	45	15	.48862	.56003	1.7856	.87250	45
16	358	769	.8598	075	44	16	888	041	.7844	235	44
17	383	807	.8585	062	43	17	913	079	.7832	221	43
18	409	844	.8572	048	42	18	938	117	.7820	207	42
19	434	882	.8559	034	41	19	964	156	.7808	193	41
20	.47460	.53920	1.8546	.88020	40	20	.48989	.56194	1.7796	.87178	40
21	186	957	.8533	.88006	39	21	.49014	232	.7783	164	39
22	511	.53995	.8520	.87993	38	22	040	270	.7771	150	38
23	537	.54032	.8507	979	37	23	065	309	.7759	136	37
24	562	070	.8495	965	36	24	090	347	.7747	121	36
25	.47588	.54107	1.8482	.87951	35	25	.49116	.56385	1.7735	.87107	35
26	614	145	.8469	937	34	26	141	424	.7723	093	34
27	639	183	.8456	923	33	27	166	462	.7711	079	33
28	665	220	.8443	909	32	28	192	501	.7699	064	32
29	690	258	.8430	896	31	29	217	539	.7687	050	31
30	.47716	.54296	1.8418	.87882	30	30	.49242	.56577	1.7675	.87036	30
31	741	333	.8405	868	29	31	268	616	.7663	021	29
32	767	371	.8392	854	28	32	293	654	.7651	.87007	28
33	793	409	.8379	840	27	33	318	693	.7639	.86993	27
34	818	446	.8367	826	26	34	344	731	.7627	978	26
35	.47844	.54484	1.8354	.87812	25	35	.49369	.56769	1.7615	.86964	25
36	869	522	.8341	798	24	36	394	808	.7603	949	24
37	895	560	.8329	784	23	37	419	846	.7591	935	23
38	920	597	.8316	770	22	38	445	885	.7579	921	22
39	946	635	.8303	756	21	39	470	923	.7567	906	21
40	.47971	.54673	1.8291	.87743	20	40	.49495	.56962	1.7556	.86892	20
41	.47997	711	.8278	729	19	41	521	.57000	.7544	878	19
42	.48022	748	.8265	715	18	42	546	039	.7532	863	18
43	048	786	.8253	701	17	43	571	078	.7520	849	17
44	073	824	.8240	687	16	44	596	116	.7508	834	16
45	.48099	.54862	1.8228	.87673	15	45	.49622	.57155	1.7496	.86820	15
46	124	900	.8215	659	14	46	647	193	.7485	805	14
47	150	938	.8202	645	13	47	672	232	.7473	791	13
48	175	.54975	.8190	631	12	48	697	271	.7461	777	12
49	201	.55013	.8177	617	11	49	723	309	.7449	762	11
50	.48226	.55051	1.8165	.87603	10	50	.49748	.57348	1.7437	.86748	10
51	252	089	.8152	589	9	51	773	386	.7426	733	9
52	277	127	.8140	575	8	52	798	425	.7414	719	8
53	303	165	.8127	561	7	53	824	464	.7402	704	7
54	328	203	.8115	546	6	54	849	503	.7391	690	6
55	.48354	.55241	1.8103	.87532	5	55	.49874	.57541	1.7379	.86675	5
56	379	279	.8090	518	4	56	899	580	.7367	661	4
57	405	317	.8078	504	3	57	924	619	.7355	646	3
58	430	355	.8065	490	2	58	950	657	.7344	632	2
59	456	393	.8053	476	1	59	.49975	696	.7332	617	1
60	.48481	.55431	1.8040	.87462	0	60	.50000	.57735	1.7321	.86603	0
	Cos	Ctn	Tan	Sin	′		Cos	Ctn	Tan	Sin	′

61°   **60°**

Table XV.
30° — Values of Trigonometric Functions — 31°

′	Sin	Tan	Ctn	Cos		′	Sin	Tan	Ctn	Cos	
0	.50000	.57735	1.7321	.86603	60	0	.51504	.60086	1.6643	.85717	60
1	025	774	.7309	588	59	1	529	126	.6632	702	59
2	050	813	.7297	573	58	2	554	165	.6621	687	58
3	076	851	.7286	559	57	3	579	205	.6610	672	57
4	101	890	.7274	544	56	4	604	245	.6599	657	56
5	.50126	.57929	1.7262	.86530	55	5	.51628	.60284	1.6588	.85642	55
6	151	.57968	.7251	515	54	6	653	324	.6577	627	54
7	176	.58007	.7239	501	53	7	678	364	.6566	612	53
8	201	046	.7228	486	52	8	703	403	.6555	597	52
9	227	085	.7216	471	51	9	728	443	.6545	582	51
10	.50252	.58124	1.7205	.86457	50	10	.51753	.60483	1.6534	.85567	50
11	277	162	.7193	442	49	11	778	522	.6523	551	49
12	302	201	.7182	427	48	12	803	562	.6512	536	48
13	327	240	.7170	413	47	13	828	602	.6501	521	47
14	352	279	.7159	398	46	14	852	642	.6490	506	46
15	.50377	.58318	1.7147	.86384	45	15	.51877	.60681	1.6479	.85491	45
16	403	357	.7136	369	44	16	902	721	.6469	476	44
17	428	396	.7124	354	43	17	927	761	.6458	461	43
18	453	435	.7113	340	42	18	952	801	.6447	446	42
19	478	474	.7102	325	41	19	.51977	841	.6436	431	41
20	.50503	.58513	1.7090	.86310	40	20	.52002	.60881	1.6426	.85416	40
21	528	552	.7079	295	39	21	026	921	.6415	401	39
22	553	591	.7067	281	38	22	051	.60960	.6404	385	38
23	578	631	.7056	266	37	23	076	.61000	.6393	370	37
24	603	670	.7045	251	36	24	101	040	.6383	355	36
25	.50628	.58709	1.7033	.86237	35	25	.52126	.61080	1.6372	.85340	35
26	654	748	.7022	222	34	26	151	120	.6361	325	34
27	679	787	.7011	207	33	27	175	160	.6351	310	33
28	704	826	.6999	192	32	28	200	200	.6340	294	32
29	729	865	.6988	178	31	29	225	240	.6329	279	31
30	.50754	.58905	1.6977	.86163	30	30	.52250	.61280	1.6319	.85264	30
31	779	944	.6965	148	29	31	275	320	.6308	249	29
32	804	.58983	.6954	133	28	32	299	360	.6297	234	28
33	829	.59022	.6943	119	27	33	324	400	.6287	218	27
34	854	061	.6932	104	26	34	349	440	.6276	203	26
35	.50879	.59101	1.6920	.86089	25	35	.52374	.61480	1.6265	.85188	25
36	904	140	.6909	074	24	36	399	520	.6255	173	24
37	929	179	.6898	059	23	37	423	561	.6244	157	23
38	954	218	.6887	045	22	38	448	601	.6234	142	22
39	.50979	258	.6875	030	21	39	473	641	.6223	127	21
40	.51004	.59297	1.6864	.86015	20	40	.52498	.61681	1.6212	.85112	20
41	029	336	.6853	.86000	19	41	522	721	.6202	096	19
42	054	376	.6842	.85985	18	42	547	761	.6191	081	18
43	079	415	.6831	970	17	43	572	801	.6181	066	17
44	104	454	.6820	956	16	44	597	842	.6170	051	16
45	.51129	.59494	1.6808	.85941	15	45	.52621	.61882	1.6160	.85035	15
46	154	533	.6797	926	14	46	646	922	.6149	020	14
47	179	573	.6786	911	13	47	671	.61962	.6139	.85005	13
48	204	612	.6775	896	12	48	696	.62003	.6128	.84989	12
49	229	651	.6764	881	11	49	720	043	.6118	974	11
50	.51254	.59691	1.6753	.85866	10	50	.52745	.62083	1.6107	.84959	10
51	279	730	.6742	851	9	51	770	124	.6097	943	9
52	304	770	.6731	836	8	52	794	164	.6087	928	8
53	329	809	.6720	821	7	53	819	204	.6076	913	7
54	354	849	.6709	806	6	54	844	245	.6066	897	6
55	.51379	.59888	1.6698	.85792	5	55	.52869	.62285	1.6055	.84882	5
56	404	928	.6687	777	4	56	893	325	.6045	866	4
57	429	.59967	.6676	762	3	57	918	366	.6034	851	3
58	454	.60007	.6665	747	2	58	943	406	.6024	836	2
59	479	046	.6654	732	1	59	967	446	.6014	820	1
60	.51504	.60086	1.6643	.85717	0	60	.52992	.62487	1.6003	.84805	0
	Cos	Ctn	Tan	Sin	′		Cos	Ctn	Tan	Sin	′

32° — Values of Trigonometric Functions — 33°

′	Sin	Tan	Ctn	Cos		′	Sin	Tan	Ctn	Cos	
0	.52992	.62487	1.6003	.84805	60	0	.54464	.64941	1.5399	.83867	60
1	.53017	527	.5993	789	59	1	488	.64982	.5389	851	59
2	041	568	.5983	774	58	2	513	.65024	.5379	835	58
3	066	608	.5972	759	57	3	537	065	.5369	819	57
4	091	649	.5962	743	56	4	561	106	.5359	804	56
5	.53115	.62689	1.5952	.84728	55	5	.54586	.65148	1.5350	.83788	55
6	140	730	.5941	712	54	6	610	189	.5340	772	54
7	164	770	.5931	697	53	7	635	231	.5330	756	53
8	189	811	.5921	681	52	8	659	272	.5320	740	52
9	214	852	.5911	666	51	9	683	314	.5311	724	51
10	.53238	.62892	1.5900	.84650	50	10	.54708	.65355	1.5301	83708	50
11	263	933	.5890	635	49	11	732	397	.5291	692	49
12	288	.62973	.5880	619	48	12	756	438	.5282	676	48
13	312	.63014	.5869	604	47	13	781	480	.5272	660	47
14	337	055	.5859	588	46	14	805	521	.5262	645	46
15	.53361	.63095	1.5849	.84573	45	15	.54829	.65563	1.5253	.83629	45
16	386	136	.5839	557	44	16	854	604	.5243	613	44
17	411	177	.5829	542	43	17	878	646	.5233	597	43
18	435	217	.5818	526	42	18	902	688	.5223	581	42
19	460	258	.5808	511	41	19	927	729	.5214	565	41
20	.53484	.63299	1.5798	.84495	40	20	.54951	.65771	1.5204	.83549	40
21	509	340	.5788	480	39	21	975	813	.5195	533	39
22	534	380	.5778	464	38	22	.54999	854	.5185	517	38
23	558	421	.5768	448	37	23	.55024	896	.5175	501	37
24	583	462	.5757	433	36	24	048	938	.5166	485	36
25	.53607	.63503	1.5747	.84417	35	25	.55072	.65980	1.5156	.83469	35
26	632	544	.5737	402	34	26	097	.66021	.5147	453	34
27	656	584	.5727	386	33	27	121	063	.5137	437	33
28	681	625	.5717	370	32	28	145	105	.5127	421	32
29	705	666	.5707	355	31	29	169	.147	.5118	405	31
30	.53730	.63707	1.5697	.84339	30	30	.55194	.66189	1.5108	.83389	30
31	754	748	.5687	324	29	31	218	230	.5099	373	29
32	779	789	.5677	308	28	32	242	272	.5089	356	28
33	804	830	.5667	292	27	33	266	314	.5080	340	27
34	828	871	.5657	277	26	34	291	356	.5070	324	26
35	.53853	.63912	1.5647	.84261	25	35	.55315	.66398	1.5061	.83308	25
36	877	953	.5637	245	24	36	339	440	.5051	292	24
37	902	.63994	.5627	230	23	37	363	482	.5042	276	23
38	926	.64035	.5617	214	22	38	388	524	.5032	260	22
39	951	076	.5607	198	21	39	412	566	.5023	244	21
40	.53975	.64117	1.5597	.84182	20	40	.55436	.66608	1.5013	.83228	20
41	.54000	158	.5587	167	19	41	460	650	.5004	212	19
42	024	199	.5577	151	18	42	484	692	.4994	195	18
43	049	240	.5567	135	17	43	509	734	.4985	179	17
44	073	281	.5557	120	16	44	533	776	.4975	163	16
45	.54097	.64322	1.5547	.84104	15	45	.55557	.66818	1.4966	.83147	15
46	122	363	.5537	088	14	46	581	860	.4957	131	14
47	146	404	.5527	072	13	47	605	902	.4947	115	13
48	171	446	.5517	057	12	48	630	944	.4938	098	12
49	195	487	.5507	041	11	49	654	.66986	.4928	082	11
50	.54220	.64528	1.5497	.84025	10	50	.55678	.67028	1.4919	.83066	10
51	244	569	.5487	.84009	9	51	702	071	.4910	050	9
52	269	610	.5477	.83994	8	52	726	113	.4900	034	8
53	293	652	.5468	978	7	53	750	155	.4891	017	7
54	317	693	.5458	962	6	54	775	197	.4882	.83001	6
55	.54342	.64734	1.5448	.83946	5	55	.55799	.67239	1.4872	.82985	5
56	366	775	.5438	930	4	56	823	282	.4863	969	4
57	391	817	.5428	915	3	57	847	324	.4854	953	3
58	415	858	.5418	899	2	58	871	366	.4844	936	2
59	440	899	.5408	883	1	59	895	409	.4835	920	1
60	.54464	.64941	1.5399	.83867	0	60	.55919	.67451	1.4826	.82904	0
	Cos	Ctn	Tan	Sin	′		Cos	Ctn	Tan	Sin	′

′	Sin	Tan	Ctn	Cos		′	Sin	Tan	Ctn	Cos	
0	.55919	.67451	1.4826	.82904	60	0	.57358	.70021	1.4281	.81915	60
1	943	493	.4816	887	59	1	381	064	.4273	899	59
2	968	536	.4807	871	58	2	405	107	.4264	882	58
3	.55992	578	.4798	855	57	3	429	151	.4255	865	57
4	.56016	620	.4788	839	56	4	453	194	.4246	848	56
5	.56040	.67663	1.4779	.82822	55	5	.57477	.70238	1.4237	.81832	55
6	064	705	.4770	806	54	6	501	281	.4229	815	54
7	088	748	.4761	790	53	7	524	325	.4220	798	53
8	112	790	.4751	773	52	8	548	368	.4211	782	52
9	136	832	.4742	757	51	9	572	412	.4202	765	51
10	.56160	.67875	1.4733	.82741	50	10	.57596	.70455	1.4193	.81748	50
11	184	917	.4724	724	49	11	619	499	.4185	731	49
12	208	.67960	.4715	708	48	12	643	542	.4176	714	48
13	232	.68002	.4705	692	47	13	667	586	.4167	698	47
14	256	045	.4696	675	46	14	691	629	.4158	681	46
15	.56280	.68088	1.4687	.82659	45	15	.57715	.70673	1.4150	.81664	45
16	305	130	.4678	643	44	16	738	717	.4141	647	44
17	329	173	.4669	626	43	17	762	760	.4132	631	43
18	353	215	.4659	610	42	18	786	804	.4124	614	42
19	377	258	.4650	593	41	19	810	848	.4115	597	41
20	.56401	.68301	1.4641	.82577	40	20	.57833	.70891	1.4106	.81580	40
21	425	343	.4632	561	39	21	857	935	.4097	563	39
22	449	386	.4623	544	38	22	881	.70979	.4089	546	38
23	473	429	.4614	528	37	23	904	.71023	.4080	530	37
24	497	471	.4605	511	36	24	928	066	.4071	513	36
25	.56521	.68514	1.4596	.82495	35	25	.57952	.71110	1.4063	.81496	35
26	545	557	.4586	478	34	26	976	154	.4054	479	34
27	569	600	.4577	462	33	27	.57999	198	.4045	462	33
28	593	642	.4568	446	32	28	.58023	242	.4037	445	32
29	617	685	.4559	429	31	29	047	285	.4028	428	31
30	.56641	.68728	1.4550	.82413	30	30	.58070	.71329	1.4019	.81412	30
31	665	771	.4541	396	29	31	094	373	.4011	395	29
32	689	814	.4532	380	28	32	118	417	.4002	378	28
33	713	857	.4523	363	27	33	141	461	.3994	361	27
34	736	900	.4514	347	26	34	165	505	.3985	344	26
35	.56760	.68942	1.4505	.82330	25	35	.58189	.71549	1.3976	.81327	25
36	784	.68985	.4496	314	24	36	212	593	.3968	310	24
37	808	.69028	.4487	297	23	37	236	637	.3959	293	23
38	832	071	.4478	281	22	38	260	681	.3951	276	22
39	856	114	.4469	264	21	39	283	725	.3942	259	21
40	.56880	.69157	1.4460	.82248	20	40	.58307	.71769	1.3934	.81242	20
41	904	200	.4451	231	19	41	330	813	.3925	225	19
42	928	243	.4442	214	18	42	354	857	.3916	208	18
43	952	286	.4433	198	17	43	378	901	.3908	191	17
44	.56976	329	.4424	181	16	44	401	946	.3899	174	16
45	.57000	.69372	1.4415	.82165	15	45	.58425	.71990	1.3891	.81157	15
46	024	416	.4406	148	14	46	449	.72034	.3882	140	14
47	047	459	.4397	132	13	47	472	078	.3874	123	13
48	071	502	.4388	115	12	48	496	122	.3865	106	12
49	095	545	.4379	098	11	49	519	167	.3857	089	11
50	.57119	.69588	1.4370	.82082	10	50	.58543	.72211	1.3848	.81072	10
51	143	631	.4361	065	9	51	567	255	.3840	055	9
52	167	675	.4352	048	8	52	590	299	.3831	038	8
53	191	718	.4344	032	7	53	614	344	.3823	021	7
54	215	761	.4335	.82015	6	54	637	388	.3814	.81004	6
55	.57238	.69804	1.4326	.81999	5	55	.58661	.72432	1.3806	.80987	5
56	262	847	.4317	982	4	56	684	477	.3798	970	4
57	286	891	.4308	965	3	57	708	521	.3789	953	3
58	310	934	.4299	949	2	58	731	565	.3781	936	2
59	334	.69977	.4290	932	1	59	755	610	.3772	919	1
60	.57358	.70021	1.4281	.81915	0	60	.58779	.72654	1.3764	.80902	0
	Cos	Ctn	Tan	Sin	′		Cos	Ctn	Tan	Sin	′

′	Sin	Tan	Ctn	Cos		′	Sin	Tan	Ctn	Cos	
0	.58779	.72654	1.3764	.80902	60	0	.60182	.75355	1.3270	.79864	60
1	802	699	.3755	885	59	1	205	401	.3262	846	59
2	826	743	.3747	867	58	2	228	447	.3254	829	58
3	849	788	.3739	850	57	3	251	492	.3246	811	57
4	873	832	.3730	833	56	4	274	538	.3238	793	56
5	.58896	.72877	1.3722	.80816	55	5	.60298	.75584	1.3230	.79776	55
6	920	921	.3713	799	54	6	321	629	.3222	758	54
7	943	.72966	.3705	782	53	7	344	675	.3214	741	53
8	967	.73010	.3697	765	52	8	367	721	.3206	723	52
9	.58990	055	.3688	748	51	9	390	767	.3198	706	51
10	.59014	.73100	1.3680	.80730	50	10	.60414	.75812	1.3190	.79688	50
11	037	144	.3672	713	49	11	437	858	.3182	671	49
12	061	189	.3663	696	48	12	460	904	.3175	653	48
13	084	234	.3655	679	47	13	483	950	.3167	635	47
14	108	278	.3647	662	46	14	506	.75996	.3159	618	46
15	.59131	.73323	1.3638	.80644	45	15	.60529	.76042	1.3151	.79600	45
16	154	368	.3630	627	44	16	553	088	.3143	583	44
17	178	413	.3622	610	43	17	576	134	.3135	565	43
18	201	457	.3613	593	42	18	599	180	.3127	547	42
19	225	502	.3605	576	41	19	622	226	.3119	530	41
20	.59248	.73547	1.3597	.80558	40	20	.60645	.76272	1.3111	.79512	40
21	272	592	.3588	541	39	21	668	318	.3103	494	39
22	295	637	.3580	524	38	22	691	364	.3095	477	38
23	318	681	.3572	507	37	23	714	410	.3087	459	37
24	342	726	.3564	489	36	24	738	456	.3079	441	36
25	.59365	.73771	1.3555	.80472	35	25	.60761	.76502	1.3072	.79424	35
26	389	816	.3547	455	34	26	784	548	.3064	406	34
27	412	861	.3539	438	33	27	807	594	.3056	388	33
28	436	906	.3531	420	32	28	830	640	.3048	371	32
29	459	951	.3522	403	31	29	853	686	.3040	353	31
30	.59482	.73996	1.3514	.80386	30	30	.60876	.76733	1.3032	.79335	30
31	506	.74041	.3506	368	29	31	899	779	.3024	318	29
32	529	086	.3498	351	28	32	922	825	.3017	300	28
33	552	131	.3490	334	27	33	945	871	.3009	282	27
34	576	176	.3481	316	26	34	968	918	.3001	264	26
35	.59599	.74221	1.3473	.80299	25	35	.60991	.76964	1.2993	.79247	25
36	622	267	.3465	282	24	36	.61015	.77010	.2985	229	24
37	646	312	.3457	264	23	37	038	057	.2977	211	23
38	669	357	.3449	247	22	38	061	103	.2970	193	22
39	693	402	.3440	230	21	39	084	149	.2962	176	21
40	.59716	.74447	1.3432	.80212	20	40	.61107	.77196	1.2954	.79158	20
41	739	492	.3424	195	19	41	130	242	.2946	140	19
42	763	538	.3416	178	18	42	153	289	.2938	122	18
43	786	583	.3408	160	17	43	176	335	.2931	105	17
44	809	628	.3400	143	16	44	199	382	.2923	087	16
45	.59832	.74674	1.3392	.80125	15	45	.61222	.77428	1.2915	.79069	15
46	856	719	.3384	108	14	46	245	475	.2907	051	14
47	879	764	.3375	091	13	47	268	521	.2900	033	13
48	902	810	.3367	073	12	48	291	568	.2892	.79016	12
49	926	855	.3359	056	11	49	314	615	.2884	.78998	11
50	.59949	.74900	1.3351	.80038	10	50	.61337	.77661	1.2876	.78980	10
51	972	946	.3343	021	9	51	360	708	.2869	962	9
52	.59995	.74991	.3335	.80003	8	52	383	754	.2861	944	8
53	.60019	.75037	.3327	.79986	7	53	406	801	.2853	926	7
54	042	082	.3319	968	6	54	429	848	.2846	908	6
55	.60065	.75128	1.3311	.79951	5	55	.61451	.77895	1.2838	.78891	5
56	089	173	.3303	934	4	56	474	941	.2830	873	4
57	112	219	.3295	916	3	57	497	.77988	.2822	855	3
58	135	264	.3287	899	2	58	520	.78035	.2815	837	2
59	158	310	.3278	881	1	59	543	082	.2807	819	1
60	.60182	.75355	1.3270	.79864	0	60	.61566	.78129	1.2799	.78801	0
	Cos	Ctn	Tan	Sin	′		Cos	Ctn	Tan	Sin	′

38° — Values of Trigonometric Functions — 39°

′	Sin	Tan	Ctn	Cos	
0	.61566	.78129	1.2799	.78801	60
1	589	175	.2792	783	59
2	612	222	.2784	765	58
3	635	269	.2776	747	57
4	658	316	.2769	729	56
5	.61681	.78363	1.2761	.78711	55
6	704	410	.2753	694	54
7	726	457	.2746	676	53
8	749	504	.2738	658	52
9	772	551	.2731	640	51
10	.61795	.78598	1.2723	.78622	50
11	818	645	.2715	604	49
12	841	692	.2708	586	48
13	864	739	.2700	568	47
14	887	786	.2693	550	46
15	.61909	.78834	1.2685	.78532	45
16	932	881	.2677	514	44
17	955	928	.2670	496	43
18	.61978	.78975	.2662	478	42
19	.62001	.79022	.2655	460	41
20	.62024	.79070	1.2647	.78442	40
21	046	117	.2640	424	39
22	069	164	.2632	405	38
23	092	212	.2624	387	37
24	115	259	.2617	369	36
25	.62138	.79306	1.2609	.78351	35
26	160	354	.2602	333	34
27	183	401	.2594	315	33
28	206	449	.2587	297	32
29	229	496	.2579	279	31
30	.62251	.79544	1.2572	.78261	30
31	274	591	.2564	243	29
32	297	639	.2557	225	28
33	320	686	.2549	206	27
34	342	734	.2542	188	26
35	.62365	.79781	1.2534	.78170	25
36	388	829	.2527	152	24
37	411	877	.2519	134	23
38	433	924	.2512	116	22
39	456	.79972	.2504	098	21
40	.62479	.80020	1.2497	.78079	20
41	502	067	.2489	061	19
42	524	115	.2482	043	18
43	547	163	.2475	025	17
44	570	211	.2467	.78007	16
45	.62592	.80258	1.2460	.77988	15
46	615	306	.2452	970	14
47	638	354	.2445	952	13
48	660	402	.2437	934	12
49	683	450	.2430	916	11
50	.62706	.80498	1.2423	.77897	10
51	728	546	.2415	879	9
52	751	594	.2408	861	8
53	774	642	.2401	843	7
54	796	690	.2393	824	6
55	.62819	.80738	1.2386	.77806	5
56	842	786	.2378	788	4
57	864	834	.2371	769	3
58	887	882	.2364	751	2
59	909	930	.2356	733	1
60	.62932	.80978	1.2349	.77715	0
	Cos	Ctn	Tan	Sin	′

′	Sin	Tan	Ctn	Cos	
0	.62932	.80978	1.2349	.77715	60
1	955	.81027	.2342	696	59
2	.62977	075	.2334	678	58
3	.63000	123	.2327	660	57
4	022	171	.2320	641	56
5	.63045	.81220	1.2312	.77623	55
6	068	268	.2305	605	54
7	090	316	.2298	586	53
8	113	364	.2290	568	52
9	135	413	.2283	550	51
10	.63158	.81461	1.2276	.77531	50
11	180	510	.2268	513	49
12	203	558	.2261	494	48
13	225	606	.2254	476	47
14	248	655	.2247	458	46
15	.63271	.81703	1.2239	.77439	45
16	293	752	.2232	421	44
17	316	800	.2225	402	43
18	338	849	.2218	384	42
19	361	898	.2210	366	41
20	.63383	.81946	1.2203	.77347	40
21	406	.81995	.2196	329	39
22	428	.82044	.2189	310	38
23	451	092	.2181	292	37
24	473	141	.2174	273	36
25	.63496	.82190	1.2167	.77255	35
26	518	238	.2160	236	34
27	540	287	.2153	218	33
28	563	336	.2145	199	32
29	585	385	.2138	181	31
30	.63608	.82434	1.2131	.77162	30
31	630	483	.2124	144	29
32	653	531	.2117	125	28
33	675	580	.2109	107	27
34	698	629	.2102	088	26
35	.63720	.82678	1.2095	.77070	25
36	742	727	.2088	051	24
37	765	776	.2081	033	23
38	787	825	.2074	.77014	22
39	810	874	.2066	.76996	21
40	.63832	.82923	1.2059	.76977	20
41	854	.82972	.2052	959	19
42	877	.83022	.2045	940	18
43	899	071	.2038	921	17
44	922	120	.2031	903	16
45	.63944	.83169	1.2024	.76884	15
46	966	218	.2017	866	14
47	.63989	268	.2009	847	13
48	.64011	317	.2002	828	12
49	033	366	.1995	810	11
50	.64056	.83415	1.1988	.76791	10
51	078	465	.1981	772	9
52	100	514	.1974	754	8
53	123	564	.1967	735	7
54	145	613	.1960	717	6
55	.64167	.83662	1.1953	.76698	5
56	190	712	.1946	679	4
57	212	761	.1939	661	3
58	234	811	.1932	642	2
59	256	860	.1925	623	1
60	.64279	.83910	1.1918	.76604	0
	Cos	Ctn	Tan	Sin	′

51°   **50°**

′	Sin	Tan	Ctn	Cos		′	Sin	Tan	Ctn	Cos	
0	.64279	.83910	1.1918	.76604	60	0	.65606	.86929	1.1504	.75471	60
1	301	.83960	.1910	586	59	1	628	.86980	.1497	452	59
2	323	.84009	.1903	567	58	2	650	.87031	.1490	433	58
3	346	059	.1896	548	57	3	672	082	.1483	414	57
4	368	108	.1889	530	56	4	694	133	.1477	395	56
5	.64390	.84158	1.1882	.76511	55	5	.65716	.87184	1.1470	.75375	55
6	412	208	.1875	492	54	6	738	236	.1463	356	54
7	435	258	.1868	473	53	7	759	287	.1456	337	53
8	457	307	.1861	455	52	8	781	338	.1450	318	52
9	479	357	.1854	436	51	9	803	389	.1443	299	51
10	.64501	.84407	1.1847	.76417	50	10	.65825	.87441	1.1436	.75280	50
11	524	457	.1840	398	49	11	847	492	.1430	261	49
12	546	507	.1833	380	48	12	869	543	.1423	241	48
13	568	556	.1826	361	47	13	891	595	.1416	222	47
14	590	606	.1819	342	46	14	913	646	.1410	203	46
15	.64612	.84656	1.1812	.76323	45	15	.65935	.87698	1.1403	.75184	45
16	635	706	.1806	304	44	16	956	749	.1396	165	44
17	657	756	.1799	286	43	17	.65978	801	.1389	146	43
18	679	806	.1792	267	42	18	.66000	852	.1383	126	42
19	701	856	.1785	248	41	19	022	904	.1376	107	41
20	.64723	.84906	1.1778	.76229	40	20	.66044	.87955	1.1369	.75088	40
21	746	.84956	.1771	210	39	21	066	.88007	.1363	069	39
22	768	.85006	.1764	192	38	22	088	059	.1356	050	38
23	790	057	.1757	173	37	23	109	110	.1349	030	37
24	812	107	.1750	154	36	24	131	162	.1343	.75011	36
25	.64834	.85157	1.1743	.76135	35	25	.66153	.88214	1.1336	.74992	35
26	856	207	.1736	116	34	26	175	265	.1329	973	34
27	878	257	.1729	097	33	27	197	317	.1323	953	33
28	901	308	.1722	078	32	28	218	369	.1316	934	32
29	923	358	.1715	059	31	29	240	421	.1310	915	31
30	.64945	.85408	1.1708	.76041	30	30	.66262	.88473	1.1303	.74896	30
31	967	458	.1702	022	29	31	284	524	.1296	876	29
32	.64989	509	.1695	.76003	28	32	306	576	.1290	857	28
33	.65011	559	.1688	.75984	27	33	327	628	.1283	838	27
34	033	609	.1681	965	26	34	349	680	.1276	818	26
35	.65055	.85660	1.1674	.75946	25	35	.66371	.88732	1.1270	.74799	25
36	077	710	.1667	927	24	36	393	784	.1263	780	24
37	100	761	.1660	908	23	37	414	836	.1257	760	23
38	122	811	.1653	889	22	38	436	888	.1250	741	22
39	144	862	.1647	870	21	39	458	940	.1243	722	21
40	.65166	.85912	1.1640	.75851	20	40	.66480	.88992	1.1237	.74703	20
41	188	.85963	.1633	832	19	41	501	.89045	.1230	683	19
42	210	.86014	.1626	813	18	42	523	097	.1224	664	18
43	232	064	.1619	794	17	43	545	149	.1217	644	17
44	254	115	.1612	775	16	44	566	201	.1211	625	16
45	.65276	.86166	1.1606	.75756	15	45	.66588	.89253	1.1204	.74606	15
46	298	216	.1599	738	14	46	610	306	.1197	586	14
47	320	267	.1592	719	13	47	632	358	.1191	567	13
48	342	318	.1585	700	12	48	653	410	.1184	548	12
49	364	368	.1578	680	11	49	675	463	.1178	528	11
50	.65386	.86419	1.1571	.75661	10	50	.66697	.89515	1.1171	.74509	10
51	408	470	.1565	642	9	51	718	567	.1165	489	9
52	430	521	.1558	623	8	52	740	620	.1158	470	8
53	452	572	.1551	604	7	53	762	672	.1152	451	7
54	474	623	.1544	585	6	54	783	725	.1145	431	6
55	.65496	.86674	1.1538	.75566	5	55	.66805	.89777	1.1139	.74412	5
56	518	725	.1531	547	4	56	827	830	.1132	392	4
57	540	776	.1524	528	3	57	848	883	.1126	373	3
58	562	827	.1517	509	2	58	870	935	.1119	353	2
59	584	878	.1510	490	1	59	891	.89988	.1113	334	1
60	.65606	.86929	1.1504	.75471	0	60	.66913	.90040	1.1106	.74314	0
	Cos	Ctn	Tan	Sin	′		Cos	Ctn	Tan	Sin	′

49° 48°

42° — Values of Trigonometric Functions — 43°

′	Sin	Tan	Ctn	Cos		′	Sin	Tan	Ctn	Cos	
0	.66913	.90040	1.1106	.74314	60	0	.68200	.93252	1.0724	.73135	60
1	935	093	.1100	295	59	1	221	306	.0717	116	59
2	956	146	.1093	276	58	2	242	360	.0711	096	58
3	978	199	.1087	256	57	3	264	415	.0705	076	57
4	.66999	251	.1080	237	56	4	285	469	.0699	056	56
5	.67021	.90304	1.1074	.74217	55	5	.68306	.93524	1.0692	.73036	55
6	043	357	.1067	198	54	6	327	578	.0686	.73016	54
7	064	410	.1061	178	53	7	349	633	.0680	.72996	53
8	086	463	.1054	159	52	8	370	688	.0674	976	52
9	107	516	.1048	139	51	9	391	742	.0668	957	51
10	.67129	.90569	1.1041	.74120	50	10	.68412	.93797	1.0661	.72937	50
11	151	621	.1035	100	49	11	434	852	.0655	917	49
12	172	674	.1028	080	48	12	455	906	.0649	897	48
13	194	727	.1022	061	47	13	476	.93961	.0643	877	47
14	215	781	.1016	041	46	14	497	.94016	.0637	857	46
15	.67237	.90834	1.1009	.74022	45	15	.68518	.94071	1.0630	.72837	45
16	258	887	.1003	.74002	44	16	539	125	.0624	817	44
17	280	940	.0996	.73983	43	17	561	180	.0618	797	43
18	301	.90993	.0990	963	42	18	582	235	.0612	777	42
19	323	.91046	.0983	944	41	19	603	290	.0606	757	41
20	.67344	.91099	1.0977	.73924	40	20	.68624	.94345	1.0599	.72737	40
21	366	153	.0971	904	39	21	645	400	.0593	717	39
22	387	206	.0964	885	38	22	666	455	.0587	697	38
23	409	259	.0958	865	37	23	688	510	.0581	677	37
24	430	313	.0951	846	36	24	709	565	.0575	657	36
25	.67452	.91366	1.0945	.73826	35	25	.68730	.94620	1.0569	.72637	35
26	473	419	.0939	806	34	26	751	676	.0562	617	34
27	495	473	.0932	787	33	27	772	731	.0556	597	33
28	516	526	.0926	767	32	28	793	786	.0550	577	32
29	538	580	.0919	747	31	29	814	841	.0544	557	31
30	.67559	.91633	1.0913	.73728	30	30	.68835	.94896	1.0538	.72537	30
31	580	687	.0907	708	29	31	857	.94952	.0532	517	29
32	602	740	.0900	688	28	32	878	.95007	.0526	497	28
33	623	794	.0894	669	27	33	899	062	.0519	477	27
34	645	847	.0888	649	26	34	920	118	.0513	457	26
35	.67666	.91901	1.0881	.73629	25	35	.68941	.95173	1.0507	.72437	25
36	688	.91955	.0875	610	24	36	962	229	.0501	417	24
37	709	.92008	.0869	590	23	37	.68983	284	.0495	397	23
38	730	062	.0862	570	22	38	.69004	340	.0489	377	22
39	752	116	.0856	551	21	39	025	395	.0483	357	21
40	.67773	.92170	1.0850	.73531	20	40	.69046	.95451	1.0477	.72337	20
41	795	224	.0843	511	19	41	067	506	.0470	317	19
42	816	277	.0837	491	18	42	088	562	.0464	297	18
43	837	331	.0831	472	17	43	109	618	.0458	277	17
44	859	385	.0824	452	16	44	130	673	.0452	257	16
45	.67880	.92439	1.0818	.73432	15	45	.69151	.95729	1.0446	.72236	15
46	901	493	.0812	413	14	46	172	785	.0440	216	14
47	923	547	.0805	393	13	47	193	841	.0434	196	13
48	944	601	.0799	373	12	48	214	897	.0428	176	12
49	965	655	.0793	353	11	49	235	.95952	.0422	156	11
50	.67987	.92709	1.0786	.73333	10	50	.69256	.96008	1.0416	.72136	10
51	.68008	763	.0780	314	9	51	277	064	.0410	116	9
52	029	817	.0774	294	8	52	293	120	.0404	095	8
53	051	872	.0768	274	7	53	319	176	.0398	075	7
54	072	926	.0761	254	6	54	340	232	.0392	055	6
55	.68093	.92980	1.0755	.73234	5	55	.69361	.96288	1.0385	.72035	5
56	115	.93034	.0749	215	4	56	382	344	.0379	.72015	4
57	136	088	.0742	195	3	57	403	400	.0373	.71995	3
58	157	143	.0736	175	2	58	424	457	.0367	974	2
59	179	197	.0730	155	1	59	445	513	.0361	954	1
60	.68200	.93252	1.0724	.73135	0	60	.69466	.96569	1.0355	.71934	0
	Cos	Ctn	Tan	Sin	′		Cos	Ctn	Tan	Sin	′

47°   46°

44° — Values of Trigonometric Functions

′	Sin	Tan	Ctn	Cos	
0	.69466	.96569	1.0355	.71934	60
1	487	625	.9349	914	59
2	508	681	.0343	894	58
3	529	738	.0337	873	57
4	549	794	.0331	853	56
5	.69570	.96850	1.0325	.71833	55
6	591	907	.0319	813	54
7	612	.96963	.0313	792	53
8	633	.97020	.0307	772	52
9	654	076	.0301	752	51
10	.69675	.97133	1.0295	.71732	50
11	696	189	.0289	711	49
12	717	246	.0283	691	48
13	737	302	.0277	671	47
14	758	359	.0271	650	46
15	.69779	.97416	1.0265	.71630	45
16	800	472	.0259	610	44
17	821	529	.0253	590	43
18	842	586	.0247	569	42
19	862	643	.0241	549	41
20	.69883	.97700	1.0235	.71529	40
21	904	756	.0230	508	39
22	925	813	.0224	488	38
23	946	870	.0218	468	37
24	966	927	.0212	447	36
25	.69987	.97984	1.0206	.71427	35
26	.70008	.98041	.0200	407	34
27	029	098	.0194	386	33
28	049	155	.0188	366	32
29	070	213	.0182	345	31
30	.70091	.98270	1.0176	.71325	30
31	112	327	.0170	305	29
32	132	384	.0164	284	28
33	153	441	.0158	264	27
34	174	499	.0152	243	26
35	.70195	.98556	1.0147	.71223	25
36	215	613	.0141	203	24
37	236	671	.0135	182	23
38	257	728	.0129	162	22
39	277	786	.0123	141	21
40	.70298	.98843	1.0117	.71121	20
41	319	901	.0111	100	19
42	339	.98958	.0105	080	18
43	360	.99016	.0099	059	17
44	381	073	.0094	039	16
45	.70401	.99131	1.0088	.71019	15
46	422	189	.0082	.70998	14
47	443	247	.0076	978	13
48	463	304	.0070	957	12
49	484	362	.0064	937	11
50	.70505	.99420	1.0058	.70916	10
51	525	478	.0052	896	9
52	546	536	.0047	875	8
53	567	594	.0041	855	7
54	587	652	.0035	834	6
55	.70608	.99710	1.0029	.70813	5
56	628	768	.0023	793	4
57	649	826	.0017	772	3
58	670	884	.0012	752	2
59	690	.99942	.0006	731	1
60	.70711	1.0000	1.0000	.70711	0
	Cos	Ctn	Tan	Sin	′

45°

′	0° Vers.	Exsec.	1° Vers.	Exsec.	2° Vers.	Exsec.	3° Vers.	Exsec.	′
0	.00000	.00000	.00015	.00015	.00061	.00061	.00137	.00137	0
1	.00000	.00000	.00016	.00016	.00062	.00062	.00139	.00139	1
2	.00000	.00000	.00016	.00016	.00063	.00063	.00140	.00140	2
3	.00000	.00000	.00017	.00017	.00064	.00064	.00142	.00142	3
4	.00000	.00000	.00017	.00017	.00065	.00065	.00143	.00143	4
5	.00000	.00000	.00018	.00018	.00066	.00066	.00145	.00145	5
6	.00000	.00000	.00018	.00018	.00067	.00067	.00147	.00147	6
7	.00000	.00000	.00019	.00019	.00068	.00068	.00148	.00148	7
8	.00000	.00000	.00020	.00020	.00069	.00069	.00150	.00150	8
9	.00000	.00000	.00020	.00020	.00070	.00070	.00151	.00151	9
10	.00000	.00000	.00021	.00021	.00071	.00072	.00153	.00153	10
11	.00001	.00001	.00021	.00021	.00073	.00073	.00154	.00155	11
12	.00001	.00001	.00022	.00022	.00074	.00074	.00156	.00156	12
13	.00001	.00001	.00023	.00023	.00075	.00075	.00158	.00158	13
14	.00001	.00001	.00023	.00023	.00076	.00076	.00159	.00159	14
15	.00001	.00001	.00024	.00024	.00077	.00077	.00161	.00161	15
16	.00001	.00001	.00024	.00024	.00078	.00078	.00162	.00163	16
17	.00001	.00001	.00025	.00025	.00079	.00079	.00164	.00164	17
18	.00001	.00001	.00026	.00026	.00081	.00081	.00166	.00166	18
19	.00002	.00002	.00026	.00026	.00082	.00082	.00167	.00168	19
20	.00002	.00002	.00027	.00027	.00083	.00083	.00169	.00169	20
21	.00002	.00002	.00028	.00028	.00084	.00084	.00171	.00171	21
22	.00002	.00002	.00028	.00028	.00085	.00085	.00173	.00173	22
23	.00002	.00002	.00029	.00029	.00087	.00087	.00174	.00175	23
24	.00002	.00002	.00030	.00030	.00088	.00088	.00176	.00176	24
25	.00003	.00003	.00031	.00031	.00089	.00089	.00178	.00178	25
26	.00003	.00003	.00031	.00031	.00090	.00090	.00179	.00180	26
27	.00003	.00003	.00032	.00032	.00091	.00091	.00181	.00182	27
28	.00003	.00003	.00033	.00033	.00093	.00093	.00183	.00183	28
29	.00004	.00004	.00034	.00034	.00094	.00094	.00185	.00185	29
30	.00004	.00004	.00034	.00034	.00095	.00095	.00187	.00187	30
31	.00004	.00004	.00035	.00035	.00096	.00097	.00188	.00189	31
32	.00004	.00004	.00035	.00036	.00098	.00098	.00190	.00190	32
33	.00005	.00005	.00037	.00037	.00099	.00099	.00192	.00192	33
34	.00005	.00005	.00037	.00037	.00100	.00100	.00194	.00194	34
35	.00005	.00005	.00038	.00038	.00102	.00102	.00196	.00196	35
36	.00005	.00005	.00039	.00039	.00103	.00103	.00197	.00198	36
37	.00006	.00006	.00040	.00040	.00104	.00104	.00199	.00200	37
38	.00006	.00006	.00041	.00041	.00106	.00106	.00201	.00201	38
39	.00006	.00006	.00041	.00041	.00107	.00107	.00203	.00203	39
40	.00007	.00007	.00042	.00042	.00108	.00108	.00205	.00205	40
41	.00007	.00007	.00043	.00043	.00110	.00110	.00207	.00207	41
42	.00007	.00007	.00044	.00044	.00111	.00111	.00208	.00209	42
43	.00008	.00008	.00045	.00045	.00112	.00113	.00210	.00211	43
44	.00008	.00008	.00046	.00046	.00114	.00114	.00212	.00213	44
45	.00009	.00009	.00047	.00047	.00115	.00115	.00214	.00215	45
46	.00009	.00009	.00048	.00048	.00117	.00117	.00216	.00216	46
47	.00009	.00009	.00048	.00048	.00118	.00118	.00218	.00218	47
48	.00010	.00010	.00049	.00049	.00119	.00120	.00220	.00220	48
49	.00010	.00010	.00050	.00050	.00121	.00121	.00222	.00222	49
50	.00011	.00011	.00051	.00051	.00122	.00122	.00224	.00224	50
51	.00011	.00011	.00052	.00052	.00124	.00124	.00226	.00226	51
52	.00011	.00011	.00053	.00053	.00125	.00125	.00228	.00228	52
53	.00012	.00012	.00054	.00054	.00127	.00127	.00230	.00230	53
54	.00012	.00012	.00055	.00055	.00128	.00128	.00232	.00232	54
55	.00013	.00013	.00056	.00056	.00130	.00130	.00234	.00234	55
56	.00013	.00013	.00057	.00057	.00131	.00131	.00236	.00236	56
57	.00014	.00014	.00058	.00058	.00133	.00133	.00238	.00238	57
58	.00014	.00014	.00059	.00059	.00134	.00134	.00240	.00240	58
59	.00015	.00015	.00060	.00060	.00136	.00136	.00242	.00242	59
60	.00015	.00015	.00061	.00061	.00137	.00137	.00244	.00244	60

| ′ | 4° | | 5° | | 6° | | 7° | | ′ |
	Vers.	Exsec.	Vers.	Exsec.	Vers.	Exsec.	Vers.	Exsec.	
0	.00244	.00244	.00381	.00382	.00548	.00551	.00745	.00751	0
1	.00246	.00246	.00383	.00385	.00551	.00554	.00749	.00755	1
2	.00248	.00248	.00386	.00387	.00554	.00557	.00752	.00758	2
3	.00250	.00250	.00388	.00390	.00557	.00560	.00756	.00762	3
4	.00252	.00252	.00391	.00392	.00560	.00563	.00760	.00765	4
5	.00254	.00254	.00393	.00395	.00563	.00566	.00763	.00769	5
6	.00256	.00257	.00396	.00397	.00566	.00569	.00767	.00773	6
7	.00258	.00259	.00398	.00400	.00569	.00573	.00770	.00776	7
8	.00260	.00261	.00401	.00403	.00572	.00576	.00774	.00780	8
9	.00262	.00263	.00404	.00405	.00576	.00579	.00778	.00784	9
10	.00264	.00265	.00406	.00408	.00579	.00582	.00781	.00787	10
11	.00266	.00267	.00409	.00411	.00582	.00585	.00785	.00791	11
12	.00269	.00269	.00412	.00413	.00585	.00588	.00789	.00795	12
13	.00271	.00271	.00414	.00416	.00588	.00592	.00792	.00799	13
14	.00273	.00274	.00417	.00419	.00591	.00595	.00796	.00802	14
15	.00275	.00276	.00420	.00421	.00594	.00598	.00800	.00806	15
16	.00277	.00278	.00422	.00424	.00598	.00601	.00803	.00810	16
17	.00279	.00280	.00425	.00427	.00601	.00604	.00807	.00813	17
18	.00281	.00282	.00428	.00429	.00604	.00608	.00811	.00817	18
19	.00284	.00284	.00430	.00432	.00607	.00611	.00814	.00821	19
20	.00286	.00287	.00433	.00435	.00610	.00614	.00818	.00825	20
21	.00288	.00289	.00436	.00438	.00614	.00617	.00822	.00828	21
22	.00290	.00291	.00438	.00440	.00617	.00621	.00825	.00832	22
23	.00292	.00293	.00441	.00443	.00620	.00624	.00829	.00836	23
24	.00295	.00296	.00444	.00446	.00623	.00627	.00833	.00840	24
25	.00297	.00298	.00447	.00449	.00626	.00630	.00837	.00844	25
26	.00299	.00300	.00449	.00451	.00630	.00634	.00840	.00848	26
27	.00301	.00302	.00452	.00454	.00633	.00637	.00844	.00851	27
28	.00304	.00305	.00455	.00457	.00636	.00640	.00848	.00855	28
29	.00306	.00307	.00458	.00460	.00640	.00644	.00852	.00859	29
30	.00308	.00309	.00460	.00463	.00643	.00647	.00856	.00863	30
31	.00311	.00312	.00463	.00465	.00646	.00650	.00859	.00867	31
32	.00313	.00314	.00466	.00468	.00649	.00654	.00863	.00871	32
33	.00315	.00316	.00469	.00471	.00653	.00657	.00867	.00875	33
34	.00317	.00318	.00472	.00474	.00656	.00660	.00871	.00878	34
35	.00320	.00321	.00474	.00477	.00659	.00664	.00875	.00882	35
36	.00322	.00323	.00477	.00480	.00663	.00667	.00878	.00886	36
37	.00324	.00326	.00480	.00482	.00666	.00671	.00882	.00890	37
38	.00327	.00328	.00483	.00485	.00669	.00674	.00886	.00894	38
39	.00329	.00330	.00486	.00488	.00673	.00677	.00890	.00898	39
40	.00332	.00333	.00489	.00491	.00676	.00681	.00894	.00902	40
41	.00334	.00335	.00492	.00494	.00680	.00684	.00898	.00906	41
42	.00336	.00337	.00494	.00497	.00683	.00688	.00902	.00910	42
43	.00339	.00340	.00497	.00500	.00686	.00691	.00906	.00914	43
44	.00341	.00342	.00500	.00503	.00690	.00695	.00909	.00918	44
45	.00343	.00345	.00503	.00506	.00693	.00698	.00913	.00922	45
46	.00346	.00347	.00506	.00509	.00697	.00701	.00917	.00926	46
47	.00348	.00349	.00509	.00512	.00700	.00705	.00921	.00930	47
48	.00351	.00352	.00512	.00515	.00703	.00708	.00925	.00934	48
49	.00353	.00354	.00515	.00518	.00707	.00712	.00929	.00938	49
50	.00356	.00357	.00518	.00521	.00710	.00715	.00933	.00942	50
51	.00358	.00359	.00521	.00524	.00714	.00719	.00937	.00946	51
52	.00361	.00362	.00524	.00527	.00717	.00722	.00941	.00950	52
53	.00363	.00364	.00527	.00530	.00721	.00726	.00945	.00954	53
54	.00365	.00367	.00530	.00533	.00724	.00730	.00949	.00958	54
55	.00368	.00369	.00533	.00536	.00728	.00733	.00953	.00962	55
56	.00370	.00372	.00536	.00539	.00731	.00737	.00957	.00966	56
57	.00373	.00374	.00539	.00542	.00735	.00740	.00961	.00970	57
58	.00375	.00377	.00542	.00545	.00738	.00744	.00965	.00975	58
59	.00378	.00379	.00545	.00548	.00742	.00747	.00969	.00979	59
60	.00381	.00382	.00548	.00551	.00745	.00751	.00973	.00983	60

′	8°		9°		10°		11°		′
	Vers.	**Exsec.**	**Vers.**	**Exsec.**	**Vers.**	**Exsec.**	**Vers.**	**Exsec.**	
0	.00973	.00983	.01231	.01247	.01519	.01543	.01837	.01872	0
1	.00977	.00987	.01236	.01251	.01524	.01548	.01843	.01877	1
2	.00981	.00991	.01240	.01256	.01529	.01553	.01848	.01883	2
3	.00985	.00995	.01245	.01261	.01534	.01558	.01854	.01889	3
4	.00989	.00999	.01249	.01265	.01539	.01564	.01860	.01895	4
5	.00994	.01004	.01254	.01270	.01545	.01569	.01865	.01901	**5**
6	.00998	.01008	.01259	.01275	.01550	.01574	.01871	.01906	6
7	.01002	.01012	.01263	.01279	.01555	.01579	.01876	.01912	7
8	.01006	.01016	.01268	.01284	.01560	.01585	.01882	.01918	8
9	.01010	.01020	.01272	.01289	.01565	.01590	.01888	.01924	9
10	.01014	.01024	.01277	.01294	.01570	.01595	.01893	.01930	**10**
11	.01018	.01029	.01282	.01298	.01575	.01601	.01899	.01936	11
12	.01022	.01033	.01286	.01303	.01580	.01606	.01904	.01941	12
13	.01027	.01037	.01291	.01308	.01586	.01611	.01910	.01947	13
14	.01031	.01041	.01296	.01313	.01591	.01616	.01916	.01953	14
15	.01035	.01046	.01300	.01317	.01596	.01622	.01921	.01959	**15**
16	.01039	.01050	.01305	.01322	.01601	.01627	.01927	.01965	16
17	.01043	.01054	.01310	.01327	.01606	.01633	.01933	.01971	17
18	.01047	.01059	.01314	.01332	.01611	.01638	.01939	.01977	18
19	.01052	.01063	.01319	.01337	.01617	.01643	.01944	.01983	19
20	.01056	.01067	.01324	.01342	.01622	.01649	.01950	.01989	**20**
21	.01060	.01071	.01329	.01346	.01627	.01654	.01956	.01995	21
22	.01064	.01076	.01333	.01351	.01632	.01659	.01961	.02001	22
23	.01069	.01080	.01338	.01356	.01638	.01665	.01967	.02007	23
24	.01073	.01084	.01343	.01361	.01643	.01670	.01973	.02013	24
25	.01077	.01089	.01348	.01366	.01648	.01676	.01979	.02019	**25**
26	.01081	.01093	.01352	.01371	.01653	.01681	.01984	.02025	26
27	.01086	.01097	.01357	.01376	.01659	.01687	.01990	.02031	27
28	.01090	.01102	.01362	.01381	.01664	.01692	.01996	.02037	28
29	.01094	.01106	.01367	.01386	.01669	.01698	.02002	.02043	29
30	.01098	.01111	.01371	.01391	.01675	.01703	.02008	.02049	**30**
31	.01103	.01115	.01376	.01395	.01680	.01709	.02013	.02055	31
32	.01107	.01119	.01381	.01400	.01685	.01714	.02019	.02061	32
33	.01111	.01124	.01386	.01405	.01690	.01720	.02025	.02067	33
34	.01116	.01128	.01391	.01410	.01696	.01725	.02031	.02073	34
35	.01120	.01133	.01396	.01415	.01701	.01731	.02037	.02079	**35**
36	.01124	.01137	.01400	.01420	.01706	.01736	.02042	.02085	36
37	.01129	.01142	.01405	.01425	.01712	.01742	.02048	.02091	37
38	.01133	.01146	.01410	.01430	.01717	.01747	.02054	.02097	38
39	.01137	.01151	.01415	.01435	.01723	.01753	.02060	.02103	39
40	.01142	.01155	.01420	.01440	.01728	.01758	.02066	.02110	**40**
41	.01146	.01160	.01425	.01445	.01733	.01764	.02072	.02116	41
42	.01151	.01164	.01430	.01450	.01739	.01769	.02078	.02122	42
43	.01155	.01169	.01435	.01455	.01744	.01775	.02084	.02128	43
44	.01159	.01173	.01439	.01460	.01750	.01781	.02090	.02134	44
45	.01164	.01178	.01444	.01466	.01755	.01786	.02095	.02140	**45**
46	.01168	.01182	.01449	.01471	.01760	.01792	.02101	.02146	46
47	.01173	.01187	.01454	.01476	.01766	.01798	.02107	.02153	47
48	.01177	.01191	.01459	.01481	.01771	.01803	.02113	.02159	48
49	.01182	.01196	.01464	.01486	.01777	.01809	.02119	.02165	49
50	.01186	.01200	.01469	.01491	.01782	.01815	.02125	.02171	**50**
51	.01191	.01205	.01474	.01496	.01788	.01820	.02131	.02178	51
52	.01195	.01209	.01479	.01501	.01793	.01826	.02137	.02184	52
53	.01200	.01214	.01484	.01506	.01799	.01832	.02143	.02190	53
54	.01204	.01219	.01489	.01512	.01804	.01837	.02149	.02196	54
55	.01209	.01223	.01494	.01517	.01810	.01843	.02155	.02203	**55**
56	.01213	.01228	.01499	.01522	.01815	.01849	.02161	.02209	56
57	.01218	.01233	.01504	.01527	.01821	.01854	.02167	.02215	57
58	.01222	.01237	.01509	.01532	.01826	.01860	.02173	.02221	58
59	.01227	.01242	.01514	.01537	.01832	.01866	.02179	.02228	59
60	.01231	.01247	.01519	.01543	.01837	.01872	.02185	.02234	**60**

′	12° Vers.	Exsec.	13° Vers.	Exsec.	14° Vers.	Exsec.	15° Vers.	Exsec.	′
0	.02185	.02234	.02563	.02630	.02970	.03061	.03407	.03528	0
1	.02191	.02240	.02570	.02637	.02977	.03069	.03415	.03536	1
2	.02197	.02247	.02576	.02644	.02985	.03076	.03422	.03544	2
3	.02203	.02253	.02583	.02651	.02992	.03084	.03430	.03552	3
4	.02209	.02259	.02589	.02658	.02999	.03091	.03438	.03560	4
5	.02216	.02266	.02596	.02665	.03006	.03099	.03445	.03568	5
6	.02222	.02272	.02602	.02672	.03013	.03106	.03453	.03576	6
7	.02228	.02279	.02609	.02679	.03020	.03114	.03460	.03584	7
8	.02234	.02285	.02616	.02686	.03027	.03121	.03468	.03592	8
9	.02240	.02291	.02622	.02693	.03034	.03129	.03476	.03601	9
10	.02246	.02298	.02629	.02700	.03041	.03137	.03483	.03609	10
11	.02252	.02304	.02635	.02707	.03048	.03144	.03491	.03617	11
12	.02258	.02311	.02642	.02714	.03055	.03152	.03498	.03625	12
13	.02265	.02317	.02649	.02721	.03063	.03159	.03506	.03633	13
14	.02271	.02323	.02655	.02728	.03070	.03167	.03514	.03642	14
15	.02277	.02330	.02662	.02735	.03077	.03175	.03521	.03650	15
16	.02283	.02336	.02669	.02742	.03084	.03182	.03529	.03658	16
17	.02289	.02343	.02675	.02749	.03091	.03190	.03537	.03666	17
18	.02295	.02349	.02682	.02756	.03098	.03197	.03544	.03674	18
19	.02302	.02356	.02689	.02763	.03106	.03205	.03552	.03683	19
20	.02308	.02362	.02696	.02770	.03113	.03213	.03560	.03691	20
21	.02314	.02369	.02702	.02777	.03120	.03220	.03567	.03699	21
22	.02320	.02375	.02709	.02784	.03127	.03228	.03575	.03708	22
23	.02327	.02382	.02716	.02791	.03134	.03236	.03583	.03716	23
24	.02333	.02388	.02722	.02799	.03142	.03244	.03590	.03724	24
25	.02339	.02395	.02729	.02806	.03149	.03251	.03598	.03732	25
26	.02345	.02402	.02736	.02813	.03156	.03259	.03606	.03741	26
27	.02352	.02408	.02743	.02820	.03163	.03267	.03614	.03749	27
28	.02358	.02415	.02749	.02827	.03171	.03275	.03621	.03758	28
29	.02364	.02421	.02756	.02834	.03178	.03282	.03629	.03766	29
30	.02370	.02428	.02763	.02842	.03185	.03290	.03637	.03774	30
31	.02377	.02435	.02770	.02849	.03193	.03298	.03645	.03783	31
32	.02383	.02441	.02777	.02856	.03200	.03306	.03653	.03791	32
33	.02389	.02448	.02783	.02863	.03207	.03313	.03660	.03799	33
34	.02396	.02454	.02790	.02870	.03214	.03321	.03668	.03808	34
35	.02402	.02461	.02797	.02878	.03222	.03329	.03676	.03816	35
36	.02408	.02468	.02804	.02885	.03229	.03337	.03684	.03825	36
37	.02415	.02474	.02811	.02892	.03236	.03345	.03692	.03833	37
38	.02421	.02481	.02818	.02899	.03244	.03353	.03699	.03842	38
39	.02427	.02488	.02824	.02907	.03251	.03360	.03707	.03850	39
40	.02434	.02494	.02831	.02914	.03258	.03368	.03715	.03858	40
41	.02440	.02501	.02838	.02921	.03266	.03376	.03723	.03867	41
42	.02447	.02508	.02845	.02928	.03273	.03384	.03731	.03875	42
43	.02453	.02515	.02852	.02936	.03281	.03392	.03739	.03884	43
44	.02459	.02521	.02859	.02943	.03288	.03400	.03747	.03892	44
45	.02466	.02528	.02866	.02950	.03295	.03408	.03754	.03901	45
46	.02472	.02535	.02873	.02958	.03303	.03416	.03762	.03909	46
47	.02479	.02542	.02880	.02965	.03310	.03424	.03770	.03918	47
48	.02485	.02548	.02887	.02972	.03318	.03432	.03778	.03927	48
49	.02492	.02555	.02894	.02980	.03325	.03439	.03786	.03935	49
50	.02498	.02562	.02900	.02987	.03333	.03447	.03794	.03944	50
51	.02504	.02569	.02907	.02994	.03340	.03455	.03802	.03952	51
52	.02511	.02576	.02914	.03002	.03347	.03463	.03810	.03961	52
53	.02517	.02582	.02921	.03009	.03355	.03471	.03818	.03969	53
54	.02523	.02589	.02928	.03017	.03362	.03479	.03826	.03978	54
55	.02530	.02596	.02935	.03024	.03370	.03487	.03834	.03987	55
56	.02537	.02603	.02942	.03032	.03377	.03495	.03842	.03995	56
57	.02543	.02610	.02949	.03039	.03385	.03503	.03850	.04004	57
58	.02550	.02617	.02956	.03046	.03392	.03511	.03858	.04013	58
59	.02556	.02624	.02963	.03054	.03400	.03520	.03866	.04021	59
60	.02563	.02630	.02970	.03061	.03407	.03528	.03874	.04030	60

′	16°		17°		18°		19°		′
	Vers.	Exsec.	Vers.	Exsec.	Vers.	Exsec.	Vers.	Exsec.	
0	.03874	.04030	.04370	.04569	.04894	.05146	.05448	.05762	0
1	.03882	.04039	.04378	.04578	.04903	.05156	.05458	.05773	1
2	.03890	.04047	.04387	.04588	.04912	.05166	.05467	.05783	2
3	.03898	.04056	.04395	.04597	.04921	.05176	.05477	.05794	3
4	.03906	.04065	.04404	.04606	.04930	.05186	.05486	.05805	4
5	.03914	.04073	.04412	.04616	.04939	.05196	.05496	.05815	5
6	.03922	.04082	.04421	.04625	.04948	.05206	.05505	.05826	6
7	.03930	.04091	.04429	.04635	.04957	.05216	.05515	.05836	7
8	.03938	.04100	.04438	.04644	.04967	.05226	.05524	.05847	8
9	.03946	.04108	.04446	.04653	.04976	.05236	.05534	.05858	9
10	.03954	.04117	.04455	.04663	.04985	.05246	.05543	.05869	10
11	.03963	.04126	.04464	.04672	.04994	.05256	.05553	.05879	11
12	.03971	.04135	.04472	.04682	.05003	.05266	.05562	.05890	12
13	.03979	.04144	.04481	.04691	.05012	.05276	.05572	.05901	13
14	.03987	.04152	.04489	.04700	.05021	.05286	.05582	.05911	14
15	.03995	.04161	.04498	.04710	.05030	.05297	.05591	.05922	15
16	.04003	.04170	.04507	.04719	.05039	.05307	.05601	.05933	16
17	.04011	.04179	.04515	.04729	.05048	.05317	.05610	.05944	17
18	.04019	.04188	.04524	.04738	.05057	.05327	.05620	.05955	18
19	.04028	.04197	.04533	.04748	.05067	.05337	.05630	.05965	19
20	.04036	.04206	.04541	.04757	.05076	.05347	.05639	.05976	20
21	.04044	.04214	.04550	.04767	.05085	.05357	.05649	.05987	21
22	.04052	.04223	.04559	.04776	.05094	.05367	.05658	.05998	22
23	.04060	.04232	.04567	.04786	.05103	.05378	.05668	.06009	23
24	.04069	.04241	.04576	.04795	.05112	.05388	.05678	.06020	24
25	.04077	.04250	.04585	.04805	.05122	.05398	.05687	.06030	25
26	.04085	.04259	.04593	.04815	.05131	.05408	.05697	.06041	26
27	.04093	.04268	.04602	.04824	.05140	.05418	.05707	.06052	27
28	.04102	.04277	.04611	.04834	.05149	.05429	.05716	.06063	28
29	.04110	.04286	.04620	.04843	.05158	.05439	.05726	.06074	29
30	.04118	.04295	.04628	.04853	.05168	.05449	.05736	.06085	30
31	.04126	.04304	.04637	.04863	.05177	.05460	.05746	.06096	31
32	.04135	.04312	.04646	.04872	.05186	.05470	.05755	.06107	32
33	.04143	.04322	.04655	.04882	.05195	.05480	.05765	.06118	33
34	.04151	.04331	.04663	.04891	.05205	.05490	.05775	.06129	34
35	.04159	.04340	.04672	.04901	.05214	.05501	.05785	.06140	35
36	.04168	.04349	.04681	.04911	.05223	.05511	.05794	.06151	36
37	.04176	.04358	.04690	.04920	.05232	.05521	.05804	.06162	37
38	.04184	.04367	.04699	.04930	.05242	.05532	.05814	.06173	38
39	.04193	.04376	.04707	.04940	.05251	.05542	.05824	.06184	39
40	.04201	.04385	.04716	.04950	.05260	.05552	.05833	.06195	40
41	.04209	.04394	.04725	.04959	.05270	.05563	.05843	.06206	41
42	.04218	.04403	.04734	.04969	.05279	.05573	.05853	.06217	42
43	.04226	.04413	.04743	.04979	.05288	.05584	.05863	.06228	43
44	.04234	.04422	.04752	.04989	.05298	.05594	.05873	.06239	44
45	.04243	.04431	.04760	.04998	.05307	.05604	.05882	.06250	45
46	.04251	.04440	.04769	.05008	.05316	.05615	.05892	.06261	46
47	.04260	.04449	.04778	.05018	.05326	.05625	.05902	.06272	47
48	.04268	.04458	.04787	.05028	.05335	.05636	.05912	.06283	48
49	.04276	.04468	.04796	.05038	.05344	.05646	.05922	.06295	49
50	.04285	.04477	.04805	.05047	.05354	.05657	.05932	.06306	50
51	.04293	.04486	.04814	.05057	.05363	.05667	.05942	.06317	51
52	.04302	.04495	.04823	.05067	.05373	.05678	.05951	.06328	52
53	.04310	.04504	.04832	.05077	.05382	.05688	.05961	.06339	53
54	.04319	.04514	.04841	.05087	.05391	.05699	.05971	.06350	54
55	.04327	.04523	.04850	.05097	.05401	.05709	.05981	.06362	55
56	.04336	.04532	.04858	.05107	.05410	.05720	.05991	.06373	56
57	.04344	.04541	.04867	.05116	.05420	.05730	.06001	.06384	57
58	.04353	.04551	.04876	.05126	.05429	.05741	.06011	.06395	58
59	.04361	.04560	.04885	.05136	.05439	.05751	.06021	.06407	59
60	.04370	.04569	.04894	.05146	.05448	.05762	.06031	.06418	60

′	20° Vers.	Exsec.	21° Vers.	Exsec.	22° Vers.	Exsec.	23° Vers.	Exsec.	′
0	.06031	.06418	.06642	.07114	.07282	.07853	.07950	.08636	0
1	.06041	.06429	.06652	.07126	.07293	.07866	.07961	.08649	1
2	.06051	.06440	.06663	.07138	.07303	.07879	.07972	.08663	2
3	.06061	.06452	.06673	.07150	.07314	.07892	.07984	.08676	3
4	.06071	.06463	.06684	.07162	.07325	.07904	.07995	.08690	4
5	.06081	.06474	.06694	.07174	.07336	.07917	.08006	.08703	5
6	.06091	.06486	.06705	.07186	.07347	.07930	.08018	.08717	6
7	.06101	.06497	.06715	.07199	.07358	.07943	.08029	.08730	7
8	.06111	.06508	.06726	.07211	.07369	.07955	.08041	.08744	8
9	.06121	.06520	.06736	.07223	.07380	.07968	.08052	.08757	9
10	.06131	.06531	.06747	.07235	.07391	.07981	.08064	.08771	10
11	.06141	.06542	.06757	.07247	.07402	.07994	.08075	.08784	11
12	.06151	.06554	.06768	.07259	.07413	.08006	.08086	.08798	12
13	.06161	.06565	.06778	.07271	.07424	.08019	.08098	.08811	13
14	.06171	.06577	.06789	.07283	.07435	.08032	.08109	.08825	14
15	.06181	.06588	.06799	.07295	.07446	.08045	.08121	.08839	15
16	.06191	.06600	.06810	.07307	.07457	.08058	.08132	.08852	16
17	.06201	.06611	.06820	.07320	.07468	.08071	.08144	.08866	17
18	.06211	.06622	.03831	.07332	.07479	.08084	.08155	.08880	18
19	.06221	.06634	.06841	.07344	.07490	.08097	.08167	.08893	19
20	.06231	.06645	.06852	.07356	.07501	.08109	.08178	.08907	20
21	.06241	.06657	.06863	.07368	.07512	.08122	.08190	.08920	21
22	.06252	.06668	.06873	.07380	.07523	.08135	.08201	.08934	22
23	.06262	.06680	.06884	.07393	.07534	.08148	.08213	.08948	23
24	.06272	.06691	.06894	.07405	.07545	.08161	.08225	.08962	24
25	.06282	.06703	.06905	.07417	.07556	.08174	.08236	.08975	25
26	.06292	.06715	.06916	.07429	.07568	.08187	.08248	.08989	26
27	.06302	.06726	.06926	.07442	.07579	.08200	.08259	.09003	27
28	.06312	.06738	.06937	.07454	.07590	.08213	.08271	.09017	28
29	.06323	.06749	.06948	.07466	.07601	.08226	.08282	.09030	29
30	.06333	.06761	.06958	.07479	.07312	.08239	.08294	.09044	30
31	.06343	.06773	.06969	.07491	.07623	.08252	.08306	.09058	31
32	.06353	.06784	.06980	.07503	.07634	.08265	.08317	.09072	32
33	.06363	.06796	.06990	.07516	.07645	.03278	.08329	.09086	33
34	.06374	.06807	.07001	.07528	.07657	.08291	.08340	.09099	34
35	.06384	.06819	.07012	.07540	.07668	.08305	.08352	.09113	35
36	.06394	.06831	.07022	.07553	.07679	.08318	.08364	.09127	36
37	.06404	.06842	.07033	.07565	.07690	.08331	.08375	.09141	37
38	.03415	.06854	.07044	.07578	.07701	.08344	.08387	.09155	38
39	.06425	.06866	.07055	.07590	.07713	.08357	.08399	.09169	39
40	.06435	.06878	.07065	.07602	.07724	.08370	.08410	.09183	40
41	.06445	.06889	.07076	.07615	.07735	.08383	.08422	.09197	41
42	.06456	.06901	.07087	.07627	.07746	.08397	.08434	.09211	42
43	.06466	.06913	.07098	.07640	.07757	.08410	.08445	.09224	43
44	.06476	.06925	.07108	.07652	.07769	.08423	.08457	.09238	44
45	.06486	.06936	.07119	.07665	.07780	.08436	.08469	.09252	45
46	.06497	.06948	.07130	.07677	.07791	.08449	.08481	.09266	46
47	.03507	.06960	.07141	.07690	.07802	.08463	.08492	.09280	47
48	.06517	.06972	.07151	.07702	.07814	.08476	.08504	.09294	48
49	.06528	.06984	.07162	.07715	.07825	.08489	.08516	.09308	49
50	.06538	.06995	.07173	.07727	.07836	.08503	.08528	.09323	50
51	.06548	.07007	.07184	.07740	.07848	.08516	.08539	.09337	51
52	.06559	.07019	.07195	.07752	.07859	.08529	.08551	.09351	52
53	.06569	.07031	.07206	.07765	.07870	.08542	.08563	.09365	53
54	.06580	.07043	.07216	.07778	.07881	.08556	.08575	.09379	54
55	.06590	.07055	.07227	.07790	.07893	.08569	.08586	.09393	55
56	.06600	.07067	.07238	.07803	.07904	.08582	.08598	.09407	56
57	.03611	.07079	.07249	.07816	.07915	.08596	.08610	.09421	57
58	.06621	.07091	.07260	.07828	.07927	.08609	.08622	.09435	58
59	.06632	.07103	.07271	.07841	.07938	.08623	.08634	.09449	59
60	.06642	.07114	.07282	.07853	.07950	.08636	.08645	.09464	60

′	24° Vers.	24° Exsec.	25° Vers.	25° Exsec.	26° Vers.	26° Exsec.	27° Vers.	27° Exsec.	′
0	.08645	.09464	.09369	.10338	.10121	.11260	.10899	.12233	0
1	.08657	.09478	.09382	.10353	.10133	.11276	.10913	.12249	1
2	.08669	.09492	.09394	.10368	.10146	.11292	.10926	.12266	2
3	.08681	.09506	.09406	.10383	.10159	.11308	.10939	.12283	3
4	.08693	.09520	.09418	.10398	.10172	.11323	.10952	.12299	4
5	.08705	.09535	.09431	.10413	.10184	.11339	.10965	.12316	5
6	.08717	.09549	.09443	.10428	.10197	.11355	.10979	.12333	6
7	.08728	.09563	.09455	.10443	.10210	.11371	.10992	.12349	7
8	.08740	.09577	.09468	.10458	.10223	.11387	.11005	.12366	8
9	.08752	.09592	.09480	.10473	.10236	.11403	.11019	.12383	9
10	.08764	.09606	.09493	.10488	.10248	.11419	.11032	.12400	10
11	.08776	.09620	.09505	.10503	.10261	.11435	.11045	.12416	11
12	.08788	.09635	.09517	.10518	.10274	.11451	.11058	.12433	12
13	.08800	.09649	.09530	.10533	.10287	.11467	.11072	.12450	13
14	.08812	.09663	.09542	.10549	.10300	.11483	.11085	.12467	14
15	.08824	.09678	.09554	.10564	.10313	.11499	.11098	.12484	15
16	.08836	.09692	.09567	.10579	.10326	.11515	.11112	.12501	16
17	.08848	.09707	.09579	.10594	.10338	.11531	.11125	.12518	17
18	.08860	.09721	.09592	.10609	.10351	.11547	.11138	.12534	18
19	.08872	.09735	.09604	.10625	.10364	.11563	.11152	.12551	19
20	.08884	.09750	.09617	.10640	.10377	.11579	.11165	.12568	20
21	.08896	.09764	.09629	.10655	.10390	.11595	.11178	.12585	21
22	.08908	.09779	.09642	.10670	.10403	.11611	.11192	.12602	22
23	.08920	.09793	.09654	.10686	.10416	.11627	.11205	.12619	23
24	.08932	.09808	.09666	.10701	.10429	.11643	.11218	.12636	24
25	.08944	.09822	.09679	.10716	.10442	.11659	.11232	.12653	25
26	.08956	.09837	.09691	.10731	.10455	.11675	.11245	.12670	26
27	.08968	.09851	.09704	.10747	.10468	.11691	.11259	.12687	27
28	.08980	.09866	.09716	.10762	.10481	.11708	.11272	.12704	28
29	.08992	.09880	.09729	.10777	.10494	.11724	.11285	.12721	29
30	.09004	.09895	.09741	.10793	.10507	.11740	.11299	.12738	30
31	.09016	.09909	.09754	.10808	.10520	.11756	.11312	.12755	31
32	.09028	.09924	.09767	.10824	.10533	.11772	.11326	.12772	32
33	.09040	.09939	.09779	.10839	.10546	.11789	.11339	.12789	33
34	.09052	.09953	.09792	.10854	.10559	.11805	.11353	.12807	34
35	.09064	.09968	.09804	.10870	.10572	.11821	.11366	.12824	35
36	.09076	.09982	.09817	.10885	.10585	.11838	.11380	.12841	36
37	.09089	.09997	.09829	.10901	.10598	.11854	.11393	.12858	37
38	.09101	.10012	.09842	.10916	.10611	.11870	.11407	.12875	38
39	.09113	.10026	.09854	.10932	.10624	.11886	.11420	.12892	39
40	.09125	.10041	.09867	.10947	.10637	.11903	.11434	.12910	40
41	.09137	.10056	.09880	.10963	.10650	.11919	.11447	.12927	41
42	.09149	.10071	.09892	.10978	.10663	.11936	.11461	.12944	42
43	.09161	.10085	.09905	.10994	.10676	.11952	.11474	.12961	43
44	.09174	.10100	.09918	.11009	.10689	.11968	.11488	.12979	44
45	.09186	.10115	.09930	.11025	.10702	.11985	.11501	.12996	45
46	.09198	.10130	.09943	.11041	.10715	.12001	.11515	.13013	46
47	.09210	.10144	.09955	.11056	.10728	.12018	.11528	.13031	47
48	.09222	.10159	.09968	.11072	.10741	.12034	.11542	.13048	48
49	.09234	.10174	.09981	.11087	.10755	.12051	.11555	.13065	49
50	.09247	.10189	.09993	.11103	.10768	.12067	.11569	.13083	50
51	.09259	.10204	.10006	.11119	.10781	.12083	.11583	.13100	51
52	.09271	.10218	.10019	.11134	.10794	.12100	.11596	.13117	52
53	.09283	.10233	.10032	.11150	.10807	.12117	.11610	.13135	53
54	.09296	.10248	.10044	.11166	.10820	.12133	.11623	.13152	54
55	.09308	.10263	.10057	.11181	.10833	.12150	.11637	.13170	55
56	.09320	.10278	.10070	.11197	.10847	.12166	.11651	.13187	56
57	.09332	.10293	.10082	.11213	.10860	.12183	.11664	.13205	57
58	.09345	.10308	.10095	.11229	.10873	.12199	.11678	.13222	58
59	.09357	.10323	.10108	.11244	.10886	.12216	.11692	.13239	59
60	.09369	.10338	.10121	.11260	.10899	.12233	.11705	.13257	60

′	28° Vers.	Exsec.	29° Vers.	Exsec.	30° Vers.	Exsec.	31° Vers.	Exsec.	′
0	.11705	.13257	.12538	.14335	.13397	.15470	.14283	.16663	0
1	.11719	.13275	.12552	.14354	.13412	.15489	.14298	.16684	1
2	.11733	.13292	.12566	.14372	.13427	.15509	.14313	.16704	2
3	.11746	.13310	.12580	.14391	.13441	.15528	.14328	.16725	3
4	.11760	.13327	.12594	.14409	.13456	.15548	.14343	.16745	4
5	.11774	.13345	.12609	.14428	.13470	.15567	.14358	.16766	5
6	.11787	.13362	.12623	.14446	.13485	.15587	.14373	.16786	6
7	.11801	.13380	.12637	.14465	.13499	.15606	.14388	.16806	7
8	.11815	.13398	.12651	.14483	.13514	.15626	.14403	.16827	8
9	.11828	.13415	.12665	.14502	.13529	.15645	.14418	.16848	9
10	.11842	.13433	.12679	.14521	.13543	.15665	.14433	.16868	10
11	.11856	.13451	.12694	.14539	.13558	.15684	.14449	.16889	11
12	.11870	.13468	.12708	.14558	.13573	.15704	.14464	.16909	12
13	.11883	.13486	.12722	.14576	.13587	.15724	.14479	.16930	13
14	.11897	.13504	.12736	.14595	.13602	.15743	.14494	.16950	14
15	.11911	.13521	.12750	.14614	.13616	.15763	.14509	.16971	15
16	.11925	.13539	.12765	.14632	.13631	.15782	.14524	.16992	16
17	.11938	.13557	.12779	.14651	.13646	.15802	.14539	.17012	17
18	.11952	.13575	.12793	.14670	.13660	.15822	.14554	.17033	18
19	.11966	.13593	.12807	.14689	.13675	.15841	.14569	.17054	19
20	.11980	.13610	.12822	.14707	.13690	.15861	.14584	.17075	20
21	.11994	.13628	.12836	.14726	.13705	.15881	.14599	.17095	21
22	.12007	.13646	.12850	.14745	.13719	.15901	.14615	.17116	22
23	.12021	.13664	.12864	.14764	.13734	.15920	.14630	.17137	23
24	.12035	.13682	.12879	.14782	.13749	.15940	.14645	.17158	24
25	.12049	.13700	.12893	.14801	.13763	.15960	.14660	.17178	25
26	.12063	.13718	.12907	.14820	.13778	.15980	.14675	.17199	26
27	.12077	.13735	.12921	.14839	.13793	.16000	.14690	.17220	27
28	.12091	.13753	.12936	.14858	.13808	.16019	.14706	.17241	28
29	.12104	.13771	.12950	.14877	.13822	.16039	.14721	.17262	29
30	.12118	.13789	.12964	.14896	.13837	.16059	.14736	.17283	30
31	.12132	.13807	.12979	.14914	.13852	.16079	.14751	.17304	31
32	.12146	.13825	.12993	.14933	.13867	.16099	.14766	.17325	32
33	.12160	.13843	.13007	.14952	.13881	.16119	.14782	.17346	33
34	.12174	.13861	.13022	.14971	.13896	.16139	.14797	.17367	34
35	.12188	.13879	.13036	.14990	.13911	.16159	.14812	.17388	35
36	.12202	.13897	.13051	.15009	.13926	.16179	.14827	.17409	36
37	.12216	.13915	.13065	.15028	.13941	.16199	.14843	.17430	37
38	.12230	.13934	.13079	.15047	.13955	.16219	.14858	.17451	38
39	.12244	.13952	.13094	.15066	.13970	.16239	.14873	.17472	39
40	.12257	.13970	.13108	.15085	.13985	.16259	.14888	.17493	40
41	.12271	.13988	.13122	.15105	.14000	.16279	.14904	.17514	41
42	.12285	.14006	.13137	.15124	.14015	.16299	.14919	.17535	42
43	.12299	.14024	.13151	.15143	.14030	.16319	.14934	.17556	43
44	.12313	.14042	.13166	.15162	.14044	.16339	.14949	.17577	44
45	.12327	.14061	.13180	.15181	.14059	.16359	.14965	.17598	45
46	.12341	.14079	.13195	.15200	.14074	.16380	.14980	.17620	46
47	.12355	.14097	.13209	.15219	.14089	.16400	.14995	.17641	47
48	.12369	.14115	.13223	.15239	.14104	.16420	.15011	.17662	48
49	.12383	.14134	.13238	.15258	.14119	.16440	.15026	.17683	49
50	.12397	.14152	.13252	.15277	.14134	.16460	.15041	.17704	50
51	.12411	.14170	.13267	.15296	.14149	.16481	.15057	.17726	51
52	.12425	.14188	.13281	.15315	.14164	.16501	.15072	.17747	52
53	.12439	.14207	.13296	.15335	.14179	.16521	.15087	.17768	53
54	.12454	.14225	.13310	.15354	.14194	.16541	.15103	.17790	54
55	.12468	.14243	.13325	.15373	.14208	.16562	.15118	.17811	55
56	.12482	.14262	.13339	.15393	.14223	.16582	.15134	.17832	56
57	.12496	.14280	.13354	.15412	.14238	.16602	.15149	.17854	57
58	.12510	.14299	.13368	.15431	.14253	.16623	.15164	.17875	58
59	.12524	.14317	.13383	.15451	.14268	.16643	.15180	.17896	59
60	.12538	.14335	.13397	.15470	.14283	.16663	.15195	.17918	60

′	32° Vers.	Exsec.	33° Vers.	Exsec.	34° Vers.	Exsec.	35° Vers.	Exsec.	′
0	.15195	.17918	.16133	.19236	.17096	.20622	.18085	.22077	0
1	.15211	.17939	.16149	.19259	.17113	.20645	.18101	.22102	1
2	.15226	.17961	.16165	.19281	.17129	.20669	.18118	.22127	2
3	.15241	.17982	.16181	.19304	.17145	.20693	.18135	.22152	3
4	.15257	.18004	.16196	.19327	.17161	.20717	.18152	.22177	4
5	.15272	.18025	.16212	.19349	.17178	.20740	.18168	.22202	**5**
6	.15288	.18047	.16228	.19372	.17194	.20764	.18185	.22227	6
7	.15303	.18068	.16244	.19394	.17210	.20788	.18202	.22252	7
8	.15319	.18090	.16260	.19417	.17227	.20812	.18218	.22277	8
9	.15334	.18111	.16276	.19440	.17243	.20836	.18235	.22302	9
10	.15350	.18133	.16292	.19463	.17259	.20859	.18252	.22327	**10**
11	.15365	.18155	.16308	.19485	.17276	.20883	.18269	.22352	11
12	.15381	.18176	.16324	.19508	.17292	.20907	.18286	.22377	12
13	.15396	.18198	.16340	.19531	.17308	.20931	.18302	.22402	13
14	.15412	.18220	.16355	.19553	.17325	.20955	.18319	.22428	14
15	.15427	.18241	.16371	.19576	.17341	.20979	.18336	.22453	**15**
16	.15443	.18263	.16387	.19599	.17357	.21003	.18353	.22478	16
17	.15458	.18285	.16403	.19622	.17374	.21027	.18369	.22503	17
18	.15474	.18307	.16419	.19645	.17390	.21051	.18386	.22528	18
19	.15489	.18328	.16435	.19668	.17407	.21075	.18403	.22554	19
20	.15505	.18350	.16451	.19691	.17423	.21099	.18420	.22579	**20**
21	.15520	.18372	.16467	.19713	.17439	.21123	.18437	.22604	21
22	.15536	.18394	.16483	.19736	.17456	.21147	.18454	.22629	22
23	.15552	.18416	.16499	.19759	.17472	.21171	.18470	.22655	23
24	.15567	.18437	.16515	.19782	.17489	.21195	.18487	.22680	24
25	.15583	.18459	.16531	.19805	.17505	.21220	.18504	.22706	**25**
26	.15598	.18481	.16547	.19828	.17522	.21244	.18521	.22731	26
27	.15614	.18503	.16563	.19851	.17538	.21268	.18538	.22756	27
28	.15630	.18525	.16579	.19874	.17554	.21292	.18555	.22782	28
29	.15645	.18547	.16595	.19897	.17571	.21316	.18572	.22807	29
30	.15661	.18569	.16611	.19920	.17587	.21341	.18588	.22833	**30**
31	.15676	.18591	.16627	.19944	.17604	.21365	.18605	.22858	31
32	.15692	.18613	.16644	.19967	.17620	.21389	.18622	.22884	32
33	.15708	.18635	.16660	.19990	.17637	.21414	.18639	.22909	33
34	.15723	.18657	.16676	.20013	.17653	.21438	.18656	.22935	34
35	.15739	.18679	.16692	.20036	.17670	.21462	.18673	.22960	**35**
36	.15755	.18701	.16708	.20059	.17686	.21487	.18690	.22986	36
37	.15770	.18723	.16724	.20083	.17703	.21511	.18707	.23012	37
38	.15786	.18745	.16740	.20106	.17719	.21535	.18724	.23037	38
39	.15802	.18767	.16756	.20129	.17736	.21560	.18741	.23063	39
40	.15818	.18790	.16772	.20152	.17752	.21584	.18758	.23089	**40**
41	.15833	.18812	.16788	.20176	.17769	.21609	.18775	.23114	41
42	.15849	.18834	.16805	.20199	.17786	.21633	.18792	.23140	42
43	.15865	.18856	.16821	.20222	.17802	.21658	.18809	.23166	43
44	.15880	.18878	.16837	.20246	.17819	.21682	.18826	.23192	44
45	.15896	.18901	.16853	.20269	.17835	.21707	.18843	.23217	**45**
46	.15912	.18923	.16869	.20292	.17852	.21731	.18860	.23243	46
47	.15928	.18945	.16885	.20316	.17868	.21756	.18877	.23269	47
48	.15943	.18967	.16902	.20339	.17885	.21781	.18894	.23295	48
49	.15959	.18990	.16918	.20363	.17902	.21805	.18911	.23321	49
50	.15975	.19012	.16934	.20386	.17918	.21830	.18928	.23347	**50**
51	.15991	.19034	.16950	.20410	.17935	.21855	.18945	.23373	51
52	.16006	.19057	.16966	.20433	.17952	.21879	.18962	.23398	52
53	.16022	.19079	.16983	.20457	.17968	.21904	.18979	.23424	53
54	.16038	.19102	.16999	.20480	.17985	.21929	.18996	.23450	54
55	.16054	.19124	.17015	.20504	.18001	.21953	.19013	.23476	**55**
56	.16070	.19146	.17031	.20527	.18018	.21978	.19030	.23502	56
57	.16085	.19169	.17047	.20551	.18035	.22003	.19047	.23529	57
58	.16101	.19191	.17064	.20575	.18051	.22028	.19064	.23555	58
59	.16117	.19214	.17080	.20598	.18068	.22053	.19081	.23581	59
60	.16133	.19236	.17096	.20622	.18085	.22077	.19098	.23607	**60**

′	36° Vers.	36° Exsec.	37° Vers.	37° Exsec.	38° Vers.	38° Exsec.	39° Vers.	39° Exsec.	′
0	.19098	.23607	.20136	.25214	.21199	.26902	.22285	.28676	0
1	.19115	.23633	.20154	.25241	.21217	.26931	.22304	.28706	1
2	.19133	.23659	.20171	.25269	.21235	.26960	.22322	.28737	2
3	.19150	.23685	.20189	.25296	.21253	.26988	.22340	.28767	3
4	.19167	.23711	.20207	.25324	.21271	.27017	.22359	.28797	4
5	.19184	.23738	.20224	.25351	.21289	.27046	.22377	.28828	**5**
6	.19201	.23764	.20242	.25379	.21306	.27075	.22395	.28858	6
7	.19218	.23790	.20259	.25406	.21324	.27104	.22414	.28889	7
8	.19235	.23816	.20277	.25434	.21342	.27133	.22432	.28919	8
9	.19252	.23843	.20294	.25462	.21360	.27162	.22450	.28950	9
10	.19270	.23869	.20312	.25489	.21378	.27191	.22469	.28980	**10**
11	.19287	.23895	.20329	.25517	.21396	.27221	.22487	.29011	11
12	.19304	.23922	.20347	.25545	.21414	.27250	.22506	.29042	12
13	.19321	.23948	.20365	.25572	.21432	.27279	.22524	.29072	13
14	.19338	.23975	.20382	.25600	.21450	.27308	.22542	.29103	14
15	.19356	.24001	.20400	.25628	.21468	.27337	.22561	.29133	**15**
16	.19373	.24028	.20417	.25656	.21486	.27366	.22579	.29164	16
17	.19390	.24054	.20435	.25683	.21504	.27396	.22598	.29195	17
18	.19407	.24081	.20453	.25711	.21522	.27425	.22616	.29226	18
19	.19424	.24107	.20470	.25739	.21540	.27454	.22634	.29256	19
20	.19442	.24134	.20488	.25767	.21558	.27483	.22653	.29287	**20**
21	.19459	.24160	.20506	.25795	.21576	.27513	.22671	.29318	21
22	.19476	.24187	.20523	.25823	.21595	.27542	.22690	.29349	22
23	.19493	.24213	.20541	.25851	.21613	.27572	.22708	.29380	23
24	.19511	.24240	.20559	.25879	.21631	.27601	.22727	.29411	24
25	.19528	.24267	.20576	.25907	.21649	.27630	.22745	.29442	**25**
26	.19545	.24293	.20594	.25935	.21667	.27660	.22764	.29473	26
27	.19562	.24320	.20612	.25963	.21685	.27689	.22782	.29504	27
28	.19580	.24347	.20629	.25991	.21703	.27719	.22801	.29535	28
29	.19597	.24373	.20647	.26019	.21721	.27748	.22819	.29566	29
30	.19614	.24400	.20665	.26047	.21739	.27778	.22838	.29597	**30**
31	.19632	.24427	.20682	.26075	.21757	.27807	.22856	.29628	31
32	.19649	.24454	.20700	.26104	.21775	.27837	.22875	.29659	32
33	.19666	.24481	.20718	.26132	.21794	.27867	.22893	.29690	33
34	.19684	.24508	.20736	.26160	.21812	.27896	.22912	.29721	34
35	.19701	.24534	.20753	.26188	.21830	.27926	.22930	.29752	**35**
36	.19718	.24561	.20771	.26216	.21848	.27956	.22949	.29784	36
37	.19736	.24588	.20789	.26245	.21866	.27985	.22967	.29815	37
38	.19753	.24615	.20807	.26273	.21884	.28015	.22986	.29846	38
39	.19770	.24642	.20824	.26301	.21902	.28045	.23004	.29877	39
40	.19788	.24669	.20842	.26330	.21921	.28075	.23023	.29909	**40**
41	.19805	.24696	.20860	.26358	.21939	.28105	.23041	.29940	41
42	.19822	.24723	.20878	.26387	.21957	.28134	.23060	.29971	42
43	.19840	.24750	.20895	.26415	.21975	.28164	.23079	.30003	43
44	.19857	.24777	.20913	.26443	.21993	.28194	.23097	.30034	44
45	.19875	.24804	.20931	.26472	.22012	.28224	.23116	.30066	**45**
46	.19892	.24832	.20949	.26500	.22030	.28254	.23134	.30097	46
47	.19909	.24859	.20967	.26529	.22048	.28284	.23153	.30129	47
48	.19927	.24886	.20984	.26557	.22066	.28314	.23172	.30160	48
49	.19944	.24913	.21002	.26586	.22084	.28344	.23190	.30192	49
50	.19962	.24940	.21020	.26615	.22103	.28374	.23209	.30223	**50**
51	.19979	.24967	.21038	.26643	.22121	.28404	.23228	.30255	51
52	.19997	.24995	.21056	.26672	.22139	.28434	.23246	.30287	52
53	.20014	.25022	.21074	.26701	.22157	.28464	.23265	.30318	53
54	.20032	.25049	.21092	.26729	.22176	.28495	.23283	.30350	54
55	.20049	.25077	.21109	.26758	.22194	.28525	.23302	.30382	**55**
56	.20066	.25104	.21127	.26787	.22212	.28555	.23321	.30413	56
57	.20084	.25131	.21145	.26815	.22231	.28585	.23339	.30445	57
58	.20101	.25159	.21163	.26844	.22249	.28615	.23358	.30477	58
59	.20119	.25186	.21181	.26873	.22267	.28646	.23377	.30509	59
60	.20136	.25214	.21199	.26902	.22285	.28676	.23396	.30541	**60**

′	40° Vers.	Exsec.	41° Vers.	Exsec.	42° Vers.	Exsec.	43° Vers.	Exsec.	′
0	.23396	.30541	.24529	.32501	.25686	.34563	.26865	.36733	0
1	.23414	.30573	.24548	.32535	.25705	.34599	.26884	.36770	1
2	.23433	.30605	.24567	.32568	.25724	.34634	.26904	.36807	2
3	.23452	.30636	.24586	.32602	.25744	.34669	.26924	.36844	3
4	.23470	.30668	.24605	.32636	.25763	.34704	.26944	.36881	4
5	.23489	.30700	.24625	.32669	.25783	.34740	.26964	.36919	5
6	.23508	.30732	.24644	.32703	.25802	.34775	.26984	.36956	6
7	.23527	.30764	.24663	.32737	.25822	.34811	.27004	.36993	7
8	.23545	.30796	.24682	.32770	.25841	.34846	.27024	.37030	8
9	.23564	.30829	.24701	.32804	.25861	.34882	.27043	.37068	9
10	.23583	.30861	.24720	.32838	.25880	.34917	.27063	.37105	10
11	.23602	.30893	.24739	.32872	.25900	.34953	.27083	.37143	11
12	.23620	.30925	.24759	.32905	.25920	.34988	.27103	.37180	12
13	.23639	.30957	.24778	.32939	.25939	.35024	.27123	.37218	13
14	.23658	.30989	.24797	.32973	.25959	.35060	.27143	.37255	14
15	.23677	.31022	.24816	.33007	.25978	.35095	.27163	.37293	15
16	.23696	.31054	.24835	.33041	.25998	.35131	.27183	.37330	16
17	.23714	.31086	.24854	.33075	.26017	.35167	.27203	.37368	17
18	.23733	.31119	.24874	.33109	.26037	.35203	.27223	.37406	18
19	.23752	.31151	.24893	.33143	.26056	.35238	.27243	.37443	19
20	.23771	.31183	.24912	.33177	.26076	.35274	.27263	.37481	20
21	.23790	.31216	.24931	.33211	.26096	.35310	.27283	.37519	21
22	.23808	.31248	.24950	.33245	.26115	.35346	.27303	.37556	22
23	.23827	.31281	.24970	.33279	.26135	.35382	.27323	.37594	23
24	.23846	.31313	.24989	.33314	.26154	.35418	.27343	.37632	24
25	.23865	.31346	.25008	.33348	.26174	.35454	.27363	.37670	25
26	.23884	.31378	.25027	.33382	.26194	.35490	.27383	.37708	26
27	.23903	.31411	.25047	.33416	.26213	.35526	.27403	.37746	27
28	.23922	.31443	.25066	.33451	.26233	.35562	.27423	.37784	28
29	.23941	.31476	.25085	.33485	.26253	.35598	.27443	.37822	29
30	.23959	.31509	.25104	.33519	.26272	.35634	.27463	.37860	30
31	.23978	.31541	.25124	.33554	.26292	.35670	.27483	.37898	31
32	.23997	.31574	.25143	.33588	.26312	.35707	.27503	.37936	32
33	.24016	.31607	.25162	.33622	.26331	.35743	.27523	.37974	33
34	.24035	.31640	.25182	.33657	.26351	.35779	.27543	.38012	34
35	.24054	.31672	.25201	.33691	.26371	.35815	.27563	.38051	35
36	.24073	.31705	.25220	.33726	.26390	.35852	.27583	.38089	36
37	.24092	.31738	.25240	.33760	.26410	.35888	.27603	.38127	37
38	.24111	.31771	.25259	.33795	.26430	.35924	.27623	.38165	38
39	.24130	.31804	.25278	.33830	.26449	.35961	.27643	.38204	39
40	.24149	.31837	.25297	.33864	.26469	.35997	.27663	.38242	40
41	.24168	.31870	.25317	.33899	.26489	.36034	.27683	.38280	41
42	.24187	.31903	.25336	.33934	.26509	.36070	.27703	.38319	42
43	.24206	.31936	.25356	.33968	.26528	.36107	.27723	.38357	43
44	.24225	.31969	.25375	.34003	.26548	.36143	.27743	.38396	44
45	.24244	.32002	.25394	.34038	.26568	.36180	.27764	.38434	45
46	.24262	.32035	.25414	.34073	.26587	.36217	.27784	.38473	46
47	.24281	.32068	.25433	.34108	.26607	.36253	.27804	.38512	47
48	.24300	.32101	.25452	.34142	.26627	.36290	.27824	.38550	48
49	.24320	.32134	.25472	.34177	.26647	.36327	.27844	.38589	49
50	.24339	.32168	.25491	.34212	.26667	.36363	.27864	.38628	50
51	.24358	.32201	.25511	.34247	.26686	.36400	.27884	.38666	51
52	.24377	.32234	.25530	.34282	.26706	.36437	.27905	.38705	52
53	.24396	.32267	.25549	.34317	.26726	.36474	.27925	.38744	53
54	.24415	.32301	.25569	.34352	.26746	.36511	.27945	.38783	54
55	.24434	.32334	.25588	.34387	.26766	.36548	.27965	.38822	55
56	.24453	.32368	.25608	.34423	.26785	.36585	.27985	.38860	56
57	.24472	.32401	.25627	.34458	.26805	.36622	.28005	.38899	57
58	.24491	.32434	.25647	.34493	.26825	.36659	.28026	.38938	58
59	.24510	.32468	.25666	.34528	.26845	.36696	.28046	.38977	59
60	.24529	.32501	.25686	.34563	.26865	.36733	.28066	.39016	60

′	44° Vers.	Exsec.	45° Vers.	Exsec.	46° Vers.	Exsec.	47° Vers.	Exsec.	′
0	.28066	.39016	.29289	.41421	.30534	.43956	.31800	.46628	0
1	.28086	.39055	.29310	.41463	.30555	.43999	.31821	.46674	1
2	.28106	.39095	.29330	.41504	.30576	.44042	.31843	.46719	2
3	.28127	.39134	.29351	.41545	.30597	.44086	.31864	.46765	3
4	.28147	.39173	.29372	.41586	.30618	.44129	.31885	.46811	4
5	.28167	.39212	.29392	.41627	.39639	.44173	.31907	.46857	**5**
6	.28187	.39251	.29413	.41669	.30660	.44217	.31928	.46903	6
7	.28208	.39291	.29433	.41710	.30381	.44260	.31949	.46949	7
8	.28228	.39330	.29454	.41752	.30702	.44304	.31971	.46995	8
9	.28248	.39369	.29475	.41793	.30723	.44347	.31992	.47041	9
10	.28268	.39409	.29495	.41835	.30744	.44391	.32013	.47087	**10**
11	.28289	.39448	.29516	.41876	.30765	.44435	.32035	.47134	11
12	.28309	.39487	.29537	.41918	.30786	.44479	.32056	.47180	12
13	.28329	.39527	.29557	.41959	.30807	.44523	.32077	.47226	13
14	.28350	.39566	.29578	.42001	.30828	.44567	.32099	.47272	14
15	.28370	.39606	.29599	.42042	.30849	.44610	.32120	.47319	**15**
16	.28390	.39646	.29619	.42084	.30870	.44654	.32141	.47365	16
17	.28410	.39685	.29640	.42126	.30891	.44698	.32163	.47411	17
18	.28431	.39725	.29661	.42168	.30912	.44742	.32184	.47458	18
19	.28451	.39764	.29681	.42209	.30933	.44787	.32205	.47504	19
20	.28471	.39804	.29702	.42251	.30954	.44831	.32227	.47551	**20**
21	.28492	.39844	.29723	.42293	.30975	.44875	.32248	.47598	21
22	.28512	.39884	.29743	.42335	.30996	.44919	.32270	.47644	22
23	.28532	.39924	.29764	.42377	.31017	.44963	.32291	.47691	23
24	.28553	.39963	.29785	.42419	.31038	.45007	.32312	.47738	24
25	.28573	.40003	.29805	.42461	.31059	.45052	.32334	.47784	**25**
26	.28593	.40043	.29826	.42503	.31080	.45096	.32355	.47831	26
27	.28614	.40083	.29847	.42545	.21101	.45141	.32377	.47878	27
28	.28634	.40123	.29868	.42587	.31122	.45185	.32398	.47925	28
29	.28655	.40163	.29888	.42630	.31143	.45229	.32420	.47972	29
39	.28675	.40203	.29909	.42672	.31165	.45274	.32441	.48019	**30**
31	.28695	.40243	.29930	.42714	.31186	.45319	.32462	.48066	31
32	.28716	.40283	.29951	.42756	.31207	.45363	.32484	.48113	32
33	.28736	.40324	.29971	.42799	.31228	.45408	.32505	.48160	33
34	.28757	.40364	.29992	.42841	.31249	.45452	.32527	.48207	34
35	.28777	.40404	.30013	.42883	.31270	.45497	.32548	.48254	**35**
36	.28797	.40444	.30034	.42926	.31291	.45542	.32570	.48301	36
37	.28818	.40485	.30054	.42968	.31312	.45587	.32591	.48349	37
38	.28838	.40525	.30075	.43011	.31334	.45631	.32613	.48396	38
39	.28859	.40565	.30096	.43053	.31355	.45676	.32634	.48443	39
40	.28879	.40606	.30117	.43096	.31376	.45721	.32656	.48491	**40**
41	.28900	.40646	.30138	.43139	.31397	.45766	.32677	.48538	41
42	.28920	.40687	.30158	.43181	.31418	.45811	.32699	.48586	42
43	.28941	.40727	.30179	.43224	.31439	.45856	.32720	.48633	43
44	.28961	.40768	.30200	.43267	.31461	.45901	.32742	.48681	44
45	.28981	.40808	.30221	.43309	.31482	.45946	.32763	.48728	**45**
46	.29002	.40849	.30242	.43352	.31503	.45992	.32785	.48776	46
47	.29022	.40890	.30263	.43395	.31524	.46037	.32806	.48824	47
48	.29043	.40930	.30283	.43438	.31545	.46082	.32828	.48871	48
49	.29063	.40971	.30304	.43481	.31566	.46127	.32849	.48919	49
50	.29084	.41012	.30325	.43524	.31588	.46173	.32871	.48967	**50**
51	.29104	.41053	.30346	.43567	.31609	.46218	.32893	.49015	51
52	.29125	.41093	.30367	.43610	.31630	.46263	.32914	.49063	52
53	.29145	.41134	.30388	.43653	.31651	.46309	.32936	.49111	53
54	.29166	.41175	.30409	.43696	.31673	.46354	.32957	.49159	54
55	.29187	.41216	.30430	.43739	.31694	.46400	.32979	.49207	**55**
56	.29207	.41257	.30451	.43783	.31715	.46445	.33001	.49255	56
57	.29228	.41298	.30471	.43826	.31736	.46491	.33022	.49303	57
58	.29248	.41339	.30492	.43869	.31758	.46537	.33044	.49351	58
59	.29269	.41380	.30513	.43912	.31779	.46582	.33065	.49399	59
60	.29289	.41421	.30534	.43956	.31800	.46628	.33087	.49448	**60**

′	48°		49°		50°		51°		′
	Vers.	Exsec.	Vers.	Exsec.	Vers.	Exsec.	Vers.	Exsec.	
0	.33087	.49448	.34394	.52425	.35721	.55572	.37068	.58902	0
1	.33109	.49496	.34416	.52476	.35744	.55626	.37091	.58959	1
2	.33130	.49544	.34438	.52527	.35766	.55680	.37113	.59016	2
3	.33152	.49593	.34460	.52579	.35788	.55734	.37136	.59073	3
4	.33173	.49641	.34482	.52630	.35810	.55789	.37158	.59130	4
5	.33195	.49690	.34504	.52681	.35833	.55843	.37181	.59188	5
6	.33217	.49738	.34526	.52732	.35855	.55897	.37204	.59245	6
7	.33238	.49787	.34548	.52784	.35877	.55951	.37226	.59302	7
8	.33260	.49835	.34570	.52835	.35900	.56005	.37249	.59360	8
9	.33282	.49884	.34592	.52886	.35922	.56060	.37272	.59418	9
10	.33303	.49933	.34614	.52938	.35944	.56114	.37294	.59475	10
11	.33325	.49981	.34636	.52989	.35967	.56169	.37317	.59533	11
12	.33347	.50030	.34658	.53041	.35989	.56223	.37340	.59590	12
13	.33368	.50079	.34680	.53092	.36011	.56278	.37362	.59648	13
14	.33390	.50128	.34702	.53144	.36034	.56332	.37385	.59706	14
15	.33412	.50177	.34724	.53196	.36056	.56387	.37408	.59764	15
16	.33434	.50226	.34746	.53247	.36078	.56442	.37430	.59822	16
17	.33455	.50275	.34768	.53299	.36101	.56497	.37453	.59880	17
18	.33477	.50324	.34790	.53351	.36123	.56551	.37476	.59938	18
19	.33499	.50373	.34812	.53403	.36146	.56606	.37498	.59996	19
20	.33520	.50422	.34834	.53455	.36168	.56661	.37521	.60054	20
21	.33542	.50471	.34856	.53507	.36190	.56716	.37544	.60112	21
22	.33564	.50521	.34878	.53559	.36213	.56771	.37567	.60171	22
23	.33586	.50570	.34900	.53611	.36235	.56826	.37589	.60229	23
24	.33607	.50619	.34923	.53663	.36258	.56881	.37612	.60287	24
25	.33629	.50669	.34945	.53715	.36280	.56937	.37635	.60346	25
26	.33651	.50718	.34967	.53768	.36302	.56992	.37658	.60404	26
27	.33673	.50767	.34989	.53820	.36325	.57047	.37680	.60463	27
28	.33694	.50817	.35011	.53872	.36347	.57103	.37703	.60521	28
29	.33716	.50866	.35033	.53924	.36370	.57158	.37726	.60580	29
30	.33738	.50916	.35055	.53977	.36392	.57213	.37749	.60639	30
31	.33760	.50966	.35077	.54029	.36415	.57269	.37771	.60698	31
32	.33782	.51015	.35099	.54082	.36437	.57324	.37794	.60756	32
33	.33803	.51065	.35122	.54134	.36460	.57380	.37817	.60815	33
34	.33825	.51115	.35144	.54187	.36482	.57436	.37840	.60874	34
35	.33847	.51165	.35166	.54240	.36504	.57491	.37862	.60933	35
36	.33869	.51215	.35188	.54292	.36527	.57547	.37885	.60992	36
37	.33891	.51265	.35210	.54345	.36549	.57603	.37908	.61051	37
38	.33912	.51314	.35232	.54398	.36572	.57659	.37931	.61111	38
39	.33934	.51364	.35254	.54451	.36594	.57715	.37954	.61170	39
40	.33956	.51415	.35277	.54504	.36617	.57771	.37976	.61229	40
41	.33978	.51465	.35299	.54557	.36639	.57827	.37999	.61288	41
42	.34000	.51515	.35321	.54610	.36662	.57883	.38022	.61348	42
43	.34022	.51565	.35343	.54663	.36684	.57939	.38045	.61407	43
44	.34044	.51615	.35365	.54716	.36707	.57995	.38068	.61467	44
45	.34065	.51665	.35388	.54769	.36729	.58051	.38091	.61526	45
46	.34087	.51716	.35410	.54822	.36752	.58108	.38113	.61586	46
47	.34109	.51766	.35432	.54876	.36775	.58164	.38136	.61646	47
48	.34131	.51817	.35454	.54929	.36797	.58221	.38159	.61705	48
49	.34153	.51867	.35476	.54982	.36820	.58277	.38182	.61765	49
50	.34175	.51918	.35499	.55035	.36842	.58333	.38205	.61825	50
51	.34197	.51968	.35521	.55089	.36865	.58390	.38228	.61885	51
52	.34219	.52019	.35543	.55143	.36887	.58447	.38251	.61945	52
53	.34241	.52069	.35565	.55196	.36910	.58503	.38274	.62005	53
54	.34262	.52120	.35588	.55250	.36932	.58560	.38296	.62065	54
55	.34284	.52171	.35610	.55303	.36955	.58617	.38319	.62125	55
56	.34306	.52222	.35632	.55357	.36978	.58674	.38342	.62185	56
57	.34328	.52273	.35654	.55411	.37000	.58731	.38365	.62245	57
58	.34350	.52323	.35677	.55465	.37023	.58788	.38388	.62305	58
59	.34372	.52374	.35699	.55518	.37045	.58845	.38411	.62366	59
60	.34394	.52425	.35721	.55572	.37068	.58902	.38434	.62427	60

′	52° Vers.	52° Exsec.	53° Vers.	53° Exsec.	54° Vers.	54° Exsec.	55° Vers.	55° Exsec.	′
0	.38434	.62427	.39818	.66164	.41221	.70130	.42642	.74345	0
1	.38457	.62487	.39842	.66228	.41245	.70198	.42666	.74417	1
2	.38480	.62548	.39865	.66292	.41269	.70267	.42690	.74490	2
3	.38503	.62609	.39888	.66357	.41292	.70335	.42714	.74562	3
4	.38526	.62669	.39911	.66421	.41316	.70403	.42738	.74635	4
5	.38549	.62730	.39935	.66486	.41339	.70472	.42762	.74708	**5**
6	.38571	.62791	.39958	.66550	.41363	.70540	.42785	.74781	6
7	.38594	.62852	.39981	.66615	.41386	.70609	.42809	.74854	7
8	.38617	.62913	.40005	.66679	.41410	.70677	.42833	.74927	8
9	.38640	.62974	.40028	.66744	.41433	.70746	.42857	.75000	9
10	.38663	.63035	.40051	.66809	.41457	.70815	.42881	.75073	**10**
11	.38686	.63096	.40075	.66873	.41481	.70884	.42905	.75146	11
12	.38709	.63157	.40098	.66938	.41504	.70953	.42929	.75219	12
13	.38732	.63218	.40121	.67003	.41528	.71022	.42953	.75293	13
14	.38755	.63279	.40144	.67068	.41551	.71091	.42976	.75366	14
15	.38778	.63341	.40168	.67133	.41575	.71160	.43000	.75440	**15**
16	.38801	.63402	.40191	.67198	.41599	.71229	.43024	.75513	16
17	.38824	.63464	.40214	.67264	.41622	.71298	.43048	.75587	17
18	.38847	.63525	.40237	.67329	.41646	.71368	.43072	.75661	18
19	.38870	.63587	.40261	.67394	.41670	.71437	.43096	.75734	19
20	.38893	.63648	.40284	.67460	.41693	.71506	.43120	.75808	**20**
21	.38916	.63710	.40307	.67525	.41717	.71576	.43144	.75882	21
22	.38939	.62772	.40331	.67591	.41740	.71646	.43168	.75956	22
23	.38962	.63834	.40354	.67656	.41764	.71715	.43192	.76031	23
24	.38985	.63895	.40378	.67722	.41788	.71785	.43216	.76105	24
25	.39009	.63957	.40401	.67788	.41811	.71855	.43240	.76179	**25**
26	.39032	.64019	.40424	.67853	.41835	.71925	.43264	.76253	26
27	.39055	.64081	.40448	.67919	.41859	.71995	.43287	.76328	27
28	.39078	.64144	.40471	.67985	.41882	.72065	.43311	.76402	28
29	.39101	.64206	.40494	.68051	.41906	.72135	.43335	.76477	29
30	.39124	.64268	.40518	.68117	.41930	.72205	.43359	.76552	**30**
31	.39147	.64330	.40541	.68183	.41953	.72275	.43383	.76626	31
32	.39170	.64393	.40564	.68250	.41977	.72346	.43407	.76701	32
33	.39193	.64455	.40588	.68316	.42001	.72416	.43431	.76776	33
34	.39216	.64518	.40611	.68382	.42024	.72487	.43455	.76851	34
35	.39239	.64580	.40635	.68449	.42048	.72557	.43479	.76926	**35**
36	.39262	.64643	.40658	.68515	.42072	.72628	.43503	.77001	36
37	.39286	.64705	.40682	.68582	.42096	.72698	.43527	.77077	37
38	.39309	.64768	.40705	.68648	.42119	.72769	.43551	.77152	38
39	.39332	.64831	.40728	.68715	.42143	.72840	.43575	.77227	39
40	.39355	.64894	.40752	.68782	.42167	.72911	.43599	.77303	**40**
41	.39378	.64957	.40775	.68848	.42190	.72982	.43623	.77378	41
42	.39401	.65020	.40799	.68915	.42214	.73053	.43647	.77454	42
43	.39424	.65083	.40822	.68982	.42238	.73124	.43671	.77530	43
44	.39447	.65146	.40846	.69049	.42262	.73195	.43695	.77606	44
45	.39471	.65209	.40869	.69116	.42285	.73267	.43720	.77681	**45**
46	.39494	.65272	.40892	.69183	.42309	.73338	.43744	.77757	46
47	.39517	.65335	.40916	.69250	.42333	.73409	.43768	.77833	47
48	.39540	.65399	.40939	.69318	.42357	.73481	.43792	.77910	48
49	.39563	.65462	.40963	.69385	.42381	.73552	.43816	.77986	49
50	.39586	.65526	.40986	.69452	.42404	.73624	.43840	.78062	**50**
51	.39610	.65589	.41010	.69520	.42428	.73696	.43864	.78138	51
52	.39633	.65653	.41033	.69587	.42452	.73768	.43888	.78215	52
53	.39656	.65717	.41057	.69655	.42476	.73840	.43912	.78291	53
54	.39679	.65780	.41080	.69723	.42499	.73911	.43936	.78368	54
55	.39702	.65844	.41104	.69790	.42523	.73983	.43960	.78445	**55**
56	.39726	.65908	.41127	.69858	.42547	.74056	.43984	.78521	56
57	.39749	.65972	.41151	.69926	.42571	.74128	.44008	.78598	57
58	.39772	.66036	.41174	.69994	.42595	.47200	.44032	.78675	58
59	.39795	.66100	.41198	.70062	.42619	.74272	.44057	.78752	59
60	.39818	.66164	.41221	.70130	.42642	.74345	.44081	.78829	**60**

′	56° Vers.	Exsec.	57° Vers.	Exsec.	58° Vers.	Exsec.	59° Vers.	Exsec.	′
0	.44081	.78829	.45536	.83608	.47008	.88708	.48496	.94160	0
1	.44105	.78906	.45560	.83690	.47033	.88796	.48521	.94254	1
2	.44129	.78984	.45585	.83773	.47057	.88884	.48546	.94349	2
3	.44153	.79061	.45609	.83855	.47082	.88972	.48571	.94443	3
4	.44177	.79138	.45634	.83938	.47107	.89060	.48596	.94537	4
5	.44201	.79216	.45658	.84020	.47131	.89148	.48621	.94632	5
6	.44225	.79293	.45683	.84103	.47156	.89237	.48646	.94726	6
7	.44250	.79371	.45707	.84186	.47181	.89325	.48671	.94821	7
8	.44274	.79449	.45731	.84269	.47206	.89414	.48696	.94916	8
9	.44298	.79527	.45756	.84352	.47230	.89503	.48721	.95011	9
10	.44322	.79604	.45780	.84435	.47255	.89591	.48746	.95106	10
11	.44346	.79682	.45805	.84518	.47280	.89680	.48771	.95201	11
12	.44370	.79761	.45829	.84601	.47304	.89769	.48769	.95296	12
13	.44395	.79839	.45854	.84685	.47329	.89858	.48821	.95392	13
14	.44419	.79917	.45878	.84768	.47354	.89948	.48846	.95487	14
15	.44443	.79995	.45903	.84852	.47379	.90037	.48871	.95583	15
16	.44467	.80074	.45927	.84935	.47403	.90126	.48896	.95678	16
17	.44491	.80152	.45951	.85019	.47428	.90216	.48921	.95774	17
18	.44516	.80231	.45976	.85103	.47453	.90305	.48946	.95870	18
19	.44540	.80309	.46000	.85187	.47478	.90395	.48971	.95966	19
20	.44564	.80388	.46025	.85271	.47502	.90485	.48996	.96062	20
21	.44588	.80467	.46049	.85355	.47527	.90575	.49021	.96158	21
22	.44612	.80546	.46074	.85439	.47552	.90665	.49046	.96255	22
23	.44637	.80625	.46098	.85523	.47577	.90755	.49071	.96351	23
24	.44661	.80704	.46123	.85608	.47601	.90845	.49096	.96448	24
25	.44685	.80783	.46147	.85692	.47626	.90935	.49121	.96544	25
26	.44709	.80862	.46172	.85777	.47651	.91026	.49146	.96641	26
27	.44734	.80942	.46196	.85861	.47676	.91116	.49171	.96738	27
28	.44758	.81021	.46221	.85946	.47701	.91207	.49196	.96835	28
29	.44782	.81101	.46246	.86031	.47725	.91297	.49221	.96932	29
30	.44806	.81180	.46270	.86116	.47750	.91388	.49246	.97029	30
31	.44831	.81260	.46295	.86201	.47775	.91479	.49271	.97127	31
32	.44855	.81340	.46319	.86286	.47800	.91570	.49296	.97224	32
33	.44879	.81419	.46344	.86371	.47825	.91661	.49321	.97322	33
34	.44903	.81499	.46368	.86457	.47849	.91752	.49346	.97421	34
35	.44928	.81579	.46393	.86542	.47874	.91844	.49372	.97517	35
36	.44952	.81659	.46417	.86627	.47899	.91935	.49397	.97615	36
37	.44976	.81740	.46442	.86713	.47924	.92027	.49422	.97713	37
38	.45001	.81820	.46466	.86799	.47949	.92118	.49447	.97811	38
39	.45025	.81900	.46491	.86885	.47974	.92210	.49472	.97910	39
40	.45049	.81981	.46516	.86970	.47998	.92302	.49497	.98008	40
41	.45073	.82061	.46540	.87056	.48023	.92394	.49522	.98107	41
42	.45098	.82142	.46565	.87142	.48048	.92486	.49547	.98205	42
43	.45122	.82222	.46589	.87229	.48073	.92578	.49572	.98304	43
44	.45146	.82303	.46614	.87315	.48098	.92670	.49597	.98403	44
45	.45171	.82384	.46639	.87401	.48123	.92762	.49623	.98502	45
46	.45195	.82465	.46663	.87488	.48148	.92855	.49648	.98601	46
47	.45219	.82546	.46688	.87574	.48172	.92947	.49673	.98700	47
48	.45244	.82627	.46712	.87661	.48197	.93040	.49698	.98799	48
49	.45268	.82709	.46737	.87748	.48222	.93133	.49723	.98899	49
50	.45292	.82790	.46762	.87834	.48247	.93226	.49748	.98998	50
51	.45317	.82871	.46786	.87921	.48272	.93319	.49773	.99098	51
52	.45341	.82953	.46811	.88008	.48297	.93412	.49799	.99198	42
53	.45365	.83034	.46836	.88095	.48322	.93505	.49824	.99298	53
54	.45390	.83116	.46860	.88183	.48347	.93598	.49849	.99398	54
55	.45414	.83198	.46885	.88270	.48372	.93692	.49874	.99498	55
56	.45439	.83280	.46909	.88357	.48396	.93785	.49899	.99598	56
57	.45463	.38362	.46934	.88445	.48421	.93879	.49924	.99698	57
58	.45487	.83444	.46959	.88532	.48446	.93973	.49950	.99799	58
59	.45512	.83526	.46983	.88620	.48471	.94066	.49975	.99899	59
60	.45536	.83608	.47008	.88708	.48496	.94160	.50000	1.00000	60

′	60° Vers.	60° Exsec.	61° Vers.	61° Exsec.	62° Vers.	62° Exsec.	63° Vers.	63° Exsec.	′
0	.50000	1.00000	.51519	1.03267	.53053	1.13005	.54601	1.20269	0
1	.50025	1.00101	.51544	1.03375	.53079	1.13122	.54627	1.20395	1
2	.50050	1.00202	.51570	1.06483	.53104	1.13239	.54653	1.20521	2
3	.50076	1.00303	.51595	1.06592	.53130	1.13356	.54679	1.20647	3
4	.50101	1.00404	.51621	1.06701	.53156	1.13473	.54705	1.20773	4
5	.50126	1.00505	.51646	1.06809	.53181	1.13590	.54731	1.20900	5
6	.50151	1.00607	.51672	1.06918	.53207	1.13707	.54757	1.21026	6
7	.50176	1.00708	.51697	1.07027	.53233	1.13825	.54782	1.21153	7
8	.50202	1.00810	.51723	1.07137	.53258	1.13942	.54808	1.21280	8
9	.50227	1.00912	.51748	1.07246	.53284	1.14060	.54834	1.21407	9
10	.50252	1.01014	.51774	1.07356	.53310	1.14178	.54860	1.21535	10
11	.50277	1.01116	.51799	1.07465	.53336	1.14296	.54886	1.21662	11
12	.50303	1.01218	.51825	1.07575	.53361	1.14414	.54912	1.21790	12
13	.50328	1.01320	.51850	1.07685	.53387	1.14533	.54938	1.21918	13
14	.50353	1.01422	.51876	1.07795	.53413	1.14651	.54964	1.22045	14
15	.50378	1.01525	.51901	1.07905	.53439	1.14770	.54990	1.22174	15
16	.50404	1.01628	.51927	1.08015	.53564	1.14889	.55016	1.22302	16
17	.50429	1.01730	.51952	1.08126	.53490	1.15008	.55042	1.22430	17
18	.50454	1.01833	.51978	1.08236	.53516	1.15127	.55068	1.22559	18
19	.50479	1.01936	.52003	1.08347	.53542	1.15246	.55094	1.22688	19
20	.50505	1.02039	.52029	1.08458	.53567	1.15366	.55120	1.22817	20
21	.50530	1.02143	.52054	1.08569	.53593	1.15485	.55146	1.22946	21
22	.50555	1.02246	.52080	1.08680	.53619	1.15605	.55172	1.23075	22
23	.50581	1.02349	.52105	1.08791	.53645	1.15725	.55198	1.23205	23
24	.50606	1.02453	.52131	1.08903	.53670	1.15845	.55224	1.23334	24
25	.50631	1.02557	.52156	1.09014	.53696	1.15965	.55250	1.23464	25
26	.50656	1.02661	.52182	1.09126	.53722	1.16085	.55276	1.23594	26
27	.50682	1.02765	.52207	1.09238	.53748	1.16206	.55302	1.23724	27
28	.50707	1.02869	.52233	1.09350	.53774	1.16326	.55328	1.23855	28
29	.50732	1.02973	.52259	1.09462	.53799	1.16447	.55354	1.23985	29
30	.50758	1.03077	.52284	1.09574	.53825	1.16568	.55380	1.24116	30
31	.50783	1.03182	.52310	1.09686	.53851	1.16689	.55406	1.24247	31
32	.50808	1.03286	.52335	1.09799	.53877	1.16810	.55432	1.24378	32
33	.50834	1.03391	.52361	1.09911	.53903	1.16932	.55458	1.24509	33
34	.50859	1.03496	.52386	1.10024	.53928	1.17053	.55484	1.24640	34
35	.50884	1.03601	.52412	1.10137	.53954	1.17175	.55510	1.24772	35
36	.50910	1.03706	.52438	1.10250	.53980	1.17297	.55536	1.24903	36
37	.50935	1.03811	.52463	1.10363	.54006	1.17419	.55563	1.25035	37
38	.50960	1.03916	.52489	1.10477	.54032	1.17541	.55589	1.25167	38
39	.50986	1.04022	.52514	1.10590	.54058	1.17663	.55615	1.25300	39
40	.51011	1.04128	.52540	1.10704	.54083	1.17786	.55641	1.25432	40
41	.51036	1.04233	.52566	1.10817	.54109	1.17909	.55667	1.25565	41
42	.51062	1.04339	.52591	1.10931	.54135	1.18031	.55693	1.25697	42
43	.51087	1.04445	.52617	1.11045	.54161	1.18154	.55719	1.25830	43
44	.51112	1.04551	.52642	1.11159	.54187	1.18277	.55745	1.25963	44
45	.51138	1.04657	.52668	1.11274	.54213	1.18401	.55771	1.26097	45
46	.51163	1.04764	.52694	1.11388	.54238	1.18524	.55797	1.26230	46
47	.51189	1.04870	.52719	1.11503	.54264	1.18648	.55823	1.26364	47
48	.51214	1.04977	.52745	1.11617	.54290	1.18772	.55849	1.26498	48
49	.51239	1.05084	.52771	1.11732	.54316	1.18895	.55876	1.26632	49
50	.51265	1.05191	.52796	1.11847	.54342	1.19019	.55902	1.26766	50
51	.51290	1.05298	.52822	1.11963	.54368	1.19144	.55928	1.26900	51
52	.51316	1.05405	.52847	1.12078	.54394	1.19268	.55954	1.27035	52
53	.51341	1.05512	.52873	1.12193	.54420	1.19393	.55980	1.27169	53
54	.51366	1.05619	.52899	1.12309	.54446	1.19517	.56006	1.27304	54
55	.51392	1.05727	.52924	1.12425	.54471	1.19642	.56032	1.27439	55
56	.51417	1.05835	.52950	1.12540	.54497	1.19767	.56058	1.27574	56
57	.51443	1.05942	.52976	1.12657	.54523	1.19892	.56084	1.27710	57
58	.51468	1 96050	.53001	1.12773	.54549	1.20018	.56111	1.27845	58
59	.51494	1.06158	.53027	1.12889	.54575	1.20143	.56137	1.27981	59
60	.51519	1.06267	.53053	1.13005	.54601	1.20269	.56163	1.28117	60

′	64°		65°		66°		67°		′
	Vers.	Exsec.	Vers.	Exsec.	Vers.	Exsec.	Vers.	Exsec.	
0	.56163	1.28117	.57738	1.36620	.59326	1.45859	.60927	1.55930	0
1	.56189	1.28253	.57765	1.36768	.59353	1.46020	.60954	1.56106	1
2	.56215	1.28390	.57791	1.36916	.59379	1.46181	.60980	1.56282	2
3	.56241	1.28526	.57817	1.37064	.59406	1.46342	.61007	1.56458	3
4	.56267	1.28663	.57844	1.37212	.59433	1.46504	.61034	1.56634	4
5	.56294	1.28800	.57870	1.37361	.59459	1.46665	.61061	1.56811	5
6	.56320	1.28937	.57896	1.37509	.59486	1.46827	.61088	1.56988	6
7	.56346	1.29074	.57923	1.37658	.59512	1.46989	.61114	1.57165	7
8	.56372	1.29211	.57949	1.37808	.59539	1.47152	.61141	1.57342	8
9	.56398	1.29349	.57976	1.37957	.59566	1.47314	.61168	1.57520	9
10	.56425	1.29487	.58002	1.38107	.59592	1.47477	.61195	1.57698	10
11	.56451	1.29625	.58028	1.38256	.59619	1.47640	.61222	1.57876	11
12	.56477	1.29763	.58055	1.38406	.59645	1.47804	.61248	1.58054	12
13	.56503	1.29901	.58081	1.38556	.59672	1.47967	.61275	1.58233	13
14	.56529	1.30040	.58108	1.38707	.59699	1.48131	.61302	1.58412	14
15	.56555	1.30179	.58134	1.38857	.59725	1.48295	.61329	1.58591	15
16	.56582	1.30318	.58160	1.39008	.59752	1.48459	.61356	1.58771	16
17	.56608	1.30457	.58187	1.39159	.59779	1.48624	.61383	1.58950	17
18	.56634	1.30596	.58213	1.39311	.59805	1.48789	.61409	1.59130	18
19	.56660	1.30735	.58240	1.39462	.59832	1.48594	.61436	1.59311	19
20	.56687	1.30875	.58266	1.39614	.59859	1.49119	.61463	1.59491	20
21	.56713	1.31015	.58293	1.39766	.59885	1.49284	.61490	1.59672	21
22	.56739	1.31155	.58319	1.39918	.59912	1.49450	.61517	1.59853	22
23	.56765	1.31295	.58345	1.40070	.59938	1.49616	.61544	1.60035	23
24	.56791	1.31436	.58372	1.40222	.59965	1.49782	.61570	1.60217	24
25	.56818	1.31576	.58398	1.40375	.59992	1.49948	.61597	1.60399	25
26	.56844	1.31717	.58425	1.40528	.60018	1.50115	.61624	1.60581	26
27	.56870	1.31858	.58451	1.40681	.60045	1.50282	.61651	1.60763	27
28	.56896	1.31999	.58478	1.40835	.60072	1.50449	.61678	1.60946	28
29	.56923	1.32140	.58504	1.40988	.60098	1.50617	.61705	1.61129	29
30	.56949	1.32282	.58531	1.41142	.60125	1.50784	.61732	1.61313	30
31	.56975	1.32424	.58557	1.41296	.60152	1.50952	.61759	1.61496	31
32	.57001	1.32566	.58584	1.41450	.60178	1.51120	.61785	1.61680	32
33	.57028	1.32708	.58610	1.41605	.60205	1.51289	.61812	1.61864	33
34	.57054	1.32850	.58637	1.41760	.60232	1.51457	.61839	1.62049	34
35	.57080	1.32993	.58663	1.41914	.60259	1.51626	.61866	1.62234	35
36	.57106	1.33135	.58790	1.42070	.60285	1.51795	.61893	1.62419	36
37	.57133	1.33278	.58716	1.42225	.60312	1.51965	.61920	1.62604	37
38	.57159	1.33422	.58743	1.42380	.60339	1.52134	.61947	1.62790	38
39	.57185	1.33565	.58769	1.42536	.60365	1.52304	.61974	1.62976	39
40	.57212	1.33708	.58796	1.42692	.60392	1.52474	.62001	1.63162	40
41	.57238	1.33852	.58822	1.42848	.60419	1.52645	.62027	1.63348	41
42	.57264	1.33996	.58849	1.43005	.60445	1.52815	.62054	1.63535	42
43	.57291	1.34140	.58875	1.43162	.60472	1.52986	.62081	1.63722	43
44	.57317	1.34284	.58902	1.43318	.60499	1.53157	.62108	1.63909	44
45	.57343	1.34429	.58928	1.43476	.60526	1.53329	.62135	1.64097	45
46	.57369	1.34573	.58955	1.43633	.60552	1.53500	.62162	1.64285	46
47	.57396	1.34718	.58981	1.43790	.60579	1.53672	.62189	1.64473	47
48	.57422	1.34863	.59008	1.43948	.60606	1.53845	.62216	1.64662	48
49	.57448	1.35009	.59034	1.44106	.60633	1.54017	.62243	1.64851	49
50	.57475	1.35154	.59061	1.44264	.60659	1.54190	.62270	1.65040	50
51	.57501	1.35300	.59087	1.44423	.60686	1.54363	.62297	1.65229	51
52	.57527	1.35446	.59114	1.44582	.60713	1.54536	.62324	1.65419	52
53	.57554	1.35592	.59140	1.44741	.60740	1.54709	.62351	1.65609	53
54	.57580	1.35738	.59167	1.44900	.60766	1.54883	.62378	1.65799	54
55	.57603	1.35885	.59194	1.45059	.60793	1.55057	.62405	1.65989	55
56	.57633	1.36031	.59220	1.45219	.60820	1.55231	.62431	1.66180	56
57	.57659	1.36178	.59247	1.45378	.60847	1.55405	.62458	1.66371	57
58	.57685	1.36325	.59273	1.45539	.60873	1.55580	.62485	1.66563	58
59	.57712	1.36473	.59300	1.45699	.60900	1.55755	.62512	1.66755	59
60	.57738	1.36620	.59326	1.45859	.60927	1.55930	.62539	1.66947	60

′	68° Vers.	Exsec.	69° Vers.	Exsec.	70° Vers.	Exsec.	71° Vers.	Exsec.	′
0	.62539	1.66947	.64163	1.79043	.65798	1.92380	.67443	2.07155	0
1	.62566	1.67139	.64190	1.79254	.65825	1.92614	.67471	2.07415	1
2	.62593	1.67332	.64218	1.79466	.65853	1.92849	.67498	2.07675	2
3	.62620	1.67525	.64245	1.79679	.65880	1.93083	.67526	2.07936	3
4	.62647	1.67718	.64272	1.79891	.65907	1.93318	.67553	2.08197	4
5	.62674	1.67911	.64299	1.80104	.65935	1.93554	.67581	2.08459	5
6	.62701	1.68105	.64326	1.80318	.65962	1.93790	.67608	2.08721	6
7	.62728	1.68299	.64353	1.80531	.65989	1.94026	.67636	2.08983	7
8	.62755	1.68494	.64381	1.80746	.66017	1.94263	.67663	2.09246	8
9	.62782	1.68689	.64408	1.80960	.66044	1.94500	.67691	2.09510	9
10	.62809	1.68884	.64435	1.81175	.66071	1.94737	.67718	2.09774	10
11	.62836	1.69079	.64462	1.81390	.66099	1.94975	.67746	2.10038	11
12	.62863	1.69275	.64489	1.81605	.66126	1.95213	.67773	2.10303	12
13	.62890	1.69471	.64516	1.81821	.66154	1.95452	.67801	2.10568	13
14	.62917	1.69667	.64544	1.82037	.66181	1.95691	.67829	2.10834	14
15	.62944	1.69864	.64571	1.82254	.66208	1.95931	.67856	2.11101	15
16	.62971	1.70061	.64598	1.82471	.66236	1.96171	.67884	2.11367	16
17	.62998	1.70258	.64625	1.82688	.66263	1.96411	.67911	2.11635	17
18	.63025	1.70455	.64653	1.82906	.66290	1.96652	.67939	2.11903	18
19	.63052	1.70653	.64680	1.83124	.66318	1.96893	.67966	2.12171	19
20	.63079	1.70851	.64707	1.83342	.66345	1.97135	.67994	2.12440	20
21	.63106	1.71050	.64734	1.83561	.66373	1.97377	.68021	2.12709	21
22	.63133	1.71249	.64761	1.83780	.66400	1.97619	.68049	2.12979	22
23	.63161	1.71448	.64789	1.83999	.66427	1.97862	.68077	2.13249	23
24	.63188	1.71647	.64816	1.84219	.66455	1.98106	.68104	2.13520	24
25	.63215	1.71847	.64843	1.84439	.66482	1.98349	.68132	2.13791	25
26	.63242	1.72047	.64870	1.84659	.66510	1.98594	.68159	2.14033	26
27	.63269	1.72247	.64898	1.84880	.66537	1.98838	.68187	2.14335	27
28	.63296	1.72448	.64925	1.85102	.66564	1.99083	.68214	2.14608	28
29	.63323	1.72649	.64952	1.85323	.66592	1.99329	.68242	2.14881	29
30	.63350	1.72850	.64979	1.85545	.66619	1.99574	.68270	2.15155	30
31	.63377	1.73052	.65007	1.85767	.66647	1.99821	.68297	2.15429	31
32	.63404	1.73254	.65034	1.85990	.66674	2.00067	.68325	2.15704	32
33	.63431	1.73456	.65061	1.86213	.66702	2.00315	.68352	2.15979	33
34	.63458	1.73659	.65088	1.86437	.66729	2.00562	.68380	2.16255	34
35	.63485	1.73862	.65116	1.86661	.66756	2.00810	.68407	2.16531	35
36	.63512	1.74065	.65143	1.86885	.66784	2.01059	.68435	2.16808	36
37	.63539	1.74269	.65180	1.87109	.66811	2.01308	.68463	2.17085	37
38	.63566	1.74473	.65197	1.87334	.66839	2.01557	.68490	2.17363	38
39	.63594	1.74677	.65225	1.87560	.66866	2.01807	.68518	2.17641	39
40	.63621	1.74881	.65252	1.87785	.66894	2.02057	.68546	2.17920	40
41	.63648	1.75086	.65279	1.88011	.66921	2.02308	.68573	2.18199	41
42	.63675	1.75292	.65306	1.88238	.66949	2.02559	.68601	2.18479	42
43	.63702	1.75497	.65334	1.88465	.66976	2.02810	.68628	2.18759	43
44	.63729	1.75703	.65361	1.88692	.67003	2.03062	.68656	2.19040	44
45	.63756	1.75909	.65388	1.88920	.67031	2.03315	.68684	2.19322	45
46	.63783	1.76116	.65416	1.89148	.67058	2.03568	.68711	2.19604	46
47	.63810	1.76323	.65443	1.89376	.67085	2.03821	.68739	2.19886	47
48	.63838	1.76530	.65470	1.89605	.67113	2.04075	.68767	2.20169	48
49	.63865	1.76737	.65497	1.89834	.67141	2.04329	.68794	2.20453	49
50	.63892	1.76945	.65525	1.90063	.67168	2.04584	.68822	2.20737	50
51	.63919	1.77154	.65552	1.90293	.67196	2.04839	.68849	2.21021	51
52	.63946	1.77362	.65579	1.90524	.67223	2.05094	.68877	2.21306	52
53	.63973	1.77571	.65607	1.90754	.67251	2.05350	.68905	2.21592	53
54	.64000	1.77780	.65634	1.90985	.67278	2.05607	.68932	2.21878	54
55	.64027	1.77990	.65661	1.91217	.67303	2.05864	.68960	2.22165	55
56	.64055	1.78200	.65689	1.91449	.67333	2.06121	.68988	2.22452	56
57	.64082	1.78410	.65716	1.91681	.67361	2.06379	.69015	2.22740	57
58	.64109	1.78621	.65743	1.91914	.67388	2.06637	.69043	2.23028	58
59	.64136	1.78832	.65771	1.92147	.67416	2.06896	.69071	2.23317	59
60	.64163	1.79043	.65798	1.92380	.67443	2.07155	.69098	2.23607	60

′	72° Vers.	Exsec.	73° Vers.	Exsec.	74° Vers.	Exsec.	75° Vers.	Exsec.	′
0	.69098	2.23607	.70763	2.42030	.72436	2.62796	.74118	2.86370	0
1	.69126	2.23897	.70791	2.42356	.72464	2.63164	.74146	2.86790	1
2	.69154	2.24187	.70818	2.42683	.72492	2.63533	.74174	2.87211	2
3	.69181	2.24478	.70846	2.43010	.72520	2.63903	.74202	2.87633	3
4	.69209	2.24770	.70874	2.43337	.72548	2.64274	.74231	2.88056	4
5	.69237	2.25062	.70902	2.43666	.72576	2.64645	.74259	2.88479	**5**
6	.69264	2.25355	.70930	2.43995	72604	2.65018	.74287	2.88904	6
7	.69292	2.25648	.70958	2.44324	.72632	2.65391	.74315	2.89330	7
8	.69320	2.25942	.70985	2.44655	.72660	2.65765	.74343	2.89756	8
9	.69347	2.26237	.71013	2.44986	.72688	2.66140	.74371	2.90184	9
10	.69375	2.26531	.71041	2.45317	.72716	2.66515	.74399	2.90613	**10**
11	.69403	2.26827	.71069	2.45650	.72744	2.66892	.74427	2.91042	11
12	.69430	2.27123	.71097	2.45983	.72772	2.67269	.74455	2.91473	1?
13	.69458	2.27420	.71125	2.46316	.72800	2.67647	.74484	2.91904	13
14	.69486	2.27717	.71153	2.46651	.72828	2.68025	.74512	2.92337	14
15	.69514	2.28015	.71180	2.46986	.72856	2.68405	.74540	2.92770	**15**
16	.69541	2.28313	.71208	2.47321	.72884	2.68785	.74568	2.93204	16
17	.69569	2.28612	.71236	2.47658	.72912	2.69167	.74596	2.93640	17
18	.69597	2.28912	.71264	2.47995	.72940	2.69549	.74624	2.94076	18
19	.69624	2.29212	.71292	2.48333	.72968	2.69931	.74652	2.94514	19
20	.69652	2.29512	.71320	2.48761	.72996	2.70315	.74680	2.94952	**20**
21	.69680	2.29814	.71348	2.49010	.73024	2.70700	.74709	2.95392	21
22	.69708	2.30115	.71375	2.49350	.73052	2.71085	.74737	2.95832	22
23	.69735	2.30418	.71413	2.49691	.73080	2.71471	.74765	2.96274	23
24	.69763	2.30721	.71431	2.50032	.73108	2.71858	.74793	2.96716	24
25	.69791	2.31024	.71459	2.50374	.73136	2.72246	.74821	2.97160	**25**
26	.69818	2.31328	.71487	2.50716	.73164	2.72635	.74849	2.97604	26
27	.69846	2.31633	.71515	2.51060	.73192	2.73024	.74878	2.98050	27
28	.69874	2.31939	.71543	2.51404	.73220	2.73414	.74906	2.98497	28
29	.69902	2.32244	.71571	2.51748	.73248	2.73806	.74934	2.98944	29
30	.69929	2.32551	.71598	2.52094	.73276	2.74198	.74962	2.99393	**30**
31	.69957	2.32858	.71626	2.52440	.73304	2.74591	.74990	2.99843	31
32	.69985	2.33166	.71654	2.52787	.73332	2.74984	.75018	3.00293	32
33	.70013	2.33474	.71682	2.53134	.73360	2.75379	.75046	3.00745	33
34	.70040	2.33783	.71710	2.53482	.73388	2.75775	.75075	3.01198	34
35	.70068	2.34092	.71738	2.53831	.73416	2.76171	.75103	3.01652	**35**
36	.70096	2.34403	.71766	2.54181	.73444	2.76568	.75131	3.02107	36
37	.70124	2.34713	.71794	2.54531	.73472	2.76966	.75159	3.02563	37
38	.70151	2.35025	.71822	2.54833	.73500	2.77365	.75187	3.03020	38
39	.70179	2.35336	.71850	2.55234	.73529	2.77765	.75216	3.03479	39
40	.70207	2.35649	.71877	2.55587	.73557	2.78166	.75244	3.03938	**40**
41	.70235	2.35962	.71905	2.55940	.73585	2.78568	.75272	3.04398	41
42	.70263	2.36276	.71933	2.56294	.73613	2.78970	.75300	3.04860	42
43	.70290	2.36590	.71961	2.56649	.73641	2.79374	.75328	3.05322	43
44	.70318	2.36905	.71989	2.57005	.73669	2.79778	.75356	3.05786	44
45	.70346	2.37221	.72017	2.57361	.73697	2.80183	.75385	3.06251	**45**
46	.70374	2.37537	.72045	2.57718	.73725	2.80589	.75413	3.06717	46
47	.70401	2.37854	.72073	2.58076	.73753	2.80996	.75441	3.07184	47
48	.70429	2.38171	.72101	2.58434	.73781	2.81404	.75469	3.07652	48
49	.70457	2.38489	.72129	2.58794	.73809	2.81813	.75497	3.08121	49
50	.70485	2.38808	.72157	2.59154	.73837	2.82223	.75526	3.08591	**50**
51	.70513	2.39128	.72185	2.59514	.73865	2.82633	.75554	3.09063	51
52	.70540	2.39448	.72213	2.59876	.73893	2.83045	.75582	3.09535	52
53	.70568	2.39768	.72241	2.60238	.73921	2.83457	.75610	3.10009	53
54	.70596	2.40089	.72269	2.60601	.73950	2.83871	.75638	3.10484	54
55	.70624	2.40411	.72296	2.60965	.73978	2.84285	.75667	3.10960	**55**
56	.70652	2.40734	.72324	2.61330	.74006	2.84700	.75695	3.11437	56
57	.70679	2.41057	.72352	2.61695	.74034	2.85116	.75723	3.11915	57
58	.70707	2.41381	.72380	2.62061	.74062	2.85533	.75751	3.12394	58
59	.70735	2.41705	.72408	2.62428	.74090	2.85951	.75780	3.12875	59
60	.70763	2.42030	.72436	2.62796	.74118	2.86370	.75808	3.13357	**60**

′	76° Vers.	76° Exsec.	77° Vers.	77° Exsec.	78° Vers.	78° Exsec.	79° Vers.	79° Exsec.	′
0	.75808	3.13357	.77505	3.44541	.79209	3.80973	.80919	4.24801	0
1	.75836	3.13839	.77533	3.45102	.79237	3.81633	.80948	4.24870	1
2	.75864	3.14323	.77562	3.45664	.79266	3.82294	.80976	4.25658	2
3	.75892	3.14809	.77590	3.46228	.79294	3.82956	.81005	4.26448	3
4	.75921	3.15295	.77618	3.46793	.79323	3.83621	.81033	4.27241	4
5	.75949	3.15782	.77647	3.47360	.79351	3.84288	.81062	4.28036	**5**
6	.75977	3.16271	.77675	3.47928	.79380	3.84956	.81090	4.28833	6
7	.76005	3.16761	.77703	3.48498	.79408	3.85627	.81119	4.29634	7
8	.76034	3.17252	.77732	3.49069	.79437	3.86299	.81148	4.30435	8
9	.76062	3.17744	.77760	3.49642	.79465	3.86973	.81176	4.31241	9
10	.76090	3.18238	.77788	3.50216	.79493	3.87649	.81205	4.32049	**10**
11	.76118	3.18733	.77817	3.50791	.79522	3.88327	.81233	4.32859	11
12	.76147	3.19228	.77845	3.51368	.79550	3.89007	.81262	4.33671	12
13	.76175	3.19725	.77874	3.51947	.79579	3.89689	.81290	4.34486	13
14	.76203	3.20224	.77902	3.52527	.79607	3.90373	.81319	4.35304	14
15	.76231	3.20723	.77930	3.53109	.79636	3.91058	.81348	4.36124	**15**
16	.76260	3.21224	.77959	3.53692	.79664	3.91746	.81376	4.36947	16
17	.76288	3.21726	.77987	3.54277	.79693	3.92436	.81405	4.37772	17
18	.76316	3.22229	.78015	3.54863	.79721	3.93128	.81433	4.38600	18
19	.76344	3.22734	.78044	3.55451	.79750	3.93821	.81462	4.39430	19
20	.76373	3.23239	.78072	3.56041	.79778	3.94517	.81491	4.40263	**20**
21	.76401	3.23746	.78101	3.56632	.79807	3.95215	.81519	4.41099	21
22	.76429	3.24255	.78129	3.57224	.79835	3.95914	.81548	4.41937	22
23	.76458	3.24764	.78157	3.57819	.79864	3.96616	.81576	4.42778	23
24	.76486	3.25275	.78186	3.58414	.79892	3.97320	.81605	4.43622	24
25	.76514	3.25787	.78214	3.59012	.79921	3.98025	.81633	4.44468	**25**
26	.76542	3.26300	.78242	3.59611	.79949	3.98733	.81662	4.45317	26
27	.76571	3.26814	.78271	3.60211	.79978	3.99443	.81691	4.46169	27
28	.76599	3.27330	.78299	3.60813	.80006	4.00155	.81719	4.47023	28
29	.76627	3.27847	.78328	3.61417	.80035	4.00689	.81748	4.47881	29
30	.76655	3.28366	.78356	3.62023	.80063	4.01585	.81776	4.48740	**30**
31	.76684	3.28885	.78384	3.62630	.80092	4.02303	.81805	4.49603	31
32	.76712	3.29406	.78413	3.63238	.80120	4.03024	.81834	4.50468	32
33	.76740	3.29929	.78441	3.63849	.80149	4.03746	.81862	4.51337	33
34	.76769	3.30452	.78470	3.64461	.80177	4.04471	.81891	4.52208	34
35	.76797	3.30977	.78498	3.65074	.80206	4.05197	.81919	4.53081	**35**
36	.76825	3.31503	.78526	3.65690	.80234	4.05926	.81948	4.53958	36
37	.76854	3.32031	.78555	3.66307	.80263	4.06657	.81977	4.54837	37
38	.76882	3.32560	.78583	3.66925	.80291	4.07390	.82005	4.55720	38
39	.76910	3.33090	.78612	3.67545	.80320	4.08125	.82034	4.56605	39
40	.76938	3.33622	.78640	3.68167	.80348	4.08863	.82063	4.57493	**40**
41	.76967	3.34154	.78669	3.68791	.80377	4.09602	.82091	4.58383	41
42	.76995	3.34689	.78697	3.69417	.80405	4.10344	.82120	4.59277	42
43	.77023	3.35224	.78725	3.70044	.80434	4.11088	.82148	4.60174	43
44	.77052	3.35761	.78754	3.70673	.80462	4.11835	.82177	4.61073	44
45	.77080	3.36299	.78782	3.71303	.80491	4.12583	.82206	4.61976	**45**
46	.77108	3.36839	.78811	3.71935	.80519	4.13334	.82234	4.62881	46
47	.77137	3.37380	.78839	3.72569	.80548	4.14087	.82263	4.63790	47
48	.77165	3.37923	.78868	3.73205	.80577	4.14842	.82292	4.64701	48
49	.77193	3.38466	.78896	3.73843	.80605	4.15599	.82320	4.65616	49
50	.77222	3.39012	.78924	3.74482	.80634	4.16359	.82349	4.66533	**50**
51	.77250	3.39558	.79953	3.75123	.80662	4.17121	.82377	4.67454	51
52	.77278	3.40103	.79981	3.75766	.80691	4.17886	.82406	4.68377	52
53	.77307	3.40656	.79010	3.76411	.80719	4.18652	.82435	4.69304	53
54	.77335	3.41206	.79038	3.77057	.80748	4.19421	.82463	4.70234	54
55	.77363	3.41759	.79067	3.77705	.80776	4.20193	.82492	4.71166	**55**
56	.77392	3.42312	.79095	3.78355	.80805	4.20966	.82521	4.72102	56
57	.77420	3.42867	.79123	3.79007	.80833	4.21742	.82549	4.73041	57
58	.77448	3.43424	.79152	3.79661	.80862	4.22521	.82578	4.73983	58
59	.77477	3.43982	.79180	3.80316	.80891	4.23301	.82607	4.74929	59
60	.77505	3.44541	.79209	3.80973	.80919	4.24084	.82635	4.75877	**60**

′	80°		81°		82°		83°		′
	Vers.	Exsec.	Vers.	Exsec.	Vers.	Exsec.	Vers.	Exsec.	
0	.82635	4.75877	.84357	5.39245	.86083	6.18530	.87813	7.20551	0
1	.82664	4.76829	.84385	5.40422	.86111	6.20020	.87842	7.22500	1
2	.82692	4.77783	.84414	5.41602	.86140	6.21517	.87871	7.24457	2
3	.82721	4.78742	.84443	5.42787	.86169	6.23019	.87900	7.26425	3
4	.82750	4.79703	.84471	5.43977	.86198	6.24529	.87929	7.28402	4
5	.82778	4.80667	.84500	5.45171	.86227	6.26044	.87957	7.30388	5
6	.82807	4.81635	.84529	5.46369	.86256	6.27566	.87986	7.32384	6
7	.82836	4.82606	.84558	5.47572	.86284	6.29095	.88015	7.34390	7
8	.82864	4.83581	.84586	5.48779	.86313	6.30630	.88044	7.36405	8
9	.82893	4.84558	.84615	5.49991	.86342	6.32171	.88073	7.38431	9
10	.82922	4.85539	.84644	5.51208	.86371	6.33719	.88102	7.40466	10
11	.82950	4.86524	.84673	5.52429	.86400	6.35274	.88131	7.42511	11
12	.82979	4.87511	.84701	5.53655	.86428	6.36835	.88160	7.44566	12
13	.83008	4.88502	.84730	5.54886	.86457	6.38403	.88188	7.46632	13
14	.83036	4.89497	.84759	5.56121	.86486	6.39978	.88217	7.48707	14
15	.83065	4.90495	.84788	5.57361	.86515	6.41560	.88246	7.50793	15
16	.83094	4.91496	.84816	5.58606	.86544	6.43148	.88275	7.52889	16
17	.83122	4.92501	.84845	5.59855	.86573	6.44743	.88304	7.54996	17
18	.83151	4.93509	.84874	5.61110	.86601	6.46346	.88333	7.57113	18
19	.83180	4.94521	.84903	5.62369	.86630	6.47955	.88362	7.59241	19
20	.83208	4.95536	.84931	5.63633	.86659	6.49571	.88391	7.61379	20
21	.83237	4.96555	.84960	5.64902	.86688	6.51194	.88420	7.63528	21
22	.83266	4.97577	.84989	5.66176	.86717	6.52825	.88448	7.65688	22
23	.83294	4.98603	.85018	5.67454	.86746	6.54462	.88477	7.67859	23
24	.83323	4.99633	.85046	5.68738	.86774	6.56107	.88506	7.70041	24
25	.83352	5.00666	.85075	5.70027	.86803	6.57759	.88535	7.72234	25
26	.83380	5.01702	.85104	5.71321	.86832	6.59418	.88564	7.74438	26
27	.83409	5.02743	.85133	5.72620	.86861	6.61085	.88593	7.76653	27
28	.83438	5.03787	.85162	5.73924	.86890	6.62759	.88622	7.78880	28
29	.83467	5.04834	.85190	5.75233	.86919	6.64441	.88651	7.81118	29
30	.83495	5.05886	.85219	5.76547	.86947	6.66130	.88680	7.83367	30
31	.83524	5.06941	.85248	5.77866	.86976	6.67826	.88709	7.85628	31
32	.83553	5.08000	.85277	5.79191	.87005	6.69530	.88737	7.87901	32
33	.83581	5.09062	.85305	5.80521	.87034	6.71242	.88766	7.90186	33
34	.83610	5.10129	.85334	5.81856	.87063	6.72962	.88795	7.92482	34
35	.83639	5.11199	.85363	5.83196	.87092	6.74689	.88824	7.94791	35
36	.83667	5.12273	.85392	5.84542	.87120	6.76424	.88853	7.97111	36
37	.83696	5.13350	.85420	5.85893	.87149	6.78167	.88882	7.99444	37
38	.83725	5.14432	.85449	5.87250	.87178	6.79918	.88911	8.01788	38
39	.83753	5.15517	.85478	5.88612	.87207	6.81677	.88940	8.04146	39
40	.83782	5.16607	.85507	5.89979	.87236	6.83443	.88969	8.06515	40
41	.83811	5.17700	.85536	5.91352	.87265	6.85218	.88998	8.08897	41
42	.83840	5.18797	.85564	5.92731	.87294	6.87001	.89027	8.11292	42
43	.83868	5.19898	.85593	5.94115	.87322	6.88792	.89055	8.13699	43
44	.83897	5.21004	.85622	5.95505	.87351	6.90592	.89084	8.16120	44
45	.83926	5.22113	.85651	5.96900	.87380	6.92399	.89113	8.18553	45
46	.83954	5.23226	.85680	5.98301	.87409	6.94216	.89142	8.20999	46
47	.83983	5.24343	.85708	5.99708	.87438	6.96040	.89171	8.23459	47
48	.84012	5.25464	.85737	6.01120	.87467	6.97873	.89200	8.25931	48
49	.84041	5.26590	.85766	6.02538	.87496	6.99714	.89229	8.28417	49
50	.84069	5.27719	.85795	6.03962	.87524	7.01565	.89258	8.30917	50
51	.84098	5.28853	.85823	6.05392	.87553	7.03423	.89287	8.33430	51
52	.84127	5.29991	.85852	6.06828	.87582	7.05291	.89316	8.35957	52
53	.84155	5.31133	.85881	6.08269	.87611	7.07167	.89345	8.33497	53
54	.84184	5.32279	.85910	6.09717	.87640	7.09052	.89374	8.41052	54
55	.84213	5.33429	.85939	6.11171	.87669	7.10946	.89403	8.43620	55
56	.84242	5.34584	.85967	6.12630	.87698	7.12849	.89431	8.46203	56
57	.84270	5.35743	.85996	6.14096	.87726	7.14760	.89460	8.48800	57
58	.84299	5.36906	.86025	6.15568	.87755	7.16681	.89489	8.51411	58
59	.84328	5.38073	.86054	6.17046	.87784	7.18612	.89518	8.54037	59
60	.84357	5.39245	.86083	6.18530	.87813	7.20551	.89547	8.56677	60

′	84° Vers.	Exsec.	85° Vers.	Exsec.	86° Vers.	Exsec.	′
0	.89547	8.56677	.91284	10.47371	.93024	13.33559	0
1	.89576	8.59332	.91313	10.51199	.93053	13.39547	1
2	.89605	8.62002	.91342	10.55052	.93082	13.45586	2
3	.89634	8.64687	.91371	10.58932	.93111	13.51676	3
4	.89663	8.67387	.91400	10.62837	.93140	13.57817	4
5	.89692	8.70103	.91429	10.66769	.93169	13.64011	5
6	.89721	8.72833	.91458	10.70728	.93198	13.70258	6
7	.89750	8.75579	.91487	10.74714	.93227	13.76558	7
8	.89779	8.78341	.91516	10.78727	.93257	13.82913	8
9	.89808	8.81119	.91545	10.82768	.93286	13.89323	9
10	.89836	8.83912	.91574	10.86837	.93315	13.95788	10
11	.89865	8.86722	.91603	10.90934	.93344	14.02310	11
12	.89894	8.89547	.91632	10.95050	.93373	14.08890	12
13	.89923	8.92389	.91661	10.99214	.93402	14.15527	13
14	.89952	8.95248	.91690	11.03397	.93431	14.22223	14
15	.89981	8.98123	.91719	11.07610	.93460	14.28979	15
16	.90010	9.01015	.91748	11.11852	.93489	14.35795	16
17	.90039	9.03923	.91777	11.16125	.93518	14.42672	17
18	.90068	9.06849	.91806	11.20427	.93547	14.49611	18
19	.90097	9.09792	.91835	11.24761	.93576	14.56613	19
20	.90126	9.12752	.91864	11.29125	.93605	14.63679	20
21	.90155	9.15730	.91893	11.33521	.93634	14.70810	21
22	.90184	9.18725	.91922	11.37948	.93663	14.78005	22
23	.90213	9.21739	.91951	11.42408	.93692	14.85268	23
24	.90242	9.24770	.91980	11.46900	.93721	14.92597	24
25	.90271	9.27819	.92009	11.51424	.93750	14.99995	25
26	.90300	9.30887	.92038	11.55981	.93779	15.07462	26
27	.90329	9.33973	.92067	11.60572	.93808	15.14999	27
28	.90358	9.37077	.92096	11.65197	.93837	15.22607	28
29	.90386	9.40201	.92125	11.69856	.93866	15.30287	29
30	.90415	9.43343	.92154	11.74549	.93895	15.38041	30
31	.90444	9.46505	.92183	11.79278	.93924	15.45869	31
32	.90473	9.49685	.92212	11.84042	.93953	15.53772	32
33	.90502	9.52886	.92241	11.88841	.93982	15.61751	33
34	.90531	9.56106	.92270	11.93677	.94011	15.69808	34
35	.90560	9.59346	.92299	11.98549	.94040	15.77944	35
36	.90589	9.62605	.92328	12.03458	.94069	15.86159	36
37	.90618	9.65885	.92357	12.08404	.94098	15.94456	37
38	.90647	9.69186	.92386	12.13388	.94127	16.02835	38
39	.90676	9.72507	.92415	12.18411	.94156	16.11297	39
40	.90705	9.75849	.92444	12.23472	.94186	16.19843	40
41	.90734	9.79212	.92473	12.28572	.94215	16.28476	41
42	.90763	9.82596	.92502	12.33712	.94244	16.37196	42
43	.90792	9.86001	.92531	12.38891	.94273	16.46005	43
44	.90821	9.89428	.92560	12.44112	.94302	16.54903	44
45	.90850	9.92877	.92589	12.49373	.94331	16.63893	45
46	.90879	9.96348	.92618	12.54676	.94360	16.72975	46
47	.90908	9.99841	.92647	12.60021	.94389	16.82152	47
48	.90937	10.03356	.92676	12.65408	.94418	16.91424	48
49	.90966	10.06894	.92705	12.70838	.94447	17.00794	49
50	.90995	10.10455	.92734	12.76311	.94476	17.10262	50
51	.91024	10.14039	.92763	12.81829	.94505	17.19830	51
52	.91053	10.17646	.92792	12.87391	.94534	17.29500	52
53	.91082	10.21277	.92821	12.92999	.94563	17.39274	53
54	.91111	10.24932	.92850	12.98651	.94592	17.49153	54
55	.91140	10.28610	.92879	13.04350	.94621	17.59139	55
56	.91169	10.32313	.92908	13.10096	.94650	17.69233	56
57	.91197	10.36040	.92937	13.15889	.94679	17.79438	57
58	.91226	10.39792	.92966	13.21730	.94708	17.89755	58
59	.91255	10.43569	.92995	13.27620	.94737	18.00185	59
60	.91284	10.47371	.93024	13.33559	.94766	18.10732	60

′	87°		88°		89°		′
	Vers.	**Exsec.**	**Vers.**	**Exsec.**	**Vers.**	**Exsec.**	
0	.94766	18.10732	.96510	27.65371	.98255	56.29869	0
1	.94795	18.21397	.96539	27.89440	.98284	57.26975	1
2	.94825	18.32182	.96568	28.13917	.98313	58.27431	2
3	.94854	18.43088	.96597	28.38812	.98342	59.31411	3
4	.94883	18.54119	.96626	28.64137	.98371	60.39105	4
5	.94912	18.65275	.96655	28.89903	.98400	61.50715	**5**
6	.94941	18.76560	.96684	29.16120	.98429	62.66460	6
7	.94970	18.87976	.96714	29.42802	.98458	63.86572	7
8	.94999	18.99524	.96743	29.69960	.98487	65.11304	8
9	.95028	19.11207	.96772	29.97607	.98517	66.40927	9
10	.95057	19.23028	.96801	30.25758	.98546	67.75736	**10**
11	.95086	19.34989	.96830	30.54425	.98575	69.16047	11
12	.95115	19.47093	.96859	30.83623	.98604	70.62205	12
13	.95144	19.59341	.96888	31.13366	.98633	72.14583	13
14	.95173	19.71737	.96917	31.43671	.98662	73.73586	14
15	.95202	19.84283	.96946	31.74554	.98691	75.39655	**15**
16	.95231	19.96982	.96975	32.06030	.98720	77.13274	16
17	.95260	20.09838	.97004	32.38118	.98749	78.94968	17
18	.95289	20.22852	.97033	32.70835	.98778	80.85315	18
19	.95318	20.36027	.97062	33.04199	.98807	82.84947	19
20	.95347	20.49368	.97092	33.38232	.98836	84.94561	**20**
21	.95377	20.62876	.97121	33.72951	.98866	87.14924	21
22	.95406	20.76555	.97150	34.08380	.98895	89.46886	22
23	.95435	20.90409	.97179	34.44539	.98924	91.91387	23
24	.95464	21.04440	.97208	34.81542	.98953	94.49471	24
25	.95493	21.18653	.97237	35.19141	.98982	97.22303	**25**
26	.95522	21.33050	.97266	35.57633	.99011	100.11185	26
27	.95551	21.47635	.97295	35.96953	.99040	103.17574	27
28	.95580	21.62413	.97324	36.37127	.99069	106.43114	28
29	.95609	21.77386	.97353	36.78185	.99098	109.89656	29
30	.95638	21.92559	.97382	37.20155	.99127	113.59301	**30**
31	.95667	22.07935	.97411	37.63068	.99156	117.54440	31
32	.95696	22.23520	.97440	38.06957	.99186	121.77803	32
33	.95725	22.39316	.97470	38.51855	.99215	126.32526	33
34	.95754	22.55329	.97499	38.97797	.99244	131.22229	34
35	.95783	22.71563	.97528	39.44820	.99273	136.51108	**35**
36	.95812	22.88022	.97557	39.92963	.99302	142.24061	36
37	.95841	23.04712	.97586	40.42266	.99331	148.46837	37
38	.95871	23.21637	.97615	40.92772	.99360	155.26228	38
39	.95900	23.38802	.97644	41.44525	.99389	162.70325	39
40	.95929	23.56212	.97673	41.97571	.99418	170.88831	**40**
41	.95958	23.73873	.97702	42.51961	.99447	179.93496	41
42	.95987	23.91790	.97731	43.07746	.99476	189.98680	42
43	.96016	24.09969	.97760	43.64980	.99505	201.22122	43
44	.96045	24.28414	.97789	44.23719	.99535	213.85995	44
45	.96074	24.47134	.97819	44.84026	.99564	228.18385	**45**
46	.96103	24.66132	.97848	45.45963	.99593	244.55402	46
47	.96132	24.85417	.97877	46.09596	.99622	263.44269	47
48	.96161	25.04994	.97906	46.74997	.99651	285.47948	48
49	.96190	25.24869	.97935	47.42241	.99680	311.52297	49
59	.96219	25.45051	.97964	48.11406	.99709	342.77516	**50**
51	.96248	25.65545	.97993	48.82576	.99738	380.97230	51
52	.96277	25.86360	.98022	49.55840	.99767	428.71873	52
53	.96307	26.07503	.98051	50.31290	.99796	490.10702	53
54	.96336	26.28981	.98080	51.09027	.99825	571.95809	54
55	.96365	26.50804	.98109	51.89156	.99855	686.54960	**55**
56	.96394	26.72978	.98138	52.71790	.99884	858.43859	56
57	.96423	26.95512	.98168	53.57046	.99913	1144.91574	57
58	.96452	27.18417	.98197	54.45053	.99942	1717.87348	58
59	.96481	27.41700	.98226	55.35946	.99971	3436.74682	59
60	.96510	27.65371	.98255	56.29869	1.00000	∞	**60**

n	n²	√n	√10 n	n³	∛n	∛10 n	∛100 n	1/n
1.00	1.0000	1.00000	3.16228	1.00000	1.00000	2.15443	4.64159	1.00000
1.01	1.0201	1.00499	3.17805	1.03030	1.00332	2.16159	4.65701	.990099
1.02	1.0404	1.00995	3.19374	1.06121	1.00662	2.16870	4.67233	.980392
1.03	1.0609	1.01489	3.20936	1.09273	1.00990	2.17577	4.68755	.970874
1.04	1.0816	1.01980	3.22490	1.12486	1.01316	2.18279	4.70267	.961538
1.05	1.1025	1.02470	3.24037	1.15762	1.01640	2.18976	4.71769	.952381
1.06	1.1236	1.02956	3.25576	1.19102	1.01961	2.19669	4.73262	.943396
1.07	1.1449	1.03441	3.27109	1.22504	1.02281	2.20358	4.74746	.934579
1.08	1.1664	1.03923	3.28634	1.25971	1.02599	2.21042	4.76220	.925926
1.09	1.1881	1.04403	3.30151	1.29503	1.02914	2.21722	4.77686	.917431
1.10	1.2100	1.04881	3.31662	1.33100	1.03228	2.22398	4.79142	.909091
1.11	1.2321	1.05357	3.33167	1.36763	1.03540	2.23070	4.80590	.900901
1.12	1.2544	1.05830	3.34664	1.40493	1.03850	2.23738	4.82028	.892857
1.13	1.2769	1.06301	3.36155	1.44290	1.04158	2.24402	4.83459	.884956
1.14	1.2996	1.06771	3.37639	1.48154	1.04464	2.25062	4.84881	.877193
1.15	1.3225	1.07238	3.39116	1.52088	1.04769	2.25718	4.86294	.869565
1.16	1.3456	1.07703	3.40588	1.56090	1.05072	2.26370	4.87700	.862069
1.17	1.3689	1.08167	3.42053	1.60161	1.05373	2.27019	4.89097	.854701
1.18	1.3924	1.08628	3.43511	1.64303	1.05672	2.27664	4.90487	.847458
1.19	1.4161	1.09087	3.44964	1.68516	1.05970	2.28305	4.91868	.840336
1.20	1.4400	1.09545	3.46410	1.72800	1.06266	2.28943	4.93242	.833333
1.21	1.4641	1.10000	3.47851	1.77156	1.06560	2.29577	4.94609	.826446
1.22	1.4884	1.10454	3.49285	1.81585	1.06853	2.30208	4.95968	.819672
1.23	1.5129	1.10905	3.50714	1.86087	1.07144	2.30835	4.97319	.813008
1.24	1.5376	1.11355	3.52136	1.90662	1.07434	2.31459	4.98663	.806452
1.25	1.5625	1.11803	3.53553	1.95312	1.07722	2.32079	5.00000	.800000
1.26	1.5876	1.12250	3.54965	2.00038	1.08008	2.32697	5.01330	.793651
1.27	1.6129	1.12694	3.56371	2.04838	1.08293	2.33311	5.02653	.787402
1.28	1.6384	1.13137	3.57771	2.09715	1.08577	2.33921	5.03968	.781250
1.29	1.6641	1.13578	3.59166	2.14669	1.08859	2.34529	5.05277	.775194
1.30	1.6900	1.14018	3.60555	2.19700	1.09139	2.35133	5.06580	.769231
1.31	1.7161	1.14455	3.61939	2.24809	1.09418	2.35735	5.07875	.763359
1.32	1.7424	1.14891	3.63318	2.29997	1.09696	2.36333	5.09164	.757576
1.33	1.7689	1.15326	3.64692	2.35264	1.09972	2.36928	5.10447	.751880
1.34	1.7956	1.15758	3.66060	2.40610	1.10247	2.37521	5.11723	.746269
1.35	1.8225	1.16190	3.67423	2.46038	1.10521	2.38110	5.12993	.740741
1.36	1.8496	1.16619	3.68782	2.51546	1.10793	2.38697	5.14256	.735294
1.37	1.8769	1.17047	3.70135	2.57135	1.11064	2.39280	5.15514	.729927
1.38	1.9044	1.17473	3.71484	2.62807	1.11334	2.39861	5.16765	.724638
1.39	1.9321	1.17898	3.72827	2.68562	1.11602	2.40439	5.18010	.719424
1.40	1.9600	1.18322	3.74166	2.74400	1.11869	2.41014	5.19249	.714286
1.41	1.9881	1.18743	3.75500	2.80322	1.12135	2.41587	5.20483	.709220
1.42	2.0164	1.19164	3.76829	2.86329	1.12399	2.42156	5.21710	.704225
1.43	2.0449	1.19583	3.78153	2.92421	1.12662	2.42724	5.22932	.699301
1.44	2.0736	1.20000	3.79473	2.98598	1.12924	2.43288	5.24148	.694444
1.45	2.1025	1.20416	3.80789	3.04862	1.13185	2.43850	5.25359	.689655
1.46	2.1316	1.20830	3.82099	3.11214	1.13445	2.44409	5.26564	.684932
1.47	2.1609	1.21244	3.83406	3.17652	1.13703	2.44966	5.27763	.680272
1.48	2.1904	1.21655	3.84708	3.24179	1.13960	2.45520	5.28957	.675676
1.49	2.2201	1.22066	3.86005	3.30795	1.14216	2.46072	5.30146	.671141
1.50	2.2500	1.22474	3.87298	3.37500	1.14471	2.46621	5.31329	.666667
n	n²	√n	√10 n	n³	∛n	∛10 n	∛100 n	1/n

n	n^2	$\sqrt{n}$	$\sqrt{10\,n}$	n^3	$\sqrt[3]{n}$	$\sqrt[3]{10\,n}$	$\sqrt[3]{100\,n}$	$1/n$
1.50	2.2500	1.22474	3.87298	3.37500	1.14471	2.46621	5.31329	.666667
1.51	2.2801	1.22882	3.88587	3.44295	1.14725	2.47168	5.32507	.662252
1.52	2.3104	1.23288	3.89872	3.51181	1.14978	2.47712	5.33680	.657895
1.53	2.3409	1.23693	3.91152	3.58158	1.15230	2.48255	5.34848	.653595
1.54	2.3716	1.24097	3.92428	3.65226	1.15480	2.48794	5.36011	.649351
1.55	2.4025	1.24499	3.93700	3.72338	1.15729	2.49332	5.37169	.645161
1.56	2.4336	1.24900	3.94968	3.79642	1.15978	2.49867	5.38321	.641026
1.57	2.4649	1.25300	3.96232	3.86989	1.16225	2.50399	5.39469	.636943
1.58	2.4964	1.25698	3.97492	3.94431	1.16471	2.50930	5.40612	.632911
1.59	2.5281	1.26095	3.98748	4.01968	1.16717	2.51458	5.41750	.628931
1.60	2.5600	1.26491	4.00000	4.09600	1.16961	2.51984	5.42884	.625000
1.61	2.5921	1.26886	4.01248	4.17328	1.17204	2.52508	5.44012	.621118
1.62	2.6244	1.27279	4.02492	4.25153	1.17446	2.53030	5.45136	.617284
1.63	2.6569	1.27671	4.03733	4.33075	1.17687	2.53549	5.46256	.613497
1.64	2.6896	1.28062	4.04969	4.41094	1.17927	2.54067	5.47370	.609756
1.65	2.7225	1.28452	4.06202	4.49212	1.18167	2.54582	5.48481	.606061
1.66	2.7556	1.28841	4.07431	4.57430	1.18405	2.55095	5.49586	.602410
1.67	2.7889	1.29228	4.08656	4.65746	1.18642	2.55607	5.50688	.598802
1.68	2.8224	1.29615	4.09878	4.74163	1.18878	2.56116	5.51785	.595238
1.69	2.8561	1.30000	4.11096	4.82681	1.19114	2.56623	5.52877	.591716
1.70	2.8900	1.30384	4.12311	4.91300	1.19348	2.57128	5.53966	.588235
1.71	2.9241	1.30767	4.13521	5.00021	1.19582	2.57631	5.55050	.584795
1.72	2.9584	1.31149	4.14729	5.08845	1.19815	2.58133	5.56130	.581395
1.73	2.9929	1.31529	4.15933	5.17772	1.20046	2.58632	5.57205	.578035
1.74	3.0276	1.31909	4.17133	5.26802	1.20277	2.59129	5.58277	.574713
1.75	3.0625	1.32288	4.18330	5.35938	1.20507	2.59625	5.59344	.571429
1.76	3.0976	1.32665	4.19524	5.45178	1.20736	2.60118	5.60408	.568182
1.77	3.1329	1.33041	4.20714	5.54523	1.20964	2.60610	5.61467	.564972
1.78	3.1684	1.33417	4.21900	5.63975	1.21192	2.61100	5.62523	.561798
1.79	3.2041	1.33791	4.23084	5.73534	1.21418	2.61588	5.63574	.558659
1.80	3.2400	1.34164	4.24264	5.83200	1.21644	2.62074	5.64622	.555556
1.81	3.2761	1.34536	4.25441	5.92974	1.21869	2.62559	5.65665	.552486
1.82	3.3124	1.34907	4.26615	6.02857	1.22093	2.63041	5.66705	.549451
1.83	3.3489	1.35277	4.27785	6.12849	1.22316	2.63522	5.67741	.546448
1.84	3.3856	1.35647	4.28952	6.22950	1.22539	2.64001	5.68773	.543478
1.85	3.4225	1.36015	4.30116	6.33162	1.22760	2.64479	5.69802	.540541
1.86	3.4596	1.36382	4.31277	6.43486	1.22981	2.64954	5.70827	.537634
1.87	3.4969	1.36748	4.32435	6.53920	1.23201	2.65428	5.71848	.534759
1.88	3.5344	1.37113	4.33590	6.64467	1.23420	2.65901	5.72865	.531915
1.89	3.5721	1.37477	4.34741	6.75127	1.23639	2.66371	5.73879	.529101
1.90	3.6100	1.37840	4.35890	6.85900	1.23856	2.66840	5.74890	.526316
1.91	3.6481	1.38203	4.37035	6.96787	1.24073	2.67307	5.75897	.523560
1.92	3.6864	1.38564	4.38178	7.07789	1.24289	2.67773	5.76900	.520833
1.93	3.7249	1.38924	4.39318	7.18906	1.24505	2.68237	5.77900	.518135
1.94	3.7636	1.39284	4.40454	7.30138	1.24719	2.68700	5.78896	.515464
1.95	3.8025	1.39642	4.41588	7.41488	1.24933	2.69161	5.79889	.512821
1.96	3.8416	1.40000	4.42719	7.52954	1.25146	2.69620	5.80879	.510204
1.97	3.8809	1.40357	4:43847	7.64537	1.25359	2.70078	5.81865	.507614
1.98	3.9204	1.40712	4.44972	7.76239	1.25571	2.70534	5.82848	.505051
1.99	3.9601	1.41067	4.46094	7.88060	1.25782	2.70989	5.83827	.502513
2.00	4.0000	1.41421	4.47214	8.00000	1.25992	2.71442	5.84804	.500000
n	n^2	$\sqrt{n}$	$\sqrt{10\,n}$	n^3	$\sqrt[3]{n}$	$\sqrt[3]{10\,n}$	$\sqrt[3]{100\,n}$	$1/n$

n	n^2	$\sqrt{n}$	$\sqrt{10\,n}$	n^3	$\sqrt[3]{n}$	$\sqrt[3]{10\,n}$	$\sqrt[3]{100\,n}$	$1/n$
2.00	4.0000	1.41421	4.47214	8.00000	1.25992	2.71442	5.84804	.500000
2.01	4.0401	1.41774	4.48330	8.12060	1.26202	2.71893	5.85777	.497512
2.02	4.0804	1.42127	4.49444	8.24241	1.26411	2.72344	5.86746	.495050
2.03	4.1209	1.42478	4.50555	8.36543	1.26619	2.72792	5.87713	.492611
2.04	4.1616	1.42829	4.51664	8.48966	1.26827	2.73239	5.88677	.490196
2.05	4.2025	1.43178	4.52769	8.61512	1.27033	2.73685	5.89637	.487805
2.06	4.2436	1.43527	4.53872	8.74182	1.27240	2.74129	5.90594	.485437
2.07	4.2849	1.43875	4.54973	8.86974	1.27445	2.74572	5.91548	.483092
2.08	4.3264	1.44222	4.56070	8.99891	1.27650	2.75014	5.92499	.480769
2.09	4.3681	1.44568	4.57165	9.12933	1.27854	2.75454	5.93447	.478469
2.10	4.4100	1.44914	4.58258	9.26100	1.28058	2.75892	5.94392	.476190
2.11	4.4521	1.45258	4.59347	9.39393	1.28261	2.76330	5.95334	.473934
2.12	4.4944	1.45602	4.60435	9.52813	1.28463	2.76766	5.96273	.471698
2.13	4.5369	1.45945	4.61519	9.66360	1.28665	2.77200	5.97209	.469434
2.14	4.5796	1.46287	4.62601	9.80034	1.28866	2.77633	5.98142	.467290
2.15	4.6225	1.46629	4.63681	9.93838	1.29066	2.78065	5.99073	.465116
2.16	4.6656	1.46969	4.64758	10.0777	1.29266	2.78495	6.00000	.462963
2.17	4.7089	1.47309	4.65833	10.2183	1.29465	2.78924	6.00925	.460829
2.18	4.7524	1.47648	4.66905	10.3602	1.29664	2.79352	6.01846	.458716
2.19	4.7961	1.47986	4.67974	10.5035	1.29862	2.79779	6.02765	.456621
2.20	4.8400	1.48324	4.69042	10.6480	1.30059	2.80204	6.03681	.454545
2.21	4.8841	1.48661	4.70106	10.7939	1.30256	2.80628	6.04594	.452489
2.22	4.9284	1.48997	4.71169	10.9410	1.30452	2.81050	6.05505	.450450
2.23	4.9729	1.49332	4.72229	11.0896	1.30648	2.81472	6.06413	.448430
2.24	5.0176	1.49666	4.73286	11.2394	1.30843	2.81892	6.07318	.446429
2.25	5.0625	1.50000	4.74342	11.3906	1.31037	2.82311	6.08220	.444444
2.26	5.1076	1.50333	4.75395	11.5432	1.31231	2.82728	6.09120	.442478
2.27	5.1529	1.50665	4.76445	11.6971	1.31424	2.83145	6.10017	.440529
2.28	5.1984	1.50997	4.77493	11.8524	1.31617	2.83560	6.10911	.438596
2.29	5.2441	1.51327	4.78539	12.0090	1.31809	2.83974	6.11803	.436681
2.30	5.2900	1.51658	4.79583	12.1670	1.32001	2.84387	6.12693	.434783
2.31	5.3361	1.51987	4.80625	12.3264	1.32192	2.84798	6.13579	.432900
2.32	5.3824	1.52315	4.81664	12.4872	1.32382	2.85209	6.14463	.431034
2.33	5.4289	1.52643	4.82701	12.6493	1.32572	2.85618	6.15345	.429185
2.34	5.4756	1.52971	4.83735	12.8129	1.32761	2.86026	6.16224	.427350
2.35	5.5225	1.53297	4.84768	12.9779	1.32950	2.86433	6.17101	.425532
2.36	5.5696	1.53623	4.85798	13.1443	1.33139	2.86838	6.17975	.423729
2.37	5.6169	1.53948	4.86826	13.3121	1.33326	2.87243	6.18846	.421941
2.38	5.6644	1.54272	4.87852	13.4813	1.33514	2.87646	6.19715	.420168
2.39	5.7121	1.54596	4.88876	13.6519	1.33700	2.88049	6.20582	.418410
2.40	5.7600	1.54919	4.89898	13.8240	1.33887	2.88450	6.21447	.416667
2.41	5.8081	1.55242	4.90918	13.9975	1.34072	2.88850	6.22308	.414938
2.42	5.8564	1.55563	4.91935	14.1725	1.34257	2.89249	6.23168	.413223
2.43	5.9049	1.55885	4.92950	14.3489	1.34442	2.89647	6.24025	.411523
2.44	5.9536	1.56205	4.93964	14.5268	1.34626	2.90044	6.24880	.409836
2.45	6.0025	1.56525	4.94975	14.7061	1.34810	2.90439	6.25732	.408163
2.46	6.0516	1.56844	4.95984	14.8869	1.34993	2.90834	6.26583	.406504
2.47	6.1009	1.57162	4.96991	15.0692	1.35176	2.91227	6.27431	.404858
2.48	6.1504	1.57480	4.97996	15.2530	1.35358	2.91620	6.28276	.403226
2.49	6.2001	1.57797	4.98999	15.4382	1.35540	2.92011	6.29119	.401606
2.50	6.2500	1.58114	5.00000	15.6250	1.35721	2.92402	6.29961	.400000
n	n^2	$\sqrt{n}$	$\sqrt{10\,n}$	n^3	$\sqrt[3]{n}$	$\sqrt[3]{10\,n}$	$\sqrt[3]{100\,n}$	$1/n$

n	n^2	$\sqrt{n}$	$\sqrt{10\,n}$	n^3	$\sqrt[3]{n}$	$\sqrt[3]{10\,n}$	$\sqrt[3]{100\,n}$	$1/n$
2.50	6.2500	1.58114	5.00000	15.6250	1.35721	2.92402	6.29961	.400000
2.51	6.3001	1.58430	5.00999	15.8133	1.35902	2.92791	6.30799	.398406
2.52	6.3504	1.58745	5.01996	16.0030	1.36082	2.93179	6.31636	.396825
2.53	6.4009	1.59060	5.02991	16.1943	1.36262	2.93567	6.32470	.395257
2.54	6.4516	1.59374	5.03984	16.3871	1.36441	2.93953	6.33303	.393701
2.55	6.5025	1.59687	5.04975	16.5814	1.36620	2.94338	6.34133	.392157
2.56	6.5536	1.60000	5.05964	16.7772	1.36798	2.94723	6.34960	.390625
2.57	6.6049	1.60312	5.06952	16.9746	1.36976	2.95106	6.35786	.389105
2.58	6.6564	1.60624	5.07937	17.1735	1.37153	2.95488	6.36610	.387597
2.59	6.7081	1.60935	5.08920	17.3740	1.37330	2.95869	6.37431	.386100
2.60	6.7600	1.61245	5.09902	17.5760	1.37507	2.96250	6.38250	.384615
2.61	6.8121	1.61555	5.10882	17.7796	1.37683	2.96629	6.39068	.383142
2.62	6.8644	1.61864	5.11859	17.9847	1.37859	2.97007	6.39883	.381679
2.63	6.9169	1.62173	5.12835	18.1914	1.38034	2.97385	6.40696	.380228
2.64	6.9696	1.62481	5.13809	18.3997	1.38208	2.97761	6.41507	.378788
2.65	7.0225	1.62788	5.14782	18.6096	1.38383	2.98137	6.42316	.377358
2.66	7.0756	1.63095	5.15752	18.8211	1.38557	2.98511	6.43123	.375940
2.67	7.1289	1.63401	5.16720	19.0342	1.38730	2.98885	6.43928	.374532
2.68	7.1824	1.63707	5.17687	19.2488	1.38903	2.99257	6.44731	.373134
2.69	7.2361	1.64012	5.18652	19.4651	1.39076	2.99629	6.45531	.371747
2.70	7.2900	1.64317	5.19615	19.6830	1.39248	3.00000	6.46330	.370370
2.71	7.3441	1.64621	5.20577	19.9025	1.39419	3.00370	6.47127	.369004
2.72	7.3984	1.64924	5.21536	20.1236	1.39591	3.00739	6.47922	.367647
2.73	7.4529	1.65227	5.22494	20.3464	1.39761	3.01107	6.48715	.366300
2.74	7.5076	1.65529	5.23450	20.5708	1.39932	3.01474	6.49507	.364964
2.75	7.5625	1.65831	5.24404	20.7969	1.40102	3.01841	6.50296	.363636
2.76	7.6176	1.66132	5.25357	21.0246	1.40272	3.02206	6.51083	.362319
2.77	7.6729	1.66433	5.26308	21.2539	1.40441	3.02570	6.51868	.361011
2.78	7.7284	1.66733	5.27257	21.4850	1.40610	3.02934	6.52652	.359712
2.79	7.7841	1.67033	5.28205	21.7176	1.40778	3.03297	6.53434	.358423
2.80	7.8400	1.67332	5.29150	21.9520	1.40946	3.03659	6.54213	.357143
2.81	7.8961	1.67631	5.30094	22.1880	1.41114	3.04020	6.54991	.355872
2.82	7.9524	1.67929	5.31037	22.4258	1.41281	3.04380	6.55767	.354610
2.83	8.0089	1.68226	5.31977	22.6652	1.41448	3.04740	6.56541	.353357
2.84	8.0656	1.68523	5.32917	22.9063	1.41614	3.05098	6.57314	.352113
2.85	8.1225	1.68819	5.33854	23.1491	1.41780	3.05456	6.58084	.350877
2.86	8.1796	1.69115	5.34790	23.3937	1.41946	3.05813	6.58853	.349650
2.87	8.2369	1.69411	5.35724	23.6399	1.42111	3.06169	6.59620	.348432
2.88	8.2944	1.69706	5.36656	23.8879	1.42276	3.06524	6.60385	.347222
2.89	8.3521	1.70000	5.37587	24.1376	1.42440	3.06878	6.61149	.346021
2.90	8.4100	1.70294	5.38516	24.3890	1.42604	3.07232	6.61911	.344828
2.91	8.4681	1.70587	5.39444	24.6422	1.42768	3.07584	6.62671	.343643
2.92	8.5264	1.70880	5.40370	24.8971	1.42931	3.07936	6.63429	.342466
2.93	8.5849	1.71172	5.41295	25.1538	1.43094	3.08287	6.64185	.341297
2.94	8.6436	1.71464	5.42218	25.4122	1.43257	3.08638	6.64940	.340136
2.95	8.7025	1.71756	5.43139	25.6724	1.43419	3.08987	6.65693	.338983
2.96	8.7616	1.72047	5.44059	25.9343	1.43581	3.09336	6.66444	.337838
2.97	8.8209	1.72337	5.44977	26.1981	1.43743	3.09684	6.67194	.336700
2.98	8.8804	1.72627	5.45894	26.4636	1.43904	3.10031	6.67942	.335570
2.99	8.9401	1.72916	5.46809	26.7309	1.44065	3.10378	6.68688	.334448
3.00	9.0000	1.73205	5.47723	27.0000	1.44225	3.10723	6.69433	.333333
n	n^2	$\sqrt{n}$	$\sqrt{10\,n}$	n^3	$\sqrt[3]{n}$	$\sqrt[3]{10\,n}$	$\sqrt[3]{100\,n}$	$1/n$

n	n^2	$\sqrt{n}$	$\sqrt{10\,n}$	n^3	$\sqrt[3]{n}$	$\sqrt[3]{10\,n}$	$\sqrt[3]{100\,n}$	$1/n$
3.00	9.0000	1.73205	5.47723	27.0000	1.44225	3.10723	6.69433	.333333
3.01	9.0601	1.73494	5.48635	27.2709	1.44385	3.11068	6.70176	.332226
3.02	9.1204	1.73781	5.49545	27.5436	1.44545	3.11412	6.70917	.331126
3.03	9.1809	1.74069	5.50454	27.8181	1.44704	3.11756	6.71657	.330033
3.04	9.2416	1.74356	5.51362	28.0945	1.44863	3.12098	6.72395	.328947
3.05	9.3025	1.74642	5.52268	28.3726	1.45022	3.12440	6.73132	.327869
3.06	9.3636	1.74929	5.53173	28.6526	1.45180	3.12781	6.73866	.326797
3.07	9.4249	1.75214	5.54076	28.9344	1.45338	3.13121	6.74600	.325733
3.08	9.4864	1.75499	5.54977	29.2181	1.45496	3.13461	6.75331	.324675
3.09	9.5481	1.75784	5.55878	29.5036	1.45653	3.13800	6.76061	.323625
3.10	9.6100	1.76068	5.56776	29.7910	1.45810	3.14138	6.76790	.322581
3.11	9.6721	1.76352	5.57674	30.0802	1.45967	3.14475	6.77517	.321543
3.12	9.7344	1.76635	5.58570	30.3713	1.46123	3.14812	6.78242	.320513
3.13	9.7969	1.76918	5.59464	30.6643	1.46279	3.15148	6.78966	.319489
3.14	9.8596	1.77200	5.60357	30.9591	1.46434	3.15483	6.79688	.318471
3.15	9.9225	1.77482	5.61249	31.2559	1.46590	3.15818	6.80409	.317460
3.16	9.9856	1.77764	5.62139	31.5545	1.46745	3.16152	6.81128	.316456
3.17	10.0489	1.78045	5.63028	31.8550	1.46899	3.16485	6.81846	.315457
3.18	10.1124	1.78326	5.63915	32.1574	1.47054	3.16817	6.82562	.314465
3.19	10.1761	1.78606	5.64801	32.4618	1.47208	3.17149	6.83277	.313480
3.20	10.2400	1.78885	5.65685	32.7680	1.47361	3.17480	6.83990	.312500
3.21	10.3041	1.79165	5.66569	33.0762	1.47515	3.17811	6.84702	.311526
3.22	10.3684	1.79444	5.67450	33.3862	1.47668	3.18140	6.85412	.310559
3.23	10.4329	1.79722	5.68331	33.6983	1.47820	3.18469	6.86121	.309598
3.24	10.4976	1.80000	5.69210	34.0122	1.47973	3.18798	6.86829	.308642
3.25	10.5625	1.80278	5.70088	34.3281	1.48125	3.19125	6.87534	.307692
3.26	10.6276	1.80555	5.70964	34.6460	1.48277	3.19452	6.88239	.306748
3.27	10.6929	1.80831	5.71839	34.9658	1.48428	3.19778	6.88942	.305810
3.28	10.7584	1.81108	5.72713	35.2876	1.48579	3.20104	6.89643	.304878
3.29	10.8241	1.81384	5.73585	35.6113	1.48730	3.20429	6.90344	.303951
3.30	10.8900	1.81659	5.74456	35.9370	1.48881	3.20753	6.91042	.303030
3.31	10.9561	1.81934	5.75326	36.2647	1.49031	3.21077	6.91740	.302115
3.32	11.0224	1.82209	5.76194	36.5944	1.49181	3.21400	6.92436	.301205
3.33	11.0889	1.82483	5.77062	36.9260	1.49330	3.21722	6.93130	.300300
3.34	11.1556	1.82757	5.77927	37.2597	1.49480	3.22044	6.93823	.299401
3.35	11.2225	1.83030	5.78792	37.5954	1.49629	3.22365	6.94515	.298507
3.36	11.2896	1.83303	5.79655	37.9331	1.49777	3.22686	6.95205	.297619
3.37	11.3569	1.83576	5.80517	38.2728	1.49926	3.23006	6.95894	.296736
3.38	11.4244	1.83848	5.81378	38.6145	1.50074	3.23325	6.96582	.295858
3.39	11.4921	1.84120	5.82237	38.9582	1.50222	3.23643	6.97268	.294985
3.40	11.5600	1.84391	5.83095	39.3040	1.50369	3.23961	6.97953	.294118
3.41	11.6281	1.84662	5.83952	39.6518	1.50517	3.24278	6.98637	.293255
3.42	11.6964	1.84932	5.84808	40.0017	1.50664	3.24595	6.99319	.292398
3.43	11.7649	1.85203	5.85662	40.3536	1.50810	3.24911	7.00000	.291545
3.44	11.8336	1.85472	5.86515	40.7076	1.50957	3.25227	7.00680	.290698
3.45	11.9025	1.85742	5.87367	41.0636	1.51103	3.25542	7.01358	.289855
3.46	11.9716	1.86011	5.88218	41.4217	1.51249	3.25856	7.02035	.289017
3.47	12.0409	1.86279	5.89067	41.7819	1.51394	3.26169	7.02711	.288184
3.48	12.1104	1.86548	5.89915	42.1442	1.51540	3.26482	7.03385	.287356
3.49	12.1801	1.86815	5.90762	42.5085	1.51685	3.26795	7.04058	.286533
3.50	12.2500	1.87083	5.91608	42.8750	1.51829	3.27107	7.04730	.285714
n	n^2	$\sqrt{n}$	$\sqrt{10\,n}$	n^3	$\sqrt[3]{n}$	$\sqrt[3]{10\,n}$	$\sqrt[3]{100\,n}$	$1/n$

n	n^2	$\sqrt{n}$	$\sqrt{10\,n}$	n^3	$\sqrt[3]{n}$	$\sqrt[3]{10\,n}$	$\sqrt[3]{100\,n}$	$1/n$
3.50	12.2500	1.87083	5.91608	42.8750	1.51829	3.27107	7.04730	.285714
3.51	12.3201	1.87350	5.92453	43.2436	1.51974	3.27418	7.05400	.284900
3.52	12.3904	1.87617	5.93296	43.6142	1.52118	3.27729	7.06070	.284091
3.53	12.4609	1.87883	5.94138	43.9870	1.52262	3.28039	7.06738	.283286
3.54	12.5316	1.88149	5.94979	44.3619	1.52406	3.28348	7.07404	.282486
3.55	12.6025	1.88414	5.95819	44.7389	1.52549	3.28657	7.08070	.281690
3.56	12.6736	1.88680	5.96657	45.1180	1.52692	3.28965	7.08734	.280899
3.57	12.7449	1.88944	5.97495	45.4993	1.52835	3.29273	7.09397	.280112
3.58	12.8164	1.89209	5.98331	45.8827	1.52978	3.29580	7.10059	.279330
3.59	12.8881	1.89473	5.99166	46.2683	1.53120	3.29887	7.10719	.278552
3.60	12.9600	1.89737	6.00000	46.6560	1.53262	3.30193	7.11379	.277778
3.61	13.0321	1.90000	6.00833	47.0459	1.53404	3.30498	7.12037	.277008
3.62	13.1044	1.90263	6.01664	47.4379	1.53545	3.30803	7.12694	.276243
3.63	13.1769	1.90526	6.02495	47.8321	1.53686	3.31107	7.13349	.275482
3.64	13.2496	1.90788	6.03324	48.2285	1.53827	3.31411	7.14004	.274725
3.65	13.3225	1.91050	6.04152	48.6271	1.53968	3.31714	7.14657	.273973
3.66	13.3956	1.91311	6.04979	49.0279	1.54109	3.32017	7.15309	.273224
3.67	13.4689	1.91572	6.05805	49.4309	1.54249	3.32319	7.15960	.272480
3.68	13.5424	1.91833	6.06630	49.8360	1.54389	3.32621	7.16610	.271739
3.69	13.6161	1.92094	6.07454	50.2434	1.54529	3.32922	7.17258	.271003
3.70	13.6900	1.92354	6.08276	50.6530	1.54668	3.33222	7.17905	.270270
3.71	13.7641	1.92614	6.09098	51.0648	1.54807	3.33522	7.18552	.269542
3.72	13.8384	1.92873	6.09918	51.4788	1.54946	3.33822	7.19197	.268817
3.73	13.9129	1.93132	6.10737	51.8951	1.55085	3.34120	7.19840	.268097
3.74	13.9876	1.93391	6.11555	52.3136	1.55223	3.34419	7.20483	.267380
3.75	14.0625	1.93649	6.12372	52.7344	1.55362	3.34716	7.21125	.266667
3.76	14.1376	1.93907	6.13188	53.1574	1.55500	3.35014	7.21765	.265957
3.77	14.2129	1.94165	6.14003	53.5826	1.55637	3.35310	7.22405	.265252
3.78	14.2884	1.94422	6.14817	54.0102	1.55775	3.35607	7.23043	.264550
3.79	14.3641	1.94679	6.15630	54.4399	1.55912	3.35902	7.23680	.263852
3.80	14.4400	1.94936	6.16441	54.8720	1.56049	3.36198	7.24316	.263158
3.81	14.5161	1.95192	6.17252	55.3063	1.56186	3.36492	7.24950	.262467
3.82	14.5924	1.95448	6.18061	55.7430	1.56322	3.36786	7.25584	.261780
3.83	14.6689	1.95704	6.18870	56.1819	1.56459	3.37080	7.26217	.261097
3.84	14.7456	1.95959	6.19677	56.6231	1.56595	3.37373	7.26848	.260417
3.85	14.8225	1.96214	6.20484	57.0666	1.56731	3.37666	7.27479	.259740
3.86	14.8996	1.96469	6.21289	57.5125	1.56866	3.37958	7.28108	.259067
3.87	14.9769	1.96723	6.22093	57.9606	1.57001	3.38249	7.28736	.258398
3.88	15.0544	1.96977	6.22896	58.4111	1.57137	3.38540	7.29363	.257732
3.89	15.1321	1.97231	6.23699	58.8639	1.57271	3.38831	7.29989	.257069
3.90	15.2100	1.97484	6.24500	59.3190	1.57406	3.39121	7.30614	.256410
3.91	15.2881	1.97737	6.25300	59.7765	1.57541	3.39411	7.31238	.255754
3.92	15.3664	1.97990	6.26099	60.2363	1.57675	3.39700	7.31861	.255102
3.93	15.4449	1.98242	6.26897	60.6985	1.57809	3.39988	7.32483	.254453
3.94	15.5236	1.98494	6.27694	61.1630	1.57942	3.40277	7.33104	.253807
3.95	15.6025	1.98746	6.28490	61.6299	1.58076	3.40564	7.33723	.253165
3.96	15.6816	1.98997	6.29285	62.0991	1.58209	3.40851	7.34342	.252525
3.97	15.7609	1.99249	6.30079	62.5708	1.58342	3.41138	7.34960	.251889
3.98	15.8404	1.99499	6.30872	63.0448	1.58475	3.41424	7.35576	.251256
3.99	15.9201	1.99750	6.31664	63.5212	1.58608	3.41710	7.36192	.250627
4.00	16.0000	2.00000	6.32456	64.0000	1.58740	3.41995	7.36806	.250000
n	n^2	$\sqrt{n}$	$\sqrt{10\,n}$	n^3	$\sqrt[3]{n}$	$\sqrt[3]{10\,n}$	$\sqrt[3]{100\,n}$	$1/n$

n	n^2	$\sqrt{n}$	$\sqrt{10\,n}$	n^3	$\sqrt[3]{n}$	$\sqrt[3]{10\,n}$	$\sqrt[3]{100\,n}$	$1/n$
4.00	16.0000	2.00000	6.32456	64.0000	1.58740	3.41995	7.36806	.250000
4.01	16.0801	2.00250	6.33246	64.4812	1.58872	3.42280	7.37420	.249377
4.02	16.1604	2.00499	6.34035	64.9648	1.59004	3.42564	7.38032	.248756
4.03	16.2409	2.00749	6.34823	65.4508	1.59136	3.42848	7.38644	.248139
4.04	16.3216	2.00998	6.35610	65.9393	1.59267	3.43131	7.39254	.247525
4.05	16.4025	2.01246	6.36396	66.4301	1.59399	3.43414	7.39864	.246914
4.06	16.4836	2.01494	6.37181	66.9234	1.59530	3.43697	7.40472	.246305
4.07	16.5649	2.01742	6.37966	67.4191	1.59661	3.43979	7.41080	.245700
4.08	16.6464	2.01990	6.38749	67.9173	1.59791	3.44260	7.41686	.245098
4.09	16.7281	2.02237	6.39531	68.4179	1.59922	3.44541	7.42291	.244499
4.10	16.8100	2.02485	6.40312	68.9210	1.60052	3.44822	7.42896	.243902
4.11	16.8921	2.02731	6.41093	69.4265	1.60182	3.45102	7.43499	.243309
4.12	16.9744	2.02978	6.41872	69.9345	1.60312	3.45382	7.44102	.242718
4.13	17.0569	2.03224	6.42651	70.4450	1.60441	3.45661	7.44703	.242131
4.14	17.1396	2.03470	6.43428	70.9579	1.60571	3.45939	7.45304	.241546
4.15	17.2225	2.03715	6.44205	71.4734	1.60700	3.46218	7.45904	.240964
4.16	17.3056	2.03961	6.44981	71.9913	1.60829	3.46496	7.46502	.240385
4.17	17.3889	2.04206	6.45755	72.5117	1.60958	3.46773	7.47100	.239808
4.18	17.4724	2.04450	6.46529	73.0346	1.61086	3.47050	7.47697	.239234
4.19	17.5561	2.04695	6.47302	73.5601	1.61215	3.47327	7.48292	.238663
4.20	17.6400	2.04939	6.48074	74.0880	1.61343	3.47603	7.48887	.238095
4.21	17.7241	2.05183	6.48845	74.6185	1.61471	3.47878	7.49481	.237530
4.22	17.8084	2.05426	6.49615	75.1514	1.61599	3.48154	7.50074	.236967
4.23	17.8929	2.05670	6.50384	75.6870	1.61726	3.48428	7.50666	.236407
4.24	17.9776	2.05913	6.51153	76.2250	1.61853	3.48703	7.51257	.235849
4.25	18.0625	2.06155	6.51920	76.7656	1.61981	3.48977	7.51847	.235294
4.26	18.1476	2.06398	6.52687	77.3088	1.62108	3.49250	7.52437	.234742
4.27	18.2329	2.06640	6.53452	77.8545	1.62234	3.49523	7.53025	.234192
4.28	18.3184	2.06882	6.54217	78.4028	1.62361	3.49796	7.53612	.233645
4.29	18.4041	2.07123	6.54981	78.9536	1.62487	3.50068	7.54199	.233100
4.30	18.4900	2.07364	6.55744	79.5070	1.62613	3.50340	7.54784	.232558
4.31	18.5761	2.07605	6.56506	80.0630	1.62739	3.50611	7.55369	.232019
4.32	18.6624	2.07846	6.57267	80.6216	1.62865	3.50882	7.55953	.231481
4.33	18.7489	2.08087	6.58027	81.1827	1.62991	3.51153	7.56535	.230947
4.34	18.8356	2.08327	6.58787	81.7465	1.63116	3.51423	7.57117	.230415
4.35	18.9225	2.08567	6.59545	82.3129	1.63241	3.51692	7.57698	.229885
4.36	19.0096	2.08806	6.60303	82.8819	1.63366	3.51962	7.58279	.229358
4.37	19.0969	2.09045	6.61060	83.4535	1.63491	3.52231	7.58858	.228833
4.38	19.1844	2.09284	6.61816	84.0277	1.63619	3.52499	7.59436	.228311
4.39	19.2721	2.09523	6.62571	84.6045	1.63740	3.52767	7.60014	.227790
4.40	19.3600	2.09762	6.63325	85.1840	1.63864	3.53035	7.60590	.227273
4.41	19.4481	2.10000	6.64078	85.7661	1.63988	3.53302	7.61166	.226757
4.42	19.5364	2.10238	6.64831	86.3509	1.64112	3.53569	7.61741	.226244
4.43	19.6249	2.10476	6.65582	86.9383	1.64236	3.53835	7.62315	.225734
4.44	19.7136	2.10713	6.66333	87.5284	1.64359	3.54101	7.62888	.225225
4.45	19.8025	2.10950	6.67083	88.1211	1.64483	3.54367	7.63461	.224719
4.46	19.8916	2.11187	6.67832	88.7165	1.64606	3.54632	7.64032	.224215
4.47	19.9809	2.11424	6.68581	89.3146	1.64729	3.54897	7.64603	.223714
4.48	20.0704	2.11660	6.69328	89.9154	1.64851	3.55162	7.65172	.223214
4.49	20.1601	2.11896	6.70075	90.5188	1.64974	3.55426	7.65741	.222717
4.50	20.2500	2.12132	6.70820	91.1250	1.65096	3.55689	7.66309	.222222
n	n^2	$\sqrt{n}$	$\sqrt{10\,n}$	n^3	$\sqrt[3]{n}$	$\sqrt[3]{10\,n}$	$\sqrt[3]{100\,n}$	$1/n$

n	n^2	$\sqrt{n}$	$\sqrt{10\,n}$	n^3	$\sqrt[3]{n}$	$\sqrt[3]{10\,n}$	$\sqrt[3]{100\,n}$	$1/n$
4.50	20.2500	2.12132	6.70820	91.1250	1.65096	3.55689	7.66309	.222222
4.51	20.3401	2.12368	6.71565	91.7339	1.65219	3.55953	7.66877	.221729
4.52	20.4304	2.12603	6.72309	92.3454	1.65341	3.56215	7.67443	.221239
4.53	20.5209	2.12838	6.73053	92.9597	1.65462	3.56478	7.68009	.220751
4.54	20.6116	2.13073	6.73795	93.5767	1.65584	3.56740	7.68573	.220264
4.55	20.7025	2.13307	6.74537	94.1964	1.65706	3.57002	7.69137	.219780
4.56	20.7936	2.13542	6.75278	94.8188	1.65827	3.57263	7.69700	.219298
4.57	20.8849	2.13776	6.76018	95.4440	1.65948	3.57524	7.70262	.218818
4.58	20.9764	2.14009	6.76757	96.0719	1.66069	3.57785	7.70824	.218341
4.59	21.0681	2.14243	6.77495	96.7026	1.66190	3.58045	7.71384	.217865
4.60	21.1600	2.14476	6.78233	97.3360	1.66310	3.58305	7.71944	.217391
4.61	21.2521	2.14709	6.78970	97.9722	1.66431	3.58564	7.72503	.216920
4.62	21.3444	2.14942	6.79706	98.6111	1.66551	3.58823	7.73061	.216450
4.63	21.4369	2.15174	6.80441	99.2528	1.66671	3.59082	7.73619	.215983
4.64	21.5296	2.15407	6.81175	99.8973	1.66791	3.59340	7.74175	.215517
4.65	21.6225	2.15639	6.81909	100.545	1.66911	3.59598	7.74731	.215054
4.66	21.7156	2.15870	6.82642	101.195	1.67030	3.59856	7.75286	.214592
4.67	21.8089	2.16102	6.83374	101.848	1.67150	3.60113	7.75840	.214133
4.68	21.9024	2.16333	6.84105	102.503	1.67269	3.60370	7.76394	.213675
4.69	21.9961	2.16564	6.84836	103.162	1.67388	3.60626	7.76946	.213220
4.70	22.0900	2.16795	6.85565	103.823	1.67507	3.60883	7.77498	.212766
4.71	22.1841	2.17025	6.86294	104.487	1.67626	3.61138	7.78049	.212314
4.72	22.2784	2.17256	6.87023	105.154	1.67744	3.61394	7.78599	.211864
4.73	22.3729	2.17486	6.87750	105.824	1.67863	3.61649	7.79149	.211416
4.74	22.4676	2.17715	6.88477	106.496	1.67981	3.61903	7.79697	.210970
4.75	22.5625	2.17945	6.89202	107.172	1.68099	3.62158	7.80245	.210526
4.76	22.6576	2.18174	6.89928	107.850	1.68217	3.62412	7.80793	.210084
4.77	22.7529	2.18403	6.90652	108.531	1.68334	3.62665	7.81339	.209644
4.78	22.8484	2.18632	6.91375	109.215	1.68452	3.62919	7.81885	.209205
4.79	22.9441	2.18861	6.92098	109.902	1.68569	3.63172	7.82429	.208768
4.80	23.0400	2.19089	6.92820	110.592	1.68687	3.63424	7.82974	.208333
4.81	23.1361	2.19317	6.93542	111.285	1.68804	3.63676	7.83517	.207900
4.82	23.2324	2.19545	6.94262	111.980	1.68920	3.63928	7.84059	.207469
4.83	23.3289	2.19773	6.94982	112.679	1.69037	3.64180	7.84601	.207039
4.84	23.4256	2.20000	6.95701	113.380	1.69154	3.64431	7.85142	.206612
4.85	23.5225	2.20227	6.96419	114.084	1.69270	3.64682	7.85683	.206186
4.86	23.6196	2.20454	6.97137	114.791	1.69386	3.64932	7.86222	.205761
4.87	23.7169	2.20681	6.97854	115.501	1.69503	3.65182	7.86761	.205339
4.88	23.8144	2.20907	6.98570	116.214	1.69619	3.65432	7.87299	.204918
4.89	23.9121	2.21133	6.99285	116.930	1.69734	3.65681	7.87837	.204499
4.90	24.0100	2.21359	7.00000	117.649	1.69850	3.65931	7.88374	.204082
4.91	24.1081	2.21585	7.00714	118.371	1.69965	3.66179	7.88909	.203666
4.92	24.2064	2.21811	7.01427	119.095	1.70081	3.66428	7.89445	.203252
4.93	24.3049	2.22036	7.02140	119.823	1.70196	3.66676	7.89979	.202840
4.94	24.4036	2.22261	7.02851	120.554	1.70311	3.66924	7.90513	.202429
4.95	24.5025	2.22486	7.03562	121.287	1.70426	3.67171	7.91046	.202020
4.96	24.6016	2.22711	7.04273	122.024	1.70540	3.67418	7.91578	.201613
4.97	24.7009	2.22935	7.04982	122.763	1.70655	3.67665	7.92110	.201207
4.98	24.8004	2.23159	7.05691	123.506	1.70769	3.67911	7.92641	.200803
4.99	24.9001	2.23383	7.06399	124.251	1.70884	3.68157	7.93171	.200401
5.00	25.0000	2.23607	7.07107	125.000	1.70998	3.68403	7.93701	.200000
n	n^2	$\sqrt{n}$	$\sqrt{10\,n}$	n^3	$\sqrt[3]{n}$	$\sqrt[3]{10\,n}$	$\sqrt[3]{100\,n}$	$1/n$

n	n^2	$\sqrt{n}$	$\sqrt{10\,n}$	n^3	$\sqrt[3]{n}$	$\sqrt[3]{10\,n}$	$\sqrt[3]{100\,n}$	$1/n$
5.00	25.0000	2.23607	7.07107	125.000	1.70998	3.68403	7.93701	.200000
5.01	25.1001	2.23830	7.07814	125.752	1.71112	3.68649	7.94229	.199601
5.02	25.2004	2.24054	7.08520	126.506	1.71225	3.68894	7.94757	.199203
5.03	25.3009	2.24277	7.09225	127.264	1.71339	3.69138	7.95285	.198807
5.04	25.4016	2.24499	7.09930	128.024	1.71452	3.69383	7.95811	.198413
5.05	25.5025	2.24722	7.10634	128.788	1.71566	3.69627	7.96337	.198020
5.06	25.6036	2.24944	7.11337	129.554	1.71679	3.69871	7.96863	.197628
5.07	25.7049	2.25167	7.12039	130.324	1.71792	3.70114	7.97387	.197239
5.08	25.8064	2.25389	7.12741	131.097	1.71905	3.70357	7.97911	.196850
5.09	25.9081	2.25610	7.13442	131.872	1.72017	3.70600	7.98434	.196464
5.10	26.0100	2.25832	7.14143	132.651	1.72130	3.70843	7.98957	.196078
5.11	26.1121	2.26053	7.14843	133.433	1.72242	3.71085	7.99479	.195695
5.12	26.2144	2.26274	7.15542	134.218	1.72355	3.71327	8.00000	.195312
5.13	26.3169	2.26495	7.16240	135.006	1.72467	3.71569	8.00520	.194932
5.14	26.4196	2.26716	7.16938	135.797	1.72579	3.71810	8.01040	.194553
5.15	26.5225	2.26936	7.17635	136.591	1.72691	3.72051	8.01559	.194175
5.16	26.6256	2.27156	7.18331	137.388	1.72802	3.72292	8.02078	.193798
5.17	26.7289	2.27376	7.19027	138.188	1.72914	3.72532	8.02596	.193424
5.18	26.8324	2.27596	7.19722	138.992	1.73025	3.72772	8.03113	.193050
5.19	26.9361	2.27816	7.20417	139.798	1.73137	3.73012	8.03629	.192678
5.20	27.0400	2.28035	7.21110	140.608	1.73248	3.73251	8.04145	.192308
5.21	27.1441	2.28254	7.21803	141.421	1.73359	3.73490	8.04660	.191939
5.22	27.2484	2.28473	7.22496	142.237	1.73470	3.73729	8.05175	.191571
5.23	27.3529	2.28692	7.23187	143.056	1.73580	3.73968	8.05689	.191205
5.24	27.4576	2.28910	7.23878	143.878	1.73691	3.74206	8.06202	.190840
5.25	27.5625	2.29129	7.24569	144.703	1.73801	3.74443	8.06714	.190476
5.26	27.6676	2.29347	7.25259	145.532	1.73912	3.74681	8.07226	.190114
5.27	27.7729	2.29565	7.25948	146.363	1.74022	3.74918	8.07737	.189753
5.28	27.8784	2.29783	7.26636	147.198	1.74132	3.75155	8.08248	.189394
5.29	27.9841	2.30000	7.27324	148.036	1.74242	3.75392	8.08758	.189036
5.30	28.0900	2.30217	7.28011	148.877	1.74351	3.75629	8.09267	.188679
5.31	28.1961	2.30434	7.28697	149.721	1.74461	3.75865	8.09776	.188324
5.32	28.3024	2.30651	7.29383	150.569	1.74570	3.76101	8.10284	.187970
5.33	28.4089	2.30868	7.30068	151.419	1.74680	3.76336	8.10791	.187617
5.34	28.5156	2.31084	7.30753	152.273	1.74789	3.76571	8.11298	.187266
5.35	28.6225	2.31301	7.31437	153.130	1.74898	3.76806	8.11804	.186916
5.36	28.7296	2.31517	7.32120	153.991	1.75007	3.77041	8.12310	.186567
5.37	28.8369	2.31733	7.32803	154.854	1.75116	3.77275	8.12814	.186220
5.38	28.9444	2.31948	7.33485	155.721	1.75224	3.77509	8.13319	.185874
5.39	29.0521	2.32164	7.34166	156.591	1.75333	3.77743	8.13822	.185529
5.40	29.1600	2.32379	7.34847	157.464	1.75441	3.77976	8.14325	.185185
5.41	29.2681	2.32594	7.35527	158.340	1.75549	3.78209	8.14828	.184843
5.42	29.3764	2.32809	7.36206	159.220	1.75657	3.78442	8.15329	.184502
5.43	29.4849	2.33024	7.36885	160.103	1.75765	3.78675	8.15831	.184162
5.44	29.5936	2.33238	7.37564	160.989	1.75873	3.78907	8.16331	.183824
5.45	29.7025	2.33452	7.38241	161.879	1.75981	3.79139	8.16831	.183486
5.46	29.8116	2.33666	7.38918	162.771	1.76088	3.79371	8.17330	.183150
5.47	29.9209	2.33880	7.39594	163.667	1.76196	3.79603	8.17829	.182815
5.48	30.0304	2.34094	7.40270	164.567	1.76303	3.79834	8.18327	.182482
5.49	30.1401	2.34307	7.40945	165.469	1.76410	3.80065	8.18824	.182149
5.50	30.2500	2.34521	7.41620	166.375	1.76517	3.80295	8.19321	.181818
n	n^2	$\sqrt{n}$	$\sqrt{10\,n}$	n^3	$\sqrt[3]{n}$	$\sqrt[3]{10\,n}$	$\sqrt[3]{100\,n}$	$1/n$

n	n^2	$\sqrt{n}$	$\sqrt{10\,n}$	n^3	$\sqrt[3]{n}$	$\sqrt[3]{10\,n}$	$\sqrt[3]{100\,n}$	$1/n$
5.50	30.2500	2.34521	7.41620	166.375	1.76517	3.80295	8.19321	.181818
5.51	30.3601	2.34734	7.42294	167.284	1.76624	3.80526	8.19818	.181488
5.52	30.4704	2.34947	7.42967	168.197	1.76731	3.80756	8.20313	.181159
5.53	30.5809	2.35160	7.43640	169.112	1.76838	3.80985	8.20808	.180832
5.54	30.6916	2.35372	7.44312	170.031	1.76944	3.81215	8.21303	.180505
5.55	30.8025	2.35584	7.44983	170.954	1.77051	3.81444	8.21797	.180180
5.56	30.9136	2.35797	7.45654	171.880	1.77157	3.81673	8.22290	.179856
5.57	31.0249	2.36008	7.46324	172.809	1.77263	3.81902	8.22783	.179533
5.58	31.1364	2.36220	7.46994	173.741	1.77369	3.82130	8.23275	.179211
5.59	31.2481	2.36432	7.47663	174.677	1.77475	3.82358	8.23766	.178891
5.60	31.3600	2.36643	7.48331	175.616	1.77581	3.82586	8.24257	.178571
5.61	31.4721	2.36854	7.48999	176.558	1.77686	3.82814	8.24747	.178253
5.62	31.5844	2.37065	7.49667	177.504	1.77792	3.83041	8.25237	.177936
5.63	31.6969	2.37276	7.50333	178.454	1.77897	3.83268	8.25726	.177620
5.64	31.8096	2.37487	7.50999	179.406	1.78003	3.83495	8.26215	.177305
5.65	31.9225	2.37697	7.51665	180.362	1.78108	3.83722	8.26703	.176991
5.66	32.0356	2.37908	7.52330	181.321	1.78213	3.83948	8.27190	.176678
5.67	32.1489	2.38118	7.52994	182.284	1.78318	3.84174	8.27677	.176367
5.68	32.2624	2.38328	7.53658	183.250	1.78422	3.84399	8.28164	.176056
5.69	32.3761	2.38537	7.54321	184.220	1.78527	3.84625	8.28649	.175747
5.70	32.4900	2.38747	7.54983	185.193	1.78632	3.84850	8.29134	.175439
5.71	32.6041	2.38956	7.55645	186.169	1.78736	3.85075	8.29619	.175131
5.72	32.7184	2.39165	7.56307	187.149	1.78840	3.85300	8.30103	.174825
5.73	32.8329	2.39374	7.56968	188.133	1.78944	3.85524	8.30587	.174520
5.74	32.9476	2.39583	7.57628	189.119	1.79048	3.85748	8.31069	.174216
5.75	33.0625	2.39792	7.58288	190.109	1.79152	3.85972	8.31552	.173913
5.76	33.1776	2.40000	7.58947	191.103	1.79256	3.86196	8.32034	.173611
5.77	33.2929	2.40208	7.59605	192.100	1.79360	3.86419	8.32515	.173310
5.78	33.4084	2.40416	7.60263	193.101	1.79463	3.86642	8.32995	.173010
5.79	33.5241	2.40624	7.60920	194.105	1.79567	3.86865	8.33476	.172712
5.80	33.6400	2.40832	7.61577	195.112	1.79670	3.87088	8.33955	.172414
5.81	33.7561	2.41039	7.62234	196.123	1.79773	3.87310	8.34434	.172117
5.82	33.8724	2.41247	7.62889	197.137	1.79876	3.87532	8.34913	.171821
5.83	33.9889	2.41454	7.63544	198.155	1.79979	3.87754	8.35390	.171527
5.84	34.1056	2.41661	7.64199	199.177	1.80082	3.87975	8.35868	.171233
5.85	34.2225	2.41868	7.64853	200.202	1.80185	3.88197	8.36345	.170940
5.86	34.3396	2.42074	7.65506	201.230	1.80288	3.88418	8.36821	.170649
5.87	34.4569	2.42281	7.66159	202.262	1.80390	3.88639	8.37297	.170358
5.88	34.5744	2.42487	7.66812	203.297	1.80492	3.88859	8.37772	.170068
5.89	34.6921	2.42693	7.67463	204.336	1.80595	3.89080	8.38247	.169779
5.90	34.8100	2.42899	7.68115	205.379	1.80697	3.89300	8.38721	.169492
5.91	34.9281	2.43105	7.68765	206.425	1.80799	3.89519	8.39194	.169205
5.92	35.0464	2.43311	7.69415	207.475	1.80901	3.89739	8.39667	.168919
5.93	35.1649	2.43516	7.70065	208.528	1.81003	3.89958	8.40140	.168634
5.94	35.2836	2.43721	7.70714	209.585	1.81104	3.90177	8.40612	.168350
5.95	35.4025	2.43926	7.71362	210.645	1.81206	3.90396	8.41083	.168067
5.96	35.5216	2.44131	7.72010	211.709	1.81307	3.90615	8.41554	.167785
5.97	35.6409	2.44336	7.72658	212.776	1.81409	3.90833	8.42025	.167504
5.98	35.7604	2.44540	7.73305	213.847	1.81510	3.91051	8.42494	.167224
5.99	35.8801	2.44745	7.73951	214.922	1.81611	3.91269	8.42964	.166945
6.00	36.0000	2.44949	7.74597	216.000	1.81712	3.91487	8.43433	.166667
n	n^2	$\sqrt{n}$	$\sqrt{10\,n}$	n^3	$\sqrt[3]{n}$	$\sqrt[3]{10\,n}$	$\sqrt[3]{100\,n}$	$1/n$

n	n^2	$\sqrt{n}$	$\sqrt{10\,n}$	n^3	$\sqrt[3]{n}$	$\sqrt[3]{10\,n}$	$\sqrt[3]{100\,n}$	$1/n$
6.00	36.0000	2.44949	7.74597	216.000	1.81712	3.91487	8.43433	.166667
6.01	36.1201	2.45153	7.75242	217.082	1.81813	3.91704	8.43901	.166389
6.02	36.2404	2.45357	7.75887	218.167	1.81914	3.91921	8.44369	.166113
6.03	36.3609	2.45561	7.76531	219.256	1.82014	3.92138	8.44836	.165837
6.04	36.4816	2.45764	7.77174	220.349	1.82115	3.92355	8.45303	.165563
6.05	36.6025	2.45967	7.77817	221.445	1.82215	3.92571	8.45769	.165289
6.06	36.7236	2.46171	7.78460	222.545	1.82316	3.92787	8.46235	.165017
6.07	36.8449	2.46374	7.79102	223.649	1.82416	3.93003	8.46700	.164745
6.08	36.9664	2.46577	7.79744	224.756	1.82516	3.93219	8.47165	.164474
6.09	37.0881	2.46779	7.80385	225.867	1.82616	3.93434	8.47629	.164204
6.10	37.2100	2.46982	7.81025	226.981	1.82716	3.93650	8.48093	.163934
6.11	37.3321	2.47184	7.81665	228.099	1.82816	3.93865	8.48556	.163666
6.12	37.4544	2.47386	7.82304	229.221	1.82915	3.94079	8.49018	.163399
6.13	37.5769	2.47588	7.82943	230.346	1.83015	3.94294	8.49481	.163132
6.14	37.6996	2.47790	7.83582	231.476	1.83115	3.94508	8.49942	.162866
6.15	37.8225	2.47992	7.84219	232.608	1.83214	3.94722	8.50403	.162602
6.16	37.9456	2.48193	7.84857	233.745	1.83313	3.94936	8.50864	.162338
6.17	38.0689	2.48395	7.85493	234.885	1.83412	3.95150	8.51324	.162075
6.18	38.1924	2.48596	7.86130	236.029	1.83511	3.95363	8.51784	.161812
6.19	38.3161	2.48797	7.86766	237.177	1.83610	3.95576	8.52243	.161551
6.20	38.4400	2.48998	7.87401	238.328	1.83709	3.95789	8.52702	.161290
6.21	38.5641	2.49199	7.88036	239.483	1.83808	3.96002	8.53160	.161031
6.22	38.6884	2.49399	7.88670	240.642	1.83906	3.96214	8.53618	.160772
6.23	38.8129	2.49600	7.89303	241.804	1.84005	3.96427	8.54075	.160514
6.24	38.9376	2.49800	7.89937	242.971	1.84103	3.96638	8.54532	.160256
6.25	39.0625	2.50000	7.90569	244.141	1.84202	3.96850	8.54988	.160000
6.26	39.1876	2.50200	7.91202	245.314	1.84300	3.97062	8.55444	.159744
6.27	39.3129	2.50400	7.91833	246.492	1.84398	3.97273	8.55899	.159490
6.28	39.4384	2.50599	7.92465	247.673	1.84496	3.97484	8.56354	.159236
6.29	39.5641	2.50799	7.93095	248.858	1.84594	3.97695	8.56808	.158983
6.30	39.6900	2.50998	7.93725	250.047	1.84691	3.97906	8.57262	.158730
6.31	39.8161	2.51197	7.94355	251.240	1.84789	3.98116	8.57715	.158479
6.32	39.9424	2.51396	7.94984	252.436	1.84887	3.98326	8.58168	.158228
6.33	40.0689	2.51595	7.95613	253.636	1.84984	3.98536	8.58620	.157978
6.34	40.1956	2.51794	7.96241	254.840	1.85082	3.98746	8.59072	.157729
6.35	40.3225	2.51992	7.96869	256.048	1.85179	3.98956	8.59524	.157480
6.36	40.4496	2.52190	7.97496	257.259	1.85276	3.99165	8.59975	.157233
6.37	40.5769	2.52389	7.98123	258.475	1.85373	3.99374	8.60425	.156986
6.38	40.7044	2.52587	7.98749	259.694	1.85470	3.99583	8.60875	.156740
6.39	40.8321	2.52784	7.99375	260.917	1.85567	3.99792	8.61325	.156495
6.40	40.9600	2.52982	8.00000	262.144	1.85664	4.00000	8.61774	.156250
6.41	41.0881	2.53180	8.00625	263.375	1.85760	4.00208	8.62222	.156006
6.42	41.2164	2.53377	8.01249	264.609	1.85857	4.00416	8.62671	.155763
6.43	41.3449	2.53574	8.01873	265.848	1.85953	4.00624	8.63118	.155521
6.44	41.4736	2.53772	8.02496	267.090	1.86050	4.00832	8.63566	.155280
6.45	41.6025	2.53969	8.03119	268.336	1.86146	4.01039	8.64012	.155039
6.46	41.7316	2.54165	8.03741	269.586	1.86242	4.01246	8.64459	.154799
6.47	41.8609	2.54362	8.04363	270.840	1.86338	4.01453	8.64904	.154560
6.48	41.9904	2.54558	8.04984	272.098	1.86434	4.01660	8.65350	.154321
6.49	42.1201	2.54755	8.05605	273.359	1.86530	4.01866	8.65795	.154083
6.50	42.2500	2.54951	8.06226	274.625	1.86626	4.02073	8.66239	.153846
n	n^2	$\sqrt{n}$	$\sqrt{10\,n}$	n^3	$\sqrt[3]{n}$	$\sqrt[3]{10\,n}$	$\sqrt[3]{100\,n}$	$1/n$

n	n^2	$\sqrt{n}$	$\sqrt{10\,n}$	n^3	$\sqrt[3]{n}$	$\sqrt[3]{10\,n}$	$\sqrt[3]{100\,n}$	$1/n$
6.50	42.2500	2.54951	8.06226	274.625	1.86626	4.02073	8.66239	.153846
6.51	42.3801	2.55147	8.06846	275.894	1.86721	4.02279	8.66683	.153610
6.52	42.5104	2.55343	8.07465	277.168	1.86817	4.02485	8.67127	.153374
6.53	42.6409	2.55539	8.08084	278.445	1.86912	4.02690	8.67570	.153139
6.54	42.7716	2.55734	8.08703	279.726	1.87008	4.02896	8.68012	.152905
6.55	42.9025	2.55930	8.09321	281.011	1.87103	4.03101	8.68455	.152672
6.56	43.0336	2.56125	8.09938	282.300	1.87198	4.03306	8.68896	.152439
6.57	43.1649	2.56320	8.10555	283.593	1.87293	4.03511	8.69338	.152207
6.58	43.2964	2.56515	8.11172	284.890	1.87388	4.03715	8.69778	.151976
6.59	43.4281	2.56710	8.11788	286.191	1.87483	4.03920	8.70219	.151745
6.60	43.5600	2.56905	8.12404	287.496	1.87578	4.04124	8.70659	.151515
6.61	43.6921	2.57099	8.13019	288.805	1.87672	4.04328	8.71098	.151286
6.62	43.8244	2.57294	8.13634	290.118	1.87767	4.04532	8.71537	.151057
6.63	43.9569	2.57488	8.14248	291.434	1.87862	4.04735	8.71976	.150830
6.64	44.0896	2.57682	8.14862	292.755	1.87956	4.04939	8.72414	.150602
6.65	44.2225	2.57876	8.15475	294.080	1.88050	4.05142	8.72852	.150376
6.66	44.3556	2.58070	8.16088	295.408	1.88144	4.05345	8.73289	.150150
6.67	44.4889	2.58263	8.16701	296.741	1.88239	4.05548	8.73726	.149925
6.68	44.6224	2.58457	8.17313	298.078	1.88333	4.05750	8.74162	.149701
6.69	44.7561	2.58650	8.17924	299.418	1.88427	4.05953	8.74598	.149477
6.70	44.8900	2.58844	8.18535	300.763	1.88520	4.06155	8.75034	.149254
6.71	45.0241	2.59037	8.19146	302.112	1.88614	4.06357	8.75469	.149031
6.72	45.1584	2.59230	8.19756	303.464	1.88708	4.06559	8.75904	.148810
6.73	45.2929	2.59422	8.20366	304.821	1.88801	4.06760	8.76338	.148588
6.74	45.4276	2.59615	8.20975	306.182	1.88895	4.06961	8.76772	.148368
6.75	45.5625	2.59808	8.21584	307.547	1.88988	4.07163	8.77205	.148148
6.76	45.6976	2.60000	8.22192	308.916	1.89081	4.07364	8.77638	.147929
6.77	45.8329	2.60192	8.22800	310.289	1.89175	4.07564	8.78071	.147710
6.78	45.9684	2.60384	8.23408	311.666	1.89268	4.07765	8.78503	.147493
6.79	46.1041	2.60576	8.24015	313.047	1.89361	4.07965	8.78935	.147275
6.80	46.2400	2.60768	8.24621	314.432	1.89454	4.08166	8.79366	.147059
6.81	46.3761	2.60960	8.25227	315.821	1.89546	4.08365	8.79797	.146843
6.82	46.5124	2.61151	8.25833	317.215	1.89639	4.08565	8.80227	.146628
6.83	46.6489	2.61343	8.26438	318.612	1.89732	4.08765	8.80657	.146413
6.84	46.7856	2.61534	8.27043	320.014	1.89824	4.08964	8.81087	.146199
6.85	46.9225	2.61725	8.27647	321.419	1.89917	4.09163	8.81516	.145985
6.86	47.0596	2.61916	8.28251	322.829	1.90009	4.09362	8.81945	.145773
6.87	47.1969	2.62107	8.28855	324.243	1.90102	4.09561	8.82373	.145560
6.88	47.3344	2.62298	8.29458	325.661	1.90194	4.09760	8.82801	.145349
6.89	47.4721	2.62488	8.30060	327.083	1.90286	4.09958	8.83228	.145138
6.90	47.6100	2.62679	8.30662	328.509	1.90378	4.10157	8.83656	.144928
6.91	47.7481	2.62869	8.31264	329.939	1.90470	4.10355	8.84082	.144718
6.92	47.8864	2.63059	8.31865	331.374	1.90562	4.10552	8.84509	.144509
6.93	48.0249	2.63249	8.32466	332.813	1.90653	4.10750	8.84934	.144300
6.94	48.1636	2.63439	8.33067	334.255	1.90745	4.10948	8.85360	.144092
6.95	48.3025	2.63629	8.33667	335.702	1.90837	4.11145	8.85785	.143885
6.96	48.4416	2.63818	8.34266	337.154	1.90928	4.11342	8.86210	.143678
6.97	48.5809	2.64008	8.34865	338.609	1.91019	4.11539	8.86634	.143472
6.98	48.7204	2.64197	8.35464	340.068	1.91111	4.11736	8.87058	.143266
6.99	48.8601	2.64386	8.36062	341.532	1.91202	4.11932	8.87481	.143062
7.00	49.0000	2.64575	8.36660	343.000	1.91293	4.12129	8.87904	.142857
n	n^2	$\sqrt{n}$	$\sqrt{10\,n}$	n^3	$\sqrt[3]{n}$	$\sqrt[3]{10\,n}$	$\sqrt[3]{100\,n}$	$1/n$

n	n^2	$\sqrt{n}$	$\sqrt{10\,n}$	n^3	$\sqrt[3]{n}$	$\sqrt[3]{10\,n}$	$\sqrt[3]{100\,n}$	$1/n$
7.00	49.0000	2.64575	8.36660	343.000	1.91293	4.12129	8.87904	.142857
7.01	49.1401	2.64764	8.37257	344.472	1.91384	4.12325	8.88327	.142653
7.02	49.2804	2.64953	8.37854	345.948	1.91475	4.12521	8.88749	.142450
7.03	49.4209	2.65141	8.38451	347.429	1.91566	4.12716	8.89171	.142248
7.04	49.5616	2.65330	8.39047	348.914	1.91657	4.12912	8.89592	.142045
7.05	49.7025	2.65518	8.39643	350.403	1.91747	4.13107	8.90013	.141844
7.06	49.8436	2.65707	8.40238	351.896	1.91838	4.13303	8.90434	.141643
7.07	49.9849	2.65895	8.40833	353.393	1.91929	4.13498	8.90854	.141443
7.08	50.1264	2.66083	8.41427	354.895	1.92019	4.13693	8.91274	.141243
7.09	50.2681	2.66271	8.42021	356.401	1.92109	4.13887	8.91693	.141044
7.10	50.4100	2.66458	8.42615	357.911	1.92200	4.14082	8.92112	.140845
7.11	50.5521	2.66646	8.43208	359.425	1.92290	4.14276	8.92531	.140647
7.12	50.6944	2.66833	8.43801	360.944	1.92380	4.14470	8.92949	.140449
7.13	50.8369	2.67021	8.44393	362.467	1.92470	4.14664	8.93367	.140252
7.14	50.9796	2.67208	8.44985	363.994	1.92560	4.14858	8.93784	.140056
7.15	51.1225	2.67395	8.45577	365.526	1.92650	4.15052	8.94201	.139860
7.16	51.2656	2.67582	8.46168	367.062	1.92740	4.15245	8.94618	.139665
7.17	51.4089	2.67769	8.46759	368.602	1.92829	4.15438	8.95034	.139470
7.18	51.5524	2.67955	8.47349	370.146	1.92919	4.15631	8.95450	.139276
7.19	51.6961	2.68142	8.47939	371.695	1.93008	4.15824	8.95866	.139082
7.20	51.8400	2.68328	8.48528	373.248	1.93098	4.16017	8.96281	.138889
7.21	51.9841	2.68514	8.49117	374.805	1.93187	4.16209	8.96696	.138696
7.22	52.1284	2.68701	8.49706	376.367	1.93277	4.16402	8.97110	.138504
7.23	52.2729	2.68887	8.50294	377.933	1.93366	4.16594	8.97524	.138313
7.24	52.4176	2.69072	8.50882	379.503	1.93455	4.16786	8.97938	.138122
7.25	52.5625	2.69258	8.51469	381.078	1.93544	4.16978	8.98351	.137931
7.26	52.7076	2.69444	8.52056	382.657	1.93633	4.17169	8.98764	.137741
7.27	52.8529	2.69629	8.52643	384.241	1.93722	4.17361	8.99176	.137552
7.28	52.9984	2.69815	8.53229	385.828	1.93810	4.17552	8.99588	.137363
7.29	53.1441	2.70000	8.53815	387.420	1.93899	4.17743	9.00000	.137174
7.30	53.2900	2.70185	8.54400	389.017	1.93988	4.17934	9.00411	.136986
7.31	53.4361	2.70370	8.54985	390.618	1.94076	4.18125	9.00822	.136799
7.32	53.5824	2.70555	8.55570	392.223	1.94165	4.18315	9.01233	.136612
7.33	53.7289	2.70740	8.56154	393.833	1.94253	4.18506	9.01643	.136426
7.34	53.8756	2.70924	8.56738	395.447	1.94341	4.18696	9.02053	.136240
7.35	54.0225	2.71109	8.57321	397.065	1.94430	4.18886	9.02462	.136054
7.36	54.1696	2.71293	8.57904	398.688	1.94518	4.19076	9.02871	.135870
7.37	54.3169	2.71477	8.58487	400.316	1.94606	4.19266	9.03280	.135685
7.38	54.4644	2.71662	8.59069	401.947	1.94694	4.19455	9.03689	.135501
7.39	54.6121	2.71846	8.59651	403.583	1.94782	4.19644	9.04097	.135318
7.40	54.7600	2.72029	8.60233	405.224	1.94870	4.19834	9.04504	.135135
7.41	54.9081	2.72213	8.60814	406.869	1.94957	4.20023	9.04911	.134953
7.42	55.0564	2.72397	8.61394	408.518	1.95045	4.20212	9.05318	.134771
7.43	55.2049	2.72580	8.61974	410.172	1.95132	4.20400	9.05725	.134590
7.44	55.3536	2.72764	8.62554	411.831	1.95220	4.20589	9.06131	.134409
7.45	55.5025	2.72947	8.63134	413.494	1.95307	4.20777	9.06537	.134228
7.46	55.6516	2.73130	8.63713	415.161	1.95395	4.20965	9.06942	.134048
7.47	55.8009	2.73313	8.64292	416.833	1.95482	4.21153	9.07347	.133869
7.48	55.9504	2.73496	8.64870	418.509	1.95569	4.21341	9.07752	.133690
7.49	56.1001	2.73679	8.65448	420.190	1.95656	4.21529	9.08156	.133511
7.50	56.2500	2.73861	8.66025	421.875	1.95743	4.21716	9.08560	.133333
n	n^2	$\sqrt{n}$	$\sqrt{10\,n}$	n^3	$\sqrt[3]{n}$	$\sqrt[3]{10\,n}$	$\sqrt[3]{100\,n}$	$1/n$

n	n^2	$\sqrt{n}$	$\sqrt{10\,n}$	n^3	$\sqrt[3]{n}$	$\sqrt[3]{10\,n}$	$\sqrt[3]{100\,n}$	$1/n$
7.50	56.2500	2.73861	8.66025	421.875	1.95743	4.21716	9.08560	.133333
7.51	56.4001	2.74044	8.66603	423.565	1.95830	4.21904	9.08964	.133156
7.52	56.5504	2.74226	8.67179	425.259	1.95917	4.22091	9.09367	.132979
7.53	56.7009	2.74408	8.67756	426.958	1.96004	4.22278	9.09770	.132802
7.54	56.8516	2.74591	8.68332	428.661	1.96091	4.22465	9.10173	.132626
7.55	57.0025	2.74773	8.68907	430.369	1.96177	4.22651	9.10575	.132450
7.56	57.1536	2.74955	8.69483	432.081	1.96264	4.22838	9.10977	.132275
7.57	57.3049	2.75136	8.70057	433.798	1.96350	4.23024	9.11378	.132100
7.58	57.4564	2.75318	8.70632	435.520	1.96437	4.23210	9.11779	.131926
7.59	57.6081	2.75500	8.71206	437.245	1.96523	4.23396	9.12180	.131752
7.60	57.7600	2.75681	8.71780	438.976	1.96610	4.23582	9.12581	.131579
7.61	57.9121	2.75862	8.72353	440.711	1.96696	4.23768	9.12981	.131406
7.62	58.0644	2.76043	8.72926	442.451	1.96782	4.23954	9.13380	.131234
7.63	58.2169	2.76225	8.73499	444.195	1.96868	4.24139	9.13780	.131062
7.64	58.3696	2.76405	8.74071	445.944	1.96954	4.24324	9.14179	.130890
7.65	58.5225	2.76586	8.74643	447.698	1.97040	4.24509	9.14577	.130719
7.66	58.6756	2.76767	8.75214	449.455	1.97126	4.24694	9.14976	.130548
7.67	58.8289	2.76948	8.75785	451.218	1.97211	4.24879	9.15374	.130378
7.68	58.9824	2.77128	8.76356	452.985	1.97297	4.25063	9.15771	.130208
7.69	59.1361	2.77308	8.76926	454.757	1.97383	4.25248	9.16169	.130039
7.70	59.2900	2.77489	8.77496	456.533	1.97468	4.25432	9.16566	.129870
7.71	59.4441	2.77669	8.78066	458.314	1.97554	4.25616	9.16962	.129702
7.72	59.5984	2.77849	8.78635	460.100	1.97639	4.25800	9.17359	.129534
7.73	59.7529	2.78029	8.79204	461.890	1.97724	4.25984	9.17754	.129366
7.74	59.9076	2.78209	8.79773	463.685	1.97809	4.26167	9.18150	.129199
7.75	60.0625	2.78388	8.80341	465.484	1.97895	4.26351	9.18545	.129032
7.76	60.2176	2.78568	8.80909	467.289	1.97980	4.26534	9.18940	.128866
7.77	60.3729	2.78747	8.81476	469.097	1.98065	4.26717	9.19335	.128700
7.78	60.5284	2.78927	8.82043	470.911	1.98150	4.26900	9.19729	.128535
7.79	60.6841	2.79106	8.82610	472.729	1.98234	4.27083	9.20123	.128370
7.80	60.8400	2.79285	8.83176	474.552	1.98319	4.27266	9.20516	.128205
7.81	60.9961	2.79464	8.83742	476.380	1.98404	4.27448	9.20910	.128041
7.82	61.1524	2.79643	8.84308	478.212	1.98489	4.27631	9.21302	.127877
7.83	61.3089	2.79821	8.84873	480.049	1.98573	4.27813	9.21695	.127714
7.84	61.4656	2.80000	8.85438	481.890	1.98658	4.27995	9.22087	.127551
7.85	61.6225	2.80179	8.86002	483.737	1.98742	4.28177	9.22479	.127389
7.86	61.7796	2.80357	8.86566	485.588	1.98826	4.28359	9.22871	.127226
7.87	61.9369	2.80535	8.87130	487.443	1.98911	4.28540	9.23262	.127065
7.88	62.0944	2.80713	8.87694	489.304	1.98995	4.28722	9.23653	.126904
7.89	62.2521	2.80891	8.88257	491.169	1.99079	4.28903	9.24043	.126743
7.90	62.4100	2.81069	8.88819	493.039	1.99163	4.29084	9.24434	.126582
7.91	62.5681	2.81247	8.89382	494.914	1.99247	4.29265	9.24823	.126422
7.92	62.7264	2.81425	8.89944	496.793	1.99331	4.29446	9.25213	.126263
7.93	62.8849	2.81603	8.90505	498.677	1.99415	4.29627	9.25602	.126103
7.94	63.0436	2.81780	8.91067	500.566	1.99499	4.29807	9.25991	.125945
7.95	63.2025	2.81957	8.91628	502.460	1.99582	4.29987	9.26380	.125786
7.96	63.3616	2.82135	8.92188	504.358	1.99666	4.30168	9.26768	.125628
7.97	63.5209	2.82312	8.92749	506.262	1.99750	4.30348	9.27156	.125471
7.98	63.6804	2.82489	8.93308	508.170	1.99833	4.30528	9.27544	.125313
7.99	63.8401	2.82666	8.93868	510.082	1.99917	4.30707	9.27931	.125156
8.00	64.0000	2.82843	8.94427	512.000	2.00000	4.30887	9.28318	.125000
n	n^2	$\sqrt{n}$	$\sqrt{10\,n}$	n^3	$\sqrt[3]{n}$	$\sqrt[3]{10\,n}$	$\sqrt[3]{100\,n}$	$1/n$

n	n^2	$\sqrt{n}$	$\sqrt{10\,n}$	n^3	$\sqrt[3]{n}$	$\sqrt[3]{10\,n}$	$\sqrt[3]{100\,n}$	$1/n$
8.00	64.0000	2.82843	8.94427	512.000	2.00000	4.30887	9.28318	.125000
8.01	64.1601	2.83019	8.94986	513.922	2.00083	4.31066	9.28704	.124844
8.02	64.3204	2.83196	8.95545	515.850	2.00167	4.31246	9.29091	.124688
8.03	64.4809	2.83373	8.96103	517.782	2.00250	4.31425	9.29477	.124533
8.04	64.6416	2.83549	8.96660	519.718	2.00333	4.31604	9.29862	.124378
8.05	64.8025	2.83725	8.97218	521.660	2.00416	4.31783	9.30248	.124224
8.06	64.9636	2.83901	8.97775	523.607	2.00499	4.31961	9.30633	.124069
8.07	65.1249	2.84077	8.98332	525.558	2.00582	4.32140	9.31018	.123916
8.08	65.2864	2.84253	8.98888	527.514	2.00664	4.32318	9.31402	.123762
8.09	65.4481	2.84429	8.99444	529.475	2.00747	4.32497	9.31786	.123609
8.10	65.6100	2.84605	9.00000	531.441	2.00830	4.32675	9.32170	.123457
8.11	65.7721	2.84781	9.00555	533.412	2.00912	4.32853	9.32553	.123305
8.12	65.9344	2.84956	9.01110	535.387	2.00995	4.33031	9.32936	.123153
8.13	66.0969	2.85132	9.01665	537.368	2.01078	4.33208	9.33319	.123001
8.14	66.2596	2.85307	9.02219	539.353	2.01160	4.33386	9.33702	.122850
8.15	66.4225	2.85482	9.02774	541.343	2.01242	4.33563	9.34084	.122699
8.16	66.5856	2.85657	9.03327	543.338	2.01325	4.33741	9.34466	.122549
8.17	66.7489	2.85832	9.03881	545.339	2.01407	4.33918	9.34847	.122399
8.18	66.9124	2.86007	9.04434	547.343	2.01489	4.34095	9.35229	.122249
8.19	67.0761	2.86182	9.04986	549.353	2.01571	4.34271	9.35610	.122100
8.20	67.2400	2.86356	9.05539	551.368	2.01653	4.34448	9.35990	.121951
8.21	67.4041	2.86531	9.06091	553.388	2.01735	4.34625	9.36370	.121803
8.22	67.5684	2.86705	9.06642	555.412	2.01817	4.34801	9.36751	.121655
8.23	67.7329	2.86880	9.07193	557.442	2.01899	4.34977	9.37130	.121507
8.24	67.8976	2.87054	9.07744	559.476	2.01980	4.35153	9.37510	.121359
8.25	68.0625	2.87228	9.08295	561.516	2.02062	4.35329	9.37889	.121212
8.26	68.2276	2.87402	9.08845	563.560	2.02144	4.35505	9.38268	.121065
8.27	68.3929	2.87576	9.09395	565.609	2.02225	4.35681	9.38646	.120919
8.28	68.5584	2.87750	9.09945	567.664	2.02307	4.35856	9.39024	.120773
8.29	68.7241	2.87924	9.10494	569.723	2.02388	4.36032	9.39402	.120627
8.30	68.8900	2.88097	9.11043	571.787	2.02469	4.36207	9.39780	.120482
8.31	69.0561	2.88271	9.11592	573.856	2.02551	4.36382	9.40157	.120337
8.32	69.2224	2.88444	9.12140	575.930	2.02632	4.36557	9.40534	.120192
8.33	69.3889	2.88617	9.12688	578.010	2.02713	4.36732	9.40911	.120048
8.34	69.5556	2.88791	9.13236	580.094	2.02794	4.36907	9.41287	.119904
8.35	69.7225	2.88964	9.13783	582.183	2.02875	4.37081	9.41663	.119760
8.36	69.8896	2.89137	9.14330	584.277	2.02956	4.37256	9.42039	.119617
8.37	70.0569	2.89310	9.14877	586.376	2.03037	4.37430	9.42414	.119474
8.38	70.2244	2.89482	9.15423	588.480	2.03118	4.37604	9.42789	.119332
8.39	70.3921	2.89655	9.15969	590.590	2.03199	4.37778	9.43164	.119190
8.40	70.5600	2.89828	9.16515	592.704	2.03279	4.37952	9.43539	.119048
8.41	70.7281	2.90000	9.17061	594.823	2.03360	4.38126	9.43913	.118906
8.42	70.8964	2.90172	9.17606	596.948	2.03440	4.38299	9.44287	.118765
8.43	71.0649	2.90345	9.18150	599.077	2.03521	4.38473	9.44661	.118624
8.44	71.2336	2.90517	9.18695	601.212	2.03601	4.38646	9.45034	.118483
8.45	71.4025	2.90689	9.19239	603.351	2.03682	4.38819	9.45407	.118343
8.46	71.5716	2.90861	9.19783	605.496	2.03762	4.38992	9.45780	.118203
8.47	71.7409	2.91033	9.20326	607.645	2.03842	4.39165	9.46152	.118064
8.48	71.9104	2.91204	9.20869	609.800	2.03923	4.39338	9.46525	.117925
8.49	72.0801	2.91376	9.21412	611.960	2.04003	4.39510	9.46897	.117786
8.50	72.2500	2.91548	9.21954	614.125	2.04083	4.39683	9.47268	.117647
n	n^2	$\sqrt{n}$	$\sqrt{10\,n}$	n^3	$\sqrt[3]{n}$	$\sqrt[3]{10\,n}$	$\sqrt[3]{100\,n}$	$1/n$

n	n^2	$\sqrt{n}$	$\sqrt{10\,n}$	n^3	$\sqrt[3]{n}$	$\sqrt[3]{10\,n}$	$\sqrt[3]{100\,n}$	$1/n$
8.50	72.2500	2.91548	9.21954	614.125	2.04083	4.39683	9.47268	.117647
8.51	72.4201	2.91719	9.22497	616.295	2.04163	4.39855	9.47640	.117509
8.52	72.5904	2.91890	9.23038	618.470	2.04243	4.40028	9.48011	.117371
8.53	72.7609	2.92062	9.23580	620.650	2.04323	4.40200	9.48381	.117233
8.54	72.9316	2.92233	9.24121	622.836	2.04402	4.40372	9.48752	.117096
8.55	73.1025	2.92404	9.24662	625.026	2.04482	4.40543	9.49122	.116959
8.56	73.2736	2.92575	9.25203	627.222	2.04562	4.40715	9.49492	.116822
8.57	73.4449	2.92746	9.25743	629.423	2.04641	4.40887	9.49861	.116686
8.58	73.6164	2.92916	9.26283	631.629	2.04721	4.41058	9.50231	.116550
8.59	73.7881	2.93087	9.26823	633.840	2.04801	4.41229	9.50600	.116414
8.60	73.9600	2.93258	9.27362	636.056	2.04880	4.41400	9.50969	.116279
8.61	74.1321	2.93428	9.27901	638.277	2.04959	4.41571	9.51337	.116144
8.62	74.3044	2.93598	9.28440	640.504	2.05039	4.41742	9.51705	.116009
8.63	74.4769	2.93769	9.28978	642.736	2.05118	4.41913	9.52073	.115875
8.64	74.6496	2.93939	9.29516	644.973	2.05197	4.42084	9.52441	.115741
8.65	74.8225	2.94109	9.30054	647.215	2.05276	4.42254	9.52808	.115607
8.66	74.9956	2.94279	9.30591	649.462	2.05355	4.42425	9.53175	.115473
8.67	75.1689	2.94449	9.31128	651.714	2.05434	4.42595	9.53542	.115340
8.68	75.3424	2.94618	9.31665	653.972	2.05513	4.42765	9.53908	.115207
8.69	75.5161	2.94788	9.32202	656.235	2.05592	4.42935	9.54274	.115075
8.70	75.6900	2.94958	9.32738	658.503	2.05671	4.43105	9.54640	.114943
8.71	75.8641	2.95127	9.33274	660.776	2.05750	4.43274	9.55006	.114811
8.72	76.0384	2.95296	9.33809	663.055	2.05828	4.43444	9.55371	.114679
8.73	76.2129	2.95466	9.34345	665.339	2.05907	4.43613	9.55736	.114548
8.74	76.3876	2.95635	9.34880	667.628	2.05986	4.43783	9.56101	.114416
8.75	76.5625	2.95804	9.35414	669.922	2.06064	4.43952	9.56466	.114286
8.76	76.7376	2.95973	9.35949	672.221	2.06143	4.44121	9.56830	.114155
8.77	76.9129	2.96142	9.36483	674.526	2.06221	4.44290	9.57194	.114025
8.78	77.0884	2.96311	9.37017	676.836	2.06299	4.44459	9.57557	.113895
8.79	77.2641	2.96479	9.37550	679.151	2.06378	4.44627	9.57921	.113766
8.80	77.4400	2.96648	9.38083	681.472	2.06456	4.44796	9.58284	.113636
8.81	77.6161	2.96816	9.38616	683.798	2.06534	4.44964	9.58647	.113507
8.82	77.7924	2.96985	9.39149	686.129	2.06612	4.45133	9.59009	.113379
8.83	77.9689	2.97153	9.39681	688.465	2.06690	4.45301	9.59372	.113250
8.84	78.1456	2.97321	9.40213	690.807	2.06768	4.45469	9.59734	.113122
8.85	78.3225	2.97489	9.40744	693.154	2.06846	4.45637	9.60095	.112994
8.86	78.4996	2.97658	9.41276	695.506	2.06924	4.45805	9.60457	.112867
8.87	78.6769	2.97825	9.41807	697.864	2.07002	4.45972	9.60818	.112740
8.88	78.8544	2.97993	9.42338	700.227	2.07080	4.46140	9.61179	.112613
8.89	79.0321	2.98161	9.42868	702.595	2.07157	4.46307	9.61540	.112486
8.90	79.2100	2.98329	9.43398	704.969	2.07235	4.46475	9.61900	.112360
8.91	79.3881	2.98496	9.43928	707.348	2.07313	4.46642	9.62260	.112233
8.92	79.5664	2.98664	9.44458	709.732	2.07390	4.46809	9.62620	.112108
8.93	79.7449	2.98831	9.44987	712.122	2.07468	4.46976	9.62980	.111982
8.94	79.9236	2.98998	9.45516	714.517	2.07545	4.47142	9.63339	.111857
8.95	80.1025	2.99166	9.46044	716.917	2.07622	4.47309	9.63698	.111732
8.96	80.2816	2.99333	9.46573	719.323	2.07700	4.47476	9.64057	.111607
8.97	80.4609	2.99500	9.47101	721.734	2.07777	4.47642	9.64415	.111483
8.98	80.6404	2.99666	9.47629	724.151	2.07854	4.47808	9.64774	.111359
8.99	80.8201	2.99833	9.48156	726.573	2.07931	4.47974	9.65132	.111235
9.00	81.0000	3.00000	9.48683	729.000	2.08008	4.48140	9.65489	.111111
n	n^2	$\sqrt{n}$	$\sqrt{10\,n}$	n^3	$\sqrt[3]{n}$	$\sqrt[3]{10\,n}$	$\sqrt[3]{100\,n}$	$1/n$

n	n^2	$\sqrt{n}$	$\sqrt{10n}$	n^3	$\sqrt[3]{n}$	$\sqrt[3]{10n}$	$\sqrt[3]{100n}$	$1/n$
9.00	81.0000	3.00000	9.48683	729.000	2.08008	4.48140	9.65489	.111111
9.01	81.1801	3.00167	9.49210	731.433	2.08085	4.48306	9.65847	.110988
9.02	81.3604	3.00333	9.49737	733.871	2.08162	4.48472	9.66204	.110865
9.03	81.5409	3.00500	9.50263	736.314	2.08239	4.48638	9.66561	.110742
9.04	81.7216	3.00666	9.50789	738.763	2.08316	4.48803	9.66918	.110619
9.05	81.9025	3.00832	9.51315	741.218	2.08393	4.48969	9.67274	.110497
9.06	82.0836	3.00998	9.51840	743.677	2.08470	4.49134	9.67630	.110375
9.07	82.2649	3.01164	9.52365	746.143	2.08546	4.49299	9.67986	.110254
9.08	82.4464	3.01330	9.52890	748.613	2.08623	4.49464	9.68342	.110132
9.09	82.6281	3.01496	9.53415	751.089	2.08699	4.49629	9.68697	.110011
9.10	82.8100	3.01662	9.53939	753.571	2.08776	4.49794	9.69052	.109890
9.11	82.9921	3.01828	9.54463	756.058	2.08852	4.49959	9.69407	.109769
9.12	83.1744	3.01993	9.54987	758.551	2.08929	4.50123	9.69762	.109649
9.13	83.3569	3.02159	9.55510	761.048	2.09005	4.50288	9.70116	.109529
9.14	83.5396	3.02324	9.56033	763.552	2.09081	4.50452	9.70470	.109409
9.15	83.7225	3.02490	9.56556	766.061	2.09158	4.50616	9.70824	.109290
9.16	83.9056	3.02655	9.57079	768.575	2.09234	4.50781	9.71177	.109170
9.17	84.0889	3.02820	9.57601	771.095	2.09310	4.50945	9.71531	.109051
9.18	84.2724	3.02985	9.58123	773.621	2.09386	4.51108	9.71884	.108932
9.19	84.4561	3.03150	9.58645	776.152	2.09462	4.51272	9.72236	.108814
9.20	84.6400	3.03315	9.59166	778.688	2.09538	4.51436	9.72589	.108696
9.21	84.8241	3.03480	9.59687	781.230	2.09614	4.51599	9.72941	.108578
9.22	85.0084	3.03645	9.60208	783.777	2.09690	4.51763	9.73293	.108460
9.23	85.1929	3.03809	9.60729	786.330	2.09765	4.51926	9.73645	108342
9.24	85.3776	3.03974	9.61249	788.889	2.09841	4.52089	9.73996	.108225
9.25	85.5625	3.04138	9.61769	791.453	2.09917	4.52252	9.74348	.108108
9.26	85.7476	3.04302	9.62289	794.023	2.09992	4.52415	9.74699	.107991
9.27	85.9329	3.04467	9.62808	796.598	2.10068	4.52578	9.75049	.107875
9.28	86.1184	3.04631	9.63328	799.179	2.10144	4.52740	9.75400	.107759
9.29	86.3041	3.04795	9.63846	801.765	2.10219	4.52903	9.75750	.107643
9.30	86.4900	3.04959	9.64365	804.357	2.10294	4.53065	9.76100	.107527
9.31	86.6761	3.05123	9.64883	806.954	2.10370	4.53228	9.76450	.107411
9.32	86.8624	3.05287	9.65401	809.558	2.10445	4.53390	9.76799	.107296
9.33	87.0489	3.05450	9.65919	812.166	2.10520	4.53552	9.77148	.107181
9.34	87.2356	3.05614	9.66437	814.781	2.10595	4.53714	9.77497	.107066
9.35	87.4225	3.05778	9.66954	817.400	2.10671	4.53876	9.77846	.106952
9.36	87.6096	3.05941	9.67471	820.026	2.10746	4.54038	9.78195	.106838
9.37	87.7969	3.06105	9.67988	822.657	2.10821	4.54199	9.78543	.106724
9.38	87.9844	3.06268	9.68504	825.294	2.10896	4.54361	9.78891	.106610
9.39	88.1721	3.06431	9.69020	827.936	2.10971	4.54522	9.79239	.106496
9.40	88.3600	3.06594	9.69536	830.584	2.11045	4.54684	9.79586	.106383
9.41	88.5481	3.06757	9.70052	833.238	2.11120	4.54845	9.79933	.106270
9.42	88.7364	3.06920	9.70567	835.897	2.11195	4.55006	9.80280	.106157
9.43	88.9249	3.07083	9.71082	838.562	2.11270	4.55167	9.80627	.106045
9.44	89.1136	3.07246	9.71597	841.232	2.11344	4.55328	9.80974	.105932
9.45	89.3025	3.07409	9.72111	843.909	2.11419	4.55488	9.81320	.105820
9.46	89.4916	3.07571	9.72625	846.591	2.11494	4.55649	9.81666	.105708
9.47	89.6809	3.07734	9.73139	849.278	2.11568	4.55809	9.82012	.105597
9.48	89.8704	3.07896	9.73653	851.971	2.11642	4.55970	9.82357	.105485
9.49	90.0601	3.08058	9.74166	854.670	2.11717	4.56130	9.82703	.105374
9.50	90.2500	3.08221	9.74679	857.375	2.11791	4.56290	9.83048	.105263
n	n^2	$\sqrt{n}$	$\sqrt{10n}$	n^3	$\sqrt[3]{n}$	$\sqrt[3]{10n}$	$\sqrt[3]{100n}$	$1/n$

n	n^2	$\sqrt{n}$	$\sqrt{10\,n}$	n^3	$\sqrt[3]{n}$	$\sqrt[3]{10\,n}$	$\sqrt[3]{100\,n}$	$1/n$
9.50	90.2500	3.08221	9.74679	857.375	2.11791	4.56290	9.83048	.105263
9.51	90.4401	3.08383	9.75192	860.085	2.11865	4.56450	9.83392	.105152
9.52	90.6304	3.08545	9.75705	862.801	2.11940	4.56610	9.83737	.105042
9.53	90.8209	3.08707	9.76217	865.523	2.12014	4.56770	9.84081	.104932
9.54	91.0116	3.08869	9.76729	868.251	2.12088	4.56930	9.84425	.104822
9.55	91.2025	3.09031	9.77241	870.984	2.12162	4.57089	9.84769	.104712
9.56	91.3936	3.09192	9.77753	873.723	2.12236	4.57249	9.85113	.104603
9.57	91.5849	3.09354	9.78264	876.467	2.12310	4.57408	9.85456	.104493
9.58	91.7764	3.09516	9.78775	879.218	2.12384	4.57567	9.85799	.104384
9.59	91.9681	3.09677	9.79285	881.974	2.12458	4.57727	9.86142	.104275
9.60	92.1600	3.09839	9.79796	884.736	2.12532	4.57886	9.86485	.104167
9.61	92.3521	3.10000	9.80306	887.504	2.12605	4.58045	9.86827	.104058
9.62	92.5444	3.10161	9.80816	890.277	2.12679	4.58204	9.87169	.103950
9.63	92.7369	3.10322	9.81326	893.056	2.12753	4.58362	9.87511	.103842
9.64	92.9296	3.10483	9.81835	895.841	2.12826	4.58521	9.87853	.103734
9.65	93.1225	3.10644	9.82344	898.632	2.12900	4.58679	9.88195	.103627
9.66	93.3156	3.10805	9.82853	901.429	2.12974	4.58838	9.88536	.103520
9.67	93.5089	3.10966	9.83362	904.231	2.13047	4.58996	9.88877	.103413
9.68	93.7024	3.11127	9.83870	907.039	2.13120	4.59154	9.89217	.103306
9.69	93.8961	3.11288	9.84378	909.853	2.13194	4.59312	9.89558	.103199
9.70	94.0900	3.11448	9.84886	912.673	2.13267	4.59470	9.89898	.103093
9.71	94.2841	3.11609	9.85393	915.499	2.13340	4.59628	9.90238	.102987
9.72	94.4784	3.11769	9.85901	918.330	2.13414	4.59786	9.90578	.102881
9.73	94.6729	3.11929	9.86408	921.167	2.13487	4.59943	9.90918	.102775
9.74	94.8676	3.12090	9.86914	924.010	2.13560	4.60101	9.91257	.102669
9.75	95.0625	3.12250	9.87421	926.859	2.13633	4.60258	9.91596	.102564
9.76	95.2576	3.12410	9.87927	929.714	2.13706	4.60416	9.91935	.102459
9.77	95.4529	3.12570	9.88433	932.575	2.13779	4.60573	9.92274	.102354
9.78	95.6484	3.12730	9.88939	935.441	2.13852	4.60730	9.92612	.102249
9.79	95.8441	3.12890	9.89444	938.314	2.13925	4.60887	9.92950	.102145
9.80	96.0400	3.13050	9.89949	941.192	2.13997	4.61044	9.93288	.102041
9.81	96.2361	3.13209	9.90454	944.076	2.14070	4.61200	9.93626	.101937
9.82	96.4324	3.13369	9.90959	946.966	2.14143	4.61357	9.93964	.101833
9.83	96.6289	3.13528	9.91464	949.862	2.14216	4.61514	9.94301	.101729
9.84	96.8256	3.13688	9.91968	952.764	2.14288	4.61670	9.94638	.101626
9.85	97.0225	3.13847	9.92472	955.672	2.14361	4.61826	9.94975	.101523
9.86	97.2196	3.14006	9.92975	958.585	2.14433	4.61983	9.95311	.101420
9.87	97.4169	3.14166	9.93479	961.505	2.14506	4.62139	9.95648	.101317
9.88	97.6144	3.14325	9.93982	964.430	2.14578	4.62295	9.95984	.101215
9.89	97.8121	3.14484	9.94485	967.362	2.14651	4.62451	9.96320	.101112
9.90	98.0100	3.14643	9.94987	970.299	2.14723	4.62607	9.96655	.101010
9.91	98.2081	3.14802	9.95490	973.242	2.14795	4.62762	9.96991	.100908
9.92	98.4064	3.14960	9.95992	976.191	2.14867	4.62918	9.97326	.100806
9.93	98.6049	3.15119	9.96494	979.147	2.14940	4.63073	9.97661	.100705
9.94	98.8036	3.15278	9.96995	982.108	2.15012	4.63229	9.97996	.100604
9.95	99.0025	3.15436	9.97497	985.075	2.15084	4.63384	9.98331	.100503
9.96	99.2016	3.15595	9.97998	988.048	2.15156	4.63539	9.98665	.100402
9.97	99.4009	3.15753	9.98499	991.027	2.15228	4.63694	9.98999	.100301
9.98	99.6004	3.15911	9.98999	994.012	2.15300	4.63849	9.99333	.100200
9.99	99.8001	3.16070	9.99500	997.003	2.15372	4.64004	9.99667	.100100
10.00	100.000	3.16228	10.0000	1000.00	2.15443	4.64159	10.0000	.100000
n	n^2	$\sqrt{n}$	$\sqrt{10\,n}$	n^3	$\sqrt[3]{n}$	$\sqrt[3]{10\,n}$	$\sqrt[3]{100\,n}$	$1/n$

Lengths of Arc for Radius of 1

Degrees						Minutes		Seconds	
0°	0.00000 00	60°	1.04719 76	120°	2.09439 51	0	0.00000 00	0	0.00000 00
1	0.01745 33	61	1.06465 08	121	2.11184 84	1	0.00029 09	1	0.00000 48
2	0.03490 66	62	1.08210 41	122	2.12930 17	2	0.00058 18	2	0.00000 97
3	0.05235 99	63	1.09955 74	123	2.14675 50	3	0.00087 27	3	0.00001 45
4	0.06981 32	64	1.11701 07	124	2.16420 83	4	0.00116 36	4	0.00001 94
5	0.08726 65	65	1.13446 40	125	2.18166 16	5	0.00145 44	5	0.00002 42
6	0.10471 98	66	1.15191 73	126	2.19911 49	6	0.00174 53	6	0.00002 91
7	0.12217 30	67	1.16937 06	127	2.21656 82	7	0.00203 62	7	0.00003 39
8	0.13962 63	68	1.18682 39	128	2.23402 14	8	0.00232 71	8	0.00003 88
9	0.15707 96	69	1.20427 72	129	2.25147 47	9	0.00261 80	9	0.00004 36
10	0.17453 29	70	1.22173 05	130	2.26892 80	10	0.00290 89	10	0.00004 85
11	0.19198 62	71	1.23918 38	131	2.28638 13	11	0.00319 98	11	0.00005 33
12	0.20943 95	72	1.25663 71	132	2.30383 46	12	0.00349 07	12	0.00005 82
13	0.22689 28	73	1.27409 04	133	2.32128 79	13	0.00378 15	13	0.00006 30
14	0.24434 61	74	1.29154 36	134	2.33874 12	14	0.00407 24	14	0.00006 79
15	0.26179 94	75	1.30899 69	135	2.35619 45	15	0.00436 33	15	0.00007 27
16	0.27925 27	76	1.32645 02	136	2.37364 78	16	0.00465 42	16	0.00007 76
17	0.29670 60	77	1.34390 35	137	2.39110 11	17	0.00494 51	17	0.00008 24
18	0.31415 93	78	1.36135 68	138	2.40855 44	18	0.00523 60	18	0.00008 73
19	0.33161 26	79	1.37881 01	139	2.42600 77	19	0.00552 69	19	0.00009 21
20	0.34906 59	80	1.39626 34	140	2.44346 10	20	0.00581 78	20	0.00009 70
21	0.36651 91	81	1.41371 67	141	2.46091 42	21	0.00610 87	21	0.00010 18
22	0.38397 24	82	1.43117 00	142	2.47836 75	22	0.00639 95	22	0.00010 67
23	0.40142 57	83	1.44862 33	143	2.49582 08	23	0.00669 04	23	0.00011 15
24	0.41887 90	84	1.46607 66	144	2.51327 41	24	0.00698 13	24	0.00011 64
25	0.43633 23	85	1.48352 99	145	2.53072 74	25	0.00727 22	25	0.00012 12
26	0.45378 56	86	1.50098 32	146	2.54818 07	26	0.00756 31	26	0.00012 61
27	0.47123 89	87	1.51843 64	147	2.56563 40	27	0.00785 40	27	0.00013 09
28	0.48869 22	88	1.53588 97	148	2.58308 73	28	0.00814 49	28	0.00013 57
29	0.50614 55	89	1.55334 30	149	2.60054 06	29	0.00843 58	29	0.00014 06
30	0.52359 88	90	1.57079 63	150	2.61799 39	30	0.00872 66	30	0.00014 54
31	0.54105 21	91	1.58824 96	151	2.63544 72	31	0.00901 75	31	0.00015 03
32	0.55850 54	92	1.60570 29	152	2.65290 05	32	0.00930 84	32	0.00015 51
33	0.57595 87	93	1.62315 62	153	2.67035 38	33	0.00959 93	33	0.00016 00
34	0.59341 19	94	1.64060 95	154	2.68780 70	34	0.00989 02	34	0.00016 48
35	0.61086 52	95	1.65806 28	155	2.70526 03	35	0.01018 11	35	0.00016 97
36	0.62831 85	96	1.67551 61	156	2.72271 36	36	0.01047 20	36	0.00017 45
37	0.64577 18	97	1.69296 94	157	2.74016 69	37	0.01076 29	37	0.00017 94
38	0.66322 51	98	1.71042 27	158	2.75762 02	38	0.01105 38	38	0.00018 42
39	0.68067 84	99	1.72787 60	159	2.77507 35	39	0.01134 46	39	0.00018 91
40	0.69813 17	100	1.74532 93	160	2.79252 68	40	0.01163 55	40	0.00019 39
41	0.71558 50	101	1.76278 25	161	2.80998 01	41	0.01192 64	41	0.00019 88
42	0.73303 83	102	1.78023 58	162	2.82743 34	42	0.01221 73	42	0.00020 36
43	0.75049 16	103	1.79768 91	163	2.84488 67	43	0.01250 82	43	0.00020 85
44	0.76794 49	104	1.81514 24	164	2.86234 00	44	0.01279 91	44	0.00021 33
45	0.78539 82	105	1.83259 57	165	2.87979 33	45	0.01309 00	45	0.00021 82
46	0.80285 15	106	1.85004 90	166	2.89724 66	46	0.01338 09	46	0.00022 30
47	0.82030 47	107	1.86750 23	167	2.91469 99	47	0.01367 17	47	0.00022 79
48	0.83775 80	108	1.88495 56	168	2.93215 31	48	0.01396 26	48	0.00023 27
49	0.85521 13	109	1.90240 89	169	2.94960 64	49	0.01425 35	49	0.00023 76
50	0.87266 46	110	1.91986 22	170	2.96705 97	50	0.01454 44	50	0.00024 24
51	0.89011 79	111	1.93731 55	171	2.98451 30	51	0.01483 53	51	0.00024 73
52	0.90757 12	112	1.95476 88	172	3.00196 63	52	0.01512 62	52	0.00025 21
53	0.92502 45	113	1.97222 21	173	3.01941 96	53	0.01541 71	53	0.00025 70
54	0.94247 78	114	1.98967 53	174	3.03687 29	54	0.01570 80	54	0.00026 18
55	0.95993 11	115	2.00712 86	175	3.05432 62	55	0.01599 89	55	0.00026 66
56	0.97738 44	116	2.02458 19	176	3.07177 95	56	0.01628 97	56	0.00027 15
57	0.99483 77	117	2.04203 52	177	3.08923 28	57	0.01658 06	57	0.00027 63
58	1.01229 10	118	2.05948 85	178	3.10668 61	58	0.01687 15	58	0.00028 12
59	1.02974 43	119	2.07694 18	179	3.12413 94	59	0.01716 24	59	0.00028 60
60	1.04719 76	120	2.09439 51	180	3.14159 27	60	0.01745 33	60	0.00029 09

Center Cut in Feet	.0	.1	.2	.3	.4	.5	.6	.7	.8	.9
0	0.0	0.0	0.1	0.3	0.6	0.9	1.3	1.8	2.4	3.0
1	3.7	4.5	5.3	6.3	7.3	8.3	9.5	10.7	12.0	13.4
2	15	16	18	20	21	23	25	27	29	31
3	33	36	38	40	43	45	48	51	54	56
4	59	62	65	68	72	75	78	82	85	89
5	93	96	100	104	108	112	116	120	125	129
6	133	138	142	147	152	156	161	166	171	176
7	181	187	192	197	203	208	214	220	225	231
8	237	243	249	255	261	268	274	280	287	293
9	300	307	313	320	327	334	341	349	356	363
10	370	378	385	393	401	408	416	424	432	440
11	448	456	465	473	481	490	498	507	516	524
12	533	542	551	560	569	579	588	597	607	616
13	626	636	645	655	665	675	685	695	705	716
14	726	736	747	757	768	779	789	800	811	822
15	833	844	856	867	878	890	901	913	925	936
16	948	960	972	984	996	1008	1021	1033	1045	1058
17	1070	1083	1096	1108	1121	1134	1147	1160	1173	1187
18	1200	1213	1227	1240	1254	1268	1281	1295	1309	1323
19	1337	1351	1365	1380	1394	1408	1423	1437	1452	1467
20	1481	1496	1511	1526	1541	1556	1572	1587	1602	1618
21	1633	1649	1665	1680	1696	1712	1728	1744	1760	1776
22	1793	1809	1825	1842	1858	1875	1892	1908	1925	1942
23	1959	1976	1993	2011	2028	2045	2063	2080	2098	2116
24	2133	2151	2169	2187	2205	2223	2241	2260	2278	2296
25	2315	2333	2352	2371	2389	2408	2427	2446	2465	2484
26	2504	2523	2542	2562	2581	2601	2621	2640	2660	2680
27	2700	2720	2740	2760	2781	2801	2821	2842	2862	2883
28	2904	2924	2945	2966	2987	3008	3029	3051	3072	3093
29	3115	3136	3158	3180	3201	3223	3245	3267	3289	3311
30	3333	3356	3378	3400	3423	3445	3468	3491	3513	3536
31	3559	3582	3605	3628	3652	3675	3698	3722	3745	3769
32	3793	3816	3840	3864	3888	3912	3936	3960	3985	4009
33	4033	4058	4082	4107	4132	4156	4181	4206	4231	4256
34	4281	4307	4332	4357	4383	4408	4434	4460	4485	4511
35	4537	4563	4589	4615	4641	4668	4694	4720	4747	4773
36	4890	4827	4853	4880	4907	4934	4961	4988	5016	5043
37	5070	5098	5125	5153	5181	5208	5236	5264	5292	5320
38	5348	5376	5405	5433	5461	5490	5518	5547	5576	5604
39	5633	5662	5691	5720	5749	5779	5808	5837	5866	5896
40	5926	5956	5985	6015	6045	6075	6105	6135	6165	6196
41	6226	6256	6287	6317	6348	6379	6409	6440	6471	6502
42	6533	6564	6596	6627	6658	6690	6721	6763	6785	6816
43	6848	6880	6912	6944	6976	7008	7041	7073	7105	7138
44	7170	7203	7236	7268	7301	7334	7367	7400	7433	7467
45	7500	7533	7567	7600	7634	7668	7701	7735	7769	7803
46	7837	7871	7905	7940	7974	8008	8043	8077	8112	8147
47	8181	8216	8251	8286	8321	8356	8392	8427	8462	8498
48	8533	8569	8605	8640	8676	8712	8748	8784	8820	8856
49	8893	8929	8965	9002	9038	9075	9112	9148	9185	9222
50	9259	9296	9333	9371	9408	9445	9483	9520	9558	9596
51	9633	9671	9709	9747	9785	9823	9861	9900	9938	9976
52	10015	10053	10092	10131	10169	10208	10247	10286	10325	10364
53	10404	10443	10482	10522	10561	10601	10641	10680	10720	10760
54	10800	10840	10880	10920	10961	11001	11041	11082	11122	11163
55	11204	11244	11285	11326	11367	11408	11449	11491	11532	11573
56	11615	11656	11698	11740	11781	11823	11865	11907	11949	11991
57	12033	12076	12118	12160	12203	12245	12288	12331	12373	12416
58	12459	12502	12545	12588	12632	12675	12718	12762	12805	12849
59	12893	12936	12980	13024	13068	13112	13156	13200	13245	13289
60	13333	....	....	....	....	....	....	....	....	....

Side Slopes 1 to 1

Center Cut in Feet	.0	.1	.2	.3	.4	.5	.6	.7	.8	.9
0	0.0	0.0	0.2	0.5	0.9	1.4	2.0	2.7	3.6	4.5
1	5.6	6.7	8.0	9.4	10.9	12.5	14.2	16.1	18.0	20.1
2	22	24	27	29	32	35	38	41	44	47
3	50	53	57	60	64	68	72	76	80	84
4	89	93	98	103	108	112	118	123	128	133
5	139	144	150	156	162	168	174	180	187	193
6	200	207	214	222	228	235	242	249	257	264
7	272	280	288	296	304	312	321	329	338	347
8	356	364	374	383	392	401	411	420	430	440
9	450	460	470	480	491	501	512	522	533	544
10	556	567	577	589	601	612	624	636	648	660
11	672	684	697	709	722	735	748	760	774	787
12	800	813	827	840	854	868	882	896	910	924
13	939	953	968	983	998	1012	1028	1043	1058	1073
14	1089	1104	1120	1136	1152	1168	1184	1200	1217	1233
15	1250	1267	1284	1300	1318	1335	1352	1369	1387	1404
16	1422	1440	1458	1476	1494	1512	1531	1549	1568	1587
17	1606	1624	1644	1663	1682	1701	1721	1740	1760	1780
18	1800	1820	1840	1860	1881	1901	1922	1943	1964	1984
19	2006	2027	2048	2069	2091	2112	2134	2156	2178	2200
20	2222	2244	2267	2289	2311	2335	2358	2380	2404	2427
21	2450	2473	2497	2520	2544	2568	2592	2616	2640	2664
22	2689	2713	2738	2763	2788	2812	2838	2863	2888	2913
23	2939	2964	2990	3016	3042	3068	3094	3120	3147	3173
24	3200	3227	3254	3280	3308	3335	3362	3389	3417	3444
25	3472	3500	3528	3556	3584	3612	3641	3669	3698	3727
26	3756	3784	3814	3843	3872	3901	3931	3960	3990	4020
27	4050	4080	4110	4140	4171	4201	4232	4263	4294	4324
28	4356	4387	4418	4449	4481	4512	4544	4576	4608	4640
29	4672	4704	4737	4769	4802	4835	4868	4900	4934	4967
30	5000	5033	5067	5100	5134	5168	5202	5236	5270	5304
31	5339	5373	5408	5443	5478	5512	5548	5583	5618	5653
32	5689	5724	5760	5796	5832	5868	5904	5940	5977	6013
33	6050	6087	6124	6160	6198	6235	6272	6309	6347	6384
34	6422	6460	6498	6536	6574	6612	6651	6689	6728	6767
35	6805	6844	6884	6923	6962	7001	7041	7080	7120	7160
36	7200	7240	7280	7320	7361	7401	7442	7483	7524	7564
37	7606	7647	7688	7729	7771	7812	7854	7896	7938	7980
38	8022	8064	8107	8149	8192	8235	8278	8320	8364	8407
39	8450	8493	8537	8580	8624	8668	8712	8756	8800	8844
40	8889	8933	8978	9023	9068	9112	9158	9203	9248	9293
41	9339	9384	9430	9476	9522	9568	9614	9660	9707	9753
42	9800	9847	9894	9940	9988	10035	10082	10129	10177	10224
43	10272	10320	10368	10416	10464	10512	10561	10609	10658	10707
44	10756	10804	10854	10903	10952	11001	11051	11100	11150	11200
45	11250	11300	11350	11400	11451	11501	11552	11603	11654	11704
46	11756	11807	11858	11909	11961	12012	12064	12116	12168	12220
47	12272	12324	12377	12429	12482	12535	12588	12640	12694	12747
48	12800	12853	12907	12960	13014	13068	13122	13176	13230	13284
49	13339	13393	13448	13503	13558	13612	13668	13723	13778	13833
50	13889	13944	14000	14056	14112	14168	14224	14280	14337	14392
51	14450	14507	14564	14620	14678	14735	14792	14849	14907	14964
52	15022	15080	15138	15196	15254	15312	15371	15430	15489	15548
53	15606	15664	15724	15783	15842	15901	15961	16020	16080	16140
54	16200	16260	16320	16380	16441	16501	16562	16623	16684	16744
55	16806	16867	16928	16989	17051	17112	17174	17236	17298	17360
56	17422	17484	17547	17609	17672	17735	17798	17860	17924	17987
57	18050	18113	18177	18240	18304	18368	18432	18496	18560	18624
58	18689	18753	18818	18883	18948	19012	19078	19143	19208	19273
59	19339	19404	19470	19536	19602	19668	19734	19800	19867	19933
60	20000	....								

Side Slopes 1½ to 1

Table XIX. Cubic Yards per 100 Lineal Feet [XIX of Level Triangular Section

Side Slopes 2 to 1

Center Cut in Feet	.0	.1	.2	.3	.4	.5	.6	.7	.8	.9
0	0.0	0.1	0.3	0.7	1.2	1.9	2.7	3.6	4.7	6.0
1	7.4	9.0	10.7	12.5	14.5	16.7	19.0	21.4	24.0	26.7
2	30	33	36	39	43	46	50	54	58	62
3	67	71	76	81	86	91	96	101	107	113
4	119	125	131	137	143	150	157	164	171	178
5	185	193	200	208	216	224	232	241	249	258
6	267	276	285	294	303	313	323	333	343	353
7	363	373	384	395	406	417	428	439	451	462
8	474	486	498	510	523	535	548	561	574	587
9	600	613	627	641	655	669	683	697	711	726
10	741	756	771	786	801	817	832	848	864	880
11	893	913	929	946	963	980	997	1014	1031	1049
12	1067	1084	1103	1121	1139	1157	1176	1195	1214	1233
13	1252	1271	1291	1310	1330	1350	1370	1390	1411	1431
14	1452	1473	1494	1515	1536	1557	1579	1601	1623	1645
15	1667	1689	1711	1734	1757	1780	1803	1826	1849	1873
16	1896	1920	1944	1968	1992	2017	2041	2066	2091	2116
17	2141	2166	2191	2217	2243	2269	2295	2321	2347	2373
18	2400	2427	2454	2481	2508	2535	2563	2590	2618	2646
19	2674	2702	2731	2759	2788	2817	2846	2875	2904	2933
20	2963	2993	3023	3053	3083	3113	3143	3174	3205	3236
21	3267	3298	3329	3361	3392	3424	3456	3488	3520	3553
22	3585	3618	3651	3684	3717	3750	3783	3817	3851	3885
23	3919	3953	3987	4021	4056	4091	4126	4161	4196	4231
24	4267	4302	4338	4374	4410	4446	4483	4519	4556	4593
25	4630	4667	4704	4741	4779	4817	4855	4893	4931	4969
26	5007	5046	5085	5124	5163	5202	5241	5281	5320	5360
27	5400	5440	5480	5521	5561	5602	5643	5684	5725	5766
28	5807	5849	5891	5933	5975	6017	6059	6101	6144	6187
29	6230	6273	6316	6359	6403	6446	6490	6534	6578	6622
30	6667	6711	6756	6801	6846	6891	6936	6981	7027	7073
31	7119	7165	7211	7257	7303	7350	7397	7444	7491	7538
32	7585	7633	7680	7728	7776	7824	7872	7921	7969	8018
33	8067	8116	8165	8214	8263	8313	8363	8413	8463	8513
34	8563	8613	8664	8715	8766	8817	8868	8919	8971	9022
35	9074	9126	9178	9230	9283	9335	9388	9441	9494	9547
36	9600	9653	9707	9761	9815	9869	9923	9977	10031	10086
37	10141	10196	10251	10306	10361	10417	10472	10528	10584	10640
38	10693	10753	10809	10866	10923	10980	11037	11094	11151	11209
39	11267	11325	11383	11441	11499	11557	11616	11675	11734	11793
40	11852	11911	11971	12030	12090	12150	12210	12270	12331	12391
41	12452	12513	12574	12635	12696	12757	12819	12881	12943	13005
42	13067	13129	13191	13254	13317	13380	13443	13506	13569	13633
43	13696	13760	13824	13888	13952	14017	14081	14146	14211	14276
44	14341	14406	14471	14537	14603	14669	14735	14801	14867	14933
45	15000	15067	15134	15201	15268	15335	15403	15470	15538	15606
46	15674	15742	15811	15879	15948	16017	16086	16155	16224	16293
47	16363	16433	16503	16573	16643	16713	16783	16854	16925	16996
48	17067	17138	17209	17281	17352	17424	17496	17568	17640	17713
49	17785	17858	17931	18004	18077	18150	18223	18297	18371	18445
50	18519	18593	18667	18741	18816	18891	18966	19041	19116	19191
51	19267	19342	19418	19494	19570	19646	19723	19799	19876	19953
52	20030	20107	20184	20261	20339	20417	20495	20573	20651	20729
53	20807	20886	20965	21044	21123	21202	21281	21361	21440	21520
54	21600	21680	21760	21841	21921	22002	22083	22164	22245	22326
55	22407	22489	22571	22653	22735	22817	22899	22981	23064	23147
56	23230	23313	23396	23479	23563	23646	23730	23814	23898	23982
57	24067	24151	24236	24321	24406	24491	24576	24661	24747	24833
58	24919	25005	25091	25177	25263	25350	25436	25524	25611	25698
59	25785	25873	25960	26048	26136	26224	26312	26401	26489	26578
60	26667	....	....	....	....	....	....	....	....	....

Center Cut in Feet	.0	.1	.2	.3	.4	.5	.6	.7	.8	.9
0	0.0	0.1	0.4	1.0	1.8	2.8	4.0	5.4	7.1	9.0
1	11.1	13.4	16.0	18.8	21.8	25.0	28.4	32.2	36.1	40.1
2	44	49	54	59	64	69	75	81	87	93
3	100	106	114	121	128	136	144	152	160	168
4	178	187	196	205	215	225	235	245	256	267
5	278	289	300	312	324	336	348	361	373	337
6	400	413	427	441	455	469	484	499	514	529
7	544	560	576	592	608	625	642	659	676	693
8	711	729	747	765	784	803	822	841	860	880
9	900	920	940	961	982	1003	1024	1045	1067	1089
10	1111	1133	1156	1179	1202	1225	1248	1272	1296	1320
11	1344	1369	1394	1419	1444	1469	1495	1521	1547	1573
12	1600	1627	1654	1681	1708	1736	1764	1792	1820	1849
13	1878	1907	1936	1965	1995	2025	2055	2085	2116	2147
14	2178	2209	2240	2272	2304	2336	2368	2401	2434	2467
15	2500	2533	2567	2601	2635	2669	2704	2739	2774	2809
16	2844	2880	2916	2952	2988	3025	3062	3099	3136	3173
17	3211	3249	3287	3325	3364	3403	3442	3481	3520	3560
18	3600	3640	3680	3721	3762	3803	3844	3885	3927	3969
19	4011	4053	4096	4139	4182	4225	4268	4312	4356	4400
20	4444	4489	4534	4579	4624	4669	4715	4761	4807	4853
21	4900	4947	4994	5041	5088	5137	5184	5232	5280	5329
22	5378	5427	5476	5525	5575	5625	5675	5725	5776	5827
23	5878	5929	5980	6032	6084	6136	6188	6240	6294	6346
24	6400	6453	6507	6561	6615	6669	6724	6779	6834	6889
25	6944	7000	7056	7112	7168	7225	7282	7339	7396	7453
26	7511	7569	7627	7685	7744	7803	7862	7921	7980	8040
27	8100	8160	8220	8281	8342	8403	8464	8525	8587	8649
28	8711	8773	8836	8899	8962	9025	9088	9152	9216	9280
29	9344	9409	9474	9539	9604	9669	9735	9801	9867	9993
30	10000	10067	10134	10201	10268	10336	10404	10472	10540	10609
31	10678	10747	10816	10885	10955	11025	11095	11165	11236	11307
32	11378	11449	11520	11592	11664	11736	11808	11881	11954	12027
33	12100	12173	12247	12321	12395	12469	12544	12619	12694	12769
34	12844	12920	12996	13072	13148	13225	13302	13379	13456	13533
35	13611	13689	13767	13845	13924	14003	14082	14161	14240	14320
36	14400	14480	14560	14641	14722	14803	14884	14965	15047	15129
37	15211	15293	15376	15459	15542	15625	15708	15792	15876	15960
38	16044	16129	16214	16299	16384	16469	16555	16641	16727	16813
39	16900	16987	17074	17161	17248	17336	17424	17512	17600	17689
40	17778	17867	17956	18045	18135	18225	18315	18405	18496	18587
41	18678	18769	18860	18952	19044	19136	19228	19321	19416	19507
42	19600	19693	19787	19881	19975	20069	20164	20259	20354	20449
43	20544	20640	20736	20832	20928	21025	21122	21219	21316	21413
44	21511	21609	21707	21805	21904	22003	22102	22201	22300	22400
45	22500	22600	22700	22801	22902	23003	23104	23205	23307	23409
46	23511	23613	23716	23819	23922	24025	24128	24232	24336	24440
47	24544	24649	24754	24859	24964	25069	25175	25281	25387	25493
48	25600	25707	25814	25921	26029	26136	26244	26352	26460	26569
49	26678	26787	26896	27005	27115	27225	27335	27445	27556	27667
50	27778	27889	28000	28112	28224	28336	28448	28561	28674	28787
51	28900	29103	29127	29241	29355	29469	29584	29699	29814	29929
52	30044	30160	30276	30392	30508	30625	30742	30859	30976	31093
53	31211	31329	31447	31565	31684	31803	31992	32041	32160	32280
54	32400	32520	32640	32671	32882	33003	33124	33245	33367	33489
55	33611	33733	33856	33979	34102	34225	34348	34472	34596	34720
56	34844	34969	35094	35219	35344	35459	35595	35721	35847	35973
57	36100	36227	36354	36481	36608	36736	36864	36992	37120	37249
58	37378	37507	37636	37765	37895	38025	38155	38285	38416	38547
59	38678	38809	38940	39072	39204	39336	39468	39601	39734	39867
60	40000	....	....	....	....	....	....	....	....	....

Side Slopes 3 to 1

EXAMPLE.   Required yardage per 100 linear feet of section.
Base = 18 feet, slope = 1½ : 1, center cut = 5 feet.

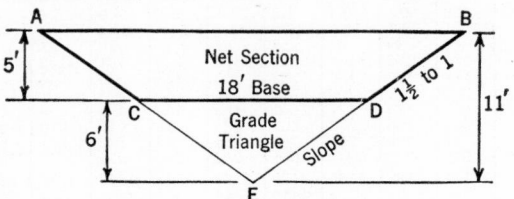

PROCEDURE.   Extend lines *AC* and *BD* until they intersect.
Height of large triangle = ⅔ (9 + 7.5) = 11 feet.
Height of small triangle = 11 − 5 = 6 feet.
Look up in Table yardages for triangular sections, slope 1½ : 1,
center cuts of 11 feet and 6 feet, respectively, and subtract.

$$672 - 200 = 472 \text{ cubic yards.}$$

This Table gives a wide range of bases.   It is most useful where the
"grade triangle" *CDE* is constant for a large number of stations.

Table XX.   Multiplying Factor to Determine · [XX
Additional Yardage for Various Transverse Slopes

Side Slopes	Transverse Slopes of Ground in Percent											
	0	10	15	20	25	39	35	40	45	50	55	60
1 : 1	1.00	1.01	1.02	1.04	1.07	1.10	1.14	1.19	1.25	1.33	1.44	1.56
1½ : 1	1.00	1.02	1.05	1.10	1.16	1.25	1.38	1.56	1.84	2.29	3.13	5.25
2 : 1	1.00	1.04	1.10	1.19	1.33	1.56	1.96	2.78	5.27			

EXAMPLE.   The yardage with 1 : 1 side slopes calculated from
Table XIX for a triangular section level transversely, must be multiplied by 1.14 if ground slopes 35% transversely.

Slope	Center Height-ft.	Base 12	Base 16	Base 20	Base 24	Base 28	Base 32	Base 36	Added Yardage per 2' of Base
1/4 : 1	1	45	60	75	90	105	119	134	7.4
	2	93	122	152	181	211	241	270	14.8
	3	142	186	231	275	319	364	408	22.2
	4	193	252	311	370	430	489	543	29.6
	5	245	319	394	468	542	616	690	37.0
	6	300	389	477	567	656	745	834	44.4
	7	356	460	564	668	771	875	979	51.9
	8	415	533	652	770	889	1007	1126	59.3
	9	475	608	742	875	1008	1141	1275	66.7
	10	537	685	833	981	1130	1278	1426	74.1
	11	601	764	927	1090	1253	1416	1579	81.5
	12	667	844	1022	1200	1378	1556	1733	88.9
	13	734	927	1119	1312	1505	1697	1890	96.3
	14	804	1011	1219	1426	1633	1841	2048	103.7
	15	875	1097	1319	1542	1764	1983	2208	111.1
	16	948	1185	1422	1659	1896	2133	2370	118.5
	17	1023	1275	1527	1779	2031	2282	2534	125.9
	18	1100	1367	1633	1900	2167	2434	2700	133.3
	19	1179	1460	1742	2023	2305	2586	2868	140.7
	20	1259	1556	1852	2148	2444	2741	3037	148.1
	21	1342	1653	1964	2275	2586	2897	3208	155.6
	22	1423	1752	2078	2404	2730	3056	3381	163.0
	23	1512	1853	2193	2534	2875	3216	3557	170.4
	24	1603	1956	2311	2667	3022	3378	3733	177.8
	25	1690	2060	2431	2801	3171	3542	3912	185.2
	30	2167	2611	3056	3500	3944	4389	4833	222.2
	35	2690	3208	3727	4245	4764	5282	5801	259.3
	40	3259	3852	4444	5037	5630	6222	6815	296.3
	45	3875	4542	5208	5875	6542	7209	7875	333.3
	50	4537	5278	6018	6759	7500	8241	8981	370.4
1/2 : 1	1	46	61	76	91	106	120	135	7.4
	2	96	126	156	185	215	244	274	14.8
	3	150	194	239	283	328	372	417	22.2
	4	207	267	326	385	444	504	563	29.6
	5	269	343	417	491	565	639	713	37.0
	6	333	422	511	600	689	778	867	44.4
	7	402	506	609	713	817	920	1024	51.9
	8	474	593	711	830	948	1067	1185	59.3
	9	550	683	817	950	1083	1217	1350	66.7
	10	630	778	926	1074	1222	1370	1519	74.1
	11	713	876	1039	1202	1365	1528	1691	81.5
	12	800	978	1156	1333	1511	1689	1867	88.9
	13	891	1083	1276	1469	1661	1854	2046	96.3
	14	985	1193	1402	1607	1815	2022	2250	103.7
	15	1083	1306	1528	1750	1972	2194	2417	111.1
	16	1185	1422	1659	1896	2133	2370	2607	118.5
	17	1291	1543	1795	2046	2298	2550	2802	125.9
	18	1403	1667	1933	2200	2467	2733	3000	133.3
	19	1513	1794	2076	2357	2639	2920	3202	140.7
	20	1630	1926	2222	2519	2815	3111	3407	148.1
	21	1750	2061	2372	2683	2994	3306	3617	155.6
	22	1874	2200	2526	2852	3178	3504	3830	163.0
	23	2002	2343	2683	3024	3365	3706	4046	170.4
	24	2133	2489	2845	3200	3556	3911	4267	177.8
	25	2269	2639	3009	3380	3750	4120	4491	185.2
	30	3000	3444	3889	4333	4778	5222	5667	222.2
	35	3824	4343	4801	5380	5898	6417	6935	259.3
	40	4741	5333	5926	6519	7111	7704	8296	296.3
	45	5750	6417	7083	7750	8417	9083	9750	333.3
	50	6852	7593	8333	9074	9815	10556	11296	370.4

Slope	Center Height-ft.	Base 12	Base 16	Base 20	Base 24	Base 28	Base 32	Base 36	Added Yardage per 2′ of Base
1 : 1	1	48	63	78	93	107	122	137	7.4
	2	104	133	163	193	222	252	281	14.8
	3	167	211	256	300	344	389	433	22.2
	4	237	296	356	415	474	533	593	29.6
	5	315	389	463	537	611	685	759	37.0
	6	400	489	578	667	756	844	933	44.4
	7	493	596	700	804	907	1011	1115	51.9
	8	593	711	830	948	1067	1185	1304	59.3
	9	700	833	967	1100	1233	1367	1500	66.7
	10	815	963	1111	1259	1407	1556	1704	74.1
	11	937	1100	1263	1426	1589	1752	1915	81.5
	12	1067	1244	1422	1600	1778	1956	2133	88.9
	13	1204	1396	1589	1781	1974	2167	2359	96.3
	14	1348	1556	1763	1970	2178	2385	2593	103.7
	15	1500	1722	1944	2167	2389	2611	2833	111.1
	16	1659	1896	2133	2370	2607	2844	3082	118.5
	17	1826	2078	2330	2581	2833	3085	3337	125.9
	18	2000	2267	2533	2800	3067	3333	3600	133.3
	19	2181	2463	2744	3026	3307	3589	3870	140.7
	20	2370	2667	2963	3259	3556	3852	4148	148.1
	21	2567	2878	3189	3500	3811	4122	4433	155.6
	22	2770	3096	3422	3748	4074	4400	4726	163.0
	23	2981	3322	3663	4004	4344	4685	5026	170.4
	24	3200	3556	3911	4267	4622	4978	5333	177.8
	25	3426	3796	4167	4537	4907	5278	5648	185.2
	30	4667	5111	5556	6000	6444	6889	7333	222.2
	35	6093	6611	7130	7648	8167	8685	9204	259.3
	40	7704	8296	8889	9481	10074	10667	11259	296.3
	45	9500	10167	10833	11500	12167	12833	13500	333.3
	50	11481	12222	12963	13704	14444	15185	15926	370.4
1-1/2 : 1	1	50	65	80	95	109	124	139	7.4
	2	111	141	170	200	230	259	289	14.8
	3	183	228	272	317	361	406	450	22.2
	4	267	326	385	444	504	563	622	29.6
	5	361	435	509	583	657	731	806	37.0
	6	467	556	644	733	822	911	1000	44.4
	7	583	687	791	895	998	1102	1206	51.9
	8	711	830	948	1067	1185	1304	1422	59.3
	9	850	983	1117	1250	1383	1517	1650	66.7
	10	1000	1148	1296	1445	1593	1741	1889	74.1
	11	1161	1324	1487	1650	1813	1976	2139	81.5
	12	1333	1511	1689	1867	2044	2222	2400	88.9
	13	1517	1709	1902	2094	2287	2480	2672	96.3
	14	1711	1919	2126	2333	2541	2748	2956	103.7
	15	1917	2139	2361	2583	2806	3028	3250	111.1
	16	2133	2370	2607	2844	3081	3319	3556	118.5
	17	2361	2613	2865	3116	3369	3620	3872	125.9
	18	2600	2867	3133	3400	3667	3933	4200	133.3
	19	2850	3131	3413	3695	3976	4257	4539	140.7
	20	3111	3407	3704	4000	4296	4593	4889	148.1
	21	3383	3694	4006	4317	4628	4939	5250	155.6
	22	3667	3993	4319	4644	4970	5296	5622	163.0
	23	3961	4302	4643	4983	5324	5665	6006	170.4
	24	4267	4622	4978	5333	5689	6044	6400	177.8
	25	4583	4954	5324	5695	6065	6435	6806	185.2
	30	6333	6778	7222	7667	8111	8556	9000	222.2
	35	8361	8880	9398	9917	10435	10954	11472	259.3
	40	10667	11259	11852	12444	13037	13630	14222	296.3
	45	13250	13917	14583	15250	15917	16583	17250	333.3
	59	16111	16852	17593	18333	19074	19815	20556	370.4

Slope	Center Height-ft.	Base 12	Base 16	Base 20	Base 24	Base 28	Base 32	Base 36	Added Yardage per 2' of Base
	1	52	67	81	96	111	126	141	7.4
	2	119	148	178	207	237	267	296	14.8
	3	200	244	289	333	378	422	467	22.2
	4	296	356	415	474	533	593	652	29.6
	5	407	481	556	630	704	778	852	37.0
	6	533	622	711	800	889	978	1067	44.4
	7	674	778	881	985	1089	1193	1296	51.9
	8	830	948	1067	1185	1304	1422	1541	59.3
	9	1000	1133	1267	1400	1533	1667	1800	66.7
	10	1185	1333	1481	1629	1778	1926	2074	74.1
	11	1385	1548	1711	1874	2037	2200	2363	81.5
	12	1600	1778	1956	2133	2311	2489	2667	88.9
	13	1830	2022	2215	2407	2600	2793	2985	96.3
	14	2074	2281	2489	2696	2904	3111	3319	103.7
2 : 1	**15**	2333	2556	2778	3000	3222	3444	3667	111.1
	16	2607	2844	3081	3318	3556	3793	4030	118.5
	17	2896	3148	3400	3652	3904	4156	4407	125.9
	18	3200	3467	3733	4000	4267	4533	4800	133.3
	19	3519	3800	4081	4363	4644	4926	5207	140.7
	20	3852	4148	4444	4744	5037	5333	5630	148.1
	21	4200	4511	4822	5133	5444	5756	6067	155.6
	22	4563	4889	5215	5540	5867	6193	6519	163.0
	23	4941	5281	5622	5963	6304	6644	6985	170.4
	24	5333	5689	6044	6400	6756	7111	7467	177.8
	25	5741	6111	6481	6852	7222	7593	7963	185.2
	30	8000	8444	8889	9333	9778	10222	10667	222.2
	35	10630	11148	11667	12185	12704	13222	13741	259.3
	40	13630	14222	14815	15407	16000	16593	17185	296.3
	45	17000	17667	18333	19000	19667	20333	21000	333.3
	50	20741	21481	22222	22963	23704	24444	25185	370.4

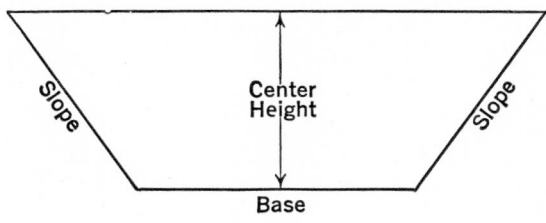

Center Height

Slope Slope

Base

from Double End Areas *

CY	2300	2200	2100	2000	1900	1800	1700	1600	1500	1400	1300	1200
0	1242	1188	1134	1080	1026	972	918	864	810	756	702	648
1.9	3	9	1135	1	7	3	9	865	1	7	3	9
3.7	4	1190	6	2	8	4	920	6	2	8	4	650
5.6	1245	1	7	3	9	975	1	7	3	9	705	1
7.4	6	2	8	4	1030	6	2	8	4	760	6	2
9.3	7	3	9	1085	1	7	3	9	815	1	7	3
11.1	8	4	1140	6	2	8	4	870	6	2	8	4
13.0	9	1195	1	7	3	9	925	1	7	3	9	655
14.8	1250	6	2	8	4	980	6	2	8	4	710	6
16.7	1	7	3	9	1035	1	7	3	9	765	1	7
18.5	2	8	4	1090	6	2	8	4	820	6	2	8
20.4	3	9	1145	1	7	3	9	875	1	7	3	9
22.2	4	1200	6	2	8	4	930	6	2	8	4	660
24.1	1255	1	7	3	9	985	1	7	3	9	715	1
25.9	6	2	8	4	1040	6	2	8	4	770	6	2
27.8	7	3	9	1095	1	7	3	9	825	1	7	3
29.6	8	4	1150	6	2	8	4	880	6	2	8	4
31.5	9	1205	1	7	3	9	935	1	7	3	9	665
33.3	1260	6	2	8	4	990	6	2	8	4	720	6
35.2	1	7	3	9	1045	1	7	3	9	775	1	7
37.0	2	8	4	1100	6	2	8	4	830	6	2	8
38.9	3	9	1155	1	7	3	9	885	1	7	3	9
40.7	4	1210	6	2	8	4	940	6	2	8	4	670
42.6	1265	1	7	3	9	995	1	7	3	9	725	1
44.4	6	2	8	4	1050	6	2	8	4	780	6	2
46.3	7	3	9	1105	1	7	3	9	835	1	7	3
48.1	8	4	1160	6	2	8	4	890	6	2	8	4
50.0	9	1215	1	7	3	9	945	1	7	3	9	675
51.9	1270	6	2	8	4	1000	6	2	8	4	730	6
53.7	1	7	3	9	1055	1	7	3	9	785	1	7
55.6	2	8	4	1110	6	2	8	4	840	6	2	8
57.4	3	9	1165	1	7	3	9	895	1	7	3	9
59.3	4	1220	6	2	8	4	950	6	2	8	4	680
61.1	1275	1	7	3	9	1005	1	7	3	9	735	1
63.0	6	2	8	4	1060	6	2	8	4	790	6	2
64.8	7	3	9	1115	1	7	3	9	845	1	7	3
66.7	8	4	1170	6	2	8	4	900	6	2	8	4
68.5	9	1225	1	7	3	9	955	1	7	3	9	685
70.4	1280	6	2	8	4	1010	6	2	8	4	740	6
72.2	1	7	3	9	1065	1	7	3	9	795	1	7
74.1	2	8	4	1120	6	2	8	4	850	6	2	8
75.9	3	9	1175	1	7	3	9	905	1	7	3	9
77.8	4	1230	6	2	8	4	960	6	2	8	4	690
79.6	1285	1	7	3	9	1015	1	7	3	9	745	1
81.5	6	2	8	4	1070	6	2	8	4	800	6	2
83.3	7	3	9	1125	1	7	3	9	855	1	7	3
85.2	8	4	1180	6	2	8	4	910	6	2	8	4
87.0	9	1235	1	7	3	9	965	1	7	3	9	695
88.9	1290	6	2	8	4	1020	6	2	8	4	750	6
90.7	1	7	3	9	1075	1	7	3	9	805	1	7
92.6	2	8	4	1130	6	2	8	4	860	6	2	8
94.4	3	9	1185	1	7	3	9	915	1	7	3	9
96.3	4	1240	6	2	8	4	970	6	2	8	4	700
98.1	1295	1	7	3	9	1025	1	7	3	9	755	1
CY	2300	2200	2100	2000	1900	1800	1700	1600	1500	1400	1300	1200

* From Missouri State Highway Commission, *Project Engineer Manual.*
EXAMPLE. Given *sum* of end areas = 518 square feet, obtain yardage for a

**Table XXIII. Yardage per 100-Foot Station— **
from Double End Areas

1100	1000	900	800	700	600	500	400	300	200	100	0	CY
594	540	486	432	378	324	270	216	162	108	54	0	0
595	1	7	3	9	325	1	7	3	9	55	1	1.9
6	2	8	4	380	6	2	8	4	110	6	2	3.7
7	3	9	435	1	7	3	9	165	1	7	3	5.6
8	4	490	6	2	8	4	220	6	2	8	4	7.4
9	545	1	7	3	9	275	1	7	3	9	5	9.3
600	6	2	8	4	330	6	2	8	4	60	6	11.1
1	7	3	9	385	1	7	3	9	115	1	7	13.0
2	8	4	440	6	2	8	4	170	6	2	8	14.8
3	9	495	1	7	3	9	225	1	7	3	9	16.7
4	550	6	2	8	4	280	6	2	8	4	10	18.5
605	1	7	3	9	335	1	7	3	9	65	1	20.4
6	2	8	4	390	6	2	8	4	120	6	2	22.2
7	3	9	445	1	7	3	9	175	1	7	3	24.1
8	4	500	6	2	8	4	230	6	2	8	4	25.9
9	555	1	7	3	9	285	1	7	3	9	15	27.8
610	6	2	8	4	340	6	2	8	4	70	6	29.6
1	7	3	9	395	1	7	3	9	125	1	7	31.5
2	8	4	450	6	2	8	4	180	6	2	8	33.3
3	9	505	1	7	3	9	235	1	7	3	9	35.2
4	560	6	2	8	4	290	6	2	8	4	20	37.0
615	1	7	3	9	345	1	7	3	9	75	1	38.9
6	2	8	4	400	6	2	8	4	130	6	2	40.7
7	3	9	455	1	7	3	9	185	1	7	3	42.6
8	4	510	6	2	8	4	240	6	2	8	4	44.4
9	565	1	7	3	9	295	1	7	3	9	25	46.3
620	6	2	8	4	350	6	2	8	4	80	6	48.1
1	7	3	9	405	1	7	3	9	135	1	7	50.0
2	8	4	460	6	2	8	4	190	6	2	8	51.9
3	9	515	1	7	3	9	245	1	7	3	9	53.7
4	570	6	2	8	4	300	6	2	8	4	30	55.6
625	1	7	3	9	355	1	7	3	9	85	1	57.4
6	2	8	4	410	6	2	8	4	140	6	2	59.3
7	3	9	465	1	7	3	9	195	1	7	3	61.1
8	4	520	6	2	8	4	250	6	2	8	4	63.0
9	575	1	7	3	9	305	1	7	3	9	35	64.8
630	6	2	8	4	360	6	2	8	4	90	6	66.7
1	7	3	9	415	1	7	3	9	145	1	7	68.5
2	8	4	470	6	2	8	4	200	6	2	8	70.4
3	9	525	1	7	3	9	255	1	7	3	9	72.2
4	580	6	2	8	4	310	6	2	8	4	40	74.1
635	1	7	3	9	365	1	7	3	9	95	1	75.9
6	2	8	4	420	6	2	8	4	150	6	2	77.8
7	3	9	475	1	7	3	9	205	1	7	3	79.6
8	4	530	6	2	8	4	260	6	2	8	4	81.5
9	585	1	7	3	9	315	1	7	3	9	45	83.3
640	6	2	8	4	370	6	2	8	4	100	6	85.2
1	7	3	9	425	1	7	3	9	155	1	7	87.0
2	8	4	480	6	2	8	4	210	6	2	8	88.9
3	9	535	1	7	3	9	265	1	7	3	9	90.7
4	590	6	2	8	4	320	6	2	8	4	50	92.6
645	1	7	3	9	375	1	7	3	9	105	1	94.4
6	2	8	4	430	6	2	8	4	160	6	2	96.3
7	3	9	485	1	7	3	9	215	1	7	3	98.1
1100	1000	900	800	700	600	500	400	300	200	100	0	CY

100-foot section. Find 518 in Table, and read 900 at top and 59.3 at right end.
Yardage = 959.3 cubic yards.

Table XXIV.
Canal Sections — Balanced Center Cut

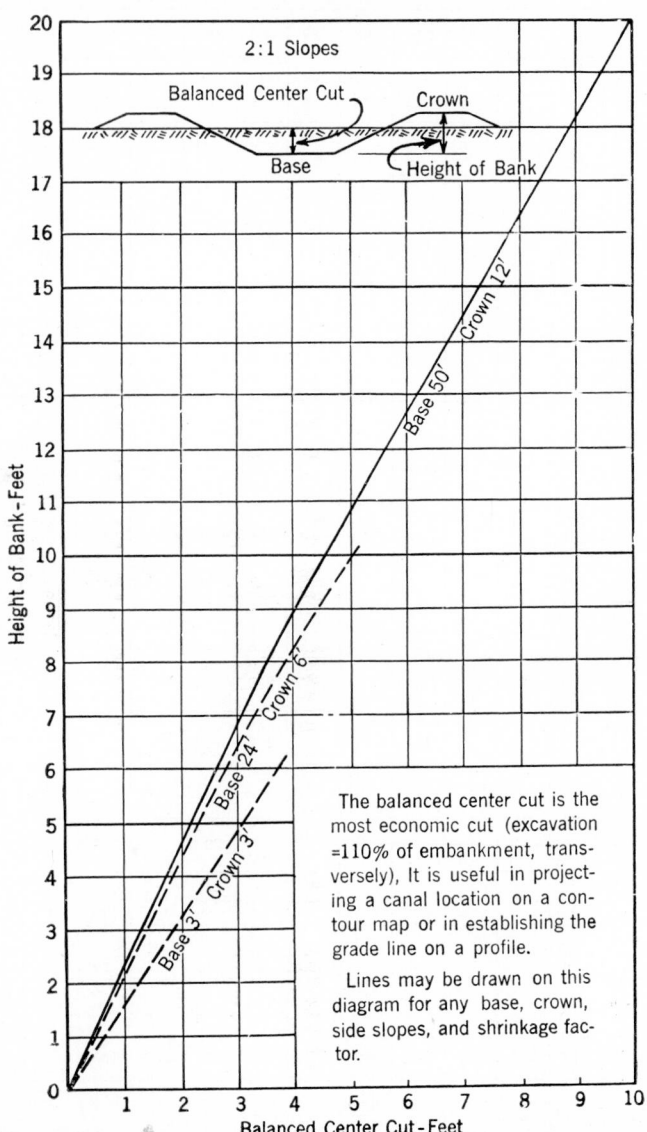

The balanced center cut is the most economic cut (excavation =110% of embankment, transversely). It is useful in projecting a canal location on a contour map or in establishing the grade line on a profile.

Lines may be drawn on this diagram for any base, crown, side slopes, and shrinkage factor.

Table XXV. Turnout and Crossover Data, A.R.E.A., 1941

	Properties of Switches			Closure Distance		Lead Curve		Gage Line Offsets							
Col. 1	Col. 2	Col. 3	Col. 4	Col. 5	Col. 6	Col. 7	Col. 8	Col. 9	Col. 10	Col. 11	Col. 12	Col. 13	Col. 14	Col. 15	Col. 16
Frog Number	Length of Switch Rail	Switch Angle	Actual Lead	Straight Closure Rail	Curved Closure Rail	Radius of Center Line	Degree of Curve							Tangent adjacent to Switch Rail	Tangent adjacent to toe of Frog
	Ft. In.	Deg. Min. Sec.	Ft. In.	Ft. In.	Ft. In	Feet	Deg. Min. Sec.	Ft In	Ft. In	Ft. In.	Inches	Inches	Ft. In	Feet	Feet
5	11-0	2-39-34	42-6$\frac{1}{2}$	28-0	28-4	177.80	32-39-56	18-0	25-0	32-0	11$\frac{13}{16}$	20$\frac{5}{8}$	2-8$\frac{7}{8}$	0.00	0.78
6	11-0	2-39-34	47-6	32-9	33-0	258.57	22-17-58	19-2$\frac{1}{4}$	27-4$\frac{1}{2}$	35-6$\frac{3}{4}$	12$\frac{3}{8}$	21$\frac{5}{8}$	2-10	0.00	1.75
7	16-6	1-46-22	62-1	40-10$\frac{1}{2}$	41-1$\frac{1}{4}$	365.59	15-43-16	26-2$\frac{1}{4}$	35-10$\frac{1}{2}$	45-6$\frac{3}{4}$	11$\frac{3}{8}$	19$\frac{9}{16}$	2-6$\frac{7}{8}$	0.01	0.00
8	16-6	1-46-22	68-0	46-5	46-7$\frac{1}{2}$	487.28	11-46-44	27-7$\frac{1}{4}$	38-8$\frac{1}{2}$	49-9$\frac{3}{4}$	11$\frac{7}{8}$	20$\frac{9}{16}$	2-8$\frac{5}{16}$	0.64	0.00
9	16-6	1-46-22	72-3$\frac{1}{2}$	49-5	49-7$\frac{1}{4}$	615.12	9-19-30	28-10$\frac{1}{4}$	41-2$\frac{1}{2}$	53-6$\frac{3}{4}$	12$\frac{5}{16}$	21$\frac{3}{8}$	2-9$\frac{7}{16}$	0.00	0.17
10	16-6	1-46-22	78-9	55-10	56-0	779.39	7-21-24	29-1$\frac{3}{4}$	43-5$\frac{1}{2}$	56-11$\frac{1}{4}$	12$\frac{1}{4}$	21	2-8$\frac{5}{8}$	2.08	0.00
11	22-0	1-19-46	91-10$\frac{1}{4}$	62-10$\frac{1}{4}$	63-0	927.27	6-10-56	37-8$\frac{1}{2}$	53-5	69-1$\frac{1}{2}$	12$\frac{1}{4}$	21$\frac{3}{8}$	2-9$\frac{3}{4}$	0.00	0.13
12	22-0	1-19-46	96-8	66-10$\frac{1}{2}$	67-0	1104.63	5-11-20	38-8$\frac{1}{2}$	55-5	72-1$\frac{1}{2}$	12$\frac{7}{16}$	21$\frac{5}{8}$	2-9$\frac{7}{8}$	0.00	0.50
14	22-0	1-19-46	107-0$\frac{3}{4}$	76-5$\frac{1}{4}$	76-6$\frac{3}{4}$	1581.20	3-37-28	41-1$\frac{1}{4}$	60-2$\frac{1}{2}$	79-3$\frac{3}{4}$	12$\frac{7}{8}$	22$\frac{5}{16}$	2-10$\frac{1}{2}$	0.24	0.00
15	30-0	0-58-30	126-4$\frac{1}{2}$	86-11$\frac{1}{2}$	87-0$\frac{3}{4}$	1720.77	3-19-48	51-9	73-6	95-3	12$\frac{1}{8}$	21$\frac{1}{4}$	2-9$\frac{3}{4}$	1.56	0.00
16	30-0	0-58-30	131-4	91-11	92-0	2007.12	2-51-18	53-0	76-0	99-0	12$\frac{7}{16}$	21$\frac{13}{16}$	2-10$\frac{5}{16}$	0.66	0.00
18	30-0	0-58-30	140-11$\frac{1}{2}$	99-11	100-0	2578.79	2-13-20	55-0	80-0	105-0	12$\frac{3}{4}$	22$\frac{1}{8}$	2-10$\frac{7}{16}$	0.57	0.00
20	30-0	0-58-30	151-11$\frac{1}{2}$	110-11	111-0	3289.29	1-44-32	57-9	85-6	113-3	13$\frac{1}{16}$	22$\frac{11}{16}$	2-11$\frac{3}{16}$	2.47	0.00

Table XXV. Turnout and Crossover Data, A.R.E.A., 1941

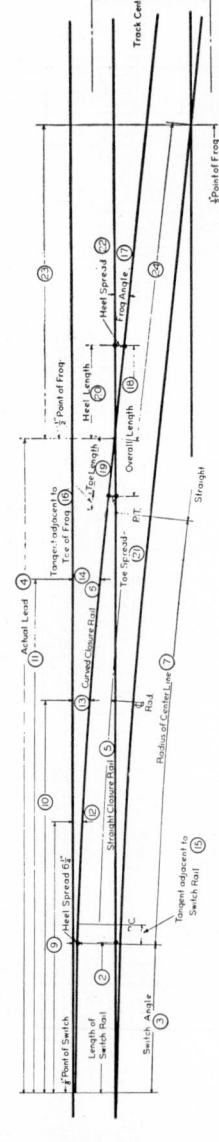

	Properties of Frogs						Data for Crossovers			
							13'-0" Track Centers		For change of 1'-0" in Track Centers	
Frog Number	Frog Angle	Overall Length	Toe Length	Heel Length	Toe Spread	Heel Spread	Straight Track	Crossover Track	Straight Track	Crossover Track
Col ①	Col ⑰	Col ⑱	Col ⑲	Col ⑳	Col ㉑	Col ㉒	Col ㉓	Col ㉔	Col ㉕	Col ㉖
	Deg-Min-Sec	Ft In	Ft In	Ft In	Inches	Inches	Ft In	Ft In	Ft In	Ft In
5	11-25-16	9-0	3-6½	5-5½	7½	13¼	16-10½	18-1¼	4-11¾	5-0¼
6	9-31-38	10-0	3-9	6-3	7	13	20-5½	21-6½	5-11⅜	6-0⅛
7	8-10-16	12-0	4-8½	7-3½	7⅞	13	24-0	24-11⅝	6-11⅞	7-0⅞
8	7-09-10	13-0	5-1	7-11	7⅞	12⅞	27-7⅝	28-4⅞	7-11⅞	8-0⅞
9	6-21-35	16-0	6-4½	9-7½	8	12⅞	31-1⅝	31-10⅝	8-11⅞	9-0⅛
10	5-43-29	16-0	6-5	10-1	7⅞	12⅞	34-8⅜	35-3⅜	9-11⅞	10-0⅛
11	5-12-18	18-8½	7-0	11-8½	7⅞	13⅛	38-2⅛	38-9⅜	10-11⅞	11-0⅛
12	4-46-19	20-4	7-9½	12-6½	7½	13⅛	41-8⅜	42-3⅜	11-11⅞	12-0⅛
14	4-05-27	23-7	8-7½	14-11½	6⅞	13¾	48-9⅜	49-2⅞	13-11⅞	14-0⅛
15	3-49-06	24-4½	9-5	14-11½	6½	13¾	52-3⅜	52-8⅞	14-11⅞	15-0⅛
16	3-34-47	26-0	9-5	16-7	6⅞	12⅞	55-9⅞	56-2⅞	15-11⅞	16-0⅛
18	3-10-56	29-3	11-0½	18-2½	6½	12⅛	62-9½	63-2⅛	17-11⅞	18-0⅛
20	2-51-51	30-10½	11-0½	19-10	6	12⅛	69-10	70-2	19-11⅞	20-0⅛

NOTES

1. TURNOUTS AND CROSSOVERS RECOMMENDED

For main line high speed movements, No. 16 or No. 20. For main line slow speed movements, No. 12 or No. 10. For yards and sidings, to meet general conditions, No. 8.

2.

The data shown are computed for turnouts out of straight standard 4'8½" gage track. If the wheel base of the equipment used requires wider gage for the switch alinement or curvature shown, the lead and alinement of curved closure rail shall be maintained, and inside stock and curved rails shall be moved out the necessary amount. The gage of straight track through switch will then be increased and the straight closure rail shall be bent to true alinement in advance of toe of frog.

3. FROG DESIGNS

For short spring rail type frogs, the straight closure, and/or solid manganese frogs, the straight and curved closures, shall be lengthened to conform.

4. MODIFICATION OF ALINEMENT

The alinement specified may be used without appreciable wear for switch points made in accordance either with Detail 4000 (thickness of point—¼"), or with Detail 5000 (thickness of point—0").

240

*Modified from a table for logging engineers by Mr. Lester Calder, Weyerhaeuser Timber Company, Springfield, Oregon.

D / c.	4°	8°	12°	16°	20°	24°	28°	32°	36°	40°
1	0.02	0.03	0.1	0.1	0.1	0.1	0.1	0.1	0.2	0.2
5	0.09	0.17	0.3	0.3	0.4	0.5	0.6	0.7	0.8	0.9
10	0.18	0.35	0.5	0.7	0.9	1.0	1.2	1.4	1.6	1.7
15	0.26	0.52	0.8	1.0	1.3	1.6	1.8	2.1	2.3	2.6
20	0.35	0.70	1.0	1.4	1.7	2.1	2.4	2.8	3.1	3.5
25	0.44	0.87	1.3	1.7	2.2	2.6	3.0	3.5	3.9	4.3
26	0.45	0.90	1.4	1.8	2.3	2.7	3.2	3.6	4.1	4.5
27	0.47	0.94	1.4	1.9	2.4	2.8	3.3	3.7	4.2	4.7
28	0.49	0.98	1.5	2.0	2.4	2.9	3.4	3.8	4.4	4.9
29	0.50	1.01	1.5	2.0	2.5	3.0	3.5	4.0	4.5	5.0
30	0.52	1.05	1.6	2.1	2.6	3.1	3.7	4.2	4.7	5.2
31	0.54	1.08	1.6	2.2	2.7	3.2	3.8	4.3	4.8	5.4
32	0.56	1.12	1.7	2.2	2.8	3.3	3.9	4.4	5.0	5.5
33	0.58	1.15	1.7	2.3	2.9	3.4	4.0	4.6	5.2	5.7
34	0.59	1.18	1.8	2.4	3.0	3.6	4.1	4.7	5.3	5.9
35	0.61	1.22	1.8	2.4	3.1	3.7	4.3	4.9	5.5	6.1
36	0.63	1.26	1.9	2.5	3.1	3.8	4.4	5.0	5.6	6.2
37	0.64	1.29	1.9	2.6	3.2	3.9	4.5	5.1	5.8	6.4
38	0.66	1.33	2.0	2.7	3.3	4.0	4.6	5.3	5.9	6.6
39	0.68	1.36	2.0	2.7	3.4	4.1	4.8	5.4	6.1	6.7
40	0.70	1.40	2.1	2.8	3.5	4.2	4.9	5.6	6.2	6.9
41	0.72	1.43	2.1	2.9	3.6	4.3	5.0	5.7	6.4	7.1
42	0.73	1.46	2.2	2.9	3.7	4.4	5.1	5.8	6.5	7.3
43	0.75	1.50	2.3	3.0	3.7	4.5	5.2	6.0	6.7	7.4
44	0.77	1.54	2.3	3.1	3.8	4.6	5.4	6.1	6.9	7.6
45	0.78	1.57	2.4	3.1	3.9	4.7	5.5	6.2	7.0	7.8
46	0.80	1.61	2.4	3.2	4.0	4.8	5.6	6.4	7.2	8.0
47	0.82	1.64	2.5	3.3	4.1	4.9	5.7	6.5	7.3	8.1
48	0.84	1.67	2.5	3.3	4.2	5.0	5.8	6.7	7.5	8.3
49	0.86	1.71	2.6	3.4	4.3	5.1	6.0	6.8	7.6	8.5
50	0.87	1.74	2.6	3.5	4.4	5.2	6.1	6.9	7.8	8.6

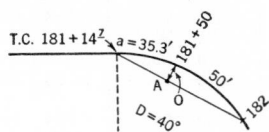

T.C. 181 + 14 a = 35.3′ 181 + 50 50′ D = 40° 182

In order to set stations and half stations near the ends of a curve, when staking the curve by tangent offsets, chord offsets, or middle ordinates, proceed as follows:

In the figure, set station 181 + 50 by tangent offset (Table IIIA). Measure ordinate ($O = 6.1'$ from Table XXVI) at station 181 + 50 perpendicular to the chord, and set point A. Sight across the T.C. and A to set station 182. Remove the temporary stake at A. Since distances are calculated on the arc, correct the chord distance, T.C. to station 182, if necessary. O may be calculated from the obvious relationship.

$$O = Lc \sin \frac{KD}{4} \text{ in which } Lc = \text{chord for 50' arc, and } K = \frac{a}{50} = \frac{35.3}{50} = 0.71.$$

Use a similar process at the far end of the curve.

Table XXVII.
Stadia Coefficients, Vertical Rod

100 cos² α and 100($\frac{1}{2}$ sin 2α)

	0°		1°		2°		3°	
	Hor. Dist.	Diff. Elev.	Hor. Dist.	Diff. Elev.	Hor. Dist.	Diff. Elev.	Hor. Dist.	Diff. Elev.
′								
0	100.00	00.00	99.97	01.74	99.88	03.49	99.73	05.23
2	100.00	00.06	99.97	01.80	99.87	03.55	99.72	05.28
4	100.00	00.12	99.97	01.86	99.87	03.60	99.71	05.34
6	100.00	00.17	99.96	01.92	99.87	03.66	99.71	05.40
8	100.00	00.23	99.96	01.98	99.86	03.72	99.70	05.46
10	100.00	00.29	99.96	02.04	99.86	03.78	99.69	05.52
12	100.00	00.35	99.96	02.09	99.85	03.84	99.69	05.57
14	100.00	00.41	99.95	02.15	99.85	03.90	99.68	05.63
16	100.00	00.47	99.95	02.21	99.84	03.95	99.68	05.69
18	100.00	00.52	99.95	02.27	99.84	04.01	99.67	05.75
20	100.00	00.58	99.95	02.33	99.83	04.07	99.66	05.80
22	100.00	00.64	99.94	02.38	99.83	04.13	99.66	05.86
24	100.00	00.70	99.94	02.44	99.82	04.18	99.65	05.92
26	99.99	00.76	99.94	02.50	99.82	04.24	99.64	05.98
28	99.99	00.81	99.93	02.56	99.81	04.30	99.63	06.04
30	99.99	00.87	99.93	02.62	99.81	04.36	99.63	06.09
32	99.99	00.93	99.93	02.67	99.80	04.42	99.62	06.15
34	99.99	00.99	99.93	02.73	99.80	04.48	99.62	06.21
36	99.99	01.05	99.92	02.79	99.79	04.53	99.61	06.27
38	99.99	01.11	99.92	02.85	99.79	04.59	99.60	06.33
40	99.99	01.16	99.92	02.91	99.78	04.65	99.59	06.38
42	99.99	01.22	99.91	02.97	99.78	04.71	99.59	06.44
44	99.98	01.28	99.91	03.02	99.77	04.76	99.58	06.50
46	99.98	01.34	99.90	03.08	99.77	04.82	99.57	06.56
48	99.98	01.40	99.90	03.14	99.76	04.88	99.56	06.61
50	99.98	01.45	99.90	03.20	99.76	04.94	99.56	06.67
52	99.98	01.51	99.89	03.26	99.75	04.99	99.55	06.73
54	99.98	01.57	99.89	03.31	99.74	05.05	99.54	06.78
56	99.97	01.63	99.89	03.37	99.74	05.11	99.53	06.84
58	99.97	01.69	99.88	03.43	99.73	05.17	99.52	06.90
60	99.97	01.74	99.88	03.49	99.73	05.23	99.51	06.96

Stadia Coefficients, Vertical Rod

$100 \cos^2 \alpha$ and $100(\frac{1}{2} \sin 2\alpha)$

	4°		5°		6°		7°	
	Hor. Dist.	Diff. Elev.	Hor. Dist.	Diff. Elev.	Hor. Dist.	Diff. Elev.	Hor. Dist.	Diff. Elev.
′								
0	99.51	06.96	99.24	08.68	98.91	10.40	98.51	12.10
2	99.51	07.02	99.23	08.74	98.90	10.45	98.50	12.15
4	99.50	07.07	99.22	08.80	98.88	10.51	98.48	12.21
6	99.49	07.13	99.21	08.85	98.87	10.57	98.47	12.26
8	99.48	07.19	99.20	08.91	98.86	10.62	98.46	12.32
10	99.47	07.25	99.19	08.97	98.85	10.68	98.44	12.38
12	99.46	07.30	99.18	09.03	98.83	10.74	98.43	12.43
14	99.46	07.36	99.17	09.08	98.82	10.79	98.41	12.49
16	99.45	07.42	99.16	09.14	98.81	10.85	98.40	12.55
18	99.44	07.48	99.15	09.20	98.80	10.91	98.39	12.60
20	99.43	07.53	99.14	09.25	98.78	10.96	98.37	12.66
22	99.42	07.59	99.13	09.31	98.77	11.02	98.36	12.72
24	99.41	07.65	99.11	09.37	98.76	11.08	98.34	12.77
26	99.40	07.71	99.10	09.43	98.74	11.13	98.33	12.83
28	99.39	07.76	99.09	09.48	98.73	11.19	98.31	12.88
30	99.38	07.82	99.08	09.54	98.72	11.25	98.29	12.94
32	99.38	07.88	99.07	09.60	98.71	11.30	98.28	13.00
34	99.37	07.94	99.06	09.65	98.69	11.36	98.27	13.05
36	99.36	07.99	99.05	09.71	98.68	11.42	98.25	13.11
38	99.35	08.05	99.04	09.77	98.67	11.47	98.24	13.17
40	99.34	08.11	99.03	09.83	98.65	11.53	98.22	13.22
42	99.33	08.17	99.01	09.88	98.64	11.59	98.20	13.28
44	99.32	08.22	99.00	09.94	98.63	11.64	98.19	13.33
46	99.31	08.28	98.99	10.00	98.61	11.70	98.17	13.39
48	99.30	08.34	98.98	10.05	98.60	11.76	98.16	13.45
50	99.29	08.40	98.97	10.11	98.58	11.81	98.14	13.50
52	99.28	08.45	98.96	10.17	98.57	11.87	98.13	13.56
54	99.27	08.51	98.94	10.22	98.56	11.93	98.11	13.61
56	99.26	08.57	98.93	10.28	98.54	11.98	98.10	13.67
58	99.25	08.63	98.92	10.34	98.53	12.04	98.08	13.73
60	99.24	08.68	98.91	10.40	98.51	12.10	98.06	13.78

Table XXVII.
Stadia Coefficients, Vertical Rod

$100 \cos^2 \alpha$ and $100(\frac{1}{2} \sin 2\alpha)$

	8°		9°		10°		11°	
′	Hor. Dist.	Diff. Elev.	Hor. Dist.	Diff. Elev.	Hor. Dist.	Diff. Elev.	Hor. Dist.	Diff. Elev.
0	98.06	13.78	97.55	15.45	96.98	17.10	96.36	18.73
2	98.05	13.84	97.53	15.51	96.96	17.16	96.34	18.78
4	98.03	13.89	97.52	15.56	96.94	17.21	96.32	18.84
6	98.01	13.95	97.50	15.62	96.92	17.26	96.29	18.89
8	98.00	14.01	97.48	15.67	96.90	17.32	96.27	18.95
10	97.98	14.06	97.46	15.73	96.88	17.37	96.25	19.00
12	97.97	14.12	97.44	15.78	96.86	17.43	96.23	19.05
14	97.95	14.17	97.43	15.84	96.84	17.48	96.21	19.11
16	97.93	14.23	97.41	15.89	96.82	17.54	96.18	19.16
18	97.92	14.28	97.39	15.95	96.80	17.59	96.16	19.21
20	97.90	14.34	97.37	16.00	96.78	17.65	96.14	19.27
22	97.88	14.40	97.35	16.06	96.76	17.70	96.12	19.32
24	97.87	14.45	97.33	16.11	96.74	17.76	96.09	19.38
26	97.85	14.51	97.31	16.17	96.72	17.81	96.07	19.43
28	97.83	14.56	97.29	16.22	96.70	17.86	96.05	19.48
30	97.82	14.62	97.28	16.28	96.68	17.92	96.03	19.54
32	97.80	14.67	97.26	16.33	96.66	17.97	96.00	19.59
34	97.78	14.73	97.24	16.39	96.64	18.03	95.98	19.64
36	97.76	14.79	97.22	16.44	96.62	18.08	95.96	19.70
38	97.75	14.84	97.20	16.50	96.60	18.14	95.93	19.75
40	97.73	14.90	97.18	16.55	96.57	18.19	95.91	19.80
42	97.71	14.95	97.16	16.61	96.55	18.24	95.89	19.86
44	97.69	15.01	97.14	16.66	96.53	18.30	95.86	19.91
46	97.68	15.06	97.12	16.72	96.51	18.35	95.84	19.96
48	97.66	15.12	97.10	16.77	96.49	18.41	95.82	20.02
50	97.64	15.17	97.08	16.83	96.47	18.46	95.79	20.07
52	97.62	15.23	97.06	16.88	96.45	18.51	95.77	20.12
54	97.61	15.28	97.04	16.94	96.42	18.57	95.75	20.18
56	97.59	15.34	97.02	16.99	96.40	18.62	95.72	20.23
58	97.57	15.40	97.00	17.05	96.38	18.68	95.70	20.28
60	97.55	15.45	96.98	17.10	96.36	18.73	95.68	20.34

Table XXVII.
Stadia Coefficients, Vertical Rod

$100 \cos^2 \alpha$ and $100(\tfrac{1}{2} \sin 2\alpha)$

	12°		13°		14°		15°	
′	Hor. Dist.	Diff. Elev.	Hor. Dist.	Diff. Elev.	Hor. Dist.	Diff. Elev.	Hor. Dist.	Diff. Elev.
0	95.68	20.34	94.94	21.92	94.15	23.47	93.30	25.00
2	95.65	20.39	94.91	21.97	94.12	23.52	93.27	25.05
4	95.63	20.44	94.89	22.02	94.09	23.58	93.24	25.10
6	95.61	20.50	94.86	22.08	94.07	23.63	93.21	25.15
8	95.58	20.55	94.84	22.13	94.04	23.68	93.18	25.20
10	95.56	20.60	94.81	22.18	94.01	23.73	93.16	25.25
12	95.53	20.66	94.79	22.23	93.98	23.78	93.13	25.30
14	95.51	20.71	94.76	22.28	93.95	23.83	93.10	25.35
16	95.49	20.76	94.73	22.34	93.93	23.88	93.07	25.40
18	95.46	20.81	94.71	22.39	93.90	23.93	93.04	25.45
20	95.44	20.87	94.68	22.44	93.87	23.99	93.01	25.50
22	95.41	20.92	94.66	22.49	93.84	24.04	92.98	25.55
24	95.39	20.97	94.63	22.54	93.81	24.09	92.95	25.60
26	95.36	21.03	94.60	22.60	93.79	24.14	92.92	25.65
28	95.34	21.08	94.58	22.65	93.76	24.19	92.89	25.70
30	95.32	21.13	94.55	22.70	93.73	24.24	92.86	25.75
32	95.29	21.18	94.52	22.75	93.70	24.29	92.83	25.80
34	95.27	21.24	94.50	22.80	93.67	24.34	92.80	25.85
36	95.24	21.29	94.47	22.85	93.65	24.39	92.77	25.90
38	95.22	21.34	94.44	22.91	93.62	24.44	92.74	25.95
40	95.19	21.39	94.42	22.96	93.59	24.49	92.71	26.00
42	95.17	21.45	94.39	23.01	93.56	24.55	92.68	26.05
44	95.14	21.50	94.36	23.06	93.53	24.60	92.65	26.10
46	95.12	21.55	94.34	23.11	93.50	24.65	92.62	26.15
48	95.09	21.60	94.31	23.16	93.47	24.70	92.59	26.20
50	95.07	21.66	94.28	23.22	93.45	24.75	92.56	26.25
52	95.04	21.71	94.26	23.27	93.42	24.80	92.53	26.30
54	95.02	21.76	94.23	23.32	93.39	24.85	92.49	26.35
56	94.99	21.81	94.20	23.37	93.36	24.90	92.46	26.40
58	94.97	21.87	94.17	23.42	93.33	24.95	92.43	26.45
60	94.94	21.92	94.15	23.47	93.30	25.00	92.40	26.50

Table XXVII.
Stadia Coefficients, Vertical Rod

100 cos² α and 100($\frac{1}{2}$ sin 2α)

′	16°		17°		18°		19°	
	Hor. Dist.	Diff. Elev.	Hor. Dist.	Diff. Elev.	Hor. Dist.	Diff. Elev.	Hor. Dist.	Diff. Elev.
0	92.40	26.50	91.45	27.96	90.45	29.39	89.40	30.78
2	92.37	26.55	91.42	28.01	90.42	29.44	89.36	30.83
4	92.34	26.59	91.39	28.06	90.38	29.48	89.33	30.87
6	92.31	26.64	91.35	28.10	90.35	29.53	89.29	30.92
8	92.28	26.69	91.32	28.15	90.31	29.58	89.26	30.97
10	92.25	26.74	91.29	28.20	90.28	29.62	89.22	31.01
12	92.22	26.79	91.26	28.25	90.24	29.67	89.18	31.06
14	92.19	26.84	91.22	28.30	90.21	29.72	89.15	31.10
16	92.15	26.89	91.19	28.34	90.18	29.76	89.11	31.15
18	92.12	26.94	91.16	28.39	90.14	29.81	89.08	31.19
20	92.09	26.99	91.12	28.44	90.11	29.86	89.04	31.24
22	92.06	27.04	91.09	28.49	90.07	29.90	89.00	31.28
24	92.03	27.09	91.06	28.54	90.04	29.95	88.96	31.33
26	92.00	27.13	91.02	28.58	90.00	30.00	88.93	31.38
28	91.97	27.18	90.99	28.63	89.97	30.04	88.89	31.42
30	91.93	27.23	90.96	28.68	89.93	30.09	88.86	31.47
32	91.90	27.28	90.92	28.73	89.90	30.14	88.82	31.51
34	91.87	27.33	90.89	28.77	89.86	30.19	88.78	31.56
36	91.84	27.38	90.86	28.82	89.83	30.23	88.75	31.60
38	91.81	27.43	90.82	28.87	89.79	30.28	88.71	31.65
40	91.77	27.48	90.79	28.92	89.76	30.32	88.67	31.69
42	91.74	27.52	90.76	28.96	89.72	30.37	88.64	31.74
44	91.71	27.57	90.72	29.01	89.69	30.41	88.60	31.78
46	91.68	27.62	90.69	29.06	89.65	30.46	88.56	31.83
48	91.65	27.67	90.66	29.11	89.61	30.51	88.53	31.87
50	91.61	27.72	90.62	29.15	89.58	30.55	88.49	31.92
52	91.58	27.77	90.59	29.20	89.54	30.60	88.45	31.96
54	91.55	27.81	90.55	29.25	89.51	30.65	88.41	32.01
56	91.52	27.86	90.52	29.30	89.47	30.69	88.38	32.05
58	91.48	27.91	90.48	29.34	89.44	30.74	88.34	32.09
60	91.45	27.96	90.45	29.39	89.40	30.78	88.30	32.14

Table XXVII.
Stadia Coefficients, Vertical Rod

$100 \cos^2 \alpha$ and $100(\frac{1}{2} \sin 2\alpha)$

	20°		21°		22°		23°	
	Hor. Dist.	Diff. Elev.	Hor. Dist.	Diff. Elev.	Hor. Dist.	Diff. Elev.	Hor. Dist.	Diff. Elev.
0	88.30	32.14	87.16	33.46	85.97	34.73	84.73	35.97
2	88.26	32.18	87.12	33.50	85.93	34.77	84.69	36.01
4	88.23	32.23	87.08	33.54	85.89	34.82	84.65	36.05
6	88.19	32.27	87.04	33.59	85.85	34.86	84.61	36.09
8	88.15	32.32	87.00	33.63	85.80	34.90	84.57	36.13
10	88.11	32.36	86.96	33.67	85.76	34.94	84.52	36.17
12	88.08	32.41	86.92	33.72	85.72	34.98	84.48	36.21
14	88.04	32.45	86.88	33.76	85.68	35.02	84.44	36.25
16	88.00	32.49	86.84	33.80	85.64	35.07	84.40	36.29
18	87.96	32.54	86.80	33.84	85.60	35.11	84.35	36.33
20	87.93	32.58	86.77	33.89	85.56	35.15	84.31	36.37
22	87.89	32.63	86.73	33.93	85.52	35.19	84.27	36.41
24	87.85	32.67	86.69	33.97	85.48	35.23	84.23	36.45
26	87.81	32.72	86.65	34.01	85.44	35.27	84.18	36.49
28	87.77	32.76	86.61	34.06	85.40	35.31	84.14	36.53
30	87.74	32.80	86.57	34.10	85.36	35.36	84.10	36.57
32	87.70	32.85	86.53	34.14	85.31	35.40	84.06	36.61
34	87.66	32.89	86.49	34.18	85.27	35.44	84.01	36.65
36	87.62	32.93	86.45	34.23	85.23	35.48	83.97	36.69
38	87.58	32.98	86.41	34.27	85.19	35.52	83.93	36.73
40	87.54	33.02	86.37	34.31	85.15	35.56	83.89	36.77
42	87.51	33.07	86.33	34.35	85.11	35.60	83.84	36.80
44	87.47	33.11	86.29	34.40	85.07	35.64	83.80	36.84
46	87.43	33.15	86.25	34.44	85.02	35.68	83.76	36.88
48	87.39	33.20	86.21	34.48	84.98	35.72	83.72	36.92
50	87.35	33.24	86.17	34.52	84.94	35.76	83.67	36.96
52	87.31	33.28	86.13	34.57	84.90	35.80	83.63	37.00
54	87.27	33.33	86.09	34.61	84.86	35.85	83.59	37.04
56	87.24	33.37	86.05	34.65	84.82	35.89	83.54	37.08
58	87.20	33.41	86.01	34.69	84.77	35.93	83.50	37.12
60	87.16	33.46	85.97	34.73	84.73	35.97	83.46	37.16

Table XXVII.
Stadia Coefficients, Vertical Rod

$100 \cos^2 \alpha$ and $100 \ (\tfrac{1}{2} \sin 2 \alpha)$

	24°		25°		26°		27°	
	Hor. Dist.	Diff. Elev.	Hor. Dist.	Diff. Elev.	Hor. Dist.	Diff. Elev.	Hor. Dist.	Diff. Elev.
′								
0	83.46	37.16	82.14	38.30	80.78	39.40	79.39	40.45
2	83.41	37.20	82.09	38.34	80.74	39.44	79.34	40.49
4	83.37	37.23	82.05	38.38	80.69	39.47	79.30	40.52
6	83.33	37.27	82.01	38.41	80.65	39.51	79.25	40.55
8	83.28	37.31	81.96	38.45	80.60	39.54	79.20	40.59
10	83.24	37.35	81.92	38.49	80.55	39.58	79.15	40.62
12	83.20	37.39	81.87	38.53	80.51	39.61	79.11	40.66
14	83.15	37.43	81.83	38.56	80.46	39.65	79.06	40.69
16	83.11	37.47	81.78	38.60	80.41	39.69	79.01	40.72
18	83.07	37.51	81.74	38.64	80.37	39.72	78.96	40.76
20	83.02	37.54	81.69	38.67	80.32	39.76	78.92	40.79
22	82.98	37.58	81.65	38.71	80.28	39.79	78.87	40.82
24	82.93	37.62	81.60	38.75	80.23	39.83	78.82	40.86
26	82.89	37.66	81.56	38.78	80.18	39.86	78.77	40.89
28	82.85	37.70	81.51	38.82	80.14	39.90	78.73	40.92
30	82.80	37.74	81.47	38.86	80.09	39.93	78.68	40.96
32	82.76	37.77	81.42	38.89	80.04	39.97	78.63	40.99
34	82.72	37.81	81.38	38.93	80.00	40.00	78.58	41.02
36	82.67	37.85	81.33	38.97	79.95	40.04	78.54	41.06
38	82.63	37.89	81.28	39.00	79.90	40.07	78.49	41.09
40	82.58	37.93	81.24	39.04	79.86	40.11	78.44	41.12
42	82.54	37.96	81.19	39.08	79.81	40.14	78.39	41.16
44	82.49	38.00	81.15	39.11	79.76	40.18	78.34	41.19
46	82.45	38.04	81.10	39.15	79.72	40.21	78.30	41.22
48	82.41	38.08	81.06	39.18	79.67	40.24	78.25	41.26
50	82.36	38.11	81.01	39.22	79.62	40.28	78.20	41.29
52	82.32	38.15	80.97	39.26	79.58	40.31	78.15	41.32
54	82.27	38.19	80.92	39.29	79.53	40.35	78.10	41.35
56	82.23	38.23	80.87	39.33	79.48	40.38	78.06	41.39
58	82.18	38.26	80.83	39.36	79.44	40.42	78.01	41.42
60	82.14	38.30	80.78	39.40	79.39	40.45	77.96	41.45

Table XXVIII.
Convergency of Meridians, Six Miles Long and Six Miles Apart, and Differences of Latitude and Longitude

LAT.	CONVERGENCY			DIFFERENCE OF LONGITUDE PER RANGE		DIFFERENCE OF LATITUDE FOR—	
	On the Parallel	Angle		In Arc	In Time	1 mi.	1 Tp.
°	Lks.	′	″	′ ″	Seconds		
25	33.9	2	25	5 44.34	22.96		
26	35.4	2	32	5 47.20	23.15	′	
27	37.0	2	39	5 50.22	23.35	0.871	5.229
28	38.6	2	46	5 53.40	23.56		
29	40.2	2	53	5 56.74	23.78		
30	41.9	3	0	6 0.26	24.02		
31	43.6	3	7	6 3.97	24.26		
32	45.4	3	15	6 7.87	24.52	0.871	5.225
33	47.2	3	23	6 11.96	24.80		
34	49.1	3	30	6 16.26	25.08		
35	50.9	3	38	6 20.78	25.39		
36	52.7	3	46	6 25.53	25.70		
37	54.7	3	55	6 30.52	26.03	0.870	5.221
38	56.8	4	4	6 35.76	26.38		
39	58.8	4	13	6 41.27	26.75		
40	60.9	4	22	6 47.06	27.14		
41	63.1	4	31	6 53.15	27.54		
42	65.4	4	41	6 59.56	27.97	0.869	5.216
43	67.7	4	51	7 6.29	28.42		
44	70.1	5	1	7 13.39	28.89		
45	72.6	5	12	7 20.86	29.39		
46	75.2	5	23	7 28.74	29.92		
47	77.8	5	34	7 37.04	30.47	0.869	5.211
48	80.6	5	46	7 45.80	31.05		
49	83.5	5	59	7 55.05	31.67		
50	86.4	6	12	8 4.83	32.32		
51	89.6	6	25	8 15.17	33.03		
52	92.8	6	39	8 26.13	33.74	0.868	5.207
53	96.2	6	54	8 37.75	34.52		
54	99.8	7	9	8 50.07	35.34		
55	103.5	7	25	9 3.18	36.22		
56	107.5	7	42	9 17.12	37.14		
57	111.6	8	0	9 31.97	38.13	0.867	5.202
58	116.0	8	19	9 47.83	39.19		
59	120.6	8	38	10 4.78	40.32		
60	125.5	8	59	10 22.94	41.52		
61	130.8	9	22	10 42.42	42.83		
62	136.3	9	46	11 3.38	44.22	0.866	5.198
63	142.2	10	11	11 25.97	45.73		
64	148.6	10	38	11 50.37	47.36		
65	155.0	11	8	12 16.82	49.12		
66	162.8	11	39	12 45.55	51.04		
67	170.7	12	13	13 16.88	53.12	0.866	5.195
68	179.3	12	51	13 51.15	55.41		
69	188.7	13	31	14 28.77	57.92		
70	199.1	14	15	15 10.26	60.68	0.866	5.193

Grade (Percent)	Hydraulic Slope	Fall per Mile	Slope Angle °	′	″	Grade (Percent)	Hydraulic Slope	Fall per Mile	Slope Angle °	′	″
.01	.0001	.528			21	.61	.0061	32.208	20	58	
.02	.0002	1.056			41	.62	.0062	32.736	21	19	
.03	.0003	1.584		1	02	.63	.0063	33.264	21	39	
.04	.0004	2.112		1	23	.64	.0064	33.792	22	00	
.05	.0005	2.640		1	43	.65	.0065	34.320	22	21	
.06	.0006	3.168		2	04	.66	.0066	34.848	22	41	
.07	.0007	3.696		2	24	.67	.0067	35.376	23	02	
.08	.0008	4.224		2	45	.68	.0068	35.904	23	23	
.09	.0009	4.752		3	06	.69	.0069	36.432	23	43	
.10	.0010	5.280		3	26	.70	.0070	36.960	24	04	
.11	.0011	5.808		3	47	.71	.0071	37.488	24	24	
.12	.0012	6.336		4	08	.72	.0072	38.016	24	45	
.13	.0013	6.864		4	28	.73	.0073	38.544	25	06	
.14	.0014	7.392		4	49	.74	.0074	39.072	25	26	
.15	.0015	7.920		5	09	.75	.0075	39.600	25	47	
.16	.0016	8.448		5	30	.76	.0076	40.128	26	08	
.17	.0017	8.976		5	51	.77	.0077	40.656	26	28	
.18	.0018	9.504		6	11	.78	.0078	41.184	26	49	
.19	.0019	10.032		6	32	.79	.0079	41.712	27	09	
.20	.0020	10.560		6	53	.80	.0080	42.240	27	30	
.21	.0021	11.088		7	13	.81	.0081	42.768	27	51	
.22	.0022	11.616		7	34	.82	.0082	43.296	28	11	
.23	.0023	12.144		7	54	.83	.0083	43.824	28	32	
.24	.0024	12.672		8	15	.84	.0084	44.352	28	53	
.25	.0025	13.200		8	36	.85	.0085	44.880	29	13	
.26	.0026	13.728		8	56	.86	.0086	45.408	29	34	
.27	.0027	14.256		9	17	.87	.0087	45.936	29	54	
.28	.0028	14.784		9	38	.88	.0088	46.464	30	15	
.29	.0029	15.312		9	58	.89	.0089	46.992	30	36	
.30	.0030	15.840		10	19	.90	.0090	47.520	30	57	
.31	.0031	16.368		10	39	.91	.0091	48.048	31	17	
.32	.0032	16.896		11	00	.92	.0092	48.576	31	38	
.33	.0033	17.424		11	21	.93	.0093	49.104	31	58	
.34	.0034	17.952		11	41	.94	.0094	49.632	32	19	
.35	.0035	18.480		12	02	.95	.0095	50.160	32	39	
.36	.0036	19.008		12	23	.96	.0096	50.688	33	00	
.37	.0037	19.536		12	43	.97	.0097	51.216	33	21	
.38	.0038	20.064		13	04	.98	.0098	51.744	33	41	
.39	.0039	20.592		13	24	.99	.0099	52.272	34	02	
.40	.0040	21.120		13	45	1.00	.0100	52.800	34	23	
.41	.0041	21.648		14	06	1.01	.0101	53.328	34	43	
.42	.0042	22.176		14	26	1.02	.0102	53.856	35	04	
.43	.0043	22.704		14	47	1.03	.0103	54.384	35	24	
.44	.0044	23.232		15	08	1.04	.0104	54.912	35	45	
.45	.0045	23.760		15	28	1.05	.0105	55.440	36	05	
.46	.0046	24.288		15	49	1.06	.0106	55.968	36	26	
.47	.0047	24.816		16	09	1.07	.0107	56.496	36	47	
.48	.0048	25.344		16	30	1.08	.0108	57.024	37	08	
.49	.0049	25.872		16	51	1.09	.0109	57.552	37	28	
.50	.0050	26.400		17	11	1.10	.0110	58.080	37	49	
.51	.0051	26.928		17	32	1.11	.0111	58.608	38	09	
.52	.0052	27.456		17	53	1.12	.0112	59.136	38	30	
.53	.0053	27.984		18	13	1.13	.0113	59.664	38	51	
.54	.0054	28.512		18	34	1.14	.0114	60.192	39	11	
.55	.0055	29.040		18	54	1.15	.0115	60.720	39	32	
.56	.0056	29.568		19	15	1.16	.0116	61.248	39	53	
.57	.0057	30.096		19	36	1.17	.0117	61.776	40	13	
.58	.0058	30.624		19	56	1.18	.0118	62.304	40	34	
.59	.0059	31.152		20	17	1.19	.0119	62.832	40	54	
.60	.0060	31.680		20	38	1.20	.0120	63.360	41	15	

Grade (Percent)	Hydraulic Slope	Fall per Mile	°	'	"	Grade (Percent)	Hydraulic Slope	Fall per Mile	°	'	"
1.21	.0121	63.888		41	35	1.81	.0181	95.568	1	02	13
1.22	.0122	64.416		41	56	1.82	.0182	96.096	1	02	34
1.23	.0123	64.944		42	17	1.83	.0183	96.624	1	02	54
1.24	.0124	65.472		42	38	1.84	.0184	97.152	1	03	15
1.25	.0125	66.000		42	58	1.85	.0185	97.680	1	03	35
1.26	.0126	66.528		43	19	1.86	.0186	98.208	1	03	56
1.27	.0127	67.056		43	39	1.87	.0187	98.736	1	04	17
1.28	.0128	67.584		44	00	1.88	.0188	99.264	1	04	37
1.29	.0129	68.112		44	21	1.89	.0189	99.792	1	04	58
1.30	.0130	68.640		44	41	1.90	.0190	100.320	1	05	19
1.31	.0131	69.168		45	02	1.91	.0191	100.848	1	05	39
1.32	.0132	69.696		45	23	1.92	.0192	101.376	1	06	00
1.33	.0133	70.224		45	43	1.93	.0193	101.904	1	06	20
1.34	.0134	70.752		46	04	1.94	.0194	102.432	1	06	41
1.35	.0135	71.280		46	24	1.95	.0195	102.960	1	07	02
1.36	.0136	71.808		46	45	1.96	.0196	103.488	1	07	22
1.37	.0137	72.336		47	06	1.97	.0197	104.016	1	07	43
1.38	.0138	72.864		47	26	1.98	.0198	104.544	1	08	04
1.39	.0139	73.392		47	47	1.99	.0199	105.072	1	08	24
1.40	.0140	73.920		48	08	2.00	.0200	105.600	1	08	45
1.41	.0141	74.448		48	28	2.10	.0210	110.880	1	12	11
1.42	.0142	74.976		48	49	2.20	.0220	116.160	1	15	37
1.43	.0143	75.504		49	09	2.30	.0230	121.440	1	19	03
1.44	.0144	76.032		49	30	2.40	.0240	126.720	1	22	29
1.45	.0145	76.560		49	51	2.50	.0250	132.000	1	25	56
1.46	.0146	77.088		50	11	2.60	.0260	137.280	1	29	22
1.47	.0147	77.616		50	32	2.70	.0270	142.560	1	32	48
1.48	.0148	78.144		50	52	2.80	.0280	147.840	1	36	14
1.49	.0149	78.672		51	13	2.90	.0290	153.120	1	39	40
1.50	.0150	79.200		51	34	3.00	.0300	158.400	1	43	06
1.51	.0151	79.728		51	54	3.10	.0310	163.680	1	46	32
1.52	.0152	80.256		52	15	3.20	.0320	168.960	1	49	58
1.53	.0153	80.784		52	36	3.30	.0330	174.240	1	53	24
1.54	.0154	81.312		52	56	3.40	.0340	179.520	1	56	50
1.55	.0155	81.840		53	17	3.50	.0350	184.800	2	00	16
1.56	.0156	82.368		53	37	3.60	.0360	190.080	2	03	42
1.57	.0157	82.896		53	58	3.70	.0370	195.360	2	07	08
1.58	.0158	83.424		54	19	3.80	.0380	200.640	2	10	34
1.59	.0159	83.952		54	39	3.90	.0390	205.920	2	14	00
1.60	.0160	84.480		55	00	4.00	.0400	211.200	2	17	26
1.61	.0161	85.008		55	21	5.0	.0500	264.000	2	51	45
1.62	.0162	85.536		55	41	6.0	.0600	316.800	3	26	01
1.63	.0163	86.064		56	02	7.0	.0700	369.600	4	0	15
1.64	.0164	86.592		56	22	8.0	.0800	422.400	4	34	26
1.65	.0165	87.120		56	43	9.0	.0900	475.200	5	08	34
1.66	.0166	87.648		57	04	10.0	.1000	528.000	5	42	38
1.67	.0167	88.176		57	24	11.0	.1100	580.800	6	16	38
1.68	.0168	88.704		57	45	12.0	.1200	633.600	6	50	34
1.69	.0169	89.232		58	06	13.0	.1300	686.400	7	24	25
1.70	.0170	89.760		58	26	14.0	.1400	739.200	7	58	10
1.71	.0171	90.288		58	47	15.0	.1500	792.000	8	31	50
1.72	.0172	90.816		59	07	16.0	.1600	844.800	9	05	25
1.73	.0173	91.344		59	28	17.0	.1700	897.600	9	38	52
1.74	.0174	91.872		59	49	18.0	.1800	950.400	10	12	14
1.75	.0175	92.400	1	00	09	19.0	.1900	1003.200	10	45	28
1.76	.0176	92.928	1	00	30	20.0	.2000	1056.000	11	18	36
1.77	.0177	93.456	1	00	51	21.0	.2100	1108.800	11	51	35
1.78	.0178	93.984	1	01	11	22.0	.2200	1161.600	12	24	27
1.79	.0179	94.512	1	01	32	23.0	.2300	1214.400	12	57	10
1.80	.0180	95.040	1	01	52	24.0	.2400	1267.200	13	29	46

Table XXX. Correction in Feet from 100 Feet of Slope Taping to the Horizontal

(100) (Versine of Slope Angle)

′	0°	1°	2°	3°	4°	5°	6°	7°	8°	9°	10°	11°	12°	13°	14°	15°	16°	17°	18°
0	0.000	0.015	0.061	0.137	0.244	0.381	0.548	0.745	0.973	1.231	1.519	1.837	2.185	2.563	2.970	3.407	3.874	4.370	4.894
2	0.000	0.016	0.063	0.140	0.248	0.386	0.554	0.752	0.981	1.240	1.529	1.848	2.197	2.576	2.985	3.422	3.890	4.387	4.912
4	0.000	0.017	0.065	0.143	0.252	0.391	0.560	0.760	0.989	1.249	1.539	1.860	2.209	2.589	2.999	3.438	3.906	4.404	4.930
6	0.000	0.018	0.067	0.146	0.256	0.396	0.566	0.767	0.998	1.259	1.550	1.871	2.222	2.602	3.013	3.453	3.922	4.421	4.948
8	0.000	0.020	0.069	0.149	0.260	0.401	0.572	0.774	1.006	1.268	1.560	1.882	2.234	2.616	3.027	3.468	3.938	4.438	4.967
10	0.000	0.021	0.071	0.153	0.264	0.406	0.579	0.781	1.014	1.277	1.570	1.893	2.246	2.629	3.041	3.483	3.954	4.455	4.985
12	0.001	0.022	0.074	0.156	0.269	0.412	0.585	0.789	1.022	1.286	1.580	1.904	2.258	2.642	3.055	3.498	3.971	4.472	5.003
14	0.001	0.023	0.076	0.159	0.273	0.417	0.591	0.796	1.031	1.296	1.591	1.916	2.271	2.655	3.070	3.514	3.987	4.489	5.021
16	0.001	0.024	0.078	0.162	0.277	0.422	0.598	0.803	1.039	1.305	1.601	1.927	2.283	2.669	3.084	3.529	4.003	4.507	5.039
18	0.001	0.026	0.081	0.166	0.281	0.428	0.604	0.811	1.047	1.314	1.611	1.939	2.295	2.682	3.098	3.544	4.019	4.524	5.057
20	0.002	0.027	0.083	0.169	0.286	0.433	0.610	0.818	1.056	1.324	1.622	1.950	2.308	2.696	3.113	3.560	4.036	4.541	5.076
22	0.002	0.028	0.085	0.173	0.290	0.438	0.617	0.825	1.064	1.333	1.632	1.961	2.320	2.709	3.127	3.575	4.052	4.559	5.094
24	0.002	0.030	0.088	0.176	0.295	0.444	0.623	0.833	1.073	1.343	1.643	1.973	2.333	2.722	3.142	3.590	4.069	4.576	5.112
26	0.003	0.031	0.090	0.179	0.299	0.449	0.630	0.840	1.081	1.352	1.653	1.984	2.345	2.736	3.156	3.606	4.085	4.593	5.131
28	0.003	0.033	0.093	0.183	0.304	0.455	0.636	0.848	1.090	1.362	1.664	1.996	2.358	2.749	3.171	3.621	4.101	4.611	5.149
30	0.004	0.034	0.095	0.187	0.308	0.460	0.643	0.856	1.098	1.371	1.675	2.008	2.370	2.763	3.185	3.637	4.118	4.628	5.168
32	0.004	0.036	0.098	0.190	0.313	0.466	0.649	0.863	1.107	1.381	1.685	2.019	2.383	2.777	3.200	3.653	4.135	4.646	5.186
34	0.005	0.037	0.100	0.194	0.318	0.472	0.656	0.871	1.116	1.391	1.696	2.031	2.396	2.790	3.214	3.668	4.151	4.663	5.205
36	0.005	0.039	0.103	0.197	0.322	0.477	0.663	0.878	1.124	1.400	1.706	2.042	2.408	2.804	3.229	3.684	4.168	4.681	5.223
38	0.006	0.041	0.106	0.201	0.327	0.483	0.669	0.886	1.133	1.410	1.717	2.054	2.421	2.818	3.244	3.699	4.184	4.699	5.242
40	0.007	0.042	0.108	0.205	0.332	0.489	0.676	0.894	1.142	1.420	1.728	2.066	2.434	2.831	3.258	3.715	4.201	4.716	5.260
42	0.007	0.044	0.111	0.208	0.336	0.494	0.683	0.902	1.151	1.430	1.739	2.078	2.447	2.845	3.273	3.731	4.218	4.734	5.279
44	0.008	0.046	0.114	0.212	0.341	0.500	0.690	0.909	1.159	1.439	1.750	2.090	2.459	2.859	3.288	3.747	4.234	4.752	5.298
46	0.009	0.048	0.117	0.216	0.346	0.506	0.697	0.917	1.168	1.449	1.761	2.101	2.472	2.873	3.303	3.762	4.251	4.769	5.316
48	0.010	0.049	0.119	0.220	0.351	0.512	0.703	0.925	1.177	1.459	1.771	2.113	2.485	2.887	3.318	3.778	4.268	4.787	5.335
50	0.011	0.051	0.122	0.224	0.356	0.518	0.710	0.933	1.186	1.469	1.782	2.125	2.498	2.900	3.333	3.794	4.285	4.805	5.354
52	0.011	0.053	0.125	0.228	0.361	0.524	0.717	0.941	1.195	1.479	1.793	2.137	2.511	2.914	3.347	3.810	4.302	4.823	5.373
54	0.012	0.055	0.128	0.232	0.365	0.530	0.724	0.949	1.204	1.489	1.804	2.149	2.524	2.928	3.362	3.826	4.319	4.841	5.391
56	0.013	0.057	0.131	0.236	0.370	0.536	0.731	0.957	1.213	1.499	1.815	2.161	2.537	2.942	3.377	3.842	4.336	4.858	5.410
58	0.014	0.059	0.134	0.240	0.375	0.542	0.738	0.965	1.222	1.509	1.826	2.173	2.550	2.956	3.392	3.858	4.353	4.876	5.429
60	0.015	0.061	0.137	0.244	0.381	0.548	0.745	0.973	1.231	1.519	1.837	2.185	2.563	2.970	3.407	3.874	4.370	4.894	5.448

Length	Area in Acres	Length	Area in Acres	Length	Area in Acres
100	.2296	1	.002296	51	.117089
200	.4591	2	.004591	52	.119375
300	.6887	3	.006887	53	.121 1
400	.9183	4	.009183	54	.123967
590	1.1478	**5**	.011478	**55**	.126262
600	1.3774	6	.013774	56	.128558
700	1.6070	7	.016070	57	.130654
800	1.8365	8	.018365	58	.133149
900	2.0661	9	.020661	59	.135445
1000	2.2957	**10**	.022957	**60**	.137741
1100	2.5252	11	.025252	61	.140036
1200	2.7548	12	.027548	62	.142332
1300	2.9844	13	.029844	63	.144628
1400	3.2140	14	.032140	64	.146924
1590	3.4435	**15**	.034435	**65**	.149219
1600	3.6731	16	.036731	66	.151515
1700	3.9027	17	.039027	67	.153811
1900	4.1322	18	.041322	68	.156106
1900	4.3618	19	.043618	69	.158402
2000	4.5914	**20**	.045914	**70**	.160698
2100	4.8209	21	.048209	71	.162993
2200	5.0505	22	.050505	72	.165289
2300	5.2801	23	.052801	73	.167585
2400	5.5096	24	.055096	74	.169880
2500	5.7392	**25**	.057392	**75**	.172176
2600	5.9688	26	.059688	76	.174472
2700	6.1983	27	.061983	77	.176767
2800	6.4279	28	.064279	78	.179063
2900	6.6575	29	.066575	79	.181359
3000	6.8870	**30**	.068870	**80**	.183654
3100	7.1166	31	.071166	81	.185950
3200	7.3462	32	.073462	82	.188246
3300	7.5757	33	.075757	83	.190541
3400	7.8053	34	.078073	84	.192837
3590	8.0349	**35**	.083349	**85**	.195133
3600	8.2644	36	.082644	86	.197428
3700	8.4940	37	.084940	87	.199724
3800	8.7236	38	.087236	88	.202020
3900	8.9532	39	.089532	89	.204316
4000	9.1827	**40**	.091827	**90**	.206611
4100	9.4123	41	.094123	91	.208907
4200	9.6419	42	.096419	92	.211203
4300	9.8714	43	.098714	93	.213498
4400	10.1010	44	.101010	94	.215794
4500	10.3306	**45**	.103306	**95**	.218090
4600	10.5601	46	.105601	96	.220385
4700	10.7897	47	.107897	97	.222681
4800	11.0193	48	.110193	98	.224977
4900	11.2488	49	.112488	99	.227272
5000	11.4784	50	.114784	**100**	.229568

EXAMPLE: Required the acres in a 150-foot right of way, 4263 feet long.

For 4200 feet	9.6419 acres	
" 63 "	0.1446 "	
" 4263 "	9.7865 "	

$$9.7865 \times 1.5 = 14.6798 \text{ acres}$$

Table XXXII. Inches in Decimals of a Foot *

Inches	1/16	1/8	3/16	1/4	5/16	3/8	7/16	1/2	9/16	5/8	11/16	3/4	13/16	7/8	15/16
0	.0000	.0052	.0104	.0156	.0208	.0260	.0313	.0365	.0417	.0469	.0521	.0573	.0625	.0677	.0729	.0781
1	.0833	.0885	.0938	.0990	.1042	.1094	.1146	.1198	.1250	.1302	.1354	.1406	.1458	.1510	.1563	.1615
2	.1667	.1719	.1771	.1823	.1875	.1927	.1979	.2031	.2083	.2135	.2188	.2240	.2292	.2344	.2396	.2448
3	.2500	.2552	.2604	.2656	.2708	.2760	.2813	.2865	.2917	.2969	.3021	.3073	.3125	.3177	.3229	.3281
4	.3333	.3385	.3458	.3490	.3542	.3594	.3646	.3698	.3750	.3802	.3854	.3906	.3958	.4010	.4063	.4115
5	.4167	.4219	.4271	.4323	.4375	.4427	.4479	.4531	.4583	.4635	.4688	.4740	.4792	.4844	.4896	.4948
6	.5000	.5052	.5104	.5156	.5208	.5260	.5313	.5365	.5417	.5469	.5521	.5573	.5625	.5677	.5729	.5781
7	.5833	.5885	.5938	.5990	.6042	.6094	.6146	.6198	.6250	.6302	.6354	.6406	.6458	.6510	.6563	.6615
8	.6667	.6719	.6771	.6823	.6875	.6927	.6979	.7031	.7083	.7135	.7188	.7240	.7292	.7344	.7396	.7448
9	.7500	.7552	.7604	.7656	.7708	.7760	.7813	.7865	.7917	.7969	.8021	.8073	.8125	.8177	.8229	.8281
10	.8333	.8385	.8438	.8490	.8542	.8594	.8646	.8698	.8750	.8802	.8854	.8906	.8958	.9010	.9063	.9115
11	.9167	.9219	.9271	.9323	.9375	.9427	.9479	.9531	.9583	.9635	.9688	.9740	.9792	.9844	.9896	.9948

One-hundredth of a foot is closely equal to one-eighth of an inch (error 4 per cent). Also, $3'' = 0.25'$, $4'' = 0.33'+$, $6'' = 0.50'$, $8'' = 0.67'-$, and $9'' = 0.75'$. By the use of these relationships, inches may be approximately converted mentally to decimals of a foot, and vice versa. For example, $0.72' = 9'' - 3/8'' = 8 5/8''$ or $7 5/8'' = 0.63'$ or $7 5/8'' = 0.67' - 0.03' = 0.64'$.

* From Missouri State Highway Commission *Project Engineer Manual*.

254

For temperatures above 50° F. the values are to be added
For temperatures below 50° F. the values are to be subtracted

Average Air Temp. °F.		Difference of Readings in Feet													
		0	20	40	60	80	100	120	140	160	180	200	220	240	260
	+ 50°	0	0	0	0	0	0	0	0	0	0	0	0	0	0
+48°	+ 52°	0	0.1	0.2	0.2	0.3	0.4	0.5	0.5	0.6	0.7	0.8	0.9	0.9	1.0
+46°	+ 54°	0	0.2	0.3	0.5	0.6	0.8	0.9	1.1	1.3	1.4	1.6	1.7	1.9	2.0
+44°	+ 56°	0	0.2	0.5	0.7	0.9	1.2	1.4	1.6	1.9	2.1	2.4	2.6	2.8	3.1
+42°	+ 58°	0	0.3	0.6	0.9	1.3	1.6	1.9	2.2	2.5	2.8	3.1	3.5	3.8	4.1
+40°	+ 60°	0	0.4	0.8	1.2	1.6	2.0	2.4	2.7	3.1	3.5	3.9	4.3	4.7	5.1
+38°	+ 62°	0	0.5	0.9	1.4	1.9	2.4	2.8	3.3	3.8	4.2	4.7	5.2	5.7	6.1
+36°	+ 64°	0	0.5	1.1	1.6	2.2	2.7	3.3	3.8	4.4	4.9	5.5	6.0	6.6	7.1
+34°	+ 66°	0	0.6	1.3	1.9	2.5	3.1	3.8	4.4	5.0	5.7	6.3	6.9	7.5	8.2
+32°	+ 68°	0	0.7	1.4	2.1	2.8	3.5	4.2	4.9	5.7	6.4	7.1	7.8	8.5	9.2
+30°	+ 70°	0	0.8	1.6	2.4	3.1	3.9	4.7	5.5	6.3	7.1	7.9	8.6	9.4	10.2
+28°	+ 72°	0	0.9	1.7	2.6	3.5	4.3	5.2	6.0	6.9	7.8	8.6	9.5	10.4	11.2
+26°	+ 74°	0	0.9	1.9	2.8	3.8	4.7	5.7	6.6	7.5	8.5	9.4	10.4	11.3	12.3
+24°	+ 76°	0	1.0	2.0	3.1	4.1	5.1	6.1	7.1	8.2	9.2	10.2	11.2	12.2	13.3
+22°	+ 78°	0	1.1	2.2	3.3	4.4	5.5	6.6	7.7	8.8	9.9	11.0	12.1	13.2	14.3
+20°	+ 80°	0	1.2	2.4	3.5	4.7	5.9	7.1	8.2	9.4	10.6	11.8	13.0	14.1	15.3
+18°	+ 82°	0	1.3	2.5	3.8	5.0	6.3	7.5	8.8	10.0	11.3	12.6	13.8	15.1	16.3
+16°	+ 84°	0	1.3	2.7	4.0	5.3	6.7	8.0	9.4	10.7	12.0	13.4	14.7	16.0	17.4
+14°	+ 86°	0	1.4	2.8	4.2	5.7	7.1	8.5	9.9	11.3	12.7	14.1	15.6	17.0	18.4
+12°	+ 88°	0	1.5	3.0	4.5	6.0	7.5	9.0	10.4	11.9	13.4	14.9	16.4	17.9	19.4
+10°	+ 90°	0	1.6	3.1	4.7	6.3	7.9	9.4	11.0	12.6	14.1	15.7	17.3	18.9	20.4
+ 8°	+ 92°	0	1.6	3.3	4.9	6.6	8.2	9.9	11.5	13.2	14.8	16.5	18.1	19.8	21.4
+ 6°	+ 94°	0	1.7	3.5	5.2	6.9	8.6	10.4	12.1	13.8	15.6	17.3	19.0	20.7	22.5
+ 4°	+ 96°	0	1.8	3.6	5.4	7.2	9.0	10.8	12.6	14.5	16.3	18.1	19.9	21.7	23.5
+ 2°	+ 98°	0	1.9	3.8	5.7	7.5	9.4	11.3	13.2	15.1	17.0	18.9	20.7	22.6	24.5
+ 0°	+100°	0	2.0	3.9	5.9	7.9	9.8	11.8	13.7	15.7	17.7	19.6	21.6	23.6	25.5
− 2°	+102°	0	2.0	4.1	6.1	8.2	10.2	12.3	14.3	16.3	18.4	20.4	22.5	24.5	26.6
− 4°	+104°	0	2.1	4.2	6.4	8.5	10.6	12.7	14.8	17.0	19.1	21.2	23.3	25.5	27.6
− 6°	+106°	0	2.2	4.4	6.6	8.8	11.0	13.2	15.4	17.6	19.8	22.0	24.2	26.4	28.6
− 8°	+108°	0	2.3	4.6	6.8	9.1	11.4	13.7	15.9	18.2	20.5	22.8	25.1	27.3	29.6
−10°	+110°	0	2.4	4.7	7.1	9.4	11.8	14.1	16.5	18.9	21.2	23.6	25.9	28.3	30.6
−12°	+112°	0	2.4	4.9	7.3	9.7	12.2	14.6	17.0	19.5	21.9	24.4	26.8	29.2	31.7
−14°	+114°	0	2.5	5.0	7.5	10.1	12.6	15.1	17.6	20.1	22.6	25.1	27.7	30.2	32.7
−16°	+116°	0	2.6	5.2	7.8	10.4	13.0	15.6	18.1	20.7	23.3	25.9	28.5	31.1	33.7
−18°	+118°	0	2.7	5.3	8.0	10.7	13.4	16.0	18.7	21.4	24.0	26.7	29.4	32.1	34.7
−20°	+120°	0	2.7	5.5	8.2	11.0	13.7	16.5	19.2	22.0	24.7	27.5	30.2	33.0	35.7
−22°	+122°	0	2.8	5.7	8.5	11.3	14.1	17.0	19.8	22.6	25.4	28.3	31.1	33.9	36.8
−24°	+124°	0	2.9	5.8	8.7	11.6	14.5	17.4	20.3	23.3	26.2	29.1	32.0	34.9	37.8
−26°	+126°	0	3.0	6.0	9.0	11.9	14.9	17.9	20.9	23.9	26.9	29.9	32.8	35.8	38.8

* From Paulin System *Manual in Altimetry.*

Table XXXIII. Average Air Temperature Correction for Barometric Leveling (in Feet) [XXXIII

For temperatures above 50° F. the values are to be added
For temperatures below 50° F. the values are to be subtracted

Average Air Temp. °F.		Difference of Readings in Feet											
		280	300	320	340	360	380	400	420	440	460	480	500
	+ 50°	0	0	0	0	0	0	0	0	0	0	0	0
+48°	+ 52°	1.1	1.2	1.3	1.3	1.4	1.5	1.6	1.6	1.7	1.8	1.9	2.0
+46°	+ 54°	2.2	2.4	2.5	2.7	2.8	3.0	3.1	3.3	3.5	3.6	3.8	3.9
+44°	+ 56°	3.3	3.5	3.8	4.0	4.2	4.5	4.7	4.9	5.2	5.4	5.7	5.9
+42°	+ 58°	4.4	4.7	5.0	5.3	5.7	6.0	6.3	6.6	6.9	7.2	7.5	7.9
+40°	+ 60°	5.5	5.9	6.3	6.7	7.1	7.5	7.9	8.2	8.6	9.0	9.4	9.8
+38°	+ 62°	6.6	7.1	7.5	8.0	8.5	9.0	9.4	9.9	10.4	10.8	11.3	11.8
+36°	+ 64°	7.7	8.2	8.8	9.3	9.9	10.4	11.0	11.5	12.1	12.6	13.2	13.7
+34°	+ 66°	8.8	9.4	10.1	10.7	11.3	11.9	12.6	13.2	13.8	14.5	15.1	15.7
+32°	+ 68°	9.9	10.6	11.3	12.0	12.7	13.4	14.1	14.8	15.6	16.3	17.0	17.7
+30°	+ 70°	11.0	11.8	12.6	13.4	14.1	14.9	15.7	16.5	17.3	18.1	18.9	19.6
+28°	+ 72°	12.1	13.0	13.8	14.7	15.6	16.4	17.3	18.2	19.0	19.9	20.7	21.6
+26°	+ 74°	13.2	14.1	15.1	16.0	17.0	17.9	18.9	19.8	20.7	21.7	22.6	23.6
+24°	+ 76°	14.3	15.3	16.3	17.4	18.4	19.4	20.4	21.4	22.5	23.5	24.5	25.5
+22°	+ 78°	15.4	16.5	17.6	18.7	19.8	20.9	22.0	23.1	24.2	25.3	26.4	27.5
+20°	+ 80°	16.5	17.7	18.8	20.0	21.2	22.4	23.6	24.7	25.9	27.1	28.3	29.5
+18°	+ 82°	17.6	18.8	20.1	21.4	22.6	23.9	25.1	26.4	27.7	28.9	30.2	31.4
+16°	+ 84°	18.7	20.0	21.4	22.7	24.0	25.4	26.7	28.0	29.4	30.7	32.1	33.4
+14°	+ 86°	19.8	21.2	22.6	24.0	25.5	26.9	28.3	29.7	31.1	32.5	33.9	35.3
+12°	+ 88°	20.9	22.4	23.9	25.4	26.9	28.4	29.9	31.3	32.8	34.3	35.8	37.3
+10°	+ 90°	22.0	23.6	25.1	26.7	28.3	29.9	31.4	33.0	34.6	36.1	37.7	39.3
+ 8°	+ 92°	23.1	24.7	26.4	28.0	29.7	31.3	33.0	34.6	36.3	37.9	39.6	41.2
+ 6°	+ 94°	24.2	25.9	27.7	29.4	31.1	32.8	34.6	36.3	38.0	39.8	41.5	43.2
+ 4°	+ 96°	25.3	27.1	28.9	30.7	32.5	34.3	36.1	37.9	39.8	41.6	43.4	45.2
+ 2°	+ 98°	26.4	28.3	30.2	32.1	33.9	35.8	37.7	39.6	41.5	43.4	45.2	47.1
+ 0°	+100°	27.5	29.5	31.4	33.4	35.4	37.3	39.3	41.2	43.2	45.2	47.1	49.1
− 2°	+102°	28.6	30.6	32.7	34.7	36.8	38.8	40.9	42.9	44.9	47.0	49.0	51.1
− 4°	+104°	29.7	31.8	33.9	36.1	38.2	40.3	42.4	44.5	46.7	48.8	50.9	53.0
− 6°	+106°	30.8	33.0	35.2	37.4	39.6	41.8	44.0	46.2	48.4	50.6	52.8	55.0
− 8°	+108°	31.9	34.2	36.5	38.7	41.0	43.3	45.6	47.8	50.1	52.4	54.7	57.0
−10°	+110°	33.0	35.4	37.7	40.1	42.4	44.8	47.1	49.5	51.8	54.2	56.6	58.9
−12°	+112°	34.1	36.5	39.0	41.4	43.8	46.3	48.7	51.1	53.6	56.0	58.4	60.9
−14°	+114°	35.2	37.7	40.2	42.7	45.3	47.8	50.3	52.8	55.3	57.8	60.3	62.8
−16°	+116°	36.3	38.9	41.5	44.1	46.7	49.3	51.9	54.4	57.0	59.6	62.2	64.8
−18°	+118°	37.4	40.1	42.7	45.4	48.1	50.8	53.4	56.1	58.8	61.4	64.1	66.8
−20°	+120°	38.5	41.2	44.0	46.7	49.5	52.2	55.0	57.7	60.5	63.2	66.0	68.7
−22°	+122°	39.6	42.4	45.2	48.1	50.9	53.7	56.6	59.4	62.2	65.1	67.9	70.7
−24°	+124°	40.7	43.6	46.5	49.4	52.3	55.2	58.1	61.0	64.0	66.9	69.8	72.7
−26°	+126°	41.8	44.8	47.8	50.8	53.7	56.7	59.7	62.7	65.7	68.7	71.7	74.6

For temperatures above 50° F. the values are to be added
For temperatures below 50° F. the values are to be subtracted

Average Air Temp. °F.		Difference of Readings in Feet													
		500	520	540	560	580	600	620	640	660	680	700	720	740	760
	+ 50°	0	0	0	0	0	0	0	0	0	0	0	0	0	0
+48°	+ 52°	2.0	2.0	2.1	2.2	2.3	2.4	2.4	2.5	2.6	2.7	2.7	2.8	2.9	3.0
+46°	+ 54°	3.9	4.1	4.2	4.4	4.6	4.7	4.9	5.0	5.2	5.3	5.5	5.7	5.8	6.0
+44°	+ 56°	5.9	6.1	6.4	6.6	6.8	7.1	7.3	7.5	7.8	8.0	8.2	8.5	8.7	9.0
+42°	+ 58°	7.9	8.2	8.5	8.8	9.1	9.4	9.7	10.1	10.4	10.7	11.0	11.3	11.6	11.9
+40°	+ 60°	9.8	10.2	10.6	11.0	11.4	11.8	12.2	12.6	13.0	13.4	13.7	14.1	14.5	14.9
+38°	+ 62°	11.8	12.3	12.7	13.2	13.7	14.1	14.6	15.1	15.5	16.0	16.5	17.0	17.4	17.9
+36°	+ 64°	13.7	14.3	14.8	15.4	15.9	16.5	17.0	17.6	18.1	18.7	19.2	19.8	20.3	20.9
+34°	+ 66°	15.7	16.3	17.0	17.6	18.2	18.9	19.5	20.1	20.7	21.4	22.0	22.6	23.3	23.9
+32°	+ 68°	17.7	18.4	19.1	19.8	20.5	21.2	21.9	22.6	23.3	24.0	24.7	25.5	26.2	26.9
+30°	+ 70°	19.6	20.4	21.2	22.0	22.8	23.6	24.4	25.1	25.9	26.7	27.5	28.3	29.1	29.9
+28°	+ 72°	21.6	22.5	23.3	24.2	25.1	25.9	26.8	27.7	28.5	29.4	30.2	31.1	32.0	32.8
+26°	+ 74°	23.6	24.5	25.5	26.4	27.3	28.3	29.2	30.2	31.1	32.1	33.0	33.9	34.9	35.8
+24°	+ 76°	25.5	26.6	27.6	28.6	29.6	30.6	31.7	32.7	33.7	34.7	35.7	36.8	37.8	38.8
+22°	+ 78°	27.5	28.6	29.7	30.8	31.9	33.0	34.1	35.2	36.3	37.4	38.5	39.6	40.7	41.8
+20°	+ 80°	29.5	30.3	31.8	33.0	34.2	35.4	36.5	37.7	38.9	40.1	41.2	42.4	43.6	44.8
+18°	+ 82°	31.4	32.7	33.9	35.2	36.5	37.7	39.0	40.2	41.5	42.7	44.0	45.3	46.5	47.8
+16°	+ 84°	33.4	34.7	36.1	37.4	38.7	40.1	41.4	42.7	44.1	45.4	46.7	48.1	49.4	50.8
+14°	+ 86°	35.3	36.8	38.2	39.6	41.0	42.4	43.8	45.2	46.7	48.1	49.5	50.9	52.3	53.7
+12°	+ 88°	37.3	38.8	40.3	41.8	43.3	44.8	46.3	47.8	49.3	50.7	52.2	53.7	55.2	56.7
+10°	+ 90°	39.3	40.9	42.4	44.0	45.6	47.1	48.7	50.3	51.8	53.4	55.0	56.6	58.1	59.7
+ 8°	+ 92°	41.2	42.9	44.5	46.2	47.8	49.5	51.1	52.8	54.4	56.1	57.7	59.4	61.0	62.7
+ 6°	+ 94°	43.2	44.9	46.7	48.4	50.1	51.9	53.6	55.3	57.0	58.8	60.5	62.2	64.0	65.7
+ 4°	+ 96°	45.2	57.0	48.8	50.6	52.4	54.2	56.0	57.8	59.6	61.4	63.2	65.1	66.9	67.8
+ 2°	+ 98°	47.1	49.0	50.9	52.8	54.7	56.6	58.4	60.3	62.2	64.1	66.0	67.9	69.8	71.6
+ 0°	+100°	49.1	51.1	53.0	55.0	57.0	58.9	60.9	62.8	64.8	66.8	68.7	70.7	72.7	74.6
− 2°	+102°	51.1	53.1	55.1	57.2	59.2	61.3	63.3	65.4	67.4	69.4	71.5	73.5	75.6	77.6
− 4°	+104°	53.0	55.2	57.3	59.4	61.5	63.6	65.8	67.9	70.0	72.1	74.2	76.4	78.5	80.6
− 6°	+106°	55.0	57.2	59.4	61.6	63.8	66.0	68.2	70.4	72.6	74.8	77.0	79.2	81. 4	83.6
− 8°	+108°	57.0	59.2	61.5	63.8	66.1	68.3	70.6	72.9	75.2	77.5	79.7	82.0	84.3	86.6
−10°	+110°	58.9	61.3	63.6	66.0	68.3	70.7	73.1	75.4	77.8	80.1	82.5	84.8	87.2	89.6
−12°	+112°	60.9	63.3	65.8	68.2	70.6	73.1	75.5	77.9	80.4	82.8	85.2	87.7	90.1	92.5
−14°	+114°	62.8	65.4	67.9	70.4	72.9	75.4	77.9	80.4	83.0	85.5	88.0	90.5	93.0	95.5
−16°	+116°	64.8	67.4	70.0	72.6	75.2	77.8	80.4	83.0	85.6	88.1	90.7	93.3	95.9	98.5
−18°	+118°	66.8	69.5	72.1	74.8	77.5	80.1	82.8	85.5	88.1	90.8	93.5	96.2	98.8	101.5
−20°	+120°	68.7	71.5	74.2	77.0	79.7	82.5	85.2	88.0	90.7	93.5	96.2	99.0	101.7	104.5
−22°	+122°	70.7	73.6	76.4	79.2	82.0	84.9	87.7	90.5	93.3	96.2	99.0	101.8	104.7	107.5
−24°	+124°	72.7	75.6	78.5	81.4	84.3	87.9	90.1	93.0	95.9	98.8	101.7	104.7	107.6	110.5
−26°	+126°	74.6	77.6	80.6	83.6	86.6	89.6	92.6	95.8	98.5	101.5	104.5	017.5	110.5	113.5

Table XXXIII. Average Air Temperature [XXXIII
Correction for Barometric Leveling (in Feet)

For temperatures above 50° F. the values are to be added
For temperatures below 50° F. the values are to be subtracted

Average Air Temp. °F.		Difference of Readings in Feet											
		780	800	820	840	860	880	900	920	940	960	980	1000
	+ 50°	0	0	0	0	0	0	0	0	0	0	0	0
+48°	+ 52°	3.1	3.1	3.2	3.3	3.4	3.5	3.5	3.6	3.7	3.8	3.8	3.9
+46°	+ 54°	6.1	6.3	6.4	6.6	6.8	6.9	7.1	7.2	7.4	7.5	7.7	7.9
+44°	+ 56°	9.1	9.4	9.7	9.9	10.1	10.4	10.6	10.8	11.1	11.3	11.5	11.8
+42°	+ 58°	12.3	12.6	12.9	13.2	13.5	13.8	14.1	14.5	14.8	15.1	15.4	15.7
+40°	+ 60°	15.3	15.7	16.1	16.5	16.9	17.3	17.7	18.1	18.5	18.8	19.2	19.0
+38°	+ 62°	18.4	18.8	19.3	19.8	20.3	20.7	21.2	21.7	22.1	22.6	23.1	23.6
+36°	+ 64°	21.4	22.0	22.5	23.1	23.6	24.2	24.7	25.3	25.8	26.4	26.9	27.5
+34°	+ 66°	24.5	25.1	25.8	26.4	27.0	27.6	28.3	28.9	29.5	30.2	30.8	31.4
+32°	+ 68°	27.6	28.3	29.0	29.7	30.4	31.1	31.8	32.5	33.2	33.9	34.6	35.4
+30°	+ 70°	30.6	31.4	32.2	33.0	33.8	34.6	35.4	36.1	36.9	37.7	38.5	39.3
+28°	+ 72°	33.7	34.6	35.4	36.3	37.2	38.0	38.9	39.8	40.6	41.5	42.3	43.2
+26°	+ 74°	36.8	37.7	38.7	39.6	40.5	41.5	42.4	43.4	44.3	45.3	46.3	47.1
+24°	+ 76°	39.8	40.9	41.9	42.9	43.9	44.9	46.0	47.0	48.0	49.0	50.0	51.1
+22°	+ 78°	42.9	44.0	45.1	46.2	47.3	48.4	49.5	50.6	51.7	52.8	53.9	55.0
+20°	+ 80°	46.0	47.1	48.3	49.5	50.7	51.8	53.0	54.2	55.4	56.6	57.7	58.9
+18°	+ 82°	49.0	50.3	51.5	52.8	54.1	55.3	56.6	57.8	59.1	60.3	61.6	62.8
+16°	+ 84°	52.1	53.4	54.8	56.1	57.4	58.8	60.1	61.4	62.8	64.1	65.4	66.8
+14°	+ 86°	55.1	56.6	58.0	59.4	60.8	62.2	63.6	65.0	66.5	67.9	69.3	70.7
+12°	+ 88°	58.2	59.7	61.2	62.7	64.2	65.7	67.2	68.7	70.2	71.6	73.1	74.0
+10°	+ 90°	61.3	62.8	64.4	66.0	67.6	69.1	70.7	72.3	73.8	75.4	77.0	78.0
+ 8°	+ 92°	64.3	66.0	67.6	69.3	70.9	72.6	74.2	75.9	77.5	79.2	80.8	82.5
+ 6°	+ 94°	67.4	69.1	70.9	72.6	74.3	76.0	77.8	79.5	81.2	83.0	84.7	86.4
+ 4°	+ 96°	70.5	72.3	74.1	75.9	77.7	79.5	81.3	83.1	84.9	86.7	88.5	90.3
+ 2°	+ 98°	73.5	75.4	77.3	79.2	81.1	83.0	84.8	86.7	88.6	90.5	92.4	94.3
+ 0°	+100°	76.6	78.6	80.5	82.5	84.5	86.4	88.4	90.3	92.3	94.3	96.2	98.2
− 2°	+102°	79.7	81.7	83.7	85.8	87.8	89.9	91.9	94.0	96.0	98.0	100.1	102.1
− 4°	+104°	82.7	84.8	87.0	89.1	91.2	93.3	95.5	97.6	99.7	101.8	103.9	106.1
− 6°	+106°	85.8	88.0	90.2	92.4	94.6	96.8	99.0	101.2	103.4	105.6	107.8	110.0
− 8°	+108°	88.8	91.1	93.4	95.7	98.0	100.2	102.5	104.8	107.1	109.4	111.6	113.9
−10°	+110°	91.9	94.3	96.6	99.0	101.3	103.7	106.1	108.4	110.8	113.1	115.5	117.8
−12°	+112°	95.0	97.4	99.9	102.3	104.7	107.2	109.6	112.0	114.5	116.9	119.3	121.8
−14°	+114°	98.0	100.6	103.1	105.6	108.1	110.6	113.1	115.6	118.2	120.7	123.2	125.7
−16°	+116°	101.1	103.7	106.3	108.9	111.5	114.1	116.7	119.3	121.9	124.5	127.0	129.6
−18°	+118°	104.2	106.8	109.5	112.2	114.9	117.5	120.2	122.9	125.5	128.2	130.9	133.6
−20°	+120°	107.2	110.0	112.7	115.5	118.2	121.0	123.7	126.5	129.2	132.0	134.7	137.5
−22°	+122°	110.3	113.1	116.0	118.8	121.6	124.3	127.3	130.1	132.9	135.8	138.6	141.1
−24°	+124°	113.4	116.3	119.2	122.1	125.0	127.9	130.8	133.7	136.6	139.5	142.4	145.3
−26°	+126°	116.4	119.4	122.4	125.4	128.4	131.4	134.4	137.3	140.3	143.3	146.3	149.3

′	0°		1°		2°		′
	Sine	Cosine	Sine	Cosine	Sine	Cosine	
0	.00000000	one	.01745241	.99984770	.03489950	.99939083	60
1	.00029089	.99999996	.01774325	.99984258	.03519021	.99938063	59
2	.00058178	.99999983	.01803409	.99983737	.03548091	.99937035	58
3	.00087266	.99999962	.01832493	.99983208	.03577162	.99935999	57
4	.00116355	.99999932	.01861577	.99982671	.03606232	.99934954	56
5	.00145444	.99999894	.01890661	.99982125	.03635301	.99933901	55
6	.00174533	.99999848	.01919744	.99981571	.03664371	.99932839	54
7	.00203622	.99999793	.01948828	.99981009	.03693440	.99931769	53
8	.00232710	.99999729	.01977911	.99980437	.03722509	.99930691	52
9	.00261799	.99999657	.02006994	.99979858	.03751577	.99929604	51
10	.00290888	.99999577	.02036077	.99979270	.03780646	.99928508	50
11	.00319976	.99999488	.02065159	.99978673	.03809713	.99927404	49
12	.00349065	.99999391	.02094242	.99978068	.03838781	.99926292	48
13	.00378154	.99999285	.02123324	.99977455	.03867848	.99925171	47
14	.00407242	.99999171	.02152407	.99976833	.03896915	.99924041	46
15	.00436331	.99999048	.02181489	.99976203	.03925982	.99922904	45
16	.00465419	.99998917	.02210570	.99975564	.03955048	.99921757	44
17	.00494508	.99998777	.02239652	.99974917	.03984114	.99920603	43
18	.00523596	.99998629	.02268733	.99974261	.04013179	.99919440	42
19	.00552685	.99998473	.02297815	.99973597	.04042244	.99918268	41
20	.00581773	.99998308	.02326896	.99972924	.04071309	.99917088	40
21	.00610861	.99998134	.02355976	.99972243	.04100374	.99915899	39
22	.00639950	.99997952	.02385057	.99971553	.04129438	.99914702	38
23	.00669038	.99997762	.02414138	.99970855	.04158502	.99913497	37
24	.00698126	.99997563	.02443218	.99970149	.04187565	.99912283	36
25	.00727214	.99997356	.02472298	.99969434	.04216629	.99911061	35
26	.00756302	.99997140	.02501378	.99968711	.04245691	.99909830	34
27	.00785390	.99996916	.02530457	.99967979	.04274754	.99908591	33
28	.00814478	.99996683	.02559537	.99967238	.04303816	.99907343	32
29	.00843566	.99996442	.02588616	.99966490	.04332877	.99906087	31
30	.00872654	.99996192	.02617695	.99965732	.04361939	.99904822	30
31	.00901741	.99995934	.02646774	.99964967	.04391000	.99903549	29
32	.00930829	.99995668	.02675852	.99964193	.04420060	.99902268	28
33	.00959916	.99995393	.02704930	.99963410	.04449120	.99900978	27
34	.00989004	.99995109	.02734008	.99962619	.04478180	.99899679	26
35	.01018091	.99994817	.02763086	.99961819	.04507240	.99898372	25
36	.01047178	.99994517	.02792164	.99961012	.04536299	.99897057	24
37	.01076266	.99994208	.02821241	.99960195	.04565357	.99895733	23
38	.01105353	.99993891	.02850318	.99959370	.04594416	.99894401	22
39	.01134440	.99993565	.02879395	.99958537	.04623474	.99893060	21
40	.01163527	.99993231	.02908472	.99957695	.04652531	.99891711	20
41	.01192613	.99992888	.02937548	.99956845	.04681588	.99890354	19
42	.01221700	.99992537	.02966624	.99955986	.04710645	.99888987	18
43	.01250787	.99992177	.02995700	.99955119	.04739701	.99887613	17
44	.01279873	.99991809	.03024776	.99954243	.04768757	.99886230	16
45	.01308960	.99991433	.03053851	.99953359	.04797813	.99884839	15
46	.01338046	.99991048	.03082926	.99952467	.04826868	.99883439	14
47	.01367132	.99990654	.03112001	.99951566	.04855923	.99882030	13
48	.01396218	.99990252	.03141076	.99950656	.04884977	.99880614	12
49	.01425304	.99989842	.03170150	.99949738	.04914031	.99879189	11
50	.01454390	.99989423	.03199224	.99948812	.04943084	.99877755	10
51	.01483475	.99988996	.03228298	.99947877	.04972137	.99876313	9
52	.01512561	.99988560	.03257372	.99946934	.05001190	.99874862	8
53	.01541646	.99988116	.03286445	.99945982	.05030242	.99873403	7
54	.01570732	.99987663	.03315518	.99945022	.05059294	.99871936	6
55	.01599817	.99987202	.03344591	.99944053	.05088345	.99870460	5
56	.01628902	.99986733	.03373663	.99943076	.05117396	.99868975	4
57	.01657987	.99986254	.03402735	.99942090	.05146447	.99867483	3
58	.01687072	.99985768	.03431807	.99941096	.05175497	.99865981	2
59	.01716156	.99985273	.03460878	.99940094	.05204546	.99864472	1
60	.01745241	.99984770	.03489950	.99939083	.05233596	.99862953	0
′	Cosine	Sine	Cosine	Sine	Cosine	Sine	′
	89°		88°		87°		

* Condensed by permission from Special Publication No. 231 of the U. S. Depart-

′	3°		4°		5°		′
	Sine	Cosine	Sine	Cosine	Sine	Cosine	
0	.05233596	.99862953	.06975647	.99756405	.08715574	.99619470	**60**
1	.05262644	.99861427	.07004665	.99754372	.08744552	.99616930	59
2	.05291693	.99859892	.07033682	.99752330	.08773529	.99614382	58
3	.05320740	.99858348	.07062699	.99750280	.08802505	.99611826	57
4	.05349788	.99856796	.07091717	.99748221	.08831481	.99609261	56
5	.05378835	.99855236	.07120730	.99746154	.08860456	.99606688	**55**
6	.05407881	.99853667	.07149744	.99744078	.08889430	.99604107	54
7	.05436927	.99852090	.07178759	.99741994	.08918403	.99601516	53
8	.05465973	.99850504	.07207772	.99739902	.08947375	.99598918	52
9	.05495018	.99848910	.07236785	.99737801	.08976347	.99596311	51
10	.05524063	.99847307	.07265797	.99735692	.09005318	.99593696	**50**
11	.05553107	.99845696	.07294809	.99733574	.09034289	.99591072	49
12	.05582150	.99844076	.07323820	.99731448	.09063258	.99588440	48
13	.05611194	.99842448	.07352830	.99729313	.09092227	.99585799	47
14	.05640236	.99840812	.07381840	.99727170	.09121195	.99583150	46
15	.05669279	.99839167	.07410849	.99725019	.09150162	.99580493	**45**
16	.05698321	.99837514	.07439858	.99722859	.09179128	.99577827	44
17	.05727362	.99835852	.07468865	.99720690	.09208094	.99575153	43
18	.05756403	.99834182	.07497873	.99718513	.09237059	.99572470	42
19	.05785443	.99832503	.07526879	.99716328	.09266023	.99569779	41
20	.05814483	.99830816	.07555885	.99714134	.09294986	.99567079	**40**
21	.05843522	.99829120	.07584891	.99711932	.09323949	.99564371	39
22	.05872561	.99827416	.07613895	.99709722	.09352910	.99561655	28
23	.05901599	.99825704	.07642899	.99707503	.09381871	.99558930	37
24	.05930637	.99823983	.07671903	.99705275	.09410831	.99556196	36
25	.05959675	.99822253	.07700906	.99703039	.09439791	.99553454	**35**
26	.05988712	.99820516	.07729908	.99700795	.09468749	.99550705	34
27	.06017748	.99818769	.07758909	.99698542	.09497707	.99547946	33
28	.06046784	.99817015	.07787910	.99696281	.09526664	.99545179	32
29	.06075819	.99815251	.07816910	.99694011	.09555620	.99542404	31
30	.06104854	.99813480	.07845910	.99691733	.09584575	.99539620	**30**
31	.06133888	.99811700	.07874908	.99689447	.09613530	.99536828	29
32	.06162922	.99809911	.07903907	.99687152	.09642483	.99534027	28
33	.06191955	.99808114	.07932904	.99684849	.09671436	.99531218	27
34	.06220988	.99806309	.07961901	.99682537	.09700388	.99528400	26
35	.06250020	.99804495	.07990897	.99680217	.09729340	.99525574	**25**
36	.06279052	.99802673	.08019892	.99677888	.09758290	.99522740	24
37	.06308083	.99800842	.08048887	.99675551	.09787240	.99519897	23
38	.06337114	.99799003	.08077881	.99673205	.09816188	.99517046	22
39	.06366144	.99797155	.08106875	.99670851	.09845136	.99514186	21
40	.06395173	.99795299	.08135867	.99668489	.09874083	.99511318	**20**
41	.06424202	.99793435	.08164860	.99666118	.09903030	.99508442	19
42	.06453231	.99791562	.08193851	.99663739	.09931975	.99505557	18
43	.06482259	.99789680	.08222842	.99661351	.09960920	.99502664	17
44	.06511286	.99787791	.08251831	.99658955	.09989863	.99499762	16
45	.06540313	.99785892	.03280821	.99656550	.10018806	.99496852	**15**
46	.06569339	.99783986	.08309809	.99654137	.10047748	.99493933	14
47	.06598365	.99782070	.08338797	.99651716	.10076689	.99491006	16
48	.06627390	.99780147	.08367784	.99649286	.10105630	.99488071	12
49	.06656415	.99778215	.08396771	.99646848	.10134569	.99485127	11
50	.06685439	.99776274	.08425757	.99644401	.10163508	.99482175	**10**
51	.06714462	.99774325	.08454742	.99641946	.10192446	.99479214	9
52	.06743485	.99772368	.08483726	.99639482	.10221382	.99476245	8
53	.06772507	.99770402	.08512709	.99637010	.10250319	.99473268	7
54	.06801529	.99768428	.08541692	.99634530	.10279254	.99470282	6
55	.06830550	.99766445	.08570674	.99632041	.10308188	.99467287	**5**
56	.06859571	.99764454	.08599656	.99629543	.10337121	.99464285	4
57	.06888591	.99762454	.08628637	.99627038	.10366054	.99461273	3
58	.06917610	.99760446	.08657617	.99624523	.10394986	.99458254	2
59	.06946629	.99758430	.08686596	.99622001	.10423916	.99455226	1
60	.06975647	.99756405	.08715574	.99619470	.10452846	.99452190	0
	Cosine	Sine	Cosine	Sine	Cosine	Sine	′
′	86°		85°		84°		

′	6° Sine	6° Cosine	7° Sine	7° Cosine	8° Sine	8° Cosine	′
0	.10452846	.99452190	.12186934	.99254615	.13917310	.99026807	60
1	.10481775	.99449145	.12215806	.99251066	.13946115	.99022754	59
2	.10510703	.99446091	.12244676	.99247508	.13974919	.99018693	58
3	.10539631	.99443030	.12273546	.99243942	.14003722	.99014624	57
4	.10568557	.99439960	.12302414	.99240368	.14032524	.99010546	56
5	.10597483	.99436881	.12331281	.99236785	.14061324	.99006460	55
6	.10626407	.99433794	.12360148	.99233194	.14090123	.99002366	54
7	.10655331	.99430699	.12389013	.99229594	.14118921	.98998263	53
8	.10684254	.99427595	.12417877	.99225986	.14147718	.98994152	52
9	.10713175	.99424483	.12446740	.99222370	.14176514	.98990032	51
10	.10742096	.99421363	.12475602	.99218745	.14205308	.98985904	50
11	.10771016	.99418234	.12504463	.99215112	.14234101	.98981768	49
12	.10799936	.99415096	.12533323	.99211470	.14262893	.98977623	48
13	.10828854	.99411951	.12562182	.99207820	.14291684	.98973470	47
14	.10857771	.99408796	.12591040	.99204162	.14320474	.98969309	46
15	.10886687	.99405634	.12619897	.99200495	.14349262	.98965139	45
16	.10915603	.99402463	.12648753	.99196820	.14378049	.98960960	44
17	.10944517	.99399283	.12677607	.99193136	.14406835	.98956774	43
18	.10973431	.99396096	.12706461	.99189444	.14435620	.98952579	42
19	.11002344	.99392899	.12735313	.99185744	.14464404	.98948376	41
20	.11031256	.99389695	.12764165	.99182035	.14493186	.98944164	40
21	.11060166	.99386482	.12793015	.99178318	.14521967	.98939944	39
22	.11089076	.99383260	.12821864	.99174592	.14550747	.98935715	38
23	.11117985	.99380030	.12850713	.99170859	.14579525	.98931478	37
24	.11146893	.99376792	.12879560	.99167116	.14608303	.98927233	36
25	.11175800	.99373545	.12908406	.99163366	.14637079	.98922980	35
26	.11204706	.99370290	.12937251	.99159606	.14665854	.98918718	34
27	.11233612	.99367027	.12966094	.99155839	.14694628	.98914447	33
28	.11262516	.99363755	.12994937	.99152063	.14723400	.98910169	32
29	.11291419	.99360474	.13023779	.99148279	.14752171	.98905882	31
30	.11320321	.99357186	.13052619	.99144486	.14780941	.98901586	30
31	.11349223	.99353888	.13081459	.99140685	.14809710	.98897283	29
32	.11378123	.99350583	.13110297	.99136876	.14838477	.98892970	28
33	.11407023	.99347269	.13139134	.99133058	.14867243	.98888650	27
34	.11435921	.99343947	.13167970	.99129232	.14896008	.98884321	26
35	.11464819	.99340616	.13196805	.99125397	.14924772	.98879984	25
36	.11493715	.99337277	.13225639	.99121554	.14953534	.98875638	24
37	.11522611	.99333929	.13254472	.99117703	.14982295	.98871284	23
38	.11551505	.99330573	.13283303	.99113843	.15011055	.98866922	22
39	.11580399	.99327209	.13312134	.99109975	.15039814	.98862551	21
40	.11609291	.99323836	.13340963	.99106098	.15068571	.98858172	20
41	.11638183	.99320455	.13369791	.99102213	.15097327	.98853784	19
42	.11667074	.99317065	.13398619	.99098320	.15126082	.98849389	18
43	.11695963	.99313667	.13427445	.99094418	.15154836	.98844984	17
44	.11724852	.99310261	.13456269	.99090508	.15183588	.98840572	16
45	.11753740	.99306846	.13485093	.99086590	.15212339	.98836151	15
46	.11782626	.99303422	.13513916	.99082663	.15241088	.98831722	14
47	.11811512	.99299991	.13542737	.99078728	.15269837	.98827284	13
48	.11840397	.99296551	.13571557	.99074784	.15298584	.98822838	12
49	.11869281	.99293102	.13600376	.99070832	.15327329	.98818384	11
50	.11898163	.99289646	.13629194	.99066872	.15356074	.98813921	10
51	.11927045	.99286180	.13658011	.99062903	.15384817	.98809450	9
52	.11955926	.99282707	.13686827	.99058926	.15413559	.98804971	8
53	.11984805	.99279225	.13715641	.99054940	.15442299	.98800483	7
54	.12013684	.99275734	.13744455	.99050946	.15471039	.98795987	6
55	.12042562	.99272235	.13773267	.99046944	.15499777	.98791482	5
56	.12071438	.99268728	.13802078	.99042933	.15528513	.98786969	4
57	.12100314	.99265212	.13830888	.99038914	.15557248	.98782448	3
58	.12129188	.99261688	.13859696	.99034887	.15585982	.98777918	2
59	.12158062	.99258156	.13888504	.99030851	.15614715	.98773380	1
60	.12186934	.99254615	.13917310	.99026807	.15643447	.98768834	0

′	Cosine	Sine	Cosine	Sine	Cosine	Sine	′
	83°		82°		81°		

Cosines to Eight Decimal Places. Since other trigonometric functions will be used

| ′ | 9° | | 10° | | 11° | | ′ |
	Sine	Cosine	Sine	Cosine	Sine	Cosine	
0	.15643447	.98768834	.17364818	.98480775	.19080900	.98162718	60
1	.15672177	.98764279	.17393464	.98475720	.19109453	.98157164	59
2	.15700905	.98759716	.17422109	.98470656	.19138005	.98151601	58
3	.15729633	.98755145	.17450752	.98465584	.19166555	.98146030	57
4	.15758359	.98750565	.17479394	.98460504	.19195104	.98140450	56
5	.15787083	.98745977	.17508034	.98455415	.19223651	.98134862	55
6	.15815807	.98741381	.17536673	.98450318	.19252197	.98129266	54
7	.15844529	.98736776	.17565310	.98445213	.19280740	.98123662	53
8	.15873249	.98732163	.17593946	.98440099	.19309283	.98118049	52
9	.15901969	.98727541	.17622580	.98434977	.19337823	.98112428	51
10	.15930687	.98722911	.17651213	.98429847	.19366362	.98106799	50
11	.15959403	.98718273	.17679844	.98424708	.19394899	.98101161	49
12	.15988119	.98713627	.17708474	.98419561	.19423435	.98095516	48
13	.16016833	.98708972	.17737102	.98414405	.19451969	.98089861	47
14	.16045545	.98704308	.17765729	.98409242	.19480501	.98084199	46
15	.16074257	.98699637	.17794355	.98404070	.19509032	.98078528	45
16	.16102966	.98694957	.17822978	.98398889	.19537561	.98072849	44
17	.16131675	.98690268	.17851601	.98393701	.19566089	.98067162	43
18	.16160382	.98685572	.17880222	.98388504	.19594614	.98061466	42
19	.16189088	.98680867	.17908841	.98383298	.19623139	.98055762	41
20	.16217792	.98676153	.17937459	.98378085	.19651661	.98050050	40
21	.16246495	.98671431	.17966075	.98372863	.19680182	.98044329	39
22	.16275197	.98666701	.17994690	.98367633	.19708701	.98038600	38
23	.16303897	.98661963	.18023303	.98362394	.19737218	.98032863	37
24	.16332596	.98657216	.18051915	.98357147	.19765734	.98027117	36
25	.16361294	.98652461	.18080525	.98351892	.19794248	.98021364	35
26	.16389990	.98647698	.18109133	.98346628	.19822761	.98015602	34
27	.16418685	.98642926	.18137740	.98341356	.19851271	.98009831	33
28	.16447378	.98638146	.18166346	.98336076	.19879780	.98004053	32
29	.16476070	.98633357	.18194950	.98330788	.19908288	.97998266	31
30	.16504761	.98628560	.18223553	.98325491	.19936793	.97992470	30
31	.16533450	.98623755	.18252153	.98320186	.19965297	.97986667	29
32	.16562138	.98618941	.18280753	.98314872	.19993800	.97980855	28
33	.16590824	.98614119	.18309351	.98309550	.20022300	.97975035	27
34	.16619509	.98609289	.18337947	.98304220	.20050799	.97969207	26
35	.16648193	.98604451	.18366542	.98298882	.20079279	.97963370	25
36	.16676875	.98599304	.18395135	.98293535	.20107792	.97957525	24
37	.16705555	.98594748	.18423727	.98288180	.20136286	.97951672	23
38	.16734235	.98589885	.18452317	.98282816	.20164778	.97945810	22
39	.16762913	.98585013	.18480905	.98277445	.20193269	.97939940	21
40	.16791589	.98580133	.18509492	.98272065	.20221757	.97934062	20
41	.16820264	.98575244	.18538078	.98266676	.20250243	.97928176	19
42	.16848938	.98570347	.18566662	.98261280	.20278730	.97922281	18
43	.16877610	.98565442	.18595244	.98255875	.20307213	.97916378	17
44	.16906281	.98560528	.18623824	.98250461	.20335695	.97910467	16
45	.16934950	.98555606	.18652404	.98245040	.20364175	.97904547	15
46	.16963618	.98550676	.18680981	.98239610	.20392654	.97898619	14
47	.16992285	.98545737	.18709557	.98234172	.20421130	.97892683	13
48	.17020950	.98540790	.18738131	.98228725	.20449605	.97886739	12
49	.17049614	.98535834	.18766704	.98223270	.20478078	.97880786	11
50	.17078276	.98530871	.18795275	.98217807	.20506550	.97874825	10
51	.17106936	.98525899	.18823845	.98212336	.20535020	.97868856	9
52	.17135596	.98520918	.18852413	.98206856	.20563488	.97862878	8
53	.17164254	.98515930	.18880979	.98201368	.20591954	.97856893	7
54	.17192910	.98510933	.18909544	.98195871	.20620419	.97850899	6
55	.17221565	.98505927	.18938108	.98190367	.20648881	.97844896	5
56	.17250218	.98500914	.18966669	.98184854	.20677342	.97838885	4
57	.17278870	.98495891	.18995229	.98179332	.20705802	.97832867	3
58	.17307521	.98490861	.19023788	.98173803	.20734259	.97826840	2
59	.17336170	.98485822	.19052344	.98168265	.20762715	.97820805	1
60	.17364818	.93480775	.19080900	.98162718	.20791169	.97814760	0
′	Cosine	Sine	Cosine	Sine	Cosine	Sine	′
	80°		79°		78°		

rarely, they can be obtained by transformation formulas. Interpolation to seconds

′	12°		13°		14°		′
	Sine	Cosine	Sine	Cosine	Sine	Cosine	
0	.20791169	.97814760	.22495105	.97437006	.24192190	.97029573	60
1	.20819621	.97808708	.22523448	.97430459	.24220413	.97022531	59
2	.20848072	.97802648	.22551788	.97423903	.24248635	.97015482	58
3	.20876521	.97796579	.22580127	.97417339	.24276855	.97008424	57
4	.20904968	.97790502	.22608463	.97410766	.24305072	.97001358	56
5	.20933413	.97784417	.22636798	.97404186	.24333288	.96994284	55
6	.20961856	.97778324	.22665131	.97397597	.24361501	.96987202	54
7	.20990298	.97772222	.22693462	.97391000	.24389713	.96980111	53
8	.21018738	.97766112	.22721791	.97384394	.24417922	.96973012	52
9	.21047176	.97759994	.22750118	.97377781	.24446129	.96965905	51
10	.21075612	.97753867	.22778443	.97371159	.24474334	.96958790	50
11	.21104047	.97747732	.22806766	.97364529	.24502558	.96951667	49
12	.21132480	.97741589	.22835087	.97357890	.24530739	.96944535	48
13	.21160911	.97735438	.22863406	.97351244	.24558938	.96937395	47
14	.21189340	.97729279	.22891724	.97344589	.24587134	.96930247	46
15	.21217767	.97723111	.22920039	.97337926	.24615329	.96923091	45
16	.21246193	.97716935	.22948353	.97331255	.24643522	.96915927	44
17	.21274617	.97710750	.22976664	.97324575	.24671713	.96908754	43
18	.21303039	.97704557	.23004974	.97317887	.24699901	.96901573	42
19	.21331459	.97698357	.23033281	.97311191	.24728088	.96894384	41
20	.21359877	.97692147	.23061587	.97304487	.24756272	.96887187	40
21	.21388294	.97685903	.23089891	.97297775	.24784454	.96879982	39
22	.21416709	.97679704	.23118193	.97291054	.24812635	.96872768	38
23	.21445122	.97673470	.23146492	.97284325	.24840813	.96865546	37
24	.21473533	.97667228	.23174790	.97277588	.24868989	.96858316	36
25	.21591942	.97660977	.23203086	.97270842	.24897163	.96851078	35
26	.21530350	.97654719	.23231380	.97264089	.24925334	.96843832	34
27	.21558755	.97648451	.23259672	.97257327	.24953504	.96836577	33
28	.21587159	.97642176	.23287962	.97250557	.24981672	.96829314	32
29	.21615561	.97635893	.23316250	.97243779	.25009837	.96822043	31
30	.21643961	.97629601	.23344536	.97236992	.25038000	.96814764	30
31	.21672360	.97623301	.23372820	.97230197	.25066162	.96807477	29
32	.21700756	.97616992	.23401103	.97223394	.25094321	.96800181	28
33	.21729151	.97610676	.23429383	.97216583	.25122478	.96792877	27
34	.21757544	.97604351	.23457661	.97209764	.25150633	.96785565	26
35	.21785935	.97598018	.23485937	.97202936	.25178785	.96778245	25
36	.21814324	.97591676	.23514211	.97196100	.25206936	.96770917	24
37	.21842711	.97585327	.23542484	.97189256	.25235084	.96763581	23
38	.21871079	.97578969	.23570734	.97182404	.25263231	.96756236	22
39	.21899481	.97572602	.23599022	.97175543	.25291375	.96748883	21
40	.21927862	.97566228	.23627288	.97168674	.25319517	.96741522	20
41	.21956242	.97559845	.23655552	.97161797	.25347657	.96734153	19
42	.21984620	.97553454	.23683815	.97154912	.25375794	.96726775	18
43	.22012997	.97547055	.23712075	.97148019	.25403930	.96719390	17
44	.22041371	.97540648	.23740333	.97141117	.25432064	.96711996	16
45	.22069744	.97534233	.23768589	.97134207	.25460195	.96704594	15
46	.22098114	.97527808	.23796843	.97127289	.25488324	.96697184	14
47	.22126483	.97521376	.23825096	.97120363	.25516451	.96689765	13
48	.22154850	.97514935	.23353346	.97113428	.25544576	.96682339	12
49	.22183215	.97508487	.23831594	.97106485	.25572698	.96674904	11
50	.22211578	.97502030	.23909840	.97099534	.25600819	.96667461	10
51	.22239939	.97495565	.23938084	.97092575	.25628937	.96660010	9
52	.22268299	.97489091	.23966326	.97085608	.25657053	.96652551	8
53	.22296656	.97482609	.23994566	.97078632	.25685167	.96645084	7
54	.22325012	.97476119	.24022804	.97071648	.25713279	.96637608	6
55	.22353365	.97469621	.24051040	.97064656	.25741389	.96630124	5
56	.22381717	.97463115	.24079274	.97057656	.25769496	.96622632	4
57	.22410067	.97456600	.24107506	.97050647	.25797602	.96615132	3
58	.22438415	.97450077	.24135736	.97043631	.25825705	.96607624	2
59	.22466761	.97443546	.24163964	.97036606	.25853806	.96600107	1
60	.22495105	.97437006	.24192190	.97029573	.25881905	.96592583	0
	Cosine	Sine	Cosine	Sine	Cosine	Sine	′
	77°		76°		75°		

,	15°		16°		17°		,
	Sine	Cosine	Sine	Cosine	Sine	Cosine	
0	.25881905	.96592583	.27563736	.96126170	.29237170	.95630476	60
1	.25910001	.96585050	.27591696	.96118148	.29264987	.95621967	59
2	.25938095	.96577509	.27619655	.96110117	.29292801	.95613450	58
3	.25966188	.96569960	.27647611	.96102079	.29320613	.95604925	57
4	.25994278	.96562402	.27675565	.96094033	.29348422	.95596392	56
5	.26022365	.96554837	.27703516	.96085978	.29376228	.95587851	55
6	.26050451	.96547263	.27731465	.96077915	.29404033	.95579301	54
7	.26078534	.96539681	.27759412	.96069845	.29431834	.95570744	53
8	.26106615	.96532091	.27787356	.96061766	.29459633	.95562179	52
9	.26134694	.96524493	.27815299	.96053679	.29487430	.95553605	51
10	.26162771	.96516887	.27843238	.96045583	.29515224	.95545024	50
11	.26190846	.96509272	.27871176	.96037480	.29543016	.95536434	49
12	.26218918	.96501649	.27899111	.96029369	.29570805	.95527836	48
13	.26246988	.96494019	.27927043	.96021249	.29598592	.95519230	47
14	.26275056	.96486380	.27954974	.96013121	.29626376	.95510616	46
15	.26303121	.96478732	.27982901	.96004985	.29654157	.95501994	45
16	.26331185	.96471077	.28010827	.95996841	.29681937	.95493364	44
17	.26359246	.96463414	.28038750	.95988689	.29709713	.95484726	43
18	.26387305	.96455742	.28066671	.95980529	.29737487	.95476080	42
19	.26415362	.96448062	.28094589	.95972361	.29765259	.95467426	41
20	.26443416	.96440374	.28122505	.95964184	.29793028	.95458763	40
21	.26471468	.96432678	.28150419	.95956000	.29820795	.95450093	39
22	.26499518	.96424974	.28178330	.95947807	.29848559	.95441414	38
23	.26527566	.96417261	.28206239	.95939606	.29876320	.95432728	37
24	.26555612	.96409540	.28234146	.95931397	.29904079	.95424033	36
25	.26583655	.96401812	.28262050	.95923180	.29931836	.95415330	35
26	.26611696	.96394075	.28289952	.95914955	.29959590	.95406619	34
27	.26639735	.96386330	.28317851	.95906722	.29987340	.95397900	33
28	.26667771	.96378576	.28345748	.95898481	.30015090	.95389173	32
29	.26695806	.96370815	.28373642	.95890231	.30042836	.95380438	31
30	.26723838	.96363045	.28401534	.95881973	.30070580	.95371695	30
31	.26751867	.96355268	.28429424	.95873708	.30098321	.95362944	29
32	.26779895	.96347482	.28457312	.95865434	.30126060	.95354185	28
33	.26807920	.96339688	.28485196	.95857152	.30153796	.95345417	27
34	.26835943	.96331886	.28513079	.95848862	.30181530	.95336642	26
35	.26863964	.96324075	.28540959	.95840564	.30209261	.95327858	25
36	.26891982	.96316257	.28568837	.95832257	.30236989	.95319067	24
37	.26919998	.96308430	.28596712	.95823943	.30264715	.95310267	23
38	.26948012	.96300595	.28624585	.95815621	.30292438	.95301459	22
39	.26976024	.96292752	.28652455	.95807290	.30320159	.95292644	21
40	.27004033	.96284901	.28680323	.95798951	.30347877	.95283820	20
41	.27032040	.96277042	.28708189	.95790604	.30375593	.95274988	19
42	.27060045	.96269175	.28736052	.95782249	.30403306	.95266148	18
43	.27088047	.96261299	.28763913	.95773886	.30431017	.95257300	17
44	.27116047	.96253415	.28791771	.95765515	.30458725	.95248444	16
45	.27144045	.96245524	.28819627	.95757136	.30486430	.95239580	15
46	.27172041	.96237624	.28847480	.95748749	.30514133	.95230708	14
47	.27200034	.96229716	.28875331	.95740353	.30541833	.95221828	13
48	.27228025	.96221799	.28903180	.95731950	.30569530	.95212939	12
49	.27256013	.96213875	.28931026	.95723538	.30597226	.95204043	11
50	.27284000	.96205942	.28958869	.95715118	.30624918	.95195139	10
51	.27311984	.96198002	.28986711	.95706691	.30652608	.95186226	9
52	.27339965	.96190053	.29014549	.95698255	.30680295	.95177306	8
53	.27367945	.96182096	.29042386	.95689811	.30707980	.95168377	7
54	.27395922	.96174131	.29070219	.95681358	.30735662	.95159440	6
55	.27423897	.96166158	.29098051	.95672898	.30763341	.95150496	5
56	.27451869	.96158176	.29125880	.95664430	.30791018	.95141543	4
57	.27479839	.96150187	.29153706	.95655953	.30818692	.95132582	3
58	.27507807	.96142189	.29181530	.95647469	.30846364	.95123613	2
59	.27535772	.96134183	.29209351	.95638976	.30874033	.95114637	1
60	.27563736	.96126170	.29237170	.95630476	.30901699	.95105652	0
	Cosine	Sine	Cosine	Sine	Cosine	Sine	,
	74°		73°		72°		

′	18° Sine	Cosine	19° Sine	Cosine	20° Sine	Cosine	′
0	.30901699	.95105652	.32556815	.94551858	.34202014	.93969262	60
1	.30929363	.95096659	.32584318	.94542383	.34229347	.93959309	59
2	.30957024	.95087658	.32611818	.94532901	.34256678	.93949348	58
3	.30984683	.95078649	.32639315	.94523410	.34284005	.93939379	57
4	.31012339	.95069631	.32666809	.94513912	.34311329	.93929403	56
5	.31039992	.95060606	.32694301	.94504406	.34338651	.93919418	55
6	.31067643	.95051573	.32721790	.94494891	.34365969	.93909425	54
7	.31095291	.95042532	.32749276	.94485369	.34393285	.93899425	53
8	.31122936	.95033483	.32776759	.94475838	.34420598	.93889416	52
9	.31150579	.95024425	.32804240	.94466300	.34447908	.93879399	51
10	.31178219	.95015360	.32831718	.94456754	.34475215	.93869375	50
11	.31205857	.95006287	.32859192	.94447199	.34502519	.93859343	49
12	.31233492	.94997205	.32886665	.94437637	.34529820	.93849302	48
13	.31261124	.94988116	.32914134	.94428067	.34557118	.93839254	47
14	.31288754	.94979018	.32941601	.94418488	.34584413	.93829198	46
15	.31316381	.94969913	.32969065	.94408902	.34611706	.93819134	45
16	.31344005	.94960799	.32996526	.94399308	.34638995	.93809061	44
17	.31371627	.94951677	.33023984	.94389705	.34666282	.93798981	43
18	.31399246	.94942548	.33051439	.94380095	.34693565	.93788893	42
19	.31426862	.94933410	.33078892	.94370477	.34720846	.93778798	41
20	.31454476	.94924264	.33106342	.94360851	.34748123	.93768694	40
21	.31482087	.94915111	.33133789	.94351216	.34775398	.93758582	39
22	.31509695	.94905949	.33161233	.94341574	.34802670	.93748462	38
23	.31537301	.94896779	.33188675	.94331924	.34829939	.93738335	37
24	.31564904	.94887601	.33216113	.94322266	.34857205	.93728199	36
25	.31592504	.94878415	.33243549	.94312600	.34884468	.93718055	35
26	.31620102	.94869221	.33270982	.94302925	.34911728	.93707904	34
27	.31647697	.94860019	.33298412	.94293243	.34938985	.93697745	33
28	.31675289	.94850810	.33325840	.94283553	.34966239	.93687577	32
29	.31702879	.94841592	.33353264	.94273855	.34993490	.93677402	31
30	.31730466	.94832366	.33380686	.94264149	.35020738	.93667219	30
31	.31758050	.94823131	.33408105	.94254435	.35047983	.93657028	29
32	.31785632	.94813889	.33435521	.94244713	.35075226	.93646829	28
33	.31813210	.94804639	.33462934	.94234983	.35102465	.93636622	27
34	.31840787	.94795381	.33490345	.94225245	.35129701	.93626407	26
35	.31868360	.94786115	.33517752	.94215499	.35156934	.93616184	25
36	.31895931	.94776841	.33545157	.94205745	.35184165	.93605954	24
37	.31923499	.94767559	.33572559	.94195983	.35211392	.93595715	23
38	.31951064	.94758269	.33599958	.94186214	.35238617	.93585468	22
39	.31978627	.94748970	.33627354	.94176436	.35265838	.93575214	21
40	.32006187	.94739664	.33654748	.94166650	.35293056	.93564952	20
41	.32033744	.94730350	.33682138	.94156856	.35320272	.93554681	19
42	.32061299	.94721028	.33709526	.94147054	.35347484	.93544403	18
43	.32088851	.94711698	.33736911	.94137245	.35374694	.93534117	17
44	.32116400	.94702359	.33764293	.94127427	.35401900	.93523823	16
45	.32143947	.94693013	.33791672	.94117602	.35429104	.93513521	15
46	.32171490	.94683659	.33819048	.94107768	.35456304	.93503211	14
47	.32199031	.94674296	.33846421	.94097926	.35483502	.93492893	13
48	.32226570	.94664926	.33873792	.94088077	.35510696	.93482568	12
49	.32254105	.94655548	.33901160	.94078219	.35537888	.93472234	11
50	.32281638	.94646161	.33928525	.94068354	.35565076	.93461893	10
51	.32309168	.94636767	.33955886	.94058481	.35592262	.93451543	9
52	.32336695	.94627365	.33983246	.94048599	.35619444	.93441186	8
53	.32364220	.94617954	.34010602	.94038710	.35646624	.93430821	7
54	.32391742	.94608536	.34037955	.94028813	.35673800	.93420447	6
55	.32419261	.94599110	.34065305	.94018907	.35700973	.93410066	5
56	.32446777	.94589675	.34092653	.94008994	.35728144	.93399677	4
57	.32474291	.94580233	.34119998	.93999073	.35755311	.93389281	3
58	.32501802	.94570782	.34147339	.93989144	.35782475	.93378876	2
59	.32529310	.94561324	.34174678	.93979207	.35809637	.93368463	1
60	.32556815	.94551858	.34202014	.93969262	.35836795	.93358043	0
′	Cosine	Sine	Cosine	Sine	Cosine	Sine	′
	71°		70°		69°		

′	21°		22°		23°		′
	Sine	Cosine	Sine	Cosine	Sine	Cosine	
0	.35836795	.93358043	.37460695	.92718385	.39073113	.92050485	**60**
1	.35863950	.93347614	.37487628	.92707485	.39099888	.92039116	59
2	.35891102	.93337178	.37514594	.92696576	.39126659	.92027738	58
3	.35918252	.93326734	.37541557	.92685660	.39153427	.92016353	57
4	.35945398	.93316281	.37568517	.92674735	.39180192	.92004959	56
5	.35972541	.93305821	.37595473	.92663803	.39206953	.91993558	**55**
6	.35999681	.93295353	.37622426	.92652863	.39233712	.91982150	54
7	.36026818	.93284878	.37649376	.92641915	.39260467	.91970733	53
8	.36053952	.93274394	.37676323	.92630960	.39287218	.91959309	52
9	.36081083	.93263902	.37703267	.92619996	.39313966	.91947877	51
10	.36108210	.93253403	.37730207	.92609025	.39340711	.91936437	**50**
11	.36135335	.93242895	.37757145	.92598046	.39367453	.91924989	49
12	.36162457	.93232380	.37784079	.92587058	.39394191	.91913534	48
13	.36189576	.93221857	.37811010	.92576064	.39420926	.91902071	47
14	.36216691	.93211326	.37837937	.92565061	.39447657	.91890600	46
15	.36243804	.93200787	.37864862	.92554050	.39474386	.91879121	**45**
16	.36270913	.93190240	.37891783	.92543032	.39501111	.91867634	44
17	.36298020	.93179685	.37918701	.92532006	.39527832	.91856140	43
18	.36325123	.93169123	.37945616	.92520972	.39554550	.91844638	42
19	.36352223	.93158552	.37972528	.92509930	.39581265	.91833128	41
20	.36379320	.93147974	.37999436	.92498880	.39607977	.91821611	**40**
21	.36406415	.93137388	.38026341	.92487823	.39634685	.91810085	39
22	.36433506	.93126793	.38053243	.92476757	.39661390	.91798552	38
23	.36460594	.93116191	.38080142	.92465684	.39688091	.91787011	37
24	.36487678	.93105582	.38107038	.92454603	.39714789	.91775463	36
25	.36514760	.93094964	.38133930	.92443515	.39741484	.91763906	**35**
26	.36541839	.93084338	.38160819	.92432418	.39768175	.91752342	34
27	.36568914	.93073705	.38187705	.92421313	.39794863	.91740770	33
28	.36595987	.93063063	.38214588	.92410201	.39821548	.91729190	32
29	.36623056	.93052414	.38241467	.92399081	.39848229	.91717603	31
30	.36650123	.93041757	.38268343	.92387953	.39874907	.91706007	**30**
31	.36677186	.93031092	.38295216	.92376818	.39901581	.91694404	29
32	.36704246	.93020419	.38322086	.92365674	.39928253	.91682794	28
33	.36731303	.93009738	.38348952	.92354523	.39954920	.91671175	27
34	.36758357	.92999049	.38375816	.92343363	.39981585	.91659549	26
35	.36785408	.92988353	.38402676	.92332197	.40008246	.91647915	**25**
36	.36812455	.92977649	.38429532	.92321022	.40034903	.91636273	24
37	.36839500	.92966936	.38456386	.92309839	.40061557	.91624623	23
38	.36866541	.92956216	.38483236	.92298649	.40088208	.91612966	22
39	.36893580	.92945488	.38510083	.92287450	.40114856	.91601301	21
40	.36920615	.92934752	.38536927	.92276244	.40141500	.91589628	**20**
41	.36947647	.92924009	.38563767	.92265031	.40168140	.91577948	19
42	.36974676	.92913257	.38590604	.92253809	.40194778	.91566259	18
43	.37001702	.92902498	.38617438	.92242579	.40221412	.91554563	17
44	.37028724	.92891730	.38644269	.92231342	.40248042	.91542859	16
45	.37055744	.92880955	.38671096	.92220097	.40274669	.91531148	**15**
46	.37082760	.92870172	.38697920	.92208844	.40301293	.91519429	14
47	.37109773	.92859381	.38724741	.92197584	.40327913	.91507702	13
48	.37136784	.92848583	.38751559	.92186315	.40354530	.91495967	12
49	.37163791	.92837776	.38778373	.92175039	.40381143	.91484224	11
50	.37190794	.92826962	.38805184	.92163755	.40407753	.91472474	**10**
51	.37217795	.92816139	.38831992	.92152463	.40434360	.91460716	9
52	.37244793	.92805309	.38858796	.92141163	.40460963	.91448950	8
53	.37271787	.92794471	.38885597	.92129856	.40487562	.91437177	7
54	.37298778	.92783625	.38912395	.92118541	.40514159	.91425396	6
55	.37325766	.92772772	.38939190	.92107218	.40540752	.91413607	**5**
56	.37352751	.92761910	.38965981	.92095887	.40567341	.91401810	4
57	.37379733	.92751041	.38992769	.92084548	.40593927	.91390005	3
58	.37406712	.92740163	.39019553	.92073202	.40620510	.91378193	2
59	.37433687	.92729278	.39046335	.92061847	.40647089	.91366373	1
60	.37460659	.92718385	.39073113	.92050485	.40673664	.91354546	0
	Cosine	Sine	Cosine	Sine	Cosine	Sine	′
′	68°		67°		66°		

′	24° Sine	24° Cosine	25° Sine	25° Cosine	26° Sine	26° Cosine	′
0	.40673664	.91354546	.42261826	.90630779	.43837115	.89879405	60
1	.40700237	.91342710	.42288188	.90618481	.43863258	.89866649	59
2	.40726805	.91330867	.42314546	.90606176	.43889397	.89853886	58
3	.40753371	.91319017	.42340900	.90593864	.43915533	.89841115	57
4	.40779933	.91307158	.42367251	.90581543	.43941664	.89828337	56
5	.40806491	.91295292	.42393599	.90569216	.43967793	.89815551	55
6	.40833046	.91283418	.42419942	.90556880	.43993917	.89802758	54
7	.40859598	.91271536	.42446282	.90544537	.44020038	.89789956	53
8	.40886146	.91259647	.42472619	.90532186	.44046155	.89777148	52
9	.40912690	.91247749	.42498952	.90519827	.44072268	.89764331	51
10	.40939231	.91235845	.42525281	.90507461	.44098377	.89751508	50
11	.40965769	.91223932	.42551607	.90495087	.44124483	.89738676	49
12	.40992303	.91212012	.42577929	.90482705	.44150585	.89725837	48
13	.41018834	.91200084	.42604248	.90470316	.44176684	.89712990	47
14	.41045361	.91188148	.42630563	.90457919	.44202778	.89700136	46
15	.41071885	.91176204	.42656874	.90445515	.44228869	.89687274	45
16	.41098406	.91164253	.42683182	.90433102	.44254956	.89674405	44
17	.41124922	.91152294	.42709486	.90420682	.44281039	.89661528	43
18	.41151436	.91140328	.42735786	.90408255	.44307119	.89648643	42
19	.41177946	.91128353	.42762083	.90395820	.44333195	.89635751	41
20	.41204452	.91116371	.42788376	.90383377	.44359267	.89622851	40
21	.41230955	.91104381	.42814666	.90370927	.44385335	.89609944	39
22	.41257455	.91092384	.42840952	.90358468	.44411400	.89597029	38
23	.41283951	.91080379	.42867235	.90346003	.44437461	.89584106	37
24	.41310443	.91068366	.42893513	.90333529	.44463518	.89571176	36
25	.41336932	.91056346	.42919788	.90321048	.44489571	.89558238	35
26	.41363417	.91044317	.42946060	.90308560	.44515621	.89545293	34
27	.41389899	.91032281	.42972328	.90296063	.44541667	.89532340	33
28	.41416378	.91020238	.42998592	.90283559	.44567709	.89519380	32
29	.41442853	.91008186	.43024853	.90271048	.44593747	.89506412	31
30	.41469324	.90996127	.43051110	.90258528	.44619781	.89493436	30
31	.41495792	.90984060	.43077363	.90246002	.44645812	.89480453	29
32	.41522257	.90971986	.43103613	.90233467	.44671829	.89467462	28
33	.41548718	.90959904	.43129859	.90220925	.44697862	.89454464	27
34	.41575175	.90947814	.43156101	.90208375	.44723881	.89441458	26
35	.41601629	.90935716	.43182340	.90195818	.44749897	.89428445	25
36	.41628079	.90923611	.43208575	.90183253	.44775909	.89415424	24
37	.41654526	.90911498	.43234806	.90170680	.44801917	.89402395	23
38	.41680969	.90899377	.43261034	.90158100	.44827921	.89389359	22
39	.41707409	.90887249	.43287258	.90145512	.44853921	.89376315	21
40	.41733845	.90875113	.43313479	.90132916	.44879918	.89363264	20
41	.41760278	.90862969	.43339695	.90120313	.44905911	.89350205	19
42	.41786707	.90850818	.43365908	.90107702	.44931900	.89337139	18
43	.41813133	.90838659	.43392118	.90095084	.44957885	.89324065	17
44	.41839555	.90826492	.43418324	.90082458	.44983866	.89310983	16
45	.41865974	.90814317	.43444526	.90069824	.45009844	.89297894	15
46	.41892389	.90802135	.43470724	.90057183	.45035818	.89284798	14
47	.41918800	.90789945	.43496919	.90044534	.45061788	.89271694	13
48	.41945208	.90777748	.43523110	.90031877	.45087754	.89258582	12
49	.41971613	.90765543	.43549297	.90019213	.45113716	.89245463	11
50	.41998013	.90753330	.43575481	.90006541	.45139675	.89232336	10
51	.42024411	.90741109	.43601661	.89993862	.45165630	.89219201	9
52	.42050805	.90728881	.43627837	.89981175	.45191581	.89206059	8
53	.42077195	.90716645	.43654010	.89968480	.45217528	.89192910	7
54	.42103581	.90704401	.43680179	.89955778	.45243471	.89179753	6
55	.42129964	.90692150	.43706344	.89943068	.45269410	.89166588	5
56	.42156344	.90679891	.43732506	.89930351	.45295346	.89153416	4
57	.42182720	.90667625	.43758663	.89917626	.45321278	.89140237	3
58	.42209092	.90655350	.43784818	.89904893	.45347206	.89127049	2
59	.42235461	.90643068	.43810968	.89892153	.45373130	.89113855	1
60	.42261826	.90630779	.43837115	.89879405	.45399050	.89100652	0
′	Cosine	Sine	Cosine	Sine	Cosine	Sine	′
	65°		64°		63°		

′	27° Sine	27° Cosine	28° Sine	28° Cosine	29° Sine	29° Cosine	′
0	.45399050	.89100652	.46947156	.88294759	.48480962	.87461971	60
1	.45424966	.89087443	.46972838	.88281099	.48506402	.87447864	59
2	.45450879	.89074225	.46998516	.88267432	.48531837	.87433751	58
3	.45476788	.89061000	.47024190	.88253757	.48557269	.87419630	57
4	.45502693	.89047768	.47049860	.88240074	.48582696	.87405501	56
5	.45528594	.89034528	.47075526	.88226384	.48608119	.87391366	55
6	.45554491	.89021280	.47101188	.88212687	.48633538	.87377222	54
7	.45580384	.89008025	.47126846	.88198982	.48658953	.87363072	53
8	.45606273	.88994763	.47152500	.88185269	.48684364	.87348914	52
9	.45632159	.88981493	.47178150	.88171549	.48709771	.87334748	51
10	.45658041	.88968215	.47203796	.88157822	.48735173	.87320575	50
11	.45683919	.88954930	.47229438	.88144087	.48760572	.87306395	49
12	.45709793	.88941637	.47255076	.88130345	.48785966	.87292208	48
13	.45735663	.88928337	.47280711	.88116596	.48811356	.87278013	47
14	.45761529	.88915029	.47306341	.88102838	.48836742	.87263810	46
15	.45787392	.88901714	.47331967	.88089074	.48862124	.87249601	45
16	.45813250	.88888391	.47357589	.88075302	.48887502	.87235384	44
17	.45839105	.88875061	.47383207	.88061522	.48912876	.87221159	43
18	.45864955	.88861723	.47408821	.88047735	.48938245	.87206927	42
19	.45890802	.88848378	.47434431	.88033941	.48963611	.87192688	41
20	.45916645	.88835025	.47460037	.88020139	.48988972	.87178441	40
21	.45942484	.88821665	.47485639	.88006330	.49014329	.87164187	39
22	.45968320	.88808297	.47511237	.87992513	.49039682	.87149926	38
23	.45994151	.88794921	.47536831	.87978689	.49065031	.87135657	37
24	.46019978	.88781539	.47562421	.87964857	.49090375	.87121381	36
25	.46045802	.88768148	.47588007	.87951018	.49115716	.87107098	35
26	.46071622	.88754750	.47613589	.87937172	.49141052	.87092807	34
27	.46097437	.88741345	.47639167	.87923318	.49166384	.87078509	33
28	.46123249	.88727932	.47664740	.87909456	.49191712	.87064203	32
29	.46149057	.88714511	.47690310	.87895588	.49217036	.87049890	31
30	.46174861	.88701083	.47715876	.87881711	.49242356	.87035570	30
31	.46200661	.88687648	.47741438	.87867828	.49267672	.87021242	29
32	.46226458	.88674205	.47766995	.87853936	.49292983	.87006907	28
33	.46252250	.88660754	.47792549	.87840038	.49318290	.86992564	27
34	.46278038	.88647296	.47818099	.87826132	.49343593	.86978215	26
35	.46303823	.88633831	.47843644	.87812218	.49368892	.86963857	25
36	.46329604	.88620358	.47869186	.87798298	.49394187	.86949493	24
37	.46355380	.88606877	.47894723	.87784369	.49419477	.86935121	23
38	.46381153	.88593389	.47920257	.87770434	.49444763	.86920742	22
39	.46406922	.88579894	.47945786	.87756490	.49470046	.86906355	21
40	.46432687	.88566391	.47971311	.87742540	.49495324	.86891961	20
41	.46458448	.88552881	.47996833	.87728582	.49520597	.86877560	19
42	.46484205	.88539363	.48022350	.87714616	.49545867	.86863151	18
43	.46509958	.88525837	.48047863	.87700644	.49571132	.86848735	17
44	.46535707	.88512304	.48073372	.87686663	.49596393	.86834312	16
45	.46561452	.88498764	.48098877	.87672676	.49621650	.86819881	15
46	.46587193	.88485216	.48124378	.87658680	.49646903	.86805443	14
47	.46612931	.88471660	.48149875	.87644678	.49672152	.86790998	13
48	.46638664	.88458098	.48175367	.87630668	.49697396	.86776545	12
49	.46664393	.88444527	.48200856	.87616651	.49722636	.86762085	11
50	.46690119	.88430949	.48226341	.87602626	.49747872	.86747618	10
51	.46715841	.88417364	.48251821	.87588594	.49773104	.86733143	9
52	.46741558	.88403771	.48277298	.87574554	.49798332	.86718661	8
53	.46767272	.88390171	.48302770	.87560507	.49823555	.86704172	7
54	.46792981	.88376563	.48328238	.87546453	.49848774	.86689675	6
55	.46818687	.88362948	.48353703	.87532391	.49873989	.86675171	5
56	.46844389	.88349325	.48379163	.87518322	.49899200	.86660659	4
57	.46870087	.88335695	.48404619	.87504245	.49924406	.86646141	3
58	.46895781	.88322057	.48430071	.87490161	.49949608	.86631615	2
59	.46921470	.88308412	.48455518	.87476070	.49974806	.86617081	1
60	.46947156	.88294759	.48480962	.87461971	.50000000	.86602540	0
′	Cosine	Sine	Cosine	Sine	Cosine	Sine	′
	62°		61°		60°		

′	30°		31°		32°		′
	Sine	Cosine	Sine	Cosine	Sine	Cosine	
0	.50000000	.86602540	.51503807	.85716730	.52991926	.84804810	60
1	.50025190	.86587992	.51528739	.85701745	.53016593	.84789391	59
2	.50050375	.86573437	.51553667	.85686752	.53041255	.84773966	58
3	.50075556	.86558874	.51578590	.85671752	.53065912	.84758533	57
4	.50100733	.86544304	.51603509	.85656745	.53090565	.84743093	56
5	.50125905	.86529727	.51628423	.85641730	.53115214	.84727646	55
6	.50151074	.86515142	.51653333	.85626708	.53139858	.84712192	54
7	.50176238	.86500550	.51678239	.85611679	.53164497	.84696731	53
8	.50201398	.86485951	.51703140	.85596643	.53189133	.84681262	52
9	.50226553	.86471344	.51728037	.85581600	.53213763	.84665787	51
10	.50251705	.86456730	.51752929	.85566549	.53238389	.84650304	50
11	.50276852	.86442109	.51777817	.85551491	.53263011	.84634814	49
12	.50301995	.86427480	.51802701	.85536426	.53287628	.84619317	48
13	.50327133	.86412844	.51827580	.85521354	.53312240	.84603812	47
14	.50352268	.86398201	.51852455	.85506274	.53336848	.84588301	46
15	.50377398	.86383551	.51877326	.85491187	.53361452	.84572782	45
16	.50402524	.86368893	.51902192	.85476093	.53386051	.84557256	44
17	.50427645	.86354228	.51927054	.85460992	.53410646	.84541723	43
18	.50452762	.86339555	.51951911	.85445883	.53435235	.84526183	42
19	.50477875	.86324875	.51976764	.85430767	.53459820	.84510636	41
20	.50502984	.86310188	.52001613	.85415644	.53484401	.84495082	40
21	.50528089	.86295494	.52026457	.85400514	.53508978	.84479520	39
22	.50553189	.86280792	.52051297	.85385376	.53533549	.84463951	38
23	.50578285	.86266083	.52076132	.85370232	.53558117	.84448376	37
24	.50603376	.86251367	.52100963	.85355080	.53582679	.84432793	36
25	.50628464	.86236643	.52125790	.85339921	.53607238	.84417202	35
26	.50653547	.86221912	.52150612	.85324754	.53631791	.84401605	34
27	.50678626	.86207174	.52175430	.85309581	.53656341	.84386001	33
28	.50703700	.86192429	.52200243	.85294400	.53680885	.84370389	32
29	.50728770	.86177676	.52225052	.85279212	.53705425	.84354770	31
30	.50753836	.86162916	.52249856	.85264016	.53729961	.84339145	30
31	.50778898	.86148149	.52274657	.85248814	.53754492	.84323512	29
32	.50803955	.86133374	.52299452	.85233604	.53779018	.84307871	28
33	.50829008	.86118592	.52324243	.85218387	.53803540	.84292224	27
34	.50854057	.86103803	.52349030	.85203163	.53828057	.84276570	26
35	.50879101	.86089006	.52373873	.85187932	.53852570	.84260908	25
36	.50904142	.86074203	.52398591	.85172693	.53877078	.84245240	24
37	.50929177	.86059392	.52423364	.85157448	.53901582	.84229564	23
38	.50954209	.86044573	.52448133	.85142195	.53926081	.84213881	22
39	.50979236	.86029748	.52472898	.85126935	.53950576	.84198191	21
40	.51004259	.86014915	.52497658	.85111667	.53975066	.84182494	20
41	.51029278	.86000075	.52522414	.85096393	.53999551	.84166790	19
42	.51054292	.85985227	.52547165	.85081111	.54024032	.84151078	18
43	.51079302	.85970372	.52571912	.85065822	.54048508	.84135360	17
44	.51104307	.85955510	.52596654	.85050526	.54072980	.84119634	16
45	.51129309	.85940641	.52621392	.85035222	.54097447	.84103902	15
46	.51154306	.85925765	.52646126	.85019912	.54121910	.84088161	14
47	.51179298	.85910881	.52670855	.85004594	.54146368	.84072414	13
48	.51204286	.85895990	.52695580	.84989269	.54170821	.84056660	12
49	.51229270	.85881091	.52720300	.84973937	.54195270	.84040899	11
50	.51254250	.85866186	.52745015	.84958598	.54219714	.84025131	10
51	.51279225	.85851273	.52769727	.84943251	.54244154	.84009355	9
52	.51304196	.85836353	.52794433	.84927898	.54268589	.83993573	8
53	.51329163	.85821425	.52819136	.84912537	.54293019	.83977783	7
54	.51354125	.85806491	.52843833	.84897169	.54317445	.83961986	6
55	.51379083	.85791549	.52868527	.84881794	.54341866	.83946183	5
56	.51404037	.85776599	.52893216	.84866411	.54366283	.83930372	4
57	.51428986	.85761643	.52917900	.84851021	.54390695	.83914554	3
58	.51453931	.85746679	.52942580	.84835625	.54415102	.83898728	2
59	.51478871	.85731708	.52967255	.84820221	.54439505	.83882896	1
60	.51503807	.85716730	.52991926	.84804810	.54463904	.83867057	0
′	Cosine	Sine	Cosine	Sine	Cosine	Sine	′
	59°		58°		57°		

′	33° Sine	33° Cosine	34° Sine	34° Cosine	35° Sine	35° Cosine	′
0	.54463904	.83867057	.55919290	.82903757	.57357644	.81915204	60
1	.54488297	.83851210	.55943404	.82887487	.57381469	.81898516	59
2	.54512686	.83835357	.55967512	.82871211	.57405290	.81881821	58
3	.54537071	.83819496	.55991616	.82854927	.57429106	.81865119	57
4	.54561450	.83803628	.56015715	.82838636	.57452917	.81848410	56
5	.54585826	.83787754	.56039810	.82822338	.57476724	.81831695	55
6	.54610196	.83771872	.56063899	.82806033	.57500525	.81814972	54
7	.54634562	.83755983	.56087984	.82789722	.57524322	.81798242	53
8	.54658923	.83740087	.56112065	.82773403	.57548113	.81781505	52
9	.54683280	.83724183	.56136140	.82757077	.57571900	.81764762	51
10	.54707632	.83708273	.56160211	.82740744	.57595682	.81748011	50
11	.54731980	.83692356	.56184277	.82724404	.57619459	.81731254	49
12	.54756322	.83676431	.56208338	.82708057	.57643232	.81714490	48
13	.54780661	.83660500	.56232394	.82691704	.57666999	.81697719	47
14	.54804994	.83644561	.56256446	.82675343	.57690761	.81680941	46
15	.54829323	.83628616	.56280493	.82658975	.57714519	.81664156	45
16	.54853647	.83612663	.56304535	.82642600	.57738272	.81647364	44
17	.54877967	.83596703	.56328572	.82626218	.57762020	.81630565	43
18	.54902282	.83580736	.56352605	.82609829	.57785762	.81613759	42
19	.54926592	.83564762	.56376633	.82593434	.57809500	.81596946	41
20	.54950898	.83548781	.56400656	.82577031	.57833234	.81580127	40
21	.54975199	.83532793	.56424674	.82560621	.57856962	.81563300	39
22	.54999495	.83516793	.56448688	.82544204	.57880685	.81546467	38
23	.55023787	.83500793	.56472696	.82527781	.57904404	.81529627	37
24	.55048074	.83484786	.56496700	.82511350	.57928117	.81512780	36
25	.55072356	.83468770	.56520700	.82494912	.57951820	.81495926	35
26	.55096634	.83452747	.56544694	.82478467	.57975530	.81479065	34
27	.55120907	.83436716	.56568684	.82462016	.57999228	.81462197	33
28	.55145176	.83420678	.56592668	.82445557	.58022922	.81445322	32
29	.55169439	.83404634	.56616648	.82429091	.58046611	.81428440	31
30	.55193699	.83388582	.56640624	.82412619	.58070296	.81411552	30
31	.55217953	.83372523	.56664594	.82396139	.58093975	.81394656	29
32	.55242203	.83356458	.56688560	.82379653	.58117649	.81377754	28
33	.55266448	.83340385	.56712521	.82363159	.58141318	.81360845	27
34	.55290688	.83324305	.56736477	.82346659	.58164983	.81343929	26
35	.55314924	.83308218	.56760428	.82330151	.58188642	.81327006	25
36	.55339155	.83292124	.56784375	.82313637	.58212297	.81310076	24
37	.55363381	.83276023	.56808316	.82297115	.58235947	.81293139	23
38	.55387603	.83259915	.56832253	.82280587	.58259591	.81276196	22
39	.55411820	.83243800	.56856185	.82264052	.58283231	.81259245	21
40	.55436032	.83227678	.56880112	.82247510	.58306866	.81242288	20
41	.55460240	.83211548	.56904035	.82230960	.58330496	.81225324	19
42	.55484443	.83195412	.56927952	.82214404	.58354121	.81208353	18
43	.55508641	.83179269	.56951865	.82197841	.58377741	.81191375	17
44	.55532834	.83163119	.56975773	.82181271	.58401356	.81174390	16
45	.55557023	.83146961	.56999676	.82164694	.58424967	.81157398	15
46	.55581207	.83130797	.57023575	.82148110	.58448572	.81140400	14
47	.55605387	.83114625	.57047468	.82131519	.58472172	.81123394	13
48	.55629562	.83098447	.57071357	.82114921	.58495767	.81106382	12
49	.55653732	.83082261	.57095241	.82098316	.58519358	.81089363	11
50	.55677897	.83066069	.57119120	.82081704	.58542943	.81072337	10
51	.55702057	.83049869	.57142994	.82065085	.58566524	.81055304	9
52	.55726213	.83033663	.57166863	.82048460	.58590099	.81038276	8
53	.55750364	.83017449	.57190728	.82031827	.58613670	.81021217	7
54	.55774511	.83001229	.57214578	.82015188	.58637236	.81004164	6
55	.55798653	.82985001	.57238442	.81998541	.58660796	.80987104	5
56	.55822790	.82968766	.57262292	.81981888	.58684352	.80970037	4
57	.55846922	.82952524	.57286137	.81965227	.58707903	.80952963	3
58	.55871049	.82936276	.57309978	.81948560	.58731449	.80935882	2
59	.55895172	.82920020	.57333813	.81931886	.58754989	.80918794	1
60	.55919290	.82903757	.57357644	.81915204	.58778525	.80901699	0

′	Cosine	Sine	Cosine	Sine	Cosine	Sine	′
	56°		55°		54°		

′	36° Sine	36° Cosine	37° Sine	37° Cosine	38° Sine	38° Cosine	′
0	.58778525	.80901699	.60181502	.79863551	.61566148	.78801075	60
1	.58802056	.80884598	.60204731	.79846042	.61589067	.78783163	59
2	.58825582	.80867490	.60227955	.79828525	.61611982	.78765244	58
3	.58849103	.80850375	.60251173	.79811002	.61634891	.78747319	57
4	.58872619	.80833253	.60274387	.79793473	.61657795	.78729387	56
5	.58896130	.80816124	.60297595	.79775936	.61680694	.78711448	55
6	.58919636	.80798988	.60320799	.79758393	.61703588	.78693502	54
7	.58943137	.80781846	.60343997	.79740843	.61726476	.78675550	53
8	.58966633	.80764697	.60367190	.79723286	.61749359	.78657591	52
9	.58990124	.80747541	.60390387	.79705723	.61772237	.78639626	51
10	.59013610	.80730378	.60413561	.79688152	.61795110	.78621654	50
11	.59037091	.80713208	.60436739	.79670576	.61817977	.78603675	49
12	.59060567	.80696031	.60459911	.79652992	.61840840	.78585689	48
13	.59084038	.80678848	.60483075	.79635401	.61863697	.78567697	47
14	.59107504	.80661658	.60506241	.79617804	.61886548	.78549698	46
15	.59130965	.80644460	.60529399	.79600200	.61909395	.78531693	45
16	.59154421	.80627257	.60552551	.79582590	.61932236	.78513681	44
17	.59177872	.80610046	.60575698	.79564970	.61955072	.78495662	43
18	.59201318	.80592828	.60598840	.79547348	.61977903	.78477637	42
19	.59224759	.80575604	.60621977	.79529717	.62000729	.78459605	41
20	.59248195	.80558373	.60645109	.79512080	.62023549	.78441566	40
21	.59271626	.80541135	.60668235	.79494435	.62046364	.78423521	39
22	.59295052	.80523890	.60691357	.79476784	.62069174	.78405469	38
23	.59318473	.80506638	.60714473	.79459127	.62091979	.78387411	37
24	.59341889	.80489380	.60737584	.79441462	.62114778	.78369346	36
25	.59365300	.80472114	.60760690	.79423791	.62137572	.78351274	35
26	.59388705	.80454842	.60783791	.79406113	.62160361	.78333196	34
27	.59412106	.80437564	.60806887	.79388428	.62183145	.78315111	33
28	.59435502	.80420278	.60829977	.79370737	.62205923	.78297019	32
29	.59458893	.80402985	.60853063	.79353039	.62228696	.78278921	31
30	.59482279	.80385686	.60876143	.79335334	.62251464	.78260816	30
31	.59505659	.80368380	.60899218	.79317623	.62274226	.78242704	29
32	.59529035	.80351067	.60922288	.79299904	.62296983	.78224586	28
33	.59552406	.80333747	.60945353	.79282179	.62319735	.78206461	27
34	.59575771	.80316421	.60968413	.79264448	.62342482	.78188330	26
35	.59599132	.80299088	.60991467	.79246709	.62365224	.78170192	25
36	.59622487	.80281748	.61014516	.79228964	.62387960	.78152047	24
37	.59645838	.80264401	.61037561	.79211213	.62410691	.78133896	23
38	.59669183	.80247047	.61060600	.79193454	.62433416	.78115738	22
39	.59692524	.80229687	.61083633	.79175689	.62456136	.78097574	21
40	.59715859	.80212319	.61106662	.79157917	.62478851	.78079403	20
41	.59739189	.80194945	.61129686	.79140139	.62501561	.78061225	19
42	.59762515	.80177564	.61152704	.79122353	.62524266	.78043041	18
43	.59785835	.80160177	.61175717	.79104561	.62546965	.78024850	17
44	.59809150	.80142782	.61198725	.79086763	.62569659	.78006652	16
45	.59832460	.80125381	.61221728	.79068957	.62592347	.77988448	15
46	.59855765	.80107973	.61244726	.79051145	.62615030	.77970238	14
47	.59879065	.80090559	.61267718	.79033327	.62637708	.77952020	13
48	.59902360	.80073137	.61290705	.79015501	.62660381	.77933796	12
49	.59925650	.80055709	.61313687	.78997669	.62683049	.77915566	11
50	.59948934	.80038274	.61336664	.78979830	.62705711	.77897329	10
51	.59972214	.80020832	.61359636	.78961985	.62728367	.77879085	9
52	.59995489	.80003383	.61382603	.78944133	.62751019	.77860835	8
53	.60018758	.79985928	.61405564	.78926274	.62773665	.77842578	7
54	.60042023	.79968466	.61428520	.78908408	.62796306	.77824315	6
55	.60065282	.79950997	.61451471	.78890536	.62818941	.77806045	5
56	.60088536	.79933521	.61474417	.78872657	.62841571	.77787768	4
57	.60111785	.79916039	.61497357	.78854772	.62864196	.77769485	3
58	.60135029	.79898550	.61520293	.78836880	.62886816	.77751195	2
59	.60158268	.79881054	.61543223	.78818981	.62909430	.77732899	1
60	.60181502	.79863551	.61566148	.78801075	.62932039	.77714596	0
′	Cosine	Sine	Cosine	Sine	Cosine	Sine	′
	53°		52°		51°		

′	39°		40°		41°		′
	Sine	Cosine	Sine	Cosine	Sine	Cosine	
0	.62932039	.77714596	.64278761	.76604444	.65605903	.75470958	60
1	.62954643	.77696287	.64301042	.76585743	.65627854	.75451871	59
2	.62977241	.77677971	.64323317	.76567035	.65649799	.75432777	58
3	.62999834	.77659648	.64345586	.76548321	.65671739	.75413677	57
4	.63022422	.77641319	.64367851	.76529601	.65693673	.75394571	56
5	.63045004	.77622983	.64390110	.76510874	.65715602	.75375458	55
6	.63067581	.77604641	.64412363	.76492140	.65737525	.75356339	54
7	.63090152	.77586292	.64434611	.76473400	.65759442	.75337214	53
8	.63112719	.77567936	.64456853	.76454654	.65781354	.75318082	52
9	.63135280	.77549574	.64479090	.76435901	.65803260	.75298944	51
10	.63157835	.77531206	.64501322	.76417141	.65825161	.75279799	50
11	.63180385	.77512831	.64523548	.76398375	.65847056	.75260648	49
12	.63202930	.77494449	.64545769	.76379603	.65868946	.75241491	48
13	.63225470	.77476061	.64567984	.76360824	.65890830	.75222327	47
14	.63248004	.77457666	.64590194	.76342039	.65912709	.75203157	46
15	.63270533	.77439264	.64612398	.76323247	.65934582	.75183981	45
16	.63293056	.77420856	.64634597	.76304449	.65956449	.75164798	44
17	.63315574	.77402442	.64656790	.76285644	.65978311	.75145609	43
18	.63338087	.77384021	.64678978	.76266833	.66000167	.75126413	42
19	.63360595	.77365593	.64701160	.76248015	.66022017	.75107212	41
20	.63383097	.77347159	.64723337	.76229191	.66043862	.75088003	40
21	.63405593	.77328719	.64745509	.76210361	.66065702	.75068789	39
22	.63428085	.77310271	.64767675	.76191524	.66087536	.75049568	38
23	.63450571	.77291818	.64789835	.76172681	.66109364	.75030341	37
24	.63473051	.77273357	.64811990	.76153831	.66131187	.75011107	36
25	.63495527	.77254891	.64834140	.76134974	.66153004	.74991867	35
26	.63517996	.77236417	.64856284	.76116112	.66174815	.74972621	34
27	.63540461	.77217937	.64878422	.76097243	.66196621	.74953368	33
28	.63562920	.77199451	.64900555	.76078367	.66218421	.74934109	32
29	.63585374	.77180958	.64922683	.76059485	.66240216	.74914844	31
30	.63607822	.77162458	.64944805	.76040597	.66262005	.74895572	30
31	.63630265	.77143952	.64966921	.76021702	.66283788	.74876294	29
32	.63652703	.77125440	.64989032	.76002800	.66305566	.74857010	28
33	.63675135	.77106921	.65011138	.75983893	.66327338	.74837719	27
34	.63697562	.77088395	.65033238	.75964978	.66349105	.74818422	26
35	.63719983	.77069863	.65055333	.75946058	.66370866	.74799119	25
36	.63742399	.77051324	.65077422	.75927131	.66392621	.74779809	24
37	.63764810	.77032779	.65099505	.75908197	.66414371	.74760493	23
38	.63787215	.77014227	.65121583	.75889257	.66436115	.74741171	22
39	.63809615	.76995669	.65143656	.75870311	.66457854	.74721842	21
40	.63832009	.76977104	.65165723	.75851358	.66479587	.74702507	20
41	.63854398	.76958533	.65187784	.75832399	.66501314	.74683166	19
42	.63876782	.76939956	.65209840	.75813434	.66523035	.74663818	18
43	.63899160	.76921371	.65231891	.75794462	.66544751	.74644464	17
44	.63921533	.76902780	.65253936	.75775483	.66566462	.74625104	16
45	.63943902	.76884183	.65275975	.75756498	.66588167	.74605737	15
46	.63966262	.76865579	.65298009	.75737507	.66609866	.74586365	14
47	.63988619	.76846969	.65320038	.75718510	.66631559	.74566985	13
48	.64010970	.76828352	.65342060	.75699506	.66653247	.74547600	12
49	.64033316	.76809729	.65364078	.75680495	.66674929	.74528208	11
50	.64055656	.76791099	.65386090	.75661478	.66696606	.74508810	10
51	.64077991	.76772463	.65408096	.75642455	.66718277	.74489406	9
52	.64100320	.75753820	.65430097	.75623425	.66739942	.74469995	8
53	.64122645	.76735171	.65452092	.75604389	.66761602	.74450578	7
54	.64144963	.76716515	.65474081	.75585347	.66783256	.74431155	6
55	.64167276	.76697853	.65496065	.75566298	.66804904	.74411725	5
56	.64189584	.76679184	.65518044	.75547243	.66826547	.74392289	4
57	.64211887	.76660509	.65540017	.75528181	.66848184	.74372847	3
58	.64234183	.76641827	.65561985	.75509113	.66869815	.74353398	2
59	.64256475	.76623139	.65583947	.75490039	.66891441	.74333944	1
60	.64278761	.76604444	.65605903	.75470958	.66913061	.74314483	0
′	Cosine	Sine	Cosine	Sine	Cosine	Sine	′
	50°		49°		48°		

,	42°		43°		44°		,
	Sine	Cosine	Sine	Cosine	Sine	Cosine	
0	.66913061	.74314483	.68199836	.73135370	.69465837	.71933980	60
1	.66934675	.74295015	.68221107	.73115529	.69486759	.71913770	59
2	.66956284	.74275542	.68242373	.73095681	.69507675	.71893554	58
3	.66977887	.74256062	.68263633	.73075827	.69528585	.71873332	57
4	.66999484	.74236575	.68284887	.73055967	.69549489	.71853104	56
5	.67021076	.74217083	.68306135	.73036100	.69570387	.71832870	55
6	.67042662	.74197584	.68327377	.73016228	.69591280	.71812630	54
7	.67064242	.74178079	.68348614	.72996349	.69612166	.71792383	53
8	.67085817	.74158568	.68369845	.72976464	.69633047	.71772131	52
9	.67107386	.74139050	.68391070	.72956573	.69653921	.71751873	51
10	.67128949	.74119526	.68412289	.72936676	.69674790	.71731608	50
11	.67150507	.74099996	.68433503	.72916772	.69695653	.71711337	49
12	.67172059	.74080460	.68454711	.72896863	.69716510	.71691061	48
13	.67193605	.74060917	.68475913	.72876947	.69737361	.71670778	47
14	.67215146	.74041368	.68497109	.72857025	.69758207	.71650489	46
15	.67236681	.74021813	.68518299	.72837097	.69779046	.71630194	45
16	.67258210	.74002251	.68539484	.72817163	.69799879	.71609893	44
17	.67279734	.73982684	.68560662	.72797222	.69820707	.71589586	43
18	.67301251	.73963109	.68581835	.72777276	.69841529	.71569273	42
19	.67322763	.73943529	.68603002	.72757323	.69862344	.71548954	41
20	.67344270	.73923943	.68624164	.72737364	.69883154	.71528629	40
21	.67365771	.73904350	.68645319	.72717399	.69903958	.71508298	39
22	.67387266	.73884751	.68666469	.72697428	.69924756	.71487961	38
23	.67408755	.73865146	.68687613	.72677451	.69945548	.71467617	37
24	.67430239	.73845534	.68708751	.72657467	.69966334	.71447268	36
25	.67451717	.73825916	.68729883	.72637477	.69987114	.71426913	35
26	.67473189	.73806292	.68751010	.72617482	.70007889	.71406551	34
27	.67494655	.73786662	.68772131	.72597480	.70028657	.71386184	33
28	.67516116	.73767025	.68793245	.72577472	.70049419	.71365810	32
29	.67537571	.73747383	.68814354	.72557457	.70070176	.71345431	31
30	.67559021	.73727734	.68835458	.72537437	.70090926	.71325045	30
31	.67580464	.73708078	.68856555	.72517411	.70111671	.71304653	29
32	.67601902	.73688417	.68877646	.72497378	.70132410	.71284256	28
33	.67623335	.73668749	.68898732	.72477339	.70153143	.71263852	27
34	.67644761	.73649075	.68919812	.72457294	.70173869	.71243442	26
35	.67666182	.73629395	.68940886	.72437243	.70194590	.71223026	25
36	.67687597	.73609709	.68961954	.72417186	.70215305	.71202605	24
37	.67709006	.73590016	.68983017	.72397123	.70236014	.71182177	23
38	.67730410	.73570317	.69004073	.72377053	.70256717	.71161743	22
39	.67751808	.73550612	.69025124	.72356978	.70277415	.71141303	21
40	.67773200	.73530901	.69046169	.72336896	.70298106	.71120857	20
41	.67794586	.73511183	.69067208	.72316808	.70318791	.71100405	19
42	.67815967	.73491460	.69088241	.72296715	.70339470	.71079947	18
43	.67837342	.73471730	.69109268	.72276615	.70360144	.71059483	17
44	.67858711	.73451993	.69130290	.72256508	.70380811	.71039014	16
45	.67880075	.73432251	.69151306	.72236396	.70401472	.71018538	15
46	.67901432	.73412502	.69172315	.72216278	.70422128	.70998056	14
47	.67922784	.73392747	.69193319	.72196153	.70442777	.70977568	13
48	.67944130	.73372986	.69214317	.72176023	.70463421	.70957074	12
49	.67965471	.73353219	.69235310	.72155886	.70484059	.70936574	11
50	.67986806	.73333446	.69256296	.72135743	.70504692	.70916068	10
51	.68008135	.73313666	.69277276	.72115594	.70525316	.70895556	9
52	.68029458	.73293880	.69298251	.72095439	.70545936	.70875038	8
53	.68050775	.73274088	.69319220	.72075278	.70566549	.70854514	7
54	.68072087	.73254290	.69340183	.72055111	.70587157	.70833984	6
55	.68093393	.73234485	.69361140	.72034938	.70607759	.70813448	5
56	.68114693	.73214675	.69382091	.72014758	.70628355	.70792906	4
57	.68135987	.73194858	.69403036	.71994573	.70648944	.70772358	3
58	.68157276	.73175035	.69423976	.71974381	.70669528	.70751804	2
59	.68178559	.73155206	.69444909	.71954184	.70690106	.70731244	1
60	.68199836	.73135370	.69465837	.71933980	.70710678	.70710678	0
	Cosine	Sine	Cosine	Sine	Cosine	Sine	,
,	47°		46°		45°		

Let A = angle BAC = arc BF, and let the radius $AF = AB = AH = 1$.
We then have

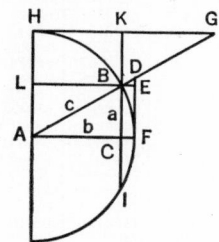

sin A	$= BC$
cos A	$= AC$
tan A	$= DF$
ctn A	$= HG$
sec A	$= AD$
cosec A	$= AG$
versin A	$= CF = BE$
covers A	$= BK = HL$
exsec A	$= BD$
coexsec A	$= PG$
chord A	$= BF$
chord $2A$	$= BI = 2BC$

In the right-angled triangle ABC
Let $AB = c$, $AC = b$, and $BC = a$.
We then have:

1. $\sin A \quad = \dfrac{a}{c} = \cos B$

2. $\cos A \quad = \dfrac{b}{c} = \sin B$

3. $\tan A \quad = \dfrac{a}{b} = \operatorname{ctn} B$

4. $\operatorname{ctn} A \quad = \dfrac{b}{a} = \tan B$

5. $\sec A \quad = \dfrac{c}{b} = \operatorname{cosec} B$

6. $\operatorname{cosec} A \quad = \dfrac{c}{a} = \sec B$

7. $\operatorname{vers} A \quad = \dfrac{c - b}{c} = \operatorname{covers} B$

8. $\operatorname{exsec} A \quad = \dfrac{c - b}{b} = \operatorname{coexsec} B$

9. $\operatorname{covers} A \quad = \dfrac{c - a}{c} = \operatorname{versin} B$

10. $\operatorname{coexsec} A = \dfrac{c - a}{a} = \operatorname{exsec} B$

11. $a = c \sin A = b \tan A$

12. $b = c \cos A = a \operatorname{ctn} A$

13. $c = \dfrac{a}{\sin A} = \dfrac{b}{\cos A}$

14. $a = c \cos B = b \operatorname{ctn} B$

15. $b = c \sin B = a \tan B$

16. $c = \dfrac{a}{\cos B} = \dfrac{b}{\sin B}$

17. $a = \sqrt{(c + b)(c - b)}$

18. $b = \sqrt{(c + a)(c - a)}$

19. $c = \sqrt{a^2 + b^2}$

20. $C = 90° = A + B$

21. area $= \dfrac{ab}{2}$

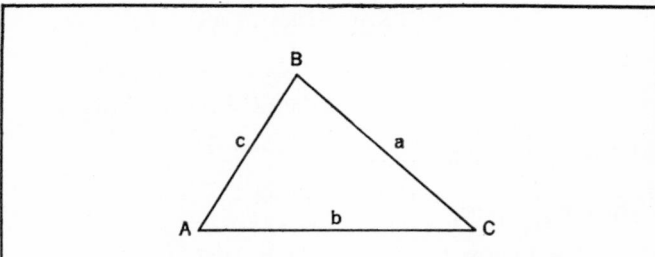

	GIVEN	SOUGHT	FORMULA
22	A, B, a	C, b, c	$C = 180° - (A + B)$, $\quad b = \dfrac{a}{\sin A} \cdot \sin B$.
			$c = \dfrac{a}{\sin A} \sin (A + B)$
23	A, a, b	B, C, c	$\sin B = \dfrac{\sin A}{a} \cdot b$, $\quad C = 180° - (A + B)$,
			$c = \dfrac{a}{\sin A} \cdot \sin C$.
24	C, a, b	$\tfrac{1}{2}(A + B)$	$\tfrac{1}{2}(A + B) = 90° - \tfrac{1}{2}C$
25		$\tfrac{1}{2}(A - B)$	$\tan \tfrac{1}{2}(A - B) = \dfrac{a - b}{a + b} \tan \tfrac{1}{2}(A + B)$
26		A, B	$A = \tfrac{1}{2}(A + B) + \tfrac{1}{2}(A - B)$, $B = \tfrac{1}{2}(A + B) - \tfrac{1}{2}(A - B)$
27		c	$c = (a + b) \dfrac{\cos \tfrac{1}{2}(A + B)}{\cos \tfrac{1}{2}(A - B)}$
28			$= \sqrt{a^2 + b^2 - 2ab \cos C}$
29	a, b, c	area	area $= \tfrac{1}{2}ab \sin C$.
		A	Let $s = \tfrac{1}{2}(a + b + c)$;
			$\sin \tfrac{1}{2}A = \sqrt{\dfrac{(s - b)(s - c)}{bc}}$
30			$\cos \tfrac{1}{2}A = \sqrt{\dfrac{s(s - a)}{bc}}$;
			$\tan \tfrac{1}{2}A = \sqrt{\dfrac{(s - b)(s - c)}{s(s - a)}}$
31			$\sin A = \dfrac{2 \sqrt{s(s - a)(s - b)(s - c)}}{bc}$;
			$\cos A = \dfrac{b^2 + c^2 - a^2}{2bc}$
32		area	area $= \sqrt{s(s - a)(s - b)(s - c)}$
33	A, B, C, a	area	area $= \dfrac{a^2 \sin B \cdot \sin C}{2 \sin A}$

GENERAL FORMULAS

$\sin A = 2 \sin \tfrac{1}{2}A \cos \tfrac{1}{2}A = \sqrt{1 - \cos^2 A} = \tan A \cos A$

$\cos A = 2 \cos^2 \tfrac{1}{2}A - 1 = 1 - 2 \sin^2 \tfrac{1}{2}A = \cos^2 \tfrac{1}{2}A - \sin^2 \tfrac{1}{2}A$

$\tan A = \dfrac{\sin A}{\cos A} = \dfrac{\sin 2A}{1 + \cos 2A}$

$\operatorname{ctn} A = \dfrac{\cos A}{\sin A} = \dfrac{\sin 2A}{1 - \cos 2A} = \dfrac{\sin 2A}{\operatorname{vers} 2A}$

$\operatorname{vers} A = 1 - \cos A = \sin A \tan \tfrac{1}{2}A = 2 \sin^2 \tfrac{1}{2}A$

$\operatorname{exsec} A = \sec A - 1 = \tan A \tan \tfrac{1}{2}A = \dfrac{\operatorname{vers} A}{\cos A}$

$\sin 2A = 2 \sin A \cos A$

$\cos 2A = 2 \cos^2 A - 1 = \cos^2 A - \sin^2 A = 1 - 2 \sin^2 A$

$\tan 2A = \dfrac{2 \tan A}{1 - \tan^2 A}$

$\operatorname{ctn} 2A = \dfrac{\operatorname{ctn}^2 A - 1}{2 \operatorname{ctn} A}$

$\operatorname{vers} 2A = 2 \sin^2 A = 2 \sin A \cos A \tan A$

$\operatorname{exsec} 2A = \dfrac{2 \tan^2 A}{1 - \tan^2 A}$

$\sin^2 A + \cos^2 A = 1$

$\sin (A \pm B) = \sin A \cdot \cos B \pm \sin B \cdot \cos A$

$\cos (A \pm B) = \cos A \cdot \cos B \mp \sin A \cdot \sin B$

$\sin A + \sin B = 2 \sin \tfrac{1}{2}(A + B) \cos \tfrac{1}{2}(A - B)$

$\sin A - \sin B = 2 \cos \tfrac{1}{2}(A + B) \sin \tfrac{1}{2}(A - B)$

$\cos A + \cos B = 2 \cos \tfrac{1}{2}(A + B) \cos \tfrac{1}{2}(A - B)$

$\cos B - \cos A = 2 \sin \tfrac{1}{2}(A + B) \sin \tfrac{1}{2}(A - B)$

$\sin^2 A - \sin^2 B = \cos^2 B - \cos^2 A = \sin (A + B) \sin (A - B)$

$\cos^2 A - \sin^2 B = \cos (A + B) \cos (A - B)$

$\tan A + \tan B = \dfrac{\sin (A + B)}{\cos A \cdot \cos B}$

$\tan A - \tan B = \dfrac{\sin (A - B)}{\cos A \cdot \cos B}$

INDEX

NOTE: Pages given are those of text, not of Tables; see also list at beginning of Tables. The Contents at the front of this volume is often useful in locating items.

Aerial surveys, 20–23, 38, 282–284, 295–303
Altimetry (see Aneroid barometer)
American Association of State Highway Officials, 271
American Railway Engineering Association Ten-Chord Spiral, 106–138 (see also Spirals)
  field notes, 117–120
  field work, 124–126
  intermediate setups, 121, 122
  offsets, 111–114, 125, 126
  osculating circle, 120–124
  precise definition of, 115–117
  properties of, 108–115
  spiraling compound curves, 112–124
  spiraling existing curves, 126–128
  tables, 126
Aneroid barometer, 11–20
  barometric correction, 16–19
  field notes, 14
  obtaining elevations with, 11–20
  temperature corrections, 13–16
Appurtenant structures, staking, 212–218
  bridges, 217
  buildings, 216
  canal structures, 217
  culverts, 216, 217

tunnels, 218
Arc definition of degree of curve, 58
Area grading, 188–192
Areas, of cross-sections, 169–177
  averaging end, 177–178
Averaging end areas, 177–178

Balance points, 203–205
Balanced cuts and fills, 50, 51
Banking of curves, 128–135
Barnett Spiral, 138
Barometric leveling (see Aneroid barometer)
Bearing power of soils, allowable, 221, 222
Bid, contractor's, 256–261
Borings, 51
Borrow pits, 187–192
Bridges, staking, 217
  waterway for, 229
Broken-back curves, 85
Building materials, strength of, 225–227, 229

Cableways, 3, facing 254
Canal engineering, 8, 10, 56
  cross-sections, 177
  flow in, 231, 232
  structures, 217
Centrifugal force, 129
Change orders, 218
Channel, flow in, 231, 232
Chief of party, duties of, 42–46
Chord definition of degree of curve, 58

Circular curves (*see* Simple circular curves)
Classification of Excavation, 193–194
Compensation of grades for curvature, 9
Compound curves, 81–86
Concrete data, 227–229
Connecting railway tracks, 146
Construction, 212–264
  data, 221–241
  engineer, 248–254
  equipment, 255
  management, 248–264
  operation after, 220
  organization, 250, 256
  procedure, 212–221
  supervision of, 220, 248–252
  surveys, 212–218
Contracting, 255–264
  as a career, 261–264
  bids, 256–261
  equipment, 255
  organization, 250, 256
Contractor-engineer, 255–264
Contracts, 129
Controlling points, 8
Conversion factors, 239
Costs of construction, 240–247, 256–261
Crossings, railway, 146
Crossovers, railway, 146
Cross-sectioning, 161–169, 212
Cross-sections, 162–177
  forms, 166, 167
  precision in measurements, 169
Cubic spiral or parabola, 105
Culverts or bridges, waterway size for, 229, 230
Curvature, choosing proper, 10
Curvature corrections, for earthwork, 184–187
Curves, simple circular, 58–80
  broken-back, 85
  compound, 81–86

  metric, 267
  parabolic and vertical, 93–102
  reverse, 86–88
  spiral, 103–138

Deeds and easements, 208
Deflection angles, 61, 62
Degree of curve, 58, 59, 265–269
  arc definition, 58
  chord definition, 58
  other definitions, 265–269

Earthwork, 161–206 (*see also* Excavation)
  settlement of embankments, 193
  tables and diagram, 181–183
Easement curves (*see* Spirals)
Easement rights, 208
Economic limit of haul, 199, 200, 205
Embankment, openings, 183
Eminent Domain, right of, 207
End areas, 169–178
  averaging, 177, 178
  by planimeter, 174
  computing, 169–174
  coordinate method of computing, 171–173
  grade triangle method, 173
Engineer-contractor, 255–264
Estimates, final, monthly, and progress, 219
Estimating, 241–247, 256–261
  by the mile, 241–245
  by units, engineer's estimates, 243–247
  contractor's bids, 256–261
Even radius curves, 265
Excavation, 51, 161–195
  center of gravity, 195
  classification of, 193–194
  exploration of, 51

mass diagram and haul, 195–206

tables and diagrams, 181–183

volumes, 177–181

Excavation and embankment, 161–194

classification, 105

general procedure, 161–166

Executives, 2, 220, 221, 251–254, 262–264

Field notes (*see type of survey desired*)

Field parties, instructions for guidance, 42–46

Field work (*see type of survey desired*)

Final estimate, 219

Final location, 47–57

re-establishing, 212

Flow of water, 231–238

in pipes and open channels, 231, 232

over weirs, 232–238

Foundations, bearing power, 221–225

Free haul, earthwork, 196

Frogs, railway, 139–146

Functions of simple curves, 59–62, 265–267

Future needs, providing for, 6

Grade contour, 49, 50

Grade rod, 168, 169

Grades, choosing proper, 8, 9

compensated, 9

Gradients, 8, 9

Grading, equipment and methods, 194

Grading over an area, computation of, 188–192

Haul, 195

Highway engineering, 8, 9, 10, 54, 99, 101, 131, 135, 271–294

Highways (*see special subject desired*)

Horizontal parabolas, 101, 102

Hydraulics, 231–238

Inspection, 218

Instructions for the guidance of field parties, 42–46

Introduction, 1–4

Kutter formula diagram for flow, 231, 232

Legal rights of surveyors, 210, 211

Length of vertical curves, 99–101

Limit of economic haul, 199, 200, 205

Location, 47–57

maps and profiles, 52–57

monumenting the, 52

procedure, 47–49

Long tape preliminary, 34–36

Management, professional, 221, 248–264

Manning formula diagram for flow, 231, 232

Map location, 47–49

Mapping, aerial (*see* Aerial surveys)

Maps, examples of, 52–57

Mass diagram, 200–206

procedure in using, 203–206

properties of, 202–203

purpose of, 203

Materials, ordering, 212

Metric curves, 267

Missouri Highway Department, 285–294

Monthly estimates, 219

Mosaic, facing 303

Notes, field (see type of survey
    desired)

Offsets, for simple curve, 70–74
    for spiral, 111–114, 125, 126
Openings, embankment, 183
Osculating circle, 120–124
Overhaul, 196–199, 205, 206

Paper location, 47–49
Parabolas, laying out hori-
    zontally with tape, 101, 102
    cubic, 105
Parabolic curves, 93–102
Permission to construct, obtain-
    ing, 51
Photogrammetry (see Aerial
    surveys)
Piles, bearing power of, 222–225
Pipe line engineering, 9, 10, 57,
    101
Pipe lines (see special subject
    desired)
    flow in, 231–232
Preliminary, 26–46
    aerial, 20–22, 282–284, 295–303
    checking and coordinating, 39
    long tape, 34
    miscellany, 40
    precision of, 38
    rapid stadia, 38
    stadia, 38
    standard type of, 26
        level party, 27
        map of, 29
        topographic party, 27
        transit party, 26
Prismoidal correction, 179–181
Prismoidal formula, 178–181
Problems, 304–315
Professional management, 221,
    248–264
Profiles, examples of, 52–57
Progress reports, 219
Project method of teaching

routes, 23
Property surveys, 207–211
Public relations, 211
Public Roads Administration
    (see U.S. Public Roads
    Administration)

Railway engineering, 8, 9, 10,
    53, 99, 131–134, 136, 137,
    139–160
Railway turnouts and track
    layouts, 139–147
Railways (see special subject
    desired)
Reconnaissance, 5–25
    general considerations, 5, 6
    importance of, 25
    instruments, 11
    procedure, 23, 24
    reports, 24–25
Reference stakes, 42, 212
Reverse curves, 86–88
Rights of way, 207–211
    agents, 208
    description, 208
    influence on selection of
        routes, 207
    surveys of, 209, 210
Routes, aesthetic factors of, 3
    selection of, 2–4
Route surveys, definition of, 1
    general types, 4
    importance of, 1, 2
    precision of, 4

Sections, canal, 177
    in earth and rock, 174
Settlement of embankment, 193
Shrinkage and swell of embank-
    ments, 192
Side slopes, 166, 167
Sight distances, 99–100, 278–
    280
Simple circular curves, 58–80
    chord offset, tangent offset,

and middle ordinate—relations between, 72, 73
curve notes, 62–65
deflection angles, 61, 62
degree of (*see* Degree of curve)
external, 60, 61
field work, 66–70
functions of, 59–62
introduction, 58
length of curve, 61
locating a curve from the center, 75
special problems, 75–80
staking by offsets and ordinates, 73, 74
staking with a tape, 70–74
tangent, 59, 60
tangent offset, 71
triangulating a curve, 75
Slope, stakes, setting, 167–169
Slopes, side, 166, 167
Soil investigations, 51
Speeds, railway and highway, 10
Spirals, 103–138 (*see* American Railway Engineering Association Ten-Chord Spiral)
Barnett, highway, 138
basic equation of, 104–106
introduction, 103, 104
length of, 135–138, 276
Stadia preliminaries, 38
Standards, highway, 271–294
Station to station method, 197–199
Station-yard, 195
Strength of building materials, 225–227, 229
String lining of curves, 148–160
chord method, 148–150
mechanized, 156–159
park roads, as applied to, 160
procedure, 150–156
tools required, 150
Structures, staking, 212

Superelevation, 128–135
Swell and shrinkage of embankments, 192
Switches, railway, 139–147

Tables (*see paging on list at beginning of tables*)
   I. Radii, etc.
   II. Lengths, tangents, and externals for a 1° curve
   III. Tangent and external corrections
   IIIA. Tangent offsets
   IV. Arc excess and true subchords for fractional stations
   V. Deflections and chords for 25-, 50-, and 100-foot arcs
   VI. Long chords for several stations
   VII. Functions of the ten-chord spiral
   VIII. Selected spirals
   IX. Spiral deflections
   X. Intermediate setup on spiral
   XI. Correction to spiral deflection angles (diagram)
   XII. Theoretical or balanced superelevation
   XIII, XIV, XV. Tables of all logarithms and functions of angles
   XVI. Natural versines and exsecs
   XVII. Powers, roots, and reciprocals
   XVIII. Arc lengths for radius of 1

XIX. Cubic yards per 100 lineal feet of level triangular section

XX. Multiplying factor to determine additional yardage for various transverse slopes

XXI. Triangular prisms (diagrams)

XXII. Cubic yards per 100-foot station

XXIII. Yardage per 100-foot station—from double end areas

XXIV. Canal sections—balanced center cut

XXV. Turnouts

XXVI. Ordinates for staking curves with tape

XXVII. Stadia coefficients. Vertical rod

XXVIII. Convergence of meridians

XXIX. Grades and grade angles

XXX. Slope taping corrections

XXXI. Right of way acreages 100 feet wide

XXXII. Inches in decimals of a foot

XXXIII. Average air temperature correction for barometric leveling

XXXIV. Eight-place natural sines and cosines

XXXV. Numbers and formulas

Talbot formula for waterway, 230

Tapes, long, 34–36
  laying out parabolas with, 101
  staking curves with, 70–75
Topography, 6–8, 27, 32
Track, *see* Railway
Track layouts, other, 139–147
Transition curves (*see* Spirals)
Transmission line engineering 9, 10, 55, 214, 215 (*see also special subject desired*)
Transportation, projects, 2
  overall policy, 285
Traverse, solution by, 89–92
Traversing around obstacles, 90, 91
Trend of the times, 6
  in transportation policy, 285
Turnouts, railway, 139–146
  on curves, 143, 144
  staking from straight track, 141–143
  tracks curved immediately after leaving, 144

U. S. Public Roads Administration, 20–23, 271–285

Vertical curves, 93–101
  adjacent, 98, 99
  length of, 99–101
  low point on, 97, 98
Vertical and other parabolic curves, 93–102
Visibility, 99–101
Volumes of earthwork, by end areas, 177, 178
  by prismoidal formula, 178–181

Water, flow of, 231–238
Waterway for culverts or bridges, 229, 230
Weights of materials, 240
Weirs, flow over, 232–238
Wye tracks, 146

Y tracks, 146